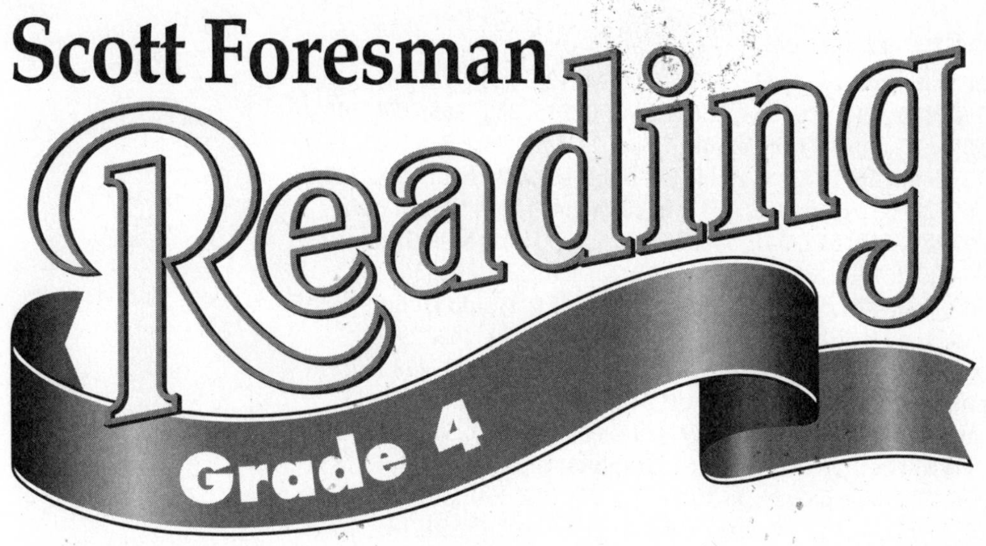

Teacher's Resource Book

Scott Foresman

Editorial Offices: Glenview, Illinois • Parsippany, New Jersey • New York, New York
Sales Offices: Parsippany, New Jersey • Duluth, Georgia • Glenview, Illinois
Coppell, Texas • Ontario, California

Credits

Illustrations

Teresa Anderko: pp. 4, 33, 60, 78, 79, 114, 121, 125, 129, 135, 136, 148, 170, 183, 192, 219, 264, 266, 271, 290, 335, 352, 365, 374, 440, 534, 559, 587 right; **Patti Corcoran:** pp. 23 right, 34, 65, 77, 87, 131, 134, 135 left, 156, 157, 158 right, 180 right, 189, 200 right, 228, 247, 258, 269, 289, 324 left, 358, 404 left, 407 right, 417, 424, 428 right, 493, 497 left, 512, 515, 541, 586, 587, 628, 657, 676; **Nelle Davis:** pp. 10, 48, 82, 153, 166, 169, 205, 213, 227 left, 279, 302, 305, 323, 341, 343, 362, 470, 500, 536, 566, 588, 647, 651; **Waldo Dunn:** pp. 35, 38, 77, 471, 544, 569; **Morissa Geller:** pp. 1, 67, 89, 202, 293, 315 right, 453, 575, 610; **Vickie Learner:** pp. 9, 21, 200, 428 left; **Mapping Specialists:** pp. 499, 501, 517; **Laurie O'Keefe:** pp. 11, 87 right, 158 left, 180 left, 191, 291, 315 left, 324, 519, 539, 540, 654, 674; **Joel Snyder:** pp. 55, 173; **TSI Graphics:** pp. 19, 41, 43, 63, 85, 399, 456, 522, 603, 633; **N. Jo Tufts:** pp. 23, 147, 190, 212, 252, 289, 318, 355, 402, 475, 478; **Jessica Wolk-Stanley:** pp. 45, 54, 145, 167, 189, 249, 340, 384, 393, 404 right, 406 right, 437, 550, 561, 586 right, 597; **Lisa Zucker:** pp. 384 right, 497.

ISBN 0-328-02233-0
ISBN 0-328-04060-6

5 6 7 8 9 10 - V004 - 10 09 08 07 06 05 04 03
5 6 7 8 9 10 - V004 - 10 09 08 07 06 05 04

Table of Contents

Unit 2

A Wider View	Family Times	Comprehension	Vocabulary	Selection Test	Writing Across Texts	Grammar	Phonics/ Word Study	Spelling	Research and Study Skills	Writing Process
from The Cricket in Times Square	114–115	116, 118, 121–122	117	119–120	123	124–128	129	130–133	134–135	
A Big-City Dream	136–137	138, 140, 143–144	139	141–142	145	146–150	151	152–155	156–157	
I Love Guinea Pigs	158–159	160, 162, 165–166	161	163–164	167	168–172	173	174–177	178–179	
The Swimming Hole	180–181	182, 184, 187–188	183	185–186	189	190–194	195	196–199	200–201	
Komodo Dragons	202–203	204, 206, 209–210	205	207–208	211	212–216	217	218–221	222–223	224–226

Unit 3

Keys to Success	Family Times	Comprehension	Vocabulary	Selection Test	Writing Across Texts	Grammar	Phonics/ Word Study	Spelling	Research and Study Skills	Writing Process
John Henry	227–228	229, 231, 234–235	230	232–233	236	237–241	242	243–246	247–248	
Marven of the Great North Woods	249–250	251, 253, 256–257	252	254–255	258	259–263	264	265–268	269–270	
On the Pampas	271–272	273, 275, 278–279	274	276–277	280	281–285	286	287–290	291–292	
The Storm	293–294	295, 297, 300–301	296	298–299	302	303–307	308	309–312	313–314	
Rikki-tikki-tavi	315–316	317, 319, 322–323	318	320–321	324	325–329	330	331–334	335–336	337–339

Unit 4

Timeless Stories	Family Times	Comprehension	Vocabulary	Selection Test	Writing Across Texts	Grammar	Phonics/ Word Study	Spelling	Research and Study Skills	Writing Process
Half-Chicken	340–341	342, 344, 347–348	343	345–346	349	350–354	355	356–359	360–361	
Blame It on the Wolf	362–363	364, 366, 369–370	365	367–368	371	372–376	377	378–381	382–383	
Lou Gehrig: The Luckiest Man	384–385	386, 388, 391–392	387	389–390	393	394–398	399	400–403	404–405	
The Disguise	406–407	408, 410, 413–414	409	411–412	415	416–420	421	422–425	426–427	
Keepers	428–429	430, 432, 435–436	431	433–434	437	438–442	443	444–447	448–449	450–452

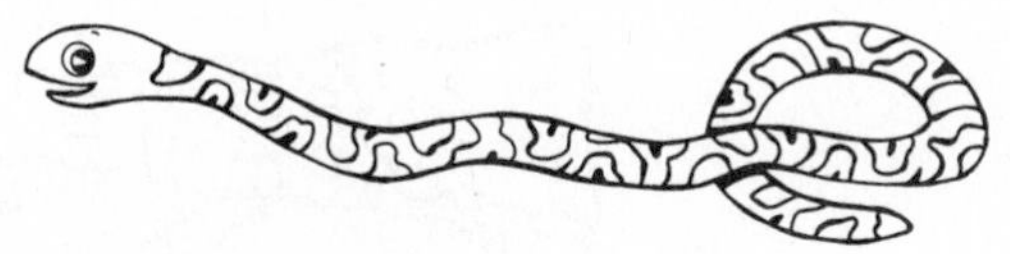

Unit 5

Other Times, Other Places	Family Times	Comprehension	Vocabulary	Selection Test	Writing Across Texts	Grammar	Phonics/ Word Study	Spelling	Research and Study Skills	Writing Process
Amazing Alice!	453–454	455, 457, 460–461	456	458–459	462	463–467	468	469–472	473–474	
A Peddler's Dream	475–476	477, 479, 482–483	478	480–481	484	485–489	490	491–494	495–496	
The Race for the North Pole	497–498	499, 501, 504–505	500	502–503	506	507–511	512	513–516	517–518	
Into the Sea	519–520	521, 523, 526–527	522	524–525	528	529–533	534	535–538	539–540	
Space Probes to the Planets	541–542	543, 545, 548–549	544	546–547	550	551–555	556	557–560	561–562	563–565

Unit 6

Express Yourself!	Family Times	Comprehension	Vocabulary	Selection Test	Writing Across Texts	Grammar	Phonics/ Word Study	Spelling	Research and Study Skills	Writing Process
Koya's Cousin Del	566–567	568, 570, 573–574	569	571–572	575	576–580	581	582–585	586–587	
Children of Clay	588–589	590, 592, 595–596	591	593–594	597	598–602	603	604–607	608–609	
Coming Home	610–611	612, 614, 617–618	613	615–616	619	620–624	625	626–629	630–631	
Out of the Blue	632–633	634, 636, 639–640	635	637–638	641	642–646	647	648–651	652–653	
Chocolate Is Missing	654–655	656, 658, 661–662	657	659–660	663	664–668	669	670–673	674–675	676–678

Family Times

Name______________________________________

Summary

Boy Finds Cooking Is Not "Women's Work"

Growing up in a house full of women, Justin feels frustrated by his mother and sisters, who are always after him to help with the household chores. He thinks doing dishes and making beds is "women's work." When Justin complains to his grandfather, Grandpa invites Justin home with him. With no women to cook and clean and make the beds, Justin discovers that it doesn't matter who does the work—and that it's not so hard after all.

Activity

Act It Out. Now that Justin sees that cooking can be a man's work, he wants to help. Act out a scene in which Justin and Grandpa make biscuits together. You can make real biscuits or make-believe ones. Don't forget to clean up!

Reading Skills

Setting

Setting is the time and place in which a story occurs. Sometimes pictures give clues to the setting of a story. Sometimes you need to use details the author has written. You may not always be able to determine the exact time a story takes place.

When Justin and his Grandpa go "riding fence," the author uses vivid details to help readers picture the setting, such as: **The early sun shone fiery red on the hilltops while the foothills were cast in shades of purple.**

Activity

Name That Place. Have your child use details to describe a place both of you know. See how quickly you can guess the place. If it takes many clues to guess the place, talk about the clues.

Family Times

Tested Vocabulary

Words to Know

Knowing the meanings of these words is important to reading "A Visit with Grandpa." Practice using these words to learn their meanings.

biscuits a kind of small, round, raised bread

dough soft, thick mixture of flour and other ingredients for baking

prairie large open grassy area with no trees

raisins dried grapes

rumpled crumpled, crushed, wrinkled

teasing trying to annoy or anger by unkind jokes or tricks

wrinkled ridged or folded irregularly; creased

Grammar

Sentences

A **sentence** is a group of words that makes a statement, a question, a command, a request, or an exclamation. Begin a sentence with a capital letter, and end it with a punctuation mark. You can tell whether a group of words is a complete sentence by checking to see if it expresses a complete idea.

These are sentences:
Justin made the bed.
Grandpa was a cowboy.

These are not sentences:
Riding fence.
Shirt for the festival.

Activity

Finish My Sentence. Pair up family members or friends. Take turns starting sentences that the other finishes.

Tested Spelling Words

____	____	____	____
____	____	____	____
____	____	____	____
____	____	____	____
____	____	____	____

Name ______________________________

Setting

- **Setting** is the time and place in which a story occurs. Sometimes the setting is important to the plot of a story. At other times, the setting is only background.
- Sometimes pictures show the setting, and sometimes you have to imagine it. Details that the author has written can help you see, hear, feel, and smell what it is like to be there.

Directions: Reread "The Red Fox." Fill in the word web with story details that would help you imagine the forest where the story takes place.

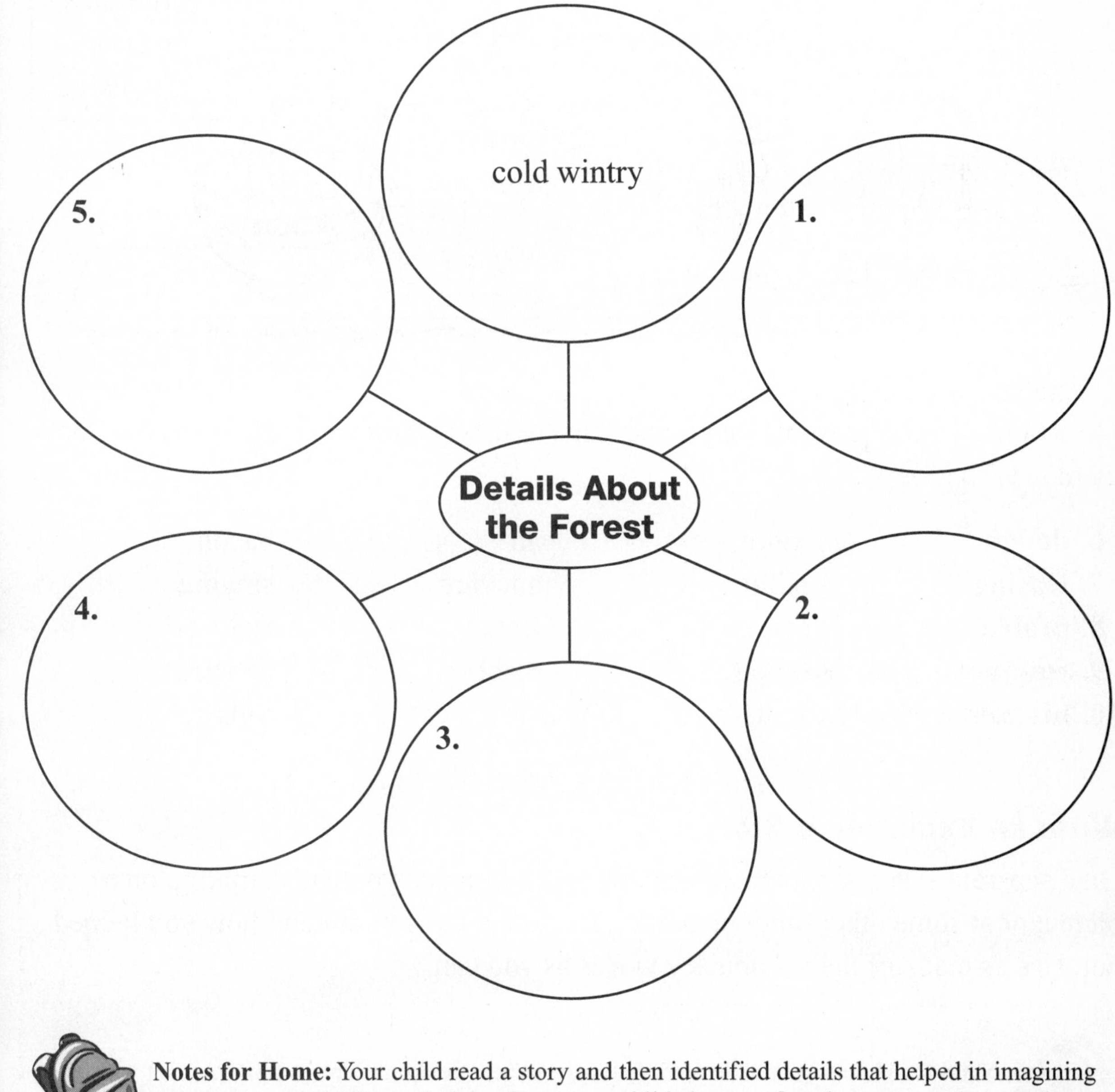

Details About the Forest

- cold wintry
- 1.
- 2.
- 3.
- 4.
- 5.

Notes for Home: Your child read a story and then identified details that helped in imagining the story's setting. ***Home Activity:*** Have your child choose a favorite room or place outdoors and give key details that would help someone who didn't know the place to imagine it.

Name ____

Vocabulary

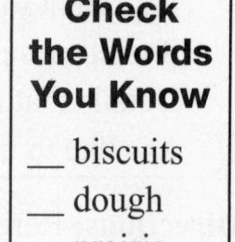

Directions: Choose the word from the box that best completes each statement. For example, *Neat* is to *messy* as *smooth* is to *rumpled.* Write the word on the line to the left.

Check the Words You Know

__ biscuits
__ dough
__ prairie
__ raisins
__ rumpled
__ teasing
__ wrinkled

____________ **1.** *Pancakes* is to *batter* as *cookies* is to _____.

____________ **2.** *Plums* is to *prunes* as *grapes* is to _____.

____________ **3.** *Sheep* is to *meadow* as *buffalo* is to _____.

____________ **4.** *Silky* is to *rough* as *unlined* is to _____.

____________ **5.** *Happy* is to *praising* as *angry* is to _____.

Directions: Circle the word that has the same or nearly the same meaning as the first word in each group.

6. dough	mixture	pan	bacon
7. teasing	honking	annoying	singing
8. prairie	beach	forest	field
9. rumpled	steamed	crushed	pressed
10. biscuits	peanuts	fruit	rolls

Write an Experience Story

On a separate sheet of paper, write about an experience you had camping, on a picnic, or at some other outdoor event. Describe what you did and how you helped out. Use as many of the vocabulary words as you can.

Notes for Home: Your child identified and learned vocabulary words from "A Visit with Grandpa." ***Home Activity:*** With your child, go through the vocabulary words and make a list of all the things the two of you think of in connection with each word.

Name ______________________________

Setting

- **Setting** is the time and place in which a story occurs.
- Sometimes pictures show the setting, and sometimes you have to visualize it from details the author has written.

Directions: Reread this passage from "A Visit with Grandpa" and try to visualize the scene it paints. Then answer the questions below.

Now the sun heated up the morning. The foothills were now varying shades of green. Shadows dotted the plains. Among the blackish green trees on the rolling hills, fog still lingered like lazy clouds. Insects buzzed. A small cloud of mosquitoes swarmed just behind their heads, and beautiful cardinals splashed their redness on the morning air. Justin felt a surge of happiness and hugged Black with his knees and heels.

1. What season of the year do you think it is? Why?

____

____

2. What can you tell about the time in which the story takes place? Explain.

____

____

3. What colors and sounds does Justin see and hear?

____

____

4. Why do you think Justin feels a "surge of happiness"?

____

5. Use a separate sheet of paper to describe a place that makes you feel the way Justin does. Remember to include vivid details about the setting.

Notes for Home: Your child has read a story and used story details to visualize its setting. ***Home Activity:*** Have your child describe in detail a place both of you know well. Then try to guess the place. Take turns describing and guessing other places.

Name ____________________

Selection Test

Directions: Choose the best answer to each item. Mark the letter for the answer you have chosen.

Part 1: Vocabulary

Find the answer choice that means about the same as the underlined word in each sentence.

1. Kenyi had never seen the prairie before.
- A. herd of cattle
- B. large, open area with no trees
- C. mountain range
- D. show put on by cowboys

2. The boy was teasing his little brother.
- F. joking with; making fun of
- G. instructing; giving a lesson to
- H. watching
- J. waiting for

3. Jenny offered me some biscuits.
- A. toast spread with jam or jelly
- B. sandwiches served with tea
- C. bread baked in small, round forms
- D. servings of meat

4. The man's clothing was rumpled.
- F. brightly colored
- G. expensive
- H. brand new
- J. crushed and messy

5. The sheets are wrinkled.
- A. torn in pieces
- B. covered with stains or dirt
- C. faded in color
- D. having many small folds or creases

6. It's time to prepare the dough.
- F. a box or trunk
- G. a favorite family recipe
- H. a mixture of flour, milk, fat, and other ingredients
- J. a simple meal cooked over a campfire

7. Be sure to bring enough raisins.
- A. fruit juices
- B. dried grapes
- C. sour apples
- D. small candies

Part 2: Comprehension

Use what you know about the story to answer each item.

8. What was Grandpa doing when Justin woke up?
- F. sleeping
- G. cooking breakfast
- H. fixing fences
- J. feeding the cattle

9. Grandpa expected Justin to—
A. tidy up after himself.
B. train the horses.
C. wash his clothes.
D. learn to rope.

10. At first, Justin thought that washing dishes was—
F. a waste of time.
G. an easy task.
H. woman's work.
J. a silly idea.

11. Where does Grandpa live?
A. in the mountains
B. on a prairie
C. in a large town
D. in a desert

12. Which sentence tells about the setting of this story?
F. "He hoped the wrinkles would disappear in time for the festival."
G. "Justin felt a surge of love for his grandpa."
H. "The foothills were now varying shades of green."
J. "Justin noticed that Grandpa had a map."

13. Justin was surprised to find out that Grandpa—
A. liked the cowboy festival.
B. had to mend the fences.
C. was a good cook.
D. enjoyed riding horseback.

14. What can you tell about Black cowboys from reading this story?
F. There were only a few Black cowboys.
G. Many books have been written about Black cowboys.
H. There are no more Black cowboys today.
J. Most people do not know about the greatest Black cowboys.

15. What was the most important thing Justin learned from Grandpa?
A. Riding fence takes a great deal of a rancher's time.
B. A mother deer will protect her fawn if she thinks people might hurt it.
C. Good bread can be made with just a few ingredients.
D. When a job needs to be done, it does not matter if a man or a woman does it.

STOP

Name ______________________________

Setting

- **Setting** is the time and place in which a story occurs.
- Sometimes pictures show the setting, and sometimes you have to imagine it from details the author has written.

Directions: Read the story below.

It was the kind of day when you don't want to move an inch. The sun beat down on us through bare windows. The air conditioning wasn't working, and the fans were useless. We were sitting in our new apartment. There were so many boxes, we could hardly see the furniture.

The heat wave seemed to have come out of nowhere. The day before, the movers had brought our things over in their truck. The weather was cool then. I hoped it would get cool again by the next week, when school started.

"When it's this hot," Ma said, "there's only one thing to do. Let's go down to the corner for an ice-cream soda."

Directions: Complete the diagram. For each question, underline the correct answer. Write a detail or a clue in each circle that helped you decide. In the middle, write a new title that tells something about the story's setting.

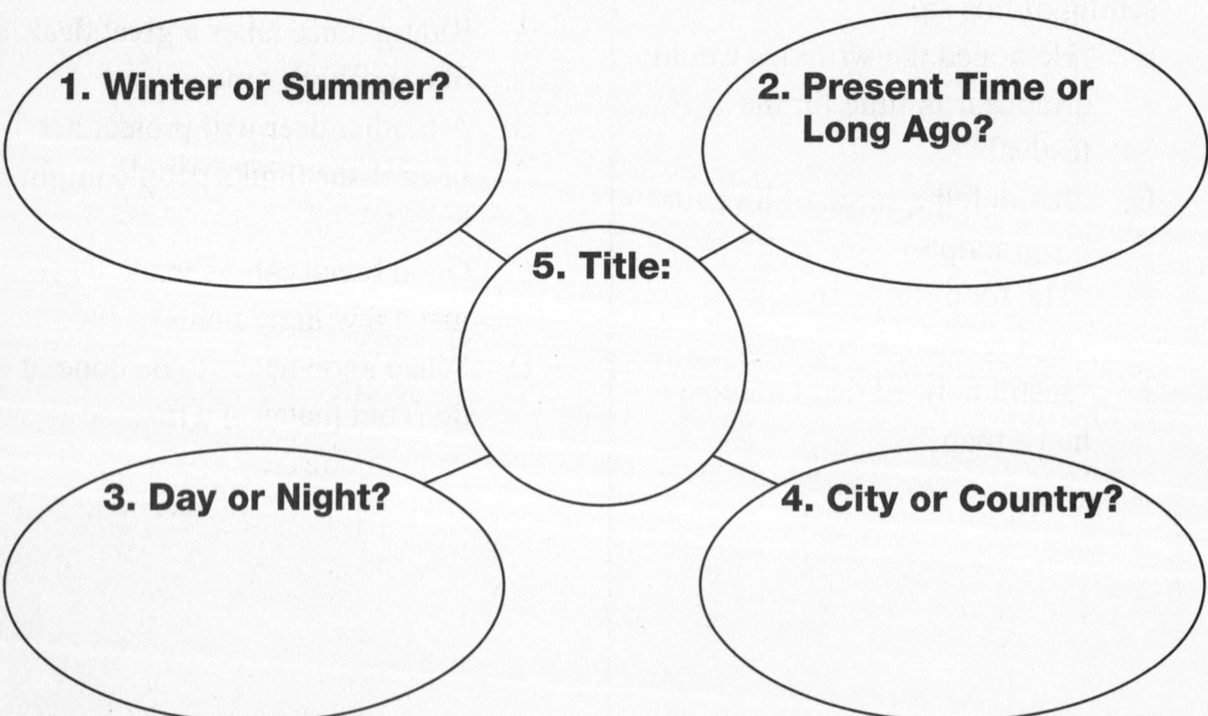

Notes for Home: Your child has read a story and used story details and clues to identify the time and place in which the story takes place. ***Home Activity:*** With your child, make a list of details that would help someone visualize a room in your home.

Name ______________________________

Sequence

REVIEW

Directions: Read the story. Then read each question about the story. Choose the best answer to each question. Mark the letter for the answer you have chosen.

But What Can I Do?

When Joe was five, he decided it was time to help around the house. Greg had already been taking out the trash for a few years. Mollie had started to help Dad vacuum. But what could he do?

He tried carrying the trash. But it was too heavy. Then he tried to vacuum. But it was too hard. The dishes were too slippery, and the beds were too big.

"I know," Joe said. "I'll cook dinner." Dad smiled. "How about if you put your toys away?"

"Aw, Dad," Joe said. "Do I have to?" Dad laughed.

1. Which story event happened first?

A. Joe decided it was time to help.
B. Mollie vacuumed.
C. Dad cooked.
D. Joe put his toys away.

2. Which list indicates the correct sequence of the tasks that Joe tried to do?

F. dishes, beds, vacuum, trash
G. vacuum, trash, beds, dishes
H. trash, vacuum, dishes, beds
J. beds, trash, vacuum, dishes

3. Which clue word in the second paragraph helps show the order of events?

A. but
B. then
C. tried
D. carrying

4. What is Joe most likely to do next?

F. put his toys away
G. eat dinner
H. cry
J. take out the trash

5. Which event took place years before Joe tried to take out the trash?

A. Mollie began to help vacuum.
B. Greg began to take out the trash.
C. Joe started to wash dishes.
D. Greg started to wash dishes.

Notes for Home: Your child has read a story and used story details to identify the order of story events. ***Home Activity:*** With your child prepare an item of food from a recipe. Go over the importance of the steps, or the sequence, of the recipe.

Name ______________________________

Writing Across Texts

Directions: Skim through "A Visit with Grandpa" and "Understanding Horses." Make notes about horses. Include at least five details from each selection about how horses act and about the work they do. Then decide whether you would make a good cowhand.

How Horses Act and the Work They Do	
A Visit with Grandpa	**Understanding Horses**
1.	**6.**
2.	**7.**
3.	**8.**
4.	**9.**
5.	**10.**

Write a Paragraph

You have learned a great deal about horses from reading "A Visit with Grandpa" and "Understanding Horses." Use information from both selections to write a paragraph telling about horses.

Notes for Home: Your child used information from different sources to write a paragraph. ***Home Activity:*** As you read a story or article with your child, discuss how its ideas connect to other reading your child has done.

Name ______________________________

REVIEW

Grammar: Statements and Questions

Directions: Write **S** if a group of words is a statement. Write **Q** if it is a question.

__________ **1.** Do you have a pet?

__________ **2.** What kind of pet do you have?

__________ **3.** Cats and dogs are the most common pets.

__________ **4.** Pets can be fun.

__________ **5.** Pet owners also have many responsibilities.

__________ **6.** Proper pet care takes time, effort, and money.

__________ **7.** Do you feed and exercise your pet every day?

__________ **8.** When did you last brush your cat or dog?

__________ **9.** Do you know the signs of a sick pet?

__________ **10.** Libraries have many books on pet care.

Directions: Add a word or a group of words to complete each sentence or question.

11. The pet I want ______________________________.

12. How do you know ______________________________?

13. I would make sure ______________________________.

14. My pet would ______________________________.

15. What animal do you ______________________________?

Notes for Home: Your child identified and wrote statements and questions. ***Home Activity:*** Take turns asking each other some simple questions and answering them using complete statements.

Practice

Name ______________________________

Grammar: Sentences

A **sentence** is a group of words that tells, asks, commands, or exclaims. It begins with a capital letter and ends with a punctuation mark. You can tell whether a group of words is a sentence by checking to see if it expresses a complete thought.

Sentence: My grandpa lives on a ranch.

Not a sentence: Lives on a ranch.

Directions: Read each group of words. Write **S** if it is a sentence. Write **NS** if it is not a sentence.

______________ **1.** Making the bed.

______________ **2.** Washing the dishes.

______________ **3.** My grandpa taught me to enjoy cleaning.

______________ **4.** In the kitchen.

______________ **5.** I like folding my clothes.

Directions: Choose the group of words in ( ) that will complete each sentence. Write the complete sentence on the line.

6. _____ helps your family. (All your hard work/Makes the bed)

____

7. Do you do _____? (in the house/chores at home)

____

8. Which chores _____? (the dirty dishes/should you do)

____

9. Someday I will have _____. (house a mess/my own house to clean)

____

10. A clean house _____. (is a happy house/without any dirt)

____

Notes for Home: Your child identified groups of words that make complete sentences. ***Home Activity:*** Talk with your child about an event that occurred at school. Have him or her describe the event, using complete sentences.

Name ______________________

Grammar: Sentences

Directions: Match each group of words on the left with a group of words on the right to make a sentence that makes the most sense. Write the matching letter on the line.

______	**1.** Have you ever gone	**a.** pancakes in the morning.
______	**2.** Wonderful things	**b.** the breakfast dishes.
______	**3.** First, we made	**c.** to visit your grandpa?
______	**4.** Then we washed	**d.** made the beds.
______	**5.** After doing the dishes, we	**e.** may be waiting for you at Grandpa's house.

Directions: Add a word or group of words to complete each sentence. Write the complete sentence on the line.

6. _____ make my bed.

____

7. The wrinkled shirt _____.

____

8. The house _____.

____

9. My grandfather cleans _____.

____

10. Everyone _____.

____

Write a Paragraph

Do you help with cleaning and other chores at home? On a separate sheet of paper, describe any tasks or chores that you do. Use complete sentences.

Notes for Home: Your child practiced completing sentences. ***Home Activity:*** Make a "To Do" list with your child of chores that need to be done. Be sure to use complete sentences.

Grammar: Sentences

RETEACHING

Look at the picture. Then underline the word group that describes it best.

All of the sheep.

All of the sheep are eating grass.

Is eating grass.

Did you underline the second group of words? It expresses a complete thought. It is a sentence.

A **sentence** is a group of words that tells, asks, commands, or exclaims. It begins with a capital letter and ends with a punctuation mark.

Directions: Underline the group of words in each pair that is a sentence.

1. The small brown cow. The cow grazed in the pasture.
2. Frogs caught flies. Their stomachs with insects.
3. Many bears in the cave. Did one bear eat fresh fish?
4. A raccoon got into our tent. Eating all our food.

Directions: Write complete sentences. Add your own words to each word group.

5. many bears

____

6. one grasshopper

____

7. chased a zebra

____

Notes for Home: Your child identified and wrote complete sentences. ***Home Activity:*** Talk with your child about what you did today. Have him or her summarize your day, using complete sentences.

Name ___________________________

Grammar: Sentences

Directions: Read the word group each animal is saying. Write each word group that is a sentence.

1. ___________________________

2. ___________________________

3. ___________________________

Directions: Underline each word group that is not a sentence. Add words to write a sentence of your own.

4. Many birds travel south.

5. Build nests.

6. Some animals migrate to warm climates.

7. Gray squirrels.

8. Need food in winter.

9. ___________________________

10. ___________________________

11. ___________________________

Notes for Home: Your child identified and wrote complete sentences. ***Home Activity:*** Have your child write five sentences about his or her favorite subject in school. Remind your child to use complete sentences.

Name ____________________

Phonics: Vowel Digraphs

Directions: Read the words in the box. Decide whether the underlined part of each word has a vowel sound like **tree, hay,** or **boat.** Write each word in the correct column.

stay	heated	soap
doe	receive	waited
slowly	feeling	plain

tree	**hay**	**boat**
1. ________	4. ________	7. ________
2. ________	5. ________	8. ________
3. ________	6. ________	9. ________

Directions: Underline the word in each sentence that has the same vowel sound as the boldfaced word to the left. Write the word on the line.

________ **10. tree** Eric had a good feeling about the day ahead.

________ **11. hay** He and his grandpa were going riding today.

________ **12. boat** They took the path through the meadow.

________ **13. boat** They saw a doe coming out of the woods.

________ **14. hay** The doe was afraid of Eric and his grandpa.

________ **15. tree** It is easy to frighten a doe.

________ **16. tree** Later, they rode home across the field.

________ **17. boat** Later, they watched as the sun slowly set.

Directions: For each word below, write three more words that have the same vowel sound spelled the same way.

18. nail ________ ________ ________

19. need ________ ________ ________

20. slow ________ ________ ________

Notes for Home: Your child learned different spellings for the vowel sounds long *e (tree, eat, deceive, niece),* long *a (play, bait),* and long *o (boat, mow, toe).* ***Home Activity:*** Pick one of these vowel sounds. Make a list of words that use each spelling.

Spelling: Vowel Sounds in *few* and *moon*

Pretest Directions: Fold back the page along the dotted line. On the blanks, write the spelling words as they are dictated. When you have finished the test, unfold the page and check your words.

1. ____________________
2. ____________________
3. ____________________
4. ____________________
5. ____________________
6. ____________________
7. ____________________
8. ____________________
9. ____________________
10. ____________________
11. ____________________
12. ____________________
13. ____________________
14. ____________________
15. ____________________
16. ____________________
17. ____________________
18. ____________________
19. ____________________
20. ____________________

1. The volcano is **huge**.
2. **Excuse** me from the table.
3. Don't **confuse** me!
4. There are a **few** left.
5. Her **nephew** is seven.
6. What time is our **curfew**?
7. This is my **usual** lunch.
8. He is a good **pupil**.
9. Gasoline is a **fuel**.
10. Is soup on the **menu**?
11. It is **cool** outside.
12. I'm in a good **mood**.
13. **Shoot** the picture.
14. This is our **school**.
15. I forgot my **shampoo**.
16. Pick **fruit** off the tree.
17. She wore a blue **suit**.
18. Drink some **juice**.
19. My **bruise** is healing.
20. **Cruise** down the river.

Notes for Home: Your child took a pretest on words that have vowel sounds such as those in *few* and *moon*. ***Home Activity:*** Help your child learn misspelled words before the final test. Your child should look at the word, say it, spell it aloud, and then spell it with eyes shut.

Name ________________________________

Spelling: Vowel Sounds in *few* and *moon*

Word List

huge	nephew	fuel	shoot	suit
excuse	curfew	menu	school	juice
confuse	usual	cool	shampoo	bruise
few	pupil	mood	fruit	cruise

Directions: Write the words from the box that have the same vowel sound as **moon.** Sort the words according to how the vowel sound is spelled.

Spelled oo	**Spelled ui**
1. ________________	6. ________________
2. ________________	7. ________________
3. ________________	8. ________________
4. ________________	9. ________________
5. ________________	10. ________________

Directions: Choose the word from the box that best matches each clue. Write the word on the line.

________________ **11.** to make unclear

________________ **12.** opposite of *niece*

________________ **13.** wood for a fire; food for your body

________________ **14.** a list of food you can order

________________ **15.** the time at which you have to be home

________________ **16.** your reason for not doing what you're supposed to

________________ **17.** immense; large

________________ **18.** someone who studies something

________________ **19.** not many

________________ **20.** ordinary

Notes for Home: Your child spelled words with the vowel sounds in *few* and *moon*. ***Home Activity:*** Together, write silly sentences that use two or more of the spelling words in each sentence.

Name ___________________________________

Spelling: Vowel Sounds in *few* and *moon*

Directions: Proofread this list. Find five spelling mistakes. Use the proofreading marks to correct each mistake.

≡	Make a capital.
/	Make a small letter.
∧	Add something.
℘	Take out something.
⊙	Add a period.
¶	Begin a new paragraph.

A Few Rules of the House

1. Curfuw: Schol nights 8:00. Weekends 9:00.
2. If you use up the soap or shampew, tell somebody.
3. Put your laundry in the basket. No exkuse will be accepted!
4. If you drink all the jewce or milk, put the container in the recycling bin.
5. If you have a few extra minutes, pick up a few things.

Spelling Tip

excuse few pupil cool juice

Watch for words that have the same vowel sounds but different spellings. The vowel sound in **few** can be spelled **u-consonant-e, ew,** or **u.** The vowel sound in **moon** can be spelled **oo** or **ui.**

Word List

huge	cool
excuse	mood
confuse	shoot
few	school
nephew	shampoo
curfew	fruit
usual	suit
pupil	juice
fuel	bruise
menu	cruise

Write Your Own Rules

On a separate sheet of paper, write your own list of rules. Try to use at least three spelling words.

Notes for Home: Your child spelled words with the vowel sounds in *few* and *moon.* ***Home Activity:*** Write a list of words with your child that rhyme with *few* and *moon.* Discuss the different spellings for these two vowel sounds.

Spelling: Vowel Sounds in *few* and *moon*

REVIEW

Directions: Choose the word from the box that completes each comparison. Write the word on the line.

Word List
huge
excuse
confuse
few
nephew
curfew
usual
pupil
fuel
menu
cool
mood
shoot
school
shampoo
fruit
suit
juice
bruise
cruise

1. song and program,
food and __________

2. aunt and uncle,
niece and __________

3. body and soap,
hair and __________

4. hot and warm,
cold and __________

5. tiny and little,
big and __________

6. knife and cut,
bump and __________

7. sailboat and wind,
car and __________

8. football and toss,
basketball and __________

9. thinking and idea,
feeling and __________

10. rare and uncommon,
ordinary and __________

Directions: Choose the word from the box that best completes each statement. Write the word on the line to the left.

_______________ **11.** To see the world, be a waiter on a _____ ship.

_______________ **12.** To learn your job, go to a training _____.

_______________ **13.** If you do well, you are a good _____.

_______________ **14.** On work days, you will have an early _____.

_______________ **15.** Don't let the passengers _____ you with their orders.

_______________ **16.** Try not to spill soup on a passenger's good _____.

_______________ **17.** Don't drop the bowl of _____ and bruise the apples.

_______________ **18.** Don't bring tomato _____ if someone orders water.

_______________ **19.** If you forget an order, don't make an _____.

_______________ **20.** After work, you will have a _____ free hours.

Notes for Home: Your child spelled words with the vowel sounds in *few* and *moon*. ***Home Activity:*** Choose a word from the box. Then give clues about the word so your child can guess and spell the word. Let your child do the same for you.

Name ______________________________

Textbook/Trade Book

Textbooks usually teach about one subject, such as social studies or math. These books are organized to help you find information quickly. Each **chapter title** tells you about a main section of the book, and the **headings** and **subheadings** show what information you can find in a particular section. **Vocabulary words** are often printed in bold and included in the margin.

Directions: Use the textbook section to answer the questions that follow.

CHAPTER 8 American History 1865–1885

A Cowboy's Life

Chefs on the Prairie

A cowboy's job involved many hours of hard work, so when dinnertime finally arrived, he was ready for hearty meals. Since cowboys used the word "chuck" to mean food, the vehicle that carried the food around was called a **chuck wagon.** These wagons, which also served as kitchens, hotels, and ranch headquarters, were driven by the cook.

chuck wagon: vehicle that carried meals to cowboys

The cook's day began at about 3:00 A.M. He would wake up the crew to help him prepare breakfast. Some cowboys complained that they had to work from sunrise to sunset, or as they put it from "can't see to can't see." To bake the biscuits, the camp chefs used cast iron **Dutch ovens.** These ovens were used to bake biscuits, cornbread, fruit cobblers, and cakes. Popular cowboy meals around the campfire included beef, beans, biscuits, rice, and dried fruit. Cowboys rarely ate fresh vegetables, milk, or eggs.

Dutch oven: a large, heavy kettle

1. How could you quickly find the definitions for vocabulary words on this page?

____

____

2. If you wanted to write an essay called "A Day in the Life of a Cowboy," do you think this textbook chapter would be helpful? Explain why or why not.

____

____

3. What part of the page tells you the time period this chapter covers?

____

____

Name ______________________________

A **trade book** is any book that is not a textbook, a periodical, or a reference book. The skills you use for understanding trade books are a lot like those you use when you read textbooks. When you choose a trade book, think about your purpose for reading, the same as you would for choosing a reference book.

Directions: Use the trade book excerpt to answer the questions that follow.

25

Chapter 3: If You Were a Wild West Wrangler

Q: Did cowboys travel with tables and chairs?

A: They usually ate their meals sitting or squatting on the ground.

Q: What other responsibilities did a cowboy cook have?

A: In addition to preparing food, it was not unusual for the cook to serve as the camp doctor and barber. The cook also drove the chuck wagon. Every night after dinner, the cook pointed the wagon toward the North Star, so he could head in the right direction the next day.

4. How is the information in this book organized? How might this be helpful for writing an essay about a cowboy's daily life?

____

____

5. In addition to cooking meals, what other responsibilities did the cook have?

____

____

Notes for Home: Your child used a textbook and a trade book to locate information and draw conclusions. ***Home Activity:*** Discuss some other resources your child might use to find information about cowboys, such as history TV channels, history magazines, and so on.

Family Times

Name____

Summary

Will Marianne Find a Home?

From the time she was left at the orphanage in New York City, Marianne had expected her mother to come back for her. When Marianne boards the train that will take her and thirteen other orphans to the Midwest, she hopes her mother will be there waiting to claim her. But doubt creeps in, and she begins to wonder if anyone will want her.

Activity

Train Talk. Imagine you're on a train in 1878 carrying orphans across the prairie to new homes. Choose characters to play, such as a conductor, an orphan, one of the adult caretakers, or another passenger. Talk about what you see out the window and how you feel about your journey.

Reading Skills

Sequence

Sequence is the order in which things happen. It can also mean the steps we follow to do something. Some ways to identify a sequence of events are:

- ❖ **Clue Words.** *First, then, next,* and *finally, while,* and *during* are some words that help you figure out the order of events. So do dates and times of day.
- ❖ **Flashback.** Watch for events that are told out of order. An event from the past that is retold is called a **flashback.**

Activity

Scrambled Events. Partner up for this activity. Have each person write down four or five events from the day on strips of paper. Use clue words in the sentences. Mix up the slips and exchange them with your partner. Try to put each other's events in order.

Family Times

Tested Vocabulary

Words to Know

Knowing the meanings of these words is important to reading *Train to Somewhere.* Practice using these words to learn their meanings.

adopt accept a child of other parents and bring up as your own

atlas a book of maps

carriage a four-wheeled vehicle that is pushed or pulled

couple two people who are married, engaged, or otherwise paired

misery great suffering or unhappiness

platform a raised level surface

Grammar

Subjects and Predicates

A sentence has two parts: a **subject** and a **predicate.** The subject is the word or group of words about which something is said: **The big, noisy train.** It usually begins the sentence. The predicate tells something about the subject and usually follows it: **pulled into the station.**

Activity

Mix and Match. Take pairs of index cards and write the subject of a sentence on one card and the predicate on the other. Make separate piles of subjects and predicates. Take turns picking a card from each pile and then putting them together. Did you make a serious or a silly sentence?

Tested Spelling Words

____	____	____	____
____	____	____	____
____	____	____	____
____	____	____	____
____	____	____	____

Name ______________________________

Sequence

- **Sequence** means the order in which things happen. **Sequence** can also mean steps we follow to do something.
- Clue words such as *first, then, next,* and *finally* help you figure out the sequence of events.
- Some events in a story may take place at the same time. Authors may use words like *meanwhile, while,* or *during* to show this.
- Sometimes events are told out of order. Verb tenses or clue words can show this.

Directions: Reread "Will Sarah Return?" On the lines below, write the story events from the box in the order that they happened. Use the letter shown next to each event.

Story Events

a. Anna sweeps the porch.
b. Anna sweeps the porch again.
c. Caleb picks up Seal.
d. Seal jumps onto the porch.
e. Anna asks her father where Sarah has gone.
f. Caleb cleans out the stove.
g. Anna watches a wagon take Mama away.
h. Caleb spills the ashes.
i. Anna and Caleb watch Sarah.
j. Anna and Caleb take lunch to their father.

1. ____________ **6.** ____________
2. ____________ **7.** ____________
3. ____________ **8.** ____________
4. ____________ **9.** ____________
5. ____________ **10.** ____________

Notes for Home: Your child read a story and identified the order in which the story events occurred. ***Home Activity:*** Work with your child to create a "My Day" list that shows all your child's activities in order from waking up in the morning to the present time.

Name ________________________________

Vocabulary

Directions: Choose the word from the box that best completes each sentence. Write the word on the matching numbered line to the right.

Check the Words You Know

__ adopt
__ atlas
__ carriage
__ couple
__ misery
__ platform

Mr. and Mrs. Garcia are the **1.** _____ next door. Last month they told me they were going to **2.** _____ a daughter. Mrs. Garcia took out her **3.** _____ and showed me the country where the baby was born. She said that she would be very happy to end the **4.** _____ of waiting so long for the baby. Yesterday I saw Mr. Garcia happily pushing a **5.** _____ with a beautiful baby girl inside.

1. ________________
2. ________________
3. ________________
4. ________________
5. ________________

Directions: Choose the word from the box that best matches each clue. Write the word in the puzzle.

Down

6. accept a child of other parents and bring it up as your own
7. book of maps
9. great unhappiness

Across

8. a raised, level surface
10. a 4-wheeled vehicle that is pulled or pushed

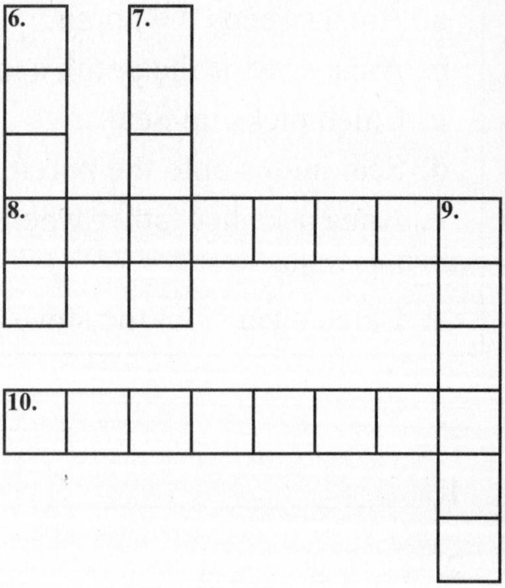

Write a Story

On a separate sheet of paper, write a story about a couple who think they are adopting a puppy, but get a very different kind of animal instead. Use as many of the vocabulary words as you can.

Notes for Home: Your child identified and used new vocabulary words from *Train to Somewhere. **Home Activity:*** With your child, make up a story about a child traveling to a new home. Encourage your child to use as many of the vocabulary words as possible.

Name ______________________________

Sequence

- **Sequence** means the order in which things happen. Clue words such as *first, then, next,* and *finally* help you figure out the sequence of events.
- Authors do not always use clue words to show sequence.

Directions: Reread what happens in *Train to Somewhere* after Marianne and eight other children leave the first stop, Porterville, Illinois. Then answer the questions below. Look for any clue words the author uses to show the sequence of events.

Nine of us are left to get back on the train. Miss Randolph says we're to keep on our good clothes. We'll be getting off again soon.

At Kilburn we are walked to a hardware store to stand in line.

"I expect they took all the biggest boys in Porterville," one man says. "But still. . . ."

Eddie Hartz, who is only seven, is taken. There's a boy who can stand on his hands and pretend to pull buttons out of people's ears. He makes the crowd laugh and he gets taken, too.

As soon as the train has loaded on wood and fresh water, the rest of us get back aboard.

1. What is the first event of this passage? ______________________________

____

2. What is the last event of this passage? ______________________________

____

3. Were the children wearing their good clothes before they got to Kilburn? How do you know?

____

4. How many children get back on the train? How do you know?

____

5. On a separate sheet of paper, write three sentences telling what happens next in the story.

Notes for Home: Your child has read a story and used story details to describe the order in which events occurred. ***Home Activity:*** Have your child make a list of tomorrow's activities. Then ask him or her to number the list in the order that the events are expected to happen.

Selection Test

Directions: Choose the best answer to each item. Mark the letter for the answer you have chosen.

Part 1: Vocabulary

Find the answer choice that means about the same as the underlined word in each sentence.

1. Wanda described her <u>misery</u> to me.
- A. way of doing things
- B. great suffering or unhappiness
- C. adventure
- D. plans for the future

2. The <u>platform</u> is large and sturdy.
- F. a chest for clothing
- G. a wall made of stone
- H. a wooden box
- J. a raised flat surface

3. The Lees will <u>adopt</u> a little boy.
- A. have happy memories of
- B. raise a child of other parents as their own
- C. pay a visit to
- D. guide someone on a long trip

4. I borrowed this <u>atlas</u> from Arnie.
- F. small suitcase
- G. old-fashioned camera
- H. book of maps
- J. heavy jacket

5. The <u>carriage</u> needs to be repaired.
- A. something to carry passengers
- B. something to eat with
- C. something to train animals
- D. something to row with

6. The <u>couple</u> ate dinner at home.
- F. the children of a family
- G. several people who are traveling together
- H. a close relative
- J. two people with a close relationship

Part 2: Comprehension

Use what you know about the story to answer each item.

7. What is the first thing Marianne does each time the train stops?
- A. has some cookies and milk
- B. changes into old clothes
- C. tries to look pleasant
- D. looks for her mother in the crowd

8. Miss Randolph's feeling about the children is that they—
- F. are hard to care for.
- G. will all be happy in their new homes.
- H. are fussy and spoiled.
- J. are very special and she will miss them.

9. Which event in this story happens before the train leaves New York?
A. Nora and Marianne sit together on the train.
B. Miss Randolph gives the children milk and cookies.
C. Marianne's mother leaves her at St. Christopher's.
D. The train stops at a town called Somewhere.

10. The feather Marianne carries in her pocket is a—
F. reminder of her mother.
G. gift from Nora.
H. decoration for her hair.
J. lucky charm.

11. How does Marianne feel when the train reaches Somewhere?
A. peaceful and content
B. tired and bored
C. excited and hopeful
D. hurt and unloved

12. What happens first when Marianne meets the Books?
F. She gives Mrs. Book her feather.
G. She notices that the Books are old.
H. She agrees to go with the Books.
J. She asks for a puppy.

13. Which sentence best describes the lesson in this story?
A. Children should learn to do the things that please adults.
B. Friends are usually more important than relatives.
C. Sometimes what you get is better than what you wished for.
D. Adults always know what is best for children.

14. Which sentence suggests that Marianne likes Mrs. Book?
F. "She's wearing a heavy black dress and a man's droopy black hat."
G. "The woman's holding a wooden toy locomotive."
H. "Somehow this woman understands about me, how it felt that nobody wanted me."
J. "She pats Mr. Book's hand and they smile at each other."

15. In this story, Marianne's biggest disappointment was—
A. leaving Miss Randolph.
B. leaving St. Christopher's.
C. being taken by the Books.
D. knowing her mother had not come for her.

STOP

Name ________________________________

Sequence

First → Next → Finally

- **Sequence** means the order in which things happen. Clue words such as *first, then, next,* and *finally* help you figure out the sequence of events.
- Authors do not always use clue words to show sequence.

Directions: Read the story below.

My great-grandmother Rose told me how she loved to visit her country cousins. It took all morning to go across town and a few miles into the next county. First, she walked to the corner of her block. There, she got on a trolley. Then, she took a train. Next, she rode a second trolley to the city limits. Finally, she took a bus out into the country!

Her uncle and cousins always picked up my great-grandmother in their buggy at the bus station. She was tired from the trip, but it was worth it. She would stay with her relatives for a few days. What fun they would have! Then, finally, it was time for her to make the long trip home.

Directions: Fill in the flowchart with the events in the order they happened.

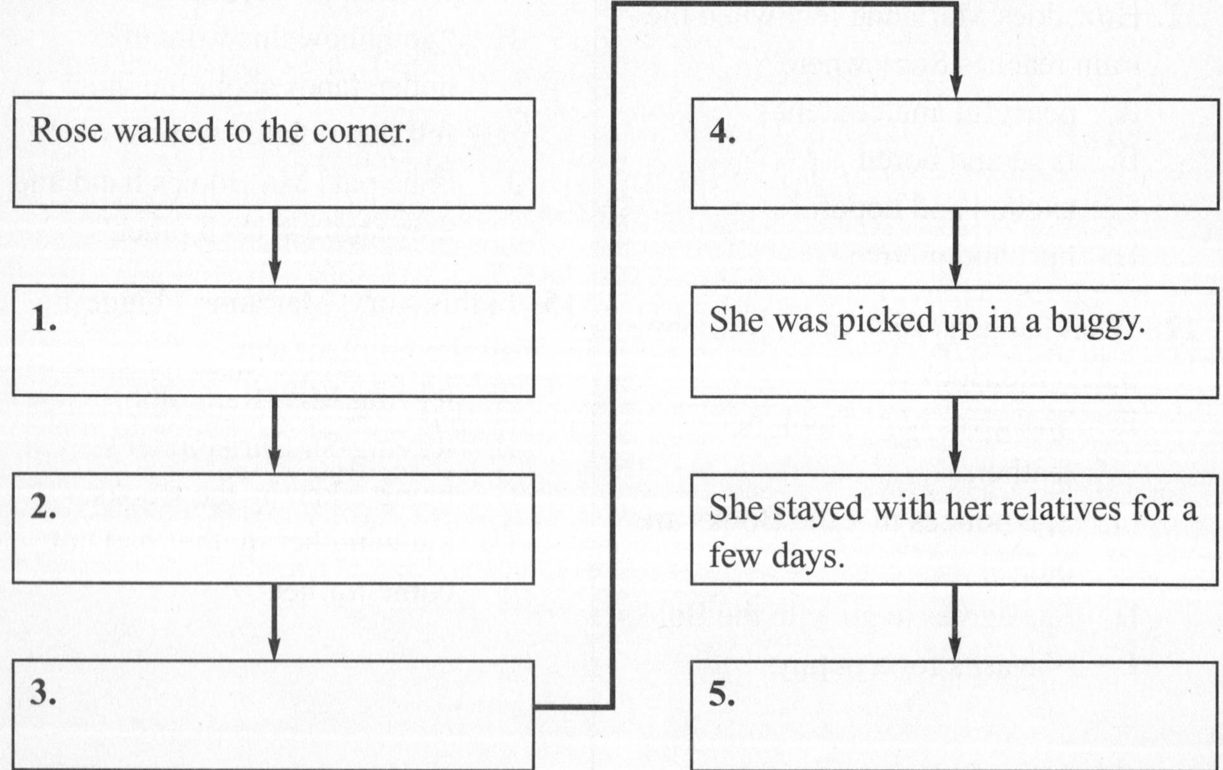

Rose walked to the corner.
1.
2.
3.
4.
She was picked up in a buggy.
She stayed with her relatives for a few days.
5.

Notes for Home: Your child has read a story and used story details to fill in a flowchart showing the sequence of events. ***Home Activity:*** The next time you take a trip with your child, such as to the grocery store, take turns recalling the sequence of events of the trip.

Name ____________________

Cause and Effect

REVIEW

Directions: Read the story. Then read each question about the story. Choose the best answer to each question. Mark the letter for the answer you have chosen.

Leaving Time

Mom told me that her family was always late leaving on vacation. That's because they didn't like to get up early. Also, it took a long time to get ready.

Mom said Grandma had too many clothes. She could never decide what to pack.

Grandpa always spotted a chore he forgot to do. Mom usually found him cleaning or fixing something. Sometimes he couldn't find the map.

My uncle David had hair that wouldn't stay down. He would spend an hour combing it. Then it would pop up again.

Mom could never decide what books to take. So she had to start reading each one.

1. Which was **not** a cause of the family leaving late?
   A. getting up late
   B. the weather
   C. Grandma's packing
   D. Mom's reading

2. What was the effect of David's hair not staying down?
   F. He forgot to comb it.
   G. He had a cowlick.
   H. His combing made the family late.
   J. His hair popped up.

3. What might Grandpa do to make the family late?
   A. go to the park
   B. comb his hair
   C. fix the lawn sprinkler
   D. eat a big breakfast

4. What might have helped the family be on time?
   F. eat breakfast together
   G. pack the night before
   H. check the weather report
   J. get gas for the car

5. In the following sentence, which word gives a clue about why something happened?
   David's hair wouldn't stay down, so he took a long time combing it.
   A. wouldn't
   B. down
   C. time
   D. so

Notes for Home: Your child identified causes and effects in a story. ***Home Activity:*** Play a game of cause and effect. When something happens at home, look for causes and effects. For example, if the timer doesn't go off (cause), then dinner may burn (effect).

Name ____________________

Writing Across Texts

Directions: The stories *Train to Somewhere* and "A Visit with Grandpa" show how an event in a person's life can have many effects. Complete the first two columns of the table by listing effects that Marianne and Justin had as a result of their experiences. Then, in the third column, list an important event in your own life and the multiple effects it has caused.

Cause: Marianne was left in an orphanage. **Effect:** She was put on an orphan train.	**Cause:** Justin went to stay with Grandpa. **Effect:** He learned that making a bed was easy.	**Cause:** **Effect:**
1.	**6.**	**11.**
2.	**7.**	**12.**
3.	**8.**	**13.**
4.	**9.**	**14.**
5.	**10.**	**15.**

Write a Cause and Effect Paragraph

On a separate sheet of paper, write a cause and effect paragraph that describes how an event in your life has caused multiple effects.

Notes for Home: Your child listed details from two different selections. ***Home Activity:*** Talk with your child about someone who has had an effect on you in your lifetime. Share how that person has changed your life in some way.

Name ______________________________

Grammar: Sentences

REVIEW

Directions: Read each group of words. Write **S** if it is a sentence. Write **NS** if it is not a sentence.

__________ **1.** A big family has many benefits.

__________ **2.** Never lonely.

__________ **3.** Lots of help with homework.

__________ **4.** You can meet the friends of your brothers and sisters.

__________ **5.** Someone will always stick up for you.

Directions: Add a word or group of words to complete each sentence. Write the complete sentence on the line. Remember to begin each sentence with a capital letter and end each one with a punctuation mark.

6. have fun together

____

7. younger brothers and sisters

____

8. share toys and games

____

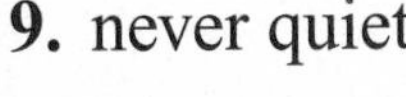

9. never quiet

____

10. have responsibilities

____

Notes for Home: Your child identified and wrote complete sentences. ***Home Activity:*** Choose a picture in a magazine. Have your child write several sentences about the picture. Check that each sentence begins with a capital letter and ends with a punctuation mark.

Name ______________________________

Practice

Grammar: Subjects and Predicates

The **subject** is the word or group of words about which something is said in the sentence. The **predicate** is the word or group of words that tells something about the subject. All the words in the subject are called the **complete subject.** All the words in the predicate are called the **complete predicate.**

All my friends love baseball.

The **simple subject** is the main noun or pronoun in the complete subject. It may be more than one word. The **simple predicate** is the verb in the complete predicate. Some simple predicates can be more than one word.

Peter Jones hit the ball hard. The fans were cheering loudly.

Directions: For each sentence, underline the complete subject once and underline the complete predicate twice.

1. A.J. is always picked last for baseball games.
2. The team captains pick all the best players first.
3. A.J. waits in the hot sun.
4. I may be team captain one day.
5. My friend A.J. will not be picked last then.

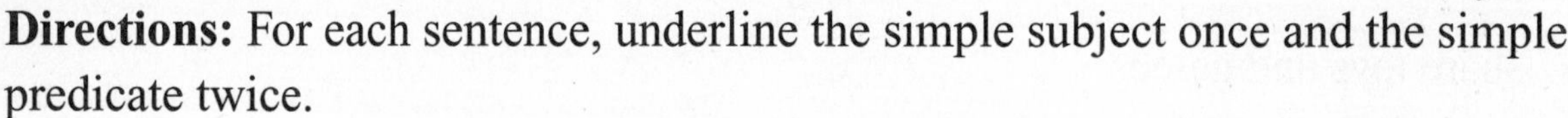

Directions: For each sentence, underline the simple subject once and the simple predicate twice.

6. I had a big surprise yesterday.
7. Ms. Martin chose A.J. as a team captain.
8. A.J. made many picks.
9. Believe it or not, I was the last one picked.
10. Suddenly, I have changed my mind about picking A.J.!

Notes for Home: Your child identified simple and complete subjects and simple and complete predicates in sentences. ***Home Activity:*** Ask your child to identify simple and complete subjects and predicates in a variety of sentences from a story or newspaper.

Name ______________________________

Grammar: Subjects and Predicates

Directions: For each sentence, underline the complete subject once. Underline the complete predicate twice. Circle the simple subject and the simple predicate.

1. Trains were slower a hundred years ago.
2. The earliest models took a long time to get anywhere.
3. A family had no other good way to travel.

4. Cars were a new invention.
5. Few people had them.
6. Our lives were much slower then.
7. Many people traveled to see new places.
8. They liked to get off at a stop and look around.
9. Most families thought cross-country travel was amazing.
10. They tried to imagine faraway places.
11. Most people never went far from home.
12. Fancy new cars had changed people's ideas about travel.
13. They made it easier to travel farther and faster.
14. Roads were appearing everywhere.
15. Trains became less important.

Write a Letter

Imagine you're traveling somewhere on a train. On a separate sheet of paper, write a letter home, describing what you see. Identify the simple and complete subjects and predicates in each sentence.

Notes for Home: Your child identified simple and complete subjects and predicates. ***Home Activity:*** Start with a sentence that has a simple subject and predicate. Take turns adding words to make the sentence longer, without losing the starting words or idea.

Name ______________________________

RETEACHING

Grammar: Subjects and Predicates

Read the sentence about Ana. Then answer the questions.

Ana plays ball.

1. Write the one word that tells whom the sentence is about. ____________
That word is the subject of the sentence.

2. Write the words that tell what Ana does. ____________
Those words are the predicate of the sentence.

A sentence has two parts. The **subject** is the word or group of words about which something is said in the sentence. The **predicate** tells about the subject.

Directions: Complete each sentence. Add a subject or a predicate from the lists.

Subjects	Predicates
You	make puppets for children
People in ancient times	are popular today

1. Puppet shows ______________________________.

2. Some adults ______________________________.

3. ____________ can give your own puppet show.

Directions: Underline the subject and circle the predicate in each sentence.

4. Some children make puppets from old socks.

5. They put the socks on their hands.

6. Their fingers make the puppet move.

7. Some of the puppets look like real people.

8. Other puppets are very unusual.

9. This puppet wears a tall hat.

Notes for Home: Your child identified and wrote subjects and predicates of sentences. ***Home Activity:*** Look at a magazine or newspaper article with your child. Have him or her underline the subjects and circle the predicates of five sentences.

Name ______________________________

Grammar: Subjects and Predicates

Directions: Draw a line between the subject and the predicate of each sentence. Then write each simple subject and simple predicate below the correct heading.

1. Many people live in Colorado.

2. The state has many mountains.

3. Few trees grow on the mountaintops.

4. The tall mountains are beautiful.

Simple Subjects	Simple Predicates
1. ______________________	**1.** ______________________
2. ______________________	**2.** ______________________
3. ______________________	**3.** ______________________
4. ______________________	**4.** ______________________

Directions: Read each sentence. Draw one line under the subject. Draw two lines under the predicate. Circle the simple subject and the simple predicate.

5. Many hikers climb the mountains.

6. The water in the streams is clear.

7. The birds in the trees sing in the morning.

8. Squirrels run around the trees.

9. Groups of campers look for campsites.

Write a Speech

On a separate sheet of paper, write a speech about your state. Use complete sentences to communicate your ideas.

Notes for Home: Your child wrote subjects and predicates of sentences. ***Home Activity:*** Provide your child with two subjects (for example, *The huge basketball, My jeans*). Have him or her make up predicates to go with the subjects and write the complete sentences.

Name____________________________________

Phonics: Vowel Digraphs

Directions: Read each sentence. Say the underlined word to yourself. Listen for the vowel sounds that the letters **ea** and **ou** represent in **feather, peak,** and **country.** Circle the word in ( ) that has the same vowel sound as the underlined word.

1. The steam train pulled into the station. (break/beat)
2. The train was taking orphan children to the country. (found/tough)
3. Many people had read about the children on the train. (sea/dead)
4. The train traveled in all kinds of weather. (bread/bead)
5. After four days, the children had had enough of riding the train. (though/tough)
6. Not knowing where their next home would be was tough on them. (fought/rough)
7. Instead of getting off the train, they waited until the next stop. (head/meat)
8. Only one couple came to meet the train at the stop. (rough/bought)
9. The woman had a white feather in her hat. (fear/head)
10. She quickly reached out to welcome the children. (seat/ready)

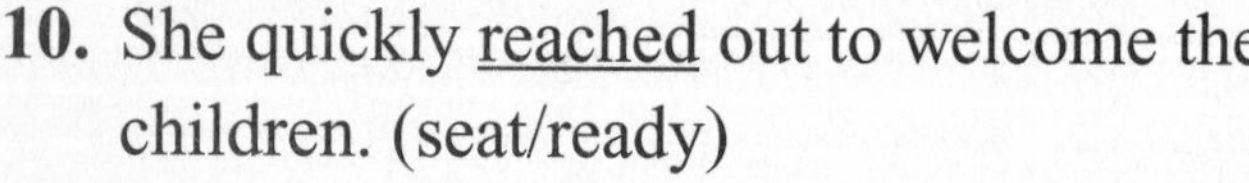

Directions: Read each word. Say it to yourself. Listen for the **vowel sound** that the underlined letters represent. Find the word with a different vowel spelling that has the same **vowel sound.** Circle the word.

11. country	cold	foul	fun
12. weather	bed	bath	bead
13. heat	height	receive	wait
14. couple	cup	cope	cop
15. heaven	heave	seven	haven

Notes for Home: Your child paired words with the same vowel sounds heard in *feather, peak,* and *country*. ***Home Activity:*** Help your child think of other words spelled with *ea* and *ou* that have these vowel sounds.

Pretest

Spelling: Short e and Long e

Pretest Directions: Fold back the page along the dotted line. On the blanks, write the spelling words as they are dictated. When you have finished the test, unfold the page and check your words.

1. ______________________
2. ______________________
3. ______________________
4. ______________________
5. ______________________
6. ______________________
7. ______________________
8. ______________________
9. ______________________
10. ______________________
11. ______________________
12. ______________________
13. ______________________
14. ______________________
15. ______________________
16. ______________________
17. ______________________
18. ______________________
19. ______________________
20. ______________________

1. Have you seen **them**?
2. Morgan **went** ice-skating.
3. Our **fence** needs fixing.
4. He got **credit** for his deed.
5. Turn the **engine** on.
6. I will enter the **contest**.
7. **Speak** up in class.
8. What **reason** do you have?
9. **Beat** the drum.
10. Which is the **least** full?
11. Mice might **steal** cheese.
12. We will have a **treat**!
13. It is the harvest **season**.
14. I save **money** in a jar.
15. Look down in the **valley**.
16. Bees make **honey**.
17. Watch the **monkey** climb.
18. Can you play **hockey**?
19. The **alley** needs sweeping.
20. Quinn rode a **donkey**.

Notes for Home: Your child took a pretest on words with the short *e* and long *e* sounds. ***Home Activity:*** Help your child learn misspelled words before the final test. Your child can underline the word parts that caused the problems and concentrate on those parts.

Name ______________________________

Spelling: Short e and Long e

Word List				
them	engine	beat	season	monkey
went	contest	least	money	hockey
fence	speak	steal	valley	alley
credit	reason	treat	honey	donkey

Directions: Write the words from the box with the **long e** vowel sound. Sort the words according to how the vowel sound is spelled.

Long e spelled ea	Long e spelled ey
1. ________________	8. ________________
2. ________________	9. ________________
3. ________________	10. ________________
4. ________________	11. ________________
5. ________________	12. ________________
6. ________________	13. ________________
7. ________________	14. ________________

Directions: Choose the word from the box that best completes each sentence. Write the word on the line to the left.

________________ **15.** Yesterday we _____ to get a present for my cousin.

________________ **16.** We had a _____ to see who could find the best present.

________________ **17.** I picked a tiny train with a working _____.

________________ **18.** My mom picked a model farm surrounded by a white picket _____.

________________ **19.** We took _____ both to the clerk.

________________ **20.** The clerk said, "Will that be cash or _____?"

Notes for Home: Your child spelled words with short *e* and long *e* vowel sounds. ***Home Activity:*** Play a word game. Take turns naming words with a short *e (went)*. Play for three minutes. Do the same with long *e* words *(speak, money)*.

Spelling: Short e and Long e

Directions: Proofread this letter. Find five spelling mistakes. Use the proofreading marks to correct each mistake.

≡	Make a capital.
/	Make a small letter.
∧	Add something.
℘	Take out something.
⊙	Add a period.
¶	Begin a new paragraph.

Dear Aunt Natalie,

Thanks for the birthday money. I used it to get a new field hocky stick. We play after school in the field behind the fenc. The grass is a little tall down there in the vally, especially this seson, but at leest we get to play!

Love,

Marcy

Spelling Tip

Short e is often spelled **e,** as in **went. Long e** can be spelled **ea,** as in **speak,** or **ey,** as in **money.**

Word List

them	steal
went	treat
fence	season
credit	money
engine	valley
contest	honey
speak	monkey
reason	hockey
beat	alley
least	donkey

Write Your Own Letter

Imagine you are Aunt Natalie. On a separate sheet of paper, write a letter back to Marcy. Try to use at least three spelling words.

Notes for Home: Your child spelled words with short *e (went)* and long *e (speak, money)* vowel sounds. ***Home Activity:*** Post paper on your refrigerator and invite your child to add words with short *e* and long *e* vowel sounds each day. Notice the different spellings for these sounds.

Spelling: Short e and Long e

REVIEW

Directions: Choose the word from the box that best matches each clue. Write the word on the line.

Word List
them
went
fence
credit
engine
contest
speak
reason
beat
least
steal
treat
season
money
valley
honey
monkey
hockey
alley
donkey

______________ **1.** You might hit the ball over it.

______________ **2.** narrow place between two buildings

______________ **3.** It is a time of year.

______________ **4.** Bees are busy making this.

______________ **5.** a long-tailed animal that likes bananas

______________ **6.** long-eared animal that can carry things

______________ **7.** what you give when you tell why

______________ **8.** You do this to cake batter or on a set of drums.

______________ **9.** This is the smallest amount.

______________ **10.** It is the part that makes a machine run.

______________ **11.** It's green but doesn't grow on trees. Hint: You could buy a tree with it.

______________ **12.** You do this when you want to be heard.

Directions: Each of the words below is hidden in a word from the box. Write the word on the line. Hint: It won't be a word you've already used.

13. hock ______________

14. test ______________

15. alley ______________

16. red ______________

17. we ______________

18. teal ______________

19. the ______________

20. eat ______________

Notes for Home: Your child spelled words with short *e* and long *e* vowel sounds. ***Home Activity:*** Hold a spelling bee for your child. Say each spelling word twice. Have your child spell it aloud.

Name ____________________

Research Process

Begin your research by asking yourself questions about your topic. Find resources, such as encyclopedias, that will help answer these questions. As you gather information, you can ask new questions. Summarize the information you find by taking notes or writing outlines. Then organize your information into a report.

Directions: Complete the table. For rows 1, 2, and 3, decide what key words would help you locate information in a reference source. For row 4, write a question based on the key word that you could answer in your research.

What I Want to Find Out	Key Words
What year did the first Orphan Train leave?	**1.**
How many people lived in New York City in 1880?	**2.**
Are any orphan-train riders alive today?	**3.**
4.	railroad

Directions: Use the information on this set of encyclopedias to answer the questions that follow.

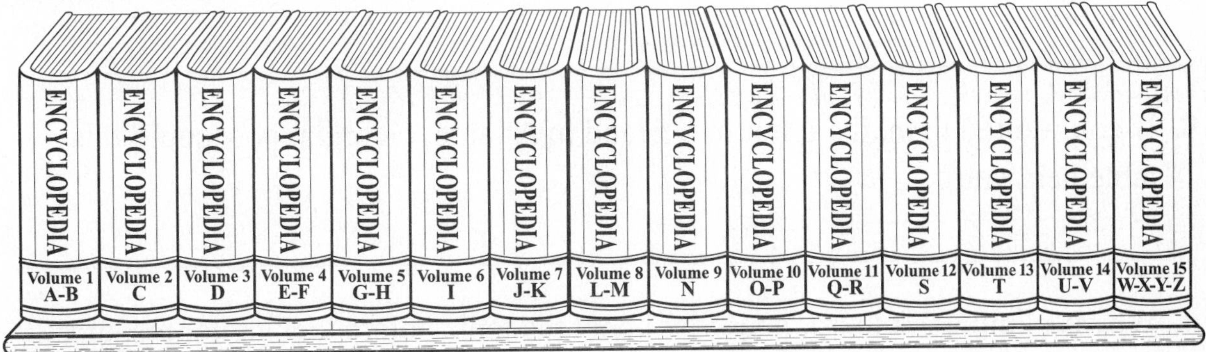

5. Which volume would help you find out what year the helicopter was invented? Explain.

____

____

6. Which volume or volumes would help you find out more about the inventor of the steam locomotive, Richard Trevithick? Explain.

____

____

7. Suppose you want to find information about "orphan trains." The library's encyclopedias are 10 years old. Will the information you find be useful to your research? Why or why not?

____

____

Directions: Use the almanac table to answer the questions below.

State	Postal Abbreviation	Date Entered Union (United States)
Florida	FL	1845
Georgia	GA	1788
Hawaii	HI	1959
Idaho	ID	1890

8. Using this almanac table, how would you find out if Florida and Georgia were part of the United States in the year 1885?

____

____

9. If you wanted to mail a letter to a friend in Atlanta, Georgia, how could this table help you?

____

10. Why is it important to ask questions about the topic before looking for resources?

____

____

Notes for Home: Your child learned about conducting research. ***Home Activity:*** Name a topic. Have your child ask a question about this topic. Then switch and let your child name the topic. Talk about where you might find answers to your questions.

Family Times

Name____

Summary

Yingtao Finds Coming to America Rough Going

Starting a new school in the middle of the year is bad enough. But imagine starting a new school in a new country, where it seems everything is different, and you don't know enough English to make friends. Add to that the fact that your violin-playing is a family joke, and you have Yingtao's life. With three strikes against him, how can Yingtao adjust to life in America?

Activity

Matthew's Story. Ask your child to tell you the story of Yingtao's early days in his new school from the point of view of Matthew, Yingtao's new friend.

Reading Skills

Compare and Contrast

When authors write about two or more characters, places, events, or situations, they often want you to compare and contrast them.

- ❖ **Compare** means telling how two or more things are alike.
- ❖ **Contrast** means telling how they are different.

One way Yingtao and Matthew are alike is that they are both in the orchestra. This is a comparison. One way they are different is in the way they eat. Yingtao has been using chopsticks since he was two. Matthew had never used them. This is a contrast.

Activity

Side by Side. Cut out pictures of two landscapes, two cars, two people, two houses, and so on. Paste them next to each other on a sheet of paper. Tell how they are alike and how they are different.

Family Times

Tested Vocabulary

Words to Know

Knowing the meanings of these words is important to reading "Yingtao's New Friend." Practice using these words to learn their meanings.

instruments devices for producing musical sounds

measures bars of music

orchestra the musicians playing at a concert, opera, or play

rehearsal practice to prepare for public performance

triangle musical instrument

Grammar

Declarative and Interrogative Sentences

A sentence that tells something is a **statement.** Another name for it is a **declarative sentence** because it declares, or tells, something. It ends with a period.

Yingtao played the violin badly.

A sentence that asks something is a **question.** Another name for it is an **interrogative sentence.** It ends with a question mark.

Do you play the trombone?

Activity

Questions and Answers. Ask a family member to ask you questions. Change the questions into statements using as many of the words from the question as possible.

Tested Spelling Words

Name ______________________________

Compare and Contrast

- To **compare** is to tell how two or more things are alike. To **contrast** is to tell how two or more things are different.
- Clue words such as *like* or *as* show comparisons. Clue words such as *but* or *unlike* show contrasts.
- Often authors don't use clue words, and readers have to compare and contrast things on their own.

Directions: Reread "Anna's New School." Then complete the table that shows the contrasts between Anna's new school and her old school. Some information has been filled in for you.

Items	New School	Old School
1. desks	in groups, hinges	
2. pencils		smaller around than Anna's thumb
3. blackboards		
4. chalk		
5. children		

Notes for Home: Your child read a story and made contrasts using word clues and their own inferences. ***Home Activity:*** Choose two objects (flowers, bowls, books, tables, and so on) and have your child list ways they are similar (comparisons) and ways they are different (contrasts).

Name ______________________________________

Vocabulary

Directions: Choose the word from the box that best completes each sentence. Write the word on the line to the left.

Check the Words You Know
__ instrument
__ measures
__ orchestra
__ rehearsal
__ triangle

______________ **1.** The members of our school _____ began to go on stage.

______________ **2.** It was their final _____ before the big performance.

______________ **3.** Each student got an _____ ready to play.

______________ **4.** From the giant tuba to the tiny _____, all the instruments were ready.

______________ **5.** As I heard the first few _____ of the music begin, I knew the concert would be a success.

Directions: Cross out the word that does not belong in each group.

6. band	stage	orchestra	group
7. measures	beats	bars	violins
8. performer	instrument	dancer	singer
9. rehearsal	practice	flute	warm-up
10. trumpet	triangle	conductor	drum

Write a Music Review

On a separate sheet of paper, tell about a concert you attended. Tell why you did or did not enjoy the concert. Use as many of the vocabulary words as you can.

Notes for Home: Your child identified and used vocabulary words from "Yingtao's New Friend." ***Home Activity:*** Have your child talk about a piece of music he or she likes. Encourage him or her to use as many of the vocabulary words as possible.

Name ______________________________

Compare and Contrast

- To **compare** is to tell how two or more things are alike. To **contrast** is to tell how two or more things are different. Clue words such as *like* or *as* show comparisons. Clue words such as *but* or *unlike* show contrasts.

Directions: Reread Yingtao's descriptions of his two older sisters in "Yingtao's New Friend." Then answer the questions below.

I think Second Sister felt the loneliest. In China, people always said she would turn out to be a real beauty. She had been popular at school there, always surrounded by friends. But in America not many people told her she was beautiful. These days she was often cranky and sad. Mother told the rest of us that we just had to be patient with Second Sister.

Third Sister had no trouble at all making friends. Even before she could speak much English, she began chatting with other kids. She could always fill the gaps with laughter.

1. Is Second Sister the same in America as she was in China or is she different? What clue word in the passage tells you?

____

2. How do you think Second Sister felt in China? Explain.

____

3. Does Third Sister act like Second Sister? Explain.

____

4. Write a sentence contrasting the two sisters' behavior in America.

____

5. Use a separate sheet of paper to tell how you think Yingtao feels in America compared with each of his sisters. Give examples from the story.

Notes for Home: Your child used story details to compare and contrast two characters. ***Home Activity:*** Work with your child to come up with a list of ways two people he or she knows well are similar (comparisons) and ways they are different (contrasts).

Name ______________________________

Selection Test

Directions: Choose the best answer to each item. Mark the letter for the answer you have chosen.

Part 1: Vocabulary

Find the answer choice that means about the same as the underlined word in each sentence.

1. Play the first six <u>measures</u>.
- A. places in line
- B. tunes
- C. bars of music
- D. numerals

2. Cecily is in the <u>orchestra</u>.
- F. a group of musicians
- G. a music class
- H. people who write music
- J. a holiday parade

3. Matt put the <u>instrument</u> away.
- A. a loud noise
- B. a device for producing musical sounds
- C. a small container
- D. a group of songs played together

4. The <u>rehearsal</u> will begin soon.
- F. dinner
- G. tryout
- H. show
- J. practice

5. I borrowed the <u>triangle</u> from Keisha.
- A. measuring tool
- B. toy
- C. musical device
- D. whistle

Part 2: Comprehension

Use what you know about the story to answer each item.

6. Yingtao's parents signed him up to—
- F. take piano lessons.
- G. play baseball.
- H. join the orchestra.
- J. learn to cook.

7. What was Second Sister doing when Yingtao brought Matthew home with him?
- A. making shelves
- B. playing the viola
- C. cooking dinner
- D. cutting tea bags

8. How was Matthew like Yingtao?
- F. His family was Chinese.
- G. His family did not have much money.
- H. He had many friends at school.
- J. He loved to play the violin.

9. How are Third Sister and Eldest Brother alike?
A. They are talented musicians.
B. They enjoy cooking.
C. They like to cut tea bags
D. They are very fun loving.

10. When Matthew said he wanted to use chopsticks to eat his dinner, Yingtao most likely felt—
F. annoyed.
G. pleased.
H. embarrassed.
J. amused.

11. Why did Yingtao slouch in his seat and interrupt his teacher?
A. He wanted to fit in with the other students.
B. Matthew dared him to be impolite.
C. He was bored and unhappy in school.
D. He wanted to bother his teacher.

12. When Matthew called Yingtao "tough," he meant that Yingtao was—
F. mean and rude.
G. unlucky and sad.
H. strong and determined.
J. cold and unfriendly.

13. After visiting Yingtao's home, Matthew could see that—
A. Yingtao's family did not get along well.
B. Yingtao's brothers and sisters were unfriendly.
C. Yingtao's parents did not work hard.
D. Yingtao's family had some customs that were different from his.

14. Yingtao's parents were probably disappointed about—
F. his friendship with Matthew.
G. the way he played the violin.
H. his poor manners.
J. how he did in school.

15. What is the most important thing that happened to Yingtao?
A. He tried out for the orchestra.
B. He had a chance to play the triangle.
C. He became friends with Matthew.
D. He got better at spelling.

STOP

Compare and Contrast

- To **compare** is to tell how two or more things are alike. To **contrast** is to tell how two or more things are different. Clue words such as *like* or *as* show comparisons. Clue words such as *but* or *unlike* show contrasts.

Directions: Read the story below.

Mr. Berg was our new music teacher. Unlike our old music teacher Mrs. Marsh, Mr. Berg let anybody join the orchestra. Some students, like my friend Jim, had taken music lessons. But some students, like my sister June and me, hadn't. That didn't matter to Mr. Berg. He told us all just to try our best.

He gave out instruments. I got a trumpet, and June got a violin. The first time she played, it sounded like a cat screeching. But at least she got her violin to do something. Jim blew a few notes on his trumpet, then asked me to try. But I couldn't make even a little squeak.

Mr. Berg wasn't upset. "You have only one way to go, Brian," he told me. "That's to get better. I'll teach you how."

Mr. Berg was right. With some lessons, I could play a few notes.

Directions: Complete the table. Use what you are told about the characters and what you can figure out to compare and contrast pairs of characters.

People	Alike	Different
Mrs. Marsh, Mr. Berg	Both are music teachers.	**1.**
Brian, June	Neither has had any lessons.	**2.**
Brian, Jim	**3.**	Brian: no lessons, no sounds; Jim: lessons, sounds
June, Jim	**4.**	**5.**

Notes for Home: Your child has read a story and used details and what he or she knows to make comparisons and contrasts. ***Home Activity:*** With your child, choose two persons, places, or things that you both know. Take turns making comparisons and contrasts.

Sequence

REVIEW

Directions: Read the story. Then read each question about the story. Choose the best answer to each question. Mark the letter for the answer you have chosen.

Hard Choices!

My mom and I were at the music store looking at instruments. Last month Mom had promised she would buy me one. She said, "You can join the school orchestra this year, Ray."

"No way, Mom!" I replied. "I want to be in a rock band. Besides, orchestra rehearsal takes place while I have track practice."

A salesperson came over to us. "May I show you an instrument?" he asked.

"Violin! Guitar!" came our answers at the same time.

"I see," said the salesperson. "Let me show you both, and you can decide which one you want . . . I hope."

1. The first event that takes place during the story is—
- **A.** Mom wanting Ray to play the violin.
- **B.** Ray wanting to play the guitar.
- **C.** Ray and his mom looking at instruments.
- **D.** Ray's mom agreeing to buy Ray an instrument.

2. Ray doesn't want to join the orchestra because it is at the same time as—
- **F.** dinner.
- **G.** math class.
- **H.** track practice.
- **J.** guitar lessons.

3. While Ray and his mom were looking at instruments—
- **A.** a salesperson came over.
- **B.** a salesperson ignored them.
- **C.** Ray's mom wrote out a check.
- **D.** Ray's mom called Ray's father.

4. While Ray asks to see a guitar, his mom—
- **F.** starts to leave.
- **G.** drops her wallet.
- **H.** asks to see a violin.
- **J.** promises to buy him a guitar.

5. Which of these events did **not** happen in the store?
- **A.** Ray said he would rather play in a rock band.
- **B.** Ray's mom said she would buy him an instrument.
- **C.** Ray's mom asked a salesperson to show her a violin.
- **D.** Ray's mom said he could join the orchestra.

Notes for Home: Your child answered questions to describe the order of events in a story. ***Home Activity:*** Have your child tell a story of something that happened recently. Try to have him or her use word clues to let you know the order of events.

Name ________________________________

Writing Across Texts

Directions: Consider what you know about Justin from "A Visit with Grandpa" and Yingtao from "Yingtao's New Friend." Use the diagram below to compare the two boys. Think about what each boy does well. Consider how the background and family traditions of the boys are similar and different. Try to include at least ten entries.

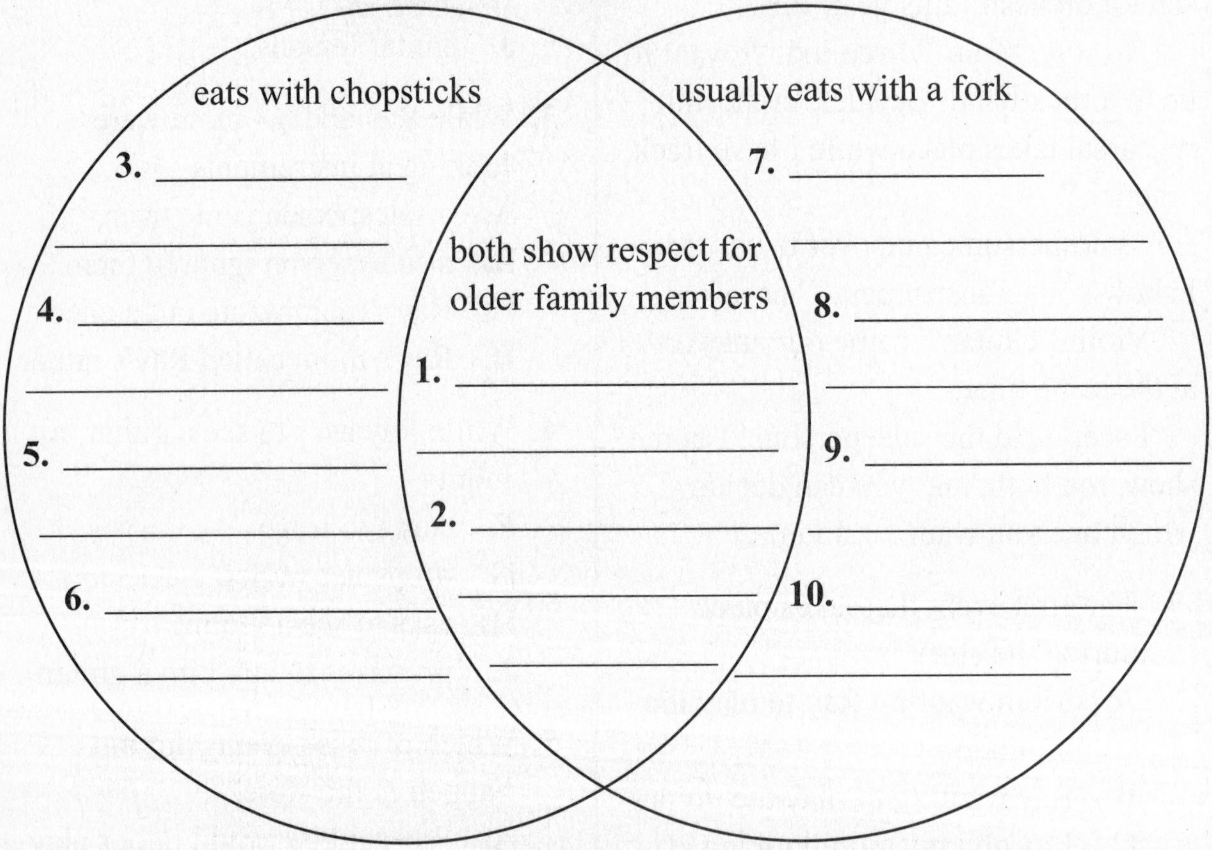

Yingtao

eats with chopsticks

3. ____________________

4. ____________________

5. ____________________

6. ____________________

Both Boys

both show respect for older family members

1. ____________________

2. ____________________

Justin

usually eats with a fork

7. ____________________

8. ____________________

9. ____________________

10. ____________________

Write a Compare/Contrast Paragraph

Yingtao and Justin have very different backgrounds and abilities. On a separate sheet of paper, write a paragraph in which you compare and contrast the boys. Use the information from your diagram to help you. Then draw a conclusion telling whether or not you think the boys could be friends.

Notes for Home: Your child used information from two reading selections to write a compare/contrast paragraph. ***Home Activity:*** As you read stories and articles with your child, talk about how ideas or characters are alike and different.

Name ______________________________

REVIEW

Grammar: Sentence End Punctuation

Directions: Add the correct punctuation mark at the end of each statement or question.

1. How many instruments are in a standard orchestra _____
2. Usually most orchestras have about 100 instruments _____
3. An orchestra is made up of four groups of instruments _____
4. Do you know what they are _____
5. The groups of instruments are strings, woodwinds, brass, and percussion_____
6. What is the most common string instrument _____
7. The violin is the most common string instrument_____
8. Some orchestras have as many as 36 violins _____
9. Can you name another string instrument _____
10. Yes, a harp is a string instrument _____

Directions: Write five sentences—four statements and one question. Write about a musical instrument you play or would like to play. Remember to begin each sentence with a capital letter and end each one with the correct punctuation.

11. ______________________________
12. ______________________________
13. ______________________________
14. ______________________________
15. ______________________________

Notes for Home: Your child identified the correct end punctuation for sentences and wrote sentences. ***Home Activity:*** Say a statement or ask a question about music your child enjoys. Have him or her tell what punctuation mark should go at the end of each sentence.

Grammar: Declarative and Interrogative Sentences

A sentence that tells something is a statement. It ends with a period. Another name for a statement is a **declarative sentence.**

I play in the orchestra at school.

A sentence that asks something is a question. It ends with a question mark. Another name for a question is an **interrogative sentence.**

Does your school have an orchestra?

Directions: For each sentence, add the correct end punctuation. Then write **D** if the sentence is declarative. Write **I** if it is interrogative.

1. Do you play a musical instrument __________ __________

2. How well do you play __________ __________

3. The violin is a beautiful instrument __________ __________

4. It isn't easy to play a violin __________ __________

5. It is important to practice every day __________ __________

6. Which musical instruments do you like __________ __________

7. You could play more than one kind of instrument __________ __________

8. Playing an instrument can make you feel proud __________ __________

9. Would you like to play in a concert __________ __________

10. Would you like to listen to some music __________ __________

11. There are many different types of music __________ __________

12. Some people don't listen to music __________ __________

13. Your family could listen to music together __________ __________

14. Everyone in my family likes music __________ __________

15. Does music make you happy __________ __________

Notes for Home: Your child identified declarative and interrogative sentences. ***Home Activity:*** Take turns making statements or asking questions about songs that you have listened to together.

Name ______________________________

Grammar: Declarative and Interrogative Sentences

Directions: For each sentence, add the correct end punctuation. Then write **D** if the sentence is declarative. Write **I** if it is interrogative.

1. Will the orchestra start to play ________ ________
2. The audience is eager to hear the musicians play ________ ________
3. The music is soft and beautiful ________ ________
4. How long do you think the concert will last ________ ________
5. I am glad that we came tonight ________ ________

Directions: Change each of these declarative sentences into an interrogative sentence. Be sure to use the correct end punctuation.

6. The orchestra played a piece by Beethoven.

____

7. The drums are loud.

____

8. The violin player can play very high notes.

____

9. There is another concert next week.

____

10. We should go again.

____

Write Questions

On a separate sheet of paper, write three questions about a musical instrument you like. Then answer each question with a declarative sentence.

Notes for Home: Your child changed statements (declarative sentences) into questions (interrogative sentences). ***Home Activity:*** To practice asking questions and making statements, take turns "interviewing" one another.

Name ______________________________

RETEACHING

Grammar: Declarative and Interrogative Sentences

Read the interrogative sentence below.

1. What do you like to ride?

Write a declarative sentence. Complete the statement below.

2. I like to ride ______________________________ .

A **declarative sentence** makes a statement. It begins with a capital letter and ends with a period. An **interrogative sentence** asks a question. It begins with a capital letter and ends with a question mark.

Directions: Decide what kind of sentence each one is. Draw a line from the sentence to **declarative** or **interrogative.**

1. His airplane just landed.	declarative
Who was the pilot?	interrogative
2. Will he rent a car?	declarative
He can take a taxi to the boat.	interrogative
3. I will ride my bicycle to the dock.	declarative
How far away is it?	interrogative

Directions: Underline the capital letter. Write the correct punctuation mark at the end of each sentence. Then write each sentence correctly.

4. The man is going to the airport _____

____

5. Will he arrive on time _____

____

Notes for Home: Your child identified and wrote declarative and interrogative sentences. ***Home Activity:*** Have your child write one declarative sentence and one interrogative sentence and explain to you the difference between them.

Name ______________________________

Grammar: Declarative and Interrogative Sentences

Directions: Write each sentence under the correct heading. Begin each sentence with a capital letter. Use periods and question marks correctly.

1. plains are grassy lands

2. are there trees on the plains

3. do crops grow on these lands

4. cows graze on the plains

Declarative Sentences

____

____

Interrogative Sentences

____

____

Directions: Change each sentence to the kind named in ( ).

5. Our country has flat land. (interrogative)

____

6. Do wheat fields grow here? (declarative)

____

7. Is this the Central Plains? (declarative)

____

Write Sentences

On a separate sheet of paper, write interrogative sentences about your town or city. Write declarative sentences to answer your questions.

Notes for Home: Your child identified and wrote declarative and interrogative sentences. ***Home Activity:*** Have your child write four interrogative sentences—sentences that ask questions—and give them to you to answer.

Phonics: Vowel Digraphs

Directions: Read the words in the box. Say the words to yourself. Decide whether each word has a **vowel sound** like **cool** or like **book.** Write each word in the correct column.

pool	shook	soon	took	food
room	stood	look	good	mood

cool	**book**
1. ____________	6. ____________
2. ____________	7. ____________
3. ____________	8. ____________
4. ____________	9. ____________
5. ____________	10. ____________

Directions: Read each sentence. Say the underlined word to yourself. Circle the word in ( ) that has the same **vowel sound** as the underlined word.

11. Band practice was held Tuesday in the music building. (suit/bin)

12. The orchestra leader shook his head when the children played. (food/good)

13. The guilty children knew they should have practiced more. (fruit/fin)

14. Julie liked playing the guitar. (build/find)

15. Matthew thought playing the violin was cool. (stood/food)

16. Matthew wore his best suit for the concert. (tool/should)

17. He stood and closed his eyes when he played. (shook/room)

18. When he was finished playing, he took a bow. (look/school)

19. They served apples, oranges, and juice after the concert. (guilty/bruise)

20. He was hungry after the concert, so he ate a piece of fruit. (build/soon)

Notes for Home: Your child distinguished between the different vowel sounds for words with *oo (boot, book)* and *ui (fruit, build)*. ***Home Activity:*** Read a newspaper or magazine article with your child to find words with *oo* and *ui*. Sort the words by their vowel sounds.

Name ____________________

Spelling: Short Vowels *a, i, o, u*

Pretest Directions: Fold back the page along the dotted line. On the blanks, write the spelling words as they are dictated. When you have finished the test, unfold the page and check your words.

1. ____________________
2. ____________________
3. ____________________
4. ____________________
5. ____________________
6. ____________________
7. ____________________
8. ____________________
9. ____________________
10. ____________________
11. ____________________
12. ____________________
13. ____________________
14. ____________________
15. ____________________
16. ____________________
17. ____________________
18. ____________________
19. ____________________
20. ____________________

1. Watch the marching **band**.
2. Put your **cash** in the bank.
3. **January** is the first month.
4. I need a warm **blanket**.
5. This **backpack** is full.
6. Float a raft down the **river**.
7. Point with your **finger**.
8. Let's **build** a tree house!
9. Can you prove his **guilt**?
10. Look out the **window**.
11. This **pond** has tadpoles.
12. Don't **block** the exit.
13. Ariel **forgot** her lunch.
14. Hang coats in the **closet**.
15. **Chop** vegetables for stew.
16. The cat gets into **trouble**.
17. My kitten is very **young**.
18. Invite your **cousin** over.
19. Bring a **couple** of cups.
20. The nut is **tough** to crack.

Notes for Home: Your child took a pretest on words that have the short vowels *a, i, o,* and *u*. ***Home Activity:*** Help your child learn misspelled words before the final test. Dictate the word and have your child spell the word aloud for you or write it on paper.

Think and Practice

Spelling: Short Vowels *a, i, o, u*

Word List			
band	river	pond	trouble
cash	finger	block	young
January	build	forgot	cousin
blanket	guilt	closet	couple
backpack	window	chop	tough

Directions: Write the words from the box with **short a, short o,** and **short u** vowel sounds. Sort the words according to how the vowel sound is spelled.

Short a Spelled a	Short o Spelled o	Short u Spelled ou
1. ________	6. ________	11. ________
2. ________	7. ________	12. ________
3. ________	8. ________	13. ________
4. ________	9. ________	14. ________
5. ________	10. ________	15. ________

Directions: Choose the word from the box that best completes each sentence. Write the word on the line to the left.

________ **16.** Lucy and her mother decided to _____ their own guitar from scratch.

________ **17.** They cut down a tree by the _____ to use for wood.

________ **18.** Each day, they sat inside by the _____ and carved.

________ **19.** Lucy felt some _____ because her mother did most of the work.

________ **20.** When the guitar was done, Lucy tried to play it, but she couldn't remember which _____ went where.

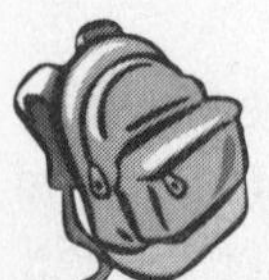

Notes for Home: Your child spelled words with short vowels *a, i, o,* and *u (band, river, build, pond, young). **Home Activity:*** Join your child on a walk around the house. Have your child point out objects that have these short vowel sounds.

Name ______________________________________

Spelling: Short Vowels *a, i, o, u*

Directions: Proofread this concert ad. Find five spelling mistakes. Use the proofreading marks to correct each mistake.

≡	Make a capital.
/	Make a small letter.
∧	Add something.
ꝭ	Take out something.
⊙	Add a period.
¶	Begin a new paragraph.

Spelling Tip

Short a, i, o, and **u** are often spelled with one vowel letter: **band, river, pond.** But **short i** can also be spelled **ui** and **short u** can also be spelled **ou: build, cousin.**

Word List

band	pond
cash	block
January	forgot
blanket	closet
backpack	chop
river	trouble
finger	young
build	cousin
guilt	couple
window	tough

Write a Concert Review

Imagine that you attended the concert in the ad. On a separate sheet of paper, write a review. Try to use at least three spelling words.

Notes for Home: Your child spelled words with the short vowels *a, i, o, u (band, river, build, pond, young). **Home Activity:*** Read a story with your child. Challenge your child to notice words in which the short *i* and short *u* sounds are spelled with two vowel letters: *build, cousin.*

Name ______________________

Spelling: Short Vowels *a, i, o, u*

REVIEW

Word List			
band	river	pond	trouble
cash	finger	block	young
January	build	forgot	cousin
blanket	guilt	closet	couple
backpack	window	chop	tough

Directions: Choose the word from the box that best completes each sentence. Write the word on the matching numbered line to the right.

Lucy sat in the **1.** _____ room waiting for rehearsal to start. She felt a terrible sense of **2.** _____. It's not that she **3.** _____ to bring her flute. It was worse. She couldn't remember where she left it. She had looked in her **4.** _____ that she carried everywhere. She had looked in her bedroom, even in the back of her messy **5.** _____. She knew she was in big **6.** _____!

Suddenly, from her seat near the **7.** _____, she saw her first **8.** _____, Mary, outside. She was about a **9.** _____ away, but Lucy could see Mary had her flute. Lucy now remembered that she had left it at Mary's house a **10.** _____ of days ago.

1. ______________

2. ______________

3. ______________

4. ______________

5. ______________

6. ______________

7. ______________

8. ______________

9. ______________

10. ______________

Directions: Write the word from the box that best fits in each group.

11. ocean, lake, __________

12. strong, firm, __________

13. creek, stream, __________

14. make, construct, __________

15. cut, saw, __________

16. youthful, immature, __________

17. quilt, comforter, __________

18. November, December, __________

19. arm, hand, __________

20. money, coins, __________

Notes for Home: Your child spelled words with the short vowels *a, i, o, u (band, river, build, pond, young)*. ***Home Activity:*** Read the newspaper with your child. Have him or her point out words that have these short vowel sounds and spellings.

Name ______________________________

Technology: Questions for Inquiry

You can learn about the traditions of another country by **asking questions** and doing research to find answers to your questions. The **Internet** is one place to find answers to your questions. You can use **search engines** to find information. After you type in key words from your questions, the search engine looks for Web sites that may have answers. A search engine home page may look something like this:

Directions: For each topic below, write a question that you could research to find out about life in China.

1. types of food prepared ______________________________

____

2. games children like to play ______________________________

____

3. languages spoken ______________________________

____

____

Name ___________________________________

Directions: A search engine may give you a list of Web sites that are related to your question or topic. Put an **X** in front of the Web site names listed below that you think may have answers to the question shown on the computer screen.

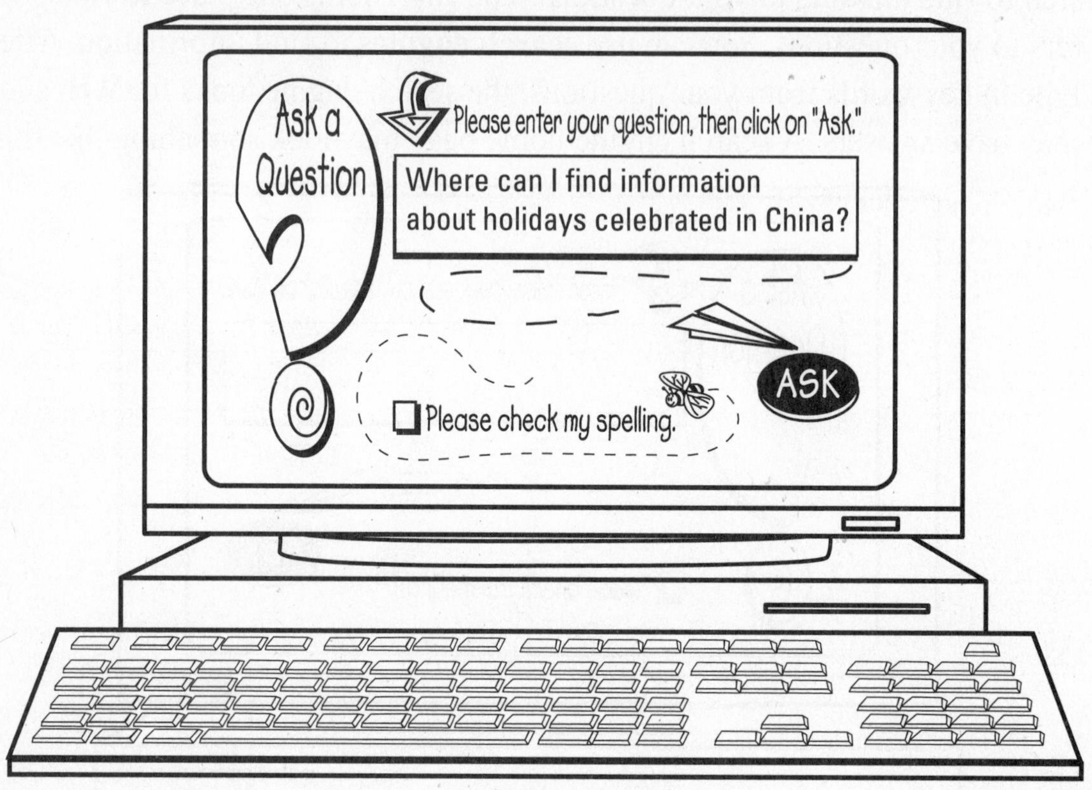

Where can I find information about holidays celebrated in China?

_______________ **4.** Folktales from China

_______________ **5.** Worldwide Holiday Calendar

_______________ **6.** China Travel and Tourism

_______________ **7.** Web site of Jamaica

_______________ **8.** Holidays and Festivals

_______________ **9.** Chinese Poetry

_______________ **10.** Holiday Traditions Around the World

Notes for Home: Your child wrote questions and identified possible Web sites that would be useful to find out more about China. ***Home Activity:*** Play a game in which you give the answer to a question, and your child asks the question that would produce that answer.

Family Times

Name____

Summary

Artist Shares Family Memories

While growing up in a Texas town near the Mexican border, Carmen Lomas Garza dreamed of becoming an artist. Now her colorful art paints a vivid picture of this time in her life—from hitting piñatas at birthday parties to making tamales in her parents' kitchen, with everyone pitching in.

Activity

Share Family Stories. Have your child tell you about his or her favorite "scene" from the story and tell why it is so appealing. Then take turns telling favorite stories from your family's past.

Reading Skills

Author's Purpose

An **author's purpose** is the reason or reasons an author has for writing. Authors usually don't tell their purposes, or reasons, for writing. You have to figure them out. Four common purposes are to inform, to entertain, to express, and to persuade.

The author of *Family Pictures* gives readers information when she describes growing up in Texas. She expresses herself when she tells how she felt about seeing a huge shark caught at the beach. Through words and pictures, readers are entertained by her story.

Activity

Your Own Family Pictures. Draw pictures or use photos to make a family picture album. Write a paragraph about each picture, keeping in mind what your purpose is. You may wish to entertain, for example, by telling a funny story about the picture.

Family Times

Tested Vocabulary

Words to Know

Knowing the meanings of these words is important to reading *Family Pictures*. Practice using these words to learn their meanings.

border boundary or edge

future what is to come

handkerchief soft piece of cloth used for wiping the face, nose, and so on

inspired filled with thought or feeling

involved took in; included

laundry clothes to be washed

memories all that a person remembers

Grammar

Imperative and Exclamatory Sentences

A sentence that tells someone to do something is called a **command,** or an **imperative sentence.** The first word is usually a verb. The subject, *you,* is not shown but it is understood. **Grab a basket.** Some commands start with *please.* **Please help me pick oranges.** Commands usually end with periods.

A sentence that shows strong feeling is called an **exclamation,** or **exclamatory sentence.** Exclamations end with an exclamation point. **These oranges taste great!**

Activity

Sentence Toss. Toss a coin. If it lands "heads" up, the tosser says a command for someone to follow. If it lands "tails" up, the tosser says an exclamation.

Tested Spelling Words

______	______	______	______
______	______	______	______
______	______	______	______
______	______	______	______
______	______	______	______

Name ___________________________________

Author's Purpose

- An **author's purpose** is the reason or reasons an author has for writing. Four common purposes are to inform, to entertain, to express, and to persuade.
- Often, people read more quickly when the author's purpose is to entertain, and more slowly and carefully when the author has another purpose.

Directions: Reread "Painting Mist and Fog." In the first row of the table, describe the author's purpose or purposes. Use the second row to give supporting reasons to explain why this is the author's purpose. In the last row, tell how quickly or slowly you read the article and why.

Author's Purposes:	**1.**
Supporting Reasons	**2.**
Read Quickly or Slowly?	**3.**

Directions: Think about the author's purpose for these types of writing. Write the purpose of each type in the table.

Comic book	**4. Purpose:**
How-to instruction book	**5. Purpose:**

Notes for Home: Your child read a magazine article and identified the author's purpose in writing it. ***Home Activity:*** Read several different kinds of articles with your child. Have your child figure out the author's purpose for each and give supporting reasons.

Name ______________________________

Vocabulary

Directions: Choose the word from the box that best completes each sentence. Write the word on the line to the left.

Check the Words You Know

- __ border
- __ future
- __ handkerchief
- __ inspired
- __ involved
- __ laundry
- __ memories
- __ scene

______________ **1.** My grandfather makes paintings that are _____ by his childhood.

______________ **2.** Once he painted a _____ of children playing ball in a meadow.

______________ **3.** Another painting ________ the toys he had when he was little.

______________ **4.** From his paintings, I guess that Grandpa has happy ____ of his childhood.

______________ **5.** People in the _____ will learn about life long ago from artwork like Grandpa's paintings.

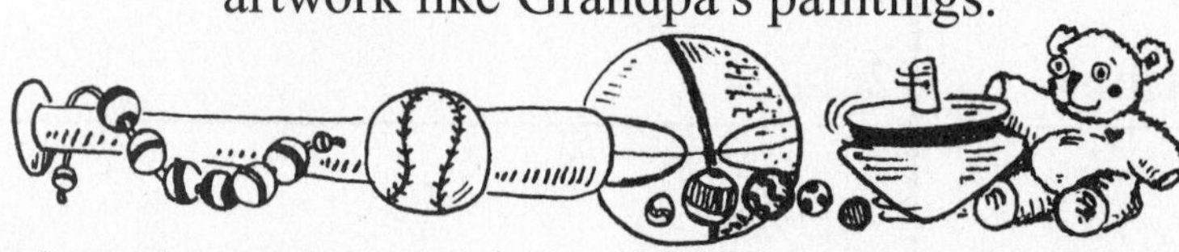

Directions: Match each word on the left with the word or words on the right that have a similar meaning. Write the letter of the similar word or words on the line.

____________	**6.** handkerchief	**a.** washing
____________	**7.** border	**b.** included
____________	**8.** laundry	**c.** encouraged
____________	**9.** inspired	**d.** soft cloth
____________	**10.** involved	**e.** boundary

Write a Paragraph

On a separate sheet of paper, write a paragraph about artwork that you saw and liked. It could be a painting in a museum, a picture or photo in your reading book, or even something you made yourself. Tell what you liked and why. Use as many vocabulary words as you can.

Notes for Home: Your child identified and used vocabulary words from *Family Pictures*. ***Home Activity:*** With your child, look at works of art in a book or magazine. Encourage him or her to talk about the artwork, using as many vocabulary words as possible.

Author's Purpose

- An **author's purpose** is the reason or reasons an author has for writing. Authors often have more than one reason for writing.
- Four common purposes are to inform, to entertain, to express, and to persuade.

1. Reread *Family Pictures.* What do you think is the author's purpose? Write the reason or reasons for writing below. Explain your answer.

____

____

Directions: Read each paragraph. Write whether the author's purpose is to inform, entertain, express, or persuade. Explain your answers.

2. The best place to go on vacation is the beach. How can you go wrong with water, sand, and sky? There are people sunning themselves and swimming. There are boats and sand castles. You'll have so much fun.

____

3. My favorite painting is of the beach. The colors of the water, sand, and sky make me remember all the happy times I had there last summer.

____

4. Seaweed is any type of plant that grows in the ocean. It can be both a place to live and a source of food for sea creatures.

____

5. On a separate sheet of paper, write a short paragraph about something that happened to you today. You might inform readers about the day's events, entertain them with a funny story, express how you felt about your day, or try to convince others that it was the best or worst day ever. Below your paragraph, tell your purpose for writing.

Notes for Home: Your child has identified the author's purpose(s) in *Family Pictures* and several short paragraphs. ***Home Activity:*** Read a short story with your child. Talk about the author's reasons for writing the piece. Was it to inform, entertain, persuade, or express a feeling or mood?

Name ________________________________

Selection Test

Directions: Choose the best answer to each item. Mark the letter for the answer you have chosen.

Part 1: Vocabulary

Find the answer choice that means about the same as the underlined word in each sentence.

1. Anna plans for the <u>future</u>.
- A. special friend
- B. favorite hobby
- C. problem or worry
- D. time to come

2. Tell us what is happening in this <u>scene</u>.
- F. time of year; season
- G. place of work
- H. a view or picture
- J. faraway land

3. The <u>border</u> is 100 miles from here.
- A. nearest neighbor
- B. boundary of a country or state
- C. grandparent's house
- D. woods or forest

4. I bought a yellow <u>handkerchief</u>.
- F. square cloth for wiping the nose
- G. colorful flag or banner
- H. pair of gloves
- J. large woolen blanket

5. Enrique shared some of his childhood <u>memories</u>.
- A. old toys
- B. things that a person remembers
- C. songs that tell a story
- D. drawings or paintings

6. Grandpa <u>inspired</u> me to write a poem.
- F. allowed
- G. ordered
- H. gave confidence to
- J. taught how

7. Please put the <u>laundry</u> away.
- A. dress-up clothes
- B. rags used for cleaning
- C. fabric to be cut and sewn
- D. clothes that have been washed

8. The girls are <u>involved</u> in their chores.
- F. proud of
- G. busy or occupied
- H. tired of
- J. skilled at

GO ON

Part 2: Comprehension

Use what you know about the selection to answer each item.

9. What did the author dream of being when she grew up?
- A. a poet
- B. an artist
- C. an actress
- D. a mother

10. What did the author do at her grandmother's house?
- F. hung laundry
- G. caught a shark
- H. picked oranges
- J. made tamales

11. Which step comes last when preparing a meal of nopal cactus?
- A. shaving off the needles
- B. boiling in hot water
- C. cutting into pieces
- D. frying with chili powder and eggs

12. Which of these was a frightening experience for the author?
- F. hitting a piñata
- G. seeing a hammerhead shark
- H. being up on the roof
- J. picking nopal cactus

13. The author probably included the part called "Beds for Dreaming" to—
- A. tell about a funny event.
- B. explain what her house was like.
- C. describe a holiday custom.
- D. express important feelings she had as a girl.

14. One of the author's main purposes for writing this selection was to—
- F. compare her family with other families.
- G. share special times she had with her family.
- H. tell how people in a family should behave.
- J. describe each member of her family.

15. Who does the author feel most grateful to for helping her make her dreams come true?
- A. her father
- B. her grandparents
- C. her sister
- D. her mother

STOP

Name ______________________________

Author's Purpose

- An **author's purpose** is the reason or reasons an author has for writing. Authors often have more then one reason for writing.
- Four common purposes are to inform, to entertain, to express, and to persuade.

Directions: Read the story below.

My sister collects junk. I know that a lot of people do. But her junk is different. She uses it to make art. You might not think that's what it is. But if you spent as much time around it as I do, you would change your mind.

Monica takes the junk and makes scenes of our everyday life. Our family is sitting at an orange-crate table. Our heads are made of dried noodles inside plastic. There's a crushed milk carton. There's an empty cake box. Monica calls the work, "The Party's Over." You really have to see it sometime!

Directions: Read each statement in the first column. For each statement, tell whether its purpose is to inform, entertain, express feelings, or persuade.

Statement	Author's Purpose
Some of the text is funny.	**1.**
The author sounds proud of Monica for being creative.	**2.**
The author tells the reader how to make one kind of "junk" sculpture.	**3.**
The author writes, "But if you spent as much time around it as I do, you would change your mind."	**4.**
The author thinks you should see the art sometime.	**5.**

Notes for Home: Your child has read a story and used story details to identify the author's purposes for writing it, such as to inform, entertain, express feelings, and persuade. ***Home Activity:*** When you read with your child, identify together the author's purposes for writing.

Name ____________________

Fact and Opinion

REVIEW

Directions: Read the story. Then read each question about the story. Choose the best answer to each question. Mark the letter for the answer you have chosen.

A Visit to the Museum

My class went to the art museum last month. I thought I would be bored, but I was in for a big surprise. We saw paintings by the artist Van Gogh. But his flowers were beautiful. One of the paintings was of a sunny field. In the art world, it is called a *landscape.*

We had pizza for lunch, which was OK. Then we saw paintings of laundry. I pass laundry every day, but I never look at it. I guess going to a museum can get a person to see things differently.

1. Which is a story fact?

A. The class went to the museum.
B. The narrator decided to become a painter.
C. Van Gogh is a cool artist.
D. The class went by bus.

2. Which sentence contains both fact and opinion?

F. I thought I would be bored.
G. Then we saw paintings of laundry.
H. In the art world, it is called a *landscape.*
J. We had pizza for lunch, which was OK.

3. Which sentence from this story states an opinion?

A. I pass laundry every day, but I never look at it.
B. I guess going to a museum can get a person to see things differently.
C. We saw paintings by the artist Van Gogh.
D. In the art world, it is called a *landscape.*

4. Which sentence states a fact about Van Gogh?

F. Van Gogh made strange-looking sculptures.
G. Van Gogh's paintings are boring.
H. Van Gogh's flowers are cool.
J. Van Gogh painted flowers and landscapes.

5. Which word or words in the last sentence are a clue that the sentence is an opinion?

A. can
B. differently
C. museum
D. I guess

Notes for Home: Your child has read a story and used story details to tell fact from opinion. ***Home Activity:*** Take turns with your child making statements that are either fact or opinion. Identify the type of statement the other person makes.

Name ____________________

Writing Across Texts

Directions: Consider what you learned about Yingtao's family in "Yingtao's New Friend" and Carmen Lomas Garza's family in *Family Pictures.* Complete the table by listing details about each family.

Yingtao's Family	Carmen Lomas Garza's Family
His father must have been a good violinist because he gave lessons.	Her father played games with the children at birthday parties.
1.	**6.**
2.	**7.**
3.	**8.**
4.	**9.**
5.	**10.**

Write a Compare/Contrast Paragraph

Think about these two families. How are they alike? How are they different? On a separate sheet of paper, write a paragraph comparing and contrasting Yingtao's family and Carmen Lomas Garza's family. Use the table you completed to help you.

Notes for Home: Your child analyzed information from two reading selections to write their own paragraph. ***Home Activity:*** As you read stories and articles with your child, discuss how ideas in these materials connect to other reading they have done.

Name ______________________________

REVIEW

Grammar: Subjects and Predicates

Directions: For each sentence, underline the complete subject once and the complete predicate twice.

1. Many pictures in a museum tell wonderful stories.

2. Pictures of things in nature are called *landscapes.*

3. Most paintings like these include water and trees.

4. Portraits show lifelike pictures of people.

5. I saw one that was a portrait of the artist's dog!

Directions: Write sentences that include the following simple subjects and predicates. Remember to begin each sentence with a capital letter and end each one with a punctuation mark.

6. I enjoy

____

7. museums look

____

8. painters use

____

9. people will pay

____

10. Mrs. Andrews studied

____

Notes for Home: Your child identified and used complete and simple subjects and predicates. ***Home Activity:*** Ask your child to point out the simple subject and predicate in several sentences that you find in a book, on a cereal box, or in a newspaper.

Name ______________________________

Practice

Grammar: Imperative and Exclamatory Sentences

A sentence that tells someone to do something is a command, or an **imperative sentence.** It usually begins with a verb. The subject of the sentence (*you*) is not shown, but it is understood. Imperative sentences end with periods.

Don't get wet. Please take an umbrella along.

An **exclamatory sentence** shows strong feeling or surprise. It ends with an exclamation mark.

What a day for walking the dog!

Directions: For each sentence, add the correct end punctuation. Then write **I** if the sentence is imperative. Write **E** if it is exclamatory.

1. Don't take too long getting ready __________ __________

2. What a wonderful day to go to a museum __________ __________

3. Leave your umbrella here __________ __________

4. That's some big painting __________ __________

5. Please follow the tour guide __________ __________

Directions: Change each of these sentences into a command. Write your new sentence on the line. (Hint: You will not use all the words in each sentence.)

6. My art teacher says to try your best. ______________________________

7. He says we should work in pairs. ______________________________

8. I tell my partner to let me do some. ______________________________

9. I tell my partner to keep helping me. ______________________________

10. My partner tells me to be quiet. ______________________________

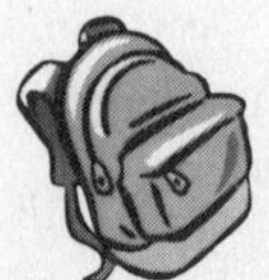

Notes for Home: Your child identified imperative and exclamatory sentences. ***Home Activity:*** To practice using commands and exclamations, make up funny dialogue in which one bossy character gives many orders that other characters don't like.

Name ____________________

Grammar: Imperative and Exclamatory Sentences

Directions: For each sentence, add the correct end punctuation. Then write **I** if the sentence is imperative. Write **E** if it is exclamatory.

1. Let's learn to draw __________ __________
2. Please be patient __________ __________
3. I am *not* impatient __________ __________
4. Please get some paper and a pencil __________ __________
5. Watch what I do __________ __________
6. Start with an outline of the face __________ __________
7. Draw the nose next __________ __________
8. Try going a little slower __________ __________
9. Please get the brown pencil __________ __________
10. Let me help you do that __________ __________
11. How wonderful it turned out __________ __________
12. I'm so excited about your drawing __________ __________
13. Please draw a picture of me __________ __________
14. Use all your talent __________ __________
15. What fun we'll have __________ __________

Write a Memo

Imagine you're in charge of getting a big mural made for school. On a separate sheet of paper, write a memo using commands and exclamations giving your friends instructions about how to get the job done.

Notes for Home: Your child decided whether sentences were commands or exclamations. ***Home Activity:*** Name a strong feeling. Have your child make up an exclamatory sentence to match the feeling. Name a task. Have your child make up a command to tell someone to do it.

Name ____________________________________

RETEACHING

Grammar: Imperative and Exclamatory Sentences

Look at the picture. Then follow these instructions.

1. Circle the end marks of each sentence in the picture.

2. Circle the command. It is an imperative sentence.

3. Underline the sentence that shows strong feeling. It is an exclamatory sentence.

An **imperative sentence** gives a command or makes a request. It begins with a capital letter and ends with a period. An **exclamatory sentence** shows strong feeling. It begins with a capital letter and ends with an exclamation mark.

Directions: Circle each imperative sentence. Underline each exclamatory sentence.

1. Pour water on the soil.

2. Find the seeds.

3. What a rare flower it is!

4. That flower smells wonderful!

5. Those flowers are amazingly tiny!

6. Please place the tree here.

Directions: Unscramble the words to make a sentence. Write each sentence. Use periods and exclamation marks correctly.

7. flowers away please put the

____

8. is so beautiful this garden

____

Notes for Home: Your child identified and wrote imperative and exclamatory sentences. ***Home Activity:*** Together, write a short story about an exciting adventure. Make sure your child writes at least two imperative sentences and two exclamatory sentences.

Name ____________________

Grammar: Imperative and Exclamatory Sentences

Directions: Look at the sentence in each space. Underline each imperative sentence. Shade each space with an exclamatory sentence.

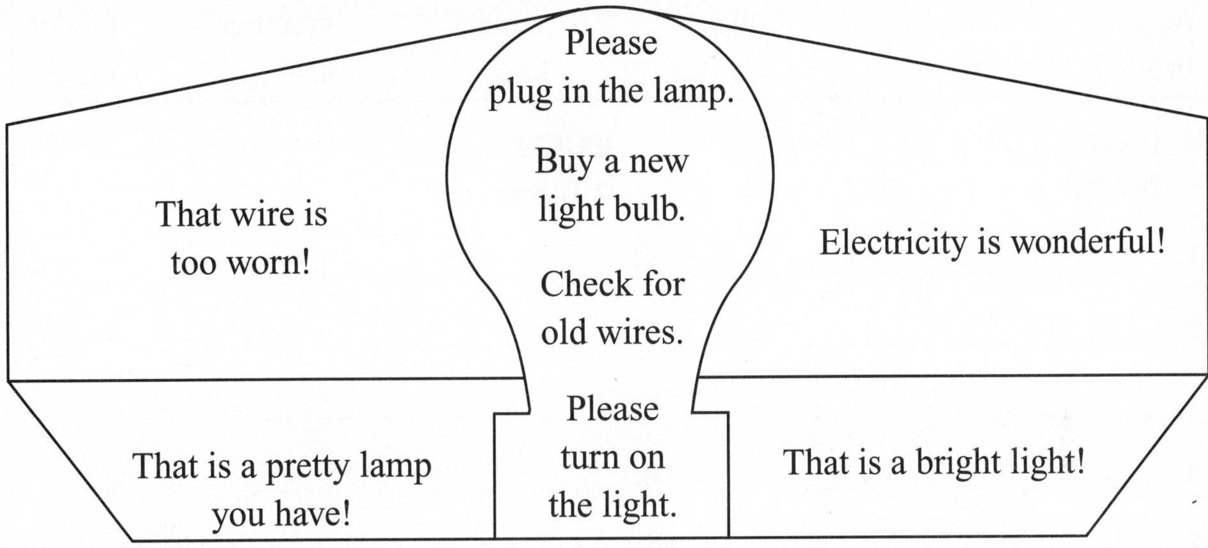
Please plug in the lamp.
Buy a new light bulb.
Check for old wires.
That wire is too worn!
Electricity is wonderful!
That is a pretty lamp you have!
Please turn on the light.
That is a bright light!

Directions: Decide if each sentence below is imperative or exclamatory. Write a period or an exclamation mark on the line. Then write **imperative** or **exclamatory.**

1. Pick up the lamp _______ ____________________
2. It was so expensive _______ ____________________
3. That old lamp still works great _______ ____________________
4. Please change the bulb _______ ____________________
5. What a cute cat he is _______ ____________________
6. Turn on the light _______ ____________________

Write Safety Rules

On a separate sheet of paper, write imperative and exclamatory sentences about how to use electricity safely.

Notes for Home: Your child identified imperative and exclamatory sentences. ***Home Activity:*** Have your child create a collage of imperative and exclamatory sentences, using words cut out from magazines. Have your child label them as *imperative* or *exclamatory.*

Name ______________________________________

Phonics: Common Word Patterns

Directions: Read each word below. Some words have a word pattern as in **home: consonant-vowel-consonant-e.** Other words have a word pattern as in **basket: vowel-consonant-consonant-vowel.** Write each word in the correct column.

rope	cactus	tale	same	summer	tender
brother	time	shelter	line	sister	make

CVCe home	**VCCV basket**
1. ____________________	**7.** ____________________
2. ____________________	**8.** ____________________
3. ____________________	**9.** ____________________
4. ____________________	**10.** ____________________
5. ____________________	**11.** ____________________
6. ____________________	**12.** ____________________

Directions: Read each sentence. Find an example of each word pattern **(CVCe, VCCV)** in each sentence. Write the words in the correct columns.

CVCe **VCCV**

________ ________ **13.** Our summer at the beach was fine.

________ ________ **14.** My mother made cookies.

________ ________ **15.** My sister hung a rope from a tree for a bird feeder.

________ ________ **16.** Birds came to the feeder and took shelter in a nearby tree.

________ ________ **17.** My aunt gave us oranges for lunch.

________ ________ **18.** We played a funny game later.

________ ________ **19.** Then my brother said we had to go home.

________ ________ **20.** It was after nine when we left.

Notes for Home: Your child learned to recognize two common word patterns: *CVCe (home)* and *VCCV (basket). **Home Activity:*** Say each word in the box. Have your child listen for the long vowel sounds in *CVCe* and the short vowel sounds in the first syllable of *VCCV* words.

Name ______________________________

Pretest

Spelling: Long Vowels *a, i, o*

Pretest Directions: Fold back the page along the dotted line. On the blanks, write the spelling words as they are dictated. When you have finished the test, unfold the page and check your words.

1. ____________	1. The fire **station** is close.
2. ____________	2. Are you in **danger**?
3. ____________	3. It rained all **April**.
4. ____________	4. Our **vacation** was great!
5. ____________	5. The **cable** pulled us up.
6. ____________	6. **Bacon** is greasy.
7. ____________	7. Wolves are **wild** animals.
8. ____________	8. Stand **behind** me.
9. ____________	9. Measure a **pint** of water.
10. ____________	10. The **lion** roared loudly.
11. ____________	11. Where did you **hide** it?
12. ____________	12. Let's **decide** on a plan.
13. ____________	13. **Invite** her to come along.
14. ____________	14. When did you **arrive**?
15. ____________	15. Bring your **whole** family.
16. ____________	16. I **broke** a glass.
17. ____________	17. He **drove** away quickly.
18. ____________	18. **Smoke** rose from the fire.
19. ____________	19. This is a **remote** island.
20. ____________	20. Who **stole** the treasure?

Notes for Home: Your child took a pretest on words that have the long vowels *a, i,* and *o*. ***Home Activity:*** Help your child learn misspelled words before the final test. Have your child divide misspelled words into parts (such as syllables) and concentrate on each part.

Think and Practice

Spelling: Long Vowels *a, i, o*

Directions: Write the words from the box with the **long i** vowel sound. Sort the words according to how the vowel sound is spelled.

Word List
station
danger
April
vacation
cable
bacon
wild
behind
pint
lion
hide
decide
invite
arrive
whole
broke
drove
smoke
remote
stole

Long i spelled i		Long i spelled i-consonant-e	
1.	________________	**5.**	________________
2.	________________	**6.**	________________
3.	________________	**7.**	________________
4.	________________	**8.**	________________

Directions: Choose the word from the box that best completes each tongue twister. Write the word on the line to the left.

____________________ **9.** Bill _____ his blue bicycle.

____________________ **10.** Who ate the _____ hog?

____________________ **11.** Apes ate eight acres of acorns in _____.

____________________ **12.** Stuart _____ silently up the steep stairs.

____________________ **13.** Curt's cousin's company sells computer _____.

____________________ **14.** Smedley's smock was smudged by smelly _____.

____________________ **15.** Dave _____ drooling drummers to dinner.

____________________ **16.** Bailey the baker baked _____ by the bay.

____________________ **17.** Doug didn't discuss the _____.

____________________ **18.** Ron and Rick wrestled for the _____ control.

____________________ **19.** Steve stood still at the _____.

____________________ **20.** Vera vanished and went on _____ .

Notes for Home: Your child spelled words with long vowels *a, i,* and *o (station, wild, hide, whole). **Home Activity:*** Choose a word with one of these long vowel sounds. Write some of the letters, but leave spaces for the others. Have your child fill in the missing letters.

Name ____

Spelling: Long Vowels *a, i, o*

Directions: Proofread this invitation. Find five spelling mistakes. Use the proofreading marks to correct each mistake.

≡	Make a capital.
/	Make a small letter.
∧	Add something.
℘	Take out something.
⊙	Add a period.
¶	Begin a new paragraph.

The Old Fire Station Gallery and Danger Safaris invit you to a new show—A Walk On The Wilde Side—opening April 10 at 150 Bacon St. Come see exciting close-up photos taken from behinde tall grass as photographers hyde from a lion.

Once you arriv, be ready for anything!

Monday–Friday 11 A.M.–5 P.M.

Spelling Tip

Long Vowels

Words with long vowels are often spelled with one letter: **station, wild.** They can also be spelled **vowel-consonant-e: whole, hide.**

Word List

station	bacon	hide	broke
danger	wild	decide	drove
April	behind	invite	smoke
vacation	pint	arrive	remote
cable	lion	whole	stole

Write an Invitation

Imagine you're a photographer. On a separate sheet of paper, write an invitation to a showing of your work. Try to use at least three spelling words.

Notes for Home: Your child spelled words with long vowels *a, i,* and *o (station, wild, hide, whole). **Home Activity:*** When you are in a grocery store, have your child call words to your attention that have these long vowel sounds, such as *whole milk* and *wild berry punch.*

Name ____________________________

Spelling: Long Vowels *a, i, o*

REVIEW

Word List

station	cable	pint	invite	drove
danger	bacon	lion	arrive	smoke
April	wild	hide	whole	remote
vacation	behind	decide	broke	stole

Directions: Choose the word from the box that is the most opposite in meaning for each word below. Write the word on the line.

1. front ____________ **4.** part ____________ **7.** safety ____________

2. tame ____________ **5.** leave ____________ **8.** work ____________

3. fixed ____________ **6.** seek ____________ **9.** ignore ____________

Directions: Choose the word from the box that matches each clue. Write the word on the line.

____________ **10.** This type of control lets you turn on a TV.

____________ **11.** You can eat it with eggs instead of sausage.

____________ **12.** The baseball player did this to second base.

____________ **13.** Where there's fire, there's this.

____________ **14.** Two cups make one of these.

____________ **15.** A ski lift runs on one.

____________ **16.** It's the past tense of *drive.*

____________ **17.** It's the month before May.

____________ **18.** Trains arrive here.

____________ **19.** This is a name for a very big cat.

____________ **20.** It's what you do when you make up your mind.

Notes for Home: Your child spelled words with long vowels *a, i,* and *o (station, wild, hide, whole). **Home Activity:*** Give your child a page of the newspaper and a highlighter. Ask your child to look for and highlight words with long vowels *a, i,* and *o*.

Name ______________________________________

Outline

Making an **outline** can help you organize information you read. Outlining helps you remember important points and understand what you read. Outlining information can also help you prepare for tests.

Directions: Read this article about flowers found in Texas. Then use the information in this article to complete the outline on the next page.

Texas Wildflowers

by William G. Morales

Many people know the old folk song, "The Yellow Rose of Texas." Texas is home to many beautiful wildflowers too.

If you see a yellow-orange flower that looks like a sombrero, you probably have found a flower called a **Mexican Hat.** These pretty flowers are also called "coneflowers" and "thimbleflowers." Mexican Hat flowers can be used for making dye.

Another flower found in the Lone Star State is the **Texas Dandelion.** These members of the sunflower family are found in pastures, near roads, and on people's lawns. When the stems of these flowers are broken, they leak a kind of milky sap. When the seeds dry, children enjoy blowing them into the air.

One of the most beautiful flowers in Texas is the **Indian Paintbrush,** also known as the "scarlet paintbrush." The paintbrush plants use the roots of other plants to help them grow. They bloom from March to May, but are the prettiest in April.

Name ______________________________________

Texas Wildflowers

I. ________________

A. Also called coneflowers and ________________

B. Used for making dye

II. ________________

A. When broken, they leak milky sap.

B. Found near pastures, roads, and on ________________

C. Children blow the seeds in the air.

III. Indian Paintbrush

A. Also known as ________________

B. Uses the roots of other plants to grow

Directions: Explain why an outline can be useful for researching and studying. Write your explanation on the lines below.

____

____

____

____

____

____

____

____

____

Notes for Home: Your child used an outline to organize information and understand what he or she read. ***Home Activity:*** Create an outline that organizes information about an interesting topic, such as your family history or wildlife in your area. Use the above outline as a model.

Family Times

Name______________________________

Summary

Heroic Girl Saves Brother and Herself

It's hard enough for a nine-year-old girl to take care of herself, her little brother, and a family friend's farm for two days. Then a prairie fire breaks out, and nothing will stop it. Addie remembers her father's advice—go where there's nothing to burn. So Addie takes her brother and heads for the well. What a spot to be in!

Activity

Act It Out. Have your child take the role of Addie or her brother Burt and act out the rest of the story, including the rescue.

Reading Skills

Character

Characters are the people or animals in a story. The main characters in "Addie in Charge" are Addie and Burt. You can learn about characters by what they think, do, and say. In a crisis, Addie stays calm and does the right thing.

You can also learn about characters from how other characters treat them and what they say about them. When the others return, they praise Addie for her courage and intelligence.

Activity

Tell a Story. Think of an exciting adventure of a heroic young girl and her brother. Have family members take turns telling a sentence or two of the story. Each person continues where the previous person left off. Remember to include details about the main characters.

Family Times

Tested Vocabulary

Words to Know

Knowing the meanings of these words is important to reading "Addie in Charge." Practice using these words to learn their meanings.

bellows makes a loud, deep noise

billows great waves of smoke, flame, or sound

crouched stooped low with bent legs

smarted felt or caused sharp pain

tufts bunches of feathers, hair, or grass held together

Grammar

Compound and Complex Sentences

A **simple sentence** has one complete thought.

A **compound sentence** contains two simple sentences joined by a comma and a conjunction, such as *and, but,* or *or*. **Addie hid in the well, and she took Burt with her.**

A **complex sentence** contains a simple sentence and a group of words that cannot stand on its own, with a connecting word such as *because* or *when*. **When the fire came close, Addie and Burt hid.**

Activity

Keeping Score. Read a favorite short story. Keep score of how many compound and complex sentences you find. Which kind of sentence was used most often?

Tested Spelling Words

___	___	___	___
___	___	___	___
___	___	___	___
___	___	___	___
___	___	___	___

Character

- **Characters** are the people or animals in a story or nonfictional article.
- You can learn about characters by what they think, do, and say.
- You can also learn about characters by seeing how other characters in the story treat them and what other characters say about them.

Directions: Reread "Ma on the Prairie." Fill in the word web with story details about Ma that help you learn about her. On the line at the bottom of the page, write your own description of this character.

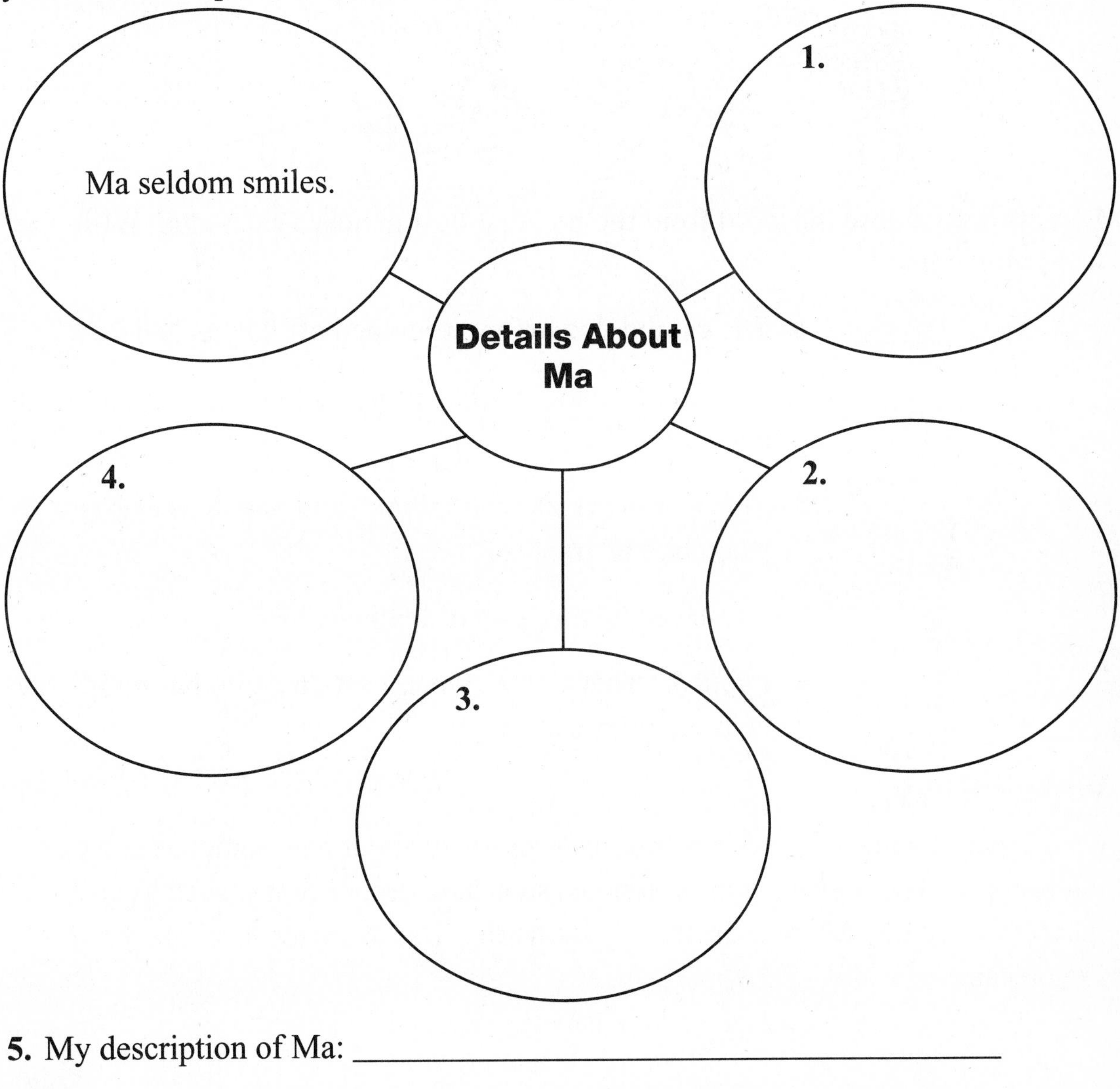

Details About Ma

Ma seldom smiles.

1.

2.

3.

4.

5. My description of Ma: ____________________

Notes for Home: Your child read a story and identified details that helped her or him understand a main character. ***Home Activity:*** Have your child try to understand a person better by making a list of things that person does and says and what other people say about the person.

Name ____________________________________

Vocabulary

Directions: Draw a line to connect each word on the left with its definition on the right.

1. tufts	roars
2. smarted	stooped
3. bellows	clumps of grass
4. crouched	waves of smoke
5. billows	stung

Check the Words You Know

__ bellows
__ billows
__ crouched
__ smarted
__ tufts

Directions: Choose the word from the box that best matches each clue. Write the word on the line.

______________ **6.** The cat did this before it jumped off the bookshelf.

______________ **7.** This word rhymes with soft things for your head on your bed.

______________ **8.** This word rhymes with *fellows,* and one fellow does it when he's angry.

______________ **9.** These can be made up of feathers, hair, or grass.

______________ **10.** I yelled, "That ____!" when I sat on a pin, but it did not help my grades at school.

Write a Story

On a separate sheet of paper, write a made-up story about how someone solves a big problem. The problem can be serious, such as a fire, or funny, such as an incredibly bad day where everything goes wrong. Use as many vocabulary words as you can.

Notes for Home: Your child identified and used vocabulary words from "Addie in Charge." ***Home Activity:*** Say the vocabulary word *crouched* and have your child act out its meaning. Take turns saying other action words that can be acted out by the other person.

Name ________________________________

Character

- **Characters** are the people or animals in a story.
- You can learn about characters by what they think, do, and say. You can also learn about characters by how other characters in the story treat them and what other characters say about them.

Directions: Reread what happens in "Addie in Charge" when she tries to save herself and her little brother from the fire. Then answer the questions below. Think about how you learn what Addie and Burt are like.

Still kneeling on the ground, Addie used one foot to carefully feel for the ladder's highest rung. Slowly, she lowered herself, balancing Burt with great effort. Down into the well she went, step over step. Now they were below ground level. It was pitch black, and the water felt cold around Addie's knees as she reached the bottom rung. "Don't let go, Burt. Don't let go," she told her brother, who buried his face into the back of her neck so that her necklace dug deep into her skin.

1. Is Addie sure of herself? How do you know?

____

2. How do you know Addie cares about her brother?

____

3. How do you think Burt feels? How do you know?

____

4. Addie's parents left her in charge. How do you think they felt about her?

____

5. On a separate sheet of paper, describe Addie in your own words. Use details from the story to support your answers.

Notes for Home: Your child has read a story and used story details to understand characters. ***Home Activity:*** Help your child understand characters in books you read together by talking about the things they think, do, or say.

Name ____________________

Selection Test

Directions: Choose the best answer to each item. Mark the letter for the answer you have chosen.

Part 1: Vocabulary

Find the answer choice that means about the same as the underlined word in each sentence.

1. Stella <u>crouched</u> on the floor.
- A. spun around quickly
- B. stooped low with bent legs
- C. walked on tiptoes
- D. pounded with the feet

2. I could hear the cow's <u>bellows</u>.
- F. deep breaths
- G. rings from a bell
- H. sweet songs
- J. loud, deep noises

3. Grains of sand <u>smarted</u> my face.
- A. caused pain in
- B. stuck to
- C. blew around
- D. covered

4. We pulled <u>tufts</u> of weeds from the garden.
- F. seeds
- G. roots
- H. bunches
- J. flowers

5. <u>Billows</u> of smoke rose from the roof.
- A. thin streams
- B. large piles
- C. great waves
- D. storm clouds

Part 2: Comprehension

Use what you know about the story to answer each item.

6. When the story begins, Addie's parents and brother were—
- F. traveling to Iowa.
- G. planting crops.
- H. visiting neighbors.
- J. building a sod home.

7. Who was Ruby Lillian?
- A. Addie's friend from Iowa
- B. the Fencys' cow
- C. Addie's little sister
- D. a doll

8. What clue shows that Addie was quite grown-up and dependable?
- F. She was left in charge of her little brother for two days.
- G. She was making a sampler.
- H. She saw a strange light in the sky.
- J. She read Burt a story.

9. What was the first sign of trouble that Addie noticed?
- A. The horizon was orange and yellow.
- B. Coyotes ran through the field.
- C. The cows were making frightened noises.
- D. Ashes were flying in the air.

10. As the fire drew closer, Addie felt—
- F. sure the firebreak would stop the fire.
- G. terrified but determined to stay safe.
- H. sure that she and Burt were going to die.
- J. nervous but certain that her parents would rescue her.

11. Why did Addie climb down into the well?
- A. She knew fire could not go there.
- B. It was quiet and dark.
- C. She and Burt needed water to drink.
- D. It was far from the fire's path.

12. In the well, Addie felt—
- F. too afraid to do anything.
- G. afraid, but responsible for her brother's safety.
- H. in control of the situation.
- J. angry that her parents had left her alone.

13. When George found a scrap of Addie's bonnet, he thought that Addie and Burt had—
- A. hidden in the well.
- B. run away from the fire.
- C. hidden in the root cellar.
- D. died in the fire.

14. For Addie, what was the best thing to come out of her experience?
- F. She would never quarrel with George again.
- G. She discovered that she was strong enough to be a pioneer.
- H. Her parents probably wouldn't leave her alone again.
- J. The Fencys would always be grateful to her.

15. What was the most important thing Addie did in this story?
- A. threw water on the Fencys' house
- B. put Anna Fency's trunk in the cellar
- C. kept herself and her brother safe
- D. untied Bess and Missy

STOP

Name ____________________

Character

- **Characters** are the people or animals in a story.
- You can learn about characters by what they think, do, and say. You can also learn about characters by how other characters in the story treat them and what other characters say about them.

Directions: Read the story below.

Matt and Bill were twins, but you couldn't tell from looking at them. They both were tall. Matt was thin, and Bill had lots of muscles. Matt had blond hair, but Bill's was brown. Matt had green eyes, and Bill's were blue.

What was important was that their parents could trust them both. When Matt and Bill's grandfather got sick, their parents had to take him in the wagon all the way to the doctor in Glenville. The twins' parents were counting on Matt and Bill to take care of things.

While they were away, Matt and Bill did the farm chores. Matt fed the animals, while Bill cleaned their stalls. Matt gathered eggs, and Bill prepared meals. Neither of them complained. They were just proud they could help out.

Directions: In the diagram below, list five things that are true of Matt, five that are true of Bill, and five that are true of both of them.

Matt	Both Matt and Bill	Bill
1. ____________	6. ____________	11. ____________
2. ____________	7. ____________	12. ____________
3. ____________	8. ____________	13. ____________
4. ____________	9. ____________	14. ____________
5. ____________	10. ____________	15. ____________

Notes for Home: Your child has read a story and used story details to describe two characters. ***Home Activity:*** With your child, fill out a diagram similar to the one above for two family members or friends.

Name ________________________________

REVIEW

Theme

Directions: Read the story. Then read each question about the story. Choose the best answer to each question. Mark the letter for the answer you have chosen.

Helping Hans

Ten-year-old Hans and his father were building a table. Hans was proud to be helping his father. Anna, his little sister, wanted to help too, but Hans said, "Go play with your dolls. You're too little to help."

When Hans and his father finished sawing, they began to put the table together. They pounded nail after nail. At last, just one leg was left, but there were no more nails.

Hans and his father searched everywhere, but they could not find any nails. Little Anna, playing quietly on the floor, suddenly pounced.

"Here they are!" she said. The nails had rolled across the floor to where she was playing.

"Thank you, Anna," said Hans. "You're a big help!"

1. A story's theme is—
- **A.** what happens.
- **B.** its big idea.
- **C.** its ending.
- **D.** why something happens.

2. Which statement best describes this story's theme?
- **F.** Don't build anything unless you have all the pieces.
- **G.** Even the littlest can help.
- **H.** Don't drop the nails before the table is finished.
- **J.** Children should be seen but not heard.

3. The theme of this passage is—
- **A.** stated by Hans.
- **B.** stated by Hans's father.
- **C.** stated by Anna.
- **D.** Not stated directly by any one character.

4. A title that suggests the theme is—
- **F.** Little Helpers.
- **G.** We Need Nails.
- **H.** Stop! Look! Listen!
- **J.** Table Building Long Ago.

5. Which statement from the story supports the theme?
- **A.** There were no more nails.
- **B.** They pounded nail after nail.
- **C.** "You're a big help!"
- **D.** Ten-year-old Hans and his father were building a table.

Notes for Home: Your child has read a story and used story details to identify its theme. ***Home Activity:*** When you and your child are watching television together, suggest that he or she tell the theme of a story and give reasons to support his or her answer.

Name ______________________________

Writing Across Texts

Directions: Consider what you know about Addie from "Addie in Charge" and Merle Block from the article "Merle Builds a Sod House." What pioneer-like qualities does each of them have? In the left-hand column, write traits that describe Addie. In the right-hand column, write traits that describe Merle Block.

Addie's Traits	Merle's Traits
She is brave and responsible.	He appreciates his ancestors.
1.	**6.**
2.	**7.**
3.	**8.**
4.	**9.**
5.	**10.**

Write a Character Description

Think about what you learned about Addie and Merle Block. What qualities would a pioneer need to survive on the prairie? On a separate sheet of paper, write a paragraph that describes the qualities of a good pioneer. Use the information you wrote in the table above to help you with ideas.

Notes for Home: Your child used information from different sources to write a character description. ***Home Activity:*** As you read stories and articles with your child, compare and contrast the characters and people in these materials.

Name ______________________________

Grammar: Simple Sentences

REVIEW

Directions: Read each group of words. Write **S** if it is a sentence. Write **NS** if it is not a sentence. For each sentence, underline the simple subject once and the simple predicate twice.

__________ **1.** Matthew will go to a new school in September.

__________ **2.** He has worried about it all summer.

__________ **3.** Meeting new teachers and students.

__________ **4.** This smart boy made some plans.

__________ **5.** Memorized a map of the school.

Directions: Think of a time you have been afraid of something. Write five sentences about that time. Underline each simple subject once and each simple predicate twice.

6. ______________________________

____

7. ______________________________

____

8. ______________________________

____

9. ______________________________

____

10. ______________________________

____

Notes for Home: Your child identified the subjects and predicates in simple sentences and wrote sentences. ***Home Activity:*** Look at comics in a newspaper. Have your child tell which statements the characters are saying are sentences that contain a subject and a predicate.

Name ______________________________

Grammar: Compound and Complex Sentences

A **simple sentence** expresses one complete thought. A **compound sentence** contains two simple sentences joined by a comma and a connecting word such as *and, but,* or *or.*

Simple sentences: My mother went out. I was home alone.
Compound sentence: My mother went out, and I was home alone.

A **complex sentence** contains a simple sentence combined with a group of words that cannot stand on its own.

Complex sentence: When my mother left, I was home alone.
group of words simple sentence

Directions: Write whether each sentence is **compound** or **complex.**

______________ **1.** When I turned the corner, I heard a strange noise.

______________ **2.** The noise grew louder, and I was scared.

______________ **3.** Before I knew it, I was running.

______________ **4.** I saw a police car, and I told the officer what I had heard.

______________ **5.** When we saw the garbage truck, we both laughed.

Directions: Write **Yes** if the underlined words can stand alone to make a sentence. Write **No** if they cannot stand alone.

________ **6.** <u>You are not alone</u>, but you wish you were.

________ **7.** <u>Because you are scared</u>, you run fast.

________ **8.** You fall, or <u>you are knocked down</u>.

________ **9.** <u>When your face is licked</u>, you start to laugh.

________ **10.** You hug your dog, and <u>you give him a treat</u>.

Notes for Home: Your child identified compound and complex sentences. ***Home Activity:*** Read a newspaper article. Challenge your child to find compound and complex sentences in it.

Name ________________________

Grammar: Compound and Complex Sentences

Directions: Make a compound sentence by joining the simple sentences with a comma and one of these words: *and, but,* or *or.*

1. We watched a TV movie. We didn't see the end.

____

2. Something went wrong with the set. The picture disappeared.

____

3. The screen went dark. The sound stopped too.

____

4. My dad would fix the set. We would replace it.

____

5. My brother turned on the radio. We listened to the news.

____

Directions: Write **Yes** if the underlined words can stand alone to make a sentence. Write **No** if they cannot stand alone.

__________ **6.** <u>Because my parents were at Open School Night,</u> I was home alone.

__________ **7.** I was reading, and <u>the lights went out.</u>

__________ **8.** Was it just my house, or <u>was it a neighborhood blackout?</u>

__________ **9.** <u>When I looked outside</u>, the whole neighborhood was dark.

__________ **10.** Since all the electric power was off, <u>I used my flashlight.</u>

Write a Paragraph

Think of a problem you solved. On a separate sheet of paper, write a paragraph that tells how you solved it. Include compound and complex sentences.

Notes for Home: Your child identified compound and complex sentences. ***Home Activity:*** Point to two objects in the room. Ask your child to make up a compound sentence (contains two simple sentences and a connecting word) that compares the objects.

Name ______________________________

Grammar: Compound and Complex Sentences

RETEACHING

Read the compound sentence. It is made of two simple sentences. Circle the word **and** in the sentence.

1. The pitcher throws the ball, and the batter hits it.

Read the complex sentence. It is made up of a simple sentence and a group of words that cannot stand alone as a sentence.

2. When I threw it as hard as I could, the ball sailed away.

A **simple sentence** expresses one complete thought. It has one subject and one predicate. A **compound sentence** contains two simple sentences joined by the word **and.** A **complex sentence** contains a simple sentence and another group of words that cannot stand alone as a complete sentence.

Directions: Read each sentence. Then circle **compound** or **complex**.

1. The catcher crouches behind the plate, and the pitcher throws the first ball. compound complex

2. When the ball comes, the batter hits it solidly. compound complex

3. The shortstop runs toward the ball because that is his job. compound complex

4. The ball hops past the shortstop, and the batter runs to first base. compound complex

Directions: Complete each compound or complex sentence.

5. When the game begins, ______________________________

6. A batter hits a high ball, and ______________________________

7. The home team wins, and ______________________________

Notes for Home: Your child identified compound and complex sentences. ***Home Activity:*** Have your child combine pairs of sentences to form compound sentences. Then write pairs of word groups for your child to combine to create complex sentences.

Name ______________________________

Grammar: Compound and Complex Sentences

Directions: Write **compound** or **complex** for each sentence.

1. Mozart was young, and he was famous. ______________
2. When he was three, he played music. ______________
3. Mozart read music, and he wrote it too. ______________
4. He wrote melodies for many instruments because he enjoyed it. ______________
5. He went on tours, and crowds cheered him. ______________
6. If you say *The Magic Flute*, someone might think of Mozart. ______________
7. Because of Mozart, more people were interested in the piano. ______________
8. It was new, and few people played it. ______________

Directions: Add a simple sentence or a group of words. Write each compound or complex sentence.

9. Music makes me smile, because ______________________________ ____.
10. I like to sing, and ______________________________ ____.
11. We can listen, and ______________________________ ____.

Write a Story

On a separate sheet of paper, write a story about a musician you like. Use compound and complex sentences. Begin with a compound sentence that starts:

I have a favorite musician, and ____________ .

Notes for Home: Your child identified and wrote compound and complex sentences. ***Home Activity:*** Read your child's story about a favorite musician. Have him or her point out to you which sentences are compound and which are complex.

Name ______________________________

Phonics: Three-letter Blends

Directions: Read each short word. Make a longer word by following the first instruction. Take that longer word and make an even longer word by following the second instruction. Write each new word on the line.

1. sash

Add an **l** after the first **s.** __________

Add a **p** after the first **s.** __________

2. tee

Add an **r** after the **t.** __________

Add an **h** after the **t.** __________

3. ream

Add a **c** before the **r.** __________

Add an **s** before the **c.** __________

4. sing

Add a **t** after the **s.** __________

Add an **r** after the **t.** __________

Directions: The sentences below are part of a diary entry about solving a problem. Six words start with a three-letter blend. Write the six words on the lines.

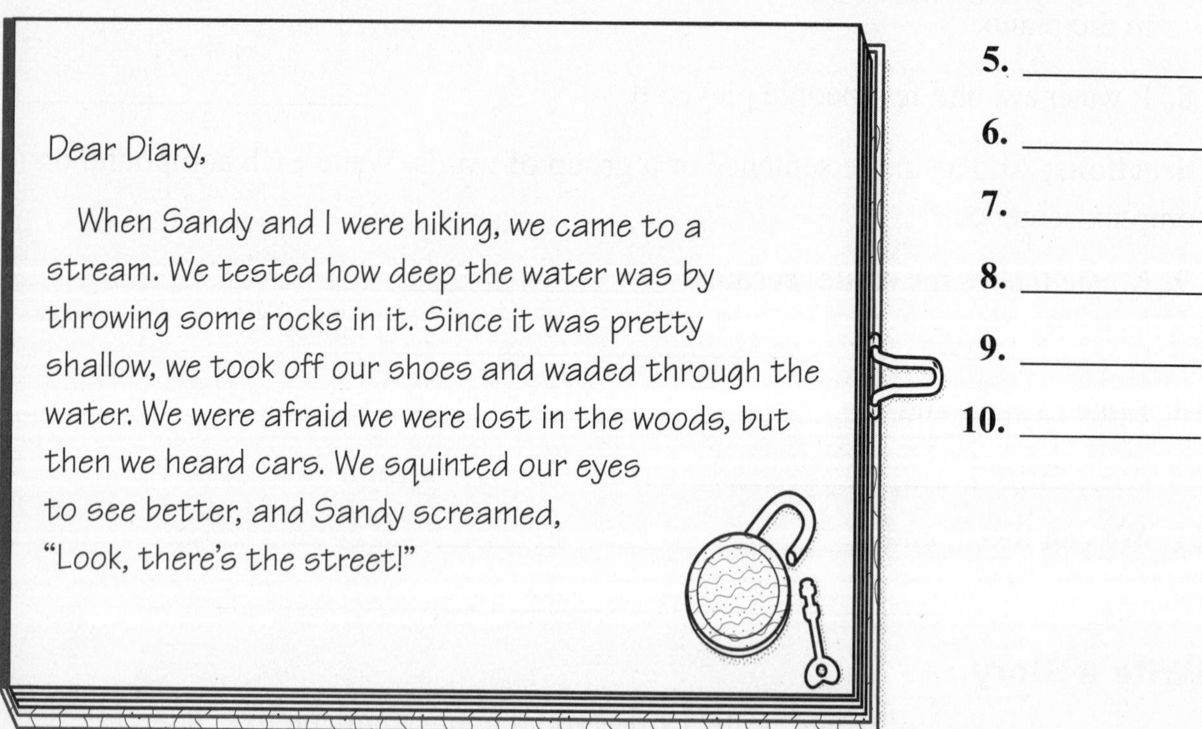

Dear Diary,

When Sandy and I were hiking, we came to a stream. We tested how deep the water was by throwing some rocks in it. Since it was pretty shallow, we took off our shoes and waded through the water. We were afraid we were lost in the woods, but then we heard cars. We squinted our eyes to see better, and Sandy screamed, "Look, there's the street!"

5. __________

6. __________

7. __________

8. __________

9. __________

10. __________

Notes for Home: Your child learned words such as *splash* that start with three-letter blend. ***Home Activity:*** Read labels with your child to help identify other three-letter blends, such as those that begin *str-, spl-, scr-, spr-, squ-,* or *thr-*. List the words you find.

Name ______________________________

Spelling: Words with *thr, scr, str, squ*

Pretest Directions: Fold back the page along the dotted line. On the blanks, write the spelling words as they are dictated. When you have finished the test, unfold the page and check your words.

1. ______________________
2. ______________________
3. ______________________
4. ______________________
5. ______________________
6. ______________________
7. ______________________
8. ______________________
9. ______________________
10. ______________________
11. ______________________
12. ______________________
13. ______________________
14. ______________________
15. ______________________
16. ______________________
17. ______________________
18. ______________________
19. ______________________
20. ______________________

1. My **throat** is sore.
2. Run **through** the field.
3. The **screen** keeps out bugs.
4. My bike has a **scratch**.
5. Did someone **scream**?
6. It is a **strange** story.
7. The **street** is empty.
8. **Strike** the piñata.
9. The windows are **square**.
10. **Squeeze** the toothpaste.
11. The bully made a **threat**.
12. The ball was **thrown** far.
13. Did the play **thrill** you?
14. **Scrub** the pots and pans.
15. Look up at the **skyscraper**!
16. Is the **strawberry** ripe?
17. Use **strength** to lift this.
18. Listen to the pig **squeal**.
19. Snakes make me **squirm**.
20. **Squirt** water on the plant.

Notes for Home: Your child took a pretest on words with *thr, scr, str,* and *squ*. ***Home Activity:*** Help your child learn misspelled words before the final test. See if there are any similar errors and discuss a memory trick that could help.

Name ______________________________

Spelling: Words with *thr, scr, str,* and *squ*

Word List			
throat	screen	strange	square
through	scratch	street	squeeze
threat	scream	strike	squeal
thrown	scrub	strawberry	squirm
thrill	skyscraper	strength	squirt

Directions: Write the words that have a three-letter **consonant blend** with **s.** Sort the words by the way they are spelled.

Spelled scr	Spelled str	Spelled squ
1. ______________	**6.** ______________	**11.** ______________
2. ______________	**7.** ______________	**12.** ______________
3. ______________	**8.** ______________	**13.** ______________
4. ______________	**9.** ______________	**14.** ______________
5. ______________	**10.** ______________	**15.** ______________

Directions: Choose the word from the box that best matches each definition. Write the word on the line.

______________ **16.** in one side and out the other

______________ **17.** a warning or promise to do harm

______________ **18.** sent through the air forcefully

______________ **19.** the front of the neck

______________ **20.** an exciting feeling

Notes for Home: Your child spelled words with *thr, scr, str,* and *squ.* ***Home Activity:*** Write *thr, scr, str,* and *squ* on index cards (one per card). On others write endings from spelling words. Let your child use the cards to build words *(str + ength = strength).*

Name ______________________________

Spelling: Words with *thr, scr, str,* and *squ*

Directions: Proofread this message. Find five spelling mistakes. Use the proofreading marks to correct each mistake.

≡	Make a capital.
/	Make a small letter.
∧	Add something.
℘	Take out something.
⊙	Add a period.
¶	Begin a new paragraph.

Thought for Today

Once you start to solve a problem, it's important to try to see it trhough. Sure, you might get stuck. At times you might even want to skream, "Enough!" But it's amazing and sttrange how much inner stirength you can find. And the thrrill of success is sweet.

Spelling Tip

Each spelling word has three letters that together represent a blended sound: **<u>thr</u>oat, <u>scr</u>eam, <u>str</u>eet, <u>squ</u>eeze.**

Word List

throat	strange
through	street
threat	strike
thrown	strawberry
thrill	strength
screen	square
scratch	squeeze
scream	squeal
scrub	squirm
skyscraper	squirt

Write About an Experience

On a separate sheet of paper, write about a problem you solved successfully. Try to use at least three spelling words.

Notes for Home: Your child spelled words with consonant blends *thr, scr, str,* and *squ.* ***Home Activity:*** Say a word that starts with one of these blends. Have your child say that word plus a new word with that blend. You say both words and add a third word. Continue taking turns.

Name ________________________________

REVIEW

Spelling: Words with *thr, scr, str,* and *squ*

Word List				
throat	thrill	scrub	strike	squeeze
through	screen	skyscraper	strawberry	squeal
threat	scratch	strange	strength	squirm
thrown	scream	street	square	squirt

Directions: Think of the word each clue describes. Then choose the word from the box that rhymes with that word. Write the word on the line.

________ **1.** two-wheeler

________ **2.** a young one is called a kid

________ **3.** you wash it off you

________ **4.** a nightcrawler

________ **5.** height, width, and _____

________ **6.** small mountain

________ **7.** home, home on the _____

________ **8.** a group of football players

________ **9.** not fake

________ **10.** it can start a fire

Directions: Choose the word that best completes each sentence. Write the word on the line to the left.

________________ **11.** Have you been to the top of a _____?

________________ **12.** You can often find them in a city's central _____.

________________ **13.** My favorite one is red like a _____.

________________ **14.** Of course, the height isn't a _____ to your safety.

________________ **15.** A _____ or fence will protect you from falling off.

________________ **16.** A ball _____ from there would go far.

________________ **17.** If you're nervous, you can _____ someone's hand.

________________ **18.** You may not want to look down at the _____ below.

________________ **19.** When you're _____ viewing, take an elevator down.

________________ **20.** Imagine having to _____ the steps clean!

Notes for Home: Your child spelled words with *thr, scr, str,* and *squ*. ***Home Activity:*** Say each of the words on the list aloud to your child and have him or her come up with another word (from the box or not) that has the same letter combination.

Name ______________________________

Parts of a Book

Knowing the **parts of a book** makes it easier to locate information. For example, a **table of contents** shows what a book is about and where to find each chapter.

Directions: Use the table of contents to answer the questions that follow.

American Pioneers of the Wild West

Table of Contents

1. What do the numbers shown on the right of the table of contents tell you?

____

2. How do the topics under each chapter head help you? ______________

____

____

3. How many different people can you read about in Chapter 2? ______________

4. If you wanted to research American Pioneers who were women, which chapter should you read? On what page does this chapter begin?

____

5. Which chapter should you read to learn more about Buffalo Bill?

____

Name ______________________________

An **index** is a list of the specific subjects covered in a book. It tells what pages have information about each subject.

Directions: Study this index from *American Pioneers of the Wild West*. Use it to answer the questions that follow.

Index

6. If you wanted to find information about a famous Native American speech, which pages would you read?

____

7. If you wanted to know what cowboys ate for dinner, which page would you read?

____

8. If you wanted to use an index to find information about a person, would you look under the first name or last name?

____

9. If you looked on pages 25–27, what information would you expect to find?

____

10. How does a table of contents and an index help you find information quickly?

____

____

Notes for Home: Your child learned about the parts of a book, such as the table of contents and the index. ***Home Activity:*** Challenge your child to locate information in a nonfiction book, using the index and table of contents.

Name ____________________

Notes for a Narrative

Directions: Fill in the graphic organizer with information about the event or experience that you plan to write about.

Possible title: ____________________

Summary

What happened? ____________________

When? ____________________

Where? ____________________

Who was there? ____________________

Details

Beginning

Middle

End

Notes for Home: Your child has been planning a personal narrative. ***Home Activity:*** Have your child tell you about the experience that he or she is writing about. Ask for details about what happened first, next, and last.

Name ____________________

Elaboration

Words That Show Emotion

- You can elaborate by adding vivid, precise **words to show emotion.**
- Adjectives can show emotion: He was *furious.* He was *annoyed.*
- Adverbs can show emotion: Clare paced *nervously.* Clare spoke *timidly.*
- Verbs can show emotion: They *waltzed* down the street. They *trudged* down the street.

Directions: Write a sentence about each scene below. Use vivid, precise words that show emotions. Use the words from the box as ideas for your sentences.

Verbs	Adjectives	Adverbs
howled	worried	excitedly
stomped	terrified	hurriedly
ripped	frantic	worriedly
celebrated	astonished	cautiously

1. The mail arrives. Judy has a letter.

____

2. Raul runs. He misses the bus. ____________________

____

3. The poster contest winner is announced. Oliver wins. ____________________

____

4. The toddler falls off of the swing. She is upset. ____________________

____

5. A puppy is lost. The owner is looking for it. ____________________

____

6. Jack hears a noise in the old house. He investigates. ____________________

____

Notes for Home: Your child has been learning to use vivid, precise words to show emotions. ***Home Activity:*** Ask your child to suggest an angry word, a sad word, and a happy word to use in place of the word *said.*

Name____

Self-Evaluation Guide

Personal Narrative Checklist

Directions: Think about the final draft of your personal narrative. Then answer each question below.

	Yes	No	Not sure
1. Does my narrative flow smoothly from beginning to middle to end?			
2. Did I use enough details to let my audience know how I feel about the event?			
3. Did I keep my audience and purpose in mind?			
4. Did I use vivid words to express myself?			
5. Did I proofread and edit carefully to avoid errors?			

6. Which sentence of your personal narrative uses the most precise, vivid words? Copy it here.

____

____

7. If you were asked to write a sequel, or continuation, of your personal narrative, what would you write about?

____

____

____

Notes for Home: Your child has just completed a self-evaluation of a personal narrative. ***Home Activity:*** Ask your child about what might make a good topic for a personal narrative.

Family Times

Name______________________________

Summary

World Turns Topsy-Turvy for Country Cricket in NY

Chester Cricket got much more than he bargained for when he climbed into a picnic basket in his Connecticut meadow. He got a trip all the way to New York City. There, in the Times Square subway station, Mario Bellini, the son of the newsstand owners, finds Chester and makes a home for him in a matchbox. One evening, after the newsstand closes, Chester makes friends with Tucker Mouse and Harry Cat, who take him above ground to see the sights of the city.

Activity

What Do You See? Imagine you're Tucker taking Chester sightseeing above ground. What sights do you see? How do they look to a tiny mouse and cricket? Try to use words that help bring the city to life for your listeners as you tell Tucker's story.

Reading Skills

Visualizing

To **visualize** means to form a picture in your mind as you read. Because everything in the subway is new to Chester, he observes and describes it in detail. Details that tell how things look, smell, sound, taste, and feel help readers create vivid pictures in their minds.

Activity

Seeing Something for the First Time. Think of a place that is familiar to your family. Describe it as if you were a cricket like Chester, seeing it for the first time. Describe the place in detail, using words that tell how things look, feel, taste, smell, and sound. Can someone else guess what place you are describing? Now let someone else take a turn.

Family Times

Tested Vocabulary

Words to Know

Knowing the meanings of these words is important to reading *The Cricket in Times Square.* Practice using these words to learn their meanings.

chirp short, sharp sound made by a cricket

furiously quickly, wildly

melody a succession of single tones in music

occasion a special event

railroad track with steel rails that trains travel on

subway underground electric railway

traffic coming and going along a way of travel

venturing daring to go

Grammar

Nouns

A **noun** is a word that names one or more persons, places, or things. A thing can be an idea, such as *freedom* or *happiness.* A noun is usually the main word in the subject of a sentence. It tells whom or what the sentence is about. **Chester had some ride!** A noun can also appear in the predicate. **Chester is visiting the city.**

Activity

Name that Noun. Play a game (the more players, the better) in which someone comes up with a sentence, such as: **The tired cricket fell asleep.** Take turns changing the noun, until you have run out of nouns or are laughing too hard to go on. Then start again with a new sentence.

Tested Spelling Words

Name ____________________

Visualizing

- To **visualize** means to form a picture in your mind as you read.
- As you read, look for details that tell how things look, smell, sound, taste, and feel.

Directions: Reread "Caught in the Kitchen." Then complete the web. Write details from the story that help you picture the characters and setting.

Gertrude and Omeletta

1.

2.

3.

Countertop

4.

"Caught in the Kitchen"

Kitchen

5.

Notes for Home: Your child pictured events and characters in his or her mind while reading. ***Home Activity:*** Ask your child to visualize a favorite place. Invite him or her to tell you sights, smells, sounds, tastes, and sensations associated with that place.

Name ________________________________

Vocabulary

Directions: Choose the word from the box that best completes each sentence. Write the word on the line to the left.

Check the Words You Know

__ chirp
__ furiously
__ melody
__ occasion
__ railroad
__ subway
__ traffic
__ venturing

_______________ **1.** It is always a special _____ when my family goes to the city.

_______________ **2.** We take the train into the city because the _____ station is close by.

_______________ **3.** Once we're in the city, we usually travel by underground _____.

_______________ **4.** Traveling underground gets us where we want to go faster than trying to drive through heavy _____.

_______________ **5.** Once, when we were at a concert in the park, I heard a cricket _____.

_______________ **6.** It wasn't exactly singing a _____, but it sounded nice anyway.

Directions: Circle the word that has the same or nearly the same meaning as the first word in each group.

7. melody	words	tune	ringing
8. furiously	wildly	softly	lightly
9. chirp	bark	tweet	growl
10. venturing	frying	risking	staying

Write a Letter

On a separate sheet of paper, write a letter to a friend about a trip to a city. Use as many vocabulary words as you can.

Notes for Home: Your child identified and used new vocabulary from *The Cricket in Times Square. **Home Activity:*** With your child, make a list of imaginary, fun trips and describe how you would travel. Use the vocabulary words, such as *railroad* or *subway,* in your planning.

Name ____________________________________

Visualizing

- **Visualizing** means creating a picture or pictures in your mind as you read.
- If you have trouble visualizing, you may want to reread parts of the story.

Directions: Reread about Tucker Mouse in *The Cricket in Times Square*. Then answer the questions below. Think about what it says in the story to help you visualize.

Tucker Mouse had been watching the Bellinis and listening to what they said. Next to scrounging, eavesdropping on human beings was what he enjoyed most. That was one of the reasons he lived in the Times Square subway station. As soon as the family disappeared, he darted out across the floor and scooted up to the newsstand. At one side the boards had separated and there was a wide space he could jump through. He'd been in a few times before—just exploring. For a moment he stood under the three legged stool, letting his eyes get used to the darkness. Then he jumped up on it.

1. Where is Tucker at the very beginning of the passage? How do you know?

____

2. Where does Tucker go when the family leaves? Is he moving quickly or slowly?

____

3. How does Tucker get into the newsstand? Is it difficult or easy? Explain.

____

4. Is it easy or hard for Tucker to see? How do you know?

____

5. Pick another scene from the story. On a separate sheet of paper, tell what mental pictures you have as you read. Give examples of words or details that help you visualize the scene.

Notes for Home: Your child has read a story and used story details to visualize it by creating a mental picture of the story. ***Home Activity:*** With your child, look at a descriptive passage in a favorite book or story. Invite your child to tell you what he or she imagines while reading.

Name ______________________________

Selection Test

Directions: Choose the best answer to each item. Mark the letter for the answer you have chosen.

Part 1: Vocabulary

Find the answer choice that means about the same as the underlined word in each sentence.

1. The boys worked furiously.
- A. without much interest
- B. in a slow, careful way
- C. quickly and wildly
- D. in a cheerful way

2. The chirp came from inside that box.
- F. short sharp sound
- G. beat of a drum
- H. loud flapping sound
- J. low moan

3. The children were venturing into the woods.
- A. shouting or calling
- B. daring to go
- C. hiking fast
- D. staring

4. I have heard that melody before.
- F. idea
- G. joke or funny story
- H. tune
- J. signal or message

5. Everyone was there for the occasion.
- A. talk or discussion
- B. special event
- C. lesson or class
- D. small meal

6. We met at the railroad station.
- F. taxi
- G. police
- H. bus
- J. train

7. Watch out for the traffic.
- A. cars and buses moving along streets
- B. rules of safe driving
- C. signs for drivers on highways
- D. rest stop for travelers

8. We decided to take the subway.
- F. ship that travels under water
- G. bridge over a city street
- H. underground electric train
- J. train that travels at night

GO ON

Name ___________________________________

Part 2: Comprehension

Use what you know about the story to answer each item.

9. At the beginning of the story, Tucker Mouse is in a—
A. subway station.
B. tree stump.
C. bus station.
D. city apartment.

10. What did Tucker Mouse give Chester to eat?
F. roast beef
G. liverwurst
H. eggs
J. chocolate

11. At the beginning of the story, how did Chester feel about being in New York?
A. excited and amazed
B. bored and sleepy
C. surprised and glad
D. nervous and uncomfortable

12. Which words match your mental picture of Chester's journey inside the picnic basket?
F. dark and cramped
G. quiet and smooth
H. cozy and comfortable
J. smelly and dirty

13. Which detail from the story helps create a mental picture of New York City at night?
A. "And there he gasped, holding his breath and crouching against the cement."
B. "They were standing at one corner of the Times building."
C. "Above the cricket, towers that seemed like mountains of light rose up into the night sky."
D. "'Well—it's—it's quite something,' Chester stuttered."

14. What was the luckiest thing that Chester did in this story?
F. hopping into a picnic basket
G. riding in a subway
H. meeting Tucker Mouse
J. climbing up the pipe

15. At the end of the story, Chester has probably decided to—
A. move to New York for good.
B. find a way to escape from Tucker Mouse and Harry Cat.
C. return to Connecticut right away.
D. let his new friends show him New York for a little while.

Name ______________________________

Visualizing

- To **visualize** means to create a picture or pictures in your mind as you read.
- If you have trouble visualizing, you may want to reread parts of the story.

Directions: Read the story below.

Marvin and Melissa Mouse lived in a small hole behind the kitchen wall. Their hole was right behind the stove, so it was warm and cozy in winter.

Both Marvin and Melissa liked to be comfortable, so they had been careful about what they took to make their nest. Marvin had found some pieces of cloth from an old T-shirt. Melissa had found some cotton balls. The cloth and cotton balls made a nice, soft place to sleep.

Sometimes it was hard to find food, so Marvin and Melissa stored as much as they could. Marvin found scraps of cheese and bacon on the kitchen floor. Melissa brought in pieces of popcorn. They kept their food in a neat pile in the corner.

Marvin and Melissa were very happy in their little mousehole. Both of them thought they had the coziest, most comfortable house in the world!

Directions: Complete the table. Use descriptive words from the story and draw pictures of what you imagine Marvin and Melissa's home is like.

Visualize	What the Story Says	What You Picture in Your Mind
Their mouse hole	small hole behind the stove	
Their nest	**1.**	**2.**
Their food	**3.**	**4.**
The characters	Marvin and Melissa were very happy in their mouse hole.	**5.**

Notes for Home: Your child has read a story and used story details to create a mental picture of what is being described. ***Home Activity:*** Name one of your child's favorite places. Ask your child to visualize, or imagine, the place. Then invite him or her to tell you more about it.

Name ________________________________

Making Judgments

REVIEW

Directions: Read the story. Then read each question about the story. Choose the best answer to each question. Mark the letter for the answer you have chosen.

The Best Place to Live

Maria lives in the big city of Chicago. Jade lives in a little town called Gladstone. Maria says that Chicago is the best place to live in the whole world. Jade says that nobody should live in a big city because small towns are best!

When Maria went to visit Jade, Jade invited all her friends to meet Maria.

When Jade visited Maria, Maria took her to the top of Chicago's tallest building. Jade felt scared being so high up, so they went down right away. Then Jade started to have a good time. She began to think that big cities might be just as nice as small towns.

Maria wants to bring Jade back to the tall building again. She hopes they go there before it's time for Jade to leave.

1. A word that describes how Maria and Jade feel about where they live is—
- **A.** embarrassed.
- **B.** proud.
- **C.** bored.
- **D.** afraid.

2. When Jade invited all her friends to meet Maria, she was probably trying to make Maria feel—
- **F.** lonely.
- **G.** welcome.
- **H.** confused.
- **J.** angry.

3. When Maria took Jade to the top of Chicago's tallest building, she probably wanted Jade to feel—
- **A.** scared.
- **B.** sick.
- **C.** excited.
- **D.** angry.

4. Jade changed her mind about big cities because she was—
- **F.** lonely.
- **G.** wishy-washy.
- **H.** confused.
- **J.** open-minded.

5. Maria wants Jade to go back to the building so that Jade will—
- **A.** feel scared again.
- **B.** like being at the top.
- **C.** get sick.
- **D.** like Maria more.

Notes for Home: Your child made judgments about characters in a short story. ***Home Activity:*** Invite your child to share times when someone was a good friend and when someone was not a good friend.

Name ______________________________

Writing Across Texts

Directions: Consider some of the likenesses and differences among animal characters in the excerpt from *The Cricket in Times Square* and "The Country Mouse and the City Mouse." Then complete the table.

	Chester	Tucker	City Mouse	Country Mouse
Types of Animals	1.	4.	mouse	8.
Where They Live	tree stump in Connecticut	5.	house in city	hole in country
What They Eat	2.	liverwurst	6.	9.
Problems They Face	3.	convincing a friend to stay in New York City	7.	10.

Write a Compare/Contrast Paragraph

On a separate sheet of paper, compare and contrast two characters from the table above. Include information about the likenesses and differences between the two characters.

Notes for Home: Your child combined and used information from more than one source. ***Home Activity:*** As you read a story or an article with your child, discuss how its ideas connect to other stories or articles. Encourage your child to compare and contrast the stories or articles.

Name ____________________________________

Grammar: Subjects

Directions: Underline the complete subject in each sentence. Then circle each simple subject. (There may be more than one in a sentence.)

1. My cousin visited New York City last week.
2. The busy, noisy streets frightened Andrew.
3. The traffic moved too fast.
4. Andrew and his brother preferred to see New York from their hotel window.
5. Andrew became braver after a few days, however.

Directions: Add a complete subject to each group of words to make your own sentence. Write your sentence on the line. Then circle the simple subject.

6. can be a good place to live

____

7. would be a wonderful place to visit

____

8. can usually be found in a big city

____

9. might be hard to find in the city

____

10. might not be very happy in a city

____

Notes for Home: Your child identified and used subjects in sentences. ***Home Activity:*** Have your child identify the subjects of some sentences in a favorite book or magazine. Suggest that your child create new sentences using the same subjects.

Name ______________________________________

Grammar: Nouns

A **noun** is a word that names one or more people, places, or things.

Persons: Many actors and musicians live in the city.
Places: Many actors live in the city and the suburbs.
Things: Tall buildings are part of a city's skyline.

Directions: One noun in each sentence is underlined. Circle the other noun or nouns.

1. I grew up in the city, near the river.
2. We lived on the first floor of a tall building.
3. Cars and buses rolled past my window.
4. A doctor and a plumber lived in two apartments down the hall.
5. My family went to see a house in the country.
6. I didn't want to move, but my parents and my brother did.
7. We left the city and drove in a big van.
8. I had never smelled such clean air or seen so many cows.
9. I thought my parents had decided to become farmers.
10. Then I heard them talking on the phone about their new store.

Directions: One of the underlined words in each sentence is a noun. Circle that noun.

11. I suppose I could get used to open spaces.
12. One problem is that it's hard to meet other people.
13. You can't just wait by your door.
14. I don't want my best friend to be a cow!
15. Where will I find new human friends?

Notes for Home: Your child identified nouns. ***Home Activity:*** Have your child look around the house and write names and other nouns for as many people, places, and things as possible.

Name ______________________________________

Grammar: Nouns

Directions: Circle all the nouns in the following sentences.

1. I grew up in the country, surrounded by farms and woods.
2. The closest village was five miles away.
3. Every single day I saw the same buildings, animals, and trees.
4. Then a letter came from my cousin.
5. He begged me to visit him at his house.
6. I couldn't make up my mind, because I had never been in the city.
7. It sounded like a rough, tough place.
8. What if I didn't get another chance?
9. I packed my best clothes, my toothbrush, and my umbrella.
10. I left under a bright, sunny sky.

Directions: Add a noun that makes sense to complete each sentence. Write the noun on the line to the left.

____________________ **11.** A car splashed through a _____, drenching me.

____________________ **12.** That was not a good _____ to begin my visit!

____________________ **13.** In my cousin's big house, I slept on a very soft _____.

____________________ **14.** Still, there wasn't a single _____ for a country cat to eat.

____________________ **15.** I was happy to scamper back to my _____.

Write a Tale

On a separate sheet of paper, write your own tale about going somewhere new and strange. Use nouns to describe whom and what you see.

Notes for Home: Your child found nouns in some sentences and supplied nouns in others. ***Home Activity:*** Take a walk or a ride around your neighborhood. Have your child make a list of as many nouns as possible. Nouns may include places, names on signs, products in stores, and so forth.

Name ______________________

from The Cricket in Times Square

RETEACHING

Grammar: Nouns

The nouns are underlined. Write one noun to answer each question.

1. Are you a boy or a girl? ______________________ (person)

2. Do you like a town or a city better? ______________________ (place)

3. Do you write with a pen or a pencil? ______________________ (thing)

A **noun** names a person, place, or thing. It gives information.

Directions: Write the three nouns in each sentence.

1. The girl threw the ball to the boy.

____

2. Many students play sports at school.

____

3. That girl kicked the ball over the tree.

____

4. Lin was a player on our team.

____

5. The teacher took the class to the playground.

____

Directions: Circle the nouns in each sentence.

6. Some athletes wear uniforms.

7. Many swimmers have red suits.

8. Sue belonged to a good team.

9. The crowd cheered the divers.

10. A student on the bench was tired.

Notes for Home: Your child identified nouns in sentences. ***Home Activity:*** Together, think of two categories. (For example: *sports; foods*) Have your child list as many nouns as possible that fit in each category.

Name ______________________________

Grammar: Nouns

Directions: On the lines below, write the three nouns that are in each sentence.

1. Chicago is a city with many fine museums.

2. Those paintings on the wall have bright colors.

3. Some of the artists drew with pencils on paper.

4. The sketches hang in frames around the room.

5. The statue in the hall is made of marble.

1. ______________ ______________ ______________

2. ______________ ______________ ______________

3. ______________ ______________ ______________

4. ______________ ______________ ______________

5. ______________ ______________ ______________

Directions: Change one noun in each sentence. Write the new sentence.

6. Jorge drew a picture of the fruit.

____

7. The colors in the painting catch my eye.

____

8. The artist used strong lines in this drawing.

____

9. The photograph shows the view from the window.

____

Write a Poem

Write a poem about a painting or a statue you have seen. Write on a separate sheet of paper. Use nouns in your sentences.

Notes for Home: Your child identified and wrote nouns in sentences. ***Home Activity:*** Have your child write sentences describing a room in your home. Make sure he or she uses at least two nouns in each sentence.

Name ____________________

Phonics: Diphthongs

Directions: Read the words in the box. Say the words to yourself. Listen to the vowel sounds. Some words have the vowel sound in **found.** Other words have the vowel sound in **boy.** Write each word in the correct column.

scrounge	enjoyed	down	pointed	about
house	voice	noise	town	boiled

found	**boy**
1. ____________	6. ____________
2. ____________	7. ____________
3. ____________	8. ____________
4. ____________	9. ____________
5. ____________	10. ____________

Directions: Read each sentence. Say the underlined word to yourself. Then read the words in ( ). Circle the word that has the same vowel sound as the underlined word.

11. New York City is a big <u>town</u>. (house/voice)

12. The cars and people make a lot of <u>noise</u>. (down/boy)

13. You have to walk <u>down</u> some stairs to get to the subway. (mouse/enjoyed)

14. Riding a bus is an easy way to get <u>around</u> in a big city. (about/boiled)

15. If you visit New York City, you will <u>enjoy</u> walking along Fifth Avenue. (town/noise)

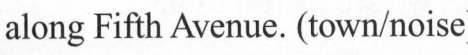

Notes for Home: Your child distinguished different sounds and spellings for the vowel sounds in *town* and *noise.* ***Home Activity:*** Help your child list words with *oi* and *oy* that stand for the vowel sound in *noise* and with *ou* and *ow* that stand for the vowel sound in *town.*

Name ______________________________

Pretest

Spelling: Vowel Sounds in *put* and *out*

Pretest Directions: Fold back the page along the dotted line. On the blanks, write the spelling words as they are dictated. When you have finished the test, unfold the page and check your words.

1. ______________	**1.** She **stood** up tall.
2. ______________	**2.** Who **took** my book?
3. ______________	**3.** Chop **wood** for the fire.
4. ______________	**4.** Throw me the **football**!
5. ______________	**5.** Wade into the **brook**.
6. ______________	**6.** The **bush** needs water.
7. ______________	**7.** **July** is hot in this city.
8. ______________	**8.** I need a seat **cushion**.
9. ______________	**9.** The **butcher** sells meat.
10. ______________	**10.** He served us **pudding**.
11. ______________	**11.** The **power** went out.
12. ______________	**12.** **However** did you find us?
13. ______________	**13.** A **shower** of rain fell.
14. ______________	**14.** Push through the **crowd**.
15. ______________	**15.** The music is too **loud**.
16. ______________	**16.** Welcome to my **house**.
17. ______________	**17.** **Outside** it is windy.
18. ______________	**18.** The **mountain** has snow.
19. ______________	**19.** A **cloud** covered the sun.
20. ______________	**20.** We are **proud** of her.

Notes for Home: Your child took a pretest on words with the vowel sounds in *put* and *out*. ***Home Activity:*** Help your child learn misspelled words before the final test. Your child should look at the word, say it, spell it aloud, and then spell it with eyes shut.

Name ______________________________

Spelling: Vowel Sounds in *put* and *out*

Word List

stood	bush	power	house
took	July	however	outside
wood	cushion	shower	mountain
football	butcher	crowd	cloud
brook	pudding	loud	proud

Directions: Choose the word from the box that rhymes with each word. Use each word only one time. Write the word on the line.

1. mouse ____________________

2. fountain ____________________

3. flower ____________________

4. tower ____________________

5. book ____________________

6. look ____________________

7. good ____________________

8. hood ____________________

Directions: Write the word from the box that belongs in each group.

9. tree, shrub, ____________

10. baseball, basketball, ____________

11. nature, outdoors, ____________

12. but, nonetheless, ____________

13. May, June, ____________

14. baker, grocer, ____________

15. audience, mob, ____________

16. noisy, high-volume, ____________

17. pillow, pad, ____________

18. fog, mist, ____________

19. pie, cake, ____________

20. happy, pleased, ____________

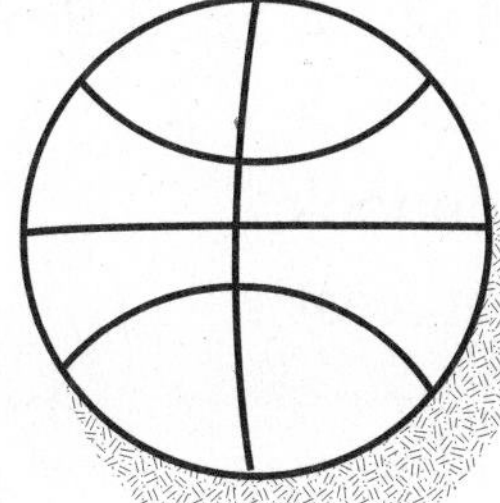

Notes for Home: Your child spelled words with the vowel sounds in *put,* spelled *oo* and *u,* and *out,* spelled *ou* and *ow*. ***Home Activity:*** Make a list with your child of other words with these vowel sounds and spellings, such as *foot, soot, push,* and *mouse, how, now.*

Name ______________________________

Spelling: Vowel Sounds in *put* and *out*

Directions: Proofread this story about a city. Find five spelling mistakes. Use the proofreading marks to correct each mistake.

≡	Make a capital.
/	Make a small letter.
∧	Add something.
℘	Take out something.
⊙	Add a period.
¶	Begin a new paragraph.

Odessa lived in a howse on Orchard Street, between the bucher shop and the shoe store. On hot Jooly days, she and the other children on the block always went to the city swimming pool. "I like swimming better than taking a shouer!" Odessa thought. "I just wish there wasn't such a big croud at the pool." However, that didn't stop her. It was more fun than the sprinkler!

Spelling Tip

The vowel sound in **put** can be spelled two different ways: **oo** in **t<u>oo</u>k** and **u** in **b<u>u</u>sh.** The vowel sound in **out** is also spelled two ways: **ow** in **p<u>ow</u>er** and **ou** in **l<u>ou</u>d.**

Word List

stood	power
took	however
wood	shower
football	crowd
brook	loud
bush	house
July	outside
cushion	mountain
butcher	cloud
pudding	proud

Write a Travel Brochure

Imagine that you are in charge of helping visitors to a city find sights to see. On a separate sheet of paper, write a travel brochure, a short pamphlet that tells visitors about something fun to do in a city. It could be your own city or a city you look up in a book or encyclopedia. Try to use at least four spelling words.

Notes for Home: Your child spelled words with the vowel sounds in *put,* spelled *oo* and *u,* and *out,* spelled *ou* and *ow.* ***Home Activity:*** Say a word with one of the two vowel sounds, like *loud* or *wood.* Ask your child to find as many rhymes for that word as possible.

Name ________________________________

Spelling: Vowel Sounds in *put* and *out*

REVIEW

Word List				
stood	brook	butcher	shower	outside
took	bush	pudding	crowd	mountain
wood	July	power	loud	cloud
football	cushion	however	house	proud

Directions: Choose the word from the box that has the same or nearly the same meaning as each word or words below. Write the word on the line.

1. noisy ________________

2. outdoors ________________

3. seventh month ________________

4. strength ________________

5. pillow ________________

6. but ________________

7. creek ________________

8. shrub ________________

9. lumber ________________

10. a huge hill ________________

Directions: Choose the word from the box that best completes each sentence. Write the word on the line to the left.

________ **11.** Ana _______ in front of the department store.

________ **12.** In the window was a TV showing the _______ game.

________ **13.** It was a great day for the game, not a _______ in the sky.

________ **14.** There was a big _______ of people watching.

________ **15.** But Ana had to go buy meat at the _______ shop.

________ **16.** If she _______ too long, dinner would be late.

________ **17.** Then she went back home to her _______.

________ **18.** Her mother had made chocolate _______ for dessert.

________ **19.** "Good job!" her mother said, "I'm _______ of you."

________ **20.** Since she was dirty, Ana went to take a _______.

Notes for Home: Your child spelled words with the vowel sounds in *put*, spelled *oo* and *u*, and *out*, spelled *ou* and *ow*. ***Home Activity:*** Write *put* and *out* on separate sheets of paper. Encourage your child to add words to each sheet that have the same vowel sound.

Name ____________________

Newspapers/Magazines/Periodicals

Newspapers are published daily or weekly and contain news, advertisements, feature stories, editorials, and other useful, current information.

Directions: Read the front page headlines of these newspapers. Use the information to answer the questions that follow.

1. Would you expect to find an article on how to make and use skateboards in the *New York City Business News Today?* Explain.

____

____

2. Is the headline for *The New York City Daily Reporter* the beginning of a news story, an editorial, or an advertisement?

____

3. A well-known actor is coming to New York City to film a movie. Which paper is most likely to cover this story?

____

4. Why are newspapers helpful sources of information? ____________________

____

5. Would you use last week's newspaper to find out about the original construction of Times Square? Explain.

____

____

Magazines, also called **periodicals,** are published at set intervals (weekly, monthly, quarterly, and so on). They may contain news articles, opinion columns, advertisements, cartoons, reports, and other current information. They often focus on a particular subject. The name of the magazine will usually tell you what subject is covered.

Directions: Use information from the magazine covers here to answer the questions that follow.

6. Which magazine might have useful information about baseball?

____

7. Will you find stories about snakes in *Dogs & Cats?* Explain. ____________

____

8. Which magazine will tell you about theater shows?

____

9. If you are doing a report on nutrition and want to find some healthful snacks to suggest, what magazine might have an article of interest?

____

10. If you needed to find out about a concert that took place in Central Park yesterday, would you look in a newspaper or a magazine? Explain.

____

____

Notes for Home: Your child learned about using newspapers and magazines as resources. ***Home Activity:*** Look at newspapers and magazines together. What does the name of the publication tell you? Use headlines or a table of contents to scan for articles of interest.

Family Times

Name____

Summary

Girl's Dream Garden Comes True

Luz Mendes might be a dreamer, but she's a doer too. When she confides her dream of turning a trash-filled lot into a vegetable and flower garden, Officer Ramirez suggests she talk to the Green Giants, a group that supports projects like hers. Just when the lot is starting to look good, somebody dumps more garbage over the fence. Things start looking hopeless, but then other people start pitching in to help.

Activity

Finish the Story. Have your child tell how Luz finally got the help she needed to get the lot ready for planting.

Reading Skills

Cause and Effect

A **cause** is why something happens. An **effect** is what happens. A cause can have more than one effect. An effect can have more than one cause. Sometimes there aren't any clue words to help you figure out what happened and why: **Lots of people showed up to help Luz clean up the lot. Her dream of having a garden came true.** The first sentence (*cause*) explains why Luz's dream came true (*effect*).

Activity

Great Chain of Cause and Effect. Play this fun game. Start with a cause-and-effect statement—for example, **Because I tripped, my open soda can went flying.** The next person continues, saying, **Because the soda can went flying, the rug got wet.** Continue until nothing more can be added.

Family Times

Tested Vocabulary

Words to Know

Knowing the meanings of these words is important to reading "A Big-City Dream." Practice using these words to learn their meanings.

blisters sores on the skin

catalog a list with pictures and prices

celebrate observe a special time with festivities

impressed influenced deeply

padlock a lock that can be put on and removed

Grammar

Proper Nouns

Proper nouns name particular people, places, or things. Begin the first word and each important word of a proper noun with a capital letter: **Luz Mendes, Officer Ramirez, Green Giants.**

Persons	Luz Mendes __________ __________
Places	First Avenue __________ __________
Things	Friday __________ __________

Activity

Make It Proper. Write a story about what you did today. In the first version, try not to use any proper nouns. For example, use **store, brother, yesterday,** and so on. Then write a version in which you change nouns to proper nouns: **Peachtree Market, Mike, Tuesday.**

Tested Spelling Words

__________	__________	__________	__________
__________	__________	__________	__________
__________	__________	__________	__________
__________	__________	__________	__________
__________	__________	__________	__________

Name ____________________________________

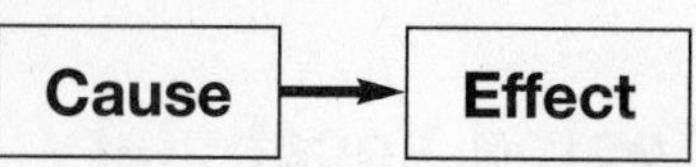

Cause and Effect

- A **cause** is why something happened. An **effect** is what happened.
- Sometimes a cause can have more than one effect.
- Sometimes there are clue words like *because, so, if, then,* or *since* to help you figure out what happened and why.

Cause → Effect

Directions: Reread "Super Cooper Scoopers." Then complete the table. Write the effect or effects for each cause given.

Cause (Why did it happen?)	Effect (What happened?)
Because the creek was dirty,	**1.**
	2.
	3.
Because garbage gets ripped apart in creeks and spreads,	**4.**
Because the creek is now clean,	**5.**

Notes for Home: Your child read a news article and explained the effects of events. ***Home Activity:*** Talk about a recent happy family event, such as a pleasant dinner together or a special trip. Help your child identify the reasons that caused the event to be so enjoyable.

Name ___________________________________

Vocabulary

Check the Words You Know
__ blisters
__ catalog
__ celebrate
__ impressed
__ padlock

Directions: Choose the word from the box that best completes each sentence. Write the word on the line to the left.

______________ **1.** The garden _____ arrived in the mail yesterday.

______________ **2.** We were _____ by how many seeds and plants it showed.

______________ **3.** When we shovel dirt in the garden, we'll wear gloves so we don't get _____ on our hands.

______________ **4.** We will _____ our beautiful garden by having a garden party when we're done.

______________ **5.** We will have to remember to put a _____ on the gate to keep our dogs out of the garden.

Directions: Choose the word from the box that best matches each clue. Write the letters of the word on the blanks. The boxed letters spell something found near a garden.

6. illustrated list **6.** ___ ___ ___ ___ ___ ___ [ ]

7. have a party **7.** ___ ___ ___ ___ ___ [ ] ___ ___ ___

8. lock you can remove **8.** ___ [ ] ___ ___ ___ ___ ___

9. sores on your skin **9.** ___ ___ ___ [ ] ___ ___ ___ ___

10. influenced deeply **10.** ___ ___ ___ ___ ___ [ ] ___ ___ ___

Something found near a garden: ___ ___ ___ ___ ___

Write Instructions

On a separate sheet of paper, give instructions for growing flowers or vegetables. Use as many of the vocabulary words as you can.

Notes for Home: Your child identified and used vocabulary words from "A Big-City Dream." ***Home Activity:*** Create a picture catalog with your child. It can show flowers, vegetables, or any items that your child can identify. Write a caption for each picture drawn.

Name ____________________

Cause and Effect

- A **cause** is why something happens. An **effect** is what happens.
- A cause may have more than one effect. An effect may have more than one cause.
- Sometimes a clue word such as *because* or *since* signals a cause-effect relationship. Sometimes there is no clue word.

Directions: Reread what happens in "A Big-City Dream" when Rosie appears. Then answer the questions below. Think about what it says in the story to help you identify causes and effects.

Lots of people walk past. Most of them don't even notice what we're doing. And nobody offers to help.

Then, all of the sudden, I see Rosie and her mom turn the corner. My heart rises straight up in my chest.

Yay! I want to shout. You're coming after all!

I wipe my sweaty face on my sleeves. I get ready to run over and open the gate extra wide to let her in. But Rosie doesn't even look at me. My heart falls down, hard, when she walks right past without even turning her head.

1. What causes the narrator's heart to rise "straight up in her chest"?

____

2. Why does the narrator want to shout "Yay! You're coming after all!"

____

3. Why do you think Rosie walks right past "without even turning her head"?

____

4. How does the narrator feel when Rosie walks past her? How do you know?

____

5. On a separate sheet of paper, tell two things that cause the narrator to feel happy and two things that cause her to feel sad.

Notes for Home: Your child has read a story and used story details to understand cause and effect. ***Home Activity:*** Play a cause and effect game with your child. You name a cause *(It started to rain.)* and invite your child to name an effect *(We got our umbrellas.)*.

Name ____________________

Selection Test

Directions: Choose the best answer to each item. Mark the letter for the answer you have chosen.

Part 1: Vocabulary

Find the answer choice that means the same as the underlined word in each sentence.

1. We will need a padlock.
- A. area enclosed with a fence
- B. gardening tool
- C. lock that can be put on and removed
- D. set of keys

2. I noticed Nell's blisters.
- F. sores on the skin
- G. small bandages
- H. rips or tears in clothing
- J. deep wrinkles

3. Mike looked at the catalog.
- A. finished project
- B. list of jobs to be done
- C. people working together
- D. book of things for sale

4. The teacher was impressed.
- F. strongly affected
- G. treated in a mean way
- H. remembered with fondness
- J. entertained or amused

5. The parents and children will celebrate together.
- A. solve a problem by talking
- B. have activities for a special day
- C. share work equally
- D. learn new skills

Part 2: Comprehension

Use what you know about the story to answer each item.

6. On Saturday morning, Luz hurried to meet—
- F. Ms. Kline.
- G. Papi.
- H. Rosie.
- J. Mami.

7. When Luz got to the corner on the first day, the first thing she looked for was—
- A. Rosie.
- B. the Green Giants.
- C. the red tulip.
- D. a rake.

8. Rosie probably did not help Luz because—
- F. she was too busy.
- G. her mother would not let her.
- H. she was upset with Luz.
- J. she didn't have work clothes.

9. Luz worked without complaining because she—

A. was so happy with the way the lot looked.

B. needed the exercise.

C. did not want to be scolded.

D. wanted to show Ms. Kline that she could do the job.

10. How did Luz feel about the Dream Garden at the end of the first day?

F. not willing to give up on it

G. relieved that it was almost done

H. ready to give up

J. happy to have so much help

11. What happened at the lot just before Ms. Kline came back to check Luz's progress?

A. Luz saw Rosie walk by.

B. Someone planted a tulip.

C. The neighbors had a party.

D. Someone dumped garbage.

12. Which sentence shows how the neighbors felt about Luz when she gave Ms. Kline a dollar?

F. "I figure lots of people will stop by and help."

G. "Everybody crowds around, shaking my hands and clapping me on the back."

H. "Ms. Kline sounds like she can hardly believe it."

J. "Everybody laughs, and the man looks a little confused."

13. The hardest part about getting the garden started was—

A. cleaning up the trash.

B. ordering from the catalog.

C. planting seeds and trees.

D. finding water.

14. When did most people in this story become truly interested in helping with the garden?

F. on the first Saturday that Luz got started

G. when Ms. Kline warned Luz to find more help

H. when someone dropped garbage in the cleaned lot

J. after the truck delivered the plants and supplies

15. Which is the best reason to think that the garden will be a success?

A. Officers Ramirez and Carter will go to the celebration.

B. Ali will let the group use his water.

C. Rosie didn't join the group.

D. The people in the neighborhood believe in it.

Name ______________________________

Cause and Effect

- A **cause** is why something happens. An **effect** is what happens.
- A cause may have more than one effect. An effect may have more than one cause.
- Sometimes a clue word such as *because* or *since* signals a cause-effect relationship. Sometimes there is no clue word.

Directions: Read the story below.

Aurelia was very excited. This year, she had her very first garden. Aurelia had decided to plant flowers. She had chosen and planted the seeds all by herself. The weather was good that year, and the plants grew tall and strong.

"You've done a good job, Aurelia," said her mother. "Because you have taken good care of your garden, you have three rows of beautiful, healthy plants."

Aurelia felt proud when she heard her mother's praise. She was glad her garden was growing so well. Then she looked more closely at her plants. What she saw made her feel very upset.

"Mama!" she cried. "I don't see any flowers blooming. In fact, *my* plants look just like *your* plants." She pointed to some feathery leaves growing in her mother's garden—and in Aurelia's garden too.

Aurelia's mother grabbed the leaves in Aurelia's garden and pulled up—a carrot! "Oh, no!" said Aurelia. "I must have gotten the seeds mixed up. I grew vegetables instead of flowers!"

Directions: Complete the flowchart. Identify each missing cause and effect.

Cause	Effect
1.	Aurelia's plants grew tall and strong.
2.	(Aurelia's plants grew tall and strong.)
3.	Aurelia felt proud and happy.
4.	(Aurelia felt proud and happy.)
Aurelia got the seeds mixed up.	5.

Notes for Home: Your child has read a story and used story details to identify causes and effects. ***Home Activity:*** As you complete a task, such as making dinner, ask your child to tell what would happen if you did something differently, for example, used salt instead of sugar.

Name ____

Compare and Contrast

REVIEW

Directions: Read the story. Then read each question about the story. Choose the best answer to each question. Mark the letter for the answer you have chosen.

Flowers and Vegetables

A famous poet once said, "My love is like a red, red rose."

I enjoy that poem because I also think red roses are beautiful. That's why I grow them in my garden.

My brother, Jesse, doesn't like flowers. He grows vegetables in *his* garden—peas, carrots, lettuce, and string beans. Jesse says that vegetables growing in a garden are the most beautiful sight on Earth.

Both Jesse and I enjoy working in our gardens. Our favorite time is early in the morning, when the weather is cool and dew covers every leaf.

This summer, I will enter my roses in the flower show. Maybe I'll win first place! Jesse doesn't like to enter contests, but he's just as proud of his peas and carrots as I am of my roses.

1. In the line, "My love is like a red, red rose," the poet compares—

A. love to a flower.
B. love to a garden.
C. a rose to a garden.
D. flowers to vegetables.

2. Both the narrator and the poet quoted—

F. like roses.
G. don't like roses.
H. grow vegetable gardens.
J. write poems.

3. One thing the narrator and Jesse have in common is that they both—

A. like vegetables.
B. like flowers.
C. grow gardens.
D. enter contests.

4. The clue word in the fourth paragraph that shows a comparison is—

F. favorite.
G. both.
H. early.
J. gardens.

5. One word that describes both Jesse and the narrator is—

A. hard-working.
B. lazy.
C. foolish.
D. cruel.

Notes for Home: Your child compared and contrasted elements in a short story. ***Home Activity:*** Think of two favorite activities that your child enjoys doing. Ask him or her to tell you some ways they are alike and ways that they are different.

Name ______________________________

Writing Across Texts

Directions: Refer to the excerpt from *The Cricket in Times Square* and "A Big-City Dream" to write sentences about the help Chester and Luz received from the other characters in the stories.

Help for Luz
Mrs. Kline brings rakes, brooms, plastic bags, and work gloves.
1.
2.
3.

Help for Chester
Tucker gives Chester a piece of liverwurst.
4.
5.

Write a Comparative Essay

Write an essay in which you tell how the other characters in the stories helped Chester and Luz. Compare and contrast the kinds of help they received.

Notes for Home: Your child combined and used information from more than one source. ***Home Activity:*** As you read a story or an article with your child, discuss how its ideas connect to other stories or articles read. Encourage your child to make comparisons.

Name ____

Grammar: Nouns

REVIEW

Directions: Circle all the nouns in the following sentences.

1. My family lives on the fifteenth floor of a building in the city.

2. Visitors to our apartment take the elevator to the top floor.

3. Although our dad loves the city, he misses his garden.

4. My father appeared one day with huge bags, tiny plants, shovels, and other tools.

5. That amazing man had decided to grow vegetables on the roof!

6. My mother and sister helped him carry the things up the stairs.

7. Our farmer poured dirt from the bags into big pots and set the plants into the soil.

8. The days were hot and sunny, and we kept pouring water on our little farm.

9. When the summer ended, we invited friends for a dinner of beans, tomatoes, and broccoli.

10. Our family and guests finished our whole crop in just one meal!

Directions: Fill in each blank with a noun that makes sense in the sentence. Write each noun on the line to the left.

____________________ **11.** If I had a garden, I would grow _____.

____________________ **12.** A garden needs lots of _____ if the plants are to grow.

____________________ **13.** A _____ is a tool that gardeners are likely to use often.

____________________ **14.** City people usually get their food from _____.

____________________ **15.** Some people, however, grow their own _____, even in the city.

Notes for Home: Your child identified nouns. ***Home Activity:*** Read a story to your child. Then go back and ask your child to pick out words that name people, places, and things.

Name ___________________________

Grammar: Proper Nouns

A **proper noun** names a particular person, place, or thing. The words *Carmen, Florida,* and *April* are proper nouns. Begin proper nouns with capital letters. Nouns that are not proper nouns are called **common nouns.** The words *girl, state,* and *month* are common nouns.

Common nouns: We walked down the street.
At the corner, an officer was directing traffic.

Proper nouns: We walked down Third Street.
At the corner, Officer Ortiz was directing traffic.

Directions: Read the following paragraph. Each underlined noun has a number next to it. Write **C** if the underlined noun is a common noun. Write **P** if the underlined noun is a proper noun. Rewrite the proper nouns correctly.

Do you love **1.** nature but live in a **2.** city? If you look carefully, you'll see plenty of natural **3.** life. You don't need to go to **4.** yellowstone national park or the **5.** florida everglades. You don't need a large outdoor place like **6.** central park in **7.** new york city. On your own **8.** block there may be a **9.** crack in the **10.** sidewalk. Start there.

1. ______________________ **6.** ______________________

2. ______________________ **7.** ______________________

3. ______________________ **8.** ______________________

4. ______________________ **9.** ______________________

5. ______________________ **10.** ______________________

Notes for Home: Your child identified common and proper nouns and used capital letters to write proper nouns. ***Home Activity:*** Ask your child to use common nouns to identify persons, places, and things in your home. Then ask your child to replace each noun with a proper noun.

Grammar: Proper Nouns

Directions: Write a proper noun to replace the underlined words in the following sentences.

____________ **1.** One day my friend and I had a real adventure.

____________ **2.** We were walking on our street.

____________ **3.** We saw our neighbor and some other people standing around.

____________ **4.** Just then, a police officer drove up.

____________ **5.** "What's this?" he asked one woman, who was holding something.

____________ **6.** "I was in the park and found this injured bird," she answered.

____________ **7.** "I can't bring a bird all the way to the animal hospital," she continued.

____________ **8.** "No, but a veterinarian has a clinic around the corner," I said.

____________ **9.** "I have to be at a downtown building in ten minutes," the woman said. "Could someone else take the bird to the clinic?"

____________ **10.** "We'll go," I told her. "Great!" said a man who had been listening to us.

Write a News Story

On a separate sheet of paper, write a news story about an interesting event that happened near where you live. Think about these reporter questions as you write: Who? What? When? Where? Why? and How? Use as many proper nouns as possible.

Notes for Home: Your child substituted proper nouns for common nouns. ***Home Activity:*** Encourage your child to tell you about the day's events, substituting proper nouns *(Jefferson Elementary School)* for common nouns *(school)*.

Name ______________________

Grammar: Proper Nouns

RETEACHING

Match the nouns. Draw a line from a common noun to the proper noun that matches it.

Common Noun	Proper Noun
1. man	Kennedy Parkway
2. country	George Washington
3. road	United States

A **common noun** names any of a kind or group of persons, places, or things. A **proper noun** names a particular person, place, or thing. Each important word in a proper noun begins with a capital letter.

Directions: Write each underlined noun in the correct column.

Laura Salerno visited her cousins in Brooklyn. The whole family rode a boat around Manhattan. They met some Italians there. Laura liked her trip.

Common Nouns	Proper Nouns
1. ______________	**5.** ______________
2. ______________	**6.** ______________
3. ______________	**7.** ______________
4. ______________	**8.** ______________

Directions: Circle the proper noun or proper nouns in each sentence.

9. The Statue of Liberty has many visitors.

10. The statue is on Liberty Island in New York Harbor.

11. France gave this gift to the United States.

12. People can climb it for a view of New York.

Notes for Home: Your child identified proper nouns. ***Home Activity:*** List familiar places or people. *(park, store, neighbor, friend)* Have your child write a proper noun for each noun you wrote. *(Lee Park, Northbrook Foods, Mrs. Washbein, Lizzie Webster)*

Name ______________________

Grammar: Proper Nouns

Directions: Write a proper noun for each common noun. Use capital letters.

1. a state ______________ **5.** a river ______________

2. a neighbor ______________ **6.** a dog ______________

3. a day ______________ **7.** a date ______________

4. a doctor ______________ **8.** a city ______________

Directions: Write each sentence. Replace the underlined noun with a proper noun.

9. Jack sails on a lake in Ohio.

____

10. Jack also fishes in a lake.

____

11. A man sails with Jack on weekends.

____

12. Jack wants to sail on an ocean someday.

____

13. Mrs. Wright will sail there on a holiday.

____

Write a List of Proper Nouns

On a separate sheet of paper, write a list of proper nouns. Write the names of a river, a president, a date, a doctor, a park, and a country.

Notes for Home: Your child identified and wrote proper nouns in sentences. ***Home Activity:*** Have your child write a description of your neighborhood, using at least five proper nouns.

Name ________________________________

Phonics: Consonant Sounds for c and g

Directions: Read the words in each box. Follow the instructions below.

celebrate
community
nice
panic

1. Write the two words with the **hard-c** sound like **cat.**

   __________, __________

2. Write the two words with the **soft-c** sound like **cell.**

   __________, __________

practice
convince

3. Write the part of each word that has the **hard-c sound.**

   __________, __________

4. Write the part of each word that has the **soft-c sound.**

   __________, __________

giant
garden
vegetable
big

5. Write the two words with the **hard-g** sound like **get.**

   __________, __________

6. Write the two words with the **soft-g** sound like **gym.**

   __________, __________

garage
garbage

7. Write the part of each word that has the **hard-g** sound.

   __________, __________

8. Write the part of each word that has the **soft-g** sound.

   __________, __________

grocery
courage

9. Write the part of each word that has a hard consonant sound.

   __________, __________

10. Write the part of each word that has a soft consonant sound.

   __________, __________

Notes for Home: Your child practiced distinguishing between hard and soft sounds for the letters *c* and *g*. ***Home Activity:*** Play a game of "I Spy." For example, say, "I spy something that begins with a hard *c,* as in *cat.*" Have your child find the object and say the name.

Name ________________________________

Pretest

Spelling: Including All the Letters

Pretest Directions: Fold back the page along the dotted line. On the blanks, write the spelling words as they are dictated. When you have finished the test, unfold the page and check your words.

1. ______________________
2. ______________________
3. ______________________
4. ______________________
5. ______________________
6. ______________________
7. ______________________
8. ______________________
9. ______________________
10. ______________________
11. ______________________
12. ______________________
13. ______________________
14. ______________________
15. ______________________
16. ______________________
17. ______________________
18. ______________________
19. ______________________
20. ______________________

1. We play here **often**.
2. He **might** visit us soon.
3. I wish I had **known** her!
4. **They** are riding bikes.
5. Do you **remember** me?
6. We **surprised** them!
7. Flora **caught** two fish.
8. The **island** is deserted.
9. It **finally** stopped raining.
10. I **really** missed you.
11. **Several** friends came by.
12. Serve food to **everyone**.
13. **Everybody** brought games.
14. This story is **interesting**.
15. I go **swimming** in summer.
16. The **camera** has film.
17. Will it snow in **December**?
18. It will be **evening** soon.
19. Start at the **beginning**.
20. We leave in **February**.

Notes for Home: Your child took a pretest on words that have difficult letter combinations. ***Home Activity:*** Help your child learn misspelled words before the final test. Have your child divide misspelled words into parts (such as syllables) and concentrate on each part.

Name ________________________________

Spelling: Including All the Letters

Word List

often	surprised	several	camera
might	caught	everyone	December
known	island	everybody	evening
they	finally	interesting	beginning
remember	really	swimming	February

Directions: Choose the words from the box that have three syllables. Write the words on the lines.

1. ____________________ **5.** ____________________

2. ____________________ **6.** ____________________

3. ____________________ **7.** ____________________

4. ____________________ **8.** ____________________

Directions: Choose the word from the box that best matches each clue. Write the word on the line.

9. not boring ____________

10. moving through water ____________

11. second month ____________

12. early part of the night ____________

13. land surrounded by water ____________

14. captured ____________

15. astonished ____________

16. many times ____________

17. opposite of *nobody* ____________

18. understood ____________

19. possibly would ____________

20. a plural pronoun ____________

Notes for Home: Your child spelled words that are often misspelled by leaving out certain letters. ***Home Activity:*** Say each word syllable by syllable. Have your child write each word. Together, correct any misspellings.

Name ____________________

Spelling: Including All the Letters

Directions: Proofread this letter written to a pen pal. Find five spelling mistakes. Use the proofreading marks to correct each mistake.

≡	Make a capital.
/	Make a small letter.
∧	Add something.
୨	Take out something.
⊙	Add a period.
¶	Begin a new paragraph.

Dear Richard,

Remember how I wrote you that I wanted my own garden? Well, I finly have one! I'm realy excited about it! There are sevral kinds of vegetables I'd like to plant there. Evrybody says that flowers are more intresting, but I don't care—I like vegetables! Are you surprised?

Love,
Yoshi

Spelling Tip

Some words have more letters than you might expect. To spell these words, pronounce each syllable carefully.

Word List

often	several
might	everyone
known	everybody
they	interesting
remember	swimming
surprised	camera
caught	December
island	evening
finally	beginning
really	February

Write a Letter

Imagine you are Richard. On a separate sheet of paper, write a letter back that tells what you would grow in a garden. Use at least three spelling words in your letter.

Notes for Home: Your child spelled words that are often misspelled by leaving letters out. ***Home Activity:*** Write some of the words listed, leaving out some letters. Ask your child to be a letter detective who finds the missing letters and tells you what they are.

Name ______________________

Spelling: Including All the Letters

REVIEW

Word List

often	surprised	several	camera
might	caught	everyone	December
known	island	everybody	evening
they	finally	interesting	beginning
remember	really	swimming	February

Directions: Choose the word from the box that is the most opposite in meaning for each word below. Write the word on the line.

1. few ______________
2. ending ______________
3. morning ______________
4. forget ______________
5. no one ______________
6. nobody ______________
7. boring ______________
8. rarely ______________

Directions: Write the word from the box that belongs in each group.

9. actually, truly, __________
10. she, he, __________
11. unexpected, astonished, __________
12. snorkeling, diving, __________
13. at last, in conclusion, __________
14. may, could, __________
15. October, November, __________
16. captured, seized, __________
17. Valentine's Day, President's Day, __________
18. photographs, film, __________
19. tropical, deserted, __________
20. familiar, recognized, __________

Notes for Home: Your child spelled words that are often misspelled by mispronouncing and then leaving out letters. ***Home Activity:*** Slowly sound out the syllables, or word parts, for each word while your child spells it. Discuss how saying words this way makes spelling them easier.

Name ____

Technology: Locate/Collect Information/Telephone Directory

A **telephone directory** lists phone numbers and addresses for individual people and businesses. The **white pages** list entries for individuals and businesses in alphabetical order. The **yellow pages** list entries for businesses and advertisements by category or type of business.

You can also find phone numbers and addresses in "yellow pages" on the Internet. You can search for businesses on the Internet by category, such as garden supplies.

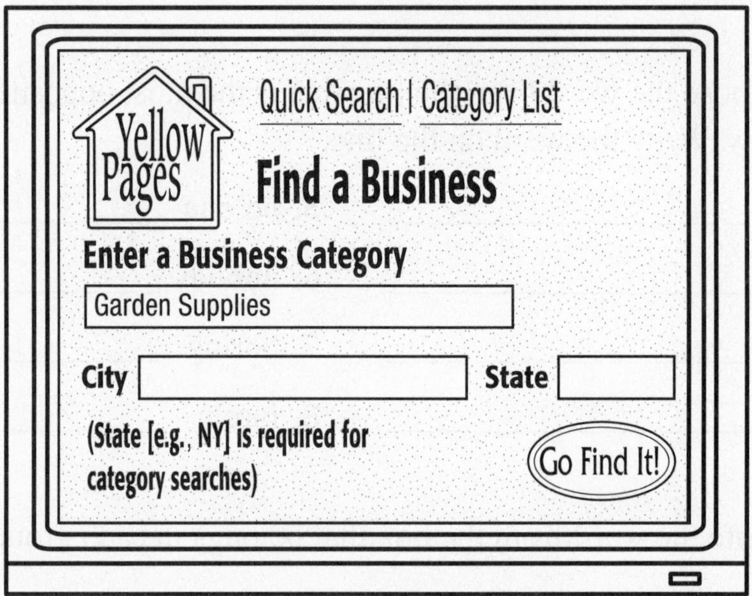

Directions: Write the category you would use to search the Internet for each store.

____________________ **1.** a store that sells games and jump ropes

____________________ **2.** a store that sells food

____________________ **3.** a store that sells windows, doors, and lumber

____________________ **4.** a store that sells baseball bats, basketballs, and sneakers

5. Look at the following categories. Write an **X** next to the category you would search to find a store that sells seeds, potting soil, and a spray to control weeds.

______________ Lawn Mowing Equipment

______________ Lawn and Garden Decorations

______________ Lawn and Garden Supplies

Name ______________________________________

When you choose a category on the Internet Yellow Pages, a listing is displayed. For gardening supplies, it might look like this:

Directions: Use the listings above to answer these questions.

6. You want to find out if a store sells what you are looking for without going there. What information could you use?

____

7. Which store is in Roxbury? ______________________________________

8. Which store is on Silver Rd.? ______________________________________

9. On the Internet, you can click on underlined words to get more information. What do you think you will get when you click on "map"?

____

10. How is searching the Internet Yellow Pages similar to searching the yellow pages in a phone book?

____

____

Notes for Home: Your child learned how to find a business on a yellow pages Web site. ***Home Activity:*** Ask your child to find a specific local store on a yellow pages Web site or in the yellow pages of a phone book.

Family Times

Name____

Summary

Author Sweet on Guinea Pigs

Guinea pigs aren't pigs, although the males are called *boars* and the females are called *sows*. These chubby rodents, originally from South America, make great pets. They live a long time (for rodents) and they're not fussy. They eat and "talk" a lot. And if you treat them well, they can become fond of you. Are they the perfect pet? Dick King-Smith, the author of *I Love Guinea Pigs,* sure thinks so!

Activity

The Perfect Pet. What's the perfect pet? Take turns in your family describing the perfect pet, giving plenty of convincing reasons to back up your choice.

Reading Skills

Text Structure

Text structure is the way a piece of writing is organized. Fiction tells stories of imaginary people and events. They are often told in the order in which things happen. Nonfiction tells of real people and events or gives information about the real world. Nonfiction may be organized by main ideas with supporting details, cause and effect, fact and opinion, or comparison and contrast.

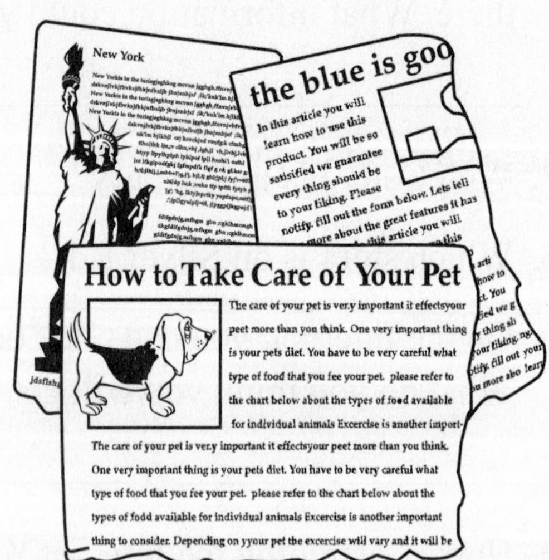

Activity

Fact or Fiction? Cut out articles from old magazines or newspapers. Look for both fiction and nonfiction articles. Work with family members to identify how information is organized in each article.

Family Times

Tested Vocabulary

Words to Know

Knowing the meanings of these words is important to reading *I Love Guinea Pigs*. Practice using these words to learn their meanings.

boars male pigs or hogs

fond loving and liking

gnawing biting and wearing away

sow fully grown female pig

varieties different kinds, types, sorts

Grammar

Regular Plural Nouns

Nouns that name more than one person, place, or thing are **plural nouns.** To make most nouns plural, add **-s** or **-es** to the singular noun: **pets, foxes, monkeys, ponies.** These are called **regular plural nouns.**

Singular Noun	Plural Noun
boar	boars
sow	____________
____________	pigs
bench	____________
baby	____________

Activity

Scavenger Hunt. Complete the table by filling in singular or plural nouns. Then go on a noun scavenger hunt. Look at every person, place, or thing around you. Find ten nouns that form regular plurals by adding **-s** or **-es.**

Tested Spelling Words

____________	____________	____________	____________
____________	____________	____________	____________
____________	____________	____________	____________
____________	____________	____________	____________
____________	____________	____________	____________

Name ______________________________

Text Structure

- **Text structure** is the way a piece of writing is organized. The two main kinds of writing are fiction and nonfiction.
- **Fiction** tells stories of imaginary people and events. Events are often told in the order in which things happen.
- **Nonfiction** tells of real people and events or tells information about the real world. One way to organize nonfiction is to have a main idea followed by supporting details. Other ways to organize nonfiction are cause and effect, problem and solution, and comparison and contrast.

Directions: Reread "Your Best Friend." Then complete the table. Tell what kind of writing it is, list details from the piece, and determine how the piece is organized.

Title	"Your Best Friend"
Fiction or Nonfiction?	1.
1st Heading	2.
Detail	3.
Detail	4.
2nd Heading	5.
Detail	6.
Detail	7.
3rd Heading	8.
Detail	9.
Method of Organization	10.

Notes for Home: Your child read an article and identified text structure. ***Home Activity:*** Ask your child about some favorite books. Encourage him or her to identify text structure by telling you whether the material is fiction or nonfiction and by saying how it is organized.

Name ____________________

Vocabulary

Directions: Choose the word from the box that best completes each sentence. Write the word on the matching numbered line below.

Check the Words You Know

__ boars
__ fond
__ gnawing
__ sow
__ varieties

There are many different **1.** _____ of pigs. Many people are **2.** _____ of the small ones because they make good pets. Unlike guinea pigs, real pigs aren't seen **3.** _____ on everything in sight. A mother pig is called a **4.** _____, and father pigs are called **5.** _____.

1. ______________ **4.** ______________

2. ______________ **5.** ______________

3. ______________

Directions: Choose the word from the box that best matches each clue. Write the word in the puzzle.

Down

6. kinds

7. female pig

9. liking

Across

8. male pigs

10. biting away

Write an Animal Care List

Imagine you are the proud owner of a guinea pig. On a separate sheet of paper, make a list of things you need to know to take care of your guinea pig. Use as many of the vocabulary words as you can.

Notes for Home: Your child has learned new vocabulary words from *I Love Guinea Pigs*. ***Home Activity:*** Talk with your child about the fun and responsibilities of having a pet. Encourage him or her to use the vocabulary words.

Name ______________________

Text Structure

- **Text structure** is the way a piece of writing is organized.
- Fiction tells stories of imaginary people and events. They are usually told in the order in which things happen. Nonfiction tells of real people and events or tells information about the real world. Some ways to organize nonfiction are cause and effect, problem and solution, or comparison and contrast.

Directions: Reread the part of *I Love Guinea Pigs* where the author explains why guinea pigs are "sensible animals." Then answer the questions below.

They don't like the cold, of course, or the damp, any more than you would, and they're not happy living in a poky little place, any more than you would be. But as long as they have a comfortable, warm, dry place to live, guinea pigs are as happy as can be.

They're hardy animals and don't often get sick. Properly cared for, they can live a long time.

I once had a crested sow named Zen. She lived two years with me and then eight more with one of my daughters. People's hair grows whiter as they age, but Zen's grew darker.

Guinea pigs need plenty of food. They love eating, just like you do. . . .

1. Is this text fiction or nonfiction? Tell why you think so.

____

2. Name three ways that guinea pigs are compared to humans.

____

____

3. Name one way that guinea pigs are contrasted to humans.

____

4. Tell two things that make guinea pigs happy.

____

5. On a separate sheet of paper, tell how the author organized the text. Give another example from the story of how he used this text structure.

Notes for Home: Your child looked at how an excerpt of a larger text was organized. ***Home Activity:*** Find two or three of your child's favorite books and ask your child to tell you whether they are fiction or nonfiction. Discuss how each book is organized.

Name ______________________________

Selection Test

Directions: Choose the best answer to each item. Mark the letter for the answer you have chosen.

Part 1: Vocabulary

Find the answer choice that means about the same as the underlined word in each sentence.

1. There are many <u>varieties</u> of cats.
- A. problems or fears
- B. habits or ways
- C. favorite foods or treats
- D. kinds or sorts

2. Henry counted seven <u>boars</u>.
- F. nests made by animals
- G. male pigs or hogs
- H. sounds made by pigs
- J. pens for small pets

3. The dog was <u>gnawing</u> on a box.
- A. biting and wearing away
- B. burrowing into
- C. batting or hitting lightly
- D. sniffing at

4. Liam decided to take the <u>sow</u>.
- F. smallest piglet in a litter
- G. piglet born in the winter
- H. fully grown female pig
- J. pig with several colors

5. The pet is <u>fond</u> of its owner.
- A. free or without need
- B. having a liking for
- C. growing tired or bored
- D. seeming afraid

Part 2: Comprehension

Use what you know about the selection to answer each item.

6. Guinea pigs belong to the same family as—
- F. horses.
- G. humans.
- H. pigs.
- J. mice.

7. The first guinea pigs came from—
- A. Australia.
- B. South America.
- C. Africa.
- D. Asia.

8. The author thinks that guinea pigs are—
- F. loud and active.
- G. shy and nervous.
- H. chubby and cuddly.
- J. fussy and messy.

9. How does the author know so much about guinea pigs?
- A. He had them as pets for much of his life.
- B. He studied them in pet shops.
- C. He read many books about guinea pigs.
- D. He is an animal doctor.

10. Which sentence tells how this selection is written?

F. It explains how someone solved a problem.

G. It gives facts and opinions.

H. It lists many events in the order they happened.

J. It describes imaginary people and animals.

11. A guinea pig will become friendly and tame if its owner—

A. holds and pets it often.

B. keeps it in a cool, dry place.

C. lets it go outdoors often.

D. feeds it many different foods.

12. How were the guinea pigs named Beach Boy and King Arthur alike?

F. They were both a bright golden color.

G. They both lived to an old age.

H. They were both buried in the yard.

J. They both loved dandelions and clover.

13. Most of the details given in this selection are used to—

A. compare baby and adult guinea pigs.

B. describe the author's favorite guinea pig.

C. explain how to feed a guinea pig that won't eat.

D. tell what it is like having guinea pigs for pets.

14. Which detail is an opinion?

F. A guinea pig sow carries her litter for about seventy days.

G. The guinea pigs are born with their eyes open.

H. Their mouths are already filled with teeth.

J. Newborn guinea pigs are a funny sight.

15. What does the author want you to remember most about guinea pigs?

A. how long they have been kept as pets

B. how much pleasure they can give

C. how much they are like other rodents

D. how hard they are to care for

STOP

Name ____________________

Text Structure

- **Text structure** is the way a piece of writing is organized.
- Fiction tells stories of imaginary people and events. They are usually told in the order in which things happen. Nonfiction tells of real people and events or tells information about the real world. Some ways to organize nonfiction are cause and effect, problem and solution, or comparison and contrast.

Directions: Read the passage below.

Which is a better pet—a fluffy rabbit or a colorful bird? Both rabbits and birds need food, water, a safe place to live, and exercise. They are both easy to take care of and are good pets.

A rabbit eats carrots, lettuce, and other green vegetables, as well as commercial rabbit food. It nibbles with its long front teeth. A bird eats birdseed of different kinds. You can watch it crack the seed with its beak and drop the husk.

Rabbits are furry and cuddly. You can take a rabbit out of the cage to hold and stroke it. You can even let it hop around. Birds' colorful feathers may be beautiful, but they aren't so cuddly. Birds fly around and dart quickly from place to place.

Rabbits are usually silent; you could say they are good listeners! Birds are noisier. Some birds talk or sing a lot during the day.

Now that you know all this, which pet would you choose?

Directions: List things that are true about only rabbits, things that are true about only birds, and the things that are true about both of them. Then tell whether this story is fiction or nonfiction.

Rabbits	Rabbits and Birds	Birds
are furry and cuddly	are easy to take care of	fly around quickly
1. ____________	**2.** ____________	**4.** ____________
____________	**3.** ____________	____________
____________	____________	____________

5. Is the passage fiction or nonfiction? ____________________

Notes for Home: Your child has read a passage, identified whether it is fiction or nonfiction, and used a diagram to examine the way it is organized. ***Home Activity:*** Read a story together. Ask your child to tell you whether it is fiction or nonfiction and how it is organized.

Name ____

Fact and Opinion

REVIEW

Directions: Read the passage. Then read each question about the passage. Choose the best answer to each question. Mark the letter for the answer you have chosen.

Down with Cats!

Cats make terrible pets!

First of all, as everyone knows, cats are hunters. They are related to lions and tigers. Today's house cats hunt mice, birds, and lizards just the way big cats hunt bigger animals.

Some people think this is a good quality. But I definitely do not. I feel sorry for the mice that my brother's cat tries to catch. Of course, my brother's cat has never yet caught a single mouse. But someday I believe he might!

Finally, dogs are much nicer than cats. That is not just my opinion. It's a fact!

1. In the first sentence, the writer gives—
- **A.** an order.
- **B.** a question.
- **C.** a statement of fact.
- **D.** a statement of opinion.

2. Which clue word in this sentence signals that it is an opinion?
"Some people think this is a good quality."
- **F.** think
- **H.** some
- **G.** good
- **J.** is

3. A statement from the story that cannot be proved true or false is—
- **A.** cats are hunters.
- **B.** they are related to lions and tigers.
- **C.** dogs are much nicer than cats.
- **D.** house cats hunt mice, birds, and lizards.

4. The third paragraph includes—
- **F.** only statements of fact.
- **G.** statements of both fact and opinion.
- **H.** only statements of opinion.
- **J.** statements of fact that cannot be proved.

5. Which is **not** a good way to prove that one of the facts is true or false?
- **A.** Check an encyclopedia.
- **B.** Check a book about animals.
- **C.** Ask a friend.
- **D.** Ask an animal expert.

Notes for Home: Your child identified statements of opinions and facts in a passage. ***Home Activity:*** Ask your child to explain the difference between opinion and fact. Then take turns making statements about a subject, such as the weather, and identifying it as opinion or fact.

Name ______________________________

Writing Across Texts

Directions: Refer to *I Love Guinea Pigs* and the excerpt from *The Cricket in Times Square* to fill in the table below. Write the sentences about guinea pigs in the left column, and the sentences about mice in the right column. The sentences that apply to both animals should be written in each column.

They like to live in a pen on the grass.
They love to eat.
They can make purring sounds.
They have teeth for gnawing.
They are chubby.
They are very often messy.
They are usually skinny.
Their teeth keep growing.
They may live in drainpipes.

Guinea Pigs	Mice
1.	**6.**
2.	**7.**
3.	**8.**
4.	**9.**
5.	**10.**

Write a Comparison/Contrast Essay

Think about what you learned about mice and guinea pigs in the excerpt from *The Cricket in Times Square* and *I Love Guinea Pigs.* On a separate sheet of paper, write an essay discussing the likenesses and differences between these animals. Use the table you created to help you.

Notes for Home: Your child combined information from more than one source. ***Home Activity:*** As you read stories and articles, encourage your child to discuss the likenesses and differences between two things or characters.

Name ____________________

REVIEW

Grammar: Common and Proper Nouns

Directions: Read the nouns in the box. Write each noun in the correct column. Capitalize the proper nouns.

kangaroo	circus
debby's pet store	dr. ruiz
new england dog show	veterinarian
elephant	harold
puppy	reed animal hospital

Common Nouns	**Proper Nouns**
1. ____________	6. ____________
2. ____________	7. ____________
3. ____________	8. ____________
4. ____________	9. ____________
5. ____________	10. ____________

Directions: Replace the underlined words in each sentence with a proper noun. Write each proper noun on the line.

____________ **11.** I was surprised when our neighbor got a new pet.

____________ **12.** I was even more surprised when the pet turned out to be a little duckling.

____________ **13.** Our neighbor got the duckling from the animal shelter.

____________ **14.** Someone had found it quacking and alone near the town lake.

____________ **15.** The duckling loved to visit people and soon learned to fly across the street to avoid cars.

Notes for Home: Your child identified and wrote common and proper nouns. ***Home Activity:*** Encourage your child to name people, animals, and places he or she knows, using common nouns first and then proper nouns.

Practice

Grammar: Regular Plural Nouns

Nouns that name one person, place, or thing are **singular nouns. Plural nouns** name more than one person, place, or thing.

- Add **-s** to form the plural of most nouns.
  monkey/monkeys pig/pigs cat/cats snake/snakes
- Add **-es** to form the plural of nouns that end in **ch, sh, s, ss,** or **x.**
  bunch/bunches wish/wishes gas/gases fox/foxes glass/glasses
- To form the plural of nouns that end in a **consonant** and a **y,** change the **y** to **i** and add **-es.**
  penny/pennies baby/babies party/parties lady/ladies

Directions: Write the plural form of each underlined noun on the line.

______________ **1.** My friend says that I live in a zoo.

______________ **2.** It all started with a stray dog.

______________ **3.** Soon after she came to live with us, she had a puppy.

______________ **4.** Yes, that means getting another animal dish.

______________ **5.** Then my friend Mel was moving to Mexico, so she gave me her hamster.

______________ **6.** Next, my little brother wanted a lizard.

______________ **7.** My sister brought home a tadpole from the lake.

______________ **8.** Before long, it turned into a frog.

______________ **9.** My older brother decided to raise a racing pigeon.

______________ **10.** "What's next?" my friend asked me. "A pony?"

Notes for Home: Your child added *-s* or *-es* to nouns to show more than one person, place, or thing. ***Home Activity:*** Take a walk through your house. Have your child name the nouns he or she sees using singular and plural nouns *(one sofa, two chairs)*.

Name ______________________________

Grammar: Regular Plural Nouns

Directions: Write **P** if the noun is plural. Write **S** if the noun is singular. Then, write the plural form of each singular noun.

1. rabbits ____________

2. pellet ____________

3. tails ____________

4. family ____________

5. kitten ____________

6. stripes ____________

7. monkey ____________

8. circus ____________

9. snake ____________

10. tanks ____________

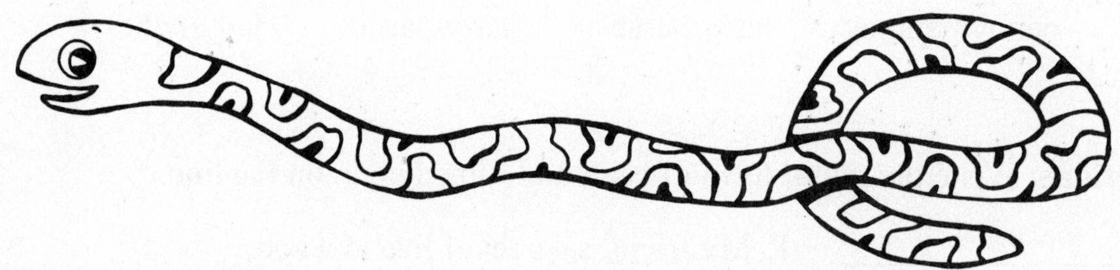

Directions: Write the plural forms of the nouns in each sentence.

____________ **11.** A ferret can be a great pet.

____________ **12.** My ferret likes to play with a ball and a bell.

____________ **13.** It likes to sleep in a special bed and on the floor of its tank.

____________ **14.** Unlike a rat, a ferret is not a rodent.

____________ **15.** Having a ferret is not as strange as having a skunk or an ocelot.

Write About a Pet

On a separate sheet of paper, write about a pet you have or would like to have. Describe where it lives, what it eats, and what things it likes to play with. Circle all the regular plural nouns.

Notes for Home: Your child wrote regular plural nouns. ***Home Activity:*** Write pairs of singular and plural nouns on index cards, one word per index card. Use nouns whose plurals are formed by adding *-s* or *-es*. Mix the cards and draw two at a time to try to match pairs.

Name ____________________

Grammar: Regular Plural Nouns

Read the chart. Circle the **-s** or **-es** ending in each plural noun.

add **-s**	days	cups	boys	paths	seas
add **-es**	riches	dishes	dresses	boxes	buses

A **singular noun** names one person, place, or thing. A **plural noun** names more than one person, place, or thing. Add **-s** or **-es** to spell the plural forms of most nouns.

Directions: Complete the chart. Write each noun in the correct column.

axes	cobra	desert	goats
brushes	colts	eagles	house
banana	couches	ferns	peaches

Singular Nouns	Plural Nouns	
1. ____________	**5.** ____________	**9.** ____________
2. ____________	**6.** ____________	**10.** ____________
3. ____________	**7.** ____________	**11.** ____________
4. ____________	**8.** ____________	**12.** ____________

Directions: Write the plural of each noun in ( ).

13. Those (store) sell (pet). ____________________

14. The (dog) saw the (bone). ____________________

15. Some (boy) sat on the (box). ____________________

16. (Student) rode the (bus). ____________________

Notes for Home: Your child identified regular plural nouns. ***Home Activity:*** Name objects in your home. Have your child write the plural forms of the names of the objects.

Name ______________________________

Grammar: Regular Plural Nouns

Directions: Replace each underlined singular noun with a plural noun. Write the plural noun on the line.

1. The student saw a movie in the morning.

____

2. The girl liked the actor in the movie.

____

3. The class rode the bus to the movie.

____

4. The movie held my attention.

____

5. Judy made lunch for the group.

____

Directions: Complete each sentence with a plural noun.

6. The actors studied their ______________ for the play.

7. The performers gave two ______________ each day.

8. Even ______________ attended the show at school.

9. Some friends sent ______________ to the actors.

10. Some people sat on ______________ .

11. The actor said his ______________ to the audience.

Write a Review

Write a review of a play or movie you enjoyed. Use plural nouns. Write on a separate sheet of paper.

Notes for Home: Your child wrote plural nouns in sentences. ***Home Activity:*** Have your child choose nouns from a page of a favorite story. Then have him or her write sentences, using plural forms of those nouns.

Name ____________________

Word Study: Compound Words

Directions: Compound words are words made by joining two words, such as **sun + shine = sunshine.** Some compound words have a hyphen. Read this paragraph. Circle each compound word. Then write the word on the line.

Throughout history, people have had dogs as pets. Some dogs have long fur. They are called long-coated. Others have short fur. They are called smooth-coated. Newborn puppies have very little fur, so it is hard to tell how long their fur will be when they are grown-up dogs.

1. ____________

2. ____________

3. ____________

4. ____________

5. ____________

Directions: Match each word in the first column with a word in the second column to make a compound word that makes sense. Write the word on the line.

6. snow	–legged	____________
7. four	storm	____________
8. any	times	____________
9. what	born	____________
10. new	out	____________
11. some	–haired	____________
12. through	ever	____________
13. long	way	____________

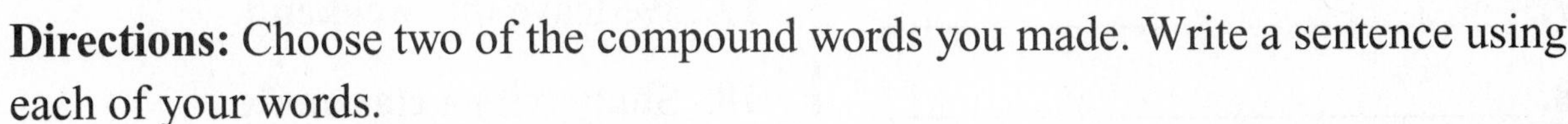

Directions: Choose two of the compound words you made. Write a sentence using each of your words.

14. ______________________________

15. ______________________________

Notes for Home: Your child wrote compound words. ***Home Activity:*** Look for compound words on directions that come with toys or games. Write each part of the word on separate slips of paper, then have your child put the words together.

Name ____________________________________

Pretest

Spelling: Compound Words

Pretest Directions: Fold back the page along the dotted line. On the blanks, write the spelling words as they are dictated. When you have finished the test, unfold the page and check your words.

1. ____________________
2. ____________________
3. ____________________
4. ____________________
5. ____________________
6. ____________________
7. ____________________
8. ____________________
9. ____________________
10. ____________________
11. ____________________
12. ____________________
13. ____________________
14. ____________________
15. ____________________
16. ____________________
17. ____________________
18. ____________________
19. ____________________
20. ____________________

1. Michelle loves **baseball**!
2. Our **basketball** team won.
3. My bedroom is **upstairs**.
4. I baked this **myself**.
5. Drive down the **highway**.
6. Our **classroom** is huge.
7. Will you come **anyway**?
8. Recycle the **newspaper**.
9. Bring **something** warm.
10. **Sometimes** we visit her.
11. Write on the **chalkboard**.
12. Those **earrings** are shiny.
13. Watch stars at **nighttime**.
14. She rode a **motorcycle**.
15. Come **downstairs** with me.
16. Do you play **softball**?
17. We leave this **weekend**.
18. Study with a **classmate**.
19. The **doorbell** rang.
20. Hose down the **driveway**.

Notes for Home: Your child took a pretest on compound words. ***Home Activity:*** Help your child learn misspelled words before the final test. Dictate the word and have your child spell the word aloud for you or write it on paper.

Name ___

Spelling: Compound Words

Word List				
baseball	highway	something	nighttime	weekend
basketball	classroom	sometimes	motorcycle	classmate
upstairs	anyway	chalkboard	downstairs	doorbell
myself	newspaper	earrings	softball	driveway

Directions: Add a word to each word below to form a compound word from the box. Write the compound word on the line.

1. up ___
2. cycle ___
3. down ___
4. basket ___
5. drive ___
6. high ___
7. night ___
8. door ___
9. rings ___
10. any ___
11. base ___
12. paper ___
13. soft ___
14. end ___

Directions: Choose the words from the box that best complete the story. Write each word on the matching numbered line to the right.

At school, we have a wonderful pet in our **15.** _____. It's a gerbil named Max. Before we got Max, our teacher wrote a list of class rules on the **16.** _____ so we'd know how to take care of Max. I take care of two gerbils by **17.** _____ at home, and I know that **18.** _____ you can forget what they need.

With Max, there's always **19.** _____ interesting to see. My **20.** _____, Lesley, says that Max is more fun than her pet goldfish!

15. ___
16. ___
17. ___
18. ___
19. ___
20. ___

Notes for Home: Your child spelled compound words in which two words are joined to make a new word. ***Home Activity:*** Together, write sentences using each part of a compound word and then the whole word. For example: *A <u>room</u> where you have a <u>class</u> is a <u>classroom</u>.*

Name ______________________________

Spelling: Compound Words

Directions: Proofread this entry from a journal. Find five spelling mistakes. Use the proofreading marks to correct each mistake.

≡	Make a capital.
/	Make a small letter.
∧	Add something.
ↄ	Take out something.
⊙	Add a period.
¶	Begin a new paragraph.

Dear Diary,

This weekkend I had fun with my cat Saucy. I chased her dowstairs and back upstairs until we both got tired of running. Then I rolled up some old newpaper and tied it to a string. She pounced on it, pretending it was a mouse. Suddenly, the dorbell rang. My friend Jaime wanted to play baskeball or softball. I told him I did, too, but first I had to feed Saucy!

Spelling Tip

baseball

A compound word is made of two or more words. Keep all the letters when spelling compounds.

Word List

baseball	highway	something	nighttime	weekend
basketball	classroom	sometimes	motorcycle	classmate
upstairs	anyway	chalkboard	downstairs	doorbell
myself	newspaper	earrings	softball	driveway

Write a Diary Entry

Imagine that you have a new pet. On a separate sheet of paper, write a diary entry telling about your pet. Include how you care for it, what it likes to eat, and how the two of you have fun. Try to use at least three spelling words.

Notes for Home: Your child spelled compound words in which two words are joined to make a new word. ***Home Activity:*** With your child, think of some other compound words, such as *mailbox, stairway,* and *daylight.*

Name ______________________________

Spelling: Compound Words

REVIEW

Word List				
baseball	highway	something	nighttime	weekend
basketball	classroom	sometimes	motorcycle	classmate
upstairs	anyway	chalkboard	downstairs	doorbell
myself	newspaper	earrings	softball	driveway

Directions: Choose the word from the box that shares a word part with the word shown. Use each word only once. Write the word on the line.

1. motorboat ______________

2. daytime ______________

3. everything ______________

4. somewhere ______________

5. weekday ______________

6. earache ______________

7. anyone ______________

8. herself ______________

9. basement ______________

10. downtown ______________

11. uptown ______________

12. newscast ______________

Directions: Choose the word from the box that best completes each sentence. Write the word on the line to the left.

______________ **13.** My dog Simon loves to go outside, even though we live near a busy _____.

______________ **14.** But we only let him go to the end of our _____.

______________ **15.** We also let him play with us on the _____ court.

______________ **16.** When I play _____, he barks when I hit the ball!

______________ **17.** I would love to take Simon to my _____ at school.

______________ **18.** My _____, Luis, would just love him.

______________ **19.** But on the _____ at school is written, "No Pets!"

______________ **20.** So Luis is coming here now to play with Simon—and I think I just heard the _____ ring!

Notes for Home: Your child spelled compound words in which two words are joined to make a new word. ***Home Activity:*** Play "word toss." You "toss" a word part at your child, who "tosses back" a compound word. For example, you say *every,* and he or she says *everyone!*

Name ________________________________

Chart/Table

A **chart** organizes information in a way that is easy to follow. A **table** is a kind of chart that presents information in rows and columns.

Directions: Use the table to answer the questions that follow.

GUIDE TO GUINEA PIG CARE

Topics	What You Need to Know
Food and Water	Guinea pigs should eat a diet of hay, pellets, fresh fruit, and vegetables such as broccoli, cauliflower, carrots, and peas. Guinea pigs need lots of fresh water daily.
Bedding	Put some shredded newspaper at the bottom of the cage. Replace with fresh newspapers daily. You can also use towels and blankets but these have to be washed every day.
Vet Visits	Guinea pigs should have a physical exam twice a year. They should also see a vet if they have a loss of appetite, bleeding, diarrhea, hair loss, or show strange behavior.
Safety	Don't put plastic toys in a guinea pig's cage. It will chew them and could choke on the pieces.

1. Which row would you look at to find out what a guinea pig needs for sleeping?

____

2. How can you use the table to find out if plastic toys are safe for guinea pigs?

____

3. What four vegetables are good for a guinea pig's diet? ________________

____

4. What information can you learn by reading the section on Vet Visits?

____

5. Suppose you were going to add another row to the table on what a guinea pig's sounds mean. What words would you use to label this topic?

____

Name ____________________________________

Directions: Study the table below. Use the table to answer the questions that follow.

"WHAT IS MY GUINEA PIG TRYING TO SAY TO ME?"

Guinea Pig Sounds	What It Probably Means
gurgles, grunts	comfort, happiness
squeaks, squeals	fear, in pain, hungry
cooing	calm, relaxed
hisses, teeth clacking	fighting, warning

6. If your guinea pig was grunting and cooing, what "Sounds" would you look under to learn more?

____

7. If you saw a guinea pig clacking its teeth, how could you use this table to figure out what this means?

____

____

8. What sound could you expect from a guinea pig that does not want to be disturbed?

____

9. Suppose you are adding a third column to this chart. It will tell how to respond to a guinea pig's sounds. What heading could you give this column?

____

10. Why are headings in a table useful? ____________________

____

____

Notes for Home: Your child used tables to answer questions about pet care. ***Home Activity:*** Create a table with your child to keep track of weekly activities. For example, on Monday, your child might play soccer; on Tuesday, your child may watch a specific TV program, and so on.

Family Times

Name____

Summary

Laura Ends up in Deep Water!

Laura loves wading in the creek of her prairie home. But when Ma and Pa take her to the swimming hole, she realizes that she loves swimming even more. Laura knows that she is never supposed to go to the swimming hole without a grownup to take her. One hot day, though, she just can't resist heading for the swimming hole's cool water. One thing that stops her from going in the water is a fierce badger that snarls at her and frightens her into returning home.

Activity

Finish the Story. Have your child tell you the rest of "The Swimming Hole," including what happens to Laura when she gets home and the lesson she learns.

Reading Skills

Theme

Theme is the underlying meaning of a story—a big idea that stands on its own outside the story. Sometimes readers have to figure out the theme on their own, using evidence from the text to support the big idea.

In "The Swimming Hole," the theme is the lesson that Laura learns: *Trust is important, and when you lose it, you have to work hard to win it back.* But the author never states this directly. Readers must figure this out for themselves by watching what Laura does and what happens to her.

Activity

Make a Poster. Read a fable or a fairy tale that tells about a lesson the main character learns. Talk about the story's big idea and make a poster telling the theme.

Family Times

Tested Vocabulary

Words to Know

Knowing the meanings of these words is important to reading "The Swimming Hole." Practice using these words to learn their meanings.

bristled made one's hair stand up straight

dugout shelter formed by digging a hole into a hillside

jointed having joints or places where two parts join together

naughty not well-behaved

punish discipline

rushes grasslike plants with hollow stems

shallow not deep

Grammar

Irregular Plural Nouns

Most plural nouns end in **-s** or **-es,** such as **birds** and **beaches.** Some nouns are made plural by changing their spelling. For example, the plural of **tooth** is **teeth.** Some nouns have the same singular and plural forms: **sheep, fish.** These are called irregular plurals.

Noun	Irregular Plural
foot	feet
ox	____________
goose	____________
tooth	teeth
mouse	____________
sheep	____________

Activity

Tell a Story. Fill in the table above. Then use plural words from the table to tell a story about the adventures of one sheep, two oxen, three mice, and four geese.

Tested Spelling Words

________	________	________	________
________	________	________	________
________	________	________	________
________	________	________	________
________	________	________	________

Name ______________________________

Theme

- **Theme** is the underlying meaning of a story—a big idea that stands on its own outside the story.
- Sometimes an author states the theme directly. Sometimes readers have to figure out the theme on their own, using evidence from the text to support their big idea.

Directions: Reread "Ant and Dove." Then complete the chart. Tell what the theme is and give supporting evidence from the story. Some sentences have been started for you.

Theme

1.

Supporting Evidence

The ant was in trouble.

2. The dove helped the ant by: ______________________________

____

3. The ant felt: ______________________________

____

The dove was in trouble.

4. The ant: ______________________________

____

5. The ant did this because: ______________________________

____

Notes for Home: Your child read a fable and identified its theme, or "big idea." ***Home Activity:*** Invite your child to tell you a favorite story. Then ask your child to identify the story's big idea and what lesson about life might be learned from it.

Name ______________________________________

Vocabulary

Directions: Choose the word from the box that best matches each definition. Write the word on the line.

Check the Words You Know
__ bristled
__ dugout
__ jointed
__ naughty
__ punish
__ rushes
__ shallow

_______________ **1.** not deep

_______________ **2.** made hair stand up straight

_______________ **3.** hollow-stemmed plants

_______________ **4.** having places where two parts join together

_______________ **5.** shelter formed by hole in hillside

_______________ **6.** not well-behaved

Directions: Choose the word from the box that best completes each sentence. Write the word on the matching numbered line to the right.

I waded out into the **7.** _____ water near where the **8.** _____ grew. I knew it was **9.** _____ of me to go into the deeper water. My mother saw what I did, and she will now **10.** _____ me. I won't do that again now that I know.

7. _______________

8. _______________

9. _______________

10. _______________

Write a Description

On a separate sheet of paper, write a paragraph describing what you might see if you lived in the prairie long ago. Use as many vocabulary words as you can.

Notes for Home: Your child identified and used new words from "The Swimming Hole." ***Home Activity:*** Imagine you and your child are pioneers living in a house on the prairie. Use the vocabulary words to help you talk about what life would have been like.

Name ______________________________

Theme

- **Theme** is the underlying meaning of a story—a "big idea" that stands on its own outside the story.

1. Reread "The Swimming Hole." Write its theme on the line below.

____

Directions: Read the story. Then answer the questions below.

Ever since Malcolm could remember, Uncle Dave had kept his promises. One day, Uncle Dave broke a promise. He said he would come visit on Malcolm's birthday, and he didn't. Malcolm felt terrible. "I can never trust him again," he thought. The next time Uncle Dave visited, he said he was sorry. He had written down the wrong date on his calendar.

Malcolm thought he could never trust Uncle Dave again. But his mother said, "Sometimes people do mean things, but sometimes they just make mistakes."

"I guess he just made a mistake," said Malcolm. "So I guess I will try trusting him again."

2. Why did Malcolm always trust Uncle Dave?

____

3. What does Uncle Dave do to make Malcolm stop trusting him?

____

4. What does Uncle Dave do to show that Malcolm can trust him again?

____

5. Use what you know about the events and characters of the story above to write about its theme. Below the theme, list all the details in the story that support this big idea. Use a separate sheet of paper.

Notes for Home: Your child has read a story and identified its theme, or big idea, as well as some details that support that theme. ***Home Activity:*** Talk together about a favorite book, movie, or television show. Invite your child to explain its theme, or "big idea."

Name ______________________________

Selection Test

Directions: Choose the best answer to each item. Mark the letter for the answer you have chosen.

Part 1: Vocabulary

Find the answer choice that means about the same as the underlined word in each sentence.

1. The wind blew the <u>rushes</u>.
- A. tall shrubs or bushes
- B. largest branches of a tree
- C. pale blue flowers
- D. grasslike plants that grow in wet soil

2. We stood in the <u>shallow</u> water.
- F. dark
- G. very cold
- H. not deep
- J. still

3. The doll's arms and legs are <u>jointed</u>.
- A. soiled or stained
- B. having places where parts join together
- C. stiff or unable to move
- D. made from cloth filled with padding

4. Trees grew around the <u>dugout</u>.
- F. valley between two mountains
- G. soil or gravel taken from the ground
- H. deepest part of a pond
- J. shelter formed by digging into the side of a hill

5. Jenna's parents will <u>punish</u> her.
- A. cause pain for doing something wrong
- B. give a reward to
- C. show her a lot of love and affection
- D. send away to somewhere else

6. The cat's coat <u>bristled</u>.
- F. became tangled
- G. trembled or shook
- H. stood up straight
- J. gleamed or shone

7. The mother spoke to the <u>naughty</u> child.
- A. worn out
- B. badly behaved
- C. lonesome
- D. confused or puzzled

Part 2: Comprehension

Use what you know about the story to answer each item.

8. Laura and her family lived near—
- F. the ocean.
- G. a creek.
- H. a lake.
- J. a river.

GO ON

9. Laura and Mary discovered many things they could make with—
A. flowers.
B. rocks.
C. rushes.
D. mud.

10. Pa and Ma did not want the girls to go to the swimming hole because—
F. it was not safe for them to swim there alone.
G. they had too many chores to do.
H. it was too far from home.
J. wild animals lived near it.

11. What does this story suggest about the outdoors?
A. Children do not enjoy the outdoors.
B. The outdoors is full of fun and wonder.
C. People spend too much time outdoors.
D. The outdoors is a dark, bad place.

12. The badger probably flattened itself because it—
F. was getting ready to sleep.
G. was afraid.
H. liked Laura.
J. was thirsty.

13. What is the theme of this story?
A. Sisters are best friends.
B. Children earn freedom when they can be trusted.
C. Growing up is fun.
D. Parents make many mistakes.

14. What bothered Laura most when she returned to the dugout after going near the swimming hole?
F. running home without getting a cool drink
G. remembering the badger she had seen
H. worrying that Ma and Pa would find out
J. knowing that she had broken a promise to Pa

15. Laura probably felt that her parents—
A. thought only of themselves.
B. should have had more rules.
C. made her work too hard.
D. tried to do what was best for her.

Name ______________________________

Theme

- **Theme** is the underlying meaning of a story—a "big idea" that stands on its own outside the story.

Directions: Read the story below.

Beth and Rosa were best friends. Beth looked forward to starting the fourth grade together. Having a friend makes everything more fun.

Then Rosa found a new best friend! She stopped walking home with Beth. She stopped having lunch with her. She stopped playing with Beth on Saturdays. Beth felt awful.

One day at lunch, Mei-Ling came over to Beth's table. "Can I sit here?" she asked shyly. The two girls had a good time. The next day, they ate together again. On Saturday, Mei-Ling came over to play. Beth began to feel much better.

It seemed as though Mei-Ling wanted to be best friends, but Beth wasn't sure she wanted a new best friend. What if Mei-Ling stopped being her friend too?

Finally, Beth decided to take a chance. She decided it was better to have a friend and lose her than not to have any friends at all. She and Mei-Ling became good friends and stayed that way for a long time.

Directions: Complete the diagram. In the first box, write the theme of the story. In each of the other boxes, write a detail that supports the theme.

1. Theme:

2. Supporting Detail:

3. Supporting Detail:

4. Supporting Detail:

5. Supporting Detail:

Notes for Home: Your child read a story, identified its theme, and gave details that support the theme. ***Home Activity:*** Talk together with your child about a book you've read together. Ask your child to describe the underlying meaning of the story.

Name ______________________________

Cause and Effect

REVIEW

Directions: Read the story. Then read each question about the story. Choose the best answer to each question. Mark the letter for the answer you have chosen.

House Rules

We have several rules in our house. My parents say that's because rules help us all get along better.

Once my sister broke the rule about calling home if you're going to be late. Dad got worried. Mama called many of my sister's friends. When my little sister saw how worried everyone was, she started to cry.

When the baby heard my sister cry, he started crying too. Mama rushed to pick him up and tripped on the rug. She hurt her leg. Just then, my sister walked in.

"I'm sorry," my sister said. "I was with Diana, and we took her dog for a long walk. I didn't realize how late it was."

When she saw what had happened, my sister was very sorry. Now she never forgets to call!

1. One clue word that signals a cause-effect relationship in the first paragraph is—
- **A.** several.
- **B.** that's.
- **C.** help.
- **D.** because.

2. This family's rules—
- **F.** make the baby cry.
- **G.** help everyone get along better.
- **H.** make the older sister sorry.
- **J.** make Dad worry.

3. Mama hurt her leg because
- **A.** Dad got worried.
- **B.** the baby was crying.
- **C.** she tripped on a rug.
- **D.** the telephone rang.

4. The sister didn't call because—
- **F.** she didn't think the rule was important.
- **G.** she didn't know how late it was.
- **H.** there wasn't a phone around.
- **J.** Diana wouldn't let her.

5. Why does the sister remember to call now?
- **A.** She was sorry for the trouble she caused.
- **B.** She got a better watch.
- **C.** She doesn't go to Diana's any more.
- **D.** She got punished for not calling.

Notes for Home: Your child identified causes and effects in a story. ***Home Activity:*** Play "Cause-Effect Chain." Name a cause *(I was late starting dinner.)*. Ask your child to name an effect *(We ate late.)*. You name an effect of *that* effect. *(We were late washing dishes.),* and so on.

Name ______________________________

Writing Across Texts

Directions: Consider what you know about taking risks and what you learned from "The Swimming Hole" and "A Big-City Dream." Is it usually a good idea to take risks? Think of examples from the stories to support each of the sentences below.

Taking a risk is usually a good idea. You can enjoy new adventures.	Taking a risk is usually not a good idea. If you fail, people may not trust you.
1.	**6.**
2.	**7.**
3.	**8.**
4.	**9.**
5.	**10.**

Write a Letter of Advice

On a separate sheet of paper, write a letter of advice about taking risks. Explain whether it is a good idea to take risks or not. Support your letter with information from "The Swimming Hole" and "A Big-City Dream." Use the table you created to help you.

Notes for Home: Your child combined and used information from more than one fictional story. ***Home Activity:*** As you read stories to your child, discuss the actions of the characters. Discuss with your child whether those actions are advisable in real life.

Name ______________________________

REVIEW

Grammar: Singular and Plural Nouns

Directions: Write **S** for nouns that are singular. After the **S,** write the plural form of the noun. Write **P** for nouns that are plural.

1. mess ____________________

2. penny ____________________

3. movies ____________________

4. crash ____________________

5. unicorn ____________________

6. glass ____________________

7. boxes ____________________

8. desks ____________________

9. treasures ____________________

10. hole ____________________

11. tray ____________________

12. hearts ____________________

13. turkey ____________________

14. lady ____________________

Directions: Write the plural form of each underlined noun on the line.

____________________ **15.** Ronald was on a trip with his <u>class</u>.

____________________ **16.** The group was crossing the river in a <u>ferry</u>.

____________________ **17.** Ronald wanted to buy a drink, but he had only a <u>quarter</u>.

____________________ **18.** He noticed some money a man had dropped under a <u>bench</u> nearby.

____________________ **19.** He picked up the money, thought for a <u>minute</u>, and went to look for the man.

____________________ **20.** The man thanked Ronald and gave him some change to buy a <u>drink</u>.

Notes for Home: Your child identified singular and plural nouns and wrote the plural form for singular nouns. ***Home Activity:*** Have your child identify singular nouns in a book or a magazine and write the plural form for each noun.

Grammar: Irregular Plural Nouns

Some plural forms of nouns do not end in **-s** or **-es.** To form these **irregular plurals,** you may have to change the spelling of the word.

Singular/Plural	
child/children	mouse/mice
foot/feet	ox/oxen
goose/geese	tooth/teeth
leaf/leaves	wolf/wolves
man/men	woman/women

A few nouns have the same form for both singular and plural.

deer	moose	sheep

Directions: Circle the correct plural noun in ( ) to complete each sentence.

1. Jenny wanted to go swimming with the other (childs/children).
2. First, she had to help the (women/womans) with chores on the farm.
3. The (sheeps/sheep) had to be brought in from the field.
4. The (oxen/oxes) had to be fed.
5. The (gooses/geese) needed more water.
6. There were (leafs/leaves) to be raked.
7. The dogs were let out to keep watch for (wolves/wolfs).
8. Jenny helped her aunt set traps for the (mouse/mice).
9. Finally, she ran to the water and jumped in with both (feet/foots).
10. The splash startled two (deer/deers) that were drinking at the stream.

Notes for Home: Your child identified irregular plural nouns that do not end in *-s* or *-es,* such as *children. **Home Activity:*** Take turns naming irregular plural nouns. Use these words to tell a story about a country adventure.

Name ______________________________

Grammar: Irregular Plural Nouns

Directions: Circle the correct plural noun in ( ) to complete each sentence.

1. Of all the (childs/children) at Olive Tree High School, Tanya was the most adventurous.

2. Every winter, she was first on the pond, her skates gleaming on her (foots/feet).

3. One day, Tanya looked up from skating and saw two big (moose/mooses).

4. She was so scared, her (teeths/teeth) started to chatter.

5. She thought, "I'm not afraid of (meece/mice), but I feel scared now!"

Directions: Write the plural form of each noun in ( ) to complete each sentence. Be careful. Don't let the rhymes fool you!

________________ **6.** What would happen if foxes were friends with (ox)?

________________ **7.** If (goose) travel on trains, do they ride in the cabooses?

________________ **8.** Those three (wolf) like to loaf.

________________ **9.** The (man) were cooking flapjacks in big pans.

________________ **10.** These boots are too small for my (foot).

Write an Adventure Story

On a separate sheet of paper, write a short adventure story that involves different animals. It can be a funny story, if you wish. Use at least five irregular plural nouns.

Notes for Home: Your child identified and wrote irregular plural nouns such as *mice*. ***Home Activity:*** Make up rhymes that use irregular plural nouns such as those listed above.

Name ______________________________

RETEACHING

Grammar: Irregular Plural Nouns

Read the chart. Underline each singular noun. Circle each plural noun.

Singular Nouns		Plural Nouns
1. loaf	(the spelling changes)	loaves
2. mouse	(the spelling changes)	mice
3. sheep	(the spelling does not change)	sheep

Some plural nouns are formed in special ways. They are called **irregular plural nouns.** Pay attention to the spelling of irregular plural nouns.

Directions: Write the plural form of each noun.

1. man ______________________

2. wolf ______________________

3. life ______________________

4. person ______________________

5. leaf ______________________

6. deer ______________________

7. moose ______________________

8. shelf ______________________

Directions: Circle each plural noun that is not formed correctly. There is one in each sentence. Then write that plural noun correctly.

9. Grandma makes us scarfs. ______________________

10. She makes up stories about deers. ______________________

11. She reads about kinds of fishs. ______________________

12. She tells tales of ancient womans. ______________________

13. She also tells stories about gooses. ______________________

14. Some tales are about childrens. ______________________

15. Their foots take them far. ______________________

Notes for Home: Your child wrote irregular plural nouns correctly. ***Home Activity:*** Write irregular nouns, such as *thief* or *deer*, and have your child write the plural forms of the nouns.

Name ____________________

Grammar: Irregular Plural Nouns

Directions: Write the plural form of each noun.

1. moose ____________________

2. tooth ____________________

3. calf ____________________

4. hoof ____________________

5. self ____________________

6. sheep ____________________

7. deer ____________________

8. woman ____________________

9. wife ____________________

10. ox ____________________

11. wolf ____________________

12. goose ____________________

13. man ____________________

14. foot ____________________

15. mouse ____________________

16. child ____________________

Directions: Write the plural form of the right noun on the line. Then choose two nouns from the list and use their plural forms in two sentences. Use one plural in each sentence.

child deer mouse wolf

17. He saw two tiny ____________________ in the bushes.

18. The ____________________ ate three bowls of fruit.

19. Several swift ____________________ ran by the house.

20. Two gray ____________________ howled at the moon.

21. ____________________

22. ____________________

Write a Silly Story

Write a silly story about what happened when two mice explored a library. Use plural nouns. Write on a separate sheet of paper.

Notes for Home: Your child wrote irregular plural nouns. ***Home Activity:*** Have your child circle irregular plural nouns in a newspaper or magazine article. Then challenge him or her to use three of the irregular plural nouns in sentences.

Name ______________________________

Phonics: Vowel Digraphs

Directions: Read the letter below. Find words that have the vowel sound in **paw, thought,** and **author.** The vowel sound in each word is the same, but the sound has three different spellings. Write the words on the lines.

Dear Billy,

I was late for school today, but it wasn't really my fault! Okay, maybe I am to blame. I guess I was naughty and slept too late. Anyway, I thought I'd ride my bike to get to school quickly. Then guess what happened! I saw this awful dog! Then I realized that it was friendly. On my way back, I brought the dog home. We are going to keep it as a pet. I ought to get up earlier, but this time I'm glad I didn't!

Your friend,

Kezia

1. __________
2. __________
3. __________
4. __________
5. __________
6. __________
7. __________

Directions: Read these sentences. Say the underlined words to yourself. Circle the word in ( ) that has the same vowel sound as the underlined word.

8. When it is too hot outside, most people feel awful. (April/thoughtful)
9. So the family thought a trip to the river would be cool. (taught/though)
10. They brought a picnic basket for lunch. (browse/pause)
11. The children fought about who could wade deepest. (fight/caught)
12. The parents warned the children not to be naughty. (note/bought)
13. As they were eating, the family saw dark clouds in the sky. (straw/sew)
14. Now the children are arguing about whose fault it is that everything got wet in the rain. (flaw/flower)

Directions: Choose one of the words you circled. Write a sentence for it.

15. ____

Notes for Home: Your child learned three spellings for the vowel sound in *paw, thought,* and *author. **Home Activity:*** Read a newspaper story with your child. Help your child recognize this vowel sound. Ask your child to write the words in three groups: *aw, ou,* and *au*.

Pretest

Spelling: Homophones

Pretest Directions: Fold back the page along the dotted line. On the blanks, write the spelling words as they are dictated. When you have finished the test, unfold the page and check your words.

1. ____	1. Gather **wood** for the fire.
2. ____	2. **Would** you help me?
3. ____	3. I want some **too**!
4. ____	4. Come **to** my house.
5. ____	5. **Two** birds flew by.
6. ____	6. I will meet you **there**.
7. ____	7. This is **their** garden.
8. ____	8. **They're** going to town.
9. ____	9. Where is **your** puppy?
10. ____	10. **You're** late today.
11. ____	11. **Beat** the rug clean.
12. ____	12. Add a **beet** to the stew.
13. ____	13. Did you **break** a bone?
14. ____	14. Use the **brake** to stop.
15. ____	15. Hang the **clothes** to dry.
16. ____	16. **Close** the window.
17. ____	17. Cut off a **piece** for me.
18. ____	18. Let me read in **peace**!
19. ____	19. The ball was **thrown** far.
20. ____	20. She sat on her **throne**.

Notes for Home: Your child took a pretest on homophones, words that sound alike but are spelled differently and have different meanings. ***Home Activity:*** Help your child learn to connect the spelling of the word with its meaning.

Name ________________________________

Spelling: Homophones

Word List				
wood	two	your	break	piece
would	there	you're	brake	peace
too	their	beat	clothes	thrown
to	they're	beet	close	throne

Directions: Choose the word from the box that best matches each clue. Write the word on the line.

1. lumber ______________

2. will ______________

3. opposite of *war* ______________

4. one part ______________

5. chair for a king ______________

6. form of *throw* ______________

7. red vegetable ______________

8. hit ______________

9. come apart ______________

10. can slow a car ______________

11. shut ______________

12. things you wear ______________

Directions: Choose the words from the box that best complete each sentence. Write each word on the matching numbered line to the right.

13. _____ friend Dylan just called you. **14.** _____ invited to a party at his house next week!

I have **15.** _____ wonderful friends, Deedee and Sam. I trust them always **16.** _____ be there when I need them. They trust me **17.** _____.

Deedee and Sam are brother and sister—in fact, **18.** _____ twins. Today I'm going to **19.** _____ house after school. I'll go **20.** _____ as soon as my last class is over.

13. ______________

14. ______________

15. ______________

16. ______________

17. ______________

18. ______________

19. ______________

20. ______________

Notes for Home: Your child practiced spelling homophones, words that sound alike but are spelled differently and have different meanings. ***Home Activity:*** Write one of the homophones from the box and have your child use it in a sentence. Switch roles and repeat.

Name ____________________

Proofread and Wri

Spelling: Homophones

Directions: Proofread this letter from one friend to another. Find five spelling mistakes. Use the proofreading marks to correct each mistake.

≡	Make a capital.
/	Make a small letter.
∧	Add something.
♪	Take out something.
⊙	Add a period.
¶	Begin a new paragraph.

Dear Tammy,

I want you too know that I'm glad you're my best friend. I know I can trust you, no matter what! You can always trust me, to. You never brake you're promises, and you always are their when I need a friend.

Your friend,
Anya

Spelling Tip

A **homophone** is a word that sounds exactly like another word but has a different spelling and meaning. Try to think of memory tricks to help you spell, such as: I'd like a **piece** of **pie.**

Word List

wood	two	your	break	piece
would	there	you're	brake	peace
too	their	beat	clothes	thrown
to	they're	beet	close	throne

Write a Friendly Letter

Imagine you are Tammy. On a separate sheet of paper, write a letter back to Anya about the trust you have for her. Use at least three spelling words in your letter.

Notes for Home: Your child learned to spell homophones, words that sound alike but are spelled differently and have different meanings. ***Home Activity:*** Work with your child to write sentences for each set of homophones. Discuss ways to remember the meaning and spelling of each word.

Name ______________________

Spelling: Homophones

REVIEW

Word List

wood	two	your	break	piece
would	there	you're	brake	peace
too	their	beat	clothes	thrown
to	they're	beet	close	throne

Directions: Use the words in ( ) to complete each sentence. Write the words on the matching numbered lines to the right.

There once was a queen who was **1.** _____ from her **2.** _____. (throne/thrown)

The queen did not know what **3.** _____ do, so she called her **4.** _____ advisors, and her jester **5.** _____. (to/too/two)

"**6.** _____ all very smart," the queen thought, "and once I see them sitting **7.** _____ in front of me, I know I'll take **8.** _____ advice." (there/their/they're)

When they arrived, the queen said, "**9.** _____ here because I want **10.** _____ opinion. How can I regain my people's trust?" (your/you're)

"It's very simple," they all said. "Bring **11.** _____ to the kingdom—and give everyone a big **12.** _____ of pie to celebrate!" (peace/piece)

1. ______________
2. ______________
3. ______________
4. ______________
5. ______________
6. ______________
7. ______________
8. ______________
9. ______________
10. ______________
11. ______________
12. ______________

Directions: Unscramble each set of letters below to form a word from the box. Write the word on the line.

13. solec ______________

14. hotcels ______________

15. odow ______________

16. ludow ______________

17. tabe ______________

18. ebet ______________

19. kareb ______________

20. kerab ______________

Notes for Home: Your child spelled homophones, words that sound alike but are spelled differently and have different meanings. ***Home Activity:*** Play a homophone game. Take turns making up sentences that use at least two homophones, such as: *The king was thrown from his throne.*

Name ________________________________

Following Directions

Following directions means doing or making something in a certain order. Be sure to:

- Read all directions carefully so you know what you need to do.
- Gather any items needed to complete the directions.
- Follow the directions in the order they are given.

Directions: Read the directions given in this recipe carefully. Then answer the questions that follow.

Apple Crisp

1. Preheat the oven to 375°F. (Ask a grown-up to help you.)
2. Peel 6 apples, and then core and slice them.
3. Mix together in a bowl:
   $\frac{1}{2}$ cup sugar
   2 tbsp. cinnamon
4. Mix together in a different bowl:
   1 cup flour
   $\frac{1}{2}$ cup sugar
   2 eggs
   $\frac{1}{2}$ cup butter, melted
   1 tsp. vanilla extract
   $2\frac{1}{2}$ tbsp. lemon juice
5. Grease a 9-by-9-inch baking pan. Put the apple slices in the pan.
6. Sprinkle <u>half</u> the sugar and cinnamon mixture over the apples.
7. Pour the mixture from step 4 over the apples. Make sure to cover the whole surface.
8. Cut about 1 tbsp. of butter into tiny bits. Add these bits of butter to the other half of the sugar and cinnamon mixture. Use your fingers to mush the butter into the sugar until crumbs form.
9. Sprinkle these crumbs over the top of the apple mixture.
10. Place the pan in the oven and bake the mixture for 45 minutes, or until the batter on the top is golden brown.
11. Cool for about 5 minutes, and then cut the apple crisp into squares.

Name ______________________________

1. When using a recipe, why is it important to read all the directions first before starting the first step?

____

____

2. What is the first step you do? ______________________________

3. How many apples are needed? ______________________________

4. How many ingredients get mixed in step 3? What are they? ______________

____

5. How many ingredients get mixed in step 4? What are they? ______________

____

____

6. How much sugar is needed? ______________________________

7. What abbreviations are used for teaspoon and tablespoon? ______________

8. If you didn't time the apple crisp cooking, what is another way to tell if it is done? What step gives you this information?

____

9. Why do you think many cookbooks include pictures? ______________

____

____

10. What might happen if you didn't follow the steps for making apple crisp in the order given in the recipe?

____

____

Notes for Home: Your child used a recipe to practice following directions. ***Home Activity:*** Show your child a recipe for a favorite family dish. Discuss the steps and write a list of what is needed to make the dish.

Family Times

Name______________________________

Summary

Dragons Found on Komodo Island!

Even though Komodo dragons don't fly or breathe fire, they do look like little dragons. These reptiles—the largest lizards in the world—live in the Komodo Island area of Indonesia. The adult dragons can grow to be more than 10 feet long and can weigh as much as 250 pounds. They are strong enough to kill a water buffalo, which can weigh more than 1,000 pounds!

Activity

Draw Dragons. Have your child draw a picture of a Komodo dragon and a picture of an imaginary dragon. Talk about how they are alike and how they are different.

Reading Skills

Context Clues

When you see an unfamiliar word, use context clues, or words around the unfamiliar word, to figure out the word's meaning. Two kinds of context clues are:

- **Definition/Explanation.** A definition or explanation may appear before or after the word: **Animals that eat other animals are called *predators.***
- **Synonym.** A word with nearly the same meaning as another word may appear in the sentence: **Komodo dragons are *carnivores,* or meat-eaters.**

Activity

Hunt for Context Clues. Look at a nonfiction book or article. Find at least three unfamiliar words. Then find the context clues—the words around those unfamiliar words—and figure out the meaning of each word. Check your meanings against those in a dictionary.

Family Times

Tested Vocabulary

Words to Know

Knowing the meanings of these words is important to reading *Komodo Dragons.* Practice using these words to learn their meanings.

armor covering worn to protect the body in fighting

fierce savage; wild

harshest roughest

lizards reptiles somewhat like snakes, but with four legs and thicker bodies

prey an animal hunted for food

reptiles one group of cold-blooded animals with backbones and lungs

roam wander

Grammar

Possessive Nouns

Nouns that show who owns, or possesses, something, are called **possessive nouns.** To make a singular noun show ownership, add an **apostrophe (')** and **-s.** To make a plural noun that ends in **-s** possessive, just add an apostrophe ('). If the plural noun doesn't end in **-s,** add an apostrophe (') and **-s.**

Person	Thing	Possessive Noun
Carlos	book	Carlos's book
Mom	ring	Mom's ring
Sara	smile	Sara's smile
cities	lights	cities' lights
children	toys	children's toys

Activity

Make a Table. Make a table like the one above. Write the names of each member of your household, two things that the person owns, and a possessive noun to show who owns what.

Tested Spelling Words

____________	____________	____________	____________
____________	____________	____________	____________
____________	____________	____________	____________
____________	____________	____________	____________
____________	____________	____________	____________

Name ______________________________

Context Clues

- When you are reading and you see an unfamiliar word, use **context clues,** or words around the unfamiliar word, to figure out its meaning.
- The context may give a definition or an explanation. Often the definition or explanation comes just before or just after the word. Sometimes a synonym, a word with nearly the same meaning as another word, is used as a context clue.

Directions: Reread "Crocodilians." Then complete the table. Use the context clues in the article to figure out the meaning of each word in the table.

Word	Meaning
osteoderms	**1.**
hides	**2.**
amphibious	**3.**
ripple	**4.**
ectothermic	**5.**

Notes for Home: Your child used context clues to figure out the meanings of five words. ***Home Activity:*** Encourage your child to use context clues to figure out the meanings of unfamiliar words as you read together.

Name ______________________________

Vocabulary

Directions: Cross out the word that does not belong in each group.

1. roam	wander	dash	travel
2. armor	shell	scales	elbow
3. reptile	snakes	chickens	alligators

Check the Words You Know

__ armor
__ fierce
__ harshest
__ lizards
__ prey
__ reptiles
__ roam

Directions: Choose the word from the box that best completes each sentence. Write the word on the matching numbered line to the right.

My friend Carrie told me a story about some **4.** _____ and scary dragons. She said that the climate where they live is one of the **5.** _____ in the world. The dragons have hard scales, like **6.** _____, to protect them. They **7.** _____ the land in search of animals to eat. The dragons are strong and swift, so they almost always catch their **8.** _____.

"I bet they are not even dragons. I bet they are only **9.** _____," I said.

"Well, maybe not," said Carrie. "But some **10.** _____ are lizards that are so large that they look like dragons."

4. ____________________

5. ____________________

6. ____________________

7. ____________________

8. ____________________

9. ____________________

10. ____________________

Write a Science Log

Imagine you are a scientist who studies reptiles. Write an entry in your log describing one of the reptiles you are studying. What does it look like? How does it act? What foods does it eat? Use as many vocabulary words as you can in your logs.

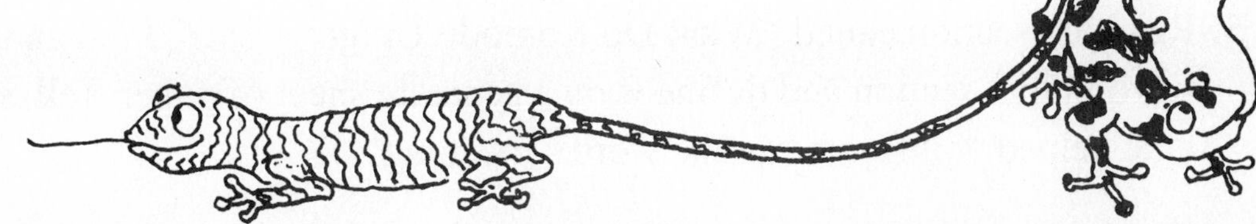

Notes for Home: Your child identified and used new words from *Komodo Dragons*. ***Home Activity:*** Talk with your child about different types of reptiles, such as snakes, lizards, turtles, or alligators. Create a picture encyclopedia. Write captions for each picture.

Name ______________________________

Context Clues

- When you are reading and see an unfamiliar word, use **context clues,** or words around the unfamiliar word, to figure out its meaning.
- **Context clues** include definitions, explanations, and synonyms (words that have the same or nearly the same meaning as other words).

Directions: Reread the part of *Komodo Dragons* that talks about where Komodo dragons live. Then answer the questions below. Look for context clues as you read.

Komodo dragons are a type of lizard called a *monitor.* They come from the Komodo Island area of Indonesia, near the northwest shore of Australia. It is one of the harshest and hottest places in the world. Often, the temperature is over 100° F. Sometimes it even gets as hot as 110° F.

On the hottest days, dragons escape the heat by getting out of the sun. They rest in underground burrows. But in the morning, when they first wake up, they lie in the sun to warm up. They do that on cooler days, too. That is because, like all lizards, they are **reptiles.** Reptiles are **cold-blooded** animals. They need outside heat (like sunlight) to warm them up.

1. What is a *monitor?* ______________________________

2. What sentence in the passage contains a clue to the meaning of *monitor?*

____

3. What does *cold-blooded* mean?

____

4. What sentence in the passage contains a clue to the meaning of *cold-blooded?*

____

____

5. Read the section called "What Do Komodo Dragons Eat?" Find an unfamiliar word in that section and define it on a separate sheet of paper. Tell what context clue helped you figure out the word's meaning.

Notes for Home: Your child practiced using context clues in a story. ***Home Activity:*** Think of a difficult word, and tell your child a sentence that makes its meaning clear ("Today I saw a bird called a *flamingo.*"). Ask your child to tell you what the word means.

Selection Test

Directions: Choose the best answer to each item. Mark the letter for the answer you have chosen.

Part 1: Vocabulary

Find the answer choice that means about the same as the underlined word in each sentence.

1. Scott wrote a report on <u>reptiles</u>.
- A. plants found in the desert
- B. mammals of South America
- C. types of building materials
- D. cold-blooded animals

2. The lion followed its <u>prey</u>.
- F. an animal hunted for food
- G. an animal's parents
- H. the way an animal behaves
- J. a smell left behind by an animal

3. Jamal caught two <u>lizards</u>.
- A. common illnesses
- B. hard balls used in a game
- C. kinds of reptiles with four legs
- D. insects with wings

4. Talia's cat likes to <u>roam</u>.
- F. wander
- G. hunt
- H. sleep
- J. hide

5. Tigers are <u>fierce</u> hunters.
- A. patient
- B. savage; wild
- C. restless
- D. skillful; clever

6. This has been the <u>harshest</u> winter ever.
- F. warmest
- G. mildest; most pleasant
- H. longest
- J. roughest; most difficult

7. That animal's skin is like <u>armor</u>.
- A. a thick hairy coat
- B. a band worn around the waist
- C. a covering worn to protect the body
- D. a kind of saddle

Part 2: Comprehension

Use what you know about the selection to answer each item.

8. Komodo dragons are—
- F. make-believe animals.
- G. alligators.
- H. birds.
- J. lizards.

9. Where do Komodo dragons live?
- A. Australia
- B. India
- C. Indonesia
- D. Africa

GO ON

10. Komodo dragons swish their tails back and forth to—
- F. show they like something.
- G. smell the air around them.
- H. hold on to their prey.
- J. help them balance.

11. How is the female Komodo dragon different from the male?
- A. She is usually smaller.
- B. She is not as strong.
- C. She digs burrows.
- D. She is active during the day.

12. What word is being defined in this sentence? "That's why the tongue is forked, or shaped like a Y."
- F. shaped
- G. forked
- H. tongue
- J. why

13. Because Komodo dragons are cold-blooded, they—
- A. prefer to eat warm food.
- B. must escape the heat by getting out of the sun.
- C. need outside heat to warm them up.
- D. can easily live in very cold places.

14. You can tell that Komodo dragons are—
- F. well suited to their surroundings.
- G. very particular about what they eat.
- H. not very intelligent animals.
- J. lazy because they sleep all day.

15. Which sentence states an opinion?
- A. Dragon eggs have a soft, smooth shell.
- B. Hatching takes about eight months.
- C. Komodo dragons live on only a few islands.
- D. Komodo dragons are very interesting creatures.

STOP

Name ________________________________

Context Clues

- When you are reading and you see an unfamiliar word, use **context clues,** or words around the unfamiliar word, to figure out its meaning.
- **Context clues** include definitions, explanations, and synonyms (words with the same or nearly the same meaning as other words).

Directions: Read the article below.

Do you know what a lemming is? It is a kind of small rodent that lives in the Arctic—the region around the North Pole.

Lemmings eat grass and plants. Lemmings produce many offspring—having up to 10 babies at a time and producing up to 30 in a year. When there are too many lemmings, reindeer, caribou (large animals that look like reindeer), and other plant-eaters begin to go hungry. However, when there are lots of lemmings, predators, or hunting animals, have plenty. The hunting animals eat the lemmings—and the lemming population goes down. When there are fewer lemmings, hunting animals have less to eat and have fewer babies—so the lemming population goes back up.

The ups and downs of the lemming population is called a *cycle.* A cycle is a process that repeats itself over and over again.

Directions: Complete the table. Find the unfamiliar words in the article. Figure out what they mean, using clues from the article. Write the missing meanings or words.

Unfamiliar Words	What It Means
lemming	**1.**
Arctic	**2.**
caribou	**3.**
predators	hunting animals
offspring	**4.**
5.	process that repeats itself

Notes for Home: Your child used context clues in a story to figure out the meanings of unfamiliar words. ***Home Activity:*** Find a difficult word on a label, a videotape box, or in a favorite book. Help your child use context clues to figure out what the word means.

Name ________________________________

REVIEW

Main Idea and Supporting Details

Directions: Read the passage. Then read each question about the passage. Choose the best answer to each question. Mark the letter for that answer.

Animals of the Arctic

Animals that live in the Arctic have found many ways to cope with the cold.

Polar bears have two main guards against the cold: extra fur and a layer of fat. These things help keep bears warm in below-freezing temperatures.

Some animals have other ways of handling the cold. Hares and reindeer can run quickly across the snow. That's because their wide "snowshoe" feet don't break through the snow's crust.

Hares in the Arctic also have very small ears. That's because body heat escapes through the ears, cooling the body down. Smaller ears allow less heat to escape.

Some animals, such as whales, birds, and caribou, handle the cold by heading south. They live in the Arctic in the summer, when temperatures are higher.

1. A key word to the main idea in the second paragraph is—

A. fat.
B. fur.
C. guards.
D. layer.

2. A detail in the third paragraph is—

F. whales head south.
G. snowshoe feet don't break through the crust.
H. hares and reindeer.
J. hares have small ears.

3. A key word to the main idea of the third paragraph is—

A. hares.
B. reindeer.
C. run.
D. break.

4. A key word to the main idea in the last paragraph is—

F. south.
G. whales.
H. birds.
J. caribou.

5. The main idea of the whole passage is that Arctic animals—

A. get cold.
B. leave during the winter.
C. have small ears.
D. find ways to cope with cold.

Notes for Home: Your child practiced identifying the main idea and its supporting details in a story. ***Home Activity:*** Ask your child to name an important family rule (main idea), such as washing hands before dinner. Have him or her give examples of why the rule is important.

Name ______________________________

Writing Across Texts

Directions: Consider what you learned about the lizards from reading *Komodo Dragons* and "Two Uncommon Lizards." What are some of the characteristics of each lizard? Add five characteristics to each column in the table.

Facts About the Komodo Dragon
It is ten feet long.
1.
2.
3.
4.
5.

Facts About the Horned Lizard
It is 3–5 inches long.
6.
7.
8.
9.
10.

Write a Compare/Contrast Paragraph

Look at the characteristics of each lizard and decide how they are alike and different. On a separate sheet of paper, write a paragraph comparing and contrasting the three kinds of lizards. Support your paragraph with facts from the boxes.

Facts About the Glass Lizard
It is over three feet long.
11.
12.
13.
14.
15.

Notes for Home: Your child compared and contrasted information about lizards. ***Home Activity:*** Read a story or article with your child and discuss how characters, events, and place descriptions are the same and different.

Name ______________________________

REVIEW

Grammar: Irregular Plural Nouns

Directions: Read each singular noun. Then circle the correct plural form for each one.

Singular	Plural
1. deer	deer / deers
2. wolf	wolfs / wolves
3. foot	feet / foots
4. tooth	tooths / teeth
5. woman	women / womans
6. ox	oxes / oxen
7. mouse	mices / mice
8. goose	geese / gooses
9. child	childrens / children
10. man	mans / men

Directions: Use the plural form of the noun in ( ) to complete each sentence. Write the plural noun on the line to the left.

__________________ **11.** The path through the woods was covered with _____. (leaf)

__________________ **12.** One hiker put her _____ down on something hard. (foot)

__________________ **13.** Bending down to look, she picked up some large _____. (tooth)

__________________ **14.** Two other _____ suggested an explanation. (woman)

__________________ **15.** They had heard _____ howling in the night. (wolf)

Notes for Home: Your child chose and wrote nouns that change form in the plural, such as *children.* ***Home Activity:*** Encourage your child to make up a short story with the irregular plural nouns that she or he circled and wrote above.

Grammar: Possessive Nouns

A noun that shows who owns, or possesses, something is a **possessive noun.**

- Add an **apostrophe (')** and **-s** to a singular noun to make it a possessive noun.
  the **bear**'s claws   the **fish**'s eggs
- Add just an **apostrophe (')** to a plural noun that ends in **-s** to make it a possessive noun.
  the two **girl**s' mother   these **familie**s' homes
- Add an **apostrophe (')** and **-s** to a plural noun that does not end in **-s** to make it a possessive noun.
  the **mice**'s nest   the **men**'s caps

Directions: Circle the possessive noun in ( ) to complete each sentence.

1. The (scientist's/scientists) work was hard, but she would not stop.
2. The (county's/counties) new road would go through the middle of the forest.
3. She had to find the four (bears/bears') den before the road was built.
4. Then she noticed a clue in a (tree's/trees') huge trunk.
5. She had discovered the (den's/dens') location!

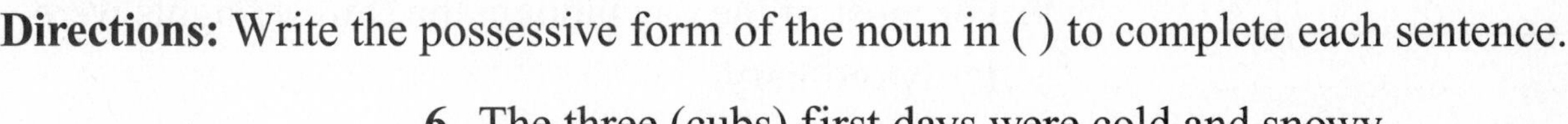

Directions: Write the possessive form of the noun in ( ) to complete each sentence.

______________ 6. The three (cubs) first days were cold and snowy.

______________ 7. The (bears) mother was sleepy, but she took good care of her babies.

______________ 8. In the spring, the (sun) rays made the cubs feel warm and frisky.

______________ 9. Once they heard bees humming and found the (bees) hive.

______________ 10. The (honey) flavor was delicious!

Notes for Home: Your child formed possessive nouns to show ownership, such as *the tree's leaves. **Home Activity:*** Ask your child to describe some favorite possessions. Then help your child make labels that use the possessive form, such as *Rosa's hat*.

Extra Practice

Grammar: Possessive Nouns

Directions: Circle the possessive noun in ( ) to complete each sentence.

1. Many (visitors/visitors') love of animals grows at Yosemite National Park.

2. A (park's/parks) wildlife includes bears, badgers, otters, and moose.

3. A (badgers/badger's) way of doing things is stubborn and fearless.

4. An (otters'/otter's) playfulness is wonderful to watch!

5. Don't you admire the (moose/moose's) huge antlers?

Directions: Write the possessive form of the noun in ( ) to complete each sentence. Then, circle **S** if the possessive noun is singular. Circle **P** if the possessive noun is plural.

S P
______________________ **6.** The two (hikers) trip to the forest had seemed dull.

S P
______________________ **7.** True, they had found three (birds) nests.

S P
______________________ **8.** Malcolm had even discovered some (rabbits) tracks.

S P
______________________ **9.** For most of the day though, the (forest) sights were fairly ordinary.

S P
______________________ **10.** Then Keisha saw a (grizzly) paw prints in the mud by a creek!

Write a Fantasy

Write a fantasy story about an animal family with human qualities. Use at least five possessive nouns in order to tell about the family members.

Notes for Home: Your child identified and wrote possessive nouns—nouns that show ownership, such as *the bear's claws.* ***Home Activity:*** Invite your child to make a list of favorite things or qualities that belong to friends and family *(my grandparents' house, Aunt Joyce's smile).*

Name ____

Grammar: Possessive Nouns

RETEACHING

Study the chart. Then complete the rules for making the possessive forms of singular and plural nouns.

Singular Noun	**Singular Possessive Noun**
parent / lady	parent's / lady's
man / deer	man's / deer's
Plural Noun	**Plural Possessive Noun**
parents / ladies	parents' / ladies'
men / deer	men's / deer's

1. If the noun is singular, add _______ .
2. If the plural noun ends in **-s**, add _______ .
3. If the plural noun does not end in **-s**, add _______ .

Singular and plural nouns can show ownership. To make the possessive form of a singular noun, add an **apostrophe (')** and **-s.** To make the possessive form of a plural noun that ends in **-s,** add an **apostrophe (').** To make the possessive form of a plural noun that does not end in **-s,** add an **apostrophe (')** and **-s.**

Directions: Add an apostrophe or an apostrophe and **-s** to each noun.

1. (plural) sheep ______ wool
2. mouse ______ holes
3. cat ______ meows
4. foxes ______ dens
5. trucks ______ wheels
6. driver ______ maps
7. dog ______ barks
8. (plural) elk ______ horns
9. (plural) deer ______ coats
10. birds ______ nests
11. roads ______ signs
12. whistles ______ blasts

Notes for Home: Your child identified and wrote singular and plural possessive nouns. ***Home Activity:*** Have your child write a story about animals and their qualities. (For example: *Once there was a giraffe with a long neck.*) Remind your child to use possessive nouns.

Name ____________________

Grammar: Possessive Nouns

Directions: Use the possessive form of each noun to fill in the blanks.

children trees birds gardener flowers park goose

1. The ________________ gates were opened for the children.
2. The children liked the ________________ bright colors.
3. The ________________ leaves were beginning to turn.
4. Fall flowers were the ________________ favorites.
5. The ________________ nests were filled with eggs.
6. The ________________ trip to the park was fun.
7. The ________________ honking made them laugh.

Directions: Underline the correct form of the noun in parentheses.

8. Our (gardens/garden's) flowers are beautiful.
9. Few flowers can survive most (deserts/deserts') hot temperatures.
10. People admire open (prairies/prairies') bright flowers.
11. A (ponds/pond's) flowers have roots in the mud bottom.
12. The (flowers/flowers') heads are lifted to the sun.
13. (Sunflowers/Sunflowers') grow very tall.
14. (Gardeners/Gardeners') flowers are carefully tended.

Write a Song

On a separate sheet of paper, write a song about a garden. Write possessive forms of nouns in your song.

Notes for Home: Your child wrote and identified singular and plural possessive nouns in sentences. ***Home Activity:*** Have your child use his or her song about a garden to explain to you how to make the possessive forms of singular and plural nouns.

Phonics: *r*-Controlled Vowels

Directions: Many vowels have a different sound when they are followed by the letter **r.** Listen to the difference in **cat** and **cart.** Read each sentence below. Each sentence has a word with a vowel followed by the letter **r.** Write the word on the line. Underline the **r-controlled vowel** you hear and see in the word.

______________ **1.** Many animals in the wild have sharp claws.

______________ **2.** An animal's fur protects it from the cold.

______________ **3.** Many wild animals today have to fight against human progress to survive.

______________ **4.** It is sometimes not wise to live too near wild animals.

______________ **5.** The birth of a wild animal in captivity is often a great accomplishment.

______________ **6.** One should be cautious around wild animals who seem curious about people.

______________ **7.** Some animals come out at night, protected by the dark.

______________ **8.** The deer come out at night to eat the leaves off low-hanging trees.

______________ **9.** I could sit and watch these animals for hours.

Directions: Read the words in the box. Some words have the same vowel sound as **for.** Other words have the same vowel sound as **word.** Write each word in the correct column.

north
armor
shore
born
predator
monitor

for	word
10. ______________	**13.** ______________
11. ______________	**14.** ______________
12. ______________	**15.** ______________

Notes for Home: Your child listened for words where the letter *r* changes the sound of the vowel that precedes it, such as *start, morning, shirt,* and *curious.* ***Home Activity:*** Read a book about animals with your child. Have your child look for words with these sounds.

Name ____________________

Pretest

Spelling: Vowels with *r*

Pretest Directions: Fold back the page along the dotted line. On the blanks, write the spelling words as they are dictated. When you have finished the test, unfold the page and check your words.

1. ____________________
2. ____________________
3. ____________________
4. ____________________
5. ____________________
6. ____________________
7. ____________________
8. ____________________
9. ____________________
10. ____________________
11. ____________________
12. ____________________
13. ____________________
14. ____________________
15. ____________________
16. ____________________
17. ____________________
18. ____________________
19. ____________________
20. ____________________

1. A **storm** is brewing.
2. It is chilly this **morning**.
3. The **forest** is lush.
4. Oranges grow in **Florida.**
5. **Form** the clay into a bird.
6. **Pour** milk on the cereal.
7. We saw **fourteen** lizards.
8. The judge is in **court**.
9. I am **fourth** in line.
10. This **course** is rocky.
11. **Serve** them lemonade.
12. She made it **herself.**
13. Are you **certain** he's here?
14. A pinched **nerve** hurts.
15. What a **perfect** day!
16. The dishes are **dirty**.
17. This is my **first** pet.
18. Invite your **girlfriend** along too!
19. Is the baby **thirsty**?
20. Her **skirt** is bright red.

Notes for Home: Your child took a pretest on words that have vowel sounds with the letter *r*. ***Home Activity:*** Help your child learn misspelled words before the final test. See if there are any similar errors and discuss a memory trick that could help.

Name ______________________________

Spelling: Vowels with *r*

Word List

storm	pour	serve	dirty
morning	fourteen	herself	first
forest	court	certain	girlfriend
Florida	fourth	nerve	thirsty
form	course	perfect	skirt

Directions: Write the words that have the same vowel sound as **for.** Sort the words according to the way the vowel sound is spelled.

Spelled our

1. ______________
2. ______________
3. ______________
4. ______________
5. ______________

Spelled or

6. ______________
7. ______________
8. ______________
9. ______________
10. ______________

Directions: Write the word from the box that belongs in each group.

11. skin, bone, ______________
12. offer, provide, ______________
13. positive, definite, ______________
14. blouse, dress, ______________
15. filthy, sloppy, ______________
16. hungry, dry, ______________
17. myself, himself, ______________
18. third, second, ______________
19. ideal, excellent, ______________
20. boyfriend, buddy, ______________

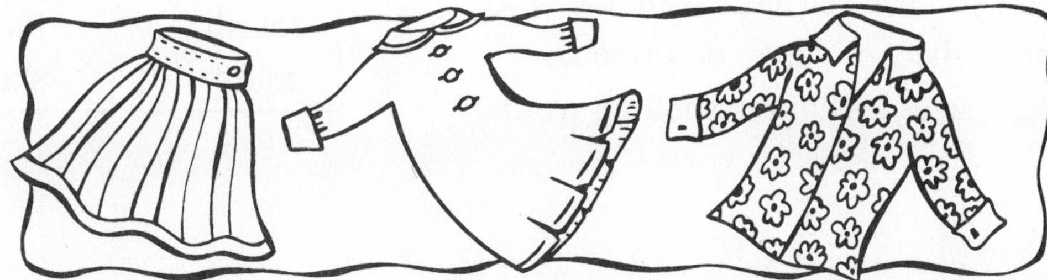

Notes for Home: Your child spelled words where the letter *r* changes the way the vowel sounds *(st<u>or</u>m, f<u>our</u>th, s<u>er</u>ve, f<u>ir</u>st)*. ***Home Activity:*** Help your child think of other words with these vowel sounds and spellings.

Name ___________________________________

Spelling: Vowels with *r*

Directions: Proofread this entry from an explorer's log. Find five spelling mistakes. Use the proofreading marks to correct each mistake.

≡	Make a capital.
/	Make a small letter.
∧	Add something.
ꝭ	Take out something.
⊙	Add a period.
¶	Begin a new paragraph.

Everglades, Flourida

Today I saw my first baby alligator! Since this is my forth day here, I had almost given up hope. I was not cirtain whether I would ever see the wildlife I was looking for. And of corse, yesterday, we had a huge storm, and I couldn't see anything then.

Then I saw a dark fourm coming out of the swamp. Was it an alligator? Yes! Hurray!

Spelling Tip

The vowel sounds in **fo<u>ur</u>th** and **st<u>or</u>m** sound the same, but are spelled differently. The same is true of **s<u>er</u>ve** and **d<u>ir</u>ty.** Check the log entry to see if the vowels with **r** have been spelled correctly.

Word List

storm	serve
morning	herself
forest	certain
Florida	nerve
form	perfect
pour	dirty
fourteen	first
court	girlfriend
fourth	thirsty
course	skirt

Write a Log Entry

Imagine that you are exploring a part of the world where you can see animals in the wild. On a separate sheet of paper, describe an experience. Use at least three spelling words.

Notes for Home: Your child spelled words where the letter *r* changes the way the vowel sounds *(storm, fourth, serve, first)*. ***Home Activity:*** Help your child divide the words on the list into four columns: words with *or, our, ir,* and *er.* Then take turns making up sentences with each word.

Name ______________________________

Spelling: Vowels with *r*

REVIEW

Word List				
storm	form	fourth	certain	first
morning	pour	course	nerve	girlfriend
forest	fourteen	serve	perfect	thirsty
Florida	court	herself	dirty	skirt

Directions: Choose the word from the box that rhymes with each word. Write the word on the line. Use a word only once.

1. thirst ______________
2. north ______________
3. dirt ______________
4. short ______________
5. more ______________
6. horse ______________
7. dorm ______________
8. norm ______________
9. verve ______________
10. swerve ______________

Directions: Choose the word from the box that best replaces the underlined word or words. Write the word on the line.

______________ **11.** One day my female friend, Malika, and I went out.

______________ **12.** It was still the early part of the day.

______________ **13.** We were on vacation in a cabin in the woods.

______________ **14.** The cabin was in a southern state.

______________ **15.** We were going to stay one more than thirteen days.

______________ **16.** Malika was sure that we would see interesting wildlife.

______________ **17.** "Everything is so dusty and filthy!" I complained.

______________ **18.** "No, it's faultless," said Malika.

______________ **19.** I was in need of a drink, so we went to the store.

______________ **20.** Malika bought some gum for her own use.

Notes for Home: Your child spelled words where the letter *r* changes the way the vowel sounds *(storm, fourth, serve, first)*. ***Home Activity:*** Have your child say one of the words on the list. Together, think of other words that rhyme. Challenge your child to spell some of the rhyming words.

Name ______________________________

Encyclopedia

An **encyclopedia** gives general information about many different subjects. Encyclopedias are organized in a set of **volumes,** or books, usually in alphabetical order. An **entry** is an encyclopedia article. Entries are listed in alphabetical order. An **entry word** is the word or phrase that begins each entry and tells its subject. To find information in an encyclopedia, use a **key word** that identifies the information you are trying to find.

Directions: Use this encyclopedia entry about Komodo Island to answer the questions that follow.

KOMODO ISLAND has only one village and fewer than 500 people. The Komodo Island National Park takes up most of the space on Komodo Island.

Many of the mountains on the island were formed by volcanoes. These volcanic mountains are usually brown and lifeless. Every year, however, during monsoon season, these mountains appear green. This color comes from small tropical plants that grow on the hill slopes.

Komodo Island is one of the few places left on Earth where the Komodo dragon can be found. About 1,000 Komodo dragons live there. Komodo dragons are giant monitor lizards that run wild on the island. They can grow to up to 10 feet long, weigh up to 300 pounds, and live for 100 years.

1. What key word would someone have looked up to find this article?

____

2. Would the entry above appear before or after an entry on Koala bears? Explain.

____

____

____

3. What key word would you use to find more information about monsoons?

____

4. What key word would you use to find information about volcanoes?

____

5. Suppose you have a volume of an encyclopedia marked "M." Name two entry words you might find in this volume.

____

Name ____________________

Directions: Read the encyclopedia entry about reptiles. Use the entry to answer the questions that follow.

REPTILES are a group of animals that include snakes, lizards, turtles, crocodiles, the tuatara, and many extinct creatures. The bodies of many snakes are covered with scales. Reptiles can be found in temperate and tropical climates around the world. They are cold-blooded animals, so most of them cannot live in polar regions.

Reptile behavior. Most reptiles lay eggs, but many lizards and snakes give birth to live offspring. When the winter is cold, some reptiles *estivate*—this means they become inactive. Most reptiles rely on the sun's heat to stay warm.

6. Would you expect to find an article about tigers before or after the reptiles entry in the encyclopedia? Explain.

____

____

7. What key word would you use to find out more about snakes?

____

8. What section of the entry contains information about how reptiles act?

____

9. What letter would likely be on the volume of the encyclopedia that contains this entry on reptiles?

____

10. If you wanted to get information about the reptile exhibit at your local zoo, would an encyclopedia be a good reference source? Explain.

____

____

Notes for Home: Your child read encyclopedia entries and answered questions about them. ***Home Activity:*** Brainstorm questions about related topics. Ask your child to tell the key words he or she would use to look up more information in an encyclopedia.

Name______________________________

Description Web

Directions: Write your topic (the person you will describe) on the line in the Topic circle. Then organize details about this person by writing them in the Details circles.

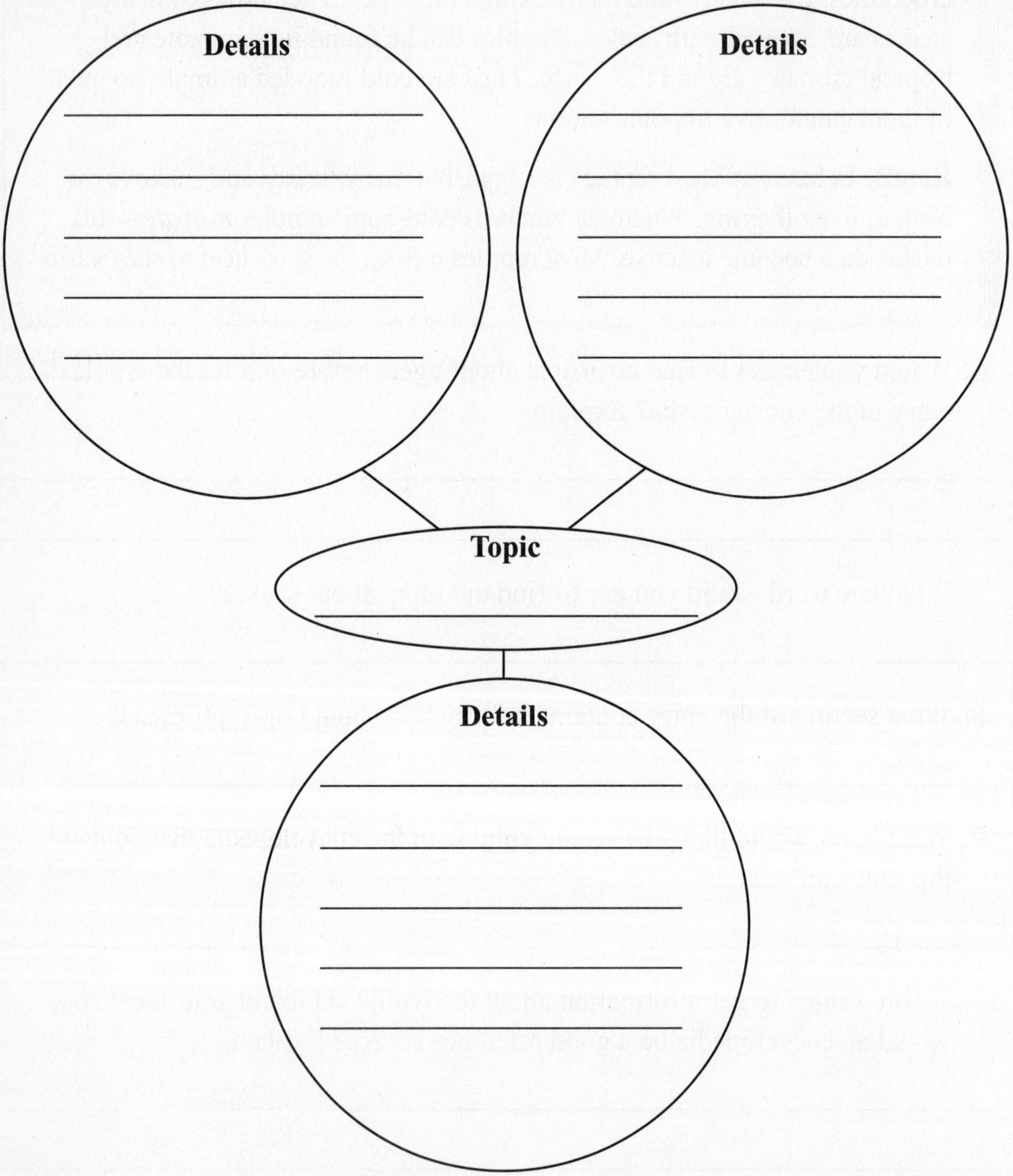

Details

____

____

____

____

____

Details

____

____

____

____

____

Topic

____

Details

____

____

____

____

____

Notes for Home: Your child recently organized information for a description. ***Home Activity:*** Have your child describe a quality of a family member in time order. *Grandma's hair was blond when she was born. It was brown when she got married. Now it's white.*

Name____

Elaboration

Sense Words

- One way to elaborate is by adding **sense words** that help readers picture things clearly.
- You can provide vivid images by telling how things look, sound, feel, taste, and smell.

Directions: Choose words from the box to make each sentence below more interesting. Write your new sentence on the line.

fragrant	warm	tasty	hurriedly	red	rickety
smoky	cluttered	bright	sparkling	wooden	excitedly
burned	frequently	noisy	messy	black	friendly

1. Our kitchen is where we get together.

____

2. We all sit around a table and talk.

____

3. We take turns cooking meals.

____

4. Smells fill other rooms.

____

5. Friends come for dinner.

____

6. We often fill all eight chairs.

____

Notes for Home: Your child recently expanded sentences by adding sense words. ***Home Activity:*** Ask your child to describe the looks, smells, and tastes of lunch today. For example: *The warm, noisy cafeteria smelled like pizza.*

Name____

Self-Evaluation Guide

Descriptive Paragraph

Directions: Think about the final draft of your description. Then answer each question below.

	Yes	No	Not sure
1. Does my description tell about a person that is special to me?			
2. Did I use descriptive words and images to give readers a good picture of this person?			
3. Did I keep my audience and purpose in mind?			
4. Did I present my ideas in an organized way?			
5. Did I proofread and edit carefully to avoid errors?			

6. What part of your description do you think gives the best picture of your special person?

____

____

7. Write one thing that you could change to make this description even better (a word, phrase, or sentence).

____

____

____

Notes for Home: Your child recently wrote a description. ***Home Activity:*** Encourage your child to tell you one way he or she tried to make this description vivid.

Family Times

Name____

Summary

John Henry Declared Winner!

Folks knew John Henry was special from the day he was born. He jumped right out of his mama's arms and grew so fast that his head and shoulders poked through the porch roof. He went on to win a race with Ferret-Faced Freddy, even though Freddy was riding a horse and John Henry was running on his own two legs. Later, he broke up a boulder that even dynamite couldn't touch.

Activity

Act Out the Story. Have your child act out the rest of the story for you, showing how John Henry won a contest with the steam drill.

Reading Skills

Making Judgments

Making judgments means thinking about and deciding how to react toward people, situations, and ideas in stories you read.

Use what you have read and your own experiences as you make judgments. Ask yourself if the author is trying to influence you and whether he succeeds.

For example, you might decide whether you'd like to have a friend like John Henry. Think about how the author wants you to feel about John Henry. He tells that John Henry helped his father with the porch and that he made Ferret-Faced Freddy be nice for a whole year.

Good Guys	Bad Guys

Activity

Make a Good Guy/Bad Guy List. Make a list of story or TV characters that are good guys and bad guys. Describe what makes one character "good" and another character "bad." Draw pictures to illustrate your list.

Family Times

Tested Vocabulary

Words to Know

Knowing the meaning of these words is important to reading *John Henry*. Practice using these words to learn their meanings.

boulder a large rock worn by water and weather

glimpse a short look

hollered cried or shouted loudly

horizon line where Earth and sky seem to meet

rhythm any movement with regular repetition of beat, accent, and so on

shivered shook with cold, fear, or excitement

tunnel underground passage

Grammar

Verbs

Words that show actions are called **action verbs.** Many verbs show action that you can see: **build, blast.** Some show actions that you cannot see: **thinks, want. Linking verbs** tell what the subject is or is like: **am, feel, seem.**

Action Verbs	Linking Verbs
pours	is
swings	was
______	______
______	______

Activity

Tell Family Stories. Add verbs to the table above. Then tell two sentences each about family members, using both action and linking verbs. **Uncle Mario pours cement. He is a construction worker.**

Tested Spelling Words

______	______	______	______
______	______	______	______
______	______	______	______
______	______	______	______
______	______	______	______

Name ______________________

Making Judgments

- **Making judgments** means thinking about and deciding how to react toward people, situations, and ideas in stories and articles that you read.
- Use what you know and your experience as you make judgments.

Directions: Reread "Welcome to McBroom's Farm." Then complete the table. For each story event, give evidence from what you know and from your own experience that makes a judgment about how realistic each event is.

Story Event	My Knowledge and Experience
Seeds burst in the ground.	**1.**
Crops shoot right up before your eyes.	**2.**
A nickel grew to a quarter.	**3.**
The hat would take a day or two to reach the ground.	**4.**
The stranger painted the no-barn in less than a second.	**5.**

Notes for Home: Your child read a story and used his or her knowledge, story details, and life experience to make judgments. ***Home Activity:*** Read a tall tale with your child. Ask him or her to find places where the author has exaggerated in order to make a funny story.

Name ___________________________________

Vocabulary

Directions: Read the story about Paul Bunyan. Choose the word from the box that best completes each sentence. You will use some words more than once. Write the word on the matching numbered line below.

Check the Words You Know

- __ boulder
- __ glimpse
- __ hollered
- __ horizon
- __ rhythm
- __ shivered
- __ tunnel

A gusty wind blew into the **1.** _____ that ran through the mountain. Paul Bunyan **2.** _____ with cold. Moving outside, he caught a **3.** _____ of a log cabin with smoke coming out its chimney. The cabin was far off on the **4.** _____. Quickly, Paul Bunyan stepped over a huge **5.** _____ and was soon on his way to getting warm.

Paul walked on with a steady, quick **6.** _____. He was getting warmer, so he no longer **7.** _____. When he **8.** _____ from a hilltop, he heard his echo. He remembered how dark it had been inside that **9.** _____. But the sun on the **10.** _____ made everything look brighter.

1. ____________________	**6.** ____________________
2. ____________________	**7.** ____________________
3. ____________________	**8.** ____________________
4. ____________________	**9.** ____________________
5. ____________________	**10.** ____________________

Write a Tall Tale

On a separate sheet of paper, create a tall tale about an amazing hero—real or imaginary. Tell how your hero gets out of a difficult situation. Use as many of the vocabulary words as you can.

Notes for Home: Your child identified and used words from *John Henry*. ***Home Activity:*** With your child, make up your own tale about an amazing person who can do incredible things. Include the vocabulary words whenever you can.

Name ________________________________

Making Judgments

- **Making judgments** means thinking about and deciding how to react to people, situations, and ideas in a story.

Directions: Reread this description of John Henry smashing the boulder. Then answer the questions below. Support each answer with story details.

"Don't see how you can do what dynamite couldn't," said the boss of the crew.

John Henry chuckled. "Just watch me." He swung one of his hammers round and round his head. It made such a wind that leaves blew off the trees and birds fell out of the sky.

RINGGGGGG!

The hammer hit the boulder. That boulder shivered like you do on a cold winter morning when it looks like the school bus is never going to come.

RINGGGGGG!

The boulder shivered like the morning when freedom came to the slaves.

1. What do you think the crew boss thinks of John Henry?

____

____

2. How do you think John Henry feels about his own abilities?

____

3. What is one way you can tell that *John Henry* is a legend?

____

____

4. Do you think the comparison, "That boulder shivered like you do on a cold winter morning when it looks like the school bus is never going to come" is a good one?

____

5. On a separate sheet of paper, write a description of the kind of person you think John Henry is. Include details from the story.

Notes for Home: Your child used story details to make judgments about a story and its characters. ***Home Activity:*** Have your child choose a character from a book or a TV show and make judgments about the character's behavior, using details from the work.

Name ____________________________

Selection Test

Directions: Choose the best answer to each item. Mark the letter for the answer you have chosen.

Part 1: Vocabulary

Find the answer choice that means about the same as the underlined word in each sentence.

1. The young boy shivered.
- A. fell asleep
- B. shook
- C. fainted
- D. disappeared

2. Tanya got a glimpse of the car.
- F. bad smell
- G. honking noise
- H. short look
- J. long report

3. The men dug a tunnel.
- A. underground passage
- B. shallow ditch
- C. canal for water
- D. deep well

4. There was a boulder in the road.
- F. large rock
- G. bump
- H. red light
- J. yellow line

5. The captain searched the horizon.
- A. forward part of a ship
- B. deepest part of the ocean
- C. person who hides on a ship
- D. line where earth and sky seem to meet

6. That song has a nice rhythm.
- F. pleasing sound
- G. regular beat
- H. musical note
- J. piano part

7. Josie hollered at us.
- A. laughed
- B. threw things
- C. yelled
- D. blew bubbles

Part 2: Comprehension

Use what you know about the story to answer each item.

8. This story is mostly about—
- F. the meanest man in the state.
- G. unicorns living in the woods.
- H. people building a railroad.
- J. the adventures of John Henry.

GO ON

9. What happened when John Henry was born?
- A. The sun did not shine that day.
- B. Birds and animals came to see him.
- C. His parents threw him a birthday party.
- D. A rainbow shined in the sky.

10. As everyone admired the new baby, he suddenly began to—
- F. grow.
- G. cry.
- H. smile.
- J. blush.

11. How was John Henry different from other newborn babies?
- A. He was quite small for his age.
- B. He liked to sleep all day.
- C. He was fully grown in one day.
- D. He was born at night.

12. Ferret-Faced Freddy became Frederick the Friendly after John Henry—
- F. beat him in a race.
- G. gave him a soda.
- H. beat him in a fight.
- J. asked for his help.

13. John Henry was like a steam drill in that he—
- A. was taller than most men.
- B. produced smoke and steam when he hammered.
- C. could hammer faster and harder than ten men.
- D. wore a rainbow on his shoulders.

14. How did John Henry feel about his special strength?
- F. He was embarrassed by it.
- G. He was happy to have it.
- H. He was ashamed of it.
- J. He felt the need to work harder because of it.

15. The author of this story would most likely agree that John Henry—
- A. did not live his life to the fullest.
- B. was an angry man who always needed to prove his strength.
- C. was foolish for racing a steam drill and dying because of it.
- D. was a hero to the people who knew him.

STOP

Making Judgments

- **Making judgments** means thinking about and reacting to people, situations, and issues in a story or an article.

Directions: Read the story below.

Mr. Jackson took care of everything in the apartment house. But the first day he was on vacation, a pipe leaked in Mrs. Dahl's kitchen. Her one-year-old son, Carl, calmly tied one of his diapers around the pipe. It stopped leaking. The amazed Mrs. Dahl told the story to Mrs. Noah.

The second day Baby Dahl unstuck a window in Mrs. Noah's apartment with baby lotion. By evening he was a legend among the neighbors. They called him Super Duper Baby.

By the end of the week he had fixed the washing machine, patched the roof, and gotten the weeds to leave and promise never to return.

Mr. Jackson decided to retire. Super Duper Baby took care of everything from then on—except at nap time.

Directions: Complete the table by making judgments and using story details to support them.

Questions	Judgment
What do you think was Mrs. Dahl's opinion of her baby?	**1.**
Why do you think Mrs. Noah had Baby Dahl fix her window?	**2.**
What do you think the neighbors thought of Baby Dahl?	**3.**
Do you think Baby Dahl could do all those things?	**4.**
How do you think the author expects you to react to the story?	**5.**

Notes for Home: Your child used story details to make judgments about characters, actions, and the author's purpose. ***Home Activity:*** Tell a story about something that happened today. Exaggerate some details. Ask your child to make judgments about what could or couldn't be true.

Name ______________________________

Character

REVIEW

Directions: Read the story. Then read each question about the story. Choose the best answer to each question. Mark the letter for the answer you have chosen.

Paul Bunyan Travels the Country

Paul Bunyan swung his ax through the forest. "Timber!" he hollered to make sure people got out of the way safely. The forest was gone in minutes. The loggers who needed wood to build houses waved happily. They shouted good-by as he left for another forest.

At the next forest, farmers were clearing the land. At first, they trembled at the sight of Paul. Then they cheered as they saw how fast he could clear their farmland.

Paul moved from forest to forest until he got tired. "I need to find other people who can clear trees and haul logs," he thought. But he never did find anyone with his size and strength. To this day, Paul Bunyan is remembered across the country for what happened when he yelled "Timber!"

1. Why did Paul holler "Timber!" to the loggers?
- **A.** to tease them
- **B.** to entertain them
- **C.** to confuse them
- **D.** to warn them

2. How did the loggers feel when Paul cut the trees?
- **F.** angry
- **G.** disgusted
- **H.** grateful
- **J.** sad

3. When the farmers first saw Paul, how did they feel?
- **A.** frightened
- **B.** mean
- **C.** rude
- **D.** quiet

4. Paul wanted to find people to help him so he could—
- **F.** plant more trees.
- **G.** be remembered.
- **H.** rest his body.
- **J.** build houses.

5. In the end, how did people treat Paul?
- **A.** They ignored him.
- **B.** They mocked him.
- **C.** They forgot him.
- **D.** They remembered him.

Notes for Home: Your child identified a character's traits through his words and actions. ***Home Activity:*** With your child, read newspaper articles about people. Take turns telling what you think the people in the story are like, based on what they did or said.

Name ______________________________________

Writing Across Texts

Directions: Think about the two versions of the legend of John Henry that you read. In many ways they are alike, but there are ways in which they differ. Fill in the boxes below with information from each version.

John Henry The Story	John Henry The Poem
John Henry's size when he was a baby	
1.	2.
How fast he grew	
3.	4.
What his parents thought he would do	
5.	6.
How John Henry died	
7.	8.
Where John Henry was buried	
9.	10.

Write a Comparison/Contrast

On a separate sheet of paper, write a paragraph in which you say what is the same and what is different about the two versions of the legend of John Henry. Use the information from the boxes above.

Notes for Home: Your child wrote a paragraph comparing two versions of the legend of John Henry. ***Home Activity:*** Read with your child two stories about the same person or topic. Discuss how each is alike and different.

Grammar: Predicates

REVIEW

Directions: Underline the complete predicate in each sentence. Then circle each simple predicate. (There may be more than one in a sentence.)

1. Paul Bunyan found Babe the Blue Ox during the winter of the blue snow.

2. Babe fell into a frozen river.

3. The icy water caused the ox's blue color.

4. Paul Bunyan rescued Babe and carried him back to the logging camp.

5. This famous logger built Babe a big barn.

Directions: Think about the life of a logger and his pet ox. Add a word or words to each subject below to form a sentence. Write the complete sentence on the line.

6. The big logger _____.

____

7. The strong ox _____.

____

8. The logger and his ox _____.

____

9. The other loggers _____.

____

10. The cook at the logging camp _____.

____

Notes for Home: Your child identified simple and complete predicates. ***Home Activity:*** Play a simple alphabet game with your child. Take turns thinking of a simple predicate, or verb, that starts with each letter of the alphabet.

Grammar: Verbs

Action verbs are words that show what action someone or something does.

The crew built the railroad tracks. The train raced down the tracks.

Every sentence has a subject and a predicate. The main word in the subject is often a noun. The verb is the main word in the predicate.

The people | cheered at the sight of the train.
Subject | Predicate

Linking verbs link, or join, the subject to a word in the predicate. The word helps tell what the subject is or what the subject is like. *Am, is, are, was,* and *were* are often used as linking verbs.

The train was noisy. I was surprised at its size and speed.

Directions: Read the paragraph. Underline the verb in each sentence below.

1. The old train left the station. **2.** At first, it moved slowly. **3.** The engineer rang the bell. **4.** The wheels of the train rolled faster and faster. **5.** Smoke poured from the smokestack. **6.** The rumbling wheels sounded loud. **7.** The train's whistle was a warning. **8.** The train sped down the tracks. **9.** Then the old locomotive slowed its speed. **10.** It stopped at the station exactly on time.

Directions: Add a verb to complete each sentence. The verb should tell what Maria does or what Maria is like. Write the verb on the line to the left.

____________________ **11.** Maria _____ out of bed early.

____________________ **12.** She _____ quickly into the kitchen.

____________________ **13.** Next, Maria _____ a huge breakfast.

____________________ **14.** She _____ a skilled carpenter.

____________________ **15.** Today, she _____ a cradle for a baby.

Notes for Home: Your child wrote action verbs and linking verbs. ***Home Activity:*** Play an action words game with your child. Say, for example, *Mrs. West [pause] the school bus.* Ask your child to supply the missing verb *(drives).* Switch roles and play again.

Grammar: Verbs

Directions: Circle the verb in each sentence. Write **A** on the line if the verb is an action verb. Write **L** if it is a linking verb. Keep in mind that some action verbs such as *know* or *decide* show actions you cannot see.

________ **1.** The construction crew worked very hard that hot summer day.

________ **2.** Frederick wanted a cold drink of water and a rest.

________ **3.** Susannah is tired and hungry.

________ **4.** Finally, the crew finished the new road.

________ **5.** They are proud of their smooth, gray highway.

Directions: Choose a verb from the box to complete each sentence. Write the verb on the line to the left.

build	grew	felt	looks	was

________________ **6.** Didn't Lydia's family _____ their own mountain cabin?

________________ **7.** At first, they _____ nervous about doing the work themselves.

________________ **8.** After a while, they _____ more confident about their skills!

________________ **9.** Pale green paint _____ their choice for the outside walls.

________________ **10.** The finished cabin now _____ great!

Write a How-To Paragraph

On a separate sheet of paper, write a paragraph telling how to do a simple task, such as tying a small child's shoelaces. Tell the reader what to do: *First, untangle any knots in the shoelaces. Next,* . . . Use at least three verbs.

Notes for Home: Your child identified and wrote verbs—words like *build* that show action, or words like *is* that tell what the subject is or is like. ***Home Activity:*** Take turns describing a character and telling what he or she did or is like.

Name ___________________________________

RETEACHING

Grammar: Verbs

Read each sentence. Complete each one with a verb from the list.

am   is   are   tame   tames

1. She ____________ a clown.   **2.** They ____________ the lion.

A **linking verb** shows being. It tells what the subject is or was. The forms of the verb **be** are often used as linking verbs. An **action verb** is a word that shows what action someone or something does.

Directions: Read each underlined verb. Circle **action verb** or **linking verb** to describe it.

1. The parade <u>was</u> colorful.	action verb	linking verb
2. Jan <u>admires</u> the costumes.	action verb	linking verb
3. The horses <u>were</u> graceful.	action verb	linking verb
4. Tiny dogs <u>danced</u> happily.	action verb	linking verb
5. I <u>am</u> a tumbler.	action verb	linking verb
6. I <u>jump</u> high into the air.	action verb	linking verb

Directions: Circle each linking verb. Underline each action verb.

7. I like the circus.

8. P. T. Barnum was the most famous circus owner.

9. His circus delighted huge crowds everywhere.

10. Circuses were small long ago.

11. A modern circus often is big.

12. Circus people are skillful performers.

13. They invent new tricks all the time.

Notes for Home: Your child identified action and linking verbs in sentences. ***Home Activity:*** Have your child look at a favorite book. Have him or her make a list of all the verbs on one page and say whether they are action or linking verbs.

Name ______________________________

Grammar: Verbs

Directions: Write an action verb to replace the underlined linking verb in each sentence. The new verb may change the meaning of the sentence. If you need ideas, pick a verb from the box. Remember to write the form of the verb that fits the subject and tense of the sentence.

float	shine	dance	wave	walk	play	howl

1. The pencil <u>is</u> on the page.

   ____

2. The sun's rays <u>are</u> in the air.

   ____

3. A cloud <u>is</u> in the sky.

   ____

4. The wind <u>was</u> outside all night.

   ____

5. The waves <u>were</u> along the shore.

   ____

Directions: Imagine that one of the sentences above is the beginning of a story. Using action and linking verbs, write the next two or three sentences of the story.

____

____

____

Notes for Home: Your child changed sentences by adding interesting verbs. ***Home Activity:*** Say simple sentences to your child. *(I walked down the street. I went there.)* Have your child replace the verbs with more interesting verbs.

Name ______________________________

Word Study: Inflected Forms with -er and -est

Directions: When you add an ending to some words, you might need to drop an **e**, change **y** to **i,** or double the final consonant. Read each word below. Change the word by adding **-er** or **-est.** Write the new word on the line.

1. fast + -er = ______________________

2. white + -er = ______________________

3. pretty + -est = ______________________

4. mean + -er = ______________________

5. big + -er = ______________________

6. funny + -est = ______________________

7. straight + -est = ______________________

Directions: Read each sentence. Write the base word of each underlined word on the line.

______________ **8.** Martha was the <u>fastest</u> worker on the road crew.

______________ **9.** Even though Joe was <u>larger</u>, he couldn't beat her record.

______________ **10.** Bill worked the <u>longest</u> hours of all the crew.

______________ **11.** Tom was the <u>noisiest</u> of the bunch.

______________ **12.** He could yell "Let's move it!" <u>louder</u> than anyone else.

______________ **13.** Despite his huge size, Anthony was one of the <u>nicest</u> people in the group.

______________ **14.** I couldn't be <u>happier</u> than to be working with this crew.

______________ **15.** Taking this job was one of my <u>smarter</u> ideas.

Notes for Home: Your child added *-er* and *-est* to base words to create longer words and identified base words in words ending in *-er* and *-est*. ***Home Activity:*** List some describing words, such as *tall, small, smooth.* Take turns adding *-er* and *-est* to each word.

Name ______________________________

Spelling: Adding *-er* and *-est*

Pretest Directions: Fold back the page along the dotted line. On the blanks, write the spelling words as they are dictated. When you have finished the test, unfold the page and check your words.

1. ______________________________
2. ______________________________
3. ______________________________
4. ______________________________
5. ______________________________
6. ______________________________
7. ______________________________
8. ______________________________
9. ______________________________
10. ______________________________
11. ______________________________
12. ______________________________
13. ______________________________
14. ______________________________
15. ______________________________
16. ______________________________
17. ______________________________
18. ______________________________
19. ______________________________
20. ______________________________

1. My shovel is **smaller** than yours.
2. Your truck is **larger** than mine.
3. Tom is **happier** than Anne.
4. Today is **hotter** than yesterday.
5. My story is **sadder** than yours.
6. His hole is **deeper**.
7. Come **closer** to the window.
8. Which noise is **scarier**?
9. Whose joke is **funnier**?
10. That dog looks **fatter** today.
11. He has the **smallest** feet.
12. Her truck has the **largest** engine.
13. He's **happiest** when he's outside.
14. August is the **hottest** month.
15. Whose story is **saddest**?
16. Whose hole is **deepest**?
17. Which house is **closest** to town?
18. I know the **scariest** story of all.
19. That's the **funniest** joke ever!
20. I want the **fattest** apple.

Notes for Home: Your child took a pretest on adding *-er* and *-est* to words. ***Home Activity:*** Help your child learn misspelled words before the final test. Your child should look at the word, say it, spell it aloud, and then spell it with eyes shut.

Name ______________________________

Spelling: Adding *-er* and -est

Word List				
smaller	happier	sadder	closer	funnier
smallest	happiest	saddest	closest	funniest
larger	hotter	deeper	scarier	fatter
largest	hottest	deepest	scariest	fattest

Directions: Choose the words from the box in which the spelling of the base word changed before **-er** or **-est** was added. Write each word in the correct column.

Final Consonant Doubled	y changed to i
1. ______________	7. ______________
2. ______________	8. ______________
3. ______________	9. ______________
4. ______________	10. ______________
5. ______________	11. ______________
6. ______________	12. ______________

Directions: Add **-er** or **-est** to each word in ( ) to form a word from the box that completes each sentence. Write the word on the line.

______________ **13.** Gerry liked to climb the (large) tree in his yard.

______________ **14.** He had never climbed a tree that was (large).

______________ **15.** His sister would climb to the (small) branch.

______________ **16.** It was (small) than a baseball bat.

______________ **17.** Gerry and his sister were the (close) of friends.

______________ **18.** They were (close) than anyone thought possible.

______________ **19.** They would go exploring in the (deep) caves.

______________ **20.** "The (deep), the better," they would say.

Notes for Home: Your child spelled words that end in *-er* and *-est*. ***Home Activity:*** Have fun playing "Can You Top This?" Write, for example, *Monday was hot*. Ask your child to write, for example, *Tuesday was hotter*. Then you write, *Wednesday was the hottest*.

Spelling: Adding -er and -est

Directions: Proofread this diary entry. Find five spelling mistakes. Use the proofreading marks to correct each mistake.

≡ Make a capital.
/ Make a small letter.
∧ Add something.
℘ Take out something.
⊙ Add a period.
¶ Begin a new paragraph.

April 1

Dear Diary,

The scarriest thing happened to me. I was kidnapped by space pigs! They were the smalest, funniest creatures I've ever seen. They were no largeer than mice. They took me to their spaceship, which was hoter than a rain forest. Then I was saved by a superhero. I don't know his name, but he was the strongest person I've ever seen. When he flew me back to Earth, it was almost scaryer than being kidnapped!

Spelling Tip

Some base words change their spelling before the endings **-er** and **-est** are added. You may need to drop a final **e** as in **larger,** double a final consonant as in **saddest,** or change **y** to **i** as in **funnier.**

Word List

smaller	deeper
smallest	deepest
larger	closer
largest	closest
happier	scarier
happiest	scariest
hotter	funnier
hottest	funniest
sadder	fatter
saddest	fattest

Write a Diary Entry

Imagine you are a larger-than-life hero. On a separate sheet of paper, write a diary entry describing one of your incredible acts of heroism. Try to use at least three spelling words.

Notes for Home: Your child spelled words that end in *-er* and *-est.* ***Home Activity:*** Help your child think of other base words to which he or she could add the endings *-er* and *-est,* such as *big, soft, white, fluffy.*

Spelling: Adding *-er* and *-est*

REVIEW

Word List

smaller	happier	sadder	closer	funnier
smallest	happiest	saddest	closest	funniest
larger	hotter	deeper	scarier	fatter
largest	hottest	deepest	scariest	fattest

Directions: Add **-er** and **-est** to each base word below to form a word from the box.

Base Word	Add -er	Add -est
happy	**1.** ________	**2.** ________
sad	**3.** ________	**4.** ________
close	**5.** ________	**6.** ________
fat	**7.** ________	**8.** ________
large	**9.** ________	**10.** ________

Directions: Choose the word from the box that completes each statement. Write the word on the line to the left.

________________ **11.** *Taller* is to *shorter* as *bigger* is to _____.

________________ **12.** *Cool* is to *cooler* as *hot* is to _____.

________________ **13.** *Longest* is to *shortest* as *shallowest* is to _____.

________________ **14.** *Weird* is to *weirder* as *scary* is to _____.

________________ **15.** *Small* is to *smaller* as *funny* is to _____.

________________ **16.** *Sad* is to *saddest* as *funny* is to _____.

________________ **17.** *Wet* is to *wettest* as *hot* is to _____.

________________ **18.** *Big* is to *biggest* as *small* is to _____.

________________ **19.** *Funny* is to *funniest* as *scary* is to _____.

________________ **20.** *Shallow* is to *shallower* as *deep* is to _____.

Notes for Home: Your child spelled words that end in *-er* and *-est.* ***Home Activity:*** Say the base word for each spelling word, such as *sad* for *sadder* and *saddest*. Have your child add *-er* and *-est* to each base word and spell the new words aloud.

Name ____

Technology: Card Catalog/Library Database

To find books in the library, you can use the **card catalog** or **library database.** You can search for a book by author, title, or subject. When searching by author, always use the last name first.

Directions: The computer screen shows how to search a library database. Tell how you would search to find each of the following books. Write **A** for author, **T** for title, or **S** for subject.

________ **1.** a book by Kathryn Lasky

________ **2.** a book about tall tales

________ **3.** a book titled *Me and My Hero*

________ **4.** a book about steam drills

________ **5.** a book by Julius Lester

Name ______________________________

Library books are sorted by call numbers, usually based on the Dewey Decimal System. Books of fiction have call numbers that use letters from the last names of the authors. They are sorted alphabetically. Books that are nonfiction are sorted by numbers and appear in a different section from fiction books.

Directions: The computer screen shows the results of a subject search on *tall tales*. Use the results to answer the questions that follow.

Subject/Titles	**Call Number**
Tall Tales—Fiction	
1) Paul and Babe	EAT
2) The Great North Wind	THR
Tall Tales—Characters	
3) Paul Bunyan and Other Tall Tale Heroes	839.1
Tall Tales—Authors	
4) Julius Lester: A Master Storyteller	860.8

Type a number to find out more about each title. ☐

Type **A, T,** or **S** to begin a new search. ☐

6. Which books listed are books of fiction? ______________________________

____

7. What does the call number THR represent? ______________________________

____

8. Will *Paul and Babe* be on the shelf before or after *The Great North Wind?* Explain.

____

9. Which of the two nonfiction books listed would be first on a shelf? Explain.

____

____

10. Which book will be about someone who writes and tells tall tales?

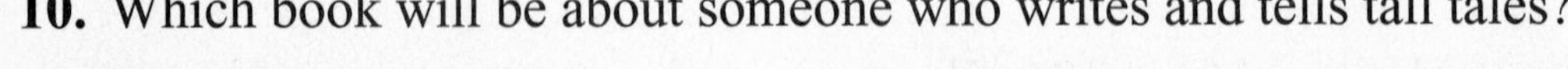

Notes for Home: Your child answered questions about a card catalog/library database. ***Home Activity:*** Take your child to the library. Have your child show how to use the card catalog or library database to find a book he or she might like to read.

Family Times

Name____

Summary

Marven Works in the Great North Woods!

Marven was only ten years old when his great-aunt died of influenza. To protect him from the disease, his family sent him far away from the city, up to the Great North Woods. There he kept the books at a logging camp. Marven was scared of the big, grouchy lumberjacks, especially Jean Louis, a "jack" whose feet were as big as skillets. But he was even more scared when he skied into the woods—and thought he saw a grizzly bear.

Reading Skills

Drawing Conclusions

A **conclusion** is a decision you reach that makes sense after you think about the details or facts that you have read. You can use the details and what you know to **draw conclusions,** or to figure out things about characters and events in what you read.

For example, in *Marven of the Great North Woods,* Jean Louis gives Marven a going-away present and takes him to the train station. You could draw the conclusion from these actions that Jean Louis likes Marven and is sorry to see him leave.

Activity

Write New Dialogue. Have your child make up a conversation between Marven and his family, in which Marven tells what happened to him at the logging camp.

Activity

Watch TV Characters. Watch a television show with your family. Draw conclusions about the main characters and their feelings based on their actions and words.

Family Times

Tested Vocabulary

Words to Know

Knowing the meaning of these words is important to reading *Marven of the Great North Woods.* Practice using these words to learn their meanings.

cord unit for measuring cut wood

depot railroad or bus station

flapjacks pancakes

grizzly large, fierce bear of North America

snowshoes shoes with wooden frame and strips of leather stretched across

Grammar

Subject-Verb Agreement

The subject and verb in a sentence must work together, or agree. For verbs that show actions happening now, follow these rules:

- ❖ If the simple subject is a singular noun or pronoun, add **-s** to the verb: **Marven chops wood. He adds the numbers.**
- ❖ If the simple subject is a plural noun, do not add an ending. **The lumberjacks chop wood. The bookkeepers add numbers.**

Activity

Play a Verb Game. The first player says a sentence with a singular subject: **The cookie tastes good.** The next player makes the subject plural and makes the verb agree: **The cookies taste good.**

Tested Spelling Words

Name ____________________________________

Drawing Conclusions

- Authors don't always tell you everything. Instead, they may give you a few details about what happens or about characters.
- You can use the details and what you know to **draw conclusions,** or figure out things about people or animals and what they do.

Directions: Reread "Winter of the Snowshoe Hare." Then complete the table. Write a conclusion for each piece of evidence given. Write evidence that supports each conclusion drawn.

Evidence (Story Details and What I Know)	Conclusions
The sounds of paws and breathing are louder.	**1.**
The master blew the whistle.	**2.**
The dog turned and trotted back to the master.	**3.**
4.	The hare didn't know the dog had turned back.
5.	The hare was safe.

Notes for Home: Your child read a story and used story details and life experience to draw conclusions. ***Home Activity:*** Watch a television show or a movie with your child. Discuss what conclusions you can draw about how the characters feel or why they behave as they do.

Name ______________________________

Vocabulary

Directions: Choose the word from the box that best matches each definition. Write the word on the line.

Check the Words You Know
__ cord
__ depot
__ flapjacks
__ grizzly
__ snowshoes

__________ **1.** large, fierce, North American bear

__________ **2.** pancakes

__________ **3.** a measure of wood

__________ **4.** railroad or bus station

__________ **5.** wooden-framed shoes

Directions: Read the letter. Choose the word from the box that best completes each sentence. Write the word on the matching numbered line to the right.

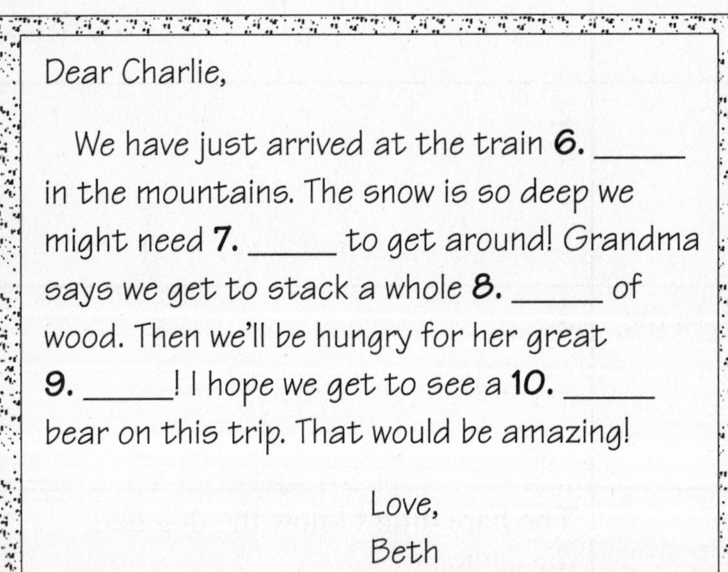
Dear Charlie,

We have just arrived at the train **6.** _____ in the mountains. The snow is so deep we might need **7.** _____ to get around! Grandma says we get to stack a whole **8.** _____ of wood. Then we'll be hungry for her great **9.** _____! I hope we get to see a **10.** _____ bear on this trip. That would be amazing!

Love,
Beth

6. __________

7. __________

8. __________

9. __________

10. __________

Write a Letter

On a separate sheet of paper, write a letter to a friend—real or imaginary—who lives in the Great North Woods. Show your excitement about going to visit your friend. Use as many vocabulary words as you can.

Notes for Home: Your child identified and used vocabulary words from *Marven of the Great North Woods*. ***Home Activity:*** With your child, use the vocabulary words to make up an adventure story about camping in the woods.

Name ______________________________

Drawing Conclusions

- As you read, use story details and what you know to **draw conclusions,** or make a sensible decision, about the characters and what they do.

Directions: Reread this passage from *Marven of the Great North Woods* in which Marven is becoming used to the logging camp. Then answer the questions below.

Every day Marven worked until midday, when he went into the cookhouse and ate baked beans and two kinds of pie with Mr. Murray and the cook. After lunch he returned to his office and worked until the jacks returned from the forest for supper.

By Friday of the second week, Marven had learned his job so well that he finished early. He had not been on his skis since he had arrived at camp. Every day the routine was simply meals and work, and Marven kept to his office and away from the lumberjacks as much as he could. But today he wanted to explore, so he put on his skis and followed the sled paths into the woods.

1. Why don't Marven and Mr. Murray eat with the lumberjacks?

____

2. Why do you think Marven could learn his job so well in so little time?

____

3. Why do you think Marven kept away from the lumberjacks?

____

4. How does Marven feel about his daily routine? How do you know?

____

____

5. How do you think Marven feels about the lumberjacks by the end of the story? On a separate sheet of paper, explain your answer.

Notes for Home: Your child drew conclusions about characters and their actions. ***Home Activity:*** Have your child draw conclusions by playing a game of "If". For example: *If your dog whines by the front door, what do you think it wants? (to go outside)*

Name ______________________________

Selection Test

Directions: Choose the best answer to each item. Mark the letter for the answer you have chosen.

Part 1: Vocabulary

Find the answer choice that means about the same as the underlined word in each sentence.

1. The hunters saw a <u>grizzly</u>.
- A. kind of tree
- B. large, fish-eating bird
- C. kind of wild cat
- D. large, fierce kind of bear

2. Do you like <u>flapjacks</u>?
- F. pancakes
- G. a game played with cards
- H. tools for lifting
- J. rabbits

3. Grant bought a <u>cord</u> of logs.
- A. a long flat-bottomed sled
- B. a certain amount of cut wood
- C. a thin, strong rope
- D. a box used to store things

4. The hikers wore <u>snowshoes</u>.
- F. heavy boots lined with fur
- G. long, narrow runners for gliding on snow
- H. skates with metal blades
- J. light frames worn on the feet for walking in deep snow

5. Tom met us at the <u>depot</u>.
- A. small restaurant
- B. camp
- C. train station
- D. hotel

Part 2: Comprehension

Use what you know about the selection to answer each item.

6. Marven spent four months at a—
- F. music camp.
- G. sports camp.
- H. logging camp.
- J. hunting camp.

7. Marven's job was to—
- A. keep the payroll.
- B. stack wood in the office.
- C. ring the morning bell.
- D. make breakfast.

8. On the first morning, Marven ran to the bunkhouse to—
- F. find an overcoat to wear.
- G. talk with Jean Louis.
- H. light the lamps.
- J. make sure the men were up.

GO ON

Name ______________________________________

9. In this selection, you can tell that "*Lève-toi!*" means—
A. Get up!
B. You're lazy!
C. It's time for breakfast!
D. Good morning!

10. You can tell that Marven was—
F. glad to be away from his family.
G. stronger than Jean Louis.
H. good with numbers.
J. afraid of snow.

11. Which word best describes Marven in his job?
A. bored
B. organized
C. lazy
D. patient

12. When he skied across the lake, Marven began to cry because—
F. the rest of his family had died.
G. Jean Louis was laughing at him.
H. his hands and feet were frozen.
J. he felt alone and afraid.

13. How did Jean Louis feel about Marven?
A. He thought Marven was a pest.
B. He did not like taking care of him.
C. He came to love him almost as a son.
D. He thought Marven acted like a baby.

14. When Marven didn't see his family at the train station, he probably thought that—
F. he was at the wrong stop.
G. they had forgotten him.
H. he should go back to the woods.
J. everyone had died from the flu.

15. How did Marven's experience away from home change him?
A. He was forced to grow up faster than most children his age.
B. He began to depend on others to take care of him.
C. He became afraid to get close to others because they would die.
D. He realized he didn't really need his family.

STOP

Name ______________________________

Drawing Conclusions

- As you read, use story details and what you know to **draw conclusions,** or make sensible decisions, about the characters and what they do.

Directions: Read the story below.

Paul and Rick did everything together. They rode bikes, played ball, hiked, and fished.

One winter there was a huge snowstorm. The next day, Paul shoveled a path to Rick's house to see if he wanted to go sledding. But when Rick came to the door, he wasn't his usual cheerful self. His mom's leg ached and was swollen. Rick's dad was out of town.

"Here's what we'll do," Paul said. "We'll tie our sleds together and pull your mom to my house. After all, my mom's a doctor."

Directions: Complete the table by drawing conclusions from what you have read.

Story Details	Conclusions I Can Draw
Paul and Rick ride bikes, play ball, hike, and fish together.	**1.**
Paul shovels a path to Rick's house.	**2.**
Rick isn't his usual cheerful self.	**3.**
Rick's mom's leg ached and was swollen.	**4.**
Paul's mom is a doctor.	**5.**

Notes for Home: Your child read a story and used story details and what he or she knows to draw conclusions. ***Home Activity:*** Tell your child a story about a friend of yours. Ask your child to draw conclusions about your friend from details in your story.

Name ______________________________

Context Clues

REVIEW

Directions: Read the story. Then read each question about the story. Choose the best answer to each question. Mark the letter for the answer you have chosen.

A Friend to Many

Frank Benson wanted to improve life for everyone in Hillsdale. His many projects helped countless people he never even met. Because Frank felt that everyone should be literate, he started a program to teach people who couldn't read. He also founded a Library on Wheels program that brought books to people living out in the country. It was the first program of its kind in the state.

When Frank passed away at the age of 92, a memorial service was held at the town's main library. Many family members and friends told stories about all the good things Frank had done in his life. Later, the town voted to rename the library after Frank. The brass plaque on the front door reads, "Frank Benson: A Friend to Many."

1. The word <u>countless</u> in this passage means—

A. many.
B. few.
C. poor.
D. mean.

2. The word <u>literate</u> in this passage means able to—

F. make money.
G. read.
H. litter.
J. teach.

3. The word <u>founded</u> in this passage means—

A. find.
B. purchased.
C. started.
D. approved.

4. The word <u>memorial</u> in this passage means something done to—

F. get a person elected to office.
G. raise funds for a good cause.
H. make people happy.
J. remember a person who has died.

5. The word <u>plaque</u> in this passage means—

A. a door.
B. a sign.
C. a wooden board.
D. a book.

Notes for Home: Your child defined words in a story using context clues. ***Home Activity:*** Give your child a list of unfamiliar words. Use each word in a sentence and challenge your child to use context clues to figure out the meaning of each unfamiliar word.

Name ____________________

Writing Across Texts

Directions: Consider what you learned about working with money in the selections *Marven of the Great North Woods* and "Counting Money." Complete each list by recording the steps for figuring out amounts of money that were described in the selections.

How Marven Did His Job
List the lumberjacks' names alphabetically.
Write the symbol for those who could not write.
1.
2.
3.

How to Subtract Money
Line up the decimals.
4.
5.

$$\begin{array}{r} \$38.52 \\ -\ 9.23 \\ \hline \$29.29 \end{array}$$

Writing About Money

Use the information you gathered from above and your own experiences to write a paragraph about a time when you have used money. What steps did you follow in dealing with money? Write about your experience on a separate sheet of paper.

Notes for Home: Your child listed details from a nonfiction story and an excerpt from a mathematics textbook. ***Home Activity:*** Play games with your child that offer him or her the opportunity to count change, add money, or calculate amounts in some way.

Name ____

REVIEW

Grammar: Verbs

Directions: Write the verb in each sentence on the line. Remember that some verbs show what action someone or something does. Other verbs link, or join, the subject to a word in the predicate. A linking verb helps to tell what the subject is or what the subject is like.

________________ **1.** Once a lonely pig wanted a friend very much.

________________ **2.** Then one day a spider appeared in the barn.

________________ **3.** The spider's name was Charlotte.

________________ **4.** Soon the pig and the spider shared a wonderful friendship.

________________ **5.** The pig Wilbur felt so happy.

Directions: Use each of the following words as the verb in a sentence. Write the sentence on the line.

6. laughed

____

7. wrote

____

8. am

____

9. *felt* as an action verb

____

10. *felt* as a linking verb

____

Notes for Home: Your child identified action and linking verbs. ***Home Activity:*** Go back over items 3 and 5 in this activity that use linking verbs. Ask your child to circle each subject and the word in each sentence that renames or describes the subject.

Name ________________________________

Practice

Grammar: Verbs in Sentences

The subject and the verb in a sentence must work together, or **agree.** Decide whether a noun subject is singular (one) or plural (more than one). Then use the verb form that agrees with it: Jay works. Lumberjacks work.

If the verb shows action that is occurring now, or if it tells what the subject is like now, follow these rules:

- Add **-s** or **-es** to many verbs to make them agree with singular noun subjects. For verbs that end in a **consonant** and **y,** change the **y** to **i** before adding **-es.**

This hot breakfast looks good!
The cook fries more eggs.

- For the verb **be,** use *is* to agree with singular noun subjects and *are* to agree with plural noun subjects.

The temperature outside the cabin is cold.
The lumberjacks are warm from the hot food.

Directions: Circle the correct form of the verb in ( ) to complete each sentence. Write **S** if the subject is singular. Write **P** if the subject is plural.

________ **1.** The snow (fall/falls) on the woods.

________ **2.** Ice (freeze/freezes) on the lake.

________ **3.** Rabbits (run/runs) across the snow.

________ **4.** Their tracks (lead/leads) to their burrows.

________ **5.** Meanwhile, the bears (sleep/sleeps) in their den.

________ **6.** All winter, the woods (is/are) very quiet.

________ **7.** A person (hear/hears) only the sound of the wind.

________ **8.** In spring, the ice (melts/melt).

________ **9.** Animals (wakes/wake) from their long sleep.

________ **10.** Life (returns/return) to the woods.

Notes for Home: Your child used the correct form of verbs with singular or plural noun subjects. ***Home Activity:*** Offer some sentences in which the subjects need verbs ("The boy [work/works] hard"), and ask your child to choose the right verb for each sentence.

Name ________________________________

Grammar: Verbs in Sentences

Directions: Circle the correct form of the verb in ( ) to complete each sentence. Write **S** if the subject is singular. Write **P** if the subject is plural. Remember that a verb must agree with its subject.

________ **1.** Logging camps (supplies/supply) wood to paper mills and furniture companies.

________ **2.** Paper mills (makes/make) paper out of wood pulp from trees.

________ **3.** That carpenter in the blue overalls (is/are) also an instructor.

________ **4.** Her helper (saw/saws) the wood carefully.

________ **5.** The customers (like/likes) their sturdy furniture.

Directions: Use the correct form of the verb in ( ) to complete each sentence. Write the verb on the line.

________________ **6.** Every morning, the sun (appear) over the frozen lake.

________________ **7.** Slowly, the lumberjacks (get) out of bed.

________________ **8.** Marc (eat) the smallest breakfast.

________________ **9.** His sister, Marcia, (eat) much more than he does!

________________ **10.** These people (need) a good meal to handle the morning's work.

Write a Description

On a separate sheet of paper, write a description of people doing hard work. Use at least five verbs. Be sure your verbs agree with their subjects. Under your description, list each verb you have used, and write whether its subject is singular or plural.

Notes for Home: Your child identified the forms of verbs for singular and plural subjects: *the dog barks, the dogs bark.* ***Home Activity:*** Name some verbs about sounds for your child *(growl, squeak, hum)*. Have your child use each verb in a sentence.

Name ______________________________

Grammar: Verbs in Sentences

Complete each sentence with the verb from the box that makes sense.

perform
holds
turns
play

1. The girl ______________ a flute.
2. She ______________ the music pages.
3. The boys ______________ the violins.
4. They ______________ at concerts.

Notice that when a singular noun or pronoun is the subject of a sentence, the verb is written with **-s** or **-es**. When a plural noun or plural pronoun is the subject of a sentence, the verb is written without **-s** or **-es**.

A verb in the present tense must agree with the subject of the sentence. With **he**, **she**, **it**, or a singular noun, add **-s** or **-es** to the verb.

Directions: Draw a line to connect each subject and verb that go together.

1. The flute	plays the trumpet.
2. We	sounds like a bird.
3. Jamal	take our music lessons.

Directions: Write the correct form of each verb in ( ).

4. Ms. Ames ________________ (teach/teaches) music.
5. The girls ________________ (dance/dances) well.
6. They ________________ (practice/practices) every day.

Notes for Home: Your child used verbs that agreed with the subjects of sentences. ***Home Activity:*** Write three subjects, such as *the cats, our house, you and I,* and have your child write sentences, using the subjects you wrote and verbs that agree.

Name ____

Grammar: Verbs in Sentences

Directions: Write the verb in ( ) that agrees with each subject.

1. The children ______________________ a song. (sing/sings)

2. Asako ______________________ the piano. (play/plays)

3. The director ______________________ the singers. (lead/leads)

4. The audience ______________________ the musical. (watch/watches)

5. We ______________________ for the children. (clap/claps)

6. The music ______________________ beautiful. (sound/sounds)

Directions: Write each sentence using the verb in ( ) correctly.

7. The singers (prepare) a song.
8. The director (train) them.
9. They (work) together.
10. The students (learn) quickly.
11. Asako (wish) for a solo.
12. Audiences (like) Asako.

7. ____

8. ____

9. ____

10. ____

11. ____

12. ____

Write About a Song

Use verbs in the present tense to write about a song you recently learned. Be sure the verbs agree with the subjects. Write on a separate sheet of paper.

Notes for Home: Your child wrote verbs in sentences correctly. ***Home Activity:*** Have your child write sentences with blanks instead of verbs. Then fill in verbs. Have your child check to make sure the verbs you wrote agree with the nouns in the sentences.

Name ______________________

Word Study: Regular Plurals

Directions: To make most nouns plural, add the letter **-s.** For nouns that end in **x, s, ss, ch,** or **sh,** add **-es.** For nouns that end in **consonant** and **y,** add **-es.** Read the paragraph below. Make each word in ( ) plural. Write the plural word on the line.

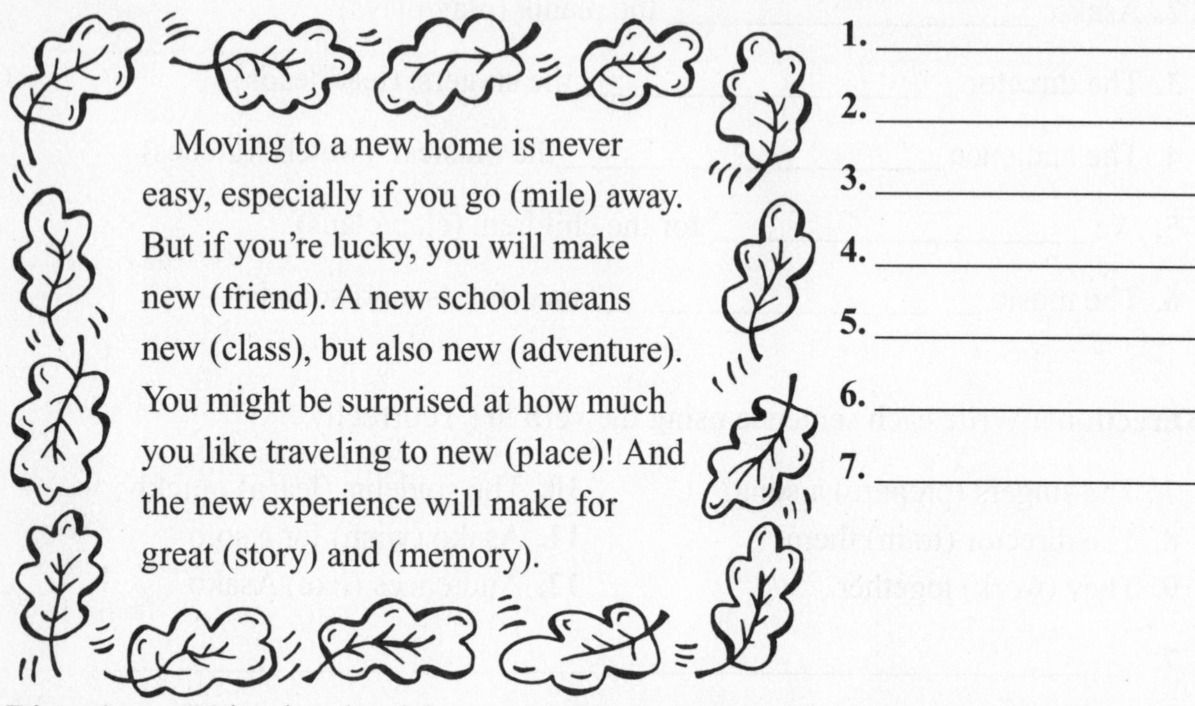

Moving to a new home is never easy, especially if you go (mile) away. But if you're lucky, you will make new (friend). A new school means new (class), but also new (adventure). You might be surprised at how much you like traveling to new (place)! And the new experience will make for great (story) and (memory).

1. ______________

2. ______________

3. ______________

4. ______________

5. ______________

6. ______________

7. ______________

Directions: Write the plural form for each word. For some words, you will add **-s.** For some you will add **-es.** You may need to change some letters before adding **-es.**

8. pencil ______________

9. candy ______________

10. ax ______________

11. city ______________

12. monkey ______________

13. lunch ______________

14. paper ______________

15. tower ______________

16. glass ______________

17. bush ______________

18. tree ______________

19. star ______________

20. fox ______________

21. horse ______________

22. flapjack ______________

23. beard ______________

24. shadow ______________

25. pony ______________

Notes for Home: Your child changed singular nouns into plurals by adding *-s* or *-es* to create words such as *tigers, babies,* and *boxes*. ***Home Activity:*** Read some coupons with your child. Look for plural words. Talk about how the singular noun changed to become a plural noun.

Name ______________________________

Spelling: Adding *-s* and *-es*

Pretest Directions: Fold back the page along the dotted line. On the blanks, write the spelling words as they are dictated. When you have finished the test, unfold the page and check your words.

1. ____________________
2. ____________________
3. ____________________
4. ____________________
5. ____________________
6. ____________________
7. ____________________
8. ____________________
9. ____________________
10. ____________________
11. ____________________
12. ____________________
13. ____________________
14. ____________________
15. ____________________
16. ____________________
17. ____________________
18. ____________________
19. ____________________
20. ____________________

1. The **monkeys** swung from trees.
2. **Holidays** are happy days.
3. There were **delays** in the march.
4. The field was full of **flowers**.
5. We all rely on our **friends**.
6. Grass hid the **tigers** from view.
7. The **supplies** were running out.
8. Tex had no **enemies**.
9. Hiking is one of her **hobbies**.
10. My **memories** of him are cloudy.
11. Life holds great **mysteries**.
12. His **eyelashes** were long.
13. The wind blew the fire's **ashes**.
14. **Beaches** have sand and stones.
15. The fruit grew in **bunches**.
16. Horses perform in **circuses**.
17. His **glasses** were broken.
18. All **classes** of people come here.
19. The country had high **taxes**.
20. Add the **suffixes** now.

Notes for Home: Your child took a pretest on adding *-s* and *-es* to nouns. ***Home Activity:*** Help your child learn misspelled words before the final test. Your child can underline the word parts that caused the problems and concentrate on those parts.

Name ______________________________

Spelling: Adding *-s* and *-es*

Word List

monkeys	friends	hobbies	ashes	glasses
holidays	tigers	memories	beaches	classes
delays	supplies	mysteries	bunches	taxes
flowers	enemies	eyelashes	circuses	suffixes

Directions: Choose the words from the box in which **-es** has been added to the base word without any spelling changes. Write the words on the lines.

1. ________________ **4.** ________________ **7.** ________________

2. ________________ **5.** ________________ **8.** ________________

3. ________________ **6.** ________________ **9.** ________________

Directions: Write the word from the box that belongs in each group.

10. festivals, celebrations, ________________

11. equipment, provisions, ________________

12. puzzles, secrets, ________________

13. rivals, opponents, ________________

14. interests, pastimes, ________________

15. remembrances, recollections, ________________

16. plants, trees, ________________

17. waits, pauses, ________________

18. lions, cougars, ________________

19. pals, buddies, ________________

20. chimpanzees, apes, ________________

Notes for Home: Your child spelled words that end in *-s* and *-es*. ***Home Activity:*** Write the singular form of each spelling word, such as *supply* for *supplies*. Have your child write the plural form by adding *-s* or *-es* to each word.

Name ______________________________

Spelling: Adding *-s* and *-es*

Directions: Proofread this description of a friend. Find five spelling mistakes. Use the proofreading marks to correct each mistake.

≡	Make a capital.
/	Make a small letter.
∧	Add something.
℘	Take out something.
⊙	Add a period.
¶	Begin a new paragraph.

Best Freinds

We were always in the same clases. We both had dark hair and wore wire-rimmed glasses. One of our favorite hobbys was woodworking. We used to go to the crafts store for suplies. We also liked to read misteries together. Then my friend moved across town. Now we can see each other only on vacations and holidays.

Spelling Tip

monkeys **supplies**

If a word ends in a **vowel** and **y,** add **-s** to make it plural. If a word ends in a **consonant** and **y,** change the **y** to **i** and add **-es.**

Word List

monkeys	mysteries
holidays	eyelashes
delays	ashes
flowers	beaches
friends	bunches
tigers	circuses
supplies	glasses
enemies	classes
hobbies	taxes
memories	suffixes

Write a Description

On a separate sheet of paper, write a description of one of your best friends. Try to use at least three spelling words.

Notes for Home: Your child spelled words that end in *-s* and *-es*. ***Home Activity:*** Have your child make a list of the things in his or her room. Have him or her use as many words ending in *-s* and *-es* as possible.

Name ______________________________

Spelling: Adding *-s* and *-es*

REVIEW

Word List				
monkeys	friends	hobbies	ashes	glasses
holidays	tigers	memories	beaches	classes
delays	supplies	mysteries	bunches	taxes
flowers	enemies	eyelashes	circuses	suffixes

Directions: Write the plural form of each word below to form a word from the box.

1. friend __________
2. memory __________
3. hobby __________
4. class __________
5. holiday __________
6. beach __________
7. glass __________
8. enemy __________
9. mystery __________
10. ash __________
11. tax __________
12. suffix __________

Directions: Choose the word from the box that answers each rhyme. Write the word on the line to the left.

__________________ **13.** We have long tails. We are not donkeys.
We like to play. Yes, we are _____.

__________________ **14.** They could take days, those shipping _____.

__________________ **15.** _____ have stripes, leopards have spots,
but both of them could scare me lots.

__________________ **16.** Stones and wood build castle towers,
but gardens grow with grass and _____.

__________________ **17.** Below your forehead, above your cheek,
raise your _____ and take a peek.

__________________ **18.** Into the big top, everyone, _____ are so much fun.

__________________ **19.** You can have _____ of flowers, bananas, or grapes,
but never camels, iguanas, or apes.

__________________ **20.** If _____ are low, you must get more.
Get on your bike and ride to the store.

Notes for Home: Your child spelled words that end in *-s* and *-es*. ***Home Activity:*** Work together to write an adventure story about monkeys and tigers. Use as many spelling words as possible.

Name ______________________________

Locate/Collect Information

To find out information about a subject, you can use resources such as books, magazines, newspapers, dictionaries, encyclopedias, videotapes, audiotapes, CD-ROMs, Internet Web sites, photographs, drawings, and diagrams. You can also talk to a reference librarian or an expert in the field.

Directions: Review these resources for information on lumberjacking. Use the resources to answer the questions that follow.

Name ________________________________

1. If you wanted to find out what the lumberjacks ate for dinner, which resources do you think would be most helpful?

2. What is one advantage of getting information by interviewing an expert?

3. Which expert would probably have the most information about logging in the 1800s? Explain.

4. What is one question you might ask expert Samuel Jones?

5. From looking at the titles, which of the audiotapes probably contains the least factual information? Explain.

Notes for Home: Your child learned about using different resources. ***Home Activity:*** List five adults your child knows. Ask your child to tell you on what subject each person could be interviewed as an expert, such as Louisa—flowers, Chico—biology.

Family Times

Name____

Summary

Summer on the Pampas Is Full of Adventure!

One summer, María goes by herself to her grandparents' ranch on the Argentine pampas. The first thing she sees when she arrives is her cousin, Susanita, on her very own horse. María gets her own horse, Pampita, and she and Susanita ride everywhere together. María also learns how to lasso a calf, herd cattle, and separate the cows from the calves—just like a regular *gaucho,* or cowboy.

Activity

Be a Storyteller. Invite your child to tell you about the rest of María's adventures, including the day she and Susanita found a *ñandú* egg.

Reading Skills

Generalizing

A **generalization** is a broad statement or rule that applies to many examples.

When you read, you are sometimes given ideas about several things or people. You can **generalize,** or make a statement about all or most of them together. Clue words like *all, many, few, seldom, always,* or *usually* signal generalizations.

For example, this is a valid, or accurate, generalization about María: **María usually had a good time at her grandparents' ranch.** You could generalize from these details: she enjoyed riding, she liked hunting *ñandú* eggs, and she had fun learning how to be a gaucho.

Activity

Make Generalizations. Take turns having one family member use one of the clue words above to make a generalization about a person, place, or thing, such as: **Our family always goes to the beach in the summer.**

Family Times

Tested Vocabulary

Words to Know

Knowing the meanings of these words is important to reading *On the Pampas*. Practice using these words to learn their meanings.

brand mark by burning skin with a hot iron

bridles part of harness that fits on horse's head

calves young cows or bulls

corral where horses are kept

herd a group of animals of one kind

initials first letters of names

manes hair on horses' necks

reins straps fastened to the bridle

Grammar

Verb Tenses: Present, Past, and Future

Verbs that tell about actions that happen now are in the **present tense.** Verbs that tell about actions that have already happened are in the **past tense.** Verbs that tell about actions that are going to happen are in the **future tense.**

Present	Past	Futur
I cook. He explores. You ride. __________	We cooked. She explored. __________ I roped.	You will c __________ He will ri We will ro

Activity

Tell About Activities. Complete the table. Use verbs in the past, present, and future tense to tell something you, or someone else, did yesterday, are doing today, and will do tomorrow.

Tested Spelling Words

__________	__________	__________	__________
__________	__________	__________	__________
__________	__________	__________	__________
__________	__________	__________	__________
__________	__________	__________	__________

Name ________________________________

Generalizing

- A **generalization** is a broad statement or rule that applies to many examples.
- Often clue words like *all, most, many, some, sometimes, usually, seldom, few,* or *generally* signal generalizations. A **valid generalization** is supported by facts and your own knowledge. A **faulty generalization** is not.

Directions: Reread "Salmon for All." Write **V** if the generalization is valid. Write **F** if it is faulty. Give evidence from the text to support your choices.

Generalization	V or F	Evidence
Many animals eat salmon.	V	Bears, foxes, birds, and people all eat salmon.
Foxes sometimes feed their pups salmon.	**1.**	**2.**
Bears never eat salmon.	**3.**	**4.**
Bears always hide their tracks.	**5.**	**6.**
There is seldom enough salmon for everyone.	**7.**	**8.**
Not everyone can catch salmon.	**9.**	**10.**

Notes for Home: Your child identified valid and faulty generalizations. ***Home Activity:*** Take turns using the clue words listed above to make generalizations. (*I seldom am wrong.*) Determine whether each generalization is valid (accurate) or faulty (not accurate).

Name ____________________________________

Vocabulary

Directions: Choose the word from the box that best completes each sentence. Write the word on the line to the left.

Check the Words You Know

- __ brand
- __ bridles
- __ calves
- __ corral
- __ herd
- __ initials
- __ manes
- __ reins

_______________ **1.** Did you know that a ranch is often known by a set of _____, or letters?

_______________ **2.** Every steer in the ranch's whole _____ is marked with these letters.

_______________ **3.** The young _____ are separated from the mother cows to be marked.

_______________ **4.** Even the horses standing in the _____ have been marked.

_______________ **5.** Cowboys groom their horses by brushing their _____.

Directions: Choose the word from the box that best matches each clue. Write the word in the puzzle.

Down

6. to mark with a hot iron

7. straps held by a horse's rider

8. pen where horses or cattle are kept

Across

9. large number of one kind of animal

10. straps that fit on horses' heads

6. 7. 8. 9. 10.

Write a Postcard

On a separate sheet of paper, write a short postcard to a friend telling about a visit to a ranch. Use as many of the vocabulary words as you can.

Notes for Home: Your child identified and used vocabulary words from *On the Pampas.* ***Home Activity:*** With your child, find out more about life on a modern ranch. Use as many of the vocabulary words as possible as you and your child discuss what you have learned.

Name ______________________________

Generalizing

- Sometimes when you read, you are given ideas about several things or people. When you make a statement about all of them together, you are making a **generalization.**
- A **valid generalization** is accurate. A **faulty generalization** is not accurate.

Directions: Reread this passage from *On the Pampas*. Then make generalizations based on what you read.

At noon, everybody would sit down around one big table and eat together. I was always hungry. Grandma, Susanita's mother, and María the cook had been working hard all morning too. They would make soup, salad, and lamb stew or pot roast, or my favorite, *carbonada,* a thick stew made of corn and peaches.

After lunch the grown-ups took a *siesta,* but not us. We liked to stay outdoors. Some afternoons, when it was too hot to do anything else, we rode out to a eucalyptus grove that was nice and cool, and stayed there until it got dark, reading comic books or cowboy stories.

1. What was true of mornings on the ranch?

____

2. What usually happened at noon?

____

3. What did all the grown-ups do after lunch?

____

4. What did the children do after lunch?

____

5. On a separate sheet of paper, write a valid generalization about life on the *pampas*.

Notes for Home: Your child used details to make generalizations about a story. ***Home Activity:*** Read a story or newspaper article with your child. Together, make generalizations—statements about several things or people in the story.

Name ________________________________

Selection Test

Directions: Choose the best answer to each item. Mark the letter for the answer you have chosen.

Part 1: Vocabulary

Find the answer choice that means about the same as the underlined word in each sentence.

1. Helen walked to the corral.
- A. building for storing hay
- B. piece of land planted with crops
- C. small country store
- D. pen where animals are kept

2. Marco grabbed the reins.
- F. seat for a rider
- G. straps used to guide a horse
- H. loops for a rider's foot
- J. long rope with a loop on the end

3. The herd headed west.
- A. group of animals of one kind
- B. great mass of clouds
- C. group of sailing ships
- D. line of covered wagons

4. Where are the bridles stored?
- F. hats with wide brims
- G. strong leather pants
- H. part of a harness for a horse
- J. metal shoes for horses

5. She brushed the horses' manes.
- A. back part of a horse's body
- B. parts of the mouth
- C. long heavy hair on a horse's neck
- D. place for an animal in a barn

6. María helped brand the cattle.
- F. mark by burning with a hot iron
- G. move to another location
- H. gather into a group
- J. give food and water to

7. The boys saw some calves.
- A. plants with no leaves
- B. large, flat rocks
- C. dark storm clouds
- D. young cows or bulls

8. Whose initials are these?
- F. first letters of a person's names
- G. coverings for the hands
- H. marks made by the tip of a finger
- J. sets of funny drawings

GO ON

Part 2: Comprehension

Use what you know about the selection to answer each item.

9. The ranch where the author spent the summer was called—
A. San Enrique.
B. La Carlota.
C. Buenos Aires.
D. La Gauchita.

10. Susanita is the author's—
F. cousin.
G. grandmother.
H. horse.
J. friend.

11. What is a *ñandú?*
A. a horse
B. a herd of cattle
C. a kind of bird
D. a fancy belt

12. Based on this selection, which generalization is most likely true?
F. All horses are friendly.
G. Few cattle live on the pampas.
H. Girls always learn faster than boys.
J. Most gauchos work very hard.

13. What can you tell about the author of this story?
A. She is willing to try new things.
B. She doesn't really have what it takes to be a gaucho.
C. She is secretly jealous of Susanita.
D. She likes to call attention to herself.

14. The author's grandmother expects her to—
F. write to her during the winter.
G. take her horse home with her.
H. come back the next summer.
J. share her horse with Susanita.

15. The author probably feels proudest that she—
A. stole a bird's egg.
B. had become a gaucho.
C. baked a birthday cake for Grandma.
D. escaped from the ñandú.

STOP

Name ____

Generalizing

- Sometimes when you read, you are given ideas about several things or people. When you make a statement about all of them together, you are making a **generalization.**
- A **valid generalization** is accurate. A **faulty generalization** is not accurate.

Directions: Read the story below.

Dad said it would be great to live on a real ranch for a week. "None of that dude ranch stuff," he said. "This is the real thing." When I didn't look excited, he looked hurt. "Every kid wants to be a cowboy."

We were treated like the cowboys the whole time. We ate the same terrible food, did the same hard work, and slept in the same hard bunks. We were always up by dawn. I was so tired. Dad was too, but he wouldn't admit it.

Home never looked so good. When we stumbled into the house, Mom took one look at us and knew we needed sleep. But all she said was, "How did it go?"

"Wonderful," said Dad. "It was just wonderful!"

Directions: Complete the table by filling in details from the story and making generalizations.

From the Story	Generalizations
1.	Dude ranches aren't for people who really want to live like cowboys.
Cowboys eat bad food, work hard, sleep in hard bunks, and get up early.	**2.**
3.	Vacations can be tiring.
4.	It feels good to be home after a long trip.
Dad said the trip was wonderful.	**5.**

Notes for Home: Your child read the story and used ideas from it to make generalizations. ***Home Activity:*** Discuss with your child a trip you took together. From things that happened, try to make generalizations about people, places, and events.

Name ______________________________

Context Clues

REVIEW

Directions: Read the story. Then read each question about the story. Choose the best answer to each question. Mark the letter for the answer you have chosen.

Life on a TV Ranch

I've never set foot on an actual ranch, but I've traveled to many in my mind. That's because TV shows made life on a ranch so enticing. It looks like so much fun.

One thing confused me about cowboy shows. I wasn't sure of the era when they were taking place.

They all showed herds of cattle and corrals. But in one they got water from a well and cooked on a wood-burning stove. In another there was a modern kitchen. In one there were cars. In another, there were only horses.

It took me a while to realize the obvious truth: Some cowboy shows took place in the Old West. Some took place in the present.

1. The word actual in the story means—
- **A.** working.
- **B.** nasty.
- **C.** make-believe.
- **D.** real.

2. The word enticing in the story means—
- **F.** dangerous.
- **G.** appealing.
- **H.** uninviting.
- **J.** boring.

3. The word confused in the story means—
- **A.** puzzled.
- **B.** dazzled.
- **C.** angered.
- **D.** entertained.

4. Which phrase gives a clue to the meaning of era?
- **F.** wasn't sure
- **G.** when they were taking place
- **H.** one thing confused me
- **J.** they all showed

5. An obvious truth is—
- **A.** sad.
- **B.** unclear.
- **C.** clear.
- **D.** whole.

Notes for Home: Your child defined words using context clues. ***Home Activity:*** Read a magazine or newspaper article with your child. Discuss which words are unfamiliar and what context clues can be used to figure out their meanings.

Writing Across Texts

Directions: Consider what you learned from reading *Marven of the Great North Woods* and *On the Pampas.* Think about the ways that the great north woods and the pampas are alike. Think about ways they are different. Use the table below to organize your thoughts.

The North Woods and the Pampas	
How They Are Alike	**How They Are Different**
They are both in remote areas.	The pampas are in Argentina; the north woods are in Minnesota.
1.	**6.**
2.	**7.**
3.	**8.**
4.	**9.**
5.	**10.**

Write a Comparison

On a separate sheet of paper, write a paragraph that tells how the pampas and the great north woods are either alike or different. Support your paragraph with information from each selection that you have listed in the table above.

Notes for Home: Your child compared and contrasted information from more than one source. ***Home Activity:*** As you read stories or articles with your child, discuss how they are alike or different from other stories or articles you have read.

Name ______________________________

Grammar: Subject-Verb Agreement

REVIEW

Directions: Circle the action verb in ( ) that agrees with the subject in each sentence. Write the verb on the line.

_______________ **1.** Today some people (visits/visit) a ranch during their vacations.

_______________ **2.** A loud bell (wakes/wake) everyone early in the morning.

_______________ **3.** The cook (makes/make) a hearty breakfast.

_______________ **4.** A ranch manager (tells/tell) the workers their chores for the day.

_______________ **5.** Sometimes grown-ups (helps/help) the ranch hands.

_______________ **6.** Occasionally they even (brands/brand) cattle.

_______________ **7.** Children often (rides/ride) horses out to the range.

_______________ **8.** At night, music (echoes/echo) across the ranch.

_______________ **9.** Visitors (practices/practice) square dances.

_______________ **10.** Soon people of all ages quickly (falls/ fall) asleep.

Directions: Circle the linking verb in ( ) that agrees with the subject in each sentence. Write the verb on the line.

_______________ **11.** Many ranches (is/are) located in the Southwest.

_______________ **12.** The Double X Ranch (has/have) been in Arizona for almost 300 years.

_______________ **13.** Luis Martinez (was/were) the original owner.

_______________ **14.** His ancestors (has/have) raised cattle there ever since.

_______________ **15.** Martinez's great-grandson (is/are) in charge there today.

Notes for Home: Your child identified verbs that agree with their subjects. ***Home Activity:*** Because oral repetition helps students become familiar with the sound of correct agreement between subjects and verbs, have your child read the sentences in this activity aloud to you.

Practice

Grammar: Verb Tenses: Present, Past, and Future

The tense of a verb is a form that tells about time. It lets you know *when* something happens. A verb in the **present tense** shows action that is happening now. A verb in the **past tense** shows action that has already happened. A verb in the **future tense** shows action that will happen.

Present Tense: My horse gallops quickly.
Past Tense: My horse galloped quickly.
Future Tense: My horse will gallop quickly.

Verbs in the past tense often end in *-ed.* Verbs in the future tense include the helping verb *will.*

Directions: Write **present, past,** or **future** to tell the tense of each underlined verb.

____________ **1.** The horses whinnied.

____________ **2.** The gauchos ride well.

____________ **3.** They will tell us stories later.

____________ **4.** Now they rope calves.

____________ **5.** Yesterday, I roped a calf by myself!

Directions: Underline the verb in each sentence. Then write **present, past,** or **future** to tell the tense of the verb.

____________ **6.** On the pampas, the grass looks very green.

____________ **7.** After the rain, the air will seem damp.

____________ **8.** We visited one very large farm.

____________ **9.** We admired the herd of cows and the big flock of sheep.

____________ **10.** I love the pampas!

Notes for Home: Your child identified verb tenses: present, past, and future. ***Home Activity:*** Name an enjoyable thing to do (shopping at the market) and a time for doing it (tomorrow). Ask your child to say a sentence, using the verb correctly.

Grammar: Verb Tenses: Present, Past, and Future

Directions: Use the correct form of the verb in ( ) to complete each sentence. Use the verb tense named in ( ). Write the verb on the line to the left.

____________________ **1.** We _____ ostrich eggs to make a birthday cake for Julia. (need—present)

____________________ **2.** Last year, we _____ her a beautiful huge cake. (bake—past)

____________________ **3.** We know the ostrich _____ us through the grass. (chase—future)

____________________ **4.** Julia _____ her cake very much. (like—future)

____________________ **5.** Last time we threw her a party, Julia never _____ it. (expect—past)

Directions: Choose a verb from the box that best completes each sentence. On the line to the left, write the verb in the tense named in ( ).

eat
help
herd
show
stay

____________________ **6.** The gauchos _____ the cattle into a large group. (present)

____________________ **7.** I _____ the gauchos on the ranch last summer. (past)

____________________ **8.** My cousin _____ me how to ride. (past)

____________________ **9.** Every night, we _____ a delicious dinner with her family. (present)

____________________ **10.** Next summer, she and I _____ at her ranch again. (future)

Write a Journal Entry

Imagine you are spending the summer on a ranch. On a separate sheet of paper, write a journal entry telling what you did today and yesterday, and what you will do tomorrow. Use different verb tenses.

Notes for Home: Your child identified verb tenses: present *(cook),* past *(cooked),* and future *(will cook).* ***Home Activity:*** Invite your child to write the present, past, and future tense forms of such verbs as *play (play, played, will play)* and use them in a story or a rhyme.

Name ______________________________

RETEACHING

Grammar: Verb Tenses: Present, Past, and Future

These sentences use the verb **bake** in three ways. Write the underlined verb in each sentence.

1. She bakes apples. ______________ (present tense)

2. She baked apples. ______________ (past tense)

3. She will bake apples. ______________ (future tense)

The **tense** of a verb shows the time of the action. A verb may be written in the **present tense, past tense**, or **future tense**.

Directions: Write **present**, **past**, or **future** beside each verb.

1. helps ______________ **5.** will want ______________

2. enjoyed ______________ **6.** walk ______________

3. will roll ______________ **7.** roasted ______________

4. learns ______________ **8.** will boil ______________

Directions: Complete each sentence. Write the past-tense verb in ( ).

9. Dad ______________ the tomatoes. (peeled/will peel)

10. Pat and I ______________ the salad. (prepare/prepared)

11. Tony ______________ fresh bread. (served/will serve)

12. Mom ______________ the meat. (carves/carved)

13. The family ______________ together. (will work/worked)

14. People ______________ themselves. (helped/help)

15. Guests ______________ the dinner. (enjoy/enjoyed)

Notes for Home: Your child wrote verbs in the present, past, and future tenses. ***Home Activity:*** Listen to a favorite song together. Have your child point out verbs in the song and tell whether they are in the present, past, or future tense.

Name ___________________________________

Grammar: Verb Tenses: Present, Past, and Future

Directions: Underline the verb in each sentence. Then write **present**, **past**, or **future** to show the tense.

1. Serge drilled a hole in the tree. ____________________
2. He pushes a peg into the hole. ____________________
3. The sap will drip into a bucket. ____________________
4. We will take it to the sugarhouse. ____________________
5. Max pulls it on a sled. ____________________
6. We boiled it for a long time. ____________________
7. The water turned to steam. ____________________
8. Pure maple syrup remains. ____________________
9. We will pour it on pancakes. ____________________

Directions: Complete each sentence. Write the past-tense form of each verb in ( ).

10. Northern Native Americans ____________________ maple syrup. (discover)
11. Pioneers ____________________ some for clothes. (trade)
12. Traders ____________________ the "sweet water." (like)
13. People ____________________ more. (want)
14. The syrup ____________________ sweet. (taste)
15. Children ____________________ it. (enjoy)

Write a Description

On a separate sheet of paper, write a description of your favorite breakfast. Use future-tense verbs in your sentences.

Notes for Home: Your child identified and wrote verbs in the present, past, and future tenses. ***Home Activity:*** Have your child write about thoughts he or she had today. Remind your child to use verbs in the present, past, and future tenses.

Name ___________________________________

Word Study: Inflected Forms with -ed, -ing, -es

Directions: You can change a verb by adding endings, such as **-ed, -ing,** or **-es.** For some verbs, you don't need to change the base word when you add these endings. For other verbs, you might need to drop the final **e,** change a **y** to **i,** or double the final consonant. Add **-ed** and **-ing** to each base word. Write the new words on the lines.

Verbs That Don't Change	-ed	-ing
stay	1. ______________	2. ______________
turn	3. ______________	4. ______________

Verbs That Drop the Final e	-ed	-ing
chase	5. ______________	6. ______________
graze	7. ______________	8. ______________

Verbs That Double the Final Consonant	-ed	-ing
stop	9. ______________	10. ______________
drag	11. ______________	12. ______________

Directions: If the verb ends in **consonant** and **y,** change the **y** to **i** before adding **-ed** or **-es.** Keep the **y** before adding **-ing.** Add **-ed, -ing,** and **-es** to the word **try.**

13. try + -ed = ______________________

14. try + -ing = ______________________

15. try + -es = ______________________

Notes for Home: Your child added *-ed, -ing,* and *-es* to verbs. ***Home Activity:*** Read a story with your child. Help your child find verbs with these endings.

Name ______________________________

Spelling: Adding *-ed* and *-ing*

Pretest Directions: Fold back the page along the dotted line. On the blanks, write the spelling words as they are dictated. When you have finished the test, unfold the page and check your words.

1. ______________________________
2. ______________________________
3. ______________________________
4. ______________________________
5. ______________________________
6. ______________________________
7. ______________________________
8. ______________________________
9. ______________________________
10. ______________________________
11. ______________________________
12. ______________________________
13. ______________________________
14. ______________________________
15. ______________________________
16. ______________________________
17. ______________________________
18. ______________________________
19. ______________________________
20. ______________________________

1. I wonder what **happened** to it.
2. She **opened** the door slowly.
3. They **danced** all night.
4. He **studied** very hard.
5. We finally **stopped** running.
6. The cat **chased** its prey.
7. He wears a **worried** look.
8. He likes **dried** flowers.
9. The snake **robbed** the nest.
10. The jewels **slipped** off her neck.
11. What's **happening**?
12. It's **opening** night at the theater.
13. We were **dancing** at the party.
14. Are you **studying** for your test?
15. Why are we **stopping**?
16. The dog's **chasing** his tail.
17. Stop **worrying**!
18. The clothes are **drying** in the sun.
19. Those men are **robbing** the store.
20. I feel my foot **slipping**.

Notes for Home: Your child took a pretest on adding *-ed* and *-ing* to words. ***Home Activity:*** Help your child learn misspelled words before the final test. Have your child divide misspelled words into parts (such as base words and endings) and concentrate on each part.

Name ___________________________

Spelling: Adding *-ed* and *-ing*

Word List				
happened	danced	stopped	worried	robbed
happening	dancing	stopping	worrying	robbing
opened	studied	chased	dried	slipped
opening	studying	chasing	drying	slipping

Directions: Choose the words from the box in which the spelling of the base word changed before **-ed** and **-ing** was added. Write each word in the correct category.

Final Consonant Doubled

1. ________________
2. ________________
3. ________________
4. ________________
5. ________________
6. ________________

Final e Dropped

7. ________________
8. ________________
9. ________________
10. ________________

Directions: Choose the word from the box that best completes each sentence. Write the word on the line to the left.

________________ **11.** What _____ today at the ranch?

________________ **12.** After the rain stopped, the ground _____ up.

________________ **13.** It was time for the dude ranch gates to be _____.

________________ **14.** But it was too wet for anything to be _____ outside.

________________ **15.** Inside, there was an _____ in one of the classes.

________________ **16.** I _____ how to build a campfire.

________________ **17.** Other people were _____ their laundry.

________________ **18.** That night I spent time _____ how to rope.

________________ **19.** It sounded fun, but I began _____ about doing it right.

________________ **20.** The other people told me that I _____ too much.

Notes for Home: Your child spelled words ending in *-ed* and *-ing*. ***Home Activity:*** Together, write each spelling word on an index card. Take turns drawing two cards at a time to try to match pairs of words with the same base word.

Spelling: Adding -*ed* and -*ing*

Directions: Proofread this section of a travel brochure. Find four spelling mistakes. Use the proofreading marks to correct each mistake.

≡	Make a capital.
/	Make a small letter.
∧	Add something.
ᒍ	Take out something.
⊙	Add a period.
¶	Begin a new paragraph.

Stop worriing about having nothing to do. The Busy Bee Ranch will soon have you riding, roping, chaseing cattle, and square danceing with real ranch folk.

Been working too hard? Been studing too hard? It's time you tried something exciting and new. Come visit the Busy Bee Ranch—you'll be glad you did!

Word List

happened	chased
happening	chasing
opened	worried
opening	worrying
danced	dried
dancing	drying
studied	robbed
studying	robbing
stopped	slipped
stopping	slipping

Spelling Tip

chasing **studied** **worrying**

With words that end in a **consonant** and **e,** the **e** is dropped before adding the ending **-ing** or **-ed.** In words that end in a **consonant** and **y,** the **y** is changed to **i** when adding **-ed.** The **y** is kept when adding **-ing.**

Write a Travel Brochure

On a separate sheet of paper, write a paragraph for a travel brochure. Describe a place that you know or have read about. Make it sound like a great place to visit. Try to use at least four spelling words.

Notes for Home: Your child spelled words ending in *-ed* and *-ing.* ***Home Activity:*** Have your child write a paragraph about a trip he or she took that was fun. Together, underline the words your child used that end in *-ed* and *-ing.*

Name ______________________________

Spelling: Adding *-ed* and *-ing* REVIEW

Word List

happened	danced	stopped	worried	robbed
happening	dancing	stopping	worrying	robbing
opened	studied	chased	dried	slipped
opening	studying	chasing	drying	slipping

Directions: Add **-ed** and **-ing** to each base word below to form a word from the box.

Base Word	Add -ed	Add -ing
happen	**1.** ________	**2.** ________
dance	**3.** ________	**4.** ________
study	**5.** ________	**6.** ________
worry	**7.** ________	**8.** ________
rob	**9.** ________	**10.** ________
slip	**11.** ________	**12.** ________
chase	**13.** ________	**14.** ________

Directions: Choose the word from the box that is the most opposite in meaning for each word below. Write the word on the line.

15. closed ________________

16. starting ________________

17. wetting ________________

18. shutting ________________

19. began ________________

20. soaked ________________

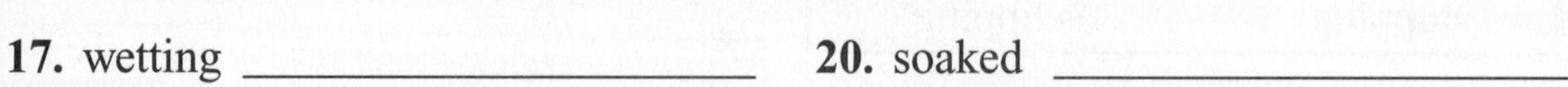

Notes for Home: Your child spelled words that end in *-ed* and *-ing*. ***Home Activity:*** Together, write the base word for each spelling word, such as *study* for *studying* and *studied*. Take turns flipping a coin. Add *-ed* to the base word if the coin shows "heads." Add *-ing* if it shows "tails."

Evaluate Information/Draw Conclusions

When you research information, you need to **evaluate** it to see if the information is accurate and up-to-date. You also need to make sure it meets the needs of your project. For example, a newspaper article might be up-to-date, but it may not have the information you need. When you find information you can use, you need to **draw conclusions** about it by deciding for yourself what the information means.

Directions: Read this encyclopedia entry about cattle. Use the information to answer the questions that follow.

Cattle: The Global Picture

In 1995, there were about $1\frac{1}{4}$ billion beef and dairy cattle in the world. More than one third of the cattle are raised in Asia. Many millions more are raised in South America. India has more cattle than any other country in the world, but the demand for meat in India is low because many people there believe that the cow is a sacred animal.

A century ago, there were 60 million cattle in the United States. In the early 1990s, the U.S. Department of Agriculture estimated that this number had grown to close to 100 million. During this same time period, each American ate about 67 pounds of beef a year and drank about 100 quarts of milk.

Name ______________________________

1. If you wanted to find information about the topic "Life on the Range," would this encyclopedia article be useful? Explain.

____

____

2. Would this encyclopedia article be considered "up-to-date" if you were trying to find out about the number of cattle in the world currently? Explain.

____

____

____

3. About how many pounds of beef does an American eat each year? About how much milk does an American drink each year? Why do you think data about milk consumption was given?

____

____

____

____

4. According to the entry, in which country are cows treated as sacred animals? Where did you find this information?

____

5. Would you say that the information presented would help you prepare a report on fast food in America? Why?

____

____

____

Notes for Home: Your child read an encyclopedia entry to gather information and draw conclusions about it. ***Home Activity:*** Discuss with your child ways to find out more information about a particular topic. Talk about what resources would have useful content.

Family Times

Name____

Summary

Boy Saves Horses and Survives a Tornado!

Ever since his accident, Jonathan has worked hard to make himself strong and capable in his wheelchair. One afternoon, his mother leaves him in charge of bringing in the horses on the family farm while she and his father are elsewhere. A huge storm is brewing. Jonathan likes most storms, but this no ordinary storm—it's a tornado. The story tells how Jonathan saves the horses—and himself.

Activity

Be a News Reporter. Invite your child to play the part of news reporter and tell you about Jonathan's adventure. Encourage your child to summarize the key events in the story and describe Jonathan's thoughts and feelings.

Reading Skills

Predicting

To **predict** means to tell what you think might happen next in a story, based on what has already happened. Your **prediction** is what you say will happen.

As you read, check and change your predictions based on new information.

For example, Jonathan holds out some sugar cubes to coax one of the horses to come to him. If you know that horses like sugar, you might predict that the horse will calm down long enough to eat. When you read that one horse calms down, you might go on to predict that the second horse will too.

Activity

Tell the Future. As a family, watch a TV show or movie. During commercial breaks, each family member writes down a prediction of what will happen next. Check everyone's predictions at the next break.

Family Times

Tested Vocabulary

Words to Know

Knowing the meanings of these words is important to reading *The Storm.* Practice using these words to learn their meanings.

accident something harmful or unlucky that happens unexpectedly

coaxed persuaded gently

nuzzled rubbed with the nose

soothing calming; comforting

tornado violent and destructive whirlwind

wail a sound that is like a long, loud cry

Grammar

Using Correct Verb Tenses

The **tense** of a verb is the time in which the action takes place—past, present, or future. When you are writing, be sure to keep the same tense for actions that happen during the same time.

The verbs in the following sentences are all in past tense. They tell about something that already happened. **Jo soothed the horses. She coaxed them back to the barn. She stroked Lightning's mane and led Thunder into his stall.**

Activity

Add on to a Story. Read the sentences above. Then add on to them to tell your own story about Jo and her horses. Be sure to keep the same tense for actions that happen during the same time.

Tested Spelling Words

______	______	______	______
______	______	______	______
______	______	______	______
______	______	______	______
______	______	______	______

Name ______________________________

Predicting

- To **predict** means to tell what you think might happen next in a story or article based on what has already happened. Your prediction is what you say will happen next.
- Predicting is a process of checking and changing your predictions as you read, based on new information.

Directions: Reread "Summer Surfers." Fill in the prediction table. For each story event, tell what logical predictions can be made based on what you have read up to that point in the story. One prediction has been done for you.

What Happened	What Might Happen
Ben and the seal surfed side by side.	Ben and the seal will become friends.
Ben couldn't take his eyes off the seal.	**1.**
Ben fell off his board and struck a rock.	**2.**
Ben was forced upward and saw sunlight again.	**3.**
The seal flipped Ben onto his board.	**4.**
Once he caught his breath, Ben felt fine.	**5.**

Notes for Home: Your child read a story and used story details and life experience to make predictions about what will happen next in a story. ***Home Activity:*** Watch a favorite TV show with your child. During the commercial breaks, predict what will happen next.

Name ________________________________

Vocabulary

Directions: Choose the word from the box that best completes each sentence. Write the word on the matching numbered line to the right.

One of the worst kinds of storms is a **1.** _____. When a bad storm is coming, the long, loud **2.** _____ of an alarm sounds a warning. During the last storm, we hid in the cellar. My dog Floppy pressed close and **3.** _____ me the whole time. He was scared too! Having him near me was **4.** _____ and comforting. After the storm passed, I **5.** _____ him to come out of the cellar by offering him a biscuit.

1. ________________
2. ________________
3. ________________
4. ________________
5. ________________

Check the Words You Know

__ accident
__ coaxed
__ nuzzled
__ soothing
__ tornado
__ wail

Directions: Cross out the word that does not belong in each group.

6. accident	disaster	plan	crash
7. wail	shout	scream	whisper
8. tornado	hurricane	breeze	storm
9. soothing	calming	quieting	annoying
10. coaxed	demanded	begged	asked

Write a TV Weather Report

On a separate sheet of paper, write a TV weather report telling listeners that a big storm is coming their way. Tell people what they should do to stay safe. Use as many of the vocabulary words as you can.

Notes for Home: Your child identified and used vocabulary words from *The Storm*. ***Home Activity:*** Talk with your child about bad storms and what to do in order to stay safe during one. Use as many vocabulary words as possible.

Name ___________________________________

Predicting

- **Predicting** means telling what you think might happen next in a story or article, based on what has already happened.
- Your prediction can change as you read, based on new information.

Directions: Reread the passage from *The Storm*. Think about the predictions you made while reading. Answer the questions below based on reading this passage.

It was so incredible that for a moment he simply stared. From the rise of the farmyard he watched the snakelike funnel slowly twist across the distant fields and broaden into a larger blackness. Before his eyes it became a black wall headed straight for the farm. Fear replaced amazement. He hurried back across the lot. The wind was shrieking now. But before he could get to the house, he heard horses.

Looking back, there were Buster and Henry tearing madly around the inner lot. How could they have gotten out? He didn't know. And not just Buster, but Henry, pride and joy of his father. Jonathan couldn't think if he had time or not, if it was safe or not.

1. Does it seem likely that the tornado will strike the farm?

____

2. Do you think Buster and Henry will go back into the barn by themselves?

____

3. What might Jonathan do to help save Buster and Henry?

____

4. What do you think might happen if Jonathan gets Buster and Henry back into the barn?

____

5. As you read *The Storm,* what predictions did you make? Did any of your predictions change as you continued reading? Explain.

Notes for Home: Your child used story details to predict what will happen next. ***Home Activity:*** Name a situation (such as forgetting to turn off the bath water). Ask your child to predict what might happen next.

Name ___________________________

Selection Test

Directions: Choose the best answer to each item. Mark the letter for the answer you have chosen.

Part 1: Vocabulary

Find the answer choice that means about the same as the underlined word in each sentence.

1. That was a coyote's <u>wail</u>.
A. baby animal
B. long, sad call
C. wild animal's home
D. mark made by a foot or paw

2. I <u>coaxed</u> the horse into the barn.
F. trapped
G. pushed from behind
H. tied with a rope
J. persuaded gently

3. We were caught in a <u>tornado</u>.
A. fast-moving water
B. trap for catching animals
C. destructive, whirling wind
D. sudden attack

4. Gus was in a bicycle <u>accident</u>.
F. something harmful that happens unexpectedly
G. important race
H. parade
J. repair shop

5. Alan was <u>soothing</u> the animals.
A. exciting
B. calming
C. feeding
D. gathering

6. The dog <u>nuzzled</u> Laura's hand.
F. rubbed with the nose
G. pushed away roughly
H. took quick small bites
J. looked at in a fearful way

Part 2: Comprehension

Use what you know about the story to answer each item.

7. What did Jonathan love?
A. street noise
B. trucks
C. hot weather
D. watching thunderstorms

8. How did Jonathan lose the use of his legs?
F. He was hit by a truck.
G. He was born that way.
H. A tree fell on his legs.
J. He fell off his bicycle.

GO ON

9. Jonathan's mom left the house to—
- A. buy a new car.
- B. have her car fixed.
- C. pick up Jonathan's dad.
- D. go food shopping.

10. When the wind rose and the sky turned a green-yellow color, you could predict that—
- F. the house would be ruined.
- G. there would be no storm.
- H. it would soon be night.
- J. a tornado was coming.

11. During the tornado, where was the safest place for Jonathan?
- A. in the root cellar
- B. inside the house
- C. outside in the yard
- D. under a tree

12. Jonathan probably cried when he found the rooster because he—
- F. had loved that bird.
- G. was worried about his parents.
- H. suddenly realized the same thing could have happened to him.
- J. knew his parents would be angry at him for leaving the animals.

13. You can tell from this story that tornadoes are—
- A. similar to snowstorms.
- B. very powerful and dangerous.
- C. impossible to escape from.
- D. nothing to be afraid of.

14. What bothered Jonathan most about being in a wheelchair?
- F. He could not play games.
- G. People saw his "condition" rather than the person he was.
- H. He could not feed the horses.
- J. He disliked having to ask other people for help.

15. As a result of his experience in the storm, Jonathan felt—
- A. guilty that he was not able to save the rooster.
- B. angry at his parents for leaving him alone during a storm.
- C. afraid that his parents would leave him alone again.
- D. better about himself and how others would see him.

STOP

Name ______________________________

Predicting

- **Predicting** means telling what you think might happen next in a story, based on what has already happened.
- Your prediction can change as you read, based on new information.

Directions: Read the story below.

When the hurricane watch came, Mom and I were on the hotel porch drinking lemonade. But the sky was blue and the water was calm. Mom just laughed and said we'd beat the storm home.

When the hurricane warning came, we were gathering shells on the beach. The sky was gray, and the water was rough. People were pulling boats out of the water. Mom said we'd be safer inside.

We sat with fifty other people in the hotel living room, behind strong shutters. We could only wait to see if the hurricane would hit. I felt calm, but Mom acted nervous. Suddenly, the wind picked up. Then came a bang at the door.

Directions: Fill in the boxes by predicting two events that could happen after each event listed. One has been done for you.

The wind picked up.	Mom acted nervous.	There was a bang at the door.
↓	↓	↓
The hurricane hit the hotel.	**2.**	**4.**
Or	**Or**	**Or**
1.	**3.**	**5.**

Notes for Home: Your child has read a story and predicted two possible events that might happen. ***Home Activity:*** Read a story with your child, pausing at various places to predict what will happen next. Continue reading, pausing to check and change predictions.

Name ____________________

Drawing Conclusions and Character

REVIEW

Directions: Read the story. Then read each question about the story. Choose the best answer to each question. Mark the letter for the answer you have chosen.

What You're Made Of

Jane's English cousins were visiting. When Jane said there was a tornado watch, Will asked if they'd watch it on TV.

"No, we have to watch *out* for one," Jane said gently.

"Should I stay by the window?" asked Violet.

"No," said Jane just as gently. But she frowned. "If it becomes a warning, then we have to go down to the shelter."

Two hours later, Jane led her cousins down to the shelter. "We'll wait out the storm here," she said. Will looked afraid. Jane put an arm around him.

"You'll be okay," she said in a soothing voice. "Show us what you're made of."

1. Will asked if he would watch the tornado on TV because—
- **A.** he was bored.
- **B.** he thought that's what Jane meant.
- **C.** nothing else was on.
- **D.** he was joking.

2. Why didn't Violet's idea make sense?
- **F.** It would be boring.
- **G.** Violet was too young to be the look-out.
- **H.** It would be dangerous.
- **J.** She wouldn't be able to see the tornado.

3. Why did Jane lead her cousins into the shelter?
- **A.** She was showing it off.
- **B.** The danger of the tornado had increased.
- **C.** The tornado hit the house.
- **D.** Everyone was bored.

4. When Jane answers gently, she shows she is—
- **F.** making fun of her cousins.
- **G.** insecure.
- **H.** afraid.
- **J.** kind.

5. Jane puts her arm around Will to try to—
- **A.** help him be less afraid.
- **B.** keep him from falling.
- **C.** make him go to the shelter.
- **D.** keep him from leaving.

Notes for Home: Your child drew conclusions about the characters in a story. ***Home Activity:*** Read or tell a story about someone who was brave. Ask your child to draw conclusions about the character and the character's actions.

Name ______________________________

Writing Across Texts

Directions: Consider what the scene looked like after the tornado hit in *The Storm.* Then recall what you learned about the effects of a tornado in "Tornado Tales." Record your ideas in the table below.

The Storm	Tornado Tales
The barn was full of litter and debris.	Stalks of straw were driven through poles.
1.	**6.**
2.	**7.**
3.	**8.**
4.	**9.**
5.	**10.**

Write a Descriptive Paragraph

Write a news story describing the scene after a tornado has hit. Use some of the details that you have recorded above. Make sure that all of the details have to do with the effects of the tornado.

Notes for Home: Your child used information from two reading selections to report on the effects of a tornado. ***Home Activity:*** Discuss severe weather that is likely to occur in your area. Help your child make a list of family safety rules in case of such an emergency.

Grammar: Verb Tenses: Past, Present, and Future

REVIEW

Directions: Circle the verb in each sentence. Write **past, present,** or **future** on the line to name the tense of each verb.

__________ **1.** Forecasters on TV predict an approaching tornado.

__________ **2.** Sometimes tornadoes will catch people outside.

__________ **3.** Last year a man saved himself.

__________ **4.** He jumped into a ditch.

__________ **5.** Tornado warnings save many lives.

Directions: Follow the directions below. Write each new sentence on the line.

6. Rewrite sentence 1 in the past tense.

____

7. Rewrite sentence 2 in the present tense.

____

8. Rewrite sentence 3 in the present tense.

____

9. Rewrite sentence 4 in the future tense.

____

10. Rewrite sentence 5 in the future tense.

____

Notes for Home: Your child identified the three main tenses of a verb. ***Home Activity:*** Ask your child to say the following verbs in all three tenses: *talk, want, laugh, watch,* and *walk.* Have your child create sentences that use each of the three tenses of *talk.*

Practice

Name ____________________________________

Grammar: Using Correct Verb Tenses

To form the **present tense** of most verbs, add **-s** or **-es** if a subject is a singular noun or is *he, she,* or *it:* A baby bird chirps. The mother watches.

Do not add an ending to the verb if the subject is plural: Birds live in nests.

To form the **past tense** of most verbs, add **-ed: raked, tasted, walked.**

When a one-syllable verb ends in a single vowel followed by a single consonant, double the final consonant before adding **-ed: hugged.**

When a verb ends in a **consonant** and **y**, change the **y** to **i** before adding **-ed: copied.**

A verb whose past tense does not end in **-ed** is called an **irregular verb.** You will need to remember how to form the past tense of irregular verbs: **held, drew, sang.**

Directions: Circle the correct verb form in ( ) to complete each sentence. Use a dictionary if you need help with irregular verbs.

1. Every year my friends (watch/watches) *The Wizard of Oz* on TV.
2. Last weekend they (see/saw) the movie again.
3. L. Frank Baum (writes/wrote) the original book.
4. Yesterday, I (asks/asked) them about the movie.
5. Tina said her favorite part (was/were) when the tornado took Dorothy to the land of Oz.
6. In Oklahoma, where we all (live/lived), we get tornadoes too.
7. Last year, a tornado (sweeps/swept) through our town.
8. We (go/went) to the cellar and stayed there for hours.
9. At first the noise of the tornado was very loud, but then suddenly it (stopped/stops).
10. After a while, we (heard/hear) the "all clear" signal and left our shelter.

Notes for Home: Your child identified verb tenses. ***Home Activity:*** Use four or five sentences to tell your child a story. Use the present tense *(A baby robin falls from its nest).* Then, have your child retell it using the past tense verbs.

Name ______________________

Grammar: Using Correct Verb Tenses

Directions: Use the correct form of the verb in ( ) to complete each sentence. Write the verb on the line to the left. Use a dictionary if you need help with irregular verbs.

______________ **1.** Usually, tornadoes (move) very swiftly.

______________ **2.** Often, the powerful wind (destroy) things in its path.

______________ **3.** Yesterday, a strange whirling cloud (appear).

______________ **4.** I was walking home when I (notice) it.

______________ **5.** I (run) to a safe place as fast as I could!

Directions: Use a verb from the box to complete each sentence. Write the verb in the correct tense on the line to the left. Use a dictionary if you need help with irregular verbs.

cry	fall	place	plant	snap

______________ **6.** Last year my favorite tree _____ in a bad storm.

______________ **7.** The strong wind _____ it in two.

______________ **8.** I was so sad that I _____ for days.

______________ **9.** An hour ago, we _____ a new tree in the yard.

______________ **10.** My father dug the hole, and I _____ the tree in it.

Write a Letter to a Friend

Were you ever caught in a bad storm? Was the experience scary? What did you do? On a separate sheet of paper, write a letter to a friend about your experience. You can describe a real experience, or you can make one up. Try to use verbs in different tenses.

Notes for Home: Your child wrote verbs in different tenses to show when something occurred. ***Home Activity:*** Play a verb game with your child. Take turns naming a verb and naming that verb's past tense.

Name ______________________________

RETEACHING

Grammar: Using Correct Verb Tenses

Read each sentence. Write the correct form of the verb in ( ) on the line.

1. The bright sun (shine—present tense) ____________________ .
2. Yesterday I (cook—past tense) ____________________ soup.
3. Then I (dip—past tense) ____________________ berries in chocolate.
4. I was late for school, so I (hurry—past tense) ____________________ .
5. I could not read what he (write—past tense) ____________________ .

Add **-s** or **-es** to form the present-tense form of most verbs if the subject is singular. Add **-ed** to form the past-tense form of most verbs. When a one-syllable verb ends in a single vowel followed by a single consonant, double the final consonant before adding **-ed**. When a verb ends in a consonant and **y**, change the **y** to **i** before adding **-ed**. A verb whose past-tense form does not end in **-ed** is an irregular verb. You will need to remember the forms of these verbs.

Directions: Underline the correct verb form in ( ) to complete each sentence. Use a dictionary if you need help with irregular verbs.

1. Usually my family (likes/liked) to eat dinner together.
2. Although we were busy, we (eat/ate) together every night last week.
3. Sometimes my mom (makes/make) dinner, and sometimes my dad does.
4. Last night my dad (hurry/hurried) home to make dinner.
5. Then my mom and I (jogged/jogs) after dinner.
6. When we got home, my stepbrother (ask/asked) for help with math.
7. I was tired, but I (finish/finished) my homework by eight o'clock.
8. Then I finally (went/go) to bed!

Notes for Home: Your child identified correct verb tenses in sentences. ***Home Activity:*** Have your child point out verbs in a story and tell what tense they are. Then have him or her write new sentences, using the verbs from the story. Challenge him or her to change the tenses of the verbs.

Name ____________________

Grammar: Using Correct Verb Tenses

Directions: Use a verb from the box to complete each sentence. Write the verb in the correct tense on the line. Use a dictionary if you need help with irregular verbs.

bake	call	decide	dry	earn	give	hug	lick
make	start	tell	wag	wash	worry	write	

____________ (present) **1.** My teacher _______ us a week to do an assignment.

____________ (past) **2.** I _______ about a kite on a string.

____________ (past) **3.** Our dog _______ his tail.

____________ (past) **4.** I wanted to play with him, so I _______ him.

____________ (past) **5.** He came over to me and he _______ my hand.

____________ (present) **6.** My older sister _______ dinner on Monday nights.

____________ (past) **7.** After dinner, Sam ______ the dishes and I ______ them.

____

____________ (past) **8.** He _______ that he wouldn't have time to play.

____________ (past) **9.** I _______ him he had an hour left before his bedtime.

____________ (past) **10.** Sam was so happy that he _______ me.

____________ (present) **11.** Renee _______ brownies and muffins to raise money for her club.

____________ (past) **12.** She and Shaunna _______ the club a year ago.

____________ (past) **13.** They _______ twenty dollars in one weekend.

____________ (past) **14.** But the club hasn't _______ what to do with the money!

Notes for Home: Your child wrote verb tenses in sentences. ***Home Activity:*** Make flashcards with your child. Help your child identify which verbs he or she has trouble remembering how to write in the present and past tenses. Then make flashcards for the difficult verbs.

Name ______________________________

Phonics: Consonant Sounds /j/, /ks/, /kw/

Directions: The sound /j/ can be spelled **dge** or **ge** as in **ledge** or **change.** The sound /ks/ can be spelled **x** or **xc** as in **fox** or **except.** The sound /kw/ can be spelled **qu** as in **quick.** Read each word below. Sort each word by the sounds you hear. Write each word in the correct column.

fidget	box	quiet	coaxed	huge
quite	sixty	ledge	explore	quilt

/j/	/ks/	/kw/
1. ____________	4. ____________	8. ____________
2. ____________	5. ____________	9. ____________
3. ____________	6. ____________	10. ____________
	7. ____________	

Directions: Read each sentence. Listen for the word that has the consonant sounds /j/, /ks/, or /kw/. Write the word on the line. Circle the letters that represent that sound.

______________ **11.** The weather forecaster changed her report to include a tornado warning.

______________ **12.** The storm hit the edge of town.

______________ **13.** It was exciting to see the storm, but frightening too.

______________ **14.** Just as quickly as it had come up, the storm died out.

______________ **15.** People who saw the tornado tried to explain what it was like.

Notes for Home: Your child practiced identifying consonant sounds: **/j/** in *ledge* and *change,* **/ks/** in *fox* and *except,* and the **/kw/** in *quick.* ***Home Activity:*** Read a newspaper story with your child. Challenge your child to listen for words with these sounds and point them out.

Name ______________________________

Pretest

Spelling: Words with /j/, /ks/, /kw/

Pretest Directions: Fold back the page along the dotted line. On the blanks, write the spelling words as they are dictated. When you have finished the test, unfold the page and check your words.

1. ______________________
2. ______________________
3. ______________________
4. ______________________
5. ______________________
6. ______________________
7. ______________________
8. ______________________
9. ______________________
10. ______________________
11. ______________________
12. ______________________
13. ______________________
14. ______________________
15. ______________________
16. ______________________
17. ______________________
18. ______________________
19. ______________________
20. ______________________

1. There's a **change** in the weather.
2. The **village** is not far away.
3. I live at the **edge** of town.
4. I know them all **except** her.
5. He's very **excited** about the party.
6. She can **explain** how it works.
7. We don't **expect** much trouble.
8. **Texas** is a large state.
9. The train was **quick** and noisy.
10. The two pies are **equal**.
11. I'm in **charge** of this project.
12. The **bridge** was his only shelter.
13. The **fudge** is still cooking.
14. That meal was **excellent**.
15. Now, we can **relax**.
16. Do you have any **extra** sugar?
17. The **queen** was in her palace.
18. Please buy a **quart** of milk.
19. What's the **liquid** in that cup?
20. This was my mother's **quilt**.

Notes for Home: Your child took a pretest on words that have the sounds /j/, /ks/, and /kw/. ***Home Activity:*** Help your child learn misspelled words before the final test. Dictate the word and have your child spell the word aloud for you or write it on paper.

Name ______________________

Spelling: Words with /j/, /ks/, /kw/

Word List				
change	bridge	explain	relax	queen
village	fudge	expect	extra	quart
edge	except	Texas	quick	liquid
charge	excited	excellent	equal	quilt

Directions: Choose the words from the box that have the sound /ks/ as in **expert** and **excuse.** Write the word on the line.

1. ______________ **4.** ______________ **7.** ______________

2. ______________ **5.** ______________ **8.** ______________

3. ______________ **6.** ______________

Directions: Choose the word from the box that best matches each clue. Write the word on the line.

______________ **9.** This means "the same as."

______________ **10.** A building ledge is one kind of this.

______________ **11.** Jack be nimble, Jack be _____.

______________ **12.** Trolls live under it.

______________ **13.** This chocolate treat is very sweet.

______________ **14.** A princess might become this.

______________ **15.** It's smaller than a city.

______________ **16.** Everyone needs some of this, or life becomes boring.

______________ **17.** Water is this, and so is milk.

______________ **18.** It's one-fourth of a gallon.

______________ **19.** Wild animals sometimes do this when they're scared.

______________ **20.** This covering keeps you warm at night.

Notes for Home: Your child spelled words with the sounds /j/ spelled *ge* or *dge,* /ks/ spelled *x* and *xc,* and /kw/ spelled *qu.* ***Home Activity:*** Have your child list more words with these sounds and spellings. Ask for which sound he or she can list the most words.

Name ____________________

Spelling: Words with /j/, /ks/, /kw/

Directions: Proofread this weather report. Find five spelling mistakes. Use the proofreading marks to correct each mistake.

≡	Make a capital.
/	Make a small letter.
∧	Add something.
ℊ	Take out something.
⊙	Add a period.
¶	Begin a new paragraph.

Report for Central Texas

Two counties in central Texxas were hit by a tornado yesterday afternoon. Residents in the whole area were told to espect high winds and heavy rain. The storm was quik, though, and there wasn't much damage. Fortunately, the storm did not hit each county with ekwel force. One villadge did report the loss of the main bridge.

Word List

change	fudge	Texas	equal
village	except	excellent	queen
edge	excited	relax	quart
charge	explain	extra	liquid
bridge	expect	quick	quilt

Spelling Tip

change edge
except explain
quick

The sound /j/ can be spelled **ge** or **dge.** The sound /ks/ can be spelled **xc** or **x.** The sound /kw/ can be spelled **qu.**

Write a Weather Report

On a separate sheet of paper, write a short weather report for your area. Try to use at least three spelling words.

Notes for Home: Your child spelled words with the sounds /j/, /ks/, and /kw/. ***Home Activity:*** Write a list of these spelling words, but deliberately misspell some of them. Challenge your child to check the list and correct any misspellings.

Name ______________________________________

REVIEW

Spelling: Words with /j/, /ks/, /kw/

Word List				
change	bridge	explain	relax	queen
village	fudge	expect	extra	quart
edge	except	Texas	quick	liquid
charge	excited	excellent	equal	quilt

Directions: Write the word from the box that belongs in each group.

1. superb, great, ____________

2. princess, king, ____________

3. same, identical, ____________

4. Utah, Oklahoma, ____________

5. eager, thrilled, ____________

6. blanket, comforter, ____________

7. calm down, rest, ____________

8. fast, swift, ____________

9. cookies, cake, ____________

10. tunnel, ferry, ____________

11. cliff, ledge, ____________

12. cup, pint, ____________

Directions: Choose the word from the box that best completes each sentence. Write the word on the line to the left.

____________ **13.** The weatherman said to _____ a tornado.

____________ **14.** He started to _____ what would happen.

____________ **15.** The _____ where we lived was put on alert.

____________ **16.** He said the sky would start to _____.

____________ **17.** He said everyone should be _____ careful.

____________ **18.** He suggested we go into our cellars with enough _____ to drink.

____________ **19.** The store owners were not allowed to _____ any more than usual.

____________ **20.** That was all we could do, _____ hope for the best.

Notes for Home: Your child spelled words with the sounds /j/, /ks/, and /kw/. ***Home Activity:*** Have your child make a list of the different ways each of the three sounds can be spelled. Together, identify which spelling words are examples of the different spellings for these sounds.

Name ____________________

Almanac

An **almanac** is a book that is published every year. It contains calendars, weather information, and dates of holidays. It also contains many charts and tables of current information about subjects such as city population and recent prize winners in science, literature, or sports.

Directions: Review this information from an almanac. Use the information to answer the questions that follow.

Tornado Facts

- The width of a tornado can vary from a few meters to a kilometer.
- Their "funnels" are made visible by dust that they suck up from the ground.
- Most tornadoes spin counterclockwise in the northern hemisphere and clockwise in the southern hemisphere.
- Tornado damage is caused by winds that often move at speeds of more than 300 miles per hour.

Notable U.S. Tornadoes Since 1980

Date	Location	Deaths
June 3, 1980	Grand Island, NE	4
March 2–4, 1982	South, Midwest	17
May 29, 1982	Southern IL	10
May 18–22, 1983	Texas	12
March 28, 1984	N. Carolina, S. Carolina	57
April 21–22, 1984	Mississippi	15

Measuring Tornadoes

Tornadoes are measured by the Fujita (or F) scale, created by T. Theodore Fujita. The F scale rates tornadoes on a scale of 0–5.

Rank	Wind Speed (mi/hr)	Damage	Strength
F-0	Up to 72 mi/hr	Light	Weak
F-1	73–112 mi/hr	Moderate	Weak
F-2	113–157 mi/hr	Considerable	Strong
F-3	158–206 mi/hr	Severe	Strong
F-4	207–260 mi/hr	Devastating	Violent
F-5	More than 261 mi/hr	Incredible	Violent

Name ______________________________

1. If you wanted to know if a strong wind where you live was tornado strength, what section of the almanac page would you look at?

2. Which notable tornado caused the greatest number of deaths? Give the date and location of this tornado. How is this information presented in the almanac?

3. What information can you find about the size of tornadoes?

4. If a tornado's wind speed is 200 mi/hr, what would the damage level be according to the Fujita scale?

5. When might you want to use an almanac as a resource instead of an encyclopedia? Explain.

Notes for Home: Your child read and interpreted information about tornadoes found in an almanac. ***Home Activity:*** Look at an almanac together. Take turns sharing interesting and/or useful information you find.

Family Times

Name____

Summary

Mongoose Kills Cobras and Saves Family!

Rikki-tikki-tavi has a big job to do. This mongoose must kill all the snakes that live in the house and garden of Teddy and his mother and father. The largest snakes are two cobras, Nag and Nagaina, who want to kill everyone in the family so that they and their babies will have the garden all to themselves. Rikki uses cunning as well as strength. He tricks the adult snakes, feeds their eggs to the ants, and succeeds in killing them all. Teddy's grateful family rewards Rikki with all he can eat, and Rikki himself is proud and satisfied with his success.

Activity

Make up New Dialogue. Pretend that another mongoose comes to visit Rikki-tikki-tavi. Help your child write or tell what Rikki would say about life in the house and garden.

Reading Skills

Drawing Conclusions

A **conclusion** is a decision you reach that makes sense after you think about details or facts in what you read. When you read, draw conclusions by looking at the details and making decisions about the characters and what happens in the story.

For example, Rikki-tikki-tavi asks Darzee where Nagaina's eggs are. Rikki has killed Nag, and we know he wants to kill Nagaina. He tells Darzee he is not going to *eat* the eggs. By everything that has happened already, you could draw the conclusion that he plans to do something to keep the baby cobras from hatching.

Activity

Play a Detective Game. Have one person think of a person, place, or thing and give three clues about its identity, for example, "I'm not in the bedroom; I'm in a room with lots of windows; You look in me when you're hungry." Have another person try to draw a conclusion about what the person, place, or thing is (a refrigerator). Don't make the clues too easy or too hard!

Family Times

Tested Vocabulary

Words to Know

Knowing the meaning of these words is important to reading *Rikki-tikki-tavi.* Practice using these words to learn their meanings.

cobra a large, poisonous snake of Asia or Africa that flattens its neck like a hood when excited

coiled wound around into a pile or a curl

lame unable to walk properly

plunged threw with force into something

triumph victory; success

Grammar

Review of Verbs

Words that show action are called **action verbs.** Many verbs show action that you can see: **jump, run.** Some verbs show action that you cannot see: **think, feel.**

Verbs that tell about actions that happen now are in the **present tense: He eats. She runs.**

Verbs that tell about actions that have already happened are in the **past tense: He ate. She ran.**

Verbs that tell about things that have not yet happened are in the **future tense: He will eat. She will run.**

Activity

Tell an Action Story. Take turns telling an action in the present tense, then in the past tense, and finally in the future tense.

Tested Spelling Words

Name ____

Drawing Conclusions

- As you read, look at the details and make decisions about the characters and what happens in the story or article.
- When you make decisions about the characters or events, you are **drawing conclusions.**

Directions: Reread "Another Death on the Ranch." Then complete the table. Write a conclusion for each piece of evidence given. Write evidence that supports each conclusion drawn.

Evidence (Story Details and What I Know)	Conclusions
1.	Hank is proud of his job.
Hank doesn't consider the milk cow a suspect.	**2.**
3.	It will be difficult for Hank to solve the crime.
Hank goes to the chickenhouse and is deep in thought about the murder.	**4.**
5.	Hank feels unappreciated.

Notes for Home: Your child read a story and used story details and life experience to draw conclusions. ***Home Activity:*** Have your child observe a pet or a neighborhood animal and draw conclusions about the animal's behavior based on observation and experience.

Name ___________________________________

Vocabulary

Directions: Cross out the word that does **not** belong in each group.

1. cobra	rattlesnake	alligator	garden snake
2. coiled	straight	curled	looped
3. lame	hurt	sure-footed	limping
4. plunged	dipped	dived	floated
5. triumph	success	victory	loss

Check the Words You Know

__ cobra
__ coiled
__ lame
__ plunged
__ triumph

Directions: Choose the word from the box that best matches each clue. Write the letters of the word on the blanks. The boxed letters spell something that is given as an award.

6. success **6.** ___ ___ ___ ___ ___ [ ] ___ ___

7. unable to walk properly **7.** ___ ___ ___ [ ]

8. wound around into a pile **8.** ___ ___ ___ ___ ___ [ ]

9. big, scary snake **9.** ___ ___ ___ ___ [ ]

10. threw with force **10.** ___ [ ] ___ ___ ___ ___ ___

Something that is given as an award: ___ ___ ___ ___ ___

Write an Animal Story

On a separate sheet of paper, write a story in which the main character is an animal. Tell what problem your character faces and solves. Use as many vocabulary words as possible.

Notes for Home: Your child identified and used vocabulary words from *Rikki-tikki-tavi.* ***Home Activity:*** With your child, recall stories you have read or seen on TV about animals that have helped humans. Try to use vocabulary words as part of your discussion.

Name ______________________________

Drawing Conclusions

- When you use details from the story and what you know to make decisions about the characters or events, you are **drawing conclusions.**

Directions: Reread this passage from *Rikki-tikki-tavi*. It takes place the morning after Rikki-tikki helped kill Nag. Then answer the questions below.

When morning came, Rikki-tikki was very stiff but well pleased with himself. "Now I have Nagaina to deal with, and she will be worse than five Nags. And there's no knowing when the eggs will hatch. I must go see Darzee," he said.

Without waiting for breakfast, Rikki-tikki ran to the thornbush where Darzee was singing a song of triumph at the top of his voice. The news of Nag's death was all over the garden, because his body had been put on the garbage heap.

"Oh, you stupid tuft of feathers!" said Rikki-tikki. "Is this the time to sing?"

1. Why does Rikki-tikki expect Nagaina to "be worse than five Nags"?

____

2. What eggs is Rikki-tikki talking about? What will happen when they hatch?

____

3. Why does Rikki-tikki say, "I must go see Darzee"?

____

4. Why doesn't Rikki-tikki think this is the time to sing?

____

____

5. On a separate sheet of paper, write a description of Rikki-tikki. Use details from the story to support your answer.

Notes for Home: Your child used story details to draw conclusions. ***Home Activity:*** Share events from work, a trip, and so on with your child. Provide details so your child can draw conclusions about why things happened or why somebody acted a certain way.

Selection Test

Directions: Choose the best answer to each item. Mark the letter for the answer you have chosen.

Part 1: Vocabulary

Find the answer choice that means about the same as the underlined word in each sentence.

1. The man caught a cobra.
- A. bad illness
- B. large cat with spots
- C. songbird
- D. poisonous snake

2. Art plunged into the lake.
- F. opened
- G. looked
- H. walked
- J. dived

3. Our game ended in triumph.
- A. victory or success
- B. loss or defeat
- C. a tie score
- D. sadness

4. The snake coiled itself.
- F. shed its skin
- G. wound around something
- H. unfolded
- J. slid away slowly

5. Terri's dog is lame.
- A. having fleas
- B. bad-tempered
- C. not able to walk right
- D. expecting puppies soon

Part 2: Comprehension

Use what you know about the story to answer each item.

6. What kind of animal is Chuchundra?
- F. a rat
- G. a muskrat
- H. a mongoose
- J. a snake

7. Nag believes that if he can rid the house of people, then—
- A. he and Nagaina can move in.
- B. Rikki-tikki will leave.
- C. a mongoose can live in the garden again.
- D. he can be crowned king.

8. Nag waits by the water jar to—
- F. take a drink.
- G. attack the man.
- H. catch Rikki-tikki.
- J. save the eggs.

GO ON

9. Darzee's wife pretends her wing is broken in order to—
A. make Nagaina angry.
B. lead the boy into a trap.
C. save Rikki-tikki.
D. trick Nagaina.

10. What can you tell about cobras from this story?
F. Cobras are very dangerous.
G. Most cobras can sing.
H. Baby cobras like to eat melon.
J. Adult cobras don't bite children.

11. How is Darzee's wife different from Darzee?
A. She is a better singer.
B. She has a broken wing.
C. She is smarter.
D. She is not as brave.

12. When Nagaina goes up on the porch, Rikki-tikki is—
F. waiting by the bathroom drain.
G. eating melons.
H. destroying her eggs.
J. looking for Nag.

13. Which word best describes Nagaina?
A. hateful
B. stupid
C. careless
D. shy

14. What was most important to Rikki-tikki?
F. having a friend
G. keeping Teddy safe
H. sleeping in the house
J. playing tricks on snakes

15. What part of this story could **not** really happen?
A. A cobra lays her eggs in the garden.
B. A bird sings loudly.
C. A mongoose kills a snake.
D. Animals talk to people.

STOP

Name ____

Drawing Conclusions

- When you use details from the story and what you know to make decisions about the characters or events, you are **drawing conclusions.**

Directions: Read the story below.

Once there was an old couple who lived in a forest. They feared that a wolf or a thief might get into their house at night, so they got a dog.

The dog thought about how to keep the couple safe. While he was chasing one wolf or thief away, another might come and attack the old couple. He couldn't do the job all by himself.

So the dog went out and brought back a stout stick. "Oh!" said the man. "This will make a bar for our door."

Then the dog went out and brought back some boards. "Oh!" said the woman. "These will make perfect shutters for the windows."

That night they all slept soundly. And they never worried about a wolf or a thief again!

Directions: Complete the table by drawing conclusions about what you have read.

What Happens in the Story	What Conclusions I Can Draw
The couple worry about a wolf or a thief breaking in.	**1.**
They get a dog.	**2.**
The dog understands what needs to be done.	**3.**
That night everyone sleeps soundly.	**4.**
They never worried about a wolf or a thief again.	**5.**

Notes for Home: Your child read a story and used story details and what he or she knows to draw conclusions about the characters or events. ***Home Activity:*** Watch a TV show or a movie with your child. Draw conclusions about what happens and the characters' actions and feelings.

Name ______________________________

Making Judgments

REVIEW

Directions: Read the story. Then read each question about the story. Choose the best answer to each question. Mark the letter for the answer you have chosen.

Flo and Bob

"'Do this!' 'Don't do that!' That's all you say," cackled Flo the hen crossly to Bob the dog.

"Someday your life may depend on it," said Bob as he went to check on the ducks.

One day a fox appeared. Flo said, "Can I help you?"

"Just looking for now," answered the fox.

That night there was a loud squawking in the henhouse. Bob ran to see what was the matter. A fox!

"Help!" cried Flo. "What should we do?"

"Join wings so the fox can't grab any one of you," said Bob. "Leave him to me."

The hens did what Bob said. Bob chased the fox away. Flo never again complained about Bob's orders.

1. Bob is—
- **A.** mean.
- **B.** angry.
- **C.** careful.
- **D.** silly.

2. Flo is—
- **F.** helpful.
- **G.** annoyed.
- **H.** gentle.
- **J.** strong.

3. When the fox says "Just looking," he means that—
- **A.** he is not sure what he wants.
- **B.** he wants to find Bob.
- **C.** he is figuring a way into the henhouse.
- **D.** he wants to make friends with the hens.

4. In the story, Bob—
- **F.** is afraid.
- **G.** is mean.
- **H.** ignores the chickens.
- **J.** knows that there are dangers in the world.

5. By the end of the story, Flo has—
- **A.** decided to leave the henhouse.
- **B.** learned her lesson.
- **C.** lost a friend.
- **D.** complained to the fox.

Notes for Home: Your child made judgments about characters and events in a story. ***Home Activity:*** Watch a TV show with your child. Invite him or her to make judgments about events and characters. Prompt your child by asking, *Is that a nice way to act? Was that smart?*

Name ______________________________________

Writing Across Texts

Directions: In this unit, you read the stories *Rikki-tikki-tavi* and *John Henry.* Each selection featured main characters who did their jobs very well. They were heroes in different ways. Think about Rikki-tikki-tavi and John Henry. Use the lists below to record details about how or why they were heroes.

Rikki-tikki-tavi
Rikki-tikki-tavi stayed guard at night and overheard the plan to kill Karait.
1.
He devised a plan to distract Nagaina.
2.
3.

John Henry
John Henry helped his father rebuild and improve his house.
4.
5.

Write a Descriptive Paragraph

Each character described above was a hero to the people he helped. Use the information in your lists to write a paragraph that describes some of the qualities of a hero. Write your paragraph on a separate sheet of paper.

Notes for Home: Your child listed details about fantasy characters in two different stories. ***Home Activity:*** Discuss some movies that you have seen with your child. Discuss the lead character. Ask the child if this character is a hero in some way.

Name ______________________________

Grammar: Using Verb Tense Correctly

REVIEW

Directions: Use the correct form of the verb in ( ) to complete each sentence. Write the verb on the line.

______________ **1.** Special dogs have (help) blind people for many years.

______________ **2.** These Seeing Eye dogs have (train) at special schools.

______________ **3.** Over the years, many people have (use) German shepherds as Seeing Eye dogs.

______________ **4.** These dogs are always (work) hard for their owners.

______________ **5.** They have (offer) independence to many.

______________ **6.** My friend Jenna is (get) a Seeing Eye dog.

______________ **7.** Last month, she (pick) out a young dog she liked.

______________ **8.** It (be) a German shepherd.

______________ **9.** Jenna is (wait) for the dog to finish its training.

______________ **10.** She will (take) the dog to school every day.

Directions: Circle the correct verb form in ( ) in each sentence.

11. Some special monkeys are (gave/given) other duties.

12. They are (teached/taught) special skills.

13. Many of these monkeys have (gone/went) to the homes of deaf people.

14. These monkeys are always (drew/drawing) their owner's attention to sounds such as a doorbell.

15. Getting one of these monkeys will (make/making) a big difference in a person's life.

Notes for Home: Your child practiced using the correct tense of verbs. ***Home Activity:*** Have your child make up sentences using the following tenses of the verb *eat: eat, am eating, ate, have eaten.*

Grammar: Review of Verbs

A word that shows action is a **verb.** Use the proper verb form to agree with a singular noun subject or with *he, she,* or *it* and use the proper verb form to agree with a plural subject.

Verbs in the **present tense** show action that is happening now. Verbs in the **past tense** show action that has already happened. Verbs in the **future tense** show action that will happen in the future.

Present: Our dog barks at strangers.

Past: Last night the dog barked once.

Future: He will bark when you ring the bell.

A verb in the past tense often ends with **-ed.** A verb whose past tense does *not* end in **-ed** is called an **irregular verb.** Since it doesn't follow a pattern, you have to remember its past tense form.

Directions: Circle the correct form of verb in ( ) to complete each sentence.

1. Some dogs (makes/make) noise when strangers appear.
2. Sometimes a cat's behavior (provide/provides) a warning.
3. Other animals (offers/offer) other kinds of protection for their young.
4. Geese (honks/honk) loudly at strangers.
5. An angry goose (looks/look) quite dangerous.

Directions: Use the correct form of the verb in ( ) to complete each sentence. Use the verb tense named in ( ). Write the verb on the line to the left.

______________________ **6.** Freckles the dog _____ on the front porch. (sit—past)

______________________ **7.** He _____ the house all day. (guard—future)

______________________ **8.** Last year, he _____ a burglar. (catch—past)

______________________ **9.** That burglar never _____ again! (come—past)

______________________ **10.** No one _____ with Freckles around. (worry—future)

Notes for Home: Your child wrote verbs for singular and plural subjects and to show present, past, and future actions. ***Home Activity:*** Name a verb. Have your child give its past, present, and future tenses.

Grammar: Review of Verbs

Directions: Circle the correct form of verb in ( ) to complete each sentence.

1. Mosquitoes (flyed/flew) freely in the summer night.

2. Then the spider (catched/caught) one in her web.

3. Spiders (protect/protects) people from harmful insects.

4. Our mosquito bites (itch/itched) all last night!

5. Right now, all of us (hope/will hope) that the spider will catch more mosquitoes!

Directions: Add a verb to complete each sentence. Write the verb in the correct tense on the line to the left.

________________ **6.** Yesterday, the sheep _____ peacefully in the meadow.

________________ **7.** They ate the grass that grew there and _____ the water from the stream.

________________ **8.** They are safe because our dogs _____ them every day.

________________ **9.** Sheepdogs _____ the sheep of a flock from wandering away.

________________ **10.** The sheep _____ asleep, but now they are awake.

Write an Animal Story

Have you ever wondered what animals would say to each other if they could talk? On a separate sheet of paper, write a story about two animal friends. Use different verbs, including two irregular verbs. Be sure to use correct verb tenses. Underline your verbs.

Notes for Home: Your child circled and wrote verbs to complete each sentence. ***Home Activity:*** Name some "fun" action verbs, such as *smile, clap, cheer, jump, spin.* Invite your child to tell you the present, past, and future tense of each verb.

Grammar: Review of Verbs

RETEACHING

Complete each sentence. Write the correct form of the verb **walk** on the line.

Present: He ________________ to the playground.

Past: Yesterday he ________________ to school.

Future: Tomorrow he ________________ to Jeremy's house.

Verbs in the **present tense** show action that is happening now. Verbs in the **past tense** show action that has already happened. Verbs in the **future tense** show what will happen.

Complete each sentence. Write the correct form of the verb **eat** on the line.

Present: Lorna ________________ lunch at home.

Past: Yesterday Lorna ________________ lunch at school.

Future: Tomorrow she ________________ lunch at her grandparents' house.

Often a verb in the past tense ends with **-ed**. A verb whose past-tense form does not end in **-ed** is called an **irregular verb.**

Directions: Use the correct form of the verb in ( ) to complete each sentence. Use the verb tense named in ( ). Write the verb on the line to the left.

________________ **1.** Celia ______ an answer to her friend. (whisper—present)

________________ **2.** I ______ my hands. (wave—past)

________________ **3.** Bruce ______ on me. (call—past)

________________ **4.** "You ______ the answer," he said. (know—future)

________________ **5.** "I ______ it is forty-two." (think—present)

________________ **6.** "You ______ smart," he said. (be—present)

Notes for Home: Your child wrote verbs for singular and plural subjects and in different tenses. ***Home Activity:*** Talk about what you did for fun when you were your child's age and about what you would like to do together. Use verbs in the present, past, and future tenses.

Name ______________________________

Grammar: Review of Verbs

Directions: Circle the correct form of the verb in ( ) to complete each sentence. Use a dictionary if you need help with irregular verbs.

1. Our neighbors (gives/gave) us an empty box.

2. We (decides/decided) to make a rocket ship.

3. The box (were/was) so big we couldn't fit it into the house.

4. Mom (tell/told) us to leave it in the backyard.

5. All of us (played/will play) with it next weekend.

6. We (put/puts) stickers on the outside of the ship.

7. Mike (run/ran) to his house to get markers.

8. Then he and Joe (drawn/drew) windows and a door.

9. Steve (will cut/cut) a hole in the top before we can climb inside.

10. I (am/will be) the first one to sit in the ship tomorrow.

11. John (was/is) finishing the decorations inside the ship right now.

12. We (is/are) very excited about our ship!

Directions: Write sentences, using the verbs and verb tenses in ( ).

(draw—future) **13.** ______________________________

(move—past) **14.** ______________________________

(fly—present) **15.** ______________________________

Notes for Home: Your child identified and wrote verbs with singular and plural subjects and in present, past, and future tenses. ***Home Activity:*** Read a magazine or newspaper article with your child. Have him or her find one example each of present, past, and future-tense verb forms.

Name ______________________

Word Study: Base Words

Directions: Many words are made by adding letters to the beginning or end of a word. The word you start with is called the **base word.** Read each word below. Find the base word for each word. Write it on the line.

1. hidden ______________________

2. sensible ______________________

3. emptied ______________________

4. frightened ______________________

5. forgotten ______________________

6. mournful ______________________

7. tingled ______________________

8. gently ______________________

9. lowered ______________________

10. misspelled ______________________

11. beautifully ______________________

12. recalled ______________________

Directions: Base words can help you figure out the meaning of new words. Read each sentence. Think about the base word for the underlined word. Then read the two definitions in ( ). Circle the correct definition.

13. The small animals were frightened by the snake. (awakened/scared)

14. The sensible thing for a hunted animal to do is to stay with a group. (foolish/smart)

15. The bird searched for hidden dangers. (out of sight/out in the open)

16. But the animals had forgotten about the family in the house. (kept in mind/not remembered)

17. They let out a mournful cry as they thought about the family's fate. (bright/sad)

18. The boy tingled with fear as he faced the snake. (a stinging feeling/a sleepy feeling)

19. The mongoose told the snake he had emptied the nest of all its eggs. (left nothing/filled up)

Directions: Write a sentence using the word **courageous.** If you're not sure what the word means, use the base word to help you.

20. ____

____

Notes for Home: Your child found base words in longer words, such as *care* in *carefully.* ***Home Activity:*** Read a magazine article with your child. As you spot longer words with base words, say, for example, "I spy the base word *near.*" Have your child find the longer word.

Name ______________________________

Spelling: Vowels in Final Syllables

Pretest Directions: Fold back the page along the dotted line. On the blanks, write the spelling words as they are dictated. When you have finished the test, unfold the page and check your words.

1. ______________________
2. ______________________
3. ______________________
4. ______________________
5. ______________________
6. ______________________
7. ______________________
8. ______________________
9. ______________________
10. ______________________
11. ______________________
12. ______________________
13. ______________________
14. ______________________
15. ______________________
16. ______________________
17. ______________________
18. ______________________
19. ______________________
20. ______________________

1. Help me find my **other** shoe.
2. We saw a **number** of birds.
3. **October** is a cool month.
4. Have **another** slice of cake.
5. What **color** are your eyes?
6. The **doctor** hasn't come yet.
7. This car has a noisy **motor**.
8. How many **people** are here?
9. The solution is **simple**.
10. The owl chose an **angle** of attack.
11. I've forgotten the book's **title**.
12. She is a **model** citizen.
13. The rain **barrel** is getting full.
14. He was an **angel** of mercy.
15. Her wing looks **broken**.
16. The attack was **sudden**.
17. Be careful, the **oven** is hot.
18. It's for the **common** good.
19. I need a **gallon** of water.
20. He needs a new **button**.

Notes for Home: Your child took a pretest on how to spell the vowel sound in final syllables. ***Home Activity:*** Help your child learn misspelled words before the final test. Your child should look at the word, say it, spell it aloud, and then spell it with eyes shut.

Spelling: Vowels in Final Syllables

Word List			
other	doctor	title	sudden
number	motor	model	oven
October	people	barrel	common
another	simple	angel	gallon
color	angle	broken	button

Directions: Choose the words from the box that end with **le** or **el.** Write each word in the correct column. Draw lines between the syllables.

Ends with le	**Ends with el**
1. ________________	**5.** ________________
2. ________________	**6.** ________________
3. ________________	**7.** ________________
4. ________________	

Directions: Write the word from the box that belongs in each group. Draw lines between the syllables.

8. different, separate, __________

9. quantity, amount, __________

10. additional, added, __________

11. snap, zipper, __________

12. pint, quart, __________

13. unexpected, quick, __________

14. average, ordinary, __________

15. stove, burner, __________

16. busted, cracked, __________

17. shade, hue, __________

18. August, September, __________

19. dentist, veterinarian, __________

20. engine, machine, __________

Notes for Home: Your child spelled words with vowels in final syllables that sound alike but are spelled differently, such as *peop<u>le</u>* and *mod<u>el</u>.* ***Home Activity:*** Work with your child to come up with more words that end similarly to the words in the box.

Name ______________________________

Spelling: Vowels in Final Syllables

Directions: Proofread this news story. Find five spelling mistakes. Use the proofreading marks to correct each mistake.

≡	Make a capital.
/	Make a small letter.
∧	Add something.
ـ୨	Take out something.
⊙	Add a period.
¶	Begin a new paragraph.

Dog Saves Boy

It was the first week of Octobor, and the leaves on the trees were all changing coler. A local boy, Jeff Blitz, went for a walk in the woods with his dog, Breck. All of a suden, Jeff realized that he was lost. There were a numbr of ways to go, and he didn't know the right one. He turned to Breck, and said, "Home." And Breck led him home. Jeff declared there was not anothor dog that was smarter than Breck!

Word List

other	color	simple	barrel	oven
number	doctor	angle	angel	common
October	motor	title	broken	gallon
another	people	model	sudden	button

Write a News Story

On a separate sheet of paper, write a short news story about an animal who makes a heroic rescue. Try to use at least three spelling words.

Spelling Tip

The vowels in final syllables often sound alike but are spelled differently: **people, model; broken, common; another, motor.** Check the story to make sure the vowels in the final syllables are spelled correctly.

Notes for Home: Your child spelled words with vowels in final syllables that are pronounced the same but are spelled differently, such as *people* and *model*. ***Home Activity:*** With your child, read stories in the newspaper. Look for words with the same final syllables as those in the box.

Name ______________________________

REVIEW

Spelling: Vowels in Final Syllables

		Word List		
other	color	simple	barrel	oven
number	doctor	angle	angel	common
October	motor	title	broken	gallon
another	people	model	sudden	button

Directions: Unscramble the letters to form a word from the box. Write the word on the line.

__________ **1.** rrable

__________ **2.** nedusd

__________ **3.** korbne

__________ **4.** pepleo

__________ **5.** munreb

__________ **6.** ctObreo

__________ **7.** monmco

__________ **8.** hoter

__________ **9.** arethon

Directions: Choose a word from the box that best matches each clue. Write the word on the line.

______________ **10.** It's who you go see when you are sick.

______________ **11.** It holds your clothes together.

______________ **12.** It's what leaves change in the fall.

______________ **13.** It is the same as four quarts.

______________ **14.** It's a figure with wings often hung on Christmas trees.

______________ **15.** It's one of four inside a square.

______________ **16.** It's the name of a book.

______________ **17.** It's another word for *easy.*

______________ **18.** It's an airplane you can build at home.

______________ **19.** It's the part of a car that makes it go.

______________ **20.** It's where you bake a pie.

Notes for Home: Your child spelled words with vowels in final syllables that are pronounced the same but are spelled differently, such as *people* and *model*. ***Home Activity:*** Have your child think of words that rhyme with words in the box. Check to see if the endings are spelled alike.

Name ___________________________________

Schedule

A **schedule** is a special kind of chart that tells you when events take place. For example, arrival and departure times for buses and trains are often organized in schedules.

Directions: Read the schedule. Use it to answer the questions that follow.

The Sun Prairie News is proud to sponsor:

Animal Rescue Stories

Meet the animals who saved their owners' lives.
Hear the amazing tales by the animals' owners.

Schedule of Presentations

(Each presentation will last 45 minutes.)

Saturday, October 3	9:00 A.M.	Mark and his dog, Pudding
	11:00 A.M.	Tonya and her cat, Pink Paws
	3:00 P.M.	J.T. and his monkey, Tippy
Sunday, October 4	11:00 A.M.	Miguel and his ferret, Freddy
	2:00 P.M.	Mark and his dog, Pudding
	3:30 P.M.	Carla and her cat, Detour

Program held in the F.W. Richey Auditorium, 100 State St., Sun Prairie, WI (920) 555-2304

Name ____________________

1. What are the names of the animals who are part of the first and last presentations of the weekend? List the times and dates when these two animals will appear.

2. Which owner and animal will be presenting twice? What are your choices in dates and times to see them?

3. What two owners will be presenting at 11:00 A.M. each day?

4. If you arrived at the auditorium at 2:00 P.M. on Saturday, October 3, which presentations could you see that day? Explain.

5. How long will Tonya and Pink Paws' presentation be? How do you know?

Notes for Home: Your child used a schedule to find dates and times of special presentations. ***Home Activity:*** Find examples of schedules you and your child use often, such as TV listings or a bus schedule. Take turns asking each other questions about the schedule.

Name____

Comparison/Contrast Organizer

Directions: Fill in the chart first. Then write your title, introductory sentence, topic sentences, and conclusion sentence.

Title ____

Introductory Sentence ____

Topic Sentence ____

Same

Food:	**Food:**
1.	**1.**
2.	**2.**

Topic Sentence ____

Different

Food:	**Food:**
1.	**1.**
2.	**2.**

Conclusion Sentence ____

Notes for Home: Your child recently completed a graphic organizer to plan a comparison/contrast essay. ***Home Activity:*** Ask your child to tell you how he or she decided upon the above similarities and differences for the essay.

Name ____

Elaboration

Adding Details

- When you write, you can elaborate by **adding details** to your examples. This will help your reader understand more clearly.

Directions: Read each sentence below. Answer the question to add details to make each sentence clearer.

Example:

The children played. (Where did they play?)

The children played in the yard.

1. Marta worked very hard. (She worked hard by doing what?)

____

2. I borrowed her book about plants. (Whose book was it?)

____

3. Maria played hopscotch. (When did she play?)

____

4. Jacob studied hard last night. (Why did he study hard?)

____

5. The five tired hikers rested. (Where did they rest?)

____

6. Juan broke the vase. (How did he break it?)

____

7. Brad made sandwiches for lunch. (What kind did he make?)

____

8. Ilene helped her friend. (She helped her friend by doing what?)

____

Notes for Home: Your child recently elaborated sentences by adding details. ***Home Activity:*** Think of activities you do at home related to mealtime. First ask your child to tell about one of these activities using simple details. Then have your child elaborate by adding more details.

Name ______________________________

Self-Evaluation

Comparison/Contrast Essay

Directions: Think about the final draft of your comparison/contrast essay. Then answer each question below.

	Yes	No	Not sure
1. Is my topic sentence clear?			
2. Are my ideas organized well so they flow smoothly?			
3. Did I use transition words when I compared and contrasted the two characters?			
4. Did I use different kinds of sentences that are easy to understand?			
5. Are there any mistakes that could make it hard for the reader to understand my paragraph?			

6. What do you think you did best in your comparison/contrast essay?

____

____

7. Write one mistake you made this time that you will avoid the next time.

____

____

Notes for Home: Your child wrote and evaluated a comparison/contrast essay. ***Home Activity:*** Ask your child to explain one new writing skill that he or she learned during this project.

Family Times

Name______________________________

Summary

Chick Born With One Wing, One Leg, One Eye

Born with only one wing, one leg, one eye, and half the feathers of other chickens, Half-Chicken soon became the center of attention—and very vain! He decided to leave the ranch and pay a visit to the viceroy in Mexico City. Along the way, Half-Chicken found time to be helpful to others. And when he himself needed help, his kindness was repaid.

Activity

Spreading a Story. The hatching of Half-Chicken was big news in the farmyard, and word of it spread quickly. Have your child act out the parts of the hen, the other chicks, the ducks, the turkeys, the pigeons, and the swallows as they spread the story of Half-Chicken.

Reading Skills

Paraphrasing

Paraphrasing is explaining something in your own words. A paraphrase should include only the author's ideas, not your own opinions. Paraphrasing can help you understand what you read.

Activity

Campfire Tales. Sit around an imaginary campfire and take turns telling favorite folk tales, such as *Stone Soup* or an Anansi story, in your own words. This storytelling activity will help you practice paraphrasing since the originals of these stories are long lost.

Family Times

Tested Vocabulary

Words to Know

Knowing the meanings of these words is important to reading *Half-Chicken*. Practice using these words to learn their meanings.

farewells good-bys

flung past tense of *fling*

suggested proposed

tangled confused, twisted

uniforms clothes worn by members of a group who are on duty

vain conceited

Grammar

Adjectives

Words that describe persons, places, and things are **adjectives.** Some adjectives tell what kind. They describe color, shape, size, sound, taste, touch, or smell: **yellow chick, pointy beak, large egg, noisy pecking, yummy corn, soft feathers, fragrant flowers** Some adjectives tell how many: **thirteen chicks, several swallows.** Some adjectives tell which one: **this chick, those turkeys.**

Activity

Dress Up Those Nouns. Go through your house. Take turns giving a descriptive adjective to each object (noun) you see. For example, **plush chair, yellow lamp.** Have family members add another adjective until you have three for each noun.

Tested Spelling Words

____	____	____	____
____	____	____	____
____	____	____	____
____	____	____	____
____	____	____	____

Name ______________________________

Paraphrasing

- **Paraphrasing** is explaining something in your own words. A paraphrase should keep the author's meaning.
- A paraphrase should include all of the author's ideas, but it should be easier to read than the original.

Directions: Reread "Blue Jay Takes the Heat." Then complete the table. Paraphrase the sentence or sentences from the story that are listed in the first column. Write your paraphrase of the text in the second column.

Author's Sentences	My Paraphrase
Paragraph 1, Sentence 2	**1.**
Paragraph 1, Last two sentences	**2.**
Paragraph 4, First sentence	**3.**
Paragraph 4, Sentences 2–5	**4.**
Last paragraph, Last sentence	**5.**

Notes for Home: Your child read a story and paraphrased parts of it in his or her own words. ***Home Activity:*** Give your child some directions, such as asking for a particular can from a cupboard. Ask your child to restate the directions simply, using his or her own words.

Name ______________________________

Vocabulary

Directions: Choose the word from the box that best matches each definition. Write the word on the line.

Check the Words You Know

__ farewells
__ flung
__ suggested
__ tangled
__ uniforms
__ vain

________________ **1.** proposed

________________ **2.** good-bys

________________ **3.** too proud of one's own looks or abilities

________________ **4.** threw with force; past tense of *fling*

________________ **5.** worn by members of a group on duty

________________ **6.** confused, twisted

Directions: Choose the word from the box that best completes each sentence. You will use some words more than once. Write the word on the line to the left.

________________ **7.** Last night's wind had _____ leaves and branches all around the yard.

________________ **8.** Lydia _____ that we check the weather report to see if it would rain today.

________________ **9.** "This afternoon is our band concert, and our _____ might get wet," she said.

________________ **10.** Just to be safe, Lydia grabbed her umbrella as she said her _____.

Write a Description

On a separate sheet of paper, write a description of a storm. Use as many vocabulary words as you can.

Notes for Home: Your child identified and used vocabulary words from *Half-Chicken*. ***Home Activity:*** Have your child give a synonym (a word with the same or nearly the same meaning as another word) for each vocabulary word *(good-bys, farewells)*.

Name ______________________________________

Paraphrasing

- **Paraphrasing** is explaining something in your own words. A paraphrase should include all of the author's ideas, but it should be easier to read than the original.

Directions: Reread what happens in *Half-Chicken* when the half-chicken hatches out of the egg. Then follow the instructions below.

Finally there was a tiny sound. The baby chick was pecking at its egg from the inside. The hen quickly helped it break open the shell, and at last the thirteenth chick came out into the world.

Yet this was no ordinary chick. He had only one wing, only one leg, only one eye, and only half as many feathers as the other chicks.

It was not long before everyone at the ranch knew that a very special chick had been born.

The ducks told the turkeys. The turkeys told the pigeons. The pigeons told the swallows. And the swallows flew over the fields, spreading the news to the cows. . . .

1. Paraphrase the first paragraph.

____

2. Paraphrase the second paragraph.

____

3. Paraphrase the third paragraph.

____

4. Paraphrase the fourth paragraph.

____

5. Reread the passage. Then, on a separate sheet of paper, paraphrase the entire passage in your own words.

Notes for Home: Your child paraphrased several paragraphs. ***Home Activity:*** With your child, find a favorite part of a book, no more than a page or two. Read the passage. Ask your child to tell you what happens in his or her own words.

Name ______________________________

Selection Test

Directions: Choose the best answer to each item. Mark the letter for the answer you have chosen.

Part 1: Vocabulary

Find the answer choice that means about the same as the underlined word in each sentence.

1. The ropes were <u>tangled</u>.
- A. tied in a bow
- B. cut by something sharp
- C. worn along the edge
- D. twisted in a confused mass

2. The cousins said their <u>farewells</u>.
- F. good-bys
- G. prayers
- H. names
- J. speeches

3. Dad <u>suggested</u> a new plan.
- A. refused to allow
- B. got ready
- C. put forward the idea
- D. forced to do

4. Ben <u>flung</u> his cards on the table.
- F. dropped
- G. set
- H. matched
- J. threw

5. Cassie's sister is <u>vain</u>.
- A. having too much pride
- B. showing feelings freely
- C. hard to understand
- D. having good manners

6. Someone stole our <u>uniforms</u>.
- F. things that bring good luck
- G. clothes worn by members of a group
- H. small copies of something
- J. directions for doing something

Part 2: Comprehension

Use what you know about the story to answer each item.

7. Which birds on the ranch had been to Mexico City before?
- A. the chickens
- B. the ducks
- C. the swallows
- D. the turkeys

8. Half-Chicken was an unusual chick because he—
- F. had only one wing, one leg, and one eye.
- G. was born thirteenth.
- H. was the last chick born.
- J. wanted to leave the ranch.

GO ON

9. Because of the attention he got, Half-Chicken became very—
- A. shy.
- B. worried.
- C. spoiled.
- D. vain.

10. Half-Chicken left his home because he wanted to—
- F. be a weather vane.
- G. see the court of the viceroy.
- H. meet the wind.
- J. do good deeds.

11. What is another way to say, "I have no time to lose"?
- A. "I'm in a hurry."
- B. "I forgot my watch."
- C. "I have plenty of time."
- D. "I've lost track of time."

12. When Half-Chicken presented himself at the kitchen door of the palace, he—
- F. hoped to be invited in to dinner.
- G. gave the cook a chicken he had brought with him.
- H. didn't realize he was about to become dinner.
- J. was surprised to see his friends were there.

13. What is another way of saying, "This chicken has been more trouble than he's worth"?
- A. "This chicken is too wild to be used in soup."
- B. "This chicken is not worth all the work I've done trying to cook him."
- C. "Now I know why I didn't have to pay for this chicken."
- D. "The trouble is that everything tastes like chicken."

14. What lesson can be learned from this story?
- F. Good things come to those who wait.
- G. People should stay home instead of traveling to see the world.
- H. A bird in the hand is worth two in the bush.
- J. It's good to help others because someday you might need their help.

15. The author was probably trying to be funny when she wrote about a "vain" rooster that—
- A. talked to the wind.
- B. became a weather vane.
- C. was flung out the window.
- D. spoke to the palace guards.

Name ______________________________

Paraphrasing

- **Paraphrasing** is explaining something in your own words.
- A paraphrase should include all of the author's ideas, but it should be easier to read than the original.

Directions: Read the story below.

One day, Fire, Water, and Wind decided to have a contest to see who was strongest. Fire went first. It burned very brightly. The flames went higher and higher into the sky. They gleamed like orange jewels. Everyone who was watching said, "Ooh!" and "Aah!" Everyone said, "Fire must be the strongest!"

Then Water came along and went, "Splash! Splash!" Pretty soon, Fire was gone. All that was left was a big, wet puddle! "Ha, ha, ha!" laughed Water. "I put out Fire! I am the strongest!"

"You are not the strongest," said Wind. Wind began to blow and blow. It blew the water into a million droplets scattered over the earth. "Ha, ha, ha!" laughed Wind. "I am the strongest!"

Then Fire came back. Fire can't burn in water, but it burns in air. So when Wind blew Water away, Fire came back, stronger than ever. Again, Water put out Fire, Wind blew away Water, and Fire ate up Wind. Who do *you* think was the strongest?

Directions: Complete the table. Use your own words to retell what happens in this story.

Paragraph	Character	What Happens?
One	Fire	burns very brightly, looks like the strongest
Two	Water	**1.**
Three	**2.**	**3.**
Four	**4.**	**5.**

Notes for Home: Your child used his or her own words to explain what happens in a story. ***Home Activity:*** Tell your child a familiar story, like "The Tortoise and the Hare." Then ask him or her to tell *you* the story in his or her own words.

Name ____

Predicting

REVIEW

Directions: Read the story. Then read each question about the story. Choose the best answer to each question. Mark the letter for the answer you have chosen.

What Will the Weather Be?

Miriam and her family were on a camping trip. Miriam had just felt a few drops of rain.

"Are you sure that was rain?" Miriam's mother asked. She pointed to the nearby lake, where Miriam's brother was swimming. "Maybe Josh splashed you."

Miriam shook her head. "Look at our campfire," she said. The wind made the flames flicker weakly. "I think that wind means a storm," said Miriam.

Miriam's father looked up at the sky. Overhead, the clouds were dark gray. But way over in the west, the sky was blue and clear. "Maybe the rain clouds will blow over," he said.

Miriam shook her head again. "No," she said. "The wind is blowing in the wrong direction." Then she heard thunder.

1. Based on what you've read, what kind of weather do you predict?

A. a hurricane
B. a rainstorm
C. bright blue skies
D. a few drops of rain

2. What is the first clue that helps you make your prediction?

F. Miriam gets splashed by her brother.
G. Miriam puts out the campfire.
H. Miriam sees dark gray clouds.
J. Miriam feels a few raindrops.

3. What is the second clue that helps you make your prediction?

A. The campfire flickers.
B. The wind blows leaves into the fire.
C. Josh splashes Miriam.
D. The rain starts.

4. Which clue might lead you to predict *good* weather?

F. The wind is blowing.
G. Part of the sky is blue.
H. Dark gray clouds are overhead.
J. The air is warm.

5. Which clue would lead you to change your "good-weather" prediction?

A. The wind has died down.
B. The fire goes out.
C. Miriam hears thunder.
D. Josh gets out of the lake.

Notes for Home: Your child made predictions about a story and identified the clues used to make the predictions. ***Home Activity:*** As you complete a task, such as preparing a meal, ask your child to predict what you will do next. Then ask how your child came up with that prediction.

Name ___________________________________

Writing Across Texts

Directions: Think about the chicken in the story *Half-Chicken*. How is he alike and different from the chickens in the selection "Chicken Farming"? Read the five statements in the box and use them to complete the table. Write the statements that are true of Half-Chicken, "real" chickens, and both in the correct places in the table. Add other information you have read to the table.

Statements

goes to visit the viceroy
probably lives on a "factory" farm
has only one leg, one wing, and one eye
says "Cock-a-doodle-do!"
produces one or more eggs a day

Half-Chicken	Real Chicken	Both
1.	**2.**	**3.**

Write a Story

On a separate sheet of paper, write a story about Half-Chicken living on a factory farm. Would he find it difficult? How might he change?

Notes for Home: Your child wrote a story about a character in a folk tale living in the real world. ***Home Activity:*** Read a folk tale with your child that features animal characters. Discuss how those animal characters are similar to and different from real animals.

Name ______________________________

REVIEW

Grammar: Complete Subjects

Directions: Underline the complete subject in each sentence.

1. Many folk tales use animals as characters.
2. These make-believe animals talk, cry, and act just like human beings.
3. Natural events become characters in folk tales too.
4. A good storyteller can make the forces of nature seem alive.
5. The mighty wind might decide to show off its power, for example.
6. A strong, fast stream is able to float a child to safety.
7. A soft breeze grows angry and turns into a raging windstorm.
8. A thunderstorm gets tired and dozes off as a gentle drizzle.
9. Some animals persuade a little spark to grow into a dangerous fire.
10. Anything can take on human qualities in a folk tale.

Directions: Add a complete subject to each predicate to create a sentence. Your subject should have at least three words. Write your sentence on the line.

11. became angry and roared down from the mountain

____

12. warmed all the people sitting around it

____

13. ruined the picnic for everyone

____

14. came running out of the cabin

____

15. appeared in the sky and frightened us

____

Notes for Home: Your child identified and used complete subjects in sentences. ***Home Activity:*** Collect four or five things from around the house. Ask your child to write a sentence about each item and underline the complete subject.

Name ______________________

Grammar: Adjectives

A word that describes a person, place, or thing is called an **adjective.** An adjective often comes before a noun, but it also can follow a noun or pronoun.

- Some adjectives tell what kind. They describe color, shape, size, sound, taste, touch, or smell: The <u>little</u> donkey trotted under its load of hay.
- Some adjectives tell how many: Are <u>two</u> men needed for the job?
- Some adjectives tell which one: Walk toward <u>that</u> restaurant.

Directions: Write the adjective or adjectives that describe each underlined noun.

______________ **1.** The <u>wind</u> and the <u>sun</u> felt irritable.

______________ **2.** They had a short <u>argument</u>.

______________ **3.** This <u>quarrel</u> was about who had more strength.

______________ **4.** A strong, cold <u>wind</u> blew across the field.

______________ **5.** The bright, hot <u>sun</u> beat down on the land.

______________ **6.** Each fierce <u>competitor</u> was determined to win.

Directions: Use the adjectives in the box to write four sentences.

cold	hot	this	bright

7. ______________________________

8. ______________________________

9. ______________________________

10. ______________________________

Notes for Home: Your child identified adjectives, words that describe persons, places, or things in sentences. ***Home Activity:*** Point to objects and ask your child to describe them, using as many different adjectives as possible.

Name ______________________________

Grammar: Adjectives

Directions: Underline the adjective or adjectives in each sentence.

1. On a beautiful morning, a kind old woman decided to bake cookies.
2. She mixed ginger with the rest of the fresh ingredients and divided the sweet dough into pieces.
3. She rolled out one piece, then carefully cut it into the shape of a little man.
4. The old woman placed her special cookie in a large pan and slid it into the hot oven.
5. After a short time, the woman smelled ginger and heard a strange sound inside the oven.
6. When she opened the door, the surprised woman couldn't believe her eyes.
7. The crispy cookie-man sat up and said, "Thank you."
8. He jumped down and ran across the kitchen as fast as his little legs could go.
9. The old woman ran after him.
10. The clever cookie-man called out in a squeaky voice, "Run, run, as fast as you can. You can't catch me—I'm the cookie-man!"

Write a Folk Tale

On a separate sheet of paper, retell a folk tale or fairy tale that you know. Use at least one adjective in each sentence to describe the characters, things, and places in the story. Underline all the adjectives you use.

Notes for Home: Your child identified adjectives—words that describe persons, places, or things—in sentences. ***Home Activity:*** Describe objects in your child's room, using only adjectives, such as *blue, fluffy, soft,* and have him or her guess what you are describing. (*a pillow*)

Name ______________________________

Grammar: Adjectives

RETEACHING

Connect the words that describe the picture.

Adjectives	Adjectives	Nouns
1. six	hard	rocks
2. some	little	turtles

Write the words you connected to complete each sentence.

3. I see ____________ ____________ ____________ .
(adjective) (adjective) (noun)

4. I see ____________ ____________ ____________ .
(adjective) (adjective) (noun)

An **adjective** describes a person, place, or thing. Adjectives can answer the questions **How many?, What kind?,** and **Which one?**

Directions: Tell more about each noun with two adjectives.

1. ________________ ________________ snails

2. ________________ ________________ fox

Directions: Circle the adjectives that tell **what kind, how many,** and **which one.**

3. Many leaves lay on the cold ground.

4. Two woodchucks crawled in long tunnels.

5. Ten bats stayed in dark caves.

6. One deer searched for some food.

Notes for Home: Your child identified adjectives. ***Home Activity:*** Have your child write a description of a perfect day. Challenge your child to use six adjectives in his or her description.

Name ________________________________

Grammar: Adjectives

Circle the adjectives that tell **what kind, how many,** and **which one.** Then write each adjective in the correct column.

1. Many craters are on this dusty moon.

2. Those pointy rocks are in several areas.

3. Deep valleys are in some places.

4. Twelve astronauts landed on its rough surface.

What Kind	How Many	Which One
5.	**9.**	**13.**
6.	**10.**	**14.**
7.	**11.**	
8.	**12.**	

Directions: Follow the correct path through the puzzle. Find the adjectives that tell **what kind.** Then write each one to tell more about a noun.

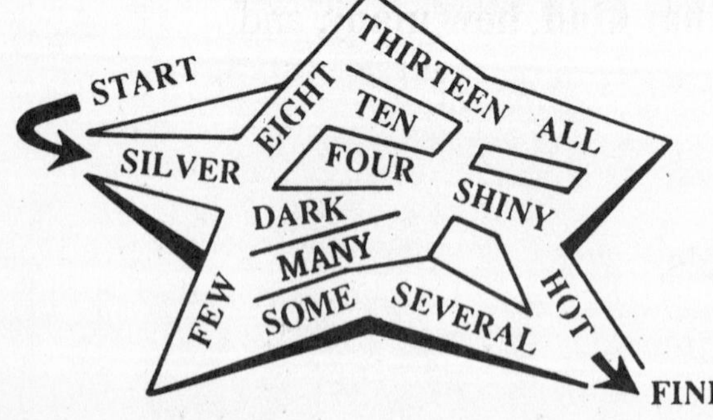

15. ______________________ star

16. ______________________ sun

17. ______________________ planets

18. ______________________ sky

Write a Poem

On a separate sheet of paper, write a poem about the night sky. Tell what you see. Use adjectives that tell what kind and how many.

Notes for Home: Your child identified adjectives that tell *what kind*, *how many*, and *which one*. ***Home Activity:*** Have your child look at a magazine article and find an example of each kind of adjective. Then have him or her use them to write new sentences.

Name ________________________________

Word Study: Inflected Forms with -es

Directions: Add **-es** to base words ending in **sh, ch, s, ss,** and **x.** Read the paragraph below. Look for words where **-es** has been added. Circle each word and write it on the line.

A mother bird perches on her nest, until one day, a baby bird hatches. A strong wind brushes through the trees. Out falls the baby bird! It passes right through the leafy greenery to the ground. A cat nearby reaches for the baby bird.

"Please don't hurt my baby!" says the mother.

"Why not?" asks the cat.

The mother thinks, then says, "Because one day I will do you a favor."

So the cat lets the baby bird go. A dog sitting nearby watches the cat and catches it. The mother bird sees what has happened. She swoops down and sits on the dog's nose, causing the dog to sneeze and drop the cat. And the cat never bothered another bird again.

1. ____________________
2. ____________________
3. ____________________
4. ____________________
5. ____________________
6. ____________________
7. ____________________

Directions: Add **-es** to each base word make a new word. Write the new word on the line.

8. fetch ____________________

9. wash ____________________

10. wish ____________________

11. match ____________________

12. toss ____________________

13. relax ____________________

14. teach ____________________

15. confess ____________________

Notes for Home: Your child added *-es* to words such as *reach (reaches)* and *pass (passes)*. ***Home Activity:*** Read a short story with your child. Take turns writing down words you find that end with *-es*.

Name ______________________________

Pretest

Spelling: Words with *sh, ch, tch, wh*

Pretest Directions: Fold back the page along the dotted line. On the blanks, write the spelling words as they are dictated. When you have finished the test, unfold the page and check your words.

1. ______________
2. ______________
3. ______________
4. ______________
5. ______________
6. ______________
7. ______________
8. ______________
9. ______________
10. ______________
11. ______________
12. ______________
13. ______________
14. ______________
15. ______________
16. ______________
17. ______________
18. ______________
19. ______________
20. ______________

1. They were **shown** into the parlor.
2. Hurry, time is **short**.
3. Don't be quick to **punish** him.
4. They looked for **shelter**.
5. Here's the **flashlight**.
6. I put it in the **trash**.
7. **March** winds can be strong.
8. I read the first **chapter**.
9. She likes **chocolate** milk.
10. The **church** is on the hill.
11. Will you **watch** them for me?
12. The cook's in the **kitchen**.
13. The **pitcher** threw the ball.
14. The **catcher** wore a face mask.
15. I'll do **whatever** it takes.
16. Dreams can take you **anywhere**.
17. Come **whenever** you want.
18. See the **wheat** in that field?
19. Sit and talk **awhile**.
20. It's here **somewhere**.

Notes for Home: Your child took a pretest on words that have the letters *sh, ch, tch,* and *wh.* ***Home Activity:*** Help your child learn misspelled words before the final test. See if there are any similar errors and discuss a memory trick that could help.

Name ______________________________

Spelling: Words with *sh, ch, tch, wh*

Word List				
shown	flashlight	chocolate	pitcher	whenever
short	trash	church	catcher	wheat
punish	March	watch	whatever	awhile
shelter	chapter	kitchen	anywhere	somewhere

Directions: Choose the word from the box that is formed by adding **sh, ch, tch,** or **wh** at the beginning or end of each group of letters below. Write the word on the line.

1. own ______________ **7.** ocolate ______________

2. tra ______________ **8.** Mar ______________

3. puni ______________ **9.** wa ______________

4. elter ______________ **10.** eat ______________

5. ort ______________ **11.** enever ______________

6. apter ______________ **12.** atever ______________

Directions: Choose the word from the box that best completes each sentence. Write the word on the line to the left.

______________ **13.** The baseball team's cook was working in the _____.

______________ **14.** He had returned from a Sunday service at _____.

______________ **15.** He poured a huge _____ of water.

______________ **16.** The team's _____ had asked the cook to make soup.

______________ **17.** The cook looked to see if there was any chicken _____.

______________ **18.** The electricity went out, so he got a _____.

______________ **19.** The catcher would have to wait _____ for the soup.

______________ **20.** Maybe the catcher would have to eat _____ else.

Notes for Home: Your child spelled words with *sh, ch, tch,* and *wh*. ***Home Activity:*** Write *sh, ch, tch,* and *wh* in four columns on a sheet of paper. Have your child sort the spelling words, writing each word in the correct column.

Name ______________________________

Proofread and Write

Spelling: Words with *sh, ch, tch, wh*

Directions: Proofread this beginning of a spooky book. Find five spelling mistakes. Use the proofreading marks to correct each mistake.

≡ Make a capital.
/ Make a small letter.
∧ Add something.
Take out something.
⊙ Add a period.
¶ Begin a new paragraph.

Chapter 1

It was a dark and stormy night in March. The wind blew. The rain fell. The ocean waves crashed against the rocky shore. Somewere, an owl hooted, alert during his nightly whatch. Lightning flashed, and wenever it did, the owl hooted louder.

Suddenly, the lightning struck an old, dead tree. The tree burst into flames. It burned awile, until the rain put it out. Just as darkness returned, a flachlight beam gleamed brightly in the distance.

Spelling Tip

Words can have two or three consonants together that are pronounced as one sound, like **punish**, **chapter**, **watch**, and **whenever.**

Word List

shown	watch
short	kitchen
punish	pitcher
shelter	catcher
flashlight	whatever
trash	anywhere
March	whenever
chapter	wheat
chocolate	awhile
church	somewhere

Write a Spooky Story

Write your own spooky story. On a separate sheet of paper, write a story that takes place during a storm, in a scary place, or with spooky characters. Use at least three spelling words.

Notes for Home: Your child spelled words with *sh, ch, tch,* and *wh.* ***Home Activity:*** Go on a word search hunt. Check a variety of print materials in the house (videos, food labels, magazines, books), looking for more words with *sh, ch, tch,* and *wh*.

Name ______________________________

Spelling: Words with *sh, ch, tch, wh*

REVIEW

Word List				
shown	flashlight	chocolate	pitcher	whenever
short	trash	church	catcher	wheat
punish	March	watch	whatever	awhile
shelter	chapter	kitchen	anywhere	somewhere

Directions: Choose the word from the box that best completes each statement. Write the word on the line to the left.

__________________ **1.** *Big* is to *little* as *tall* is to _____.

__________________ **2.** *Trumpet* is to *instrument* as *house* is to _____.

__________________ **3.** *Where* is to *wherever* as *what* is to _____.

__________________ **4.** *Week* is to *Thursday* as *month* is to _____.

__________________ **5.** *Skyscraper* is to *building* as *cathedral* is to _____.

__________________ **6.** *Finger* is to *ring* as *wrist* is to _____.

__________________ **7.** *Learn* is to *classroom* as *cook* is to _____.

__________________ **8.** *Song* is to *verse* as *book* is to _____.

Directions: Choose the word from the box that contains each word below. Write the word on the line.

9. flash __________________

10. how __________________

11. pitch __________________

12. cat __________________

13. ash __________________

14. while __________________

15. when __________________

16. any __________________

17. late __________________

18. eat __________________

19. some __________________

20. pun __________________

Notes for Home: Your child spelled words with *sh, ch, tch,* and *wh.* ***Home Activity:*** Pick one of the letter combinations. Have a contest to see who can write the greatest number of words with that combination in two minutes.

Name ___________________________________

Thesaurus

A **thesaurus** is a kind of dictionary that contains antonyms, synonyms, and other related words. Like a dictionary, the words are listed alphabetically. You can look up words in a thesaurus to better understand what you read and to find new ways of saying something.

Suppose you wanted to find a new word to replace *peaceful* in the following sentence: *News of the strange Half-Chicken spread quickly to the peaceful cows, grazing with their calves, the fierce bulls, and the swift horses.* First you look up *peaceful* in the index, and then find the entry.

> **peaceful** *(adjective)*
> *Synonyms:* nonviolent, calm, peaceable
> *Cross-reference:* cool, unruffled, steady
> *Antonyms:* disturbed, perturbed, upset

Here is what each part of the entry tells you:

- Part of speech—how a word is used
  Peaceful is an adjective. It is a word that describes nouns.
- Synonyms—words that have the same or similar meanings
  Peaceful means the same or nearly the same as *nonviolent, calm, peaceable.*
- Cross-reference—words that are related to the word you looked up
  You can look up *cool* in the thesaurus for more words with meanings similar to *peaceful.*
- Antonyms—words that have opposite meanings
  Disturbed, perturbed, and *upset* are opposite to *peaceful.*

Name ______________________________

Directions: The thesaurus entries below give you information about two more words in the sentence on the previous page about Half-Chicken. Use these entries to answer the questions that follow.

spread *(verb)*
Synonyms: circulate, distribute
Cross-reference: broadcast, communicate, pass (on), transmit, scatter, sow, peddle
Antonyms: hold (in), contain

swift *(adjective)*
Synonyms: fast, quick, rapid, snappy, speedy
Cross-reference: sudden, double-quick
Antonyms: sluggish

1. What word is opposite in meaning to *swift?* ______________________________
2. What part of speech is *spread?* ______________________________
3. What part of speech is *swift?* ______________________________
4. What words are synonyms for *spread?* ______________________________
5. Which related words could you look up to find more words similar in meaning to *swift?*

____

6. Name one antonym for *spread.* ______________________________
7. Which entry word has *pass (on)* as a related word? ______________________________
8. Which entry word is similar in meaning to *speedy?* ______________________________
9. Rewrite the sentence about Half-Chicken. Replace at least one word in the sentence. Use one of the three thesaurus entries shown.

____

____

10. Why would a thesaurus be helpful to writers? ______________________________

____

Notes for Home: Your child used thesaurus entries to locate synonyms, antonyms, and related words. ***Home Activity:*** If you have a thesaurus, have your child find a synonym for *fierce.* Or, ask your child to tell you what synonyms and antonyms are.

Family Times

Name_______________

Summary

Wolf Tries to Set Record Straight

This play lets the wolf tell his side of the story. What really happened with the three little pigs? Did the wolf threaten them as some say? And did the wolf really go after Little Red Riding Hood's grandma? Could it be that the Three Little Pigs and Little Red Riding Hood have misunderstood him? In this play, a jury hears testimony from the three pigs, Little Red, and others, and learns that there are always two sides to a story!

Activity

You Be the Jury. Have your child review the wolf's defense as though he or she was one of the jurors. Has the wolf been convincing? Why or why not? (Remind your child to ignore what they know about how the story ends.)

Reading Skills

Compare/Contrast

To **compare** means to tell how things are alike. Clue words such as *like* and *as* show comparisons. To **contrast** means to tell how things are different. Clue words such as *but* and *unlike* show contrasts. Sometimes authors don't use clue words to show comparisons and contrasts, and readers must compare and contrast on their own.

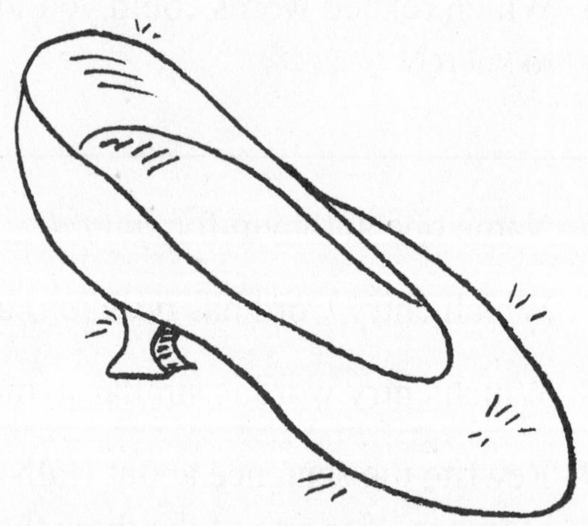

Activity

You Change the Story. Retell the story of Cinderella from the stepsisters' point of view. (Or retell another fairy tale from the villain's point of view.) Have fun changing things around! After you tell your new version of the story, talk about how the two versions are alike and how they are different.

Family Times

Tested Vocabulary

Words to Know

Knowing the meanings of these words is important to reading *Blame It on the Wolf.* Practice using these words to learn their meanings.

character person or animal in a book, play, film, story, or poem

courtroom room in which a court of law meets

evidence facts or proof

guilty having done wrong

rescued saved

Grammar

Using Adjectives to Improve Sentences

An **adjective** is a word that describes a person, place, or thing. Some adjectives tell what kind: **The wolf went to the <u>brick</u> house.** Some adjectives tell how many: **<u>Three</u> pigs met up with a wolf.** Some adjectives tell which one: **<u>That</u> pig misunderstood the wolf.** Adjectives are used to give more information and to make sentences more colorful.

Activity

Have It Both Ways. Tell a short story about a real or made-up event. Don't use any adjectives. Then tell it again. This time use adjectives to tell a more descriptive story. Which story was more fun to hear? Which was more fun to tell?

Tested Spelling Words

____________	____________	____________	____________
____________	____________	____________	____________
____________	____________	____________	____________
____________	____________	____________	____________
____________	____________	____________	____________

Name ______________________________

Compare and Contrast

- To **compare** is to tell how two or more things are alike. To **contrast** is to tell how two or more things are different.
- Clue words such as *like* or *as* show comparisons. Clue words such as *but, instead,* and *unlike* show contrasts.

Directions: Reread "Wolves." Then complete the diagram below. List things that are true about gray wolves on the left, things that are true about red wolves on the right, and things that are true about both kinds of wolves in the middle.

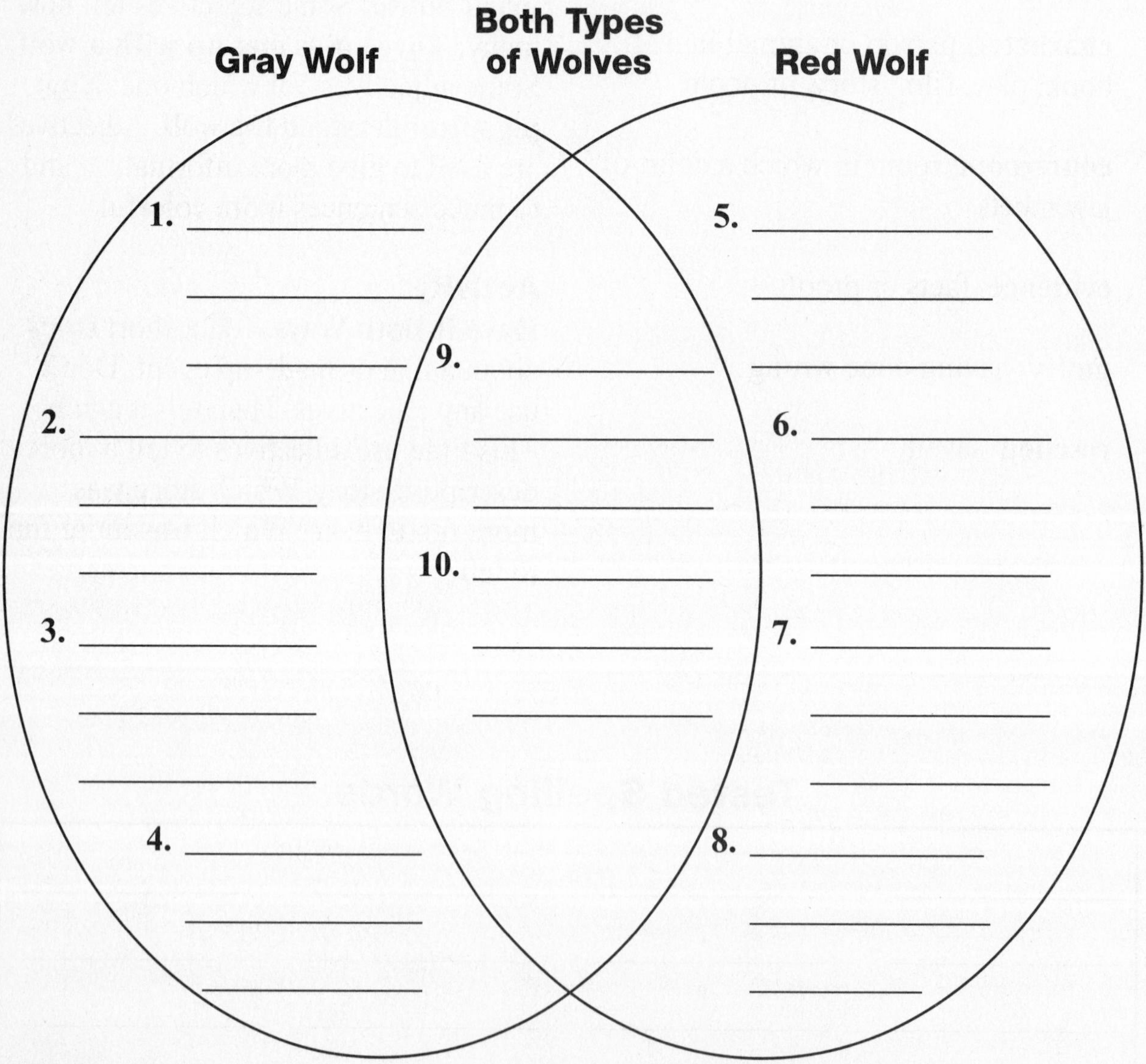

Gray Wolf	Both Types of Wolves	Red Wolf
1. ______________	9. ______________	5. ______________
2. ______________	10. ______________	6. ______________
3. ______________		7. ______________
4. ______________		8. ______________

Notes for Home: Your child read a nonfiction text and told how the wolves are alike and different. ***Home Activity:*** Ask your child to identify a favorite dessert and a favorite main dish. Then ask him or her to tell how these foods are alike and different.

Name ___________________________

Vocabulary

Directions: Choose the word from the box that best matches each definition. Write the word on the line.

Check the Words You Know

__ character
__ courtroom
__ evidence
__ guilty
__ rescued

_______________ **1.** person in a story

_______________ **2.** facts; proof

_______________ **3.** having done wrong

_______________ **4.** saved

_______________ **5.** room in which a court of law meets

Directions: Choose the word from the box that best completes each sentence. Write the word on the line to the left.

_______________ **6.** The story about the trial took place in a _____.

_______________ **7.** My favorite _____ was the lawyer, Gary the Gorilla.

_______________ **8.** He presented _____ that the chimpanzees had stolen three bunches of bananas.

_______________ **9.** A jury of leopards, lions, and panthers had to decide whether the chimps were _____.

_______________ **10.** At the last minute, the chimps were _____ by a surprise witness.

Write a Journal Entry

On a separate sheet of paper, write a journal entry as if you were the judge in the case of the chimps who stole the bananas. Use as many of the vocabulary words as you can to describe the judge's reaction to the trial.

Notes for Home: Your child identified and used vocabulary words from *Blame It on the Wolf. **Home Activity:*** Ask your child to tell you what he or she knows about trials. If necessary, ask questions such as: *Where does a trial take place? (courtroom)*

Name ______________________

Compare and Contrast

- To **compare** is to tell how two or more things are alike. To **contrast** is to tell how two or more things are different.
- Clue words such as *like* or *as* show comparisons. Clue words such as *but, instead,* and *unlike* show contrasts.

Directions: Reread what happens in *Blame It on the Wolf* when the Wolf questions the three little pigs. Then, follow the instructions below.

WOLF: What do you think I said outside your brick house? On the day in question?
IGGIE: I thought you said, "I'll huff and I'll puff and blow you into another galaxy!"
SQUIGGY: I thought he said, "My hands are rough. Can I borrow some moisturizing lotion?"
MOE: I thought he said, "I'll have a BLT on whole wheat—hold the mayo!"
WOLF: So you admit that you really aren't sure what I said. *(to JURY)* I intend to prove that sometimes we don't hear everything clearly. Some people don't pay attention …
JUDGE *(trying to get WOLF'S attention):* Mr. Wolf …
WOLF *(continuing without hearing the JUDGE):* Some people hear only what they want to hear …

1. What is one way in which the pigs' answers are different?

____

2. What is one way in which Squiggy's and Moe's answers are alike?

____

3. How is Wolf's opinion different from Iggie's opinion?

____

4. In what way does the wolf in the courtroom act like the pigs at their house?

____

5. On a separate sheet of paper, compare and contrast the wolf in this story to the wolf in other stories you know, such as "The Three Little Pigs" and "Little Red Riding Hood."

Notes for Home: Your child compared and contrasted characters in stories to show how they are alike and different. ***Home Activity:*** Find a favorite story. Ask your child how two of the characters in it are alike, and how they are different.

Name ______________________________

Selection Test

Directions: Choose the best answer to each item. Mark the letter for the answer you have chosen.

Part 1: Vocabulary

Find the answer choice that means about the same as the underlined word in each sentence.

1. The young woman was <u>guilty</u>.
- A. having done wrong
- B. not polite
- C. away on vacation
- D. feeling sick

2. I was a <u>character</u> witness.
- F. about a place
- G. colorful
- H. about a person
- J. short

3. Susie <u>rescued</u> a kitten.
- A. patted
- B. saved from harm
- C. grabbed
- D. gave food to

4. Everyone left the <u>courtroom</u>.
- F. place where people play tennis
- G. place where trials are held
- H. food court in a large mall
- J. room where a king sits

5. We need more <u>evidence</u>.
- A. lessons
- B. good ideas
- C. time to rest
- D. facts; proof

Part 2: Comprehension

Use what you know about the play to answer each item.

6. Where does the first scene of this play take place?
- F. at Iggie's brick house
- G. outside Big Red's house
- H. in a courtroom
- J. at Auntie Pot Pie's house

7. In this play, Wolf wants to—
- A. eat Little Red Riding Hood.
- B. tell his side of the story.
- C. blame Old Red for his problems.
- D. meet Hansel and Gretel.

8. Who gets to decide if Wolf is guilty of eating Grandma?
- F. the judge
- G. Iggie
- H. Moe
- J. the jury

GO ON

9. Wolf's story is different from the pigs' story because he says that he—
A. asked the pigs for help.
B. wanted to eat the pigs.
C. blew their house down.
D. wanted to take them out for supper.

10. Hansel and Gretel got lost in the woods because—
F. they didn't leave a trail.
G. they followed the wrong trail.
H. animals ate their bread crumbs.
J. it was dark out.

11. Which character doesn't seem to fit in with the rest of the story?
A. Wolf
B. Chicken Little
C. Little Red Riding Hood
D. Grandma

12. How are Auntie Pot Pie and Old Red alike?
F. They are both evil.
G. They are both sweet and kind.
H. They both dislike the wolf.
J. They are twin sisters.

13. Why was Auntie Pot Pie angry at Wolf?
A. Wolf ate Little Red Riding Hood's grandma.
B. He scared Little Red.
C. Wolf took Hansel and Gretel away from her.
D. He ate her candy house.

14. Which is the best proof that Wolf was not guilty?
F. Little Red's grandma returned.
G. The three pigs told three different stories.
H. Hansel and Gretel said that Wolf was nice to them.
J. Auntie Pot Pie wanted to eat Hansel and Gretel.

15. This play suggests that if you think someone has done something wrong, it is wise to—
A. take a trip far away.
B. listen to both sides of the story.
C. put wax in your ears.
D. keep children away from the forest.

STOP

Name ______________________________

Compare and Contrast

- To **compare** is to tell how two or more things are alike. To **contrast** is to tell how two or more things are different.
- Clue words such as *like* or *as* show comparisons. Clue words such as *but, instead,* and *unlike* show contrasts.

Directions: Read the play below.

LAWYER: Ms. Hogg, do you promise to tell the truth?
MS. HOGG: Yes.
LAWYER: You were at the store the day of the robbery. Did you see my client there?
MS. HOGG: I think I did, but I'm not sure. It might have been somebody else.
LAWYER: Then you can't tell us what happened. Next witness! Mr. Pigg! Do you promise to tell the truth?
MR. PIGG: Yes.
LAWYER: You were also at the store the day of the robbery. Did you see my client there?
MR. PIGG: Yes. I'm sure I did.
LAWYER: Good. What was he doing?
MR. PIGG: I think I saw him buying some socks—but I'm not sure. It might have been somebody else.
LAWYER: If you're not sure, you can't tell us what happened, either.
MR. PIGG: Yes, I can. Because *I'm* the one who robbed the store!

Directions: Complete the diagram. On the left, write words that describe Ms. Hogg. On the right, write words that describe Mr. Pigg. Where the circles overlap, write things both these characters have in common.

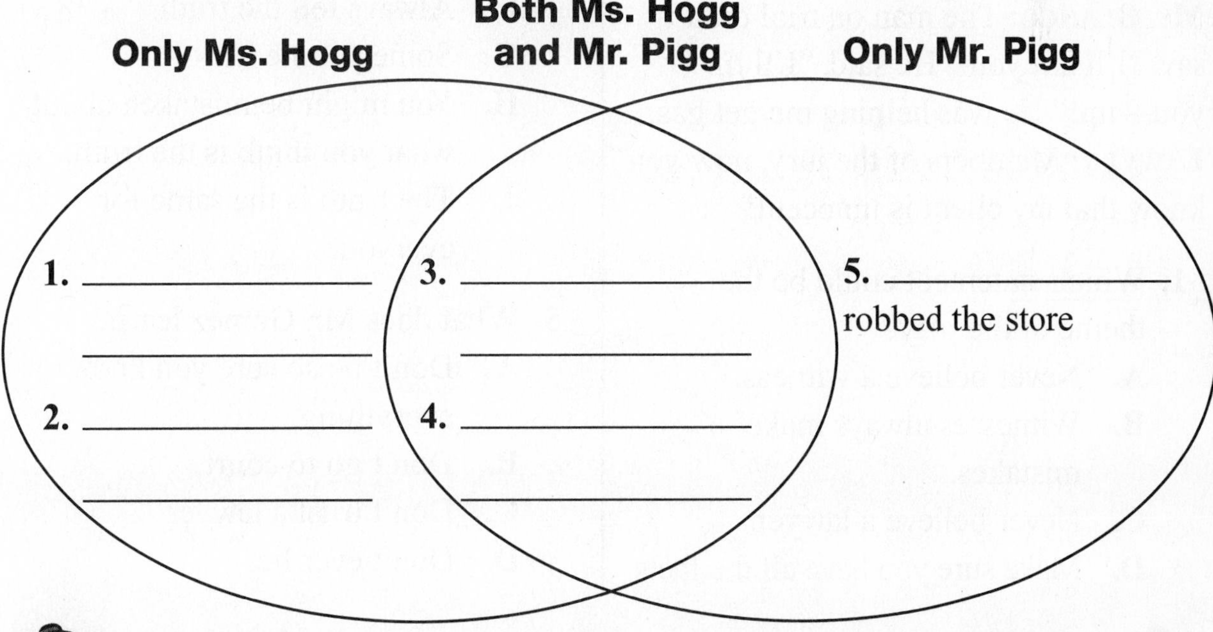

Notes for Home: Your child compared and contrasted characters in a play to show how the characters are alike and how they are different. ***Home Activity:*** Name two people that you and your child know well. Take turns telling how they are alike and how they are different.

Theme

REVIEW

Directions: Read the play. Then read each question about the play. Choose the best answer to each question. Mark the letter for the answer you have chosen.

Who Was Right?

LAWYER: Mr. Gomez, are you absolutely sure of what you heard?
MR. GOMEZ: Yes, I'm sure. The man on trial said, "I'll kill you!"
LAWYER: Did you see him?
MR. GOMEZ: No. I didn't see him. But I heard him.
LAWYER: And you're sure of what you heard?
MR. GOMEZ: Yes. He said, "I'll kill you."
LAWYER: Next witness! Ms. Blanco, were you at the same gas station?
MS. BLANCO: Yes, I was there.
LAWYER: What did you hear and see?
MS. BLANCO: The man on trial didn't say, "I'll *kill* you." He said, "I'll *fill* you—up!" He was helping me get gas.
LAWYER: Members of the jury, now you know that my client is innocent!

1. Which statement could be the theme of the play?
   - **A.** Never believe a witness.
   - **B.** Witnesses always make mistakes.
   - **C.** Never believe a lawyer.
   - **D.** Make sure you have all the facts.

2. Which statement supports the theme?
   - **F.** Mr. Gomez lied.
   - **G.** Ms. Blanco explains how Mr. Gomez was mistaken.
   - **H.** The lawyer makes a mistake.
   - **J.** Ms. Blanco was frightened.

3. Which statement is **not** a theme of the play?
   - **A.** People often make mistakes.
   - **B.** People see things differently.
   - **C.** A small detail can change a lot.
   - **D.** Guilty people should be punished harshly.

4. What did this story suggest about telling the truth?
   - **F.** Always tell the truth.
   - **G.** Some people lie.
   - **H.** You might be mistaken about what you think is the truth.
   - **J.** The truth is the same for everyone.

5. What does Mr. Gomez learn?
   - **A.** Don't be so sure you know everything.
   - **B.** Don't go to court.
   - **C.** Don't trust a lawyer.
   - **D.** Don't ever lie.

Notes for Home: Your child identified the theme, or "big idea," of a play. ***Home Activity:*** Reread a favorite story with your child. Ask your child to identify the story's theme. Discuss what events and details from the story help support the story's "big idea."

Writing Across Texts

Directions: Consider what you know about Half-Chicken from the selection *Half-Chicken* and Wolf from *Blame It on the Wolf.* Write some of the things you learned about each character in the table below.

Half-Chicken	Wolf
Half-Chicken was proud of the way he looked.	Wolf decided to be his own lawyer.
1.	**6.**
2.	**7.**
3.	**8.**
4.	**9.**
5.	**10.**

Write a Letter

Use the information in your table to compose a letter from one character to another. Think about how the character would talk and the kinds of things he would say. Write your letter on a separate sheet of paper.

Notes for Home: Your child listed details from two different stories. ***Home Activity:*** With your child, read a fairy tale. Before you finish, have your child predict how the story will end. Check his or her predictions by reading to the end of the story.

REVIEW

Grammar: Adjectives

Directions: Draw two lines under the articles **a, an,** and **the** in the sentences below. Then draw a circle around each adjective that describes the underlined noun.

1. Many <u>animals</u> were gathered for an important <u>trial</u>.
2. The noisy, crowded <u>courtroom</u> grew quiet when the judge entered.
3. Everyone admired this strong, smart <u>crow</u> in the black <u>robe</u>.
4. Chester Cow was an eager <u>witness</u>.
5. When some young <u>calves</u> waved to Chester, the judge frowned.
6. "We are here for a serious <u>trial</u>," he declared. "No waving."
7. The cows and the sheep sat on different <u>sides</u> of the courtroom.
8. The two <u>groups</u> glared at one another.
9. Who had the right to graze on the beautiful green <u>meadow</u> near the lake?
10. That important <u>question</u> would be decided here today.

Directions: Complete each sentence with an article or with an adjective that tells how many or how much. Choose a word from the box, and write it on the line to the left.

more	many	an	fifty	few

________________ 11. In the crowded courtroom sat at least _____ sheep and cows.

________________ 12. Joining them were _____ chickens, goats, pigs, and others.

________________ 13. They had waited more than _____ hour to get a seat.

________________ 14. There were very _____ animals that were not interested in today's trial.

________________ 15. The winner of the trial would have _____ grass to eat and would rule the barnyard.

Notes for Home: Your child identified and used adjectives—words that describe persons, places, or things—in sentences. ***Home Activity:*** Ask your child to name five favorite people, places, and things, and then have your child write a sentence describing each one.

Name ______________________________

Practice

Grammar: Using Adjectives to Improve Sentences

The sentence below does not paint a clear picture. It needs descriptive details.

Sentence: The king wanted clothes.

One way to revise it is by adding adjectives.

Adjectives Added: The wealthy king wanted colorful clothes.

Don't use more adjectives than necessary to express your ideas clearly.

Overuse of Adjectives: The wealthy, worldly, old king wanted elegant, fancy clothes.

Directions: Choose an adjective in ( ) to complete each sentence. Write it on the line.

______________ **1.** Once upon a time, two (unkind/nice) men played a cruel trick on their king.

______________ **2.** Someone from the (royal/tiny) palace told them the king was tired of his suits.

______________ **3.** The king wanted suits that were better than any (all/other) suits in the kingdom.

______________ **4.** (These/This) two men opened a tailoring business.

______________ **5.** The (eager/stingy) king ordered a new suit.

______________ **6.** The tailors said they used cloth that was so unusual that (marvelous/ordinary) people couldn't see it.

______________ **7.** The (vain/humble) king ordered a suit made of this cloth.

______________ **8.** The (dishonest/unsuspecting) king put on his "invisible suit."

______________ **9.** He paid the (greedy/golden) men with gold coins.

______________ **10.** A boy on the street saw the (little/foolish) ruler and exclaimed, "His Majesty forgot to put on a suit!"

Notes for Home: Your child used adjectives, words that describe nouns or pronouns, to make sentences more interesting. ***Home Activity:*** Have your child tell you about his or her day, using adjectives to give an interesting description.

Name ____________________________________

Grammar: Using Adjectives to Improve Sentences

Directions: Add an adjective to improve each sentence. Write the adjective on the line to the left.

____________________ **1.** "But I can explain!" insisted the _____ girl known as Goldilocks.

____________________ **2.** "I was sent by my _____ grandmother to the bears' house."

____________________ **3.** "My grandmother is the bears' _____ housekeeper."

____________________ **4.** "When I arrived at the _____ house, no one came to the door."

____________________ **5.** "I walked in the _____ door and looked around."

____________________ **6.** "I didn't sit in their chairs, and I didn't eat any of their _____ porridge either."

____________________ **7.** "I just put it in the _____ oven so it wouldn't get cold."

____________________ **8.** "I didn't really sleep in their _____ beds either."

____________________ **9.** "I was just putting on some _____ sheets."

____________________ **10.** "I hope you think this _____ story is interesting."

Write an Explanation

Pretend you are a character from a folk tale or fairy tale you have read, such as "Goldilocks" or "Jack and the Beanstalk." On a separate sheet of paper, write an explanation for something you did in the tale, such as wander into the three bears' cottage or buy a hatful of beans. Use colorful adjectives to help you write vivid, interesting sentences.

Notes for Home: Your child improved sentences by adding adjectives. ***Home Activity:*** Play a game of "Finish the Sentence," adding adjectives to each other's sentences.

Name ___________________________________

RETEACHING

Grammar: Using Adjectives to Improve Sentences

The sentences below do not have descriptive details. Add an adjective to each sentence. Write it on the line.

1. The person ate ________________ cake.

2. Manuel put on ________________ shoes.

This sentence has too many adjectives. Draw lines through adjectives that aren't necessary.

3. My favorite, best-liked, wonderful, nice, blue sweater was in the wash.

Adding an **adjective** to a sentence is one way to add descriptive detail. Using adjectives also helps you to express your ideas more clearly.

Directions: The story below is not very descriptive or clear. Choose an adjective from the box that best fits each sentence. Write the adjective on the line. Some adjectives will not be used.

afraid	brave	bright	colorful	dark	empty	gray	happy
heavy	huge	lonely	long	musty	new	old	tall

Darron walked down the **1.** ___________ sidewalk. He had never seen the street so **2.** ___________ . He was a little **3.** ___________ . The streetlights were **4.** ___________ , but it was still hard to see clearly. When he got to the **5.** ___________ building, he stopped. The **6.** ___________ windows looked like rectangles. The doors were **7.** ___________ . Darron closed his eyes. "I am **8.** ___________ ," he said. Then he went inside. The library smelled **9.** ___________. He reached the highest shelf and took down a **10.** ___________ book.

Notes for Home: Your child added adjectives to a story to make it more vivid and interesting. ***Home Activity:*** Read a page from a favorite story to your child, leaving out the adjectives. Have your child add adjectives of his or her choosing.

Name ______________________________

Grammar: Using Adjectives to Improve Sentences

Directions: Change seven adjectives in the story to make the mood even scarier. Use the words in the idea bank, or make up words of your own.

1.–6.

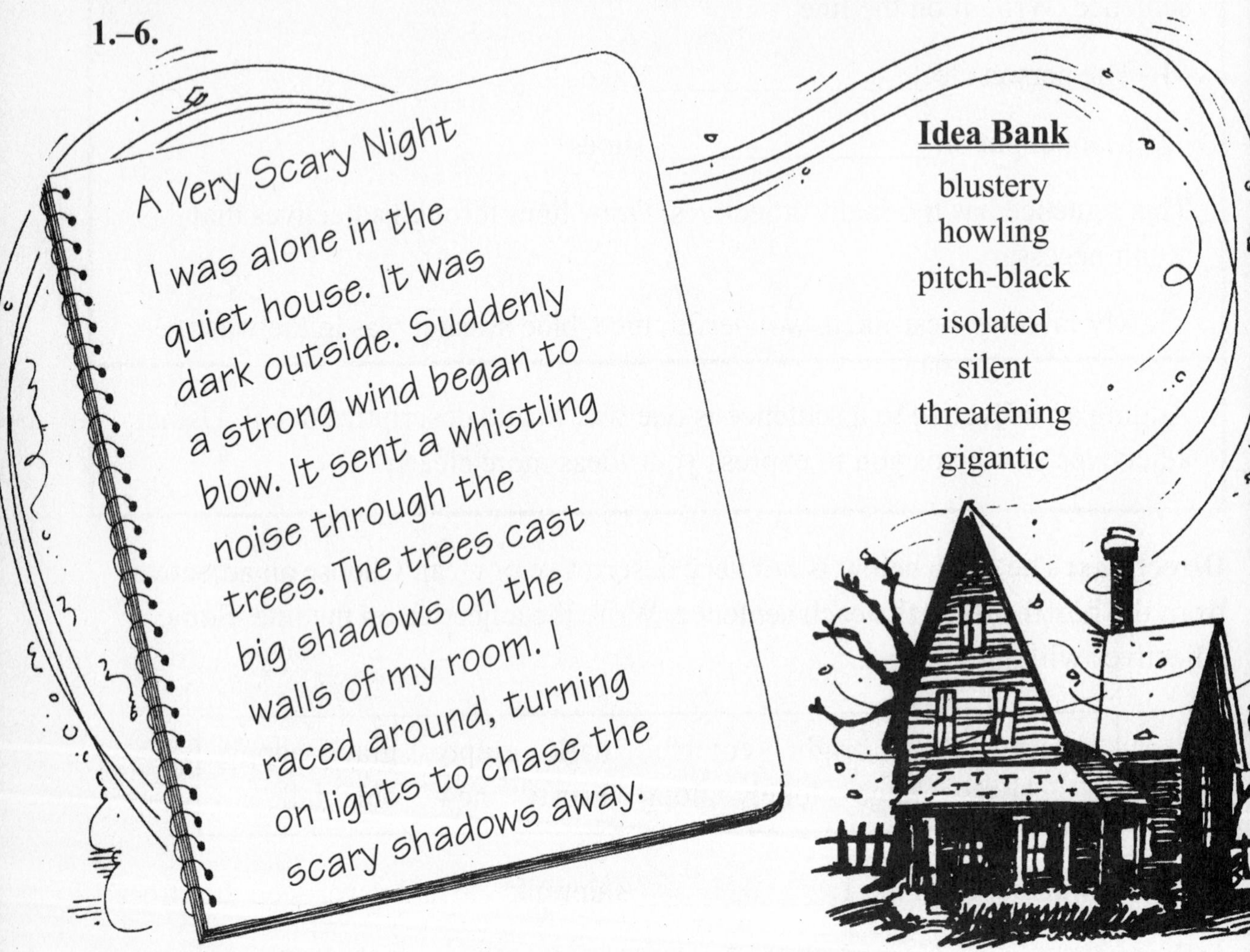

A Very Scary Night
I was alone in the quiet house. It was dark outside. Suddenly a strong wind began to blow. It sent a whistling noise through the trees. The trees cast big shadows on the walls of my room. I raced around, turning on lights to chase the scary shadows away.
Idea Bank
blustery
howling
pitch-black
isolated
silent
threatening
gigantic

Directions: Write three sentences that create a different mood of your choice. Remember to use adjectives that help create your mood.

____

____

____

Notes for Home: Your child replaced words in a story with more interesting adjectives. ***Home Activity:*** Have your child write a story about an exciting event. Challenge him or her to use descriptive adjectives in the story.

Name ________________________________

Word Study: Contractions

Directions: Some contractions are formed by joining a verb and the word **not.** An **apostrophe (')** takes the place of the **o** in **not.** Form a contraction from each pair of words below. Write the contraction on the line.

1. did + not = ____________

2. do + not = ____________

3. does + not = ____________

4. was + not = ____________

5. could + not = ____________

6. have + not = ____________

7. are + not = ____________

8. had + not = ____________

Directions: Other contractions are formed by joining a word and a verb such as **has, is, will, have,** and **are.** Read the paragraph below. Circle each contraction. Write the two words that each contraction combines on the line.

Favorite stories, such as fairy tales and folk tales, traditionally have some things in common. They're often about good people versus bad people. There's often some sort of magical element. You'll probably also read about people who've learned a lesson. The lesson could be something they've learned by doing a tremendous deed. Besides the hero and the villain, you're certain to meet some silly characters too. What's your favorite fairy tale or folk tale?

9. ____________

10. ____________

11. ____________

12. ____________

13. ____________

14. ____________

15. ____________

Notes for Home: Your child made contractions using an apostrophe to join two words. ***Home Activity:*** Work with your child to write contractions and the word pairs they represent on separate slips of paper. Take turns matching a contraction with its word pair.

Name ______________________________

Pretest

Spelling: Contractions

Pretest Directions: Fold back the page along the dotted line. On the blanks, write the spelling words as they are dictated. When you have finished the test, unfold the page and check your words.

1. ____________
2. ____________
3. ____________
4. ____________
5. ____________
6. ____________
7. ____________
8. ____________
9. ____________
10. ____________
11. ____________
12. ____________
13. ____________
14. ____________
15. ____________
16. ____________
17. ____________
18. ____________
19. ____________
20. ____________

1. I know **we'll** have fun.
2. **I'm** going to tell you.
3. **I'd** like to know.
4. I think **you'd** better tell me.
5. **I'll** have to find out later.
6. I think **we've** already been there.
7. I know **it's** a hard thing to do.
8. Yes, **that's** what I said.
9. He knows **what's** wrong.
10. It **doesn't** make any sense.
11. I bet **he'll** win the case.
12. I know **she'll** tell the truth.
13. Are you sure **they'll** come?
14. They said **they'd** come.
15. He could make it if **he'd** hurry up.
16. We **would've** been here sooner.
17. We **could've** run faster.
18. I **wouldn't** do that if I were you.
19. It **shouldn't** make a difference.
20. I say **let's** give him a chance.

Notes for Home: Your child took a pretest on words that are contractions. ***Home Activity:*** Help your child learn misspelled words before the final test. Your child can underline the word parts that caused the problems and concentrate on those parts.

Name ______________________________

Spelling: Contractions

Word List				
we'll	I'll	what's	they'll	could've
I'm	we've	doesn't	they'd	wouldn't
I'd	it's	he'll	he'd	shouldn't
you'd	that's	she'll	would've	let's

Directions: Choose the contraction from the box that is formed by combining each pair of words below. Write the contraction on the line.

1. I would ____________
2. you would ____________
3. he would ____________
4. they would ____________
5. would have ____________
6. could have ____________
7. would not ____________
8. should not ____________
9. does not ____________
10. I will ____________
11. he will ____________
12. she will ____________
13. we will ____________
14. they will ____________

Directions: Choose the word from the box that best completes each sentence. Write the word on the line to the left.

____________ 15. LAWYER: _____ going to ask the witness another question.

____________ 16. JUDGE: _____ this all about? I thought you had finished.

____________ 17. LAWYER: _____ all been wondering where the witness was during the crime.

____________ 18. WITNESS: _____ what I've been telling you! I was home with two friends!

____________ 19. LAWYER: Well, _____ hear from these friends. I'll call them to testify.

____________ 20. JUDGE: Agreed. _____ important that we hear their testimony.

Notes for Home: Your child spelled contractions. ***Home Activity:*** Write each spelling word without the apostrophe. Have your child rewrite the word correctly.

Name ______________________________

Spelling: Contractions

Directions: Proofread this dialogue from a trial. Find five spelling mistakes. Use the proofreading marks to correct each mistake.

≡	Make a capital.
/	Make a small letter.
∧	Add something.
↯	Take out something.
⊙	Add a period.
¶	Begin a new paragraph.

JUDGE: Im not happy with the way this trial is going. I'l have you know that this is a serious matter, and we'll proceed in a serious way!

LAWYER: Your honor, what did I do?

JUDGE: You have been making jokes! You shoudn't do that!

LAWYER: Your honor, I'am just naturally funny. If I culd've been born different, I would have.

Spelling Tip

Contractions use an apostrophe to take the place of letters that have been left out: **we've** is the contraction for **we have.** The letters **h** and **a** are left out. Check the dialogue to make sure that each contraction is spelled correctly.

Word List

we'll	I'll	what's	they'll	could've
I'm	we've	doesn't	they'd	wouldn't
I'd	it's	he'll	he'd	shouldn't
you'd	that's	she'll	would've	let's

Write a News Story

On a separate sheet of paper, write a news story about the trial above. Tell what you think of the characters' behavior. Use at least five contractions from the box.

Notes for Home: Your child spelled contractions. ***Home Activity:*** Say some or all of the contractions from the list. Have your child tell you what two words each contraction combines. Have your child spell the contraction and use it in a sentence.

Name ______________________________

Spelling: Contractions

REVIEW

Word List				
we'll	I'll	what's	they'll	could've
I'm	we've	doesn't	they'd	wouldn't
I'd	it's	he'll	he'd	shouldn't
you'd	that's	she'll	would've	let's

Directions: Choose the contraction from the box that is formed by combining each pair of words below. Write the contraction on the line.

1. does not ______________

2. would not ______________

3. should not ______________

4. we have ______________

5. would have ______________

6. could have ______________

7. she will ______________

8. he had ______________

9. we will ______________

10. let us ______________

11. they will ______________

12. they had ______________

Directions: Choose the contraction from the box that best replaces the underlined words. Write the contraction on the line.

______________ **13. Judge:** <u>I would</u> like to think you respect me, sir.

______________ **14. Lawyer:** Of course I do. <u>I am</u> your biggest fan.

______________ **15. Judge:** If <u>that is</u> true, why is there a pig in this court?

______________ **16. Lawyer:** <u>It is</u> here for a good reason, sir.

______________ **17. Judge:** And <u>what is</u> that reason?

______________ **18. Lawyer:** <u>He will</u> testify, if you don't mind.

______________ **19. Judge:** <u>I will</u> have to think about that.

______________ **20. Lawyer:** I knew <u>you would</u> say that.

Notes for Home: Your child spelled contractions. ***Home Activity:*** Say a sentence that includes two words that can be combined to form one of the contractions listed. Have your child repeat the sentence, replacing the two words with the contraction. Repeat for other contractions.

Evaluate Reference Sources

There are many sources you can use to find information. You can use books, magazines, encyclopedias, videotapes, audiotapes, CD-ROMs and even the Internet. When you **evaluate reference sources,** you decide which sources are reliable and up-to-date, and which are most useful for your purpose.

Directions: The table of contents can tell you at a glance what kind of information is in a book. Read the table of contents from two books. Use them to answer the questions that follow.

Wolves

Chapter 1 What do wolves look and sound like?
Chapter 2 What do wolves eat?
Chapter 3 Where do wolves live?

Stories About Wolves

Chapter 1 Little Red Riding Hood
Chapter 2 The Boy Who Cried Wolf
Chapter 3 The Three Little Pigs

1. Which book will give you factual information about how wolves live?

____

2. Which book will have fictional stories about wolves?

____

3. Suppose you want to write a report about stories that have wolves as main characters. Will *Stories About Wolves* give you useful information? Explain.

____

____

____

4. Suppose you want to write a report about wolves in the wild and how they live. Will *Wolves* give you useful information? Explain.

____

____

____

Name ______________________________

Directions: A copyright page tells when a book was written. Knowing this information can help you evaluate how up-to-date a source is. Read the copyright pages for two books. Use the copyright information to answer the questions that follow.

Wolves Copyright © 1972 by Animal Press All rights reserved. Animal Press, 537 W. 68th St., New York, NY 10015 Fifth Edition	Stories About Wolves Copyright © 1982 by Children's Book Publisher All rights reserved. Children's Book Publisher, 239 Red Rd., San Diego, CA 98716 First Edition

5. In what year was *Wolves* published? ______________________________

6. In what year was *Stories About Wolves* published? ______________________________

7. Which book is the oldest? ______________________________

8. Suppose you were writing about the number of wolves that exist today. Would you need a book about wolves published more recently than *Wolves?* Explain.

____

____

9. If you were comparing *Blame It on the Wolf* to the story "The Three Little Pigs," would you need a book published more recently than *Stories About Wolves?* Explain.

____

____

10. Is it important to think about the purpose of your research before evaluating a reference source? Explain.

____

____

Notes for Home: Your child evaluated reference sources, based on their contents and when they were published. ***Home Activity:*** Discuss different reference sources available in your home or at the library. Talk about how each source could be used for different kinds of research projects.

Family Times

Name_______________________________________

Summary

Fans Miss Slugger Who Never Missed a Game

When Lou Gehrig left college to play baseball with the Yankees, his mother thought he had ruined his life. Little did she know that he would go on to play in 2,130 straight games. He played the game so well that twice he was named the American League's Most Valuable Player. Then Lou Gehrig found out he had a fatal illness. In a speech to his fans, he called himself the "luckiest man." The Yankees honored him by retiring his uniform, something never before done in major-league baseball.

Activity

Words That Describe. Have your child tell you more about Lou Gehrig. Together think of words that describe the kind of person he was.

Reading Skills

Text Structure

Text structure is the way a piece of writing is organized. One way is to put events in time order. Biographies, like the story of Lou Gehrig, are often organized this way. Important dates and the age of the person at the time of an event can help you follow the order.

Activity

Telling About Events in Time Order. Think about the important events that have occurred in your family as you have grown up. Tell a story about a family member's life, using dates and ages to organize the events.

Family Times

Tested Vocabulary

Words to Know

Knowing the meanings of these words is important to reading *Lou Gehrig: The Luckiest Man.* Practice using these words to learn their meanings.

convinced caused to believe

courageous brave

engineer an expert in engineering

gradually slowly over a period of time

immigrants people who come to a foreign country to live

Grammar

Comparative and Superlative Adjectives

We often use adjectives to tell how people, places, and things are alike or different. Here are three ways to use adjectives to make comparisons.

- ❖ Adding *-er:* When Lou Gehrig had trouble hitting, he worked **harder** than usual.
- ❖ Adding *More* or *Most:* Lou Gehrig was voted **Most** Valuable Player twice.
- ❖ Adding *-est:* Lou Gehrig considered himself the **luckiest** man.

Activity

Exaggerate with Adjectives. People who exaggerate often use many comparative and superlative adjectives. Give an exaggerated review of a TV show, book, or movie you like—and lay it on thick!

Tested Spelling Words

______	______	______	______
______	______	______	______
______	______	______	______
______	______	______	______
______	______	______	______

Name ______________________________

Text Structure

- **Text structure** is the way a piece of writing is organized.
- One way to organize writing is to put events in **chronological,** or time, order.

Directions: Reread "Cal Ripken, Jr." Then complete the time line by listing the important events in Cal Ripken, Jr.'s life.

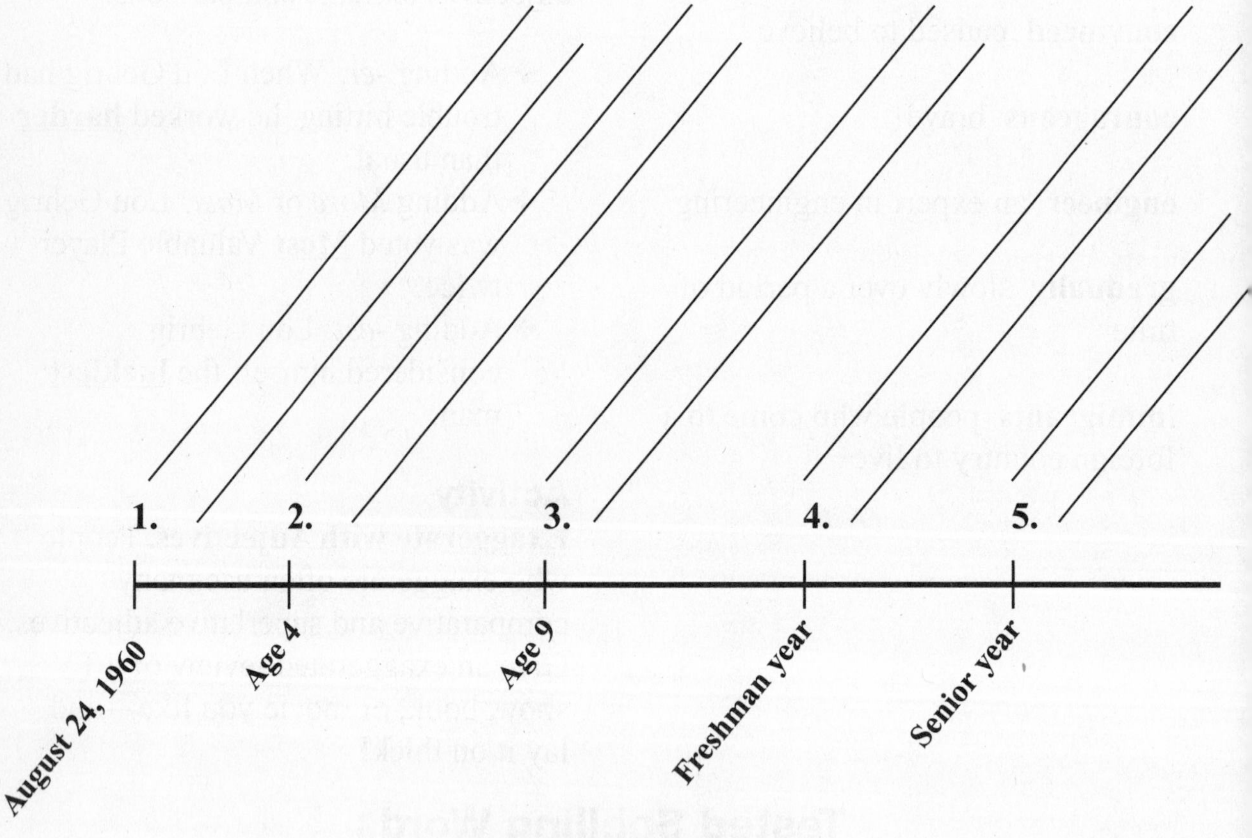

1. August 24, 1960

2. Age 4

3. Age 9

4. Freshman year

5. Senior year

Cal Ripken, Jr.

Notes for Home: Your child read a biography and used a time line to show events in the order in which they happened. ***Home Activity:*** Ask your child to tell the story of his or her life, by telling one memory each from preschool, first grade, second grade, third grade, and so on, in that order.

Name ______________________

Vocabulary

Directions: Choose the word from the box that best matches each definition. Write the word on the line.

Check the Words You Know
__ convinced
__ courageous
__ engineer
__ gradually
__ immigrants

__________ **1.** people who come from a foreign country to live

__________ **2.** caused to believe

__________ **3.** brave

__________ **4.** expert in engineering

__________ **5.** slowly over a period of time

Directions: Choose the word from the box that the best completes each sentence. Write the word on the line.

__________ **6.** You could see the _____ baseball player practicing in all kinds of weather.

__________ **7.** _____ Marta improved her game over the summer.

__________ **8.** She had come from a family of _____ and they were used to working hard.

__________ **9.** Her brother was studying hard to become an _____.

__________ **10.** Finally, the coach was _____ that Marta deserved a place on the team.

Write a Journal Entry

Imagine you are an immigrant who has recently arrived in this country. On a separate sheet of paper, write a journal entry about your hopes and dreams for your future. Use as many vocabulary words as possible.

Notes for Home: Your child identified and used vocabulary words from *Lou Gehrig: The Luckiest Man.* ***Home Activity:*** Ask your child to use each vocabulary word in a sentence. If necessary, show your child how to make up a sentence that includes one of the words.

Name ______________________________

Text Structure

- **Text structure** is the way a piece of writing is organized.
- **Fiction** tells stories of imaginary people and events. They are usually told in chronological, or time, order. **Nonfiction** tells of real people and events or tells information about the real world. Some ways to organize nonfiction are chronological order, cause and effect, problem and solution, or comparison and contrast.

Directions: Reread what happens in *Lou Gehrig: The Luckiest Man* when Lou Gehrig becomes a successful ballplayer. Then answer the questions below.

After high school Lou Gehrig went to Columbia University. He was on the baseball team there, too, and on April 26, 1923, a scout for the New York Yankees watched him play. Lou hit two long home runs in that game. Soon after that he was signed to play for the Yankees.

The Yankees offered Lou a $1,500 bonus to sign plus a good salary. His family needed the money. Lou quit college and joined the Yankees. Lou's mother was furious. She was convinced that he was ruining his life.

On June 1, 1925, the Yankee manager sent Lou to bat for the shortstop. The next day Lou played in place of first baseman Wally Pipp.

1. What happens before Lou is signed to play for the Yankees?

____

2. What happens after Lou is offered a $1,500 bonus to sign with the Yankees?

____

3. What happens on June 1, 1925?

____

4. How are events in this passage organized?

____

5. On a separate sheet of paper, tell whether this text is fiction or nonfiction. Then tell how the author organizes his writing. Do you think this is a good way to organize it? Explain.

Notes for Home: Your child looked at the way a text is organized, for example, noticing that events in stories are often told in chronological order. ***Home Activity:*** Ask your child to tell you a story about his or her day, telling about events in the order in which they happened.

Name ________________________________

Selection Test

Directions: Choose the best answer to each item. Mark the letter for the answer you have chosen.

Part 1: Vocabulary

Find the answer choice that means about the same as the underlined word in each sentence.

1. Dana <u>gradually</u> got better.
- A. suddenly
- B. at the end
- C. never
- D. slowly

2. Lee is <u>convinced</u> that he's right.
- F. sure
- G. worried
- H. sorry
- J. aware

3. Are they <u>immigrants</u>?
- A. birds that fly south
- B. persons who come to a foreign country to live
- C. persons who teach others
- D. unusual animals

4. You are very <u>courageous</u>.
- F. clever
- G. popular
- H. special
- J. brave

5. Kyle's mom is an <u>engineer</u>.
- A. one who knows the laws
- B. pilot of an airplane
- C. one who plans and builds things such as bridges
- D. person who plays sports

Part 2: Comprehension

Use what you know about the selection to answer each item.

6. Lou Gehrig was born in—
- F. Baltimore.
- G. Germany.
- H. New York City.
- J. Boston.

7. While Lou Gehrig was in college, he—
- A. became ill.
- B. had to quit school.
- C. gave a speech.
- D. signed to play for the Yankees.

8. Lou's mother was angry when he decided to play baseball because she—
- F. wanted him to be happy.
- G. thought he was ruining his life.
- H. knew he was sick.
- J. needed him to make money.

9. Lou Gehrig was known as "Iron Horse" because he—
A. never missed a game.
B. hit many home runs.
C. broke his fingers.
D. complained often.

10. The text in this selection is organized by—
F. time order.
G. causes and effects.
H. problems and solutions.
J. how things are alike or different.

11. Which of these events happened first?
A. Babe Ruth hit 60 home runs.
B. Gehrig was named MVP.
C. Babe Ruth hugged Lou Gehrig.
D. Gehrig got a $1,500 bonus.

12. During the 1938 baseball season, Lou Gehrig's playing got steadily worse because he—
F. was getting old.
G. was tired from playing so many games.
H. stopped believing in himself.
J. became ill.

13. At the end of his career, Gehrig considered himself lucky because he—
A. could finally quit baseball.
B. got a new job right away.
C. was surrounded by so many caring people.
D. was voted into the Hall of Fame.

14. The most amazing thing about Lou Gehrig is that he—
F. was named MVP twice.
G. never felt sorry for himself.
H. gave a speech to his fans.
J. did not know anything was wrong.

15. Which sentence gives an opinion?
A. Lou's hair was turning gray.
B. On June 13, 1939, Lou went to the Mayo Clinic.
C. Lou Gehrig walked to the microphone.
D. The 1927 Yankees were the best baseball team ever.

Name ______________________________

Text Structure

- **Text structure** is the way a piece of writing is organized.
- **Fiction** tells stories of imaginary people and events. They are usually told in chronological, or time, order. **Nonfiction** tells of real people and events or tells information about the real world. Some ways to organize nonfiction are chronological order, cause and effect, problem and solution, or comparison and contrast.

Directions: Read the passage below.

There wasn't always a game called baseball! It probably grew out of cricket and rounders, games Americans had learned from the English long ago.

Nobody knows exactly when baseball was invented, but it began in the 1800s. In 1876, a group of baseball teams organized themselves as the National League. In 1900, the American League was formed.

For many years, most baseball teams were located in the eastern part of the United States. Then, slowly, teams began to move west. The first team to move, the Boston Braves, went to Milwaukee, Wisconsin, in 1953. Gradually, baseball became a truly national sport, played from coast to coast.

Directions: This passage organized its information in chronological order. Complete the time line. Think about the order in which events happened. Write dates above the horizontal line. Describe events for that date below the line.

The Story of Baseball

Early 1800s	**1876**	3. ________	5. ________
1. ________	2. ________	4. ________	Boston Braves move to Milwaukee

Notes for Home: Your child used a time line to show the text's chronological organization. ***Home Activity:*** Take turns with your child telling a story of your day. Tell events in the order in which they happened. Challenge your child to write a story of your day using chronological order.

Name ______________________________

Paraphrasing

REVIEW

Directions: Read the passage. Then read each question about the passage. Choose the best answer to each question. Mark the letter for the answer you have chosen.

Satchel Paige: Baseball Hero

One of the greatest baseball players was the pitcher Satchel Paige.

For most of Paige's life, only white players were allowed in the Major Leagues. So Paige, who was African American, played in the Negro Leagues from the mid-1920s to the mid-1940s.

Paige's fast ball was legendary. Sometimes white players arranged to play against him. He pitched against the famous pitcher Dizzy Dean—and won.

In 1947, Jackie Robinson became the first African American to play in the Major Leagues. In 1948, Paige also joined the Major Leagues.

By then he was in his mid-forties—old for a ballplayer. But he still led his team to the top of the American League. Four years later, he was chosen as an American League All Star.

1. Which statement best paraphrases the first two paragraphs?
- **A.** Paige played ball for 20 years.
- **B.** Paige was a great ballplayer.
- **C.** Paige, a star player, was in the Negro Leagues for 20 years.
- **D.** Paige was one of the greatest baseball players ever.

2. Which statement does **not** paraphrase the third paragraph?
- **F.** Paige played in the Majors.
- **G.** Paige played against great white players.
- **H.** Paige was a legend in baseball.
- **J.** Paige attracted great competition.

3. Which phrase best completes this paraphrase of the fourth paragraph? Robinson and Paige both
- **A.** were stars.
- **B.** joined the Major Leagues.
- **C.** were African American.
- **D.** were great players.

4. Which statement best paraphrases the last paragraph?
- **F.** Paige still pitched at forty.
- **G.** Paige was not a young player.
- **H.** Despite his age, Paige led his team to the top.
- **J.** Paige was often tired.

5. Which detail does **not** belong in a paraphrase of the last paragraph?
- **A.** Paige was in his mid-forties.
- **B.** Robinson joined the Major Leagues.
- **C.** Paige led his team to the top.
- **D.** Paige won honors playing.

Notes for Home: Your child paraphrased—restated in his or her own words—a nonfiction passage. ***Home Activity:*** Tell your child a story about a family member. Then ask your child to retell the story in his or her own words. The paraphrase should keep the story's important ideas.

Name ____

Writing Across Texts

Directions: Consider what you learned about baseball from reading about Lou Gehrig and other players mentioned in *The Baseball Hall of Fame.* What would you teach young children about this game? List five reasons the game is enjoyable and five ways people can show they like the game.

Why Baseball Is Enjoyable	How to Show That You Like Baseball
You can play baseball just about anywhere.	You can collect baseball cards.
1.	**6.**
2.	**7.**
3.	**8.**
4.	**9.**
5.	**10.**

Write a Pamphlet

Create a pamphlet designed to encourage young children to develop an interest in playing or watching baseball. Include in the pamphlet reasons the game is enjoyable.

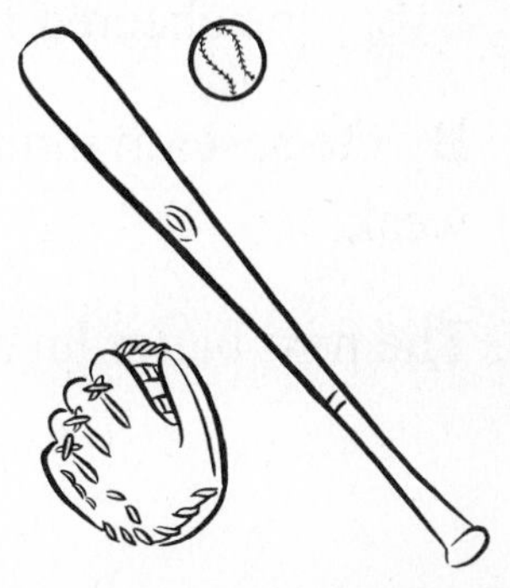

Notes for Home: Your child used information from two different selections to create a pamphlet. ***Home Activity:*** Choose a favorite sport that you and your child enjoy. Help your child make a poster about the sport to hang in his or her room.

Name ____________________

REVIEW

Grammar: Using Adjectives to Improve Sentences

Directions: Add one or more adjectives to improve each sentence. Write your new sentence on the line. Underline your adjectives.

1. The game of baseball is my favorite sport.

____

2. Baseball players must be athletes.

____

3. They have to be runners as well as hitters.

____

4. The pitcher is a player in baseball games.

____

5. Crowds help players do their best.

____

Directions: Cross out unneeded adjectives in each sentence below. Cross out any other words as needed so the revised sentences make sense.

6. My sister and I went to an exciting, wonderful, and thrilling baseball game.

7. The packed, crowded stands were filled with loud, noisy, screaming fans.

8. Everyone cheered for his or her best-liked and favorite team.

9. By the seventh inning, the tired and weary pitcher was becoming sloppy and weak.

10. The next batter hit a strong, soaring, terrific home run over the wall.

Notes for Home: Your child improved sentences by adding adjectives to give more detail and removing unnecessary adjectives. ***Home Activity:*** Have your child write sentences about something that happened today. Help your child add, take away, or replace some of the adjectives.

Name ______________________

Grammar: Comparative and Superlative Adjectives

Adjectives are often used to tell how people, places, and things are alike or different. In the sentence below, the **-er** ending in **newer** shows that two things are being compared.

Comparative: Your bat is newer than mine.

The **-est** ending of **newest** in the next sentence shows that three or more things are being compared.

Superlative: Carlos's bat is the newest of all.

Here are some patterns you can use to write comparative and superlative adjectives.

- For most adjectives that end with a consonant and **y,** change the **y** to **i** before you add **-er** or **-est: dry, drier, driest.**
- For most adjectives that end in a single consonant after a vowel, double the final consonant before adding **-er** or **-est: flat, flatter, flattest.**
- If an adjective ends with **e,** drop the final **e** before you add **-er** or **-est: safe, safer, safest.**

If you use a long adjective such as **terrific,** use **more** to compare two nouns. Use **most** to compare three or more. Never use **more** or **most** with the endings **-er** or **-est.**

The other team is more terrific than ours.
Carlos's team is the most terrific of all.

Directions: Add **-er** or **-est,** or use **more** or **most** to form comparative and superlative adjectives.

Adjective	Comparative Adjectives	Superlative Adjectives
early	**1.** ____________	**2.** ____________
late	**3.** ____________	**4.** ____________
low	**5.** ____________	**6.** ____________
thin	**7.** ____________	**8.** ____________
successful	**9.** ____________	**10.** ____________

Notes for Home: Your child wrote comparative and superlative forms of adjectives that compare people, places, and things. ***Home Activity:*** Play "Can You Top This?" Take turns. One person names an adjective, and the other person gives its comparative and superlative forms.

Extra Practice

Grammar: Comparative and Superlative Adjectives

Directions: Complete each sentence by writing the correct form of the adjective in ( ).

______________ **1.** Some people think that baseball is the (exciting) sport.

______________ **2.** They think it is (exciting) than football, even though it is not as rough.

______________ **3.** Baseball is (slow) than basketball, but these fans still prefer it.

______________ **4.** They think that going to a baseball game is the (enjoyable) way to spend an afternoon.

______________ **5.** They love to watch a player who is the (strong) hitter on the team.

______________ **6.** They like to argue about which runner is (fast) than another.

______________ **7.** They think the players on their favorite teams are the (great) players of all.

______________ **8.** If your team wins a game it's a (happy) day than if the team loses.

______________ **9.** But even if they lose, seeing the game is still (enjoyable) than staying home.

______________ **10.** For the players, sportsmanship is the (important) thing of all.

Write a Description

On a separate sheet of paper, describe your favorite sport. Use comparative adjectives to compare your sport with another sport. Use superlative adjectives to compare three or more things in your description. Circle each comparative and superlative adjective you used.

Notes for Home: Your child used the comparative and superlative forms of adjectives. ***Home Activity:*** Have your child tell you about an exciting day, using as many comparative and superlative adjectives as possible.

RETEACHING

Grammar: Comparative and Superlative Adjectives

Which dog won first prize in the dog show? Solve the riddle below.

bulldog **poodle** **Irish setter**

Riddle: The winner's tail is longer than the bulldog's tail. The winner does not have the longest tail of all. Circle the winner.

The words **longer** and **longest** are adjectives. The adjective **longer** compared two things. The adjective **longest** compared three things.

An adjective has two different forms that are useful in making comparisons. Use the **-er** form to compare two persons, places, or things. Use the **-est** form to compare three or more persons, places, or things.

Directions: Write the missing **-er** or **-est** form of each adjective.

1. clean, cleaner, ______________

2. strong, ______________, strongest

3. bright, ______________, ______________

Directions: Complete each sentence with an adjective that compares.

4. Bill's poodle is ______________ than my dog.

5. Your collie is ______________ than his collie.

6. My dog has the ______________ bark of all.

Notes for Home: Your child wrote comparative and superlative adjectives. ***Home Activity:*** Have your child choose three characters from a book, TV show, or movie, and use comparative and superlative adjectives to compare the characters.

Name ______________________

Grammar: Comparative and Superlative Adjectives

Directions: Write the missing **-er** or **-est** form of each adjective.

1. busy busier ______________

2. fat ______________ fattest

Directions: Use one adjective from the list to complete each sentence.

small smaller smallest large larger largest

3. An ant is very ______________ .

4. A lion is ______________ than a mouse.

5. A robin is ______________ than an elephant.

6. The ______________ animal of all is a whale.

Directions: Complete each comparison. Write the correct form of an adjective in the list. Then write a noun.

big slow thin noisy busy large

7. Chipmunks are ______________ than ______________ .

8. Frogs are ______________ than ______________ .

9. Snails are the ______________ ______________ of all.

10. Worker bees are the ______________ of all ______________ .

Write a Story

Write a story about a pet or a wild animal you like. Describe it well by using adjectives that compare. Write on a separate sheet of paper.

Notes for Home: Your child wrote comparative and superlative adjectives in sentences. ***Home Activity:*** Find pictures of three animals in books or magazines. Have your child label the pictures with comparative and superlative adjectives.

Name ______________________________

Word Study: Possessives

Directions: Possessive nouns are words that show ownership. Rewrite each phrase below to show possession. For example, **the scores that the players have** can be written as **the players' scores.** Write the new phrase on the line.

______________ **1.** the ball field that the school has

______________ **2.** the dream that Lou has

______________ **3.** the buildings that cities have

______________ **4.** the rules that schools have

Directions: Read the paragraph below. Several words have apostrophes, but they are not all possessive nouns. Circle each possessive noun. Write the word on the line.

Heroes and heroines in the world of sports make wonderful characters for stories. In such stories, the athletes' goal is usually to overcome an obstacle. For example, they're trying to get along with their teammates. Or a fan's rudeness makes them feel that they'd rather be doing something else. The league's rules might make it impossible for the player to try new things. It's as if the player's own skills aren't good enough for others to believe in. But true athletes are not stopped by other people's fears. Over time, everyone's learned that a strong will and an athlete's dream turn winning into a reality.

5. ______________

6. ______________

7. ______________

8. ______________

9. ______________

10. ______________

Notes for Home: Your child identified possessive nouns, such as *Chris's* and *players'*. ***Home Activity:*** Read a newspaper article with your child. Together, look for words that have apostrophes. Ask your child to decide whether or not these words show possession.

Name ______________________________

Pretest

Spelling: Easily Confused Words

Pretest Directions: Fold back the page along the dotted line. On the blanks, write the spelling words as they are dictated. When you have finished the test, unfold the page and check your words.

1. ____________________
2. ____________________
3. ____________________
4. ____________________
5. ____________________
6. ____________________
7. ____________________
8. ____________________
9. ____________________
10. ____________________
11. ____________________
12. ____________________
13. ____________________
14. ____________________
15. ____________________
16. ____________________
17. ____________________
18. ____________________
19. ____________________
20. ____________________

1. Please **set** the table for dinner.
2. Go ahead and **sit** down.
3. Tanika turned **off** the light.
4. Jack reads a lot **of** books.
5. I don't know **when** we'll be there.
6. I hope our team will **win**.
7. That's **our** house.
8. **Are** you going to the party?
9. I like carrots better **than** peas.
10. First I'll wash, **then** I'll dry.
11. He hopes his team won't **lose**.
12. Oops, this button is **loose**.
13. What **were** you saying?
14. I hope **we're** going to have fun.
15. I know **where** it is.
16. This is a **quiet** neighborhood.
17. Wow, that's **quite** a bike!
18. He says he won't **quit** trying.
19. **Whose** jacket is this?
20. **Who's** that standing by the door?

Notes for Home: Your child took a pretest on words that are easily confused with another word. ***Home Activity:*** Help your child learn misspelled words before the final test. Dictate the word in a sentence and have your child spell the word aloud for you or write it on paper.

Name ______________________________

Spelling: Easily Confused Words

Word List

set	when	than	were	quite
sit	win	then	we're	quit
off	our	lose	where	whose
of	are	loose	quiet	who's

Directions: Choose the word or words from the box that have a similar pronunciation or spelling as each word below. Write the word on the line.

1. win ______________

2. are ______________

3. whose ______________

4. sit ______________

5–6. quit ______________ ______________

7. off ______________

8. than ______________

9. lose ______________

10–11. where ______________ ______________

Directions: Choose the word in ( ) that best completes each sentence. Write the word on the line.

______________ **12.** Tim asked me to (set/sit) with him and watch TV.

______________ **13.** "(Where/We're) should I sit?" I asked.

______________ **14.** We watched the Yankees, who (our/are) my favorite team.

______________ **15.** They try hard, and never (quite/quit).

______________ **16.** They (when/win) almost every game.

______________ **17.** They never seem to (lose/loose).

______________ **18.** They're better (then/than) they were last year.

______________ **19.** "(Whose/Who's) feet are on the couch?" Tim said.

______________ **20.** "Mine," I said. "I'll take them (off/of)."

Notes for Home: Your child spelled words that are easily confused because they have similar pronunciations or spellings. ***Home Activity:*** Pick a pair or trio of words that are easily confused. Have your child spell each word and use it correctly in a sentence.

Spelling: Easily Confused Words

Directions: Proofread this article about a baseball game. Find five spelling mistakes. Use the proofreading marks to correct each mistake.

- ≡ Make a capital.
- / Make a small letter.
- ∧ Add something.
- Take out something.
- ⊙ Add a period.
- ¶ Begin a new paragraph.

SPORTS

The crowd was quit as Darryl Benton picked up the bat. They were all hoping that he would hit a home run and when the game for his team. Benton swung his bat a few times. Then he nodded. He looked like a man who would never quite until he had reached his goal. And today his goal was to win the game. "It's are turn now," he said. Than he stepped up to the plate.

Spelling Tip

Some words are easily confused because they have similar pronunciations, such as **when** and **win.** Other words have similar spellings, like **quite, quiet,** and **quit.** Check the story to make sure that these words are used and spelled correctly.

Word List

set	when	than	were	quite
sit	win	then	we're	quit
off	our	lose	where	whose
of	are	loose	quiet	who's

Write a Sports Story

On a separate sheet of paper, write your own story about a sporting event. You could write about what happened during the event, or you could tell about a specific athlete or coach. Use at least five spelling words.

Notes for Home: Your child spelled words that are easily confused because they have similar pronunciations or spellings. ***Home Activity:*** Say a spelling word, and use it in a sentence. Have your child spell the word.

Name ______________________________

Spelling: Easily Confused Words REVIEW

Word List				
set	when	than	were	quite
sit	win	then	we're	quit
off	our	lose	where	whose
of	are	loose	quiet	who's

Directions: Choose the word from the box that is the most opposite in meaning for each word below. Write the word on the line.

1. start ____________

2. on ____________

3. loud ____________

4. stand ____________

5. lose ____________

6. tight ____________

7. win ____________

8. now ____________

9. aren't ____________

10. weren't ____________

Directions: Look at the underlined word in each sentence. If it is the correct choice, write it on the line. If it is not the correct choice, write the word from the box that belongs there instead.

____________ **11.** Our coach called the team for a meeting.

____________ **12.** She had us sit down our gloves.

____________ **13.** "I want to talk about what were doing tomorrow."

____________ **14.** "Whose ready to go on a trip?" she asked.

____________ **15.** "Were to?" we asked.

____________ **16.** "To the Baseball Hall off Fame!" she announced.

____________ **17.** "When are we leaving?" we asked.

____________ **18.** "Quit early in the day," she replied.

____________ **19.** "Early is better than late," I said.

____________ **20.** Who's coach is better than ours?

Notes for Home: Your child spelled words that are easily confused because of similar pronunciations or spellings. ***Home Activity:*** Think of other easily confused words, such as *its* and *it's* or *pin* and *pen*. Ask your child to spell each word and use it in a sentence.

Name ______________________________

Technology: Order Form

An **order form** is a chart with spaces that need to be filled with specific information. You can use an order form to purchase merchandise from catalogs or to order publications, such as pamphlets, magazines, or newspapers. It is important to follow directions on order forms so that you get what you want.

Print sources, such as catalogs, have order forms that you complete by hand. Electronic sources, such as the Internet, also have order forms. Many companies have Web sites with electronic catalogs. You order items from these catalogs by clicking on pictures or descriptions. The items are automatically listed on an order form and totals are calculated for you. It is important to be careful when using online catalogs and order forms. You may accidentally click on an item you do not want.

Directions: Review these collectors' items available for sale on a baseball Web site. Use the information to answer the questions that follow.

Name ______________________________

1. Mr. Jonas wants to order a 1927 Yankees Baseball Cap. His order form is below. What mistake did he make?

____

2. Draw a line through the information that Mr. Jonas mistakenly used in the order form above. Write in the item Mr. Jonas meant to order in the row underneath. Add to the order form the Unit Price, Quantity, and Total for this item.

3. Mr. Jonas wants to add to his order. He wants two Lou Gehrig Baseball Cards. Enter this item in the order form.

4. Find the grand total of Mr. Jonas' order. Write it in the order form.

5. How is ordering electronically different from using a printed order form?

____

____

____

Item	Unit Price	Quantity	Total
1927 Yankees Baseball Bat	$72.97	1	$72.97
		Grand Total	

Notes for Home: Your child completed an order form. ***Home Activity:*** Have your child complete an order form from a catalog. Have him or her select several items. Challenge your child to make the grand total as close to $50 as possible.

Family Times

Name ____

Summary

Korean Girl Risks a Lot for Education

There was a time in Korea when school was for boys only. Imduk's mother knew her daughter could learn as well as a boy, so she thought of a way to send her. How? She disguised Imduk as a boy! Imduk learned everything that was expected of her. She made lots of friends at school too. Being a boy wasn't so bad!

Activity

All by Myself. Ask your child to tell you about Imduk's first day in school. How did she feel walking to her seat? Share a story about a challenge you faced all by yourself, such as your first day at a new school. Ask your child to share a story too.

Reading Skills

Summarizing

A **summary** is a short statement, no more than a few sentences, that tells the main idea of a selection. For a story, a summary tells the goals of the characters, how they try to reach them, and whether they reach them. A summary of an article tells the main idea and leaves out unnecessary details.

Activity

A Person of Few Words. Ask your child to summarize the story about Imduk. Together, go back over the summary and see if you can make it shorter. Finally, see if you can create the title of a magazine article or a newspaper headline from your summary.

Family Times

Tested Vocabulary

Words to Know

Knowing the meanings of these words is important to reading "The Disguise." Practice using these words to learn their meanings.

cautious very careful; not taking chances

chanting singing in one tone

dangerous likely to cause harm

disguise make a thing seem like something else

principal the head of a school

recite say over; repeat

squatted crouched on the heels

suspected believed to be guilty, false, or bad without proof

Grammar

Adverbs

An **adverb** is a word that tells how, when, or where an action happens. An adverb can come before or after a verb.

Imduk walked to school <u>quickly</u>.

<u>Tonight</u> Imduk will study hard.

Imduk climbed <u>up</u> to the roof.

Activity

Tell How, When, and Where.
Reporters ask how, when, and where an event happened to get information for a news story. Tell a news story about an event in your day. Answer the how, when, and where questions, using adverbs in your answers.

Tested Spelling Words

______	______	______	______
______	______	______	______
______	______	______	______
______	______	______	______
______	______	______	______

Name ______________________________________

Summarizing

- A **summary** is a short statement, no more than a few sentences, that tells the main idea of a selection.
- A **summary of an article** should tell the main idea, leaving out unnecessary details.

Directions: Reread "Korean Food." Then complete the web. Write a sentence summarizing the main idea for each topic given.

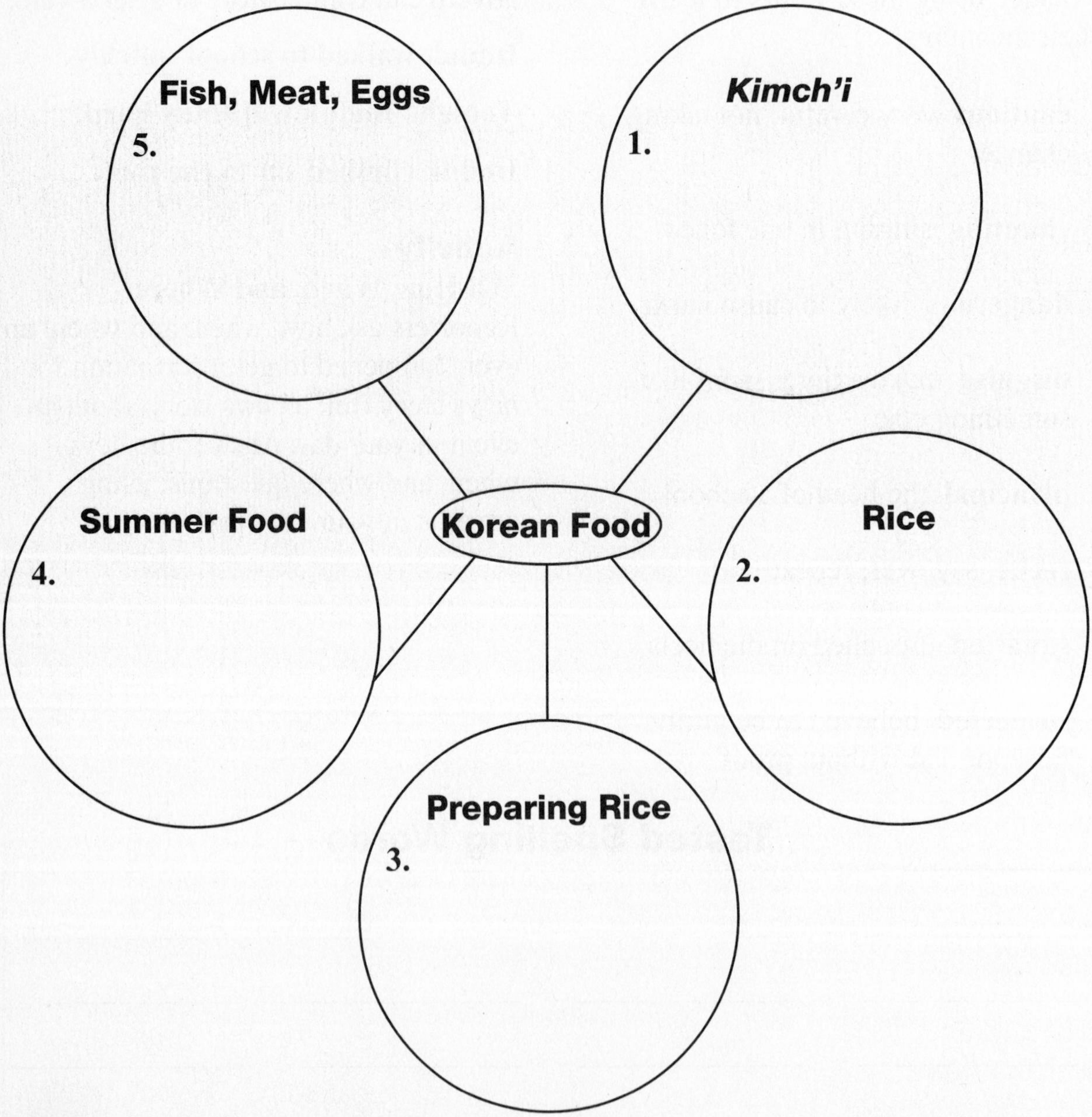

Korean Food

Kimch'i
1.

Rice
2.

Preparing Rice
3.

Summer Food
4.

Fish, Meat, Eggs
5.

Notes for Home: Your child read and summarized the main ideas in an article. ***Home Activity:*** Ask your child to identify a favorite story, movie, or television episode. Ask your child to summarize its events in no more than a few sentences.

Name ____

Vocabulary

Directions: Choose the word from the box that best matches each definition. Write the word on the line.

Check the Words You Know
__ cautious
__ chanting
__ dangerous
__ disguise
__ principal
__ recite
__ squatted
__ suspected

______________ **1.** singing in one tone

______________ **2.** believed to be guilty without proof

______________ **3.** head of a school

______________ **4.** make a thing seem like something else

______________ **5.** crouched on the heels

______________ **6.** very careful

Directions: Choose the word from the box that best completes each sentence. Write the word on the line.

______________ **7.** When Hector was little, he liked to do _____ things like sliding down stairs on his tummy.

______________ **8.** He played so many tricks that people once _____ that Hector had put salt in the punch bowl!

______________ **9.** "How could I do that?" said Hector. "I was asked to _____ a poem while everyone else was drinking punch."

______________ **10.** Now that he is older, Hector has become a lot more _____.

Write an Adventure Story

On a separate sheet of paper, write a story about two children who have an adventure. You might describe how they face danger and then tell what they do to save themselves. Use as many vocabulary words as you can.

Notes for Home: Your child identified and used vocabulary words from "The Disguise." ***Home Activity:*** Play a sentence game with your child. Taking turns, use a vocabulary word in a sentence. The other person has to then use the same word in a different sentence.

Name ______________________

Summarizing

- A **summary** is a short statement that tells the main ideas of a selection.
- A **story summary** should tell the goals of the characters, how they try to reach them, and whether they reach them. A **summary of an article** should tell the main idea, leaving out unnecessary details.

Directions: Reread what happens in "The Disguise" when Imduk and her mother move to their new home. Then follow the instructions below.

Mother's work-worn hands smoothed the fabric of her black skirt as it lay on the floor. Quickly she began cutting it.

We were in our new home, a single room, in the village of Dukdong. We had planned to live with Mother's brother, but they had quarreled.

He said Mother's idea to educate me was ridiculous. A girl couldn't learn! Where did she get such wild ideas from? No one in their family had such crazy notions!

Stubbornly, Mother clung to her plans and decided to make her own home. This decision took tremendous courage. I knew of no other woman who lived without at least one male relative in her home. By doing this, she was breaking yet another rule of our culture.

1. What is Mother's goal?

____

2. Does Mother's brother help her reach that goal?

____

3. Why did Mother's decision to make her own home take great courage?

____

4. Write a summary of this passage.

____

____

5. Write a summary of "The Disguise" on a separate sheet of paper.

Notes for Home: Your child summarized a story. ***Home Activity:*** Reread a familiar story with your child. Ask him or her to summarize it for you. Remind your child to think of the main characters, what they want, and how they try to get it.

Name ______________________________

Selection Test

Directions: Choose the best answer to each item. Mark the letter for the answer you have chosen.

Part 1: Vocabulary

Find the answer choice that means about the same as the underlined word in each sentence.

1. You must <u>disguise</u> yourself.
- A. bring shame upon
- B. become pretty
- C. save from harm
- D. dress to look like someone else

2. Who is the <u>principal</u>?
- F. person who studies
- G. the head of a school
- H. person who swims
- J. member of the police

3. People say I'm too <u>cautious</u>.
- A. polite
- B. very careful
- C. nervous
- D. very smart

4. Everyone <u>suspected</u> that he would be last.
- F. thought it likely
- G. feared
- H. argued
- J. thought well of

5. That sounds <u>dangerous</u>.
- A. comfortable
- B. unusual
- C. unsafe
- D. difficult

6. Can you <u>recite</u> a poem?
- F. explain the meaning of
- G. write over and over
- H. repeat from memory
- J. read from a book

7. The boys were <u>chanting</u>.
- A. singing in one tone
- B. running and shouting playfully
- C. fighting one another
- D. speaking with too much pride

8. Nadine <u>squatted</u> by the fire.
- F. got down on one's knees
- G. fell asleep standing up
- H. lay down
- J. crouched on one's heels

GO ON

Part 2: Comprehension

Use what you know about the story to answer each item.

9. An old man came to Imduk's home to—
A. make a pink shirt for her.
B. teach her the Korean alphabet.
C. show her Chinese characters.
D. see if she could paint.

10. Imduk's mother decided to move to Dukdong because—
F. a relative ran a school there.
G. everyone in their town knew that Imduk was a girl.
H. there were no teachers nearby.
J. Dukdong was in China.

11. How were Imduk and the Chinese girl in Mother's story alike?
A. Both fell in love.
B. Both liked to swim.
C. Both knew the alphabet.
D. Both dressed as boys.

12. Imduk's mother believed that—
F. Imduk would succeed in school.
G. girls could not learn.
H. her husband would return.
J. going to school was silly.

13. Which sentence best summarizes what happens in this story?
A. A girl pretended to be a soldier in the army.
B. Imduk dressed herself as a boy so she could go to school.
C. Boys in the school wore black ribbons in their hair.
D. Imduk's mother would not let her swim with the boys.

14. Imduk's mother is the kind of person who—
F. likes to make people angry.
G. does not value education.
H. does what she thinks is right.
J. will never be happy.

15. Which sentence about the story includes a generalization that is faulty?
A. Most people did not think a girl could be taught to read.
B. Pink was a color worn by boys.
C. All Korean girls wanted to lead an exciting life.
D. There is a risk in swimming without adults nearby.

Name ______________________________

Summarizing

- A **summary** is a short statement that tells the main ideas of a selection.
- A **story summary** should tell the goals of the characters, how they try to reach them, and whether they reach them. A **summary of an article** should tell the main idea, leaving out unnecessary details.

Directions: Read the story below.

Learning English was hard, but soon Li Chen spoke it quite well. Everyone else in her family spoke only Chinese. Li Chen felt proud. She spoke two languages! That meant she could help her family. Helping others is important to Li Chen.

Li Chen's parents were proud too. They were glad to have her help. When Li Chen's mother went shopping, she took Li Chen with her to ask questions for her. At a restaurant, Li Chen could order food for the family. Li Chen liked helping her family.

One day, a new girl who spoke only Chinese came to Li Chen's school. Li Chen could help the new girl understand the teacher. She could help the teacher understand the new girl. Sometimes helping out was a lot of work. But most of the time, Li Chen felt good that she could help.

Directions: Complete the table. Think about Li Chen's goal and how she tries to accomplish it. Then write a summary of the story.

Li Chen speaks	Chinese and English
Li Chen helps her mother by:	**1.**
Li Chen helps the new girl by:	**2.**
Li Chen helps the teacher by:	**3.**
Li Chen feels:	**4.**

5. Summary: ______________________________

____

Notes for Home: Your child gave details about a character's goals and actions and wrote a summary of a story. ***Home Activity:*** Take turns summarizing stories you and your child both know. Have the listener tell the book title, based on the summary.

Name ____________________

Predicting

REVIEW

Directions: Read the story. Then read each question about the story. Choose the best answer to each question. Mark the letter for the answer you have chosen.

In a New Country

Marc was with his family in Paris, France! Marc could hardly wait to get out and see the sights.

Marc's parents were resting in the next room. But Marc was too excited to rest.

Suddenly, there was a knock on the hotel room door. A voice said something in French. Marc didn't know what to do.

Then Marc remembered that his parents had ordered breakfast. His mother had said that breakfast was brought right to your room.

Marc went to get his parents, and they opened the door. A waiter came in with a tray with three cups of a creamy, brown liquid and a covered dish.

1. Which clues helped you predict who was at the door?
- **A.** Marc hears a knock.
- **B.** Marc's mother ordered breakfast at the hotel.
- **C.** Marc is in Paris, France.
- **D.** Marc's parents are next door.

2. Which of the following is most likely to be in the three cups?
- **F.** soup
- **G.** orange juice
- **H.** coffee or hot chocolate
- **J.** gravy

3. Which of the following is most likely to be under the covered dish?
- **A.** roast beef
- **B.** ham sandwiches
- **C.** ice cream
- **D.** rolls and butter

4. What do you predict Marc will do after breakfast?
- **F.** He will take a nap.
- **G.** He will make a phone call.
- **H.** He will go sightseeing.
- **J.** He will read a book.

5. Which clue helped you predict what Marc will do next?
- **A.** Marc hears a knock at the door.
- **B.** Marc and his parents are staying in a hotel.
- **C.** Marc hears some French.
- **D.** Marc can hardly wait to get out and see the sights.

Notes for Home: Your child made predictions based on information read in a story. ***Home Activity:*** Play a "prediction game" with your child. Take turns giving each other clues and making predictions. For example: *I'm at the gas station. What do you predict I'll do next?* (*buy gas*)

Name ____________________

Writing Across Texts

Directions: Consider what you learned about Imduk in the story "The Disguise" and Lou Gehrig in the story *Lou Gehrig: The Luckiest Man.* How are they alike? How are they different? Use the Venn Diagram to record your answers.

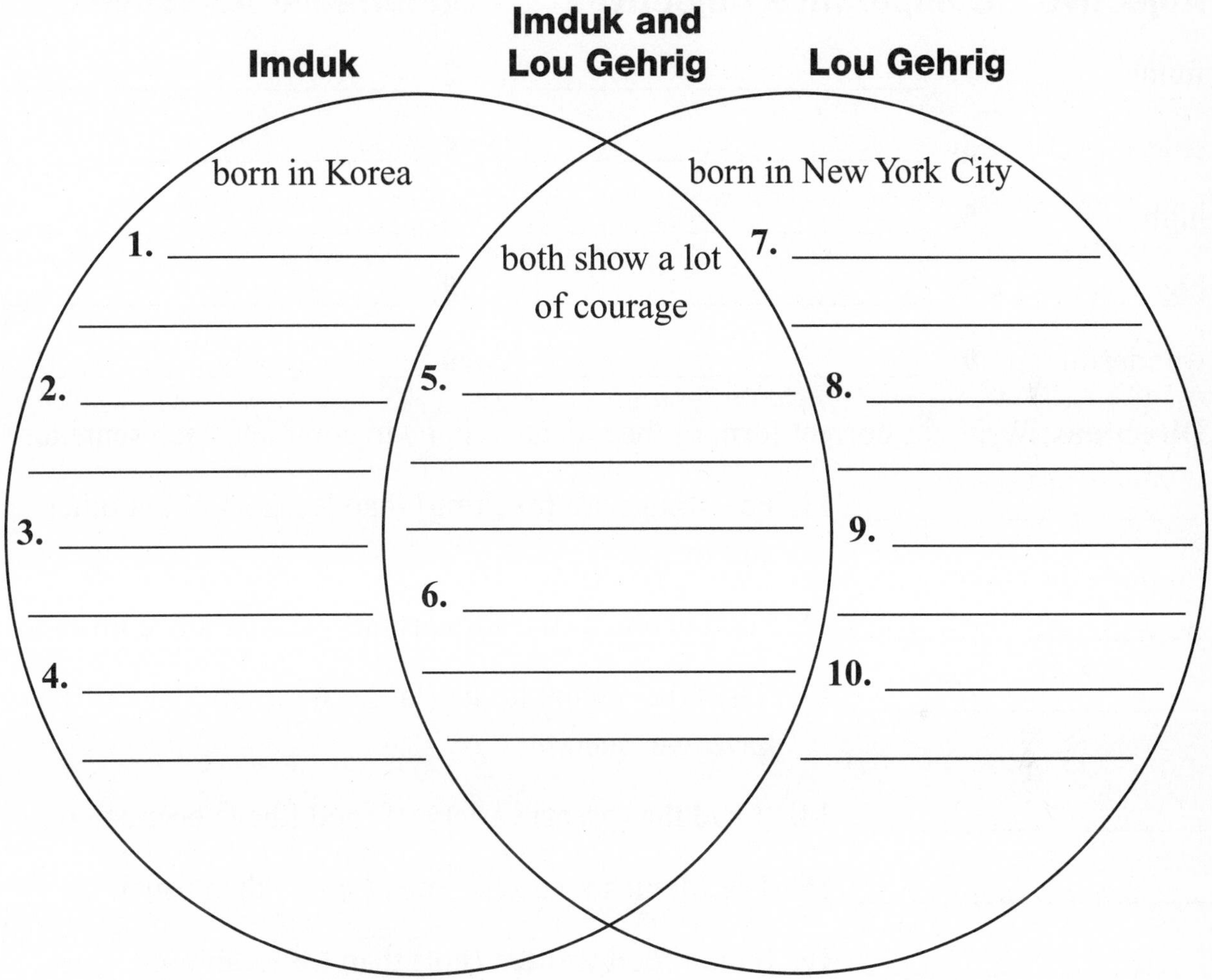

Imduk	Imduk and Lou Gehrig	Lou Gehrig
born in Korea	both show a lot of courage	born in New York City
1. ____________________	5. ____________________	7. ____________________
2. ____________________	6. ____________________	8. ____________________
3. ____________________		9. ____________________
4. ____________________		10. ____________________

Write a Compare/Contrast Paragraph

Imduk and Lou Gehrig come from very different backgrounds and have different strengths. Both characters are very successful, but they achieve success in different ways. Write a paragraph in which you compare and contrast these two characters. Use information from your diagram to help you with ideas. Write your paragraph on a separate sheet of paper.

Notes for Home: Your child used information from two reading selections to write a compare/contrast paragraph. ***Home Activity:*** As you read stories and articles with your child, talk about how the ideas in the reading materials connect to other reading you have done.

Name ______________________________

REVIEW

Grammar: Comparative and Superlative Adjectives

Directions: Add **-er, -est, more,** or **most** to the adjectives to form comparative and superlative adjectives.

Adjective	Comparative Adjectives	Superlative Adjectives
funny	**1.** ____________________	**2.** ____________________
pale	**3.** ____________________	**4.** ____________________
high	**5.** ____________________	**6.** ____________________
big	**7.** ____________________	**8.** ____________________
wonderful	**9.** ____________________	**10.** ____________________

Directions: Write the correct form of the adjective in ( ) to complete each sentence.

____________________ **11.** Few things are (exciting) than learning about other cultures.

____________________ **12.** Food is one of the (important) parts of any culture.

____________________ **13.** Yesterday I went to the (large) International Fair I have ever seen.

____________________ **14.** It had the (great) variety of food I have ever eaten.

____________________ **15.** The Mexican tacos seemed (spicy) than usual.

____________________ **16.** Indian food is often (hot) than Mexican food.

____________________ **17.** The Chinese spring rolls were (delicious) than others I have eaten elsewhere.

____________________ **18.** The Russian beet salad was (tasty) than I had expected.

____________________ **19.** The Italian gelato was the (incredible) ice cream I've ever tasted.

____________________ **20.** I have never felt (full) in my entire life!

Notes for Home: Your child used comparative forms of adjectives to compare two things and superlative forms to compare three or more things. ***Home Activity:*** Look through pictures in magazines. Use comparative and superlative forms of adjectives to compare the pictures.

Grammar: Adverbs

An **adverb** tells how, when, or where something happens. Most adverbs tell about verbs. An adverb can appear either before or after the verb. Many adverbs that tell how end in **-ly.**

How: The dancer performed gracefully.
(Other examples: beautifully, slowly, carefully)

Adverbs can also tell when or where an action happens.

When: Your new costume arrived today.
(Other examples: always, first, last)

Where: Don't leave it lying around.
(Other examples: far, out, through)

Directions: Underline the adverb in each sentence.

1. Frank was doing poorly in school.
2. Then he suddenly improved.
3. In class, he always paid attention.
4. Frank waited hopefully for Awards Day.
5. He excitedly claimed his award as the Most Improved Student.

Directions: Write the adverb that describes each underlined verb.

________________ 6. That day, Frank quickly ran home.

________________ 7. He said he would never forget how much his parents had helped him.

________________ 8. Then he immediately began his homework.

________________ 9. Frank would work first.

________________ 10. He would have fun later.

Notes for Home: Your child identified adverbs, words that tell how, when, or where an action happens. ***Home Activity:*** Ask your child questions about the day's events. Invite your child to use adverbs in his or her answers.

Extra Practice

Grammar: Adverbs

Directions: Write whether each underlined adverb tells **when, where,** or **how.**

______________________ **1.** My brother and I always enjoyed old family stories.

______________________ **2.** We eagerly listened to tales about Korea.

______________________ **3.** My brother sincerely wanted to visit Korea.

______________________ **4.** Our parents said he could study there.

______________________ **5.** My brother nervously boarded the plane.

Directions: Write an adverb for each sentence that tells whatever is named in ( ). Write your adverb on the line to the left.

______________________ **6.** John's uncle _____ told him tales from Ireland. (when)

______________________ **7.** John liked _____ the stories about leprechauns. (how)

______________________ **8.** "If you leave milk for a leprechaun," one story said, "the grateful creature will _____ work for you." (how)

______________________ **9.** The Irish _____ call leprechauns "the little people." (when)

______________________ **10.** John thinks we could use some grateful leprechauns _____! (where)

Write a Letter

On a separate sheet of paper, write a letter to a pen pal that tells about your family's culture. Describe an everyday event or a special holiday tradition. Use at least one adverb in each sentence.

Notes for Home: Your child identified adverbs telling how, when, or where something happened. ***Home Activity:*** Tell your child a story about something that happened in your family. Have your child identify each adverb and say which it tells: how, when, or where.

Name ____________________

Grammar: Adverbs

RETEACHING

Circle the adverb that tells **how.**

1. My brother ate slowly.

Circle the adverb that tells **when.**

2. He finished dinner last.

Circle the adverb that tells **where.**

3. He left his dishes sitting out.

An **adverb** tells how, when, or where something happens. Most adverbs tell about verbs. An adverb can appear before or after the verb. Many adverbs that tell how end in **-ly.**

Directions: Underline the adverb in each sentence.

1. Today the bears explore their surroundings.

2. One cub runs outside.

3. The bear family plays happily.

4. They always leave their home.

5. They travel around.

6. The three cubs never leave their mother's side.

Directions: Write an adverb that tells more about each underlined verb.

____________ **7.** The bears hunt for food.

____________ **8.** Salmon are swimming toward their destination.

____________ **9.** The mother steps into the stream.

Notes for Home: Your child identified and wrote adverbs in sentences. ***Home Activity:*** Talk with your child about what you did today. Have your child point out adverbs you use to describe how, when, or where.

Name ____________________________________

Grammar: Adverbs

Directions: Write whether each underlined adverb tells when, where, or how.

____________ **1.** Snakes don't come <u>here</u>.

____________ **2.** It is hard to find them <u>easily</u> in our town.

____________ **3.** You have to travel <u>far</u> if you want to see one.

____________ **4.** When you do spot one, you must walk <u>quietly</u>.

Directions: Write sentences, using a verb and an adverb from the box.

Verbs	Adverbs
move	quickly
run	slowly
talk	hard
eat	loudly
melt	last
try	silently

5. ____________________________________

6. ____________________________________

7. ____________________________________

8. ____________________________________

9. ____________________________________

10. ____________________________________

Notes for Home: Your child wrote adverbs in sentences. ***Home Activity:*** Have your student read a favorite story and look for adverbs. Then have him or her write new sentences with the adverbs from the story.

Name ______________________________

Word Study: Suffixes

Directions: Suffixes are letters we add to the end of base words. Some suffixes are **-ful, -ly, -ion, -ous, -less, -ness,** and **-ment.** Read the journal entry below. Find each word that has one of these suffixes and write it on a line.

Dear Diary,

Today was a wonderful day! I wanted to see if a girl could join the boys' basketball team. I know it may not be a wise decision. It might even be dangerous. Some might even say my case was hopeless. But I had to try, even if it was only to make a statement about girls being good sports. Quickly I donned my disguise. I walked uneasily onto the court. I was careful to make sure no one recognized me. As the game started, I knew that the team was about to get an education it would never forget. In all fairness, it's a lesson they need to learn.

1. ______________

2. ______________

3. ______________

4. ______________

5. ______________

6. ______________

7. ______________

8. ______________

9. ______________

10. ______________

Directions: Each word below has a base word and one or two suffixes. Write the base word in the first column. Then write the suffix or suffixes in the second column.

	Base Word	**Suffix or Suffixes**
11. beautifully	______________	______________
12. pollution	______________	______________
13. carelessly	______________	______________
14. encouragement	______________	______________
15. joyously	______________	______________

Notes for Home: Your child identified suffixes, and added them to the ends of words. ***Home Activity:*** Play a game with your child. Write a word like *encourage.* Then write some suffixes, like *-ly, -ous,* and *-ment.* Have your child choose a suffix to make a new word.

Name ______________________________

Pretest

Spelling: Suffixes *-ful*, *-ly*, *-ion*

Pretest Directions: Fold back the page along the dotted line. On the blanks, write the spelling words as they are dictated. When you have finished the test, unfold the page and check your words.

1. ______________________
2. ______________________
3. ______________________
4. ______________________
5. ______________________
6. ______________________
7. ______________________
8. ______________________
9. ______________________
10. ______________________
11. ______________________
12. ______________________
13. ______________________
14. ______________________
15. ______________________
16. ______________________
17. ______________________
18. ______________________
19. ______________________
20. ______________________

1. She's a **powerful** leader.
2. This is a **peaceful** garden.
3. What a **beautiful** place!
4. What a **cheerful** baby!
5. It was a **painful** situation.
6. She was a **thoughtful** girl.
7. He walked **slowly** to the garden.
8. He was **safely** in her arms.
9. They took a **daily** walk.
10. The sun disappeared **suddenly**.
11. Please hold it **carefully**.
12. We have a **weekly** meeting.
13. He hasn't been around **lately**.
14. I hope you spoke **truthfully**.
15. She looked at him **hopefully**.
16. What **action** would you take?
17. This is an interesting **location**.
18. The zipper was a good **invention**.
19. We need to make a **correction**.
20. **Pollution** made this place dirty.

Notes for Home: Your child took a pretest on words that have the suffixes *-ful, -ly,* and *-ion*. ***Home Activity:*** Help your child learn misspelled words before the final test. See if there are any similar errors and discuss a memory trick that could help.

Name ______________________________

Spelling: Suffixes *-ful, -ly, -ion*

Word List				
powerful	painful	daily	lately	location
peaceful	thoughtful	suddenly	truthfully	invention
beautiful	slowly	carefully	hopefully	correction
cheerful	safely	weekly	action	pollution

Directions: Choose the word from the box that is formed by adding **-ful** or **-fully** to each base word. Write the complete word on the line.

1. power ____________ **4.** thought ____________ **7.** hope ____________

2. pain ____________ **5.** peace ____________ **8.** care ____________

3. cheer ____________ **6.** truth ____________ **9.** beauty ____________

Directions: Add the suffix **-ly** or **-ion** to each word in ( ) to form a word from the box and complete each sentence. Write the word on the line.

____________ **10.** We have a (week) meeting in our class.

____________ **11.** (Late) it has been very interesting!

____________ **12.** We talk about what (day) life is like for each of us.

____________ **13.** Achmed talks (slow), but he has a lot to say.

____________ **14.** He is very concerned about (pollute).

____________ **15.** "How can we live (safe)?" he asks.

____________ **16.** "We must take (act) to protect our planet!"

____________ **17.** Sladka came to this country very (sudden).

____________ **18.** This was the best (locate) for her family's business.

____________ **19.** They sell an (invent) that her mother created.

____________ **20.** After much (correct), I know how to pronounce it.

Notes for Home: Your child spelled words with the suffixes *-ful, -ly,* and *-ion.* ***Home Activity:*** Have your child make a list of spelling words that end in *-ly*. Help your child think of additional words that end in *-ly,* such as *quickly, happily, sadly,* and *sweetly* and add them to the list.

Name ______________________________

Spelling: Suffixes *-ful, -ly, -ion*

Directions: Proofread this letter to a friend back home. Find five spelling mistakes. Use the proofreading marks to correct each mistake.

- ≡ Make a capital.
- / Make a small letter.
- ∧ Add something.
- ℘ Take out something.
- ⊙ Add a period.
- ¶ Begin a new paragraph.

Dear Hakim,

It was very thoughtfull of you to write me so soon. I miss you and all of my friends back home. I think of you dayly. We look hopefuly to a visit next summer. But this is a beautyful country too! Maybe you can come visit me. Correcttion, maybe you'll visit me soon!

Love,

Yacob

Spelling Tip

When you add **-ful, -ly,** or **-ion** to most base words, the base stays the same: **power<u>ful</u>.** For words ending in **y,** change the **y** to **i** before adding the suffix: **dai<u>ly</u>.** For words ending in **e,** drop the **e: locat<u>ion</u>.**

Word List

powerful	carefully
peaceful	weekly
beautiful	lately
cheerful	truthfully
painful	hopefully
thoughtful	action
slowly	location
safely	invention
daily	correction
suddenly	pollution

Write a Letter

Find out something about a culture that is different from your own. Then, on a separate sheet of paper, write a letter to a friend about what you found out. Try to use at least three spelling words.

Notes for Home: Your child spelled words with the suffixes *-ful, -ly,* and *-ion. **Home Activity:*** Look at the words on the list that end in *-ful*. Ask your child to add *-ly* to each word and use it in a sentence.

Name ______________________________

Spelling: Suffixes *-ful, -ly, -ion*

REVIEW

Word List				
powerful	painful	daily	lately	location
peaceful	thoughtful	suddenly	truthfully	invention
beautiful	slowly	carefully	hopefully	correction
cheerful	safely	weekly	action	pollution

Directions: Choose the word from the box that is the most opposite in meaning for each word or words below. Write the word on the line.

1. unthinking ____________

2. falsely ____________

3. pleasant ____________

4. warlike ____________

5. weak ____________

6. rest ____________

7. carelessly ____________

8. quickly ____________

9. error ____________

10. pure environment ____________

Directions: Choose the word from the box that best replaces the underlined word or words. Write the word on the line.

____________ **11.** We have a once-a-week culture fair in our class.

____________ **12.** It is a good place to learn about other cultures.

____________ **13.** Often, people show a creation from their culture.

____________ **14.** Recently, class has been very interesting.

____________ **15.** Today, Yoshi brought in some very pretty rice bowls.

____________ **16.** "I hope they have traveled in a safe way," he said.

____________ **17.** We all looked with hope at the box.

____________ **18.** All of a sudden, Yoshi smiled.

____________ **19.** It was a big, happy smile.

____________ **20.** "They're fine," he said, "and now I can tell you about the way we use these bowls every day."

Notes for Home: Your child spelled words with the suffixes *-ful, -ly,* and *-ion.* ***Home Activity:*** Say one of the suffixes *-ful, -ly,* or *-ion.* Your child can respond by saying a spelling word that uses that suffix, spelling the word, and using it in a sentence. Switch roles and repeat.

Name ______________________________

Alphabetical Order

The words in glossaries and indexes are organized in **alphabetical order** to make them easier to find. To find an entry in an alphabetical list, start by looking for the first letter of the word you wish to find. If there are multiple entries with the same first letter, look for the second letter. If there are multiple entries with the same first and second letters, look for the third letter, and so on.

You can use alphabetical order to get information from a telephone book, a dictionary, and an encyclopedia too. You'll also find fiction books in a library organized on shelves by alphabetical order using the authors' last names.

Directions: Use this index listing from an almanac to find each topic listed below. Write the page number or numbers where information about this topic can be found.

A

Abbreviations, 112
Acid rain, 44
Afghanistan, 36
Africa
  Facts, 98
  History, 104, 216–217
  Map, 398
Alabama, 235
Alaska, 389
Angola, 67
Animals, 46–50
  Classifying, 46
  Endangered species, 87
  Fastest and largest, 50
Antarctica, 77
Antigua, 32–33
Arctic Ocean, 80
Argentina, 36–37
  Map, 398
Arizona, 135
Arkansas, 136
Armenia, 38–39
Art, 79–83

1. Alabama ______________
2. Arizona ______________
3. Antigua ______________
4. a map of Africa ______________
5. endangered animals ______________
6. largest animal ______________
7. African history ______________
8. Arctic Ocean ______________
9. map of Argentina ______________
10. snakes ______________

Name ____________________________________

Directions: Some of the words from the glossary below are missing. Choose the best word from the box to complete each glossary entry. Hint: The list should be in alphabetical order.

principal	chanting	disguise
dangerous	cautious	recite

11. ____________________, very careful

chanting, singing in one tone

12. ____________________, likely to cause harm

13. ____________________, make it seem like something else

principal, head of a school

14. ____________________, say over; repeat

15. Why is alphabetical order a useful way to organize information? Give an example of a reference source that uses alphabetical order to support your answer.

____

____

____

____

____

____

____

____

Notes for Home: Your child learned ways to use alphabetical order. ***Home Activity:*** Take turns challenging each other to find names in a phone book or topics in an encyclopedia. Or, have your child list favorite television shows in alphabetical order.

Family Times

Name____

Summary

Boy Creates New Tradition from Old

Kenyon's grandmother, Little Dolly, is about to have her ninetieth birthday. Kenyon has been saving his money to buy the perfect gift. Then he sees a new baseball glove and can't help buying it. Now Kenyon has no money left for a gift, and he feels terrible. Then he thinks of the stories Little Dolly has told him and decides to write them all down. Bound in a handmade book, the stories make the most special gift of all.

Activity

Make Up a New Ending. What do you think would have happened if Kenyon returned the baseball glove right away and asked for his money back? Tell or write a new ending for the story.

Reading Skills

Plot

Plot is the important parts of a story. The parts of a plot are:

- ❖ **Conflict.** A conflict can be a problem between two characters or groups, or between a character and nature. A conflict can also be a problem within a character.
- ❖ **Rising Action.** This is the part of a story in which the conflict builds.
- ❖ **Climax.** This the place where the action of the story builds, and the conflict must be faced.
- ❖ **Resolution.** This is the place where the problem is solved.

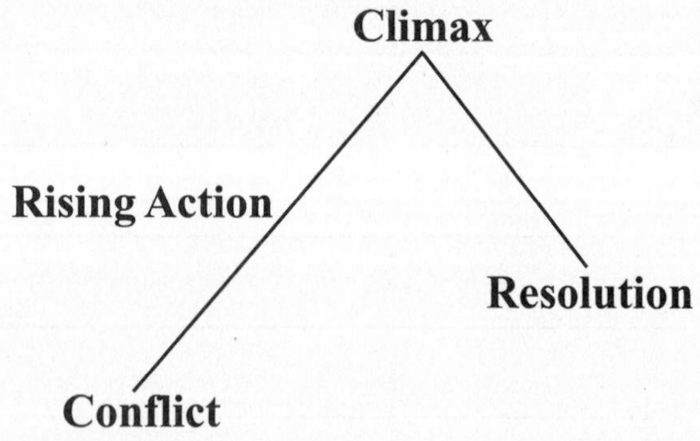

Activity

Make a Plot Map. Think of a problem your family or community has had to solve recently. Take turns making a plot map to tell the story. Start out by writing the conflict. Then list events that lead up to the climax. Finally, write how the problem is solved.

Family Times

Tested Vocabulary

Words to Know

Knowing the meanings of these words is important to reading *Keepers*. Practice using these words to learn their meanings.

considering taking into consideration

definitely surely

diamond space inside the lines that connect the bases in baseball; infield

grounders hit baseballs that hit the ground

reminder something to help one remember

stroke a sudden attack of illness when a blood vessel breaks or becomes blocked

taunted teased

Grammar

Using Adverbs to Improve Sentences

An **adverb** is a word that tells when, how, or where something happens. Adverbs tell more about the actions named by verbs.

Kenyon looked at a new glove today.

Kenyon looked longingly at the new glove.

Little Dolly stayed inside most of the time.

Activity

Don't Overdo It! Like too many adjectives, too many adverbs can make writing sound ridiculous. Declare a two-adverb day. Use two—not more—adverbs to describe important actions you did today.

Tested Spelling Words

Name ___________________________________

Plot

- Stories have **plot,** or a series of events that center on a problem, or conflict.
- A conflict can be a problem between two people or groups, between a person and nature, or within a character.
- The climax is the place where the action builds, and the conflict must be faced. The resolution is where the conflict is solved.

Directions: Reread "One Particular Small, Smart Boy." Then complete the plot map. Use the questions to help you describe the conflict, events that lead to the climax, and how the conflict is resolved.

What is the problem?

1. ______________________

What does the boy do first to solve the problem?

2. ______________________

What does the boy do next?

3. ______________________

What does the boy do last to confront the problem?

4. ______________________

What finally happens?

5. ______________________

Notes for Home: Your child read a story and described its plot. ***Home Activity:*** Ask your child to tell you the plot of a favorite story. Make sure your child tells you the main problem, the events that lead up to the problem being solved, and the way the problem is solved.

Name ______________________________

Vocabulary

Directions: Choose the word from the box that best completes each sentence. Write the word on the line to the left.

Check the Words You Know

- __ considering
- __ definitely
- __ diamond
- __ grounders
- __ reminder
- __ stroke
- __ taunted

________________ **1.** Omar is _____ the best ball player I know.

________________ **2.** He can easily scoop up those hard-to-catch _____ that batters often hit.

________________ **3.** As soon as the ball hits his glove, Omar throws it to his teammates inside the baseball _____.

________________ **4.** Last year Omar's grandmother had a sudden _____, and he quit baseball to help take care of her.

________________ **5.** Some of the other kids _____ Omar for being a quitter.

________________ **6.** _____ how mean these kids were being, I think Omar kept his temper well.

________________ **7.** "Whenever I start to get mad," he said, "I think of my grandmother. She is a good _____ to stay calm."

Directions: Cross out the word or words that do not belong in each group.

8. taunted	teased	cheered	insulted
9. definitely	certainly	surely	possibly
10. considering	forgetting	thinking about	keeping in mind

Write a Thank-You Note

On a separate page, write a letter to a relative saying "thank you" for something special he or she did for you. Use as many vocabulary words as you can.

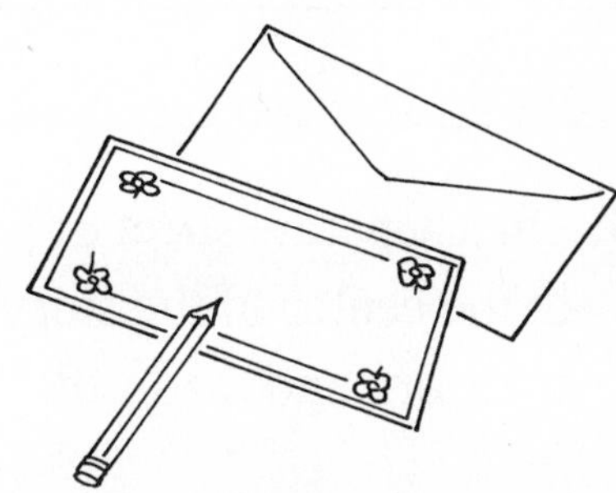

Notes for Home: Your child identified and used vocabulary words from *Keepers*. ***Home Activity:*** Play a definition game with your child. You say a vocabulary word, and he or she tells you its definition. For extra fun, have your child give a definition and you guess the word.

Plot

- A story's **plot** is the important parts of the story. The parts of a plot are the conflict, or problem, the rising action, the climax, and the resolution, or outcome.

Directions: Reread what happens in *Keepers* when Little Dolly tells her grandson, Kenyon, what a Keeper is. Then answer the questions below.

"The Keeper holds onto the past until she can pass it on to the next." Little Dolly squinched her dark brown eyes. "Don't know who I'll hand my tales to, though." Her large fingers plucked at the sleeve of her blouse.

Kenyon stopped the swing and he knelt beside her. "Little Dolly, I'll be the Keeper. I love your stories."

Her eyes looked deep into his, searching.

"Lord, honey, that's nice, but you a boy. I got to find me a girl Keeper. You can't be a Keeper if you a boy."

1. What problem does Little Dolly have?

____

2. What does Kenyon want?

____

3. Why can't he get what he wants?

____

____

4. What might Kenyon do to get what he wants?

____

____

5. On a separate sheet of paper, describe the plot of *Keepers.* Tell what problem is at the center of the story, and how this problem is faced during the climax of the story and resolved.

Notes for Home: Your child identified the plot—the important parts of a story. ***Home Activity:*** Reread a favorite story with your child. Ask him or her to tell you the plot, including the main problem, or conflict, in the story and how this problem is resolved by the end.

Name ______________________________

Selection Test

Directions: Choose the best answer to each item. Mark the letter for the answer you have chosen.

Part 1: Vocabulary

Find the answer choice that means about the same as the underlined word in each sentence.

1. The team left the <u>diamond</u>.
- A. dugout
- B. baseball field
- C. bus
- D. place where fans sit

2. Marc <u>taunted</u> his brother.
- F. greeted in a friendly way
- G. surprised
- H. teased in a mean way
- J. honored

3. Patti caught some <u>grounders</u>.
- A. baseballs hit along the ground
- B. small animals with bushy tails
- C. birds that cannot fly
- D. balls hit high into the air

4. Today is <u>definitely</u> a good day.
- F. probably
- G. usually
- H. fortunately
- J. certainly

5. Will you need a <u>reminder</u>?
- A. permit to build something
- B. something to help one remember
- C. set of instructions
- D. written statement that money has been received

6. Fiona is <u>considering</u> buying a new coat.
- F. thinking seriously about
- G. trying to keep away from
- H. making a habit of
- J. taking pleasure in

7. Terry's uncle had a <u>stroke</u>.
- A. illness caused by a broken or blocked blood vessel
- B. pain in a tooth
- C. long talk about something
- D. time of good luck

Part 2: Comprehension

Use what you know about the story to answer each item.

8. Kenyon's grandmother is a Keeper of—
- F. birthday presents.
- G. homework.
- H. stories and legends.
- J. chocolates.

GO ON

9. Kenyon is not allowed to go out and play baseball until—
A. he finishes his homework.
B. he gets a new glove.
C. his grandmother falls asleep.
D. his friends call for him.

10. Little Dolly tells Kenyon that he can't be a Keeper because he—
F. doesn't know enough stories.
G. is a boy.
H. plays too much baseball.
J. can't remember things.

11. What is Kenyon's main conflict?
A. He can't get his homework done.
B. He can't hit Mo Davis's fastball.
C. He doesn't want to take care of his grandmother.
D. He buys a new glove and has no money left for a present.

12. You can tell that a "wallop-bat day" is a day when—
F. Kenyon plays baseball.
G. everything goes well.
H. Kenyon forgets something.
J. someone makes a mistake.

13. The climax of the story comes when—
A. Kenyon goes shopping.
B. Mrs. Montgomery walks up to the house.
C. Kenyon gives the book to his grandmother.
D. Little Dolly gets some chocolates.

14. Mrs. Montgomery and the others come to the house to—
F. see Kenyon's baseball glove.
G. surprise Little Dolly with her favorite things.
H. see what Kenyon gives to his grandmother.
J. show Kenyon that they know he has made a book.

15. This story shows that—
A. baseball gloves made of real leather are expensive.
B. few people live to be ninety.
C. a birthday should be a big event.
D. some of the best presents don't cost anything.

Name ______________________________

Plot

- A story's **plot** is the important parts of the story. The parts of a plot are the conflict, or problem, the rising action, the climax, and the resolution, or outcome.

Directions: Read the story below.

Lucia loved her Uncle Harry. She wanted to get him the best present in the world. But what? Lucia thought hard. She remembered all the nice things Uncle Harry had done for her. He took her to the zoo. He came to her school play. He even gave her his old clarinet.

Suddenly, Lucia had a wonderful idea. She got out markers and paper and went to work.

The next day, Lucia gave Uncle Harry a huge envelope. He opened it—and there was a card with a drawing of the zoo, a ticket from the school play, and sheet music from a song Lucia played on her clarinet. "Do you see?" she said. "I'm giving you the wonderful memories I have of you!"

"It's the best present in the world," said Uncle Harry.

Directions: Complete the table by answering each question about the story's plot.

Characters Who is the main character?	**1.**
Conflict or Problem What problem does this character have?	**2.**
Rising Action How does this character try to solve the problem?	**3.**
Climax What happened that helped solve the problem?	**4.**
Resolution or Outcome How does the story end?	**5.**

Notes for Home: Your child described the plot of a story by telling about the story's most important parts. ***Home Activity:*** Read a book or watch a movie with your child. Discuss what the main problem of the story is, what happens because of the problem, and how the problem is solved.

Name ______________________________

REVIEW

Steps in a Process

Directions: Read the passage. Then read each question about the passage. Choose the best answer to each question. Mark the letter for the answer you have chosen.

Making a Family Album

Have you ever thought of making a family album? The first thing to do is to find an album. A nice, big sturdy album is best. Make sure that the album has pages made out of paper, not plastic. It's hard to paste things onto plastic.

The next thing to do is collect family treasures to go in the album. Some treasures you might collect are photographs, tickets or programs from special events, or postcards.

After that, you'll want to organize the treasures. You could give each family member a page or try to put things in chronological order.

Finally, label each treasure and write something about it. Ask family members to help.

1. What is the first step in the process?
   - **A.** putting things in order
   - **B.** talking to the family
   - **C.** finding an album
   - **D.** pasting things onto paper

2. What clue word tells you what the second step is?
   - **F.** second
   - **G.** after
   - **H.** finally
   - **J.** next

3. What is the third step in the process?
   - **A.** organizing the treasures
   - **B.** asking for treasures
   - **C.** collecting treasures
   - **D.** labeling each treasure

4. What clue word or words tells you what the third step is?
   - **F.** after that
   - **G.** could give
   - **H.** organize
   - **J.** chronological order

5. What clue word tells you what the last step is?
   - **A.** finally
   - **B.** after that
   - **C.** next
   - **D.** share

Notes for Home: Your child identified steps in a process that tell the order of steps to be done to complete an action. ***Home Activity:*** Choose a familiar activity, such as making a sandwich. Have your child tell you four or five steps in the process of that activity. The steps should be told in order.

Name ____

Writing Across Texts

Directions: In the story *Keepers*, Little Dolly's family celebrates her birthday with a strawberry shortcake. Kenyon might prefer the cake featured in "Have-a-Ball! Cake" on his birthday. Compare Little Dolly's party with your predictions of the kind of party Kenyon might like on his birthday. Put your ideas in the boxes below.

Little Dolly's party	Your predictions of Kenyon's party
the cake	
1.	2.
the guests	
3.	4.
where the party is held	
5.	6.
gifts	
7.	8.
party activities	
9.	10.

Write a Recipe

Think about a food you like to make or help make. On a separate sheet of paper, write the recipe. List the ingredients first, then tell the steps involved in making the dish.

Notes for Home: Your child wrote the recipe of a favorite food. ***Home Activity:*** Invite your child to help you in preparing dinner. Give him or her practice in measuring and combining ingredients.

Name ______________________________

Keepers

REVIEW

Grammar: Adverbs

Directions: Identify the adverb that tells about the underlined verb in each sentence. Write the adverb on the line.

______________ **1.** When I was little, my father often told me stories.

______________ **2.** I got into bed and waited eagerly for my story.

______________ **3.** My father sat on my bed and spoke softly.

______________ **4.** Sometimes he told me made-up stories.

______________ **5.** As I got older, though, he usually told real stories.

______________ **6.** The stories I really liked were about my father as a boy.

______________ **7.** As I lay there, I tried to picture him at that age.

______________ **8.** Once, as a little boy, he looked outside and saw a red glow in the sky.

______________ **9.** Thinking the world was on fire, he ran downstairs.

______________ **10.** "You've seen your first sunset," his mother said to him gently.

Directions: Write the comparative or superlative form of the adverb in ( ) to complete each sentence.

______________ **11.** "Please walk (fast)," said my brother.

______________ **12.** We wanted to get to our grandparents' house (early) than our parents.

______________ **13.** We arrived (soon) than anyone else, and we listened eagerly to my grandfather's wonderful stories.

______________ **14.** I laughed (loudly) of all when he told us about our father's adventures as a boy.

______________ **15.** When our parents arrived (late), we looked at my father and giggled.

Notes for Home: Your child identified adverbs—words that tell how, where, or when something happens—and wrote comparative and superlative adverbs. ***Home Activity:*** Talk with your child about a TV show. Ask questions using *how, when,* and *where.*

Grammar: Using Adverbs to Improve Sentences

The sentence below does not paint a clear picture. It needs descriptive details.

The storyteller spoke.

One way to revise the sentence is by adding an adverb.

The storyteller spoke quietly. (tells how)
The storyteller spoke later. (tells when)
The storyteller spoke outside. (tells where)

Never use more adverbs than you need for expressing ideas clearly.

The storyteller spoke confidently, strongly, easily, and fast.

Directions: Add adverbs to make the sentences more interesting. For each sentence, supply the kind of adverb named in ( ). Write the adverb on the line to the left.

______________ **1.** There is someone in our family who _____ likes telling family stories. (how)

______________ **2.** Uncle Bruce will _____ tell a good story. (how)

______________ **3.** I _____ like the stories about me as a baby. (when)

______________ **4.** He _____ tells about our visit to the country. (when)

______________ **5.** We rented a little house on a lake, and I learned to swim _____. (where)

______________ **6.** My uncle used to hold me _____ in the water. (how)

______________ **7.** One day he _____ let go of me in the water. (how)

______________ **8.** _____ I was swimming! (when)

______________ **9.** He enjoys seeing how _____ I swim now. (now)

______________ **10.** _____ I will teach others how to swim. (when)

Notes for Home: Your child added adverbs to make sentences more interesting. ***Home Activity:*** Have your child tell you about his or her day. Ask questions your child can answer using adverbs.

Name ______________________________________ Keepers

Extra Practice

Grammar: Using Adverbs to Improve Sentences

Directions: Add an adverb to improve each sentence. Remember that an adverb can tell how, when, or where the action takes place. Write the new sentence with the adverb on the line.

1. Nellie's girlfriend wanted to go to a sleep over.

____

2. She explained, "My parents think I am too young."

____

____

3. Nellie told her parents she wanted to join her friends.

____

____

4. Nellie's mother answered her daughter.

____

5. She told Nellie, "Act grown-up, and we will allow you to go."

____

____

Write a Diary Entry

On a separate sheet of paper, write a diary entry. Tell about a time when you showed your family that you were grown-up enough to do something new. Use adverbs to tell how, when, or where things happened.

Notes for Home: Your child added adverbs to sentences. ***Home Activity:*** Play "Who Am I?" by taking turns describing familiar people, using adverbs to describe how they perform actions.

Name ______________________________

Grammar: Using Adverbs to Improve Sentences

RETEACHING

Choose a word from the box to finish each sentence.

now	outside	happily

Add an adverb that tells **how.**

1. The young cub played ______________ .

Add an adverb that tells **when.**

2. He wanted to eat ______________ .

Add an adverb that tells **where.**

3. Then he took a nap ______________ .

One way to add descriptive detail to a sentence is by using an **adverb.** Adverbs can tell more about **how, when,** or **where** something happens. Do not use more adverbs than you need. Too many adverbs can make a sentence confusing.

Directions: Add descriptive detail to each sentence by choosing an adverb from the box. Write the adverb on the line.

later	quickly	gently	quietly	down

1. Water filled the cold pool ______________ .

2. The bright sun melted the ice ______________ .

3. Magda whispered ______________ to her mother.

4. The trees bent ______________ in the wind.

5. Our brown horse took us home ______________ .

Notes for Home: Your child wrote adverbs in sentences. ***Home Activity:*** Write five verbs on cards. Have your child choose a card and write a sentence using that verb and any adverb that he or she would like to use.

Name ______________________________

Grammar: Using Adverbs to Improve Sentences

Directions: The verb is underlined in each sentence. Write the adverb that tells more about it.

1. The run rises first. ____________
2. A bird sings clearly. ____________
3. Next, the waves break. ____________
4. The boat sails smoothly. ____________
5. Sails flap slowly. ____________
6. The wind blows there. ____________
7. Sailors work carefully. ____________

Directions: Find the adverb in each sentence. Then write it in the spaces next to the sentence.

8. The scientists work hard. ___ ___ [ ] ___
9. The boat moves fast. ___ [ ] ___ ___
10. The team works well. ___ ___ ___ [ ]
11. The gulls dive quickly. ___ ___ ___ [ ] ___ ___ ___
12. The scientists watch quietly. ___ ___ ___ [ ] ___ ___ ___

Unscramble the letters in the squares and write the word that completes the sentence.

The captain speaks ___ ___ ___ ___ ___ l y.

Write a Deep-Sea Tale

On a separate sheet of paper, write about a sea creature. Use abverbs to give details about how the creature might move.

Notes for Home: Your child identified and wrote adverbs in sentences. ***Home Activity:*** Have your child explain to you the role of adverbs in sentences. (Adverbs tell more about the action named by the verb.)

Name ____________________

Keepers

Word Study: Syllabication

Directions: Syllables are the individual parts of a word that you hear. For example, when you say the word **syllable,** you hear three separate parts: **syl • la • ble.** Read the sentences below. Say the underlined word to yourself. Write the syllables on the lines like this: **syl • la • ble.**

____________ **1.** The class was so interested in the story that they never <u>interrupted</u> the storyteller.

____________ **2.** A good storyteller makes <u>characters</u> come to life.

____________ **3.** <u>Muttering</u> is no way to tell a good story.

____________ **4.** My <u>grandmother</u> is a great storyteller.

____________ **5.** My <u>favorite</u> part of her stories is when the characters learn a lesson.

Directions: Read the words in the box. Count how many syllables each word has. Sort the words according to the number of syllables. Write each word in the correct column.

neighborhood	letters	dollars	holidays

Words with Two Syllables	**Words with Three Syllables**
6. ____________	**8.** ____________
7. ____________	**9.** ____________

Directions: Read this word and say it to yourself: **apologizing.** Write the number of syllables in the word, and then write each syllable.

10. Number of syllables: ________ Syllables: ____________

Notes for Home: Your child divided longer words into individual syllables. ***Home Activity:*** Read a poem with your child. Select important words from the poem for you and your child to read and say together. Help your child say each word and count the syllables.

Name ______________________________

Keepers

Pretest

Spelling: Words with Double Consonants

Pretest Directions: Fold back the page along the dotted line. On the blanks, write the spelling words as they are dictated. When you have finished the test, unfold the page and check your words.

1. ______________	**1.** We will come again **tomorrow**.
2. ______________	**2.** May I **borrow** your gloves?
3. ______________	**3.** That's a **different** story!
4. ______________	**4.** We're having **supper** now.
5. ______________	**5.** What's the **matter**?
6. ______________	**6.** I should have **written** sooner.
7. ______________	**7.** The **bottle** is almost empty.
8. ______________	**8.** He's **ridden** many trails today.
9. ______________	**9.** This cold makes me feel **odd**.
10. ______________	**10.** Can you blow a **bubble**?
11. ______________	**11.** What do you have to **offer**?
12. ______________	**12.** I don't want her to **suffer**.
13. ______________	**13.** Where is the other **slipper**?
14. ______________	**14.** The **grasshopper** jumped away.
15. ______________	**15.** Don't **worry**, we'll find it.
16. ______________	**16.** What is your **current** address?
17. ______________	**17.** My rabbit likes to eat **lettuce**.
18. ______________	**18.** The boy dropped his **paddle**.
19. ______________	**19.** He gave a **shudder** of fright.
20. ______________	**20.** Reading is a good **hobby**.

Notes for Home: Your child took a pretest on words with double consonants. ***Home Activity:*** Help your child learn misspelled words before the final test. Have your child divide misspelled words into parts (such as syllables) and concentrate on each part.

Name ____________________

Spelling: Words with Double Consonants

Word List				
tomorrow	matter	odd	slipper	lettuce
borrow	written	bubble	grasshopper	paddle
different	bottle	offer	worry	shudder
supper	ridden	suffer	current	hobby

Directions: Choose the words in the box with **rr, ff,** or **dd.** Write each word in the correct column.

Words with Double r	Words with Double f	Words with Double d
1. ____________	5. ____________	8. ____________
2. ____________	6. ____________	9. ____________
3. ____________	7. ____________	10. ____________
4. ____________		11. ____________

Directions: Choose a word from the box that best matches each clue. Write the word on the line.

____________ **12.** a word with two *b*'s that is what you do for fun

____________ **13.** a word with two *p*'s that is the name of a meal

____________ **14.** a word with two *t*'s that you eat in a salad

____________ **15.** a word with two *p*'s that you wear on your foot

____________ **16.** a word with two double consonants

____________ **17.** a word with two *t*'s that holds liquid

____________ **18.** a word with two *t*'s that is the opposite of *spoken*

____________ **19.** a word with two *b*'s that you might find in a bathtub

____________ **20.** a word with two *t*'s that means "problem or trouble"

Notes for Home: Your child spelled words with double consonants. **Home Activity:** Play a doubles game with your child. Choose a consonant and ask your child to say and spell as many words as he or she can think of that have that double consonant.

Spelling: Words with Double Consonants

≡	Make a capital.
/	Make a small letter.
∧	Add something.
ℓ	Take out something.
⊙	Add a period.
¶	Begin a new paragraph.

Directions: Proofread this journal entry that tells a family history. Find five spelling mistakes. Use the proofreading marks to correct each mistake.

Our family comes from Puerto Rico. My grandparents grew letuce and other vegetables in their garden. They made wonderful food for super, and they taught my father how to make those dishes too. But when Papa makes them, they always taste a little different! Papa used to wery about that, but now he just laughs. "It doesn't mater," he says. "Maybe tomorow I'll get it right."

Spelling Tip

supper

Sometimes double consonants stand for one sound. For example, you hear the sound /p/ one time in supper. To help you remember to use a double consonant, think: I like **peas** for **supper.**

Word List

tomorrow	offer
borrow	suffer
different	slipper
supper	grasshopper
matter	worry
written	current
bottle	lettuce
ridden	paddle
odd	shudder
bubble	hobby

Write a Journal Entry

Think of an interesting story about your family's history. On a separate sheet of paper, write a journal entry telling the story. Try to use at least three spelling words.

Notes for Home: Your child spelled words with double consonants. **Home Activity:** Write each spelling word, but leave out the second letter of the double consonant. Ask your child to tell you which consonant should be doubled for each word.

Name ______________________________

Spelling: Words with Double Consonants

REVIEW

Word List				
tomorrow	matter	odd	slipper	lettuce
borrow	written	bubble	grasshopper	paddle
different	bottle	offer	worry	shudder
supper	ridden	suffer	current	hobby

Directions: Unscramble the letters to form a word from the box. Write the word on the line.

1. tulcete ________________

2. rwobor ________________

3. uedrhsd ________________

4. prepils ________________

5. fuserf ________________

6. prasghorpes ________________

7. trenruc ________________

8. tiferdenf ________________

9. termat ________________

10. lettob ________________

11. belbub ________________

12. lepadd ________________

Directions: Choose the word from the box that best completes each sentence. Write the word on the line to the left.

________________ **13.** I can't wait for the day after _____!

________________ **14.** That's when we'll eat _____ with my aunt.

________________ **15.** She has _____ a book about our family history.

________________ **16.** She has done many _____ and unusual things.

________________ **17.** For example, she has _____ on a camel in Egypt.

________________ **18.** I always _____ to help her cook when we visit.

________________ **19.** "Don't _____," she will say. "I like to cook!"

________________ **20.** "In fact, it's my favorite _____."

Notes for Home: Your child spelled words with double consonants. **Home Activity:** With your child, think of some other words with double consonants, such as *coffee, lobby, add,* and *rubber.*

Name ______________________________

Time Line

A **time line** is a special kind of chart that shows events in the order in which they happened or will happen. The bar of a time line is divided into units of time, such as months, years, or decades. It is labeled with the event.

Directions: Think of ten events that have become often-told family stories about you and your family, such as a camping trip to the Rockies or the birth of a little sister. Describe the events on the lines below. Tell how old you were for each event. Then figure out the year each event took place. Record the month the event took place, if you can.

Family Events	My Age	Year/Month
__________	__________	__________
__________	__________	__________
__________	__________	__________
__________	__________	__________
__________	__________	__________
__________	__________	__________
__________	__________	__________
__________	__________	__________
__________	__________	__________
__________	__________	__________
__________	__________	__________
__________	__________	__________
__________	__________	__________
__________	__________	__________

Name ____________________________________

Directions: Use the bar below to make a time line of your family events. First, divide the bar into equal parts to show the number of years your time line will cover. For example, if your events cover a 10-year period, divide the bar into 10 equal parts. Then write the year (and month if you know it) that each event took place above the line. Write a short description of each event below the line. Draw lines connecting the labels to the bar. Make sure that the events and years match and that events are listed in the order in which they happened.

Notes for Home: Your child made a time line of family events. ***Home Activity:*** Tell your child some of your favorite family stories about special events. Together, make a time line of these events.

Name ____________________

How-to Chart

Directions: Fill in the how-to chart with information about your project.

Explain task. ____________________

Materials ____________________

____

Introduction ____________________

____

Steps ____________________

____

____

____

____

____

Conclusion ____________________

____

Notes for Home: Your child has been preparing to write a how-to report. ***Home Activity:*** Ask your child to outline the steps in the process of a regular home activity, such as preparing for bed or playing a video game. Try it out. Are there any steps missing?

Name ______________________________

Elaboration

Add Details

- When you write, you can elaborate by **adding vivid and specific** details that help readers picture your subject clearly.
- You can provide vivid and specific details by telling how things look, sound, feel, taste, and smell.

Directions: Read each sentence below. Pick words from the box to tell more about the process of making a book. Write your new sentences using the details.

unique	felt-tip	creative	wrapping
unusual	interesting	thick	special
hand-drawn	decorate	large	bright
cloth adhesive	small	thin	hard

1. You need paper for the pages.

____

2. Some cardboard will do for the covers.

____

3. You can cover your book with paper.

____

4. Pictures will add life to your cover.

____

5. Use pens to add different colors.

____

6. Hide the staples with tape.

____

Notes for Home: Your child expanded sentences by adding vivid and specific details. ***Home Activity:*** Discuss with your child how-to steps that occur in everyday life. Take turns giving examples and elaborating on the steps to make them as clear as possible.

Name ______________________________

Self-Evaluation Guide

How-to Report

Directions: Think about the final draft of your how-to report. Then answer each question below.

	Yes	No	Not sure
1. Are there any steps missing?			
2. Are all the steps in the right order?			
3. Are the steps clearly written and easy to follow?			
4. Did I provide all of the necessary information?			
5. Did I use words like *first* to indicate order?			
6. Did I proofread carefully for spelling, capitalization, and punctuation?			
7. Did I accomplish what I set out to accomplish?			
8. Did I learn anything new from this report?			

9. In what way would you improve your report if you rewrote it?

____

____

Notes for Home: Your child recently completed a self-evaluation of a writing assignment. ***Home Activity:*** Discuss the how-to report with your child. Consider the following questions: *What did you learn from the exercise? Are there other areas where this experience is applicable?*

Family Times

Name ____________________

Summary

Teen Joins Historic Cross-Country Trip!

Hermine Jahns, a 15-year-old girl, has the chance of a lifetime! It's 1909, and she's going cross-country by car with Alice Ramsey and Alice's sisters-in-law. Alice Ramsey is the first woman to ever try such a feat. The women have many adventures. Without reliable road maps, it's hard to find their way. When a bolt falls out, Alice Ramsey repairs the car with baling wire and hairpins. They almost get swamped by flash floods in Utah. Despite these setbacks, they make it to San Francisco in a record-breaking 59 days!

Activity

Getting There Is All the Fun. Trace the women's route on a map. Talk about what it would be like to travel the same route today. What would be the same? What would be different?

Reading Skills

Summarizing

A **summary** gives the main ideas of an article, or it tells what happened in a story. A summary is short; it doesn't include unimportant details. A summary will help you recall and organize information.

Activity

What's the Big Idea? Take turns telling stories about journeys you've taken. These could be trips around town or to far away places. Have someone else give a summary of each travel story.

Family Times

Tested Vocabulary

Words to Know

Knowing the meanings of these words is important to reading "Amazing Alice!" Practice using these words to learn their meanings.

blacksmith ironworker

crank part of a machine that sets it in motion

dependable reliable

forge blacksmith's shop

ravines deep, narrow valleys

telegraph a device used to send coded messages over wires

Grammar

Pronouns

A **pronoun** is a word that replaces a noun or a noun phrase. A pronoun may be singular or plural. *I, you, he, she, it, me, him,* and *her* are singular pronouns. *We, you, they,* and *us* are plural pronouns. Always capitalize the pronoun *I.*

Alice drove the car.
<u>She</u> drove the car.

The blacksmith gave Alice the tire.
<u>He</u> gave <u>her</u> the tire.

Activity

Talking in Pronouns. Have a conversation with a family member. Repeat one another's sentences, replacing nouns or noun phrases with pronouns.

Tested Spelling Words

______	______	______	______
______	______	______	______
______	______	______	______
______	______	______	______
______	______	______	______

Name ______________________________

Summarizing

- A **summary** gives the main ideas of an article, or it tells what happens in a story.
- A summary is short, and it doesn't include unimportant details.

Directions: Reread "Stagecoaches Then . . . and Now." Then complete the table. List details that belong with each topic. Then write a sentence summarizing the article.

Topic	Summary
Movie image of stages vs. reality	Movie Image: exciting, almost always ambushed by robbers **1.** Reality:
How stages began	**2.**
How stages got name	**3.**
How stages made money	**4.**

Summary of Article

5. ______________________________

____

____

Notes for Home: Your child read an article and summarized its main idea. ***Home Activity:*** Read an article from a children's magazine or watch a TV documentary with your child. Ask him or her to summarize the main idea.

Name ____________________

Vocabulary

Check the Words You Know

__ blacksmith
__ crank
__ dependable
__ forge
__ ravines
__ telegraph

Directions: Choose the word from the box that best matches each definition. Write the word on the line.

____________ **1.** deep, narrow valleys

____________ **2.** a way of sending coded messages over wires

____________ **3.** part of a machine that sets it in motion

____________ **4.** ironworker

____________ **5.** blacksmith's shop

____________ **6.** reliable

Directions: Read the help wanted ad. Choose the word from the box that best completes each sentence. Write the word on the matching numbered line.

Blacksmith Needed

We need a **7.** _____ person that can be trusted to work hard. The new blacksmith would work in the **8.** _____ with five other workers. You must be willing to travel across two deep **9.** _____ to get to work each day. If interested, please use a **10.** _____ to send your response because we don't have a telephone.

7. ____________

8. ____________

9. ____________

10. ____________

Write Dictionary Entries

Make dictionary entries for three of the vocabulary words. Each dictionary entry should have the word, a definition, and a picture. You may wish to look at pictures in a history book or encyclopedia. Pictures make the words easier to understand!

Notes for Home: Your child identified and used new vocabulary words from "Amazing Alice!" ***Home Activity:*** Work with your child to write a story about hiring a blacksmith to fix something for you.

Name ______________________________________

Summarizing

- A **summary** is a short statement that tells the main idea of a selection, leaving out unimportant details.

Directions: Reread this passage from "Amazing Alice!" Then answer the questions below. Use what you know about summarizing.

There were only 20 more miles to go until we reached the ferry house at Oakland, where we would board a boat taking us across the wide, blue bay to San Francisco. Time sped by too quickly. We arrived at the Oakland boat dock within an hour after breakfast. Once on the ferry, we set the Maxwell's brakes and raced to the front end of the boat to watch San Francisco bobbing in the water. Great golliwogs! To think that those same Pacific Ocean waves touch the shores of the Chinese Empire!

Our ferry slid out into the bay. Gulls were squawking like New York street vendors. Buoys were clanging. We heard foghorns hoot, though there was no fog. The other passengers seemed very excited to get a look at the Maxwell and us. Who told them I don't know, but everyone knew where we were from and what Alice had done. We did not have a single quiet moment, as every rider wanted to congratulate us.

1. Why isn't the following sentence a good example of a summary for the first paragraph? *It was 20 more miles to the ferry house.*

____

2. Write a summary of the first paragraph.

____

3. Is the following sentence a good summary of the second paragraph? Explain. *The ferry boat ride was noisy.*

____

4. What is the main idea of the second paragraph?

____

5. On a separate sheet of paper, write a summary of "Amazing Alice!"

Notes for Home: Your child used story details to summarize a passage. ***Home Activity:*** Take turns with your child reading short articles from a newspaper or magazine and summarizing them. Decide what is the main idea of each article and what are unimportant details.

Name ___________________________

Selection Test

Directions: Choose the best answer to each item. Mark the letter for the answer you have chosen.

Part 1: Vocabulary

Find the answer choice that means about the same as the underlined word in each sentence.

1. He will telegraph his answer.
- A. send a message by wire
- B. look for
- C. watch from a distance
- D. join

2. Joan is a dependable person.
- F. interesting
- G. able to be counted on
- H. clever
- J. funny or amusing

3. This is the crank.
- A. sheet of metal
- B. type of map
- C. a narrow bridge
- D. handle on a machine

4. He found a blacksmith.
- F. ironworker
- G. storyteller
- H. driver
- J. news reporter

5. Tell us about the ravines.
- A. strong winds
- B. small streams
- C. words of praise
- D. deep, narrow valleys

6. The forge is open now.
- F. place to cross a river
- G. shelter or station
- H. shop for metal work
- J. place for meetings

Part 2: Comprehension

Use what you know about the selection to answer each item.

7. Alice was the first woman to—
- A. drive across the country.
- B. own a car.
- C. fix cars for a living.
- D. enter a contest.

8. This selection is written as if it were told by—
- F. Alice.
- G. Minna.
- H. Maggie.
- J. Nettie.

GO ON

9. How did Minna feel about Alice?
- A. She was jealous of her.
- B. She thought she was strange.
- C. She admired her.
- D. She thought she was bossy.

10. What did the women learn about the "Blue Book"?
- F. It was easy to use.
- G. Parts of it were out of date.
- H. It had very good maps.
- J. Most of it was about the West.

11. Which sentence best summarizes what happened in Wyoming?
- A. The women walked across a railroad bridge to get a permit to drive across it.
- B. The bridge across the river had been washed away.
- C. A train came along while the women were crossing the trestle bridge.
- D. Alice got a case of "jolt-itis."

12. The entries in this journal tell mostly about—
- F. what Alice was like.
- G. how the women got along.
- H. the challenges of the trip.
- J. how homesick Minna felt.

13. Which sentence best summarizes this selection?
- A. Alice drove over a prairie dog hole and broke an axle.
- B. Alice Ramsey and three other women drove across the United States in 59 days.
- C. Alice and her friends drove all day and stayed in a different hotel every night.
- D. Alice drove the car and told Minna what to write in her journal.

14. Which sentence gives an opinion?
- F. "There were only 20 more miles to go."
- G. "Time sped by too quickly."
- H. "We arrived at the Oakland boat dock."
- J. "Our ferry slid out into the bay."

15. What made Alice an unusual woman for her time?
- A. She was smart.
- B. She had a good friend.
- C. She liked traveling.
- D. She was an expert driver.

STOP

Name ________________________________

Summarizing

- A **summary** is a short statement that tells the main idea of a selection, leaving out unimportant details.

Directions: Read the passage below.

In the summer of 1899, William K. Vanderbilt and his new bride arrived in Newport, Rhode Island. But the Vanderbilts did not stay long in Newport. It was all because of William K. Vanderbilt's motor car. The people of Newport didn't like it. That's because he liked to drive fast. Sometimes he drove as fast as a train, people said.

Newport leaders set speed limits. Did that slow Vanderbilt down? Not a chance. The wealthy Vanderbilt was willing to pay the fines for going fast.

Vanderbilt and his wife left Newport in 1901 for Long Island. Here, Vanderbilt came up with the idea for the nation's first international auto race and also built a road especially for cars.

Directions: Complete the table by listing important details for each paragraph. Then write a summary of the passage.

Paragraph	Story Details
Paragraph 1	**1.**
Paragraph 2	**2.**
	3.
Paragraph 3	**4.**

Summary

5.

Notes for Home: Your child identified important details of a passage and used them to write a summary of the passage's main idea. ***Home Activity:*** With your child, read a short article from a newspaper or magazine. Underline important details and use them to write a short summary.

Graphic Sources

REVIEW

Directions: Read the passage and look at the bar graph. Then read each question about the passage and the bar graph. Choose the best answer to each question. Mark the letter for the answer you have chosen.

Henry Ford's Car

In 1903, Ford Motor Company sold its first car. But real success came in 1908, with the Model T car.

Then in 1913, Ford's assembly line greatly cut the time it took to make a Model T car. The price also kept coming down. By the mid-1920s, many working people could afford a Model T car and the company's sales soared.

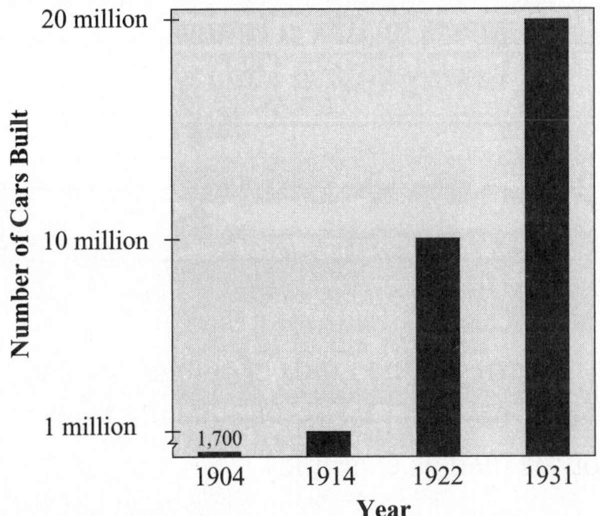

1. Ford Motor Company built its millionth car in—
   - **A.** 1914.
   - **B.** 1922.
   - **C** 1908.
   - **D.** 1931.

2. About how many cars did Ford build in 1922?
   - **F.** 1,000
   - **G.** 1 million
   - **H.** 10 million
   - **J.** 20 million

3. The price of the Model T car dropped because of—
   - **A.** the assembly line.
   - **B.** the Depression.
   - **C.** cheaper materials.
   - **D.** their bumpy ride.

4. How long after it built its 10 millionth car did Ford build its 20 millionth car?
   - **F.** about 20 years
   - **G.** about 10 years
   - **H.** only one year
   - **J.** 31 years later

5. In what year did the Ford Motor Company build its 30 millionth car?
   - **A.** 1933
   - **B.** 1943
   - **C.** 1922
   - **D.** can't tell from facts given

Notes for Home: Your child read a passage and interpreted a bar graph. ***Home Activity:*** Look for graphs in the newspaper with your child. Take turns asking one another questions based on information in the graph. Discuss how you used the graph to answer each question.

Name ______________________________

Writing Across Texts

Directions: Think about the journal entries in *Amazing Alice!* Take the information from one day of Hermine's journal of her trip with Alice Ramsey and put it onto a journal page similar to one from "Keeping a Road Journal."

1. Date: ______________________________
2. Time: ______________________________
3. Location: ______________________________
   ____
4. Weather: ______________________________
   ____
5. What happened today: ______________________________
   ____
   ____
   ____
   ____

Write an Essay

On a separate sheet of paper, write an essay describing the kinds of things you can learn from reading stories that are set in other times and places. Use details from your road journal entry and other stories you've read as examples.

Notes for Home: Your child thought about how the details in a story tie to the unit's theme, "Journeys in Time and Space." ***Home Activity:*** When watching television shows or movies set in other times and places, talk about things you can learn from these shows and movies.

Name ____________________________________

Grammar: Possessive Nouns and Pronouns

REVIEW

Directions: Make each underlined noun possessive. Write the possessive noun on the line.

1. that <u>car</u> color ____________________
2. the <u>people</u> choice ____________________
3. <u>Bess</u> bicycle ____________________
4. his <u>parents</u> automobile ____________________
5. the <u>child</u> tricycle ____________________

Directions: Underline each possessive pronoun. Write **S** above the pronoun if it is singular. Write **P** if it is plural.

6. Rosa, do you have your ticket to the car show?
7. My family drove there in our old jalopy.
8. Many people showed off their antique cars.
9. Tina found the car of her dreams.
10. Bryan, however, preferred his motorcycle.

Directions: Circle the correct word in ( ) to complete each sentence.

11. Does that red car belong to (you're/your) parents?
12. No, that is my cousin (Iris/Iris's) car.
13. She set up her (baby's/babies) car seat in the back.
14. The dog lies on (it's/its) pillow in the front.
15. Her passengers will have to look around for (they/their) own place to sit.

Notes for Home: Your child used possessive nouns and pronouns—nouns and pronouns that show ownership. ***Home Activity:*** Point to things around the house. Have your child use possessive nouns and pronouns to tell who owns each object.

Name ______________________________________

Practice

Grammar: Pronouns

Pronouns are words that replace nouns or noun phrases. *I, you, he, she, it, me, him,* and *her* are singular pronouns. *We, you, they, us,* and *them* are plural pronouns. The singular pronoun *I* is always capitalized.

Scruffy likes to ride in the car.
She is the first to jump into it when we go for a drive.

Directions: Underline each singular pronoun once and each plural pronoun twice.

1. Jane said she wanted to bike all the way to Maine.
2. We told Jane the idea was foolish and dangerous.
3. Jane said it wasn't dangerous; five other high school students and two gym teachers would be in the group.
4. "Just call us if you find the trip too hard," Mom told Jane.
5. "Call me collect anytime," Dad added.
6. Jane just smiled. "I won't need to do it," she said.
7. "You say so *now*," Dad pointed out.
8. "I know you all mean well," Jane said.
9. "However, I am a big girl now, and we will be careful."
10. "Well, stay alert and be sure you call home every night," Mom directed.

Directions: Choose a pronoun in ( ) to replace each underlined noun or noun phrase. Write the pronoun on the line.

____________________ 11. Jane did call us every night. (She/I)

____________________ 12. She spoke to Mom and Dad. (us/them)

____________________ 13. They gave Jane advice. (her/it)

____________________ 14. Jane listened to Mom. (her/me)

____________________ 15. Jane listened to Dad too. (them/him)

Notes for Home: Your child identified singular and plural pronouns and wrote pronouns. ***Home Activity:*** Name objects and people and have your child suggest pronouns for them.

Name ______________________________

Grammar: Pronouns

Directions: Choose a pronoun in ( ) to replace each underlined noun or noun phrase. Write the pronoun on the line.

______________ **1.** I couldn't wait to go on vacation in our new mobile home. (it/them)

______________ **2.** Our next-door neighbors had fun going on a trip last year. (We/They)

______________ **3.** Somebody had given our neighbors many good suggestions. (us/them)

______________ **4.** They passed the suggestions on to my family and me. (it/us)

______________ **5.** My family and I made sure we didn't drive too far in a single day. (We/They)

______________ **6.** The trip was very interesting. (I/It)

______________ **7.** Mom found some shorter routes. (She/They)

______________ **8.** My brother found campsites. (He/They)

______________ **9.** My sister just had fun. (She/We)

______________ **10.** Mom and Dad say that next year we'll feel like expert travelers. (We/They)

Write a Postcard

On a separate sheet of paper, write a postcard to a friend about a trip you have taken. The trip can be a real one or one you have imagined. Make sure you use some pronouns as well as nouns. Circle all the pronouns you use.

Notes for Home: Your child used pronouns to replace nouns. ***Home Activity:*** Think of one or more people or objects in the room. Give a pronoun, such as *they,* and play a questions game with your child to identify those people or objects.

Name ___________________________________

Grammar: Pronouns

Read the sentences. Arrows connect each pronoun with a noun.

Eli plants seeds. He likes to plant them.

1. Write the pronoun that stands for the noun Eli. ____________

2. Write the pronoun that stands for the noun seeds. ____________

A **pronoun** takes the place of a noun or nouns. Singular pronouns are **I, you, she, he, it, me, her,** and **him.** Plural pronouns are **we, you, they, us,** and **them.**

Directions: Circle the pronoun in each sentence.

1. I carry some tools for Flo.

2. We ask the teacher for the small rake.

3. She does not have the rake.

4. Flo asks her for the vegetable seeds.

5. The teacher gives them to Flo.

Directions: Write the correct pronoun to stand for each underlined noun.

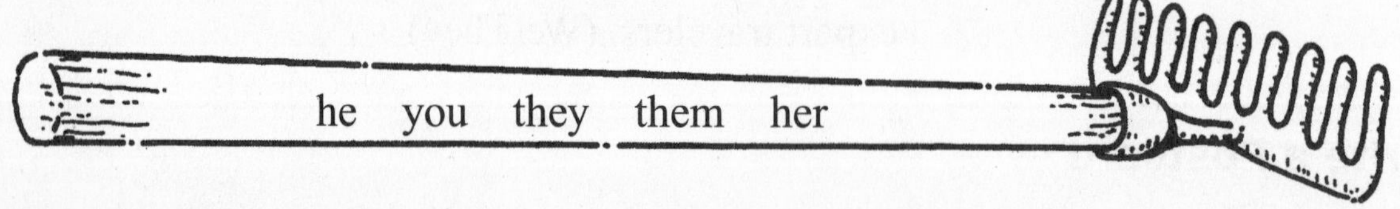

6. Eli planted seeds. ____________ enjoyed the work.

7. Janet wanted to help. Eli gave ____________ pepper seeds.

8. Janet took the seeds. She planted ____________ in the ground.

9. Bill and Tanya watched. ____________ held water buckets.

10. Eli said to Tanya, "Now ____________ can water the plants."

Notes for Home: Your child identified and wrote pronouns in sentences. ***Home Activity:*** Read a news article with your child. Have him or her point out the pronouns and use three of them in new sentences.

Name ___________________________________

Grammar: Pronouns

Directions: Circle six pronouns in the puzzle. Then write the pronouns in the sentences to replace the words in ( ).

h	e	r	s	s	a
i	s	t	h	e	y
m	o	h	e	i	t

1. (Marla and Joe) live in the Painted Desert. ______________
2. (The Painted Desert) is beautiful. ______________
3. (Marla) likes the colors of the desert. ______________
4. I bring (Marla) colored sand. ______________
5. (Joe) likes the weather in the desert. ______________
6. We ask (Joe) questions. ______________

Directions: Write a pronoun to complete each sentence.

My family traveled to the Painted Desert. **7.** ____________ marveled at the animal life. Lizards and toads moved along the ground near **8.** ____________ . **9.** ____________ are strange creatures. My father spotted some bats high above **10.** ____________ last night. **11.** ____________ exclaimed, **12.** "____________ watched **13.** ____________ . **14.** ____________ can fly very fast!"

Write a Short Description

On a separate sheet of paper, write a short description of a place you have read about. Use pronouns in your sentences to avoid repeating nouns.

Notes for Home: Your child identified and wrote pronouns in sentences. ***Home Activity:*** Have your child write about a trip your family has taken. Challenge him or her to use pronouns to avoid repeating nouns.

Name ______________________________

Word Study: Prefixes

Directions: Letters added to the beginning of words are called **prefixes.** Prefixes can change the meaning of the base word. Add the prefix to each word below to make a new word. Write each new word on the line.

	Prefix		Base Word		New Word
1.	dis	+	obey	=	______________
2.	re	+	paint	=	______________
3.	mis	+	lead	=	______________
4.	un	+	hooked	=	______________
5.	il	+	logical	=	______________

Directions: Read the journal entry below. Look for words with the prefix: **dis-, re, mis-, un-, il-, sub-, en-,** or **in-.** Circle each word and write it on the line.

March 31
My family and I are starting our trip today. We are driving across the country! It's not an uncommon trip, but it's new to me. My parents have always encouraged me to try new things. I watched as familiar sights disappeared. We'd only gone a few hours, when my father misread the map! He could not make an illegal U-turn to head us back in the right direction. But we were not discouraged! We drove to where we could turn around, retraced our steps, and started again. My father is not often incorrect about directions. Maybe we should have a subtitle for this trip—"Our Unpredictable Adventure."

6. ______________ 

7. ______________

8. ______________

9. ______________ 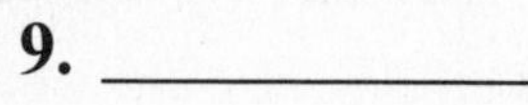

10. ______________ 

11. ______________

12. ______________

13. ______________

14. ______________

15. ______________

Notes for Home: Your child wrote and identified words with prefixes, such as *disappear (dis + appear). **Home Activity:*** Read a newspaper story with your child. Work together to find words with the prefixes listed above.

Name ______________________

Spelling: Prefixes *dis-*, *in-*, *mis-*, *re-*

Pretest

Pretest Directions: Fold back the page along the dotted line. On the blanks, write the spelling words as they are dictated. When you have finished the test, unfold the page and check your words.

1. ______________	1. She doesn't **dislike** anyone.
2. ______________	2. He made the food **disappear**.
3. ______________	3. Don't **distrust** people too much.
4. ______________	4. Lying is **dishonest**.
5. ______________	5. I **disagree** with that.
6. ______________	6. This collection is **incomplete**.
7. ______________	7. She is an **independent** girl.
8. ______________	8. This answer is **incorrect**.
9. ______________	9. The crack is almost **invisible**.
10. ______________	10. The volcano is **inactive** now.
11. ______________	11. I never **misplace** my homework.
12. ______________	12. Did I **misspell** your name?
13. ______________	13. Their lies **misled** the jury.
14. ______________	14. Don't **mistreat** the dog.
15. ______________	15. Babies, don't **misbehave**!
16. ______________	16. We need to **rebuild** our house.
17. ______________	17. I can **reuse** this jar.
18. ______________	18. How should you **react** to that?
19. ______________	19. Please **replace** the light bulb.
20. ______________	20. He can't **recall** what happened.

Notes for Home: Your child took a pretest on words that begin with *dis-*, *in-*, *mis-*, and *re-*. ***Home Activity:*** Help your child learn misspelled words before the final test. Your child should look at the word, say it, spell it aloud, and then spell it with eyes shut.

Name ______________________________

Spelling: Prefixes *dis-*, *in-*, *mis-*, *re-*

Word List			
dislike	incomplete	misplace	rebuild
disappear	independent	misspell	reuse
distrust	incorrect	misled	react
dishonest	invisible	mistreat	replace
disagree	inactive	misbehave	recall

Directions: Add the prefix **dis-**, **in-**, **mis-**, or **re-** to each base word to form a word from the box. Write the word on the line.

1. appear ____________

2. call ____________

3. place ____________

4. active ____________

5. visible ____________

6. like ____________

7. correct ____________

8. honest ____________

9. dependent ____________

10. use ____________

11. build ____________

12. spell ____________

13. treat ____________

14. complete ____________

Directions: Choose the word from the box that best replaces the underlined word or words. Write the word on the line.

____________ **15.** I <u>don't trust</u> Billy.

____________ **16.** Why didn't he <u>put back</u> the toy car that he broke?

____________ **17.** I don't know why he <u>deceived</u> us.

____________ **18.** Why does he always <u>behave badly</u>?

____________ **19.** Maybe I shouldn't <u>respond</u> so strongly.

____________ **20.** After all, he and I always <u>think different things</u>.

Notes for Home: Your child spelled words with the prefixes *dis-*, *in-*, *mis-*, and *re-*. ***Home Activity:*** Make up a matching game. Write the prefixes from the lesson on one set of cards and the base words on another. Have your child match the cards to make words *(dis- + like = dislike)*.

Name ____________________

Spelling: Prefixes *dis-, in-, mis-, re-*

Directions: Proofread this ad for car repair. Find five spelling mistakes. Use the proofreading marks to correct each mistake.

≡	Make a capital.
/	Make a small letter.
∧	Add something.
℘	Take out something.
⊙	Add a period.
¶	Begin a new paragraph.

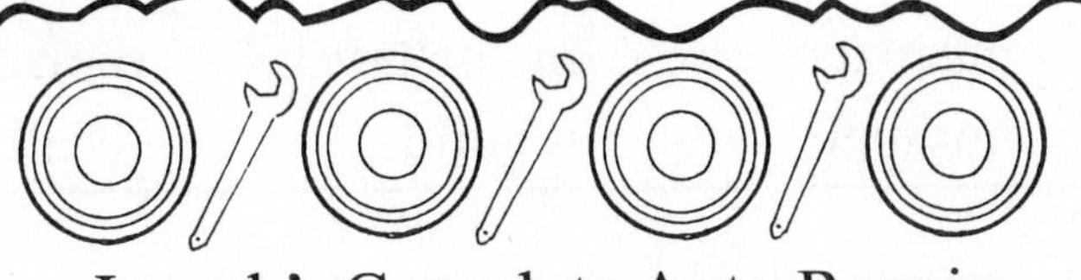

Joseph's Complete Auto Repair

Don't be missled by other repair shops. Don't distrust us just because you have had bad service elsewhere. Don't settle for inncomplete work. We will riplace any bad part at a low cost. We will rebild any part we can. We will make your worries dissappear.

Word List

dislike	misplace
disappear	misspell
distrust	misled
dishonest	mistreat
disagree	misbehave
incomplete	rebuild
independent	reuse
incorrect	react
invisible	replace
inactive	recall

Spelling Tip

When prefixes **dis-**, **in-**, **mis-**, and **re-** are added to words, make no change in the spelling of the base word: **dis-** + **like** = **dislike.**

Write an Ad

On a separate sheet of paper, write your own ad for a car dealership, repair shop, car wash, or other car-related business. Try to use at least three spelling words.

Notes for Home: Your child spelled words with the prefixes *dis-, in-, mis-,* and *re-*. ***Home Activity:*** Give your child clues about the meaning of each spelling word. Have him or her guess the word as quickly as possible.

Name ___________________________________

Spelling: Prefixes *dis-*, *in-*, *mis-*, *re-* REVIEW

Word List

dislike	disagree	invisible	misled	reuse
disappear	incomplete	inactive	mistreat	react
distrust	independent	misplace	misbehave	replace
dishonest	incorrect	misspell	rebuild	recall

Directions: Choose the word from the box that is the most opposite in meaning for each word or words below. Write the word on the line.

1. appear ____________

2. treat well ____________

3. find ____________

4. successfully guided ____________

5. relying on someone ____________

6. agree ____________

7. complete ____________

8. easily seen ____________

9. write correctly ____________

10. active ____________

11. act properly ____________

12. like ____________

Directions: Choose the word from the box that best completes each sentence. Write the word on the line to the left.

________________ **13.** You _____ negatively about all mechanics.

________________ **14.** Not every car-repair shop is _____.

________________ **15.** Do you _____ the shop we used in June?

________________ **16.** You were ready to _____ everything they said.

________________ **17.** You worried that they were _____ about what was wrong.

________________ **18.** But they were able to _____ the engine using good parts.

________________ **19.** They were able to _____ a crank shaft from another car.

________________ **20.** They were also able to _____ the old battery with a new one.

Notes for Home: Your child spelled words with the prefixes *dis-*, *in-*, *mis-*, and *re-*. ***Home Activity:*** Take turns with your child naming and spelling other words that use the same prefixes.

Name ______________________________________

Technology: Manual

A **manual** is a written set of directions, usually in the form of a booklet or book, that helps readers understand or use something. To understand a manual, you need to know how to follow directions.

Directions: The *Everyday Spelling* CD-ROM contains lessons, games, and activities that can help you learn to spell. Use this page from the manual to answer the questions on the next page.

The *Everyday Spelling* textbook program consists of weekly spelling lessons, review lessons, and cross-cultural lessons. The lockers ("cubbies" in grades 1 and 2) on this screen represent lessons. Selecting locker 1, for example, lets you use the words from Lesson 1. Move the cursor to a number and click on it to choose the words you will use.

Lockers numbered 1–5, 7–11, 13–17, 19–23, 25–29, and 31–35 will take you to the Classroom area, where you will work with that lesson's spelling words. Every sixth lesson is a review lesson. Lockers numbered 6, 12, 18, 24, 30, and 36 will take you to the Testing Center, where you will work with spelling words in review lessons.

Note: In grade 1 there are no spelling lessons 1–6.

Name ______________________________

1. What are three different kinds of lessons in the textbook program?

____

2. What does each locker represent? ______________________________

3. How can you get to the spelling words for Lesson 5? ______________________________

____

4. Which locker would you click on if you wanted to review spelling words for Lessons 1–5?

____

5. Clicking on lockers will take you to two different areas to work with spelling words. To what two areas can you go?

____

6. When you click on locker 22, what will happen? ______________________________

____

7. When you click on locker 12, what will happen?

____

8. Which lessons are review lessons? ______________________________

9. Why do you think the manual shows the program's computer screens?

____

____

10. Why is it important to know how to follow directions to use a manual?

____

____

____

Notes for Home: Your child read a manual for a CD-ROM program and answered questions about it. ***Home Activity:*** Find a user's manual for an appliance or a computer program. Look through the manual with your child and discuss the kinds of information that can be found in it.

Family Times

Name___________________________________

Summary

American Dream Is Alive and Well

Solomon Joseph Azar left his home in the mountains of Lebanon and came to the United States to seek his fortune. A man from the old country gave him advice—to become a peddler. Not long after he began peddling his wares, he was robbed. A farm family took him in. He exchanged work for food—until one day he got a job in a dry goods store in town. This was not the end of Solomon's troubles, but he never gave up on his dream.

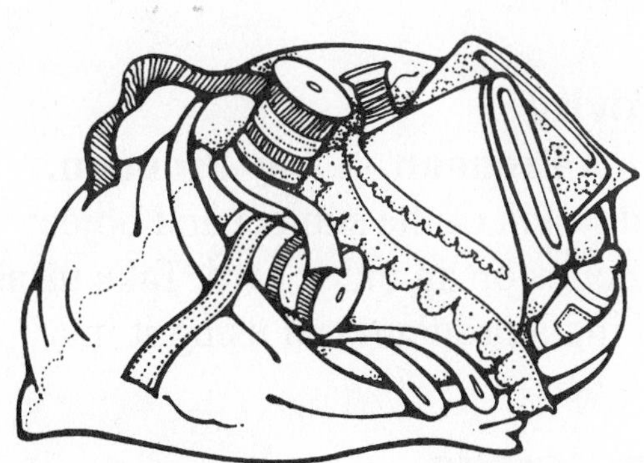

Activity

Draw the Dream. Map the story of Solomon and his dream. Start by drawing a line across a sheet of paper. At one end draw a picture that shows Solomon coming to America. At the other, show Solomon and his shop. In between, show what happens to Solomon.

Reading Skills

Plot

A story's **plot** is the important parts of a story. The parts of a plot are:

- ❖ **Conflict.** A conflict can be a problem between two characters or groups, or between a character and nature. A conflict can also be a problem within a character.
- ❖ **Rising Action.** This is the part of a story in which the conflict builds.
- ❖ **Climax.** This is the high point of a story when the conflict must be faced.
- ❖ **Resolution.** This is the place where the problem is solved.

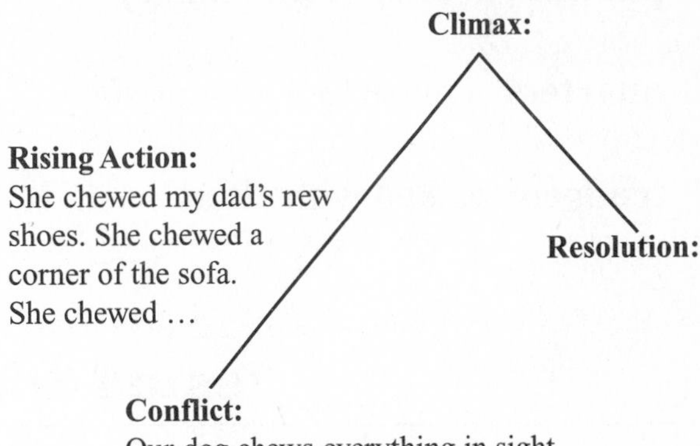
Climax:
Rising Action:
She chewed my dad's new shoes. She chewed a corner of the sofa. She chewed …
Resolution:
Conflict:
Our dog chews everything in sight.

Activity

Plot Your Own Problem. Choose a favorite book or story and make a plot line (like a time line) to show the plot of this story. Begin with the conflict. Then add events that lead up to the climax. Finish by telling how the problem was resolved.

Family Times

Tested Vocabulary

Words to Know

Knowing the meanings of these words is important to reading *A Peddler's Dream.* Practice using these words to learn their meanings.

bound tied together

fortune money and possessions amassed

mission a center or headquarters for religious or social work

peddling carrying from place to place and selling

purchased bought with money

quarters a place to live in or stay

trudged walked with effort

Grammar

Subject and Object Pronouns

A **pronoun** is a word that replaces a noun or a noun phrase. It may be singular or plural.

- **Subject Pronouns.** *I, you, he, she, it, we,* and *they* can be the subjects of sentences.
- **Object Pronouns.** *Me, you, him, her, it, us,* and *them* can follow action verbs.
- **Talking About Yourself.** Whenever you talk about yourself and another person, name yourself last: **Solomon and I walked to town.**

Activity

Pick a Pronoun — Any Pronoun. Write each of the subject and object pronouns on an index card. Take turns picking a pronoun and using it in a sentence.

Tested Spelling Words

Name ______________________

Plot

- Stories have a **plot,** or a series of events that center on a problem, or conflict.
- A **conflict** can be a problem between two people or groups, between a person and nature, or within a character.
- The **climax** is where the action of the story builds and the conflict must be faced. The **resolution** is where the conflict is solved.

Directions: Reread "Atalanta's Race." Then complete the plot map.

Which event is the climax of the story?

4. ______________________

What does Hippomenes do to try to solve the conflict?

3. ______________________

How is the conflict resolved?

5. ______________________

How does Hippomenes become involved?

2. ______________________

What is the conflict?

1. ______________________

Notes for Home: Your child read a story and described its plot. ***Home Activity:*** With your child, watch a live or animated TV show about a hero. When it's over, have him or her describe the main parts of the plot.

Name ______________________________________

Vocabulary

Directions: Choose the word from the box that best matches each definition. Write the word on the line.

Check the Words You Know
- __ bound
- __ fortune
- __ mission
- __ peddling
- __ purchased
- __ quarters
- __ trudged

____________________ **1.** bought with money

____________________ **2.** tied together

____________________ **3.** a center for social work

____________________ **4.** a place to live or stay

____________________ **5.** a great deal of money or possessions

Directions: Choose the word from the box that best completes each sentence. Write the word on the line to the left.

____________________ **6.** Laura came to this country hoping to make her _____.

____________________ **7.** She began earning money by _____ fish around her neighborhood.

____________________ **8.** Each morning, she tiredly _____ down to the docks.

____________________ **9.** At the docks, she _____ fish to sell to others.

____________________ **10.** With her earnings, Laura was able to rent new _____.

Write a Letter

Imagine that you are an immigrant. On a separate sheet of paper, write to your family back home telling about your life. Use as many vocabulary words as you can.

Notes for Home: Your child identified and used vocabulary words from *A Peddler's Dream.* ***Home Activity:*** Take turns, sentence by sentence, telling a story about a traveling peddler who sells goods along the way. Try to use all the vocabulary words.

Name ____

Plot

- A story's **plot** is the important parts of a story. These parts include the conflict, or problem, the climax, and the resolution, or outcome.

Directions: Reread this passage from *A Peddler's Dream* in which Solomon wakes up to the noise of fire trucks. Then answer the questions below.

Late one night the clanging of fire trucks awakened him. He jumped from bed and looked out the window. A red glow filled the sky over State House Avenue.

"The store! Marie, it's the store!" he cried.

"Oh, Solomon," she gasped. "It can't be."

Hurriedly he pulled on his trousers and ran out the door.

But it was the store. As Solomon stood watching it burn, Marie joined him, clutching Isaac and Nora by the hand. Rebecca and Ruth were right behind, their eyes big.

"Papa," cried Rebecca, with tears running down her cheeks, "it's ruined. Our nice store is all ruined."

Solomon put one arm around her shoulders, the other around Marie. "Yes, Rebecca, ruined but not finished."

Solomon was true to his word. He rented temporary quarters and purchased new merchandise. In two weeks he reopened for business with a fire sale on the sidewalk.

1. Who are the characters in this passage?

____

2. What is the problem these characters have?

____

3. What important thing does Solomon say that shows how he will face the problem?

____

4. How is the problem solved?

____

5. What if Solomon chose to solve the problem differently? On a separate sheet of paper, write a new ending for this passage.

Notes for Home: Your child used story details to identify the plot of a story. ***Home Activity:*** Read a short folk tale with your child and have him or her identify its most important parts. Discuss the problem that is central to the story and how this problem is resolved.

Selection Test

Directions: Choose the best answer to each item. Mark the letter for the answer you have chosen.

Part 1: Vocabulary

Find the answer choice that means about the same as the underlined word in each sentence.

1. She wants to make her <u>fortune</u>.
- A. strong statement
- B. wish for good luck
- C. large amount of money or property
- D. place built with walls

2. Let's go to the <u>mission</u>.
- F. store that sells many goods
- G. gathering place for travelers
- H. center for religious or social work
- J. large, stately house

3. His hands were <u>bound</u>.
- A. tied together
- B. hurt or wounded
- C. icy cold
- D. clasped or folded

4. The children <u>trudged</u> inside.
- F. moved in a group
- G. stumbled and fell
- H. stayed or remained
- J. walked slowly with effort

5. He earned money by <u>peddling</u>.
- A. riding a bicycle
- B. carrying and selling goods
- C. fixing things
- D. writing letters

6. We have new <u>quarters</u>.
- F. problems or worries
- G. dream or plan
- H. place to live or work in
- J. work done by a shopkeeper

7. She <u>purchased</u> some cloth.
- A. made clothes from
- B. bought
- C. had need of
- D. saved

Part 2: Comprehension

Use what you know about the story to answer each item.

8. Solomon went to America to—
- F. find a wife.
- G. learn to speak English.
- H. explore new lands.
- J. make his fortune.

GO ON

9. At first Solomon worked as a—
A. store clerk.
B. peddler.
C. farmer.
D. builder.

10. In this story, Solomon faced the problem of how to—
F. marry a rich woman.
G. become governor of his state.
H. own his own store.
J. return to Lebanon for good.

11. What did Solomon do after working two years at Hart's?
A. became the owner of Joseph's
B. built a house for himself
C. returned to Lebanon for Marie
D. became Mr. Hart's partner

12. More and more people shopped at Hart's Dry Goods when Solomon worked there because he—
F. lowered the prices.
G. made the store run better.
H. asked Mr. Hart to retire.
J. told his friends to shop there.

13. The climax of this story comes when—
A. Solomon lands in America.
B. Mr. Hart hires Solomon.
C. Joseph's burns down.
D. Solomon opens a new store.

14. What was most important to Solomon's success?
F. believing in his dream
G. learning from Mr. Hart
H. living in a city
J. meeting the governor

15. In what way was the fire a good thing for Solomon?
A. It gave him time to rest from work.
B. It made people feel sorry for him.
C. It gave him a chance to build the store he wanted.
D. It made him more careful about preventing fires.

STOP

Name ______________________________

Plot

- A story's **plot** is the important parts of a story. These parts include the conflict, or problem, the climax, and the resolution, or outcome.

Directions: Read the story below.

When gold was discovered in California in 1848, Karl was a tailor in San Francisco. Suddenly people left their work and rushed to the gold fields. Karl bought mining tools and went with the others.

After a year and a half of digging for gold, Karl was tired and discouraged. He had not found a fortune. He made just enough to feed himself. Karl wondered if he should keep on.

One day, while Karl was buying work pants, the storekeeper said, "That Levi Strauss is really something. He makes the best work pants!" Karl asked what the man meant. "I can't keep enough in stock!"

Karl was excited. He found Levi Strauss in his small San Francisco pants factory and convinced him that Strauss needed his tailoring skills. Karl sold his miner's tools and went to work making sturdy work pants called *denims* or *jeans*. He was successful, as was Strauss's factory.

Directions: Add story details to complete the plot map.

4. Climax: ______________________

____

3. Event Leading to Climax:

____

____

____

5. Resolution:

____

____

____

1. Setting: ______________________

____

Characters: ______________

____

2. Problem: ______________________

____

____

Notes for Home: Your child used a plot map to describe the important parts of a story. ***Home Activity:*** Use a plot map to plan a story with your child. Decide what problems your characters will face and how they will solve them.

Name ______________________________

Visualizing

REVIEW

Directions: Read the story. Then read each question about the story. Choose the best answer to each question. Mark the letter for the answer you have chosen.

Across the Border

July 4, 1976. Pedro was in the car, heading up the west coast. He gazed at the ocean waves crashing against the shore. Just last week, he had been living across the border in Mexico with his aunt. Then his mother had come to take Pedro and his sister, Pilar, to California. They were all going to live in America.

Pedro could hardly sit still. He imagined his new home with the whitewashed walls, the picket fence, and the yard with chickens. He could smell his mother's cooking.

The car headed away from the coast. It climbed through some hills. Then it went down into a small valley.

The sky darkened. Pedro heard a booming noise. To the right he saw brilliant flashes of color sparkle in the night sky. What a way to celebrate his coming to America!

1. In the car, Pedro—
- **A.** gets carsick.
- **B.** sees the ocean.
- **C.** sees Mexico.
- **D.** spots his new home.

2. When Pedro imagines his new home, he—
- **F.** wants to return to Mexico.
- **G.** feels excited.
- **H.** laughs at his mother.
- **J.** tells Pilar.

3. The car ride was probably—
- **A.** uncomfortable.
- **B.** interesting.
- **C.** frightening.
- **D.** boring.

4. Pedro's new home is probably in—
- **F.** an apartment building.
- **G.** the city.
- **H.** a suburban house.
- **J.** the country.

5. The booming noise Pedro hears and the colorful sparkles of light are—
- **A.** signs of danger.
- **B.** signs of a thunderstorm.
- **C.** fireworks.
- **D.** especially created for Pedro.

Notes for Home: Your child used story details to visualize or imagine what is happening in a story. ***Home Activity:*** Have your child look carefully at a room, and then give vivid details that would help someone else mentally picture this place.

Name ______________________________

Writing Across Texts

Directions: Compare information from *A Peddler's Dream,* the *Welcome to America* graph, and one other source to give an educated guess about the city where Solomon Azar arrived when he first came to the United States. Organize the information in the following table.

Name of the City
1.
Evidence and Rationale from Story
2.
Evidence and Rationale from Graph
3.
Evidence and Rationale from Other Source
4.
Persuasive Opening Sentence
5.

Write a Persuasive Paragraph

On a separate sheet of paper, write a persuasive paragraph that tells which city you think Solomon Azar landed in and why. Include the information from your table.

Notes for Home: Your child compared information from several sources to take a persuasive stance and support it in writing. ***Home Activity:*** With your child, review the source material and encourage a discussion about which places were best for newcomers to the United States.

Name ______________________________

Grammar: Pronouns

REVIEW

Directions: Underline each pronoun in the sentences below.

1. For years Ben and I hoped we could sail to America.
2. In 1919 the dream came true for us.
3. We grew up in a little Polish town, but now we were leaving it forever.
4. "I cannot say good-bye to you," sobbed Ben's mother.
5. Watching Ben leave for America was the hardest thing she had ever done.

Directions: Choose a pronoun in ( ) to replace the underlined noun or noun phrase in each sentence. Circle the pronoun you chose.

6. Ben and I were beginning a new life in New York City. (We/Us)
7. After our little Polish town, the city seemed so big. (they/it)
8. The size and the noise frightened Ben and me. (him/us)
9. Some people seemed nice, though, and we became friends with people. (you/them)
10. These people helped us find our way around. (They/It)
11. We did not know English, so we studied the language. (him/it)
12. Our friend Anna spoke English well, and Anna helped us study. (we/she)
13. Her husband was a tailor, and the husband found a job for Ben. (he/you)
14. We were so grateful to Anna and her husband. (them/us)
15. Life was still very hard, but life got better every day. (she/it)

Notes for Home: Your child identified and used pronouns—words that take the place of nouns. ***Home Activity:*** Ask your child to tell you some jokes or funny stories. Help your child list the pronouns he or she uses.

Practice

Grammar: Subject and Object Pronouns

Subject pronouns are pronouns that are used as the subjects of sentences.

Moesha and I like to travel.

Singular subject pronouns: I, you, he, she, it
Plural subject pronouns: we, you, they

Object pronouns follow action verbs.

Dan Nehmi's parents brought him to this country.

Singular object pronouns: me, you, him, her, it
Plural object pronouns: us, you, them

Directions: Circle the correct pronoun in ( ) to complete each sentence. Write **S** on the line if it is a subject pronoun. Write **O** if it is an object pronoun.

_______________ **1.** My brother and (I/me) longed to go to America.

_______________ **2.** (Us/We) heard people say newcomers quickly became rich.

_______________ **3.** Our mother said not to believe (them/they).

_______________ **4.** "But (us/you) must go and find out for yourselves."

_______________ **5.** Our sister kissed both of (we/us).

_______________ **6.** "Come with us," (I/me) said.

_______________ **7.** "(I/You) want to stay here with our parents," my sister answered.

_______________ **8.** Our father was sorry that we were leaving (him/he).

_______________ **9.** "(Them/They) have a dream," our mother told him.

_______________ **10.** "Someday you and (me/I) may live in America too."

Notes for Home: Your child chose subject and object pronouns to complete sentences. ***Home Activity:*** Say a sentence with nouns as subject and object: *Mrs. Nehmi told Dan about new customs.* Have your child replace the nouns with pronouns: *She told him about new customs.*

Name ______________________________

Grammar: Subject and Object Pronouns

Directions: Choose the correct pronoun in ( ) to complete each sentence. Write the pronoun on the line.

________________ **1.** Have (you/she) ever wondered what *success* really means?

________________ **2.** The best way to define (it/her) is by giving examples.

________________ **3.** At first, Amy was afraid of the water, but then (her/she) learned how to swim.

________________ **4.** Luis decided to get 100% on his test, and (he/they) did.

________________ **5.** The twins earned enough money, so their parents let (them/they) go to summer camp.

________________ **6.** Ms. Chang convinced her boss to give (she/her) a better job.

________________ **7.** Aaron's little brother couldn't catch a ball, so Aaron showed (he/him) how.

________________ **8.** Laura and Sandy were confused about math, so they asked Mr. Franklin to help (him/them).

________________ **9.** Some people think success means being rich and famous, but (they/it) may be wrong.

________________ **10.** Now that you've read these examples, what do (they/you) think?

Write an Ad

On a separate sheet of paper, write a Back-to-School ad listing the "Top 5" ways to have success in school. Use both subject pronouns and object pronouns. Underline the pronouns in your ad.

Notes for Home: Your child replaced nouns with subject pronouns such as: *I, we, you, he, she, it,* and *they* or object pronouns such as: *me, us, you, him, her, it,* and *them*. ***Home Activity:*** Together, read about a famous person. Ask your child to identify the subject and object pronouns.

Name ______________________________________

RETEACHING

Grammar: Subject and Object Pronouns

Read each pair of sentences. Write a pronoun on each line.

1. A clown and a dog came to school. __________ performed tricks.

2. The dog was good at jumping. The class liked watching __________ .

A **subject pronoun** is used in the subject of a sentence. Subject pronouns are **I, you, she, he, it, we,** and **they.** An object pronoun is used in the predicate of a sentence or in a prepositional phrase. Object pronouns are **me, you, him, her, it, us,** and **them.**

Directions: Circle the subject pronoun in each sentence. Then write it on the line.

1. I have learned many facts about space from Mr. Turner. __________

2. He taught the class how to spot a shooting star. __________

3. It is difficult for my sister to do. __________

4. She will be in Mr. Turner's class in three years. __________

5. One day we will watch shooting stars together. __________

6. They are beautiful to see! __________

Directions: Circle the object pronoun in each sentence. Then write it on the line.

7. Mark gave her a drawing of the Big Dipper. __________

8. Did Mark give you a picture too? __________

9. Mr. Gomez gave us star maps. __________

10. Mr. Gomez keeps them in the classroom. __________

11. The star map fascinates me. __________

12. Nina and Leon looked at it carefully. __________

Notes for Home: Your child identified subject and object pronouns in sentences. ***Home Activity:*** Together, read an article in a newspaper. Have your child circle three subject or object pronouns. Then have him or her write new sentences, using pronouns from the article.

Name ____

Grammar: Subject and Object Pronouns

Directions: Read the paragraph. Then circle the correct pronoun in ( ) that completes each sentence. Remember:

- **Subject pronouns** are used as subjects in a sentence:
  I, you, he, she, it, we, and **they.**
- **Object pronouns** are used after action verbs:
  me, you, him, her, it, us, and **them.**

1.–8.

Grandma invited Tim and (I, me) to spend the holidays with her. Mom and Dad drove (we, us) to the airport. (They, Them) waved as the plane took off into the sky. (We, Us) slept on the plane. A flight attendant had to wake (I, me) up when we landed. (He, Him) carried our bags off the plane. Grandma seemed really excited to see (we, us). (She, Her) had balloons for each of us!

Write a Travel Journal

Write about a trip you would like to take with a friend or a book character. It might be a trip to a place in your town or a trip to a faraway place. Check to make sure you used subject and object pronouns correctly in your description.

Notes for Home: Your child identified subject and object pronouns in a paragraph. ***Home Activity:*** Have your child reread his or her travel journal. Then ask your child to circle the subject pronouns and underline the object pronouns that he or she wrote.

Name ______________________________

Phonics: Words with Silent Consonants *kn, gn, wr, mb*

Directions: Read the words below. One consonant in each word is silent. Write the silent consonant on the line.

1. knee ____________

2. resigned ____________

3. wrote ____________

4. comb ____________

5. wrap ____________

6. numb ____________

7. gnarled ____________

8. knitted ____________

9. wreck ____________

10. dumb ____________

Directions: Read the words in the box. Cross out the words that do **not** have silent consonants. Use the remaining words to complete the sentences below. Write the words on the lines to the left.

knocking	bit	wrong	calling	incorrect
designs	gnawed	created	knots	butterflies

____________ **11.** Like many Europeans of his time, Jan heard opportunity _____ in America.

____________ **12.** Young Jan followed his dream and came to America, where he _____ clothing for a new store.

____________ **13.** Now Jan's stomach twisted into _____ as he wondered whether the shop would be a success.

____________ **14.** He _____ his lips nervously as he unlocked the door for the first day of business.

____________ **15.** The crowd of eager customers showed Jan that his creative ideas had not been _____.

Notes for Home: Your child identified words with *kn, gn, wr,* and *mb* where one consonant in each pair is silent, like *know, sign, write,* and *comb. **Home Activity:*** Read a newspaper article with your child. Help your child find words that have silent consonants.

Name ____________________

Spelling: Words with *kn, gn, wr, mb*

Pretest Directions: Fold back the page along the dotted line. On the blanks, write the spelling words as they are dictated. When you have finished the test, unfold the page and check your words.

1. ____________	**1.** This rope has a **knot** in it.
2. ____________	**2.** Where it came from is **unknown**.
3. ____________	**3.** I do not **know** how much it costs.
4. ____________	**4.** We can **knit** these yarns together.
5. ____________	**5.** The door **knob** is brass.
6. ____________	**6.** Please **kneel** down.
7. ____________	**7.** What does the **sign** say?
8. ____________	**8.** What a beautiful **design**!
9. ____________	**9.** She will **assign** your work later.
10. ____________	**10.** He's **writing** the information.
11. ____________	**11.** Wear it on your **wrist**.
12. ____________	**12.** He saw the **wreck** from shore.
13. ____________	**13.** Here is a **wreath** of flowers.
14. ____________	**14.** I need a **wrench** to fix this.
15. ____________	**15.** The **wren** is in that tree.
16. ____________	**16.** Can you **climb** this hill?
17. ____________	**17.** It is bigger than your **thumb**.
18. ____________	**18.** That tree **limb** should be cut off.
19. ____________	**19.** **Comb** your hair first.
20. ____________	**20.** The **lamb** bleated for its mother.

Notes for Home: Your child took a pretest on words that have the letters *kn, gn, wr,* and *mb.* ***Home Activity:*** Help your child learn misspelled words before the final test. Your child can underline the word parts that caused the problems and concentrate on those parts.

Think and Practice

Spelling: Words with *kn, gn, wr, mb*

Word List				
knot	knob	assign	wreath	thumb
unknown	kneel	writing	wrench	limb
know	sign	wrist	wren	comb
knit	design	wreck	climb	lamb

Directions: Choose the words from the box where the consonants **k** and **w** are silent. Write the words in the correct column.

Silent k	Silent w
1. ______	7. ______
2. ______	8. ______
3. ______	9. ______
4. ______	10. ______
5. ______	11. ______
6. ______	12. ______

Directions: Choose the word from the box that best matches each clue. Write the word on the line.

______ **13.** It's the favorite animal of a mother sheep.

______ **14.** You don't want a hammer to meet this.

______ **15.** You use this to get tangles out of your hair.

______ **16.** An architect draws one before starting a new building.

______ **17.** It's how you get to the top.

______ **18.** Going out on one of these can be dangerous.

______ **19.** Your teacher does this with homework.

______ **20.** This is how deaf people communicate.

Notes for Home: Your child spelled words with *kn, gn, wr,* and *mb*. ***Home Activity:*** Read a story or newspaper article together. Have your child look for other words that use these letter combinations where one letter is silent.

Proofread and Write

Spelling: Words with *kn, gn, wr, mb*

Directions: Proofread this postcard. Find five spelling mistakes. Use the proofreading marks to correct each mistake.

≡	Make a capital.
/	Make a small letter.
∧	Add something.
℘	Take out something.
⊙	Add a period.
¶	Begin a new paragraph.

October 4

I am writting just before arriving in port. I am a reck. The trip has been very tough. I tried to clime to the top deck to get some air, but it wasn't allowed. Now I'm a little scared, because it's time to face the unnown. Even though I will live with Cousin Bill, I don't no how it will be. Wish me luck.

Love,

Charlie

Spelling Tip

The underlined consonants stand for only one sound: **knot, sign, wrist, comb.**

Write a Postcard Home

Imagine you have traveled far to live in a new country. On a separate sheet of paper, write a postcard home to your family or a friend. Try to use at least three spelling words.

Word List

knot	wrist
unknown	wreck
know	wreath
knit	wrench
knob	wren
kneel	climb
sign	thumb
design	limb
assign	comb
writing	lamb

Notes for Home: Your child spelled words with *kn-, gn-, wr-,* and *mb-*. ***Home Activity:*** Write each spelling word, but leave out the silent consonant (*thum*). Have your child write each word correctly *(thumb)*.

Name ______________________________

Spelling: Words with *kn, gn, wr, mb*

REVIEW

Word List				
knot	knob	assign	wreath	thumb
unknown	kneel	writing	wrench	limb
know	sign	wrist	wren	comb
knit	design	wreck	climb	lamb

Directions: Write the word from the box that belongs in each group.

1. sparrow, canary, __________

2. brush, barrette, __________

3. sew, weave, __________

4. billboard, flyer, __________

5. bend, squat, __________

6. chick, calf, __________

7. hammer, screwdriver, __________

8. pinkie, pointer, __________

9. knee, elbow, __________

10. bouquet, bunch, __________

11. branch, arm, __________

12. crash, shatter, __________

Directions: Choose the word from the box that best completes each sentence. Write the word on the matching numbered line on the right.

When immigrants came to this country, they faced the **13.** _____. Some immigrants tried to **14.** _____ a plan for their lives. They tried to **15.** _____ the ladder of success. Others had jobs where someone else had to **16.** _____ them work to do. Since factories needed people to do low-paying work, a job might be shaping a **17.** _____ for a door or tying a **18.** _____ in the leather cord that holds a baseball glove together. Reading and **19.** _____ were learned in night school. It was important to **20.** _____ how to use the language in order to succeed in a new country.

13. __________

14. __________

15. __________

16. __________

17. __________

18. __________

19. __________

20. __________

Notes for Home: Your child spelled words with *kn, gn, wr,* and *mb*. ***Home Activity:*** Have your child sort the spelling words by the letter pairs. Together, add other words that use each letter pair *(knight, gnat, wrong, dumb)*.

Graphs

Graphs show information visually and make it easier for readers to compare types of information. The graph below is called a **circle graph.** It shows how a group of people can be divided into smaller groups. The large group this graph describes is the people who moved to Texas in 1995 from another country. The graph divides the people into five groups: Those who came to Texas from Mexico, Vietnam, India, the Philippines, and elsewhere.

Directions: Use the circle graph to answer the questions that follow.

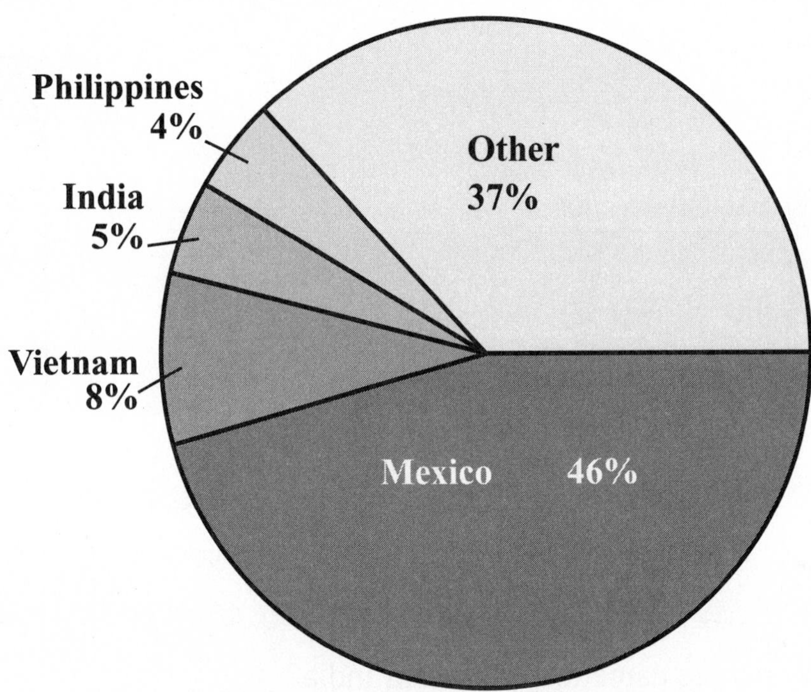

Immigration to Texas, 1995

Source: Department of Justice, Immigration and Naturalization Services

1. From which country did the most number of people come? ____________

2. From which country did the least number of people come? ____________

3. From which two countries did about the same number of people come?

____

4. Did more people come from Mexico or from Vietnam, India, and the Philippines combined? How do you know?

____

____

Name ______________________

Another type of graph is a **bar graph.** The length or height of each bar stands for a number. The bars in this graph show the number of people who moved to Texas in 1995 from another country. The bar graph shows the same data as the circle graph, but in a different way.

Directions: Use the bar graph to answer the questions that follow.

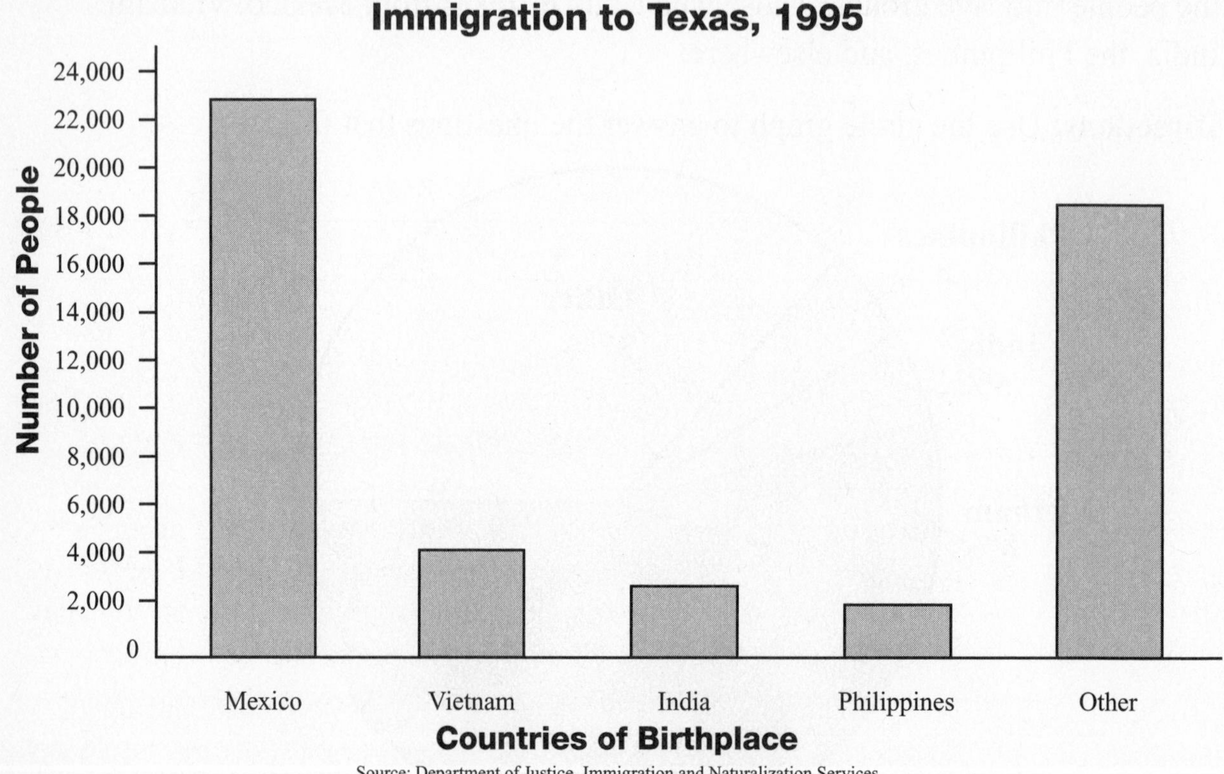

5. About how many people came to Texas from India? ______________

6. From which country did the greatest number of people come? ______________

7. From which country did about 4,000 people come? ______________

8. From which two countries did about 2,000 people come? ______________

9. About how many more people came from Vietnam than India? ______________

10. Tell how the two graphs are alike and different. ______________

____

____

Notes for Home: Your child read data from two different graphs. ***Home Activity:*** Look at graphs in a newspaper with your child. Ask your child questions about the data in these graphs. Let your child ask you questions too.

Family Times

Name____

Summary

Matthew Henson Sets Off for North Pole!

From the time he was a small boy, Matthew Henson wanted adventure. In 1879, when he was only 13 years old, he walked 40 miles to Baltimore's harbor and got a job on a ship. When he was 20 years old he went on his first expedition with explorer Robert Peary. Soon after, he and Robert Peary were bound for the biggest adventure of all—the search for the North Pole.

Activity

Summarize the Story. Have your child tell you what Robert Peary and Matthew Henson did together and what happened to Matthew Henson after the famous expedition.

Reading Skills

Graphic Sources

Charts, graphs, maps, diagrams, time lines, and scale drawings are all kinds of graphic sources. Maps are graphic sources that show places. A physical map shows landforms and bodies of water. A map key explains symbols used and the scale of miles or kilometers.

In "The Race for the North Pole," using a map of the North Pole and the Arctic region can help you follow the journey taken by Matthew Henson and Robert Peary. Seeing their route on the map can help you picture what they did.

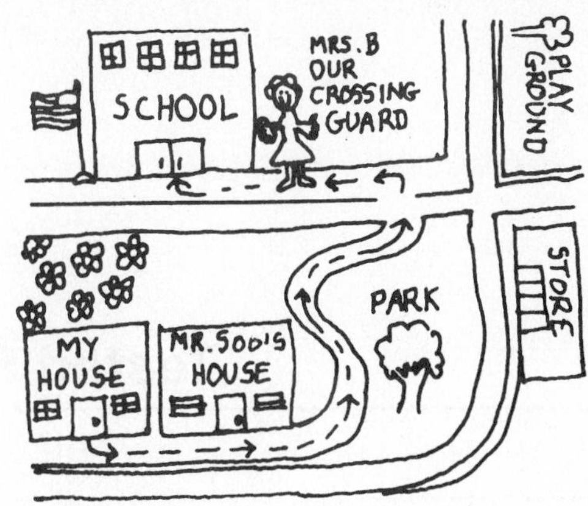

Activity

Make a Map. Think of a journey that *you* frequently take—to school, to the park, or to another favorite place. Make a map showing how to get there. Be sure to put in special landmarks along the way.

Family Times

Tested Vocabulary

Words to Know

Knowing the meanings of these words is important to reading "The Race for the North Pole." Practice using these words to learn their meanings.

adventure an unusual or exciting experience

glaciers large masses of ice

navigate sail or steer a ship or aircraft

region a place or an area

walruses large sea animals of arctic areas

Grammar

Pronouns and Referents

A **pronoun** is a word that can replace a noun or noun phrase. The word that a pronoun replaces is known as its **referent.**

Matthew looked for the North Pole. He looked for it a long time.

Pronoun	Referent
He	Matthew
it	North Pole
________	Matthew and Robert

Activity

Play a Pronoun Game. Complete the chart. Then play this game: One person says a sentence. The next person replaces all the nouns in the sentence with pronouns. For example, one person says: **Marta likes cookies.** The next person says: **She likes them.**

Tested Spelling Words

________	________	________	________
________	________	________	________
________	________	________	________
________	________	________	________
________	________	________	________

Name ______________________________

Graphic Sources

- Illustrations, charts, graphs, maps, diagrams, tables, lists, time lines, and scale drawings are kinds of **graphic sources.**
- Maps show places. A **physical map** shows landforms and bodies of water. A **map key** explains symbols used and the scale of distances.

Directions: Reread the introduction to *Polar Lands*. Then use the map to help you answer the questions below.

1. Where is the map key? What does it show? ______________________________

____

2. What is the only U.S. state on the map? ______________________________

3. What three oceans are shown? ______________________________

4. In which ocean is the North Pole? ______________________________

5. How does the map help you to better understand the article? ______________________________

____

____

Notes for Home: Your child studied a map and answered questions about it. ***Home Activity:*** Look at different maps with your child. Take turns asking and answering questions about the maps, such as what areas are shown and how to get from one place to another.

Name________________________________

Vocabulary

Directions: Choose the word from the box that best matches each definition. Write the word on the line.

Check the Words You Know
__ adventure
__ glaciers
__ navigate
__ region
__ walruses

__________________ **1.** an exciting experience

__________________ **2.** a place or area

__________________ **3.** sail or steer a ship

__________________ **4.** large masses of ice

__________________ **5.** large sea animals of arctic areas

Directions: Choose the word from the box that best completes each sentence. Write the word on the line to the left.

__________________ **6.** Ice floated in the water. In the distance, Malcolm and Brenna could see enormous _____.

__________________ **7.** "What an _____!" exclaimed Malcolm. "I never thought I would see anything like that!"

__________________ **8.** "Can you _____ the ship through that narrow passage?" Brenna asked.

__________________ **9.** "Yes," said Malcolm. "I've sailed through a _____ like this before."

__________________ **10.** "Quick! Follow those _____. They seem to know a way out."

Write About a Scientific Expedition

On a separate sheet of paper, tell what happens to Malcolm and Brenna. Describe what Malcolm has to do to steer the ship in the dangerous Arctic Ocean. Tell what Brenna finds out about icebergs. Use as many vocabulary words as you can.

Notes for Home: Your child identified and used new vocabulary words from "The Race for the North Pole." ***Home Activity:*** Pretend that you and your child are at the North Pole. Use the vocabulary words to act out an adventure.

Name ____________________

Graphic Sources

- A **graphic source** is an illustration, a graph, a chart, a map, a diagram, or other visual aid that helps you by showing you what the words say, or by organizing information in a useful way.

Directions: Reread this passage from "The Race for the North Pole" and look at the map. The black arrows show some of Matthew Henson's travels. Then answer the questions below.

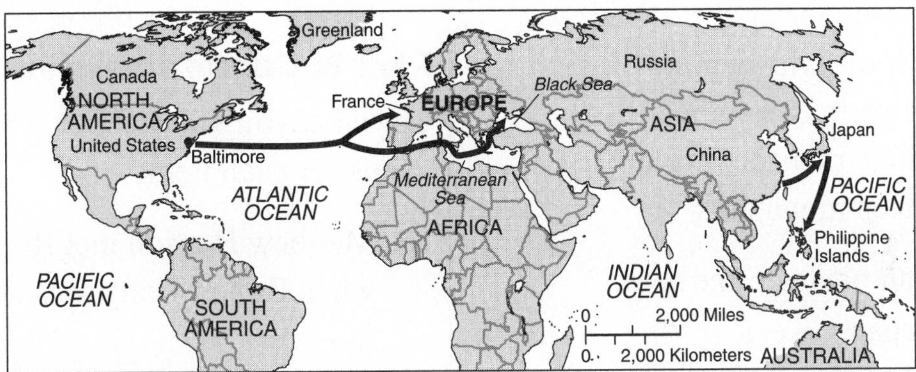

Matthew sailed from China to Japan to the Philippines. He sailed across the Atlantic Ocean to France, Africa, and southern Russia. He even sailed through the Arctic. And all the time, he continued to learn. When Matthew was 19, Captain Childs died and was buried at sea. Heartbroken, Matthew returned to Baltimore.

1. To sail from Japan to the Philippines, Matthew Henson sailed upon which ocean?

____

2. To which continents did Matthew Henson sail?

____

3. To go from Africa to southern Russia, which seas may Henson have sailed?

____

4. Where is Baltimore? ____________________

5. What information does a map give that helps you to better understand a passage like the one above? Write your answer on a separate sheet of paper.

Notes for Home: Your child read a story and used a map to understand story details better. ***Home Activity:*** Look at a map with your child (such as a newspaper weather map, a map in an atlas, or a website map). Take turns asking each other questions like the ones above.

Name ________________________________

Selection Test

Directions: Choose the best answer to each item. Mark the letter for the answer you have chosen.

Part 1: Vocabulary

Find the answer choice that means about the same as the underlined word in each sentence.

1. There are glaciers up ahead.
- A. people who explore
- B. large masses of ice
- C. shelters made of snow
- D. steep mountains

2. She can navigate the ship.
- F. repair
- G. think of a name for
- H. find
- J. steer or sail

3. I like that region.
- A. place or area
- B. type of shirt
- C. old photograph
- D. dessert

4. I described our adventure.
- F. skill or training
- G. way of living
- H. idea or opinion
- J. exciting experience

5. Jim saw two walruses.
- A. Arctic birds
- B. large fish
- C. large Arctic sea animals
- D. islands of ice

Part 2: Comprehension

Use what you know about the selection to answer each item.

6. Matthew Henson met Robert Peary when Robert Peary was about to sail to—
- F. France.
- G. Nicaragua.
- H. Japan.
- J. Russia.

7. Matthew Henson's family moved to Washington, D.C., to—
- A. start a restaurant.
- B. be with their friends.
- C. escape from racial violence.
- D. live in a big city.

8. Matthew Henson took a job on Captain Childs's ship because he—
- F. was looking for adventure.
- G. hoped to make a lot of money.
- H. knew how to sail a ship.
- J. wanted to learn to read.

GO ON

9. Captain Childs helped Matthew Henson mainly by—
A. paying him lots of money.
B. bringing him to Robert Peary.
C. telling him to work harder.
D. teaching and encouraging him.

10. Robert Peary first asked Matthew Henson to go with him to the North Pole because—
F. he enjoyed Matthew Henson's company.
G. his other men refused to go.
H. he thought Matthew Henson was the best man for the trip.
J. Matthew Henson wanted to be a hero.

11. To survive the Arctic, Matthew Henson used what he learned from—
A. his father.
B. Robert Peary.
C. the Inuit people.
D. Captain Childs's crew.

12. Robert Peary and Matthew Henson first tried for the North Pole in—
F. 1885.
G. 1893.
H. 1902.
J. 1909.

13. What did Robert Peary probably enjoy most about finally reaching the North Pole?
A. seeing what it looked like
B. sharing his victory with Matthew Henson
C. becoming famous all over the world
D. placing a flag there

14. Robert Peary probably treated Matthew Henson differently from his other men because Matthew Henson—
F. was younger than he.
G. seemed nervous and afraid.
H. had so much to learn.
J. was an African American.

15. Which sentence states an opinion?
A. "Only the bravest person would venture near the North Pole."
B. "On April 1, 1895, the three men set out for the North Pole."
C. "They made it as far as Independence Bay."
D. "On August 3, 1895, the three men returned to Washington."

STOP

Name ____________________

Graphic Sources

- A **graphic source** is an illustration, a graph, a chart, a map, a diagram, or other visual aid that helps you by showing you what the words say, or by organizing information in a useful way.

Directions: Read the passage below.

On September 20, 1519, Ferdinand Magellan and his crew of 237 were ready to sail around the world, something that no one had ever done. Three months after they left Spain, they arrived in Brazil. Then they headed south along the coast of South America.

In November, 1520, Ferdinand Magellan's ships crossed from the Atlantic to the Pacific Ocean at the tip of South America. After suffering hunger and illness, the remaining crew reached the Pacific island of Guam on March 6, 1521. By April, they were in the Philippines. But Ferdinand Magellan was killed by warriors there.

Only one ship and 18 men finished the voyage. They returned to Spain on September 8, 1522.

Directions: Write an event from the passage for each date on the time line.

1519 1520 1521 1522

Sept. Dec. Nov. April Sept.

1. ____________________

2. ____________________

3. ____________________

4. ____________________

5. ____________________

Notes for Home: Your child used a time line to show and summarize information from a passage. ***Home Activity:*** Ask your child to tell a story about his or her day. Help your child make a time line to show events in the story. Talk about the order of events as you create the time line.

Name ____________________

REVIEW

Generalizing

Directions: Read the passage. Then read each question about the passage. Choose the best answer to each question. Mark the letter for the answer you have chosen.

Born to Fly

When Beryl Markham was just three, her parents left England to start a farm in Kenya, East Africa. Most European farmers were quite successful in Kenya, but Beryl's father found his talent in breeding and training horses.

Beryl's life was always full of interesting adventures. While some daughters of European farmers may have been sent to school in England, Beryl was raised in Africa. She learned to speak several African languages and hunted wild game with a spear. She became a horse trainer like her father. Later, she learned to fly an airplane and became a bush pilot.

Few women in the 1930s had the adventures that Beryl did. She became the first person to fly a plane solo nonstop from London to North America. She wrote a best-selling book about her experiences called *West with the Night.*

1. Which word in the first paragraph signals a generalization?

A. when **C.** Kenya
B. most **D.** just

2. Which of the following statements is a valid generalization from the first paragraph?

F. Beryl's parents moved when she was three.
G. Her father became a horse breeder and trainer.
H. Her father always disliked farming.
J. Most European farmers did quite well in Kenya.

3. Which word in the second paragraph signals a generalization?

A. while **C.** later
B. always **D.** full

4. Which of these statements is a faulty generalization?

F. Beryl had many adventures.
G. Beryl was raised in Africa.
H. All horse trainers learn to fly.
J. Flying was one of Beryl's many adventures.

5. Which word in the last paragraph signals a generalization?

A. few **C.** wrote
B. fly **D.** nonstop

Notes for Home: Your child read a passage and identified valid and faulty generalizations. ***Home Activity:*** Challenge your child to use words like *always, sometimes, never,* or *all* to make a generalization. Discuss whether this generalization is accurate (valid) or not (faulty).

Name ______________________________

Writing Across Texts

Directions: Think about how Alice Ramsey from "Amazing Alice!" and Robert Peary from "The Race for the North Pole" are alike. List five ways they are alike in the following table.

How Alice Ramsey and Robert Peary Were Alike
Both Alice Ramsey and Robert Peary did something that had not been done before.
1.
2.
3.
4.
5.

Write a Paragraph

On a separate sheet of paper, write a paragraph that tells how Alice Ramsey and Robert Peary were alike. Use details from your table in the paragraph.

Notes for Home: Your child compared real-life people from two different stories. ***Home Activity:*** Read two different stories with your child. Help your child write a paragraph that tells how two characters, one from each story, are similar in personality or behavior.

Name ________________________________

REVIEW

Grammar: Subject and Object Pronouns

Directions: Underline the pronoun in each sentence. Write **S** above the pronoun if it is a subject pronoun. Write **O** if it is an object pronoun.

1. Dolores told me about the thirteenth-century explorer Marco Polo.

2. She had just read a book about this young traveler.

3. At the age of seventeen, he and two family members set out on a long journey.

4. The trip took them from Italy to China, through deserts, mountains, and wondrous cities.

5. It was a difficult journey in 1271, lasting four years.

Directions: Choose the pronoun in ( ) that completes each sentence. Circle the pronoun you chose.

6. Julia and (I/me) are writing a report about the Vikings.

7. (They/Them) were also known as Norsemen.

8. Their swift ships carried (they/them) far from their homes in Norway, Sweden, and Denmark.

9. (They/Them) sailed to North America more than a thousand years ago.

10. (We/Us) read about Leif Ericson, one of their leaders.

11. (He/Him) may have been the first European to reach North America.

12. The land pleased (he/him), and he named it Vinland.

13. The Vikings really interested Julia and (I/me).

14. One thing puzzled (she/her), though.

15. (Her/She) wondered why Christopher Columbus was so much more famous than Leif Ericson.

Notes for Home: Your child used the pronouns *I, we, you, he, she, it,* and *they* as subjects and *me, us, you, him, her,* and *them* as objects of verbs. ***Home Activity:*** Together, look for pronouns in a magazine. Decide whether each is a subject or an object pronoun.

Name ______________________________

Grammar: Pronouns and Referents

Pronouns get most of their meaning from the nouns they replace. The noun that a pronoun replaces is its **referent.** It names the person, place, or thing to which the pronoun refers. In the following sentences, the referents are underlined once, and the pronouns are underlined twice.

Jo wants to be an explorer when she grows up.

Soon, Jo and Pavel will visit the Gobi Desert. They can hardly wait!

A pronoun and its referent must agree. In the first example sentence above, the singular subject pronoun *she* agrees with its referent, the singular subject *Jo.* In the next example sentences, the plural subject pronoun *They* agrees with its referent, the compound subject *Jo and Pavel.*

Directions: Match the pronoun with the noun phrase that could be its referent. Write the letter of the referent on the line.

________ **1.** we　　**a.** Mr. Chin

________ **2.** they　　**b.** airplane

________ **3.** she　　**c.** Maggie

________ **4.** it　　**d.** Tony and Sari

________ **5.** he　　**e.** Dad and I

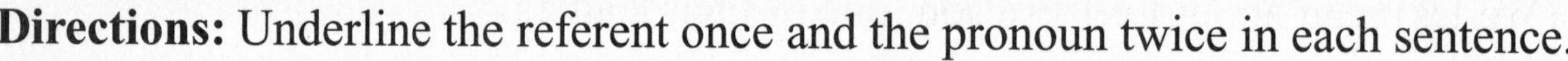

Directions: Underline the referent once and the pronoun twice in each sentence.

6. Pavel and Jo can't wait until they go to Nepal.

7. The journey will be long, but it will be fun.

8. Pavel has a new guidebook that will help him.

9. The tickets are expensive, but they are worth it!

10. Pavel went to Nepal last year. It was beautiful.

Notes for Home: Your child connected pronouns to the words to which they refer. ***Home Activity:*** Read a story together and look for nouns and pronouns. For each pronoun, name the noun it replaces.

Name ________________________________

Grammar: Pronouns and Referents

Directions: Circle the correct pronoun in ( ) to complete each sentence. The referents for the pronouns are underlined to help you.

1. Long ago, navigators steering ships had only the stars to guide (he/them).
2. The stars look different when you view (it/them) from different parts of the world.
3. Navigation takes a long time to learn, but you may find (it/you) worthwhile.
4. Sailors who want to be coastal pilots know (it/they) must learn navigation.
5. Luisa and I have decided that (she/we) will sail around the world someday.

Directions: Revise each sentence. Use pronouns to avoid repeating a noun. Cross out nouns and write new pronouns above the nouns. Circle the referent for each pronoun you used.

6. Explorers have interesting lives because explorers often visit new places.
7. Ferdinand Magellan became famous when Ferdinand Magellan sailed around the globe.
8. Luisa plans to sail around the world when Luisa grows up.
9. Luisa will be our navigator because Luisa has been studying navigation.
10. Sacajawea was the guide for Lewis and Clark. Without Sacajawea, Lewis and Clark would have been lost.

Write an Adventure Story

On a separate sheet of paper, write the story of an explorer. The explorer may be a real person that you know about or an imaginary one. Use at least five pronouns that have referents. When you are finished, identify the referent for each pronoun.

Notes for Home: Your child used pronouns to improve sentences and identified the nouns that the pronouns replaced. ***Home Activity:*** Write a few sentences that include pronouns. Ask your child to identify the noun each pronoun replaces.

Name ______________________________

RETEACHING

Grammar: Pronouns and Referents

A referent is a noun or noun phrase that gets replaced by a pronoun.

The referent is underlined. Circle the pronoun that replaces the referent.

Linnea and Jack are hungry before they eat dinner.

A **pronoun** gets most of its meaning from the noun or noun phrase it replaces. Its **referent** names the person, place, or thing to which the pronoun refers.

Directions: Circle the pronoun in each sentence. Write each referent on the line.

__________ **1.** Walter told Mrs. Chan he would water the plants.

__________ **2.** Mrs. Chan explained how she would like the plants to be watered.

__________ **3.** Many plants from stores come with information about what they need to survive.

__________ **4.** A friend sent a picture he had taken of redwood trees.

__________ **5.** The picture was beautiful, and it showed how large the trees were.

Directions: Match the pronoun with the noun or noun phrase that could be its referent. Write the letter of the referent on the line.

__________ **6.** he — **a.** Linda

__________ **7.** we — **b.** Jonathan and Chris

__________ **8.** they — **c.** the truck

__________ **9.** it — **d.** Pierre

__________ **10.** she — **e.** Flora and I

Notes for Home: Your child identified pronouns and their referents—the nouns or noun phrases to which pronouns refer. ***Home Activity:*** Together, write a poem about your family. Use at least three pronouns and their referents.

Name ______________________________________

Grammar: Pronouns and Referents

Directions: Underline the four pronouns in the paragraph. Then list the referents on the lines below.

Carlos studied the five senses with Mrs. Katz. She knows many things about the sense organs. They are the ears, nose, eyes, tongue, and skin. Carlos added a fact about the brain. It works with the eyes. Together they help people to see.

1. __________ **2.** ______________ **3.** __________ **4.** __________

Directions: Rewrite each sentence. Use a pronoun to replace the underlined referent.

5. <u>Ned and Liz</u> needed a volunteer for an experiment.

____

6. <u>Liz</u> used a handkerchief for a blindfold.

____

7. <u>Ned</u> moved an alarm clock around the room.

____

8. <u>The clock</u> ticked softly at a distance.

____

9. Now and then <u>Liz</u> asked about the clock.

____

10. <u>Volunteers</u> pointed to the sound.

____

Write Sentences About Senses

Close your eyes and listen to the sounds around you. Then, on a separate sheet of paper, write sentences about what you heard. Use pronouns and referents in some of your sentences.

Notes for Home: Your child identified pronouns and referents in sentences. ***Home Activity:*** Have your child write sentences about his or her friends. Challenge your child to use at least three pronouns and their referents.

Name ____________________

Word Study: Plural Possessives

Directions: To make most words possessive, add an **apostrophe (') and s: the dog's bone.** For plural nouns that end in **-s**, just add the **apostrophe ('): the two dogs' bones.** Complete the table by writing the plural form and the plural possessive form of each noun.

Singular Noun	Plural Noun	Plural Possessive Noun
grandmother	**1.**	**5.**
house	**2.**	**6.**
teacher	**3.**	**7.**
Mr. Reed/Mrs. Reed	**4.** The	**8.** The

Directions: Read the paragraph below. You will see many words with apostrophes, including contractions and singular possessives. Find the words that are plural possessives. Circle each plural possessive and write it on the line.

Imagine traveling to the Arctic. You'll have to pack warm clothing to keep out the Arctic's cold. You'll travel on an icebreaker. The ship's prow is built like a snow plow, using heavy blades to break through the ice. Each day's adventures will fill you with wonder. You might hear polar bears' roars or seals' barks. The icebergs' incredible sizes are breathtaking. Watch out for ice floes! The floes' instability often causes crashes. Don't miss gazing at the night sky. The stars' brilliance is amazing, and the Northern Lights' colors dance. Imagine the early explorers' experiences as they first set foot upon this snowy wilderness.

9. ____________

10. ____________

11. ____________

12. ____________

13. ____________

14. ____________

15. ____________

Notes for Home: Your child wrote and identified plural possessive nouns, such as: *the dogs' bone.* ***Home Activity:*** Read a story with your child. Point out words with apostrophes, and decide if they are possessives. Next, ask your child if they are plural possessives.

Name ______________________________

Spelling: Possessives

Pretest

Pretest Directions: Fold back the page along the dotted line. On the blanks, write the spelling words as they are dictated. When you have finished the test, unfold the page and check your words.

1. ____________________
2. ____________________
3. ____________________
4. ____________________
5. ____________________
6. ____________________
7. ____________________
8. ____________________
9. ____________________
10. ____________________
11. ____________________
12. ____________________
13. ____________________
14. ____________________
15. ____________________
16. ____________________
17. ____________________
18. ____________________
19. ____________________
20. ____________________

1. That's **Dad's** seat.
2. I'm going to a **friend's** house.
3. Where is this **girl's** brother?
4. Here are these **girls'** parents.
5. The **teacher's** bag is on the desk.
6. Two **teachers'** cars are new.
7. I lost the **baby's** rattle.
8. Both **babies'** smiles were big.
9. This is my **family's** car.
10. Tom washed both **families'** dogs.
11. I like my **grandma's** songs.
12. I like his **grandpa's** jokes.
13. That's my **brother's** backpack.
14. Those **brothers'** bikes are cool.
15. I found the **boy's** glove.
16. Three **boys'** bicycles are green.
17. My **aunt's** hat is straw.
18. Two **aunts'** houses are near ours.
19. Where is the **lady's** coat?
20. Both **ladies'** coats are black.

Notes for Home: Your child took a pretest on possessive words—words that tell who owns something. ***Home Activity:*** Help your child learn misspelled words before the final test. Singular nouns add *'s* to show possession. Plural nouns may need other changes besides adding an apostrophe.

Name ______________________________

Spelling: Possessives

Word List				
Dad's	teacher's	family's	brother's	aunt's
friend's	teachers'	families'	brothers'	aunts'
girl's	baby's	grandma's	boy's	lady's
girls'	babies'	grandpa's	boys'	ladies'

Directions: Choose the word from the box that is the possessive form of each noun below. Write the word on the line.

1. grandma ______________

2. family ______________

3. brother ______________

4. brothers ______________

5. aunt ______________

6. aunts ______________

7. lady ______________

8. ladies ______________

9. baby ______________

10. babies ______________

11. girl ______________

12. girls ______________

13. teacher ______________

14. families ______________

Directions: Use the possessive form of the word in ( ) to form a word from the box and complete each sentence. Write the word on the line.

______________ **15.** (Dad) best friend is an Arctic explorer.

______________ **16.** His (friend) book on the Arctic was great!

______________ **17.** It's my (grandpa) favorite book.

______________ **18.** The book is about one (boy) travels.

______________ **19.** The parents visited the (teachers) classrooms.

______________ **20.** He went to the Arctic, the land of (boys) dreams.

Notes for Home: Your child spelled possessives—words that show possession. ***Home Activity:*** Choose some words from the list. Work with your child to draw a picture and write a caption for each possessive, such as *My Aunts' Spotted Hats*.

Name ________________________________

Proofread and Write

Spelling: Possessives

Directions: Proofread this journal entry. Find five spelling mistakes. Use the proofreading marks to correct each mistake.

≡	Make a capital.
/	Make a small letter.
∧	Add something.
℘	Take out something.
⊙	Add a period.
¶	Begin a new paragraph.

April 11

On our remote island, the entire family lives in my grandpas hut. Dads job is to hunt. Everyone takes care of our familys children. The girls' skirts and boys pants are very colorful. My grandma's sewing skills are greatly admired. The lady's hairstyles are very pretty. It is the teachers' responsibility to help pass on the island's traditions.

Spelling Tip

To form possessives of singular nouns, add an **apostrophe (')** and an **-s.** To form possessives of plural nouns that end in **-s,** just add an **apostrophe (').**

Word List

Dad's	grandma's
friend's	grandpa's
girl's	brother's
girls'	brothers'
teacher's	boy's
teachers'	boys'
baby's	aunt's
babies'	aunts'
family's	lady's
families'	ladies'

Write a Journal Entry

Imagine what it would be like to explore a place that no one else has ever seen. On a separate sheet of paper, write a journal entry describing your experience, what you see, and how you feel. Use at least three spelling words.

Notes for Home: Your child spelled possessives—words that show possession. ***Home Activity:*** Have your child explain to you when to use an apostrophe and *-s* or just an apostrophe to form possessives. Ask him or her to identify the plural possessive spelling words.

Name ______________________

Spelling: Possessives

REVIEW

Word List

Dad's	teacher's	family's	brother's	aunt's
friend's	teachers'	families'	brothers'	aunts'
girl's	baby's	grandma's	boy's	lady's
girls'	babies'	grandpa's	boys'	ladies'

Directions: Write the possessive form of each underlined word below.

______ **1.** the father of my friend

______ **2.** the cries of the babies

______ **3.** the mother of the baby

______ **4.** the hopes of the grandma

______ **5.** the chair of the grandpa

______ **6.** the shoes of Dad

______ **7.** the rules of the teachers

______ **8.** the visit of the lady

______ **9.** the group of the ladies

______ **10.** the friend of the boy

______ **11.** the poems of the boys

______ **12.** the dreams of the families

______ **13.** the books of the teacher

______ **14.** the hat of the brother

Directions: Choose the word in ( ) that best completes each sentence. Write the word on the line.

______ **15.** The (girl's/girls') dream was to be an explorer.

______ **16.** She had all of her six (brother's/brothers') encouragement.

______ **17.** Her three (aunt's/aunts') homes were full of travel books.

______ **18.** Her one (aunt's/aunts') advice was to follow her dream.

______ **19.** "You are our (family's/families') bravest person."

______ **20.** "In our family, we care about all (girl's/girls') dreams."

Notes for Home: Your child spelled possessives—words that show possession. ***Home Activity:*** Walk around your home or neighborhood and use possessives to describe things people own. Later, make a list of the possessives you used.

Name ________________________________

Atlases/Maps

An **atlas** is a book of maps. A **map** is a drawing of a place. Maps have keys that show what the symbols on the maps mean. A compass shows directions north, south, east, and west. There are many kinds of maps. A picture map shows a place. A road map shows different types of roads. A political map shows city, state, and national boundaries. Physical maps show landforms, such as mountains and valleys. Special purpose maps may show specific information about a subject.

Directions: Admiral Peary made many attempts to reach the North Pole. This map shows the routes he took for each expedition, or trip, and the years he made each attempt. It lists the people who assisted him. Use the map to answer the questions on the next page.

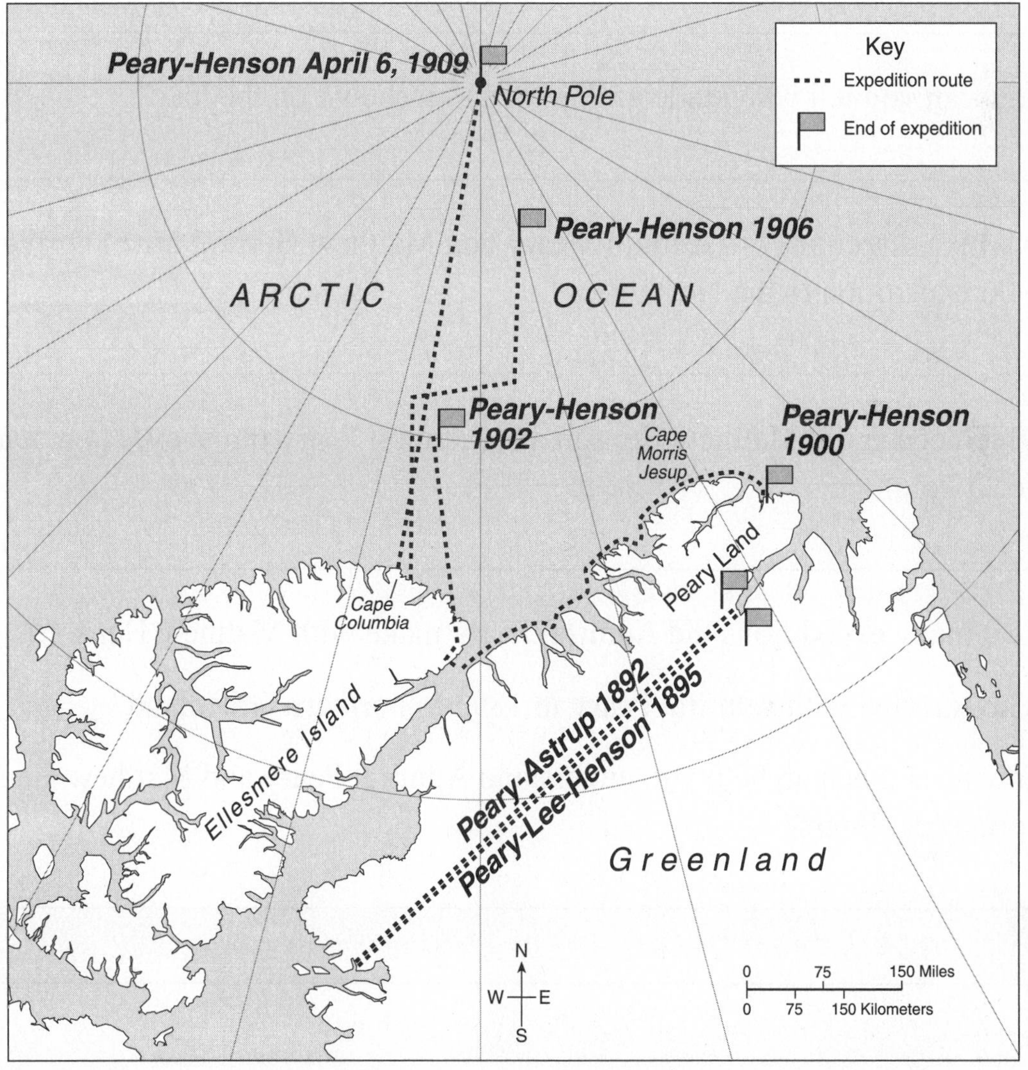

Name ________________________________

1. What special purpose does this map have? ____________________

____

2. What do the dashed lines on the map represent? ____________________

____

3. What do the flag symbols on the map represent? ____________________

____

4. Why is it important to study the map key? ____________________

____

____

5. How can you tell who made each expedition shown on the map?

____

6. In which directions did Admiral Peary and Matthew Henson travel during their 1906 expedition to the North Pole?

____

7. Which ocean did Matthew Henson and Admiral Peary travel over to reach the North Pole?

____

8. How many expeditions did Admiral Peary make with Matthew Henson? ______

9. Who traveled with Admiral Peary in 1892 to northern Greenland? ______

10. How does this map help you understand Admiral Peary and Matthew Henson's work as explorers?

____

____

Notes for Home: Your child read a map and answered questions about it. ***Home Activity:*** Ask your child to draw a map showing the route he or she takes to school. Have your child include a key that explains any symbols, such as a symbol for a post office, bridge, or school.

Family Times

Name________________________________

Summary

Tiny Sea Turtles Return to the Sea

Sea turtles start life as tiny animals not much bigger than a bottle cap. They hatch out of leathery eggs left in sandy nests dug into the beach. A baby turtle's first journey is to cross the beach and find its way into the sea. There the little turtle must stay out of the way of sea birds and fish, until it grows into a larger turtle with a big, hard shell. But the little turtle's adventures are just beginning.

Activity

Tell the Turtle's Story. What is life like for tiny turtles in a big sea? Imagine you are a baby turtle. Tell the story of a day in your life.

Reading Skills

Author's Purpose

An **author's purpose** is the reason for writing something. Some purposes for writing are to entertain, to inform, to express, and to persuade.

In *Into the Sea,* the author's purpose is to inform—to tell readers about the life of the sea turtle. Knowing this purpose can help you read more carefully, paying attention to the information that the author wants you to know.

Activity

Make a List. Take turns with someone telling short stories about your day. Try to have a different reason for telling each story. For example, tell a story about something you learned about life undersea with the purpose of informing your reader. Tell about a book you read with the purpose of persuading someone else to read it too.

Family Times

Tested Vocabulary

Words to Know

Knowing the meanings of these words is important to reading *Into the Sea.* Practice using these words to learn their meanings.

awkward uncomfortable or uncoordinated

coral substance made up of the skeletons of tiny sea animals

current a flow

flippers broad, flat animal body parts used for swimming

muscles body tissues that move body parts

protection safety

ridges raised narrow strips

underside bottom side

Grammar

Prepositions and Prepositional Phrases

A **preposition** is the first word in a group of words called a **prepositional phrase.**

Common Prepositions:
above, along, across, after, around, at, before, behind, by, down, for, from, in, near, of, on, to, toward, with.

Prepositional Phrases:
in the box
for two days
along the way

Activity
Tell Where Something Is. Play this game with a partner. One person thinks of an object in the room and uses at least three prepositional phrases to tell where it is. For example: **It is on the shelf, behind the couch, in the living room.** Then the other player guesses the object.

Tested Spelling Words

____________	____________	____________	____________
____________	____________	____________	____________
____________	____________	____________	____________
____________	____________	____________	____________
____________	____________	____________	____________

Name ____________________

Author's Purpose

- An **author's purpose** is the reason for writing something.
- Some purposes for writing are to entertain, to inform, to express, and to persuade.

Directions: Reread "Saving Our Wetlands." Then use the questions to help you determine the author's purpose or purposes for the article.

Questions	Answers
Title: What do the title and the subhead reveal about the author's purpose?	**1.**
Organization: How does the article's organization help you figure out the author's purpose?	**2.**
Key Words and Phrases: What key words or phrases does the author use that show how he feels about the wetlands?	Wetlands are home to many of the United States' birds.
	3.
	4.

Author's Purpose or Purposes

5. ____________________

____

Notes for Home: Your child read a story and used story details to determine the author's purpose. ***Home Activity:*** With your child, read the editorial page of a newspaper. Ask him or her to find places where the writers inform, entertain, express, and persuade.

Name ______________________________

Vocabulary

Directions: Choose the word from the box that best matches each definition. Write the word on the line.

Check the Words You Know

__ awkward
__ coral
__ current
__ flippers
__ muscles
__ protection
__ ridges
__ underside

________________ **1.** bottom side

________________ **2.** broad, flat animal body part used for swimming

________________ **3.** a flow of water

________________ **4.** uncomfortable; uncoordinated

________________ **5.** raised narrow strips

________________ **6.** body tissues that move body parts

Directions: Choose the word from the box that best completes each sentence. Write the word on the line to the right.

Molly dove beside the **7.** _____ reef into the warm ocean. The ocean's **8.** _____ was strong, but Molly was a good swimmer. Because she swam every day, she had strong **9.** _____ in her legs and arms. Sometimes she felt **10.** _____ and clumsy on land, but she never felt that way in the water.

7. ________________

8. ________________

9. ________________

10. ________________

Write a Description

On a separate sheet of paper, write a description of life under the ocean. You might want to find a picture in a book, encyclopedia, or magazine to help you visualize what ocean life is like. Use as many of the vocabulary words as you can in your description.

Notes for Home: Your child identified and used vocabulary words from *Into the Sea*. ***Home Activity:*** Talk with your child about the ocean, looking at pictures of it together if possible. Encourage your child to tell you how the vocabulary words are related to the ocean.

Name ______________________________________

Author's Purpose

- An **author's purpose** is the reason or reasons an author has for writing.
- Four common purposes are to entertain, to inform, to express, and to persuade.

Directions: Reread *Into the Sea.* Then answer the question below.

1. What do you think was the author's purpose or purposes for writing this story? Give examples from the story to support your answer.

____

____

Directions: Read each paragraph. Write the author's purpose on the line after each paragraph and explain your answers.

2. Tony had a "Come as a Turtle" party. Tony's dad came as a sea turtle with a HUGE foam shell, woolly arms and legs, and a ski-mask head. He had to take off the shell to sit down!

____

3. One of the really cool things about going canoeing is seeing painted turtles sunning themselves on logs. They look like kings. Their bodies seem to be covered in jewels that sparkle in the sun.

____

4. Basking turtles live in ponds, streams, lakes, and marshes. They spend most of their time in the water, but they also bask in the sun. Their bodies are encased in bony shells.

____

5. Choose your favorite story. On a separate sheet of paper, describe the author's purpose. Support your answer with examples from the story.

Notes for Home: Your child read several passages and identified the author's purpose. ***Home Activity:*** With your child, look through books, magazines, and newspapers. Find an example of writing for each of the four common purposes listed above.

Selection Test

Directions: Choose the best answer to each item. Mark the letter for the answer you have chosen.

Part 1: Vocabulary

Find the answer choice that means about the same as the underlined work in each sentence.

1. The fish's mouth has ridges.
- A. sharp teeth
- B. spots of color
- C. moving parts
- D. raised, narrow strips

2. The fish swam with the current.
- F. type of shark
- G. group of seahorses
- H. flow of water
- J. large fishing nets

3. The young horse was awkward.
- A. clumsy
- B. watchful
- C. tired
- D. hungry

4. Baby birds need protection.
- F. warm water
- G. safety or defense
- H. good food
- J. friends or mates

5. We looked at the coral reef.
- A. having valuable metals
- B. from a sunken ship
- C. filled with silver fish
- D. made from skeletons of sea animals

6. Seals and whales have flippers.
- F. keen senses
- G. skin with thick layers of fat
- H. eyes without lids
- J. broad flat body parts used for swimming

7. We'll paint the boat's underside.
- A. back section
- B. bottom
- C. wall
- D. inside

8. The turtle's muscles are strong.
- F. hard outer shells
- G. gills used for breathing
- H. habits or ways of behaving
- J. tissues that move parts of the body

GO ON

Name ____________________

Part 2: Comprehension

Use what you know about the selection to answer each item.

9. At the beginning of this selection, the turtle has just—
- A. hatched from an egg.
- B. eaten a crab.
- C. crawled out of the ocean.
- D. hidden from a fish.

10. For the first few months of its life, the turtle—
- F. builds a nest on a beach.
- G. drifts in a patch of seaweed.
- H. rests on the ocean floor.
- J. floats on the surface of water.

11. Which animal is still an enemy when the turtle is fully grown?
- A. sea gull
- B. butterfly fish
- C. shark
- D. remora

12. Getting caught in the net was dangerous for the turtle because—
- F. a whale had spotted her.
- G. she was almost out of breath.
- H. a man was pulling in the net.
- J. the net was cutting her shell.

13. The turtle returned to the island where it was born to—
- A. lay its eggs.
- B. escape from danger.
- C. find its favorite foods.
- D. prepare to die.

14. The author's main purpose in this selection is to—
- F. show how sea turtles and land turtles are different.
- G. tell a funny story about turtles.
- H. explain how people can help sea turtles.
- J. describe the life of a sea turtle.

15. The author probably thinks that sea turtles—
- A. must overcome many difficulties to survive.
- B. are the most intelligent animals in the world.
- C. take excellent care of their young.
- D. are gentle, friendly creatures.

STOP

Name ______________________________

Author's Purpose

- An **author's purpose** is the reason or reasons an author has for writing.
- Four common purposes are to entertain, to inform, to express, and to persuade.

Directions: Read the following book titles and descriptions. Then fill in the table below by providing missing purposes or explanations. You may use a purpose more than once.

My Life Among the Sea Turtles—A noted scientist tells of her love for the great beasts, along with fascinating details of their daily life.

Turtles in Space!—Another adventure of the infamous Turtle Terrors. Inside a space shuttle, they make trouble for the astronauts by chomping holes in the shuttle wall and even in a spacesuit!

Natural Beauties—This collection of poems shows the beauty and wonder of turtles—the patterns of their shells, their awkward movements on land, and their graceful swimming.

Save the Sea Turtles!—An animal activist argues for action to protect baby sea turtles and restore sea turtle nesting grounds.

The Family of Turtles—This book is filled with color photographs of turtles in the wild. The notes include facts about each turtle's habitat, food, and egg-laying behavior.

Book Title	Purpose for Writing	Explanation
My Life Among the Sea Turtles	inform, express	1.
Turtles in Space!	2.	It tells a science fiction adventure.
Natural Beauties	3.	Poems show beauty and wonder.
Save the Sea Turtles!	persuade	4.
The Family of Turtles	inform	5.

Notes for Home: Your child used book titles and descriptions to identify an author's purpose. ***Home Activity:*** Read a variety of short newspaper articles, including sports stories and comic strips, with your child. Discuss the author's purpose for each text.

Name ______________________________

Summarizing and Steps in a Process

REVIEW

Directions: Read the passage. Then read each question about the passage. Choose the best answer to each question. Mark the letter for the answer you have chosen.

Turtle Watching

Turtle watching may not be as exciting as whale watching, but you don't have to live near the ocean to do it.

Here's how to find a turtle. If you live where the winter is cold, you must first wait for spring. Then pick a sunny day. Choose a nearby stream with a soft bottom, a lake, a pond, a marsh, or a swamp. There should be a lot of plants. Turtles like them.

After you've chosen a good spot, take an adult with you. Travel on foot or in a small boat. Either way, be quiet. Don't make any sudden moves.

Finally, look for a rock or a log sticking out of the water. You just may see a turtle on it.

Now what? If you want to find out what kind of turtle you are looking at, well, that's another story.

1. The first thing you must do if you want to go turtle watching is—
- **A.** buy a telescope.
- **B.** get a boat.
- **C.** find a stream.
- **D.** be sure it is not too cold.

2. The next thing you should do is—
- **F.** learn all you can about turtles.
- **G.** pick a sunny day.
- **H.** travel in a boat.
- **J.** look for a rock.

3. To pick a spot, the first two things you should look for are—
- **A.** water and food.
- **B.** water and rocks.
- **C.** boats and people.
- **D.** water and plants.

4. Which of the following statements best summarizes the third paragraph?
- **F.** After finding a location, travel quietly and carefully with an adult by boat or on foot.
- **G.** Take an adult with you.
- **H.** Be quiet and don't move.
- **J.** Travel with an adult either on foot or by small boat.

5. Which clue word signals the last step in finding turtles?
- **A.** then
- **B.** after
- **C.** finally
- **D.** now

Notes for Home: Your child used story details to recognize steps in a process and to summarize the main idea of a passage. ***Home Activity:*** Together, tell a story about an activity you and your child do. Include steps to follow to do the activity.

Writing Across Texts

Directions: Think about the job of Norbert Wu in "I Work in the Ocean." What kinds of careers can you think of that could be connected to the sea turtles described in *Into the Sea?* Brainstorm a list of possible careers and write them in the following table. Then choose a favorite career idea and make a list of reasons why it might be a good career to have.

Possible Sea Turtle Careers	Favorite Career Idea and Why It Might Be a Good Career
1.	**Favorite Career Idea:** **6.**
2.	**Reasons It Might Be a Good Career:** **7.**
3.	**8.**
4.	**9.**
5.	**10.**

Write a Paragraph

On a separate sheet of paper, write a paragraph that explains why the career you chose might be a good career to have. Use ideas from your table in the paragraph.

Notes for Home: Your child wrote about an interesting career. ***Home Activity:*** Ask your child to tell about a career he or she might like to have. Visit the library to find books about it. Help your child make a list of things he or she needs to do to accomplish this career goal.

Name ________________________________

REVIEW

Grammar: Pronouns and Referents

Directions: Underline the pronoun in each sentence. Then draw a circle around its referent. Hint: One pronoun is a possessive pronoun.

1. Turtles may seem slow and dull, but they are really interesting creatures.
2. Jeff and Josh like turtles so much that they have a pet turtle.
3. Jeff claims that he has trained the turtle to do tricks.
4. The turtle's only "trick," though, is to pull its head inside the shell.
5. Jeff says that seems like an amazing trick to him!

Directions: Write a sentence or a pair of sentences using the nouns and pronouns given. Use each noun as the referent of each pronoun.

6. turtle, it

____

7. students, they

____

____

8. teacher, him

____

____

9. scientist, she

____

10. turtles, them

____

Notes for Home: Your child matched pronouns with their referents—the nouns they replace in sentences. ***Home Activity:*** With your child, write a story about an animal. Then ask your child to identify the referent of each pronoun in the story.

Practice

Grammar: Prepositions and Prepositional Phrases

A **preposition** is a word that shows how a word is related to other words in the sentence. A preposition begins a group of words called a **prepositional phrase.** The phrase ends with a noun or pronoun called the **object of the preposition.**

The turtle walked into the sea. The plane flew above the sea.

A prepositional phrase can be used to tell where, when, how, or which one.

Where did the turtle go? It went into the sea.

When did it go? It moved after sunset.

How did it walk? It walked with slow steps.

Which turtle was it? It was the one with a spotted shell.

Common Prepositions				
about	around	between	into	to
above	at	by	of	under
across	behind	for	on	upon
after	below	from	over	with
against	beneath	in	through	without

Directions: Underline the prepositional phrase in each sentence once. Draw a second line under the preposition.

1. The dolphins leaped over the waves.
2. They liked playing in the water.
3. At certain times, they joined the tuna.
4. Many tiny fish swam into view.
5. A baby dolphin swam after them.
6. The crabs walked on the shore.
7. Some hid under the mud.
8. Some dug into the sand.
9. One crab with a heavy shell moved slowly.
10. Another climbed over the log.

Notes for Home: Your child used prepositions, such as *in, on,* and *with,* and prepositional phrases, such as *in the sea. **Home Activity:*** Ask your child to tell you the exact location of an object that you name. Then ask the child to identify the prepositions he or she used.

Extra Practice

Grammar: Prepositions and Prepositional Phrases

Directions: Circle the prepositional phrase that best answers the question in ( ) to complete each sentence.

1. Huge mammals called whales live _____. *(Where?)*
   (in the ocean/on land and sea)

2. This has been their home _____. *(When?)*
   (for the future/for a long time)

3. Blue whales, killer whales, and others exist _____. *(Where?)*
   (on our planet/on small ponds)

4. Some countries protect whales _____. *(How?)*
   (through laws/from wild animals)

5. Whales _____ perform well in water shows. *(Which?)*
   (with kind trainers/without experience)

Directions: Add a prepositional phrase to each sentence. Begin the phrase with a preposition from the box.

for	to	at	into	toward

6. Rosa dived happily ______________________________.

7. She swam until her dad waved ______________________________.

8. Her dad was pointing ______________________________.

9. Rosa suddenly felt hungry ______________________________.

10. She waved back and swam ______________________________.

Write Directions

On a separate sheet of paper, write directions telling how to get to a place that you like to visit. Use at least five prepositions, and underline each one.

Notes for Home: Your child wrote prepositions, such as *in, for,* and *through,* and prepositional phrases, such as *in the ocean. **Home Activity:*** Describe an object's location, using prepositions. Have your child guess the object and identify the prepositions you used.

Name ____________________________________

RETEACHING

Grammar: Prepositions and Prepositional Phrases

Choose the preposition in ( ) that makes the most sense in each sentence.

1. We ran (under/down) the path.

2. T.J. called (after/against) you left.

A **preposition** shows how a word is related to one or more other words in the sentence. A preposition is the first word in a **prepositional phrase.** Prepositional phrases can answer the questions **Where? When? How?** and **Which one?** What questions do the two sentences above answer?

Directions: Draw a line from the phrase on the left to the prepositional phrase on the right that best matches it.

1. Luz told Julie to go	from the basement
2. Their mother called	in the jar."
3. "There is money	after this show."
4. "I will go	by four o'clock!"
5. "Be back	to the store.

Directions: Underline the prepositional phrase or phrases in each sentence.

6. My dog is the best dog in the world.

7. He comes when I call, and he walks behind me.

8. If I go to the park, he comes with me.

9. One time I couldn't find him anywhere around the house.

10. I looked under the stairs.

11. I also searched through my bedroom.

Notes for Home: Your child identified prepositions and prepositional phrases in sentences. ***Home Activity:*** Look for prepositional phrases in books or magazines. Have your child identify which questions—*How? When? Where? Which one?*—they answer.

Name ______________________

Grammar: Prepositions and Prepositional Phrases

about	above	across	against	behind	by	in	through	to	under	with

Directions: Choose a preposition from the box to complete each sentence. Write it on the line to the left.

_______________ **1.** Last weekend my family went _____ a movie.

_______________ **2.** The movie was _____ a lot of animals.

_______________ **3.** The animals lived _____ a forest.

_______________ **4.** Some of them liked to hide _____ the dirt.

_______________ **5.** Others swung in trees _____ the ground.

_______________ **6.** My favorites were squirrels that ran _____ tree branches.

_______________ **7.** Sometimes they flew right _____ the leaves!

_______________ **8.** They never crashed _____ anything!

_______________ **9.** My younger stepsister hid _____ her mom.

_______________ **10.** She was afraid of the fox _____ sharp teeth.

Directions: Add a prepositional phrase to each sentence. Use a preposition from the box above to begin each prepositional phrase.

11. Kenji hid ______________________________

12. He didn't want to be seen ______________________________

13. His friends looked ______________________________

14. One of them saw movement ______________________________

15. Kenji was hiding ______________________________

Notes for Home: Your child wrote prepositions and prepositional phrases. ***Home Activity:*** Have your child hide four objects in a room. Then have him or her write prepositional phrases as clues for you to find the objects.

Name ____

Phonics: Schwa Sound

Directions: The **schwa sound** is an indistinct vowel sound heard in an unstressed syllable. The **a** in **a**gainst and the **o** in **favorite** are examples of the schwa sound. Read each word below. Underline the schwa sound in each word.

1. alone
2. difficult
3. moment
4. around
5. seasonal
6. delicate
7. bottom
8. across
9. sargassum
10. surround
11. tropical
12. oppose
13. coward
14. accuse
15. compete

Directions: Read each sentence below. Say the underlined word carefully to yourself. Listen for the schwa sound. Write the word on the line. Circle the letter or letters that represent the schwa sound.

______________________ **16.** The more I learn about sea animals, the more amazed I am at how clever they are.

______________________ **17.** For example, some sea animals float with the ocean's currents as they migrate.

______________________ **18.** Some small sea animals attach themselves to larger ones to catch a ride.

______________________ **19.** Some sea creatures survive by eating small bits of plankton that float in the water.

______________________ **20.** Many sea animals camouflage themselves, using their colors to blend in with their environment.

Notes for Home: Your child identified letters that represent the schwa sound, such as the *a* in *against* and the *o* in *favorite. **Home Activity:*** Read a story with your child. List words with two or more syllables that have the schwa sound. You can check these words in a dictionary.

Name ____________________

Spelling: Vowels with No Sound Clues

Pretest Directions: Fold back the page along the dotted line. On the blanks, write the spelling words as they are dictated. When you have finished the test, unfold the page and check your words.

1. ____________	1. That's a powerful **machine**.
2. ____________	2. He's **especially** nice.
3. ____________	3. She's **usually** very quiet.
4. ____________	4. We're **probably** not going.
5. ____________	5. It was a **giant** mountain.
6. ____________	6. The **buffalo** grazed peacefully.
7. ____________	7. **Canada** is in North America.
8. ____________	8. How many can fit in the **canoe**?
9. ____________	9. Our **relatives** are coming to visit.
10. ____________	10. My **stomach** is full.
11. ____________	11. Take a **moment** to relax.
12. ____________	12. The **cement** isn't dry yet.
13. ____________	13. I went to see her **yesterday**.
14. ____________	14. The **animals** are howling.
15. ____________	15. The anchor is made of **iron**.
16. ____________	16. That's my **favorite** fish.
17. ____________	17. We feel **welcome** here.
18. ____________	18. Do you **support** this idea?
19. ____________	19. I don't **suppose** you agree.
20. ____________	20. We will see you again in **August**.

Notes for Home: Your child took a pretest on words whose vowel sounds have no sound clues. ***Home Activity:*** Help your child learn misspelled words before the final test. Have your child divide misspelled words into parts (such as syllables) and concentrate on each part.

Name ______________________________

Spelling: Vowels with No Sound Clues

Word List				
machine	giant	relatives	yesterday	welcome
especially	buffalo	stomach	animals	support
usually	Canada	moment	iron	suppose
probably	canoe	cement	favorite	August

Directions: Choose the word from the box that contains each word below. Write the word on the line.

1. special ______________
2. ant ______________
3. day ______________
4. port ______________
5. gust ______________
6. usual ______________
7. buff ______________
8. come ______________
9. pose ______________
10. favor ______________

Directions: Choose the word from the box that best matches each clue. Write the word on the line.

______________ **11.** It's the country north of the United States.

______________ **12.** These can be wild, or they can be tame.

______________ **13.** A toaster is one of these, and so is a car.

______________ **14.** It means the same as "likely."

______________ **15.** You paddle in one.

______________ **16.** They come to a family reunion.

______________ **17.** A sidewalk is made of this.

______________ **18.** Steel is made from this.

______________ **19.** It's a tiny amount of time.

______________ **20.** It's where your food goes after it's swallowed.

Notes for Home: Your child spelled words in which the vowel sound gives no clue to its spelling, such as in *animals*. ***Home Activity:*** Make up memory tricks with your child to help remember correct spellings (*I see the animals.*).

Name ______________________________

Spelling: Vowels with No Sound Clues

Directions: Proofread this description of a meeting with a turtle. Find five spelling mistakes. Use the proofreading marks to correct each mistake.

≡	Make a capital.
/	Make a small letter.
∧	Add something.
⸙	Take out something.
⊙	Add a period.
¶	Begin a new paragraph.

Wellcome to My Home

Have you ever met a turtle eye to eye? It isn't always easy because turtles don't usually let you get that close. But one time, I was on a canew trip in Cannada. We were heading toward a gient rock — or so I thought. It turned out to be probaly the largest turtle I've ever seen! Just as we passed it, the turtle stuck its head out of its shell. I think it was as surprised as I was.

Spelling Tip

In many words, the vowel sound gives no clue to its spelling: **machine, moment, animals, iron, support.** Make up memory tricks to help you remember correct spellings, such as: The **stomach** is an eating **machine.**

Word List

machine	moment
especially	cement
usually	yesterday
probably	animals
giant	iron
buffalo	favorite
Canada	welcome
canoe	support
relatives	suppose
stomach	August

Write a Paragraph

On a separate sheet of paper, write a paragraph describing an interesting experience with an animal. Try to use at least four spelling words.

Notes for Home: Your child spelled words in which the vowel sound gives no clues to its spelling, such as in *animals*. ***Home Activity:*** Say each spelling word aloud, and have your child write it. Together, check for misspellings and correct them.

Name ____________________

Spelling: Vowels with No Sound Clues

REVIEW

Word List

machine	giant	relatives	yesterday	welcome
especially	buffalo	stomach	animals	support
usually	Canada	moment	iron	suppose
probably	canoe	cement	favorite	August

Directions: Write the word from the box that belongs in each group.

1. Mexico, United States, __________
2. kayak, rowboat, __________
3. creatures, beasts, __________
4. best, preferred, __________
5. huge, immense, __________
6. extremely, unusually, __________
7. normally, commonly, __________
8. instant, second, __________
9. likely, chances are, __________
10. guess, assume, __________

Directions: Choose the word from the box that best answers each riddle. Write the word on the line.

__________ **11.** Call me tummy or belly, I like bread and jelly.

__________ **12.** The harder I get, the easier I am to walk on.

__________ **13.** You can turn me on or turn me off.

__________ **14.** This is how the doormat says, "Come in!"

__________ **15.** If you press on me, I'll press your clothes.

__________ **16.** If I leave, you might fall.

__________ **17.** My body is hairy; I live on the prairie.

__________ **18.** You can choose your friends but not these.

__________ **19.** I'm always behind you, never ahead.

__________ **20.** Enjoy this month, summer's almost over.

Notes for Home: Your child spelled words in which the vowel sound gives no clue to its spelling, such as in *anim̲al*. ***Home Activity:*** Play a word scramble game. Each player scrambles the letters of individual spelling words for others to unscramble, such as *onace* for *canoe*.

Name ____________________

Diagram/Scale Drawing/ Pictures and Captions

A **diagram** is a special drawing with labels. Diagrams often show how something is made or how it works. A **scale drawing** is a diagram that uses a mathematical scale to help you determine the actual size of the subject. For example, a scale of 1 inch = 1 foot means that one inch on the drawing represents one foot in real life.

Directions: Use this diagram of the skeleton of a sea turtle to answer the questions that follow.

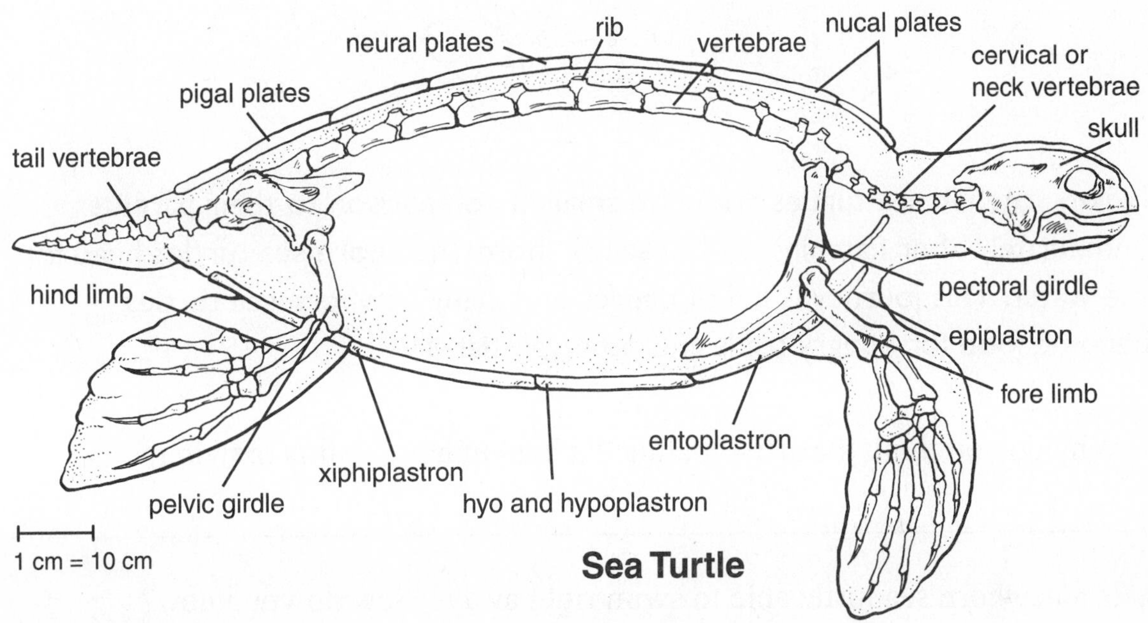

Sea Turtle

1. One centimeter on the drawing equals how many centimeters on a turtle? ______

2. About how long is the tail vertebrae of a real sea turtle? ____________

3. Where are a sea turtle's nucal plates: near the neck, on the back, or near the tail?

____

4. The vertebrae begin at the neck. Where do they end? ____________

5. What is the name of the bone that forms the sea turtle's head? ____________

6. A sea turtle has two girdles that help support its shell. What are the full names of the two girdles?

____

Name ________________________________

Pictures are photographs or artwork that tell information about characters and events in a story or an article. They can also help set a mood. Sometimes pictures have captions that explain what is happening in a drawing or photograph.

Directions: Use the picture and the caption to answer the questions that follow.

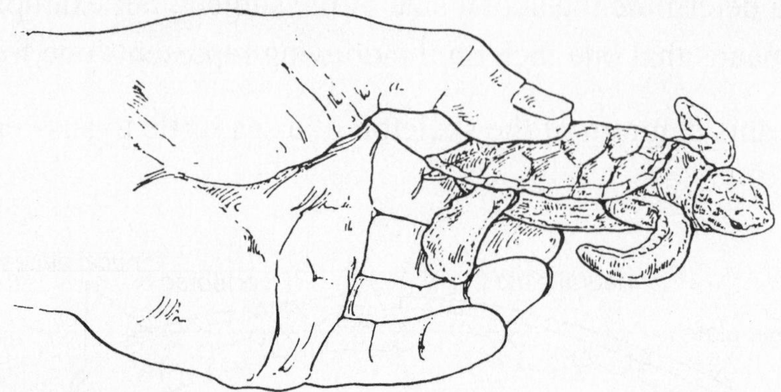

Newly hatched sea turtles are quite small in comparison to their parents. Immediately after hatching on the sandy shores, newborn sea turtles head for the water. This journey is full of danger and many newborn sea turtles become food for hungry birds and other predators.

7. Why do you think the artist included a human hand in this drawing?

____

8. Is a newborn sea turtle able to swim right away? How do you know?

____

9. Why is the trip from the hatching site to the sea a dangerous one for newborn sea turtles?

____

10. Why is it important to read the labels, scales, and captions for pictures carefully?

____

____

Notes for Home: Your child answered questions about a scale drawing and a picture with a caption. ***Home Activity:*** Ask your child to read captions from newspaper photos and tell you what information the captions provide.

Family Times

Name____

Summary

Space Probes Explore Faraway Planets!

Have you ever wondered what other planets are like? It is very difficult for people to visit the planets in our solar system: the planets are very far away, and people need special protection to live outside Earth's atmosphere. But *space probes*—spacecraft with no people on them—can visit other planets and find out lots of interesting information.

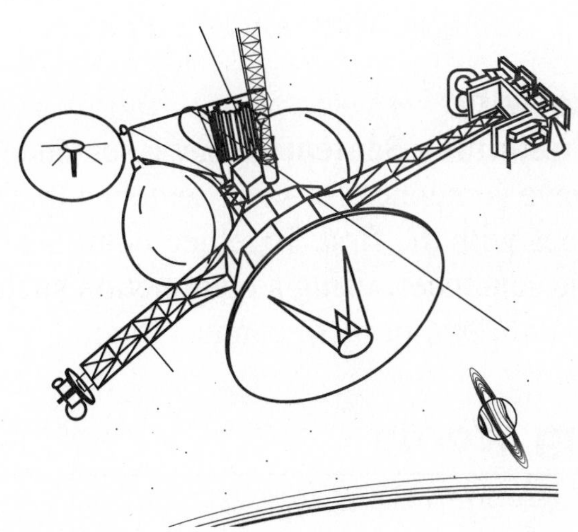

Activity

Explain Space Probes. Ask your child to tell you some more interesting facts about space probes. Pretend you are in charge of a space probe. What kinds of information would you try to find?

Reading Skills

Text Structure

Text structure is the way a piece of writing is organized. Nonfiction tells of real people and events or tells information about the real world. Some ways to organize nonfiction are cause and effect, problem and solution, and compare and contrast.

Space Probes to the Planets is nonfiction; it gives information about the real world. The author tells about a problem—it's difficult to get information about the planets. Then she explains a solution—we can use space probes to explore faraway planets.

Don't forget
to take
me out!

Activity

Tell a Problem-Solution Story. Think of an everyday problem that your family has, like people forgetting to take out the garbage. Alone or with others, tell a nonfiction story about the problem and a solution.

Family Times

Tested Vocabulary

Words to Know

Knowing the meanings of these words is important to reading *Space Probes to the Planets.* Practice using these words to learn their meanings.

atmosphere air that surrounds Earth

craters holes in the ground shaped like bowls

incredible amazing

probes spacecrafts carrying scientific instruments to record information

spacecraft vehicle used for flight in outer space

Grammar

Conjunctions

A **conjunction** is a word that can join words, phrases, and whole sentences. You can use conjunctions to make compound and complex sentences.

- ❖ A **compound sentence** contains two simple sentences joined by a conjunction such as *and, but,* or *or.* **Mercury is covered with craters, <u>and</u> it has long ridges.**
- ❖ A **complex sentence** is a simple sentence joined to a sentence part by a connecting word, such as *because.* **<u>Because</u> its surface had grooves like riverbeds, scientists thought Mars once had rivers.**

Activity

Combining Sentences. Say a sentence. Have someone else say a sentence that goes with the first. Together, combine the sentences, using a conjunction such as *and, but,* or *or* to connect them.

Tested Spelling Words

________	________	________	________
________	________	________	________
________	________	________	________
________	________	________	________
________	________	________	________

Name ______________________________

Text Structure

- **Text structure** is the way a piece of writing is organized. There are two main kinds of writing, fiction and nonfiction.
- Fiction tells stories of people and events that an author creates. It is usually organized by the order in which things happen. Nonfiction tells of real people and events or tells information about the real world. Some ways to organize nonfiction are cause and effect, problem and solution, and compare and contrast.

Directions: Reread "Out-of-This-World Rocks." Then complete the diagram below. List things that are true about space rocks on the left, things that are true about Earth rocks on the right, and things that are true about both kinds of rocks in the middle. Then describe the type of organization used for this text.

Space Rocks Facts | **Space and Earth Rocks** | **Earth Rocks Facts**

1. ______________________
2. ______________________
3. ______________________
4. ______________________
5. ______________________
6. ______________________
7. ______________________
8. ______________________
9. ______________________

Type of Organization

10. ____

Notes for Home: Your child read an article and identified how information in the article is organized. ***Home Activity:*** Have your child read a newspaper, magazine, or reference book article. Together, look at how the article organizes its information.

Name ________________________________

Vocabulary

Directions: Choose the word from the box that best matches each definition. Write the word on the line.

Check the Words You Know
__ atmosphere
__ craters
__ incredible
__ probes
__ spacecraft

____________________ **1.** amazing

____________________ **2.** gases that surround a planet

____________________ **3.** vehicle used to fly into outer space

____________________ **4.** holes in ground

____________________ **5.** spacecraft carrying scientific instruments to record information

Directions: Choose the word from the box that best completes each sentence. Write the word on the line to the left.

____________________ **6.** When astronauts land on other planets they cannot breathe because there is no oxygen in the _____.

____________________ **7.** Of course, there is plenty of oxygen inside the _____ in which they travel.

____________________ **8.** Sometimes, it is easier to send space _____ without any astronauts aboard.

____________________ **9.** The information that scientists can now collect is simply _____!

____________________ **10.** They can even explore the hills and _____ of the moon.

Write a Log Entry

Imagine you are an astronaut. On a separate sheet of paper, write an entry in your log telling about the day you landed on a new planet. Use as many vocabulary words as you can.

Notes for Home: Your child identified and used vocabulary words from *Space Probes to the Planets*. ***Home Activity:*** Say the definition of each vocabulary word, and have your child tell you what the word is. Alternately, you say the word and have your child supply the definition.

Name ____________________

Text Structure

- **Text structure** is the way a piece of writing is organized. The two main kinds of writing are fiction and nonfiction.
- Nonfiction tells about the real world. Some ways to organize nonfiction are cause and effect, problem and solution, and compare and contrast.

Directions: Reread the opening passage from *Space Probes to the Planets.* Then answer the questions below.

Have you ever wanted to visit another planet? Ever since the planets were discovered, people have dreamed of visiting them. But the planets are all very hot or very cold, and very far away. Until scientists learn more, a trip to explore them would be unsafe.

In the meantime we've learned a lot about the planets, partly because of space probes. Space probes are spacecraft with no people on them. With the help of computers and radio signals, they can travel to the planets by themselves.

1. Why would a trip to the planets be unsafe?

____

2. How have scientists learned about the planets if they couldn't send people to explore them?

____

3. Why is it safe to use space probes?

____

4. Which kind of organization does this passage use: cause and effect, problem and solution, or compare and contrast? Explain.

____

____

5. Look at the rest of the story. Choose a passage and tell how it is organized. Write your answer on a separate sheet of paper.

Notes for Home: Your child used story details to identify the ways the text was organized. ***Home Activity:*** Go to the library with your child and find examples of fiction and nonfiction books about space exploration. Discuss how the writing is organized in each book.

Selection Test

Directions: Choose the best answer to each item. Mark the letter for the answer you have chosen.

Part 1: Vocabulary

Find the answer choice that means about the same as the underlined word in each sentence.

1. I know a lot about spacecraft.
- A. science of outer space
- B. outer-space explorers
- C. rocks from outer space
- D. vehicles for traveling in space

2. It is part of Earth's atmosphere.
- F. materials a planet is made of
- G. planet's distance from the Sun
- H. mass of gases around a planet
- J. size of a planet

3. This picture is incredible.
- A. amazing
- B. unclear or hard to see
- C. colorful
- D. old or out of date

4. Probes have been very useful.
- F. space vehicles that collect and send information
- G. suits worn by astronauts
- H. rocky objects that circle the Sun
- J. maps of the solar system

5. Some planets have craters.
- A. bowl-shaped holes
- B. rings of gas
- C. thick layers of clouds
- D. mountain ranges

Part 2: Comprehension

Use what you know about the selection to answer each item.

6. Space probes are built to—
- F. carry astronauts.
- G. follow meteoroids.
- H. travel to or near other planets.
- J. circle Earth's moon.

7. Some probes have—
- A. returned to Earth.
- B. found signs of life on Jupiter.
- C. flown close to Pluto.
- D. landed on Mars and Venus.

8. One probe showed that Mercury—
- F. has many craters.
- G. is very cold.
- H. has some small moons.
- J. is getting larger.

GO ON

9. To find out about Venus, scientists needed to—
A. gather information from Earth.
B. wait for good weather.
C. build a larger probe.
D. make special cameras.

10. Why do scientists believe there might have been life on Mars?
F. It has a red-orange color.
G. It is the fourth planet from the Sun.
H. They think it once had rivers of water.
J. It has a rocky surface.

11. What makes scientists think Uranus was knocked over?
A. its hazy glow
B. the direction of its rings
C. its blue color
D the patterns on its surface

12. The author's main purpose in this selection is to—
F. describe what the probes have revealed about the planets.
G. explain how scientists solved problems with the probes.
H. tell how probes are different from other space vehicles.
J. tell a fictional story of a probe.

13. This selection presents the planets in order from—
A. largest to smallest.
B. closest to the Sun to farthest from the Sun.
C. most colorful to least colorful.
D. most like Earth to least like Earth.

14. The author probably thinks that exploring space with probes is—
F. dangerous.
G. wasteful.
H. boring.
J. useful.

15. Which sentence states an opinion?
A. "The Sun and all the planets and objects that circle it are called the solar system."
B. "The most exciting information came from pictures the space probes took."
C. "Two of the space probes carry a record that plays sounds from Earth."
D. "They are sending other space probes to the planets to learn more."

STOP

Text Structure

- **Text structure** is the way a piece of writing is organized. The two main kinds of writing are fiction and nonfiction.
- Nonfiction tells about the real world. Some ways to organize nonfiction are cause and effect, problem and solution, and compare and contrast.

Directions: Read the passage below.

Asteroids are tiny planets made of rock or metal. Most of them orbit, or travel in a path, around the Sun between Mars and Jupiter. That part of our solar system is called the *asteroid belt.* Asteroids are usually named by number in order of discovery. Some have been named for make-believe figures or people. The largest asteroid is Ceres. If you could measure it through its middle from side to side, Ceres measures more than 600 miles. The tiniest asteroids are the size of a grain of sand.

Comets are also travelers in the solar system. A comet is a huge lump of ice and rock. It zooms through space in a path around the Sun. As a comet comes close to the Sun, the ice melts. Clouds of dust and gas are released. They follow the comet, shining with reflected sunlight, like a brilliant tail in the sky. Comets are named for the people who discovered them. A comet may be only two miles across, but its tail may be 79,000 miles long!

Directions: For each feature listed in the table, fill in details to compare and contrast asteroids and comets.

Feature	Asteroids	Comets
Orbit	**1.**	They zoom in a path around the Sun.
Size	They can be 600 miles thick or the size of a grain of sand.	**2.**
Made of	**3.**	**4.**
How named	They are usually named by number in order of discovery.	**5.**

Notes for Home: Your child read a nonfiction passage that compared and contrasted asteroids and comets. ***Home Activity:*** Help your child write a short nonfiction piece about a topic he or she knows well, such as sports or music. Use comparisons and contrasts to organize the information.

Name ______________________________

REVIEW

Graphic Sources

Directions: Read the passage and the table. Then read each question about the passage and the table. Choose the best answer to each question. Mark the letter for the answer you have chosen.

On August 27, 1962, the United States sent a spacecraft to Venus. *Mariner 2* came within 22,000 miles of Venus. Then it lost contact with Earth. Since then, there have been a number of space probes sent to the planets.

Space Probes to the Planets

Spacecraft	Launch Date	Mission
Mariner 6	February 25, 1969	Mars
Pioneer 10	March 3, 1972	Jupiter
Voyager 2	August 20, 1977	Jupiter, Saturn, Uranus, Neptune
Galileo	October 18, 1989	Jupiter

1. The space probe launched in October 1989 was—
- **A.** *Voyager 2.*
- **B.** *Mariner 2.*
- **C.** *Mariner 6.*
- **D.** *Galileo.*

2. Which planet was explored more than once for the missions listed?
- **F.** Jupiter
- **G.** Mars
- **H.** Venus
- **J.** Mercury

3. According to the passage and table, the two missions launched in the 1960s were—
- **A.** *Pioneer 10* and *Mariner 2*
- **B.** *Pioneer 10* and *Mariner 6*
- **C.** *Mariner 2* and *Mariner 6*
- **D.** *Pioneer 10* and *Voyager 2*

4. How many years passed between the first and most recent launch to Jupiter?
- **F.** 5 years
- **G.** 20 years
- **H.** 17 years
- **J.** 6 years

5. Which probe went to four planets?
- **A.** *Mariner 6*
- **B.** *Galileo*
- **C.** *Voyager 2*
- **D.** *Pioneer 10*

Notes for Home: Your child answered questions based on information given in a nonfiction passage and table. ***Home Activity:*** Find other examples of tables on cereal boxes, magazines, and newspapers. Ask your child questions that can be answered using data in the tables.

Name ____________________________________

Writing Across Texts

Directions: Consider what you learned from the selections *Space Probes to the Planets* and "Meet the Universe's Main Attraction . . . Gravity." Imagine you are an astronaut who is walking on another planet for the first time. Use the following table to record ideas about your experience. Compare that planet's gravitational pull with Earth's.

Walking on ______________
What I See **1.**
What I Hear **2.**
What I Smell **3.**
What I Touch **4.**
How I Feel **5.**

Write a Journal Entry

On a separate sheet of paper, write a journal entry that describes your visit to another planet. Include ideas you compiled in the table above.

Notes for Home: Your child used the ideas from different stories to write their own journal entry. ***Home Activity:*** Select a place you could visit in a day, and make a list of what you would like to do there. Take the trip together and discuss your journey when you get home.

Name ______________________________

Grammar: Compound and Complex Sentences

REVIEW

Directions: Write **compound** or **complex** to identify each kind of sentence.

______________ **1.** Our solar system has nine planets, but it has other parts as well.

______________ **2.** Asteroids are numerous, and some come near Earth.

______________ **3.** When an asteroid enters Earth's atmosphere, it is called a *meteor.*

______________ **4.** If it reaches Earth's surface, it is called a *meteorite.*

______________ **5.** Comets seem to have tails, but these are just trails of gas and dust.

______________ **6.** Because the Sun produces both heat and light, it is called a star.

______________ **7.** Mercury is the closest planet to the Sun, and Venus is the second closest planet.

______________ **8.** Pluto is thought to be the farthest planet, but there may be more planets beyond it.

Directions: Combine each pair of sentences. Add a connecting word, such as *and, but, or, because, if,* or *when,* to make the kind of sentence shown in ( ). Write your new sentence on the line.

9. Jupiter is the largest planet. It rotates very fast for its size. (compound)

____

____

10. Mercury is close to the Sun. It moves around the Sun in only 88 days. (complex)

____

____

Notes for Home: Your child wrote compound and complex sentences. ***Home Activity:*** With your child, write simple sentences about space travel. Work together to try to combine them into compound or complex sentences.

Name ______________________________

Grammar: Conjunctions

Connecting words such as *and, but,* or *or* are called **conjunctions.** Conjunctions can be used to join words, phrases, or entire sentences. They are used to make compound subjects, predicates, and sentences.

Compound subject: Mercury and Venus are closest to the Sun.
Compound predicate: The probe circled the planet and sent signals.
Compound sentence: We can explore Venus, or we can explore Mars.

- Use *and* to join related ideas: Saturn and Uranus have rings.
- Use *but* to join different ideas: Saturn's rings go around the planet, but Uranus's rings go over it.
- Use *or* to suggest a choice: Would you rather study Saturn or Uranus?

Directions: Underline the conjunction in each sentence.

1. Telescopes and microscopes provide useful information.
2. They have been used to study large and small objects.
3. Would you rather use a telescope or a microscope to look at the moon?
4. A telescope is good for looking at planets, but a microscope is better for looking at germs!
5. An astronomer uses a telescope, but a doctor uses a microscope.

Directions: Choose the conjunction in ( ) to complete each sentence. Write the conjunction on the line.

______________ 6. The probe sent back pictures (but/and) information.

______________ 7. Was the information new (or/but) old?

______________ 8. Some of the information was old, (but/or) most of it was new.

______________ 9. Both Mercury (and/but) the moon have craters.

______________ 10. We knew about the moon's craters, (but/or) we did not know about the craters on Mercury.

Notes for Home: Your child used the conjunctions *and, or,* and *but.* ***Home Activity:*** Say some sentences that include *and, or,* or *but.* Ask your child to identify the conjunctions and to describe the words, phrases, or sentences that each conjunction joins.

Grammar: Conjunctions

Directions: Circle the correct conjunction in ( ) to complete each sentence.

1. The scientist looked through the telescope, (and/or) then she scratched her head.
2. Was something wrong with her telescope, (but/or) had she made a great discovery?
3. She blinked (and/or) then peered again at an object on the side of the planet.
4. It did not exactly twinkle, (or/but) it did look like a star!
5. The scientist was excited, (but/or) she decided to stay calm.
6. She called in a friend, (and/or) he thought he saw the same thing.
7. Was it a new star, (and/or) was it just something unimportant?
8. Would they become famous, (and/but) would other scientists respect them?
9. Together, she (and/or) he made an embarrassing but important discovery.
10. A space probe, on its way to explore the riverbeds (but/and) rocks of Mars, was what they had seen.

Write a Note

Imagine planning a long journey to explore a vast place like the ocean floor. On a separate sheet of paper, list the things that you would bring on your journey. Then write a note to yourself so you will remember to take those items. Use conjunctions to join words, phrases, and sentences.

Notes for Home: Your child used *and, or,* and *but* to join words, phrases, and sentences. ***Home Activity:*** Say each conjunction and ask your child to say a sentence that includes it. Then invite the child to name a conjunction, and you offer a sentence that includes it.

Name ____________________________________

RETEACHING

Grammar: Conjunctions

Conjunctions can be used to join words, phrases, or sentences. Choose the conjunction **and, but,** or **or** to complete each sentence.

Example A: Marta ________ Sean enjoy soccer.

Example B: Sean likes to be the goalie, ________ Marta likes to play offense.

Example C: After a game, both friends drink a glass of lemonade ________ relax in the shade.

Conjunctions can be used to form compound subjects (Example A), compound predicates (Example C), and compound sentences (Example B).

Use **and** to join related ideas. Use **but** to join contrasting ideas. Use **or** to suggest a choice.

Directions: Choose the conjunction in ( ) that best completes each sentence. Write the conjunction on the line.

________________ **1.** Tara (and/but) Jack raked the garden.

________________ **2.** They were going to plant seeds (but/and) weed the garden.

________________ **3.** Jack wanted to plant vegetables, (but/or) Tara wanted to plant flowers.

________________ **4.** They realized that they didn't have to choose one (and/or) the other.

________________ **5.** Both friends made space in the garden for flowers (and/but) vegetables.

________________ **6.** The garden would be small, (or/but) it didn't matter.

Notes for Home: Your child identified and wrote the conjunctions *and, but,* and *or* in sentences. ***Home Activity:*** Write the words *and, but,* and *or* on cards. Have your child pick a card and make up a sentence with that conjunction.

Name ______________________________________

Grammar: Conjunctions

Directions: Underline the conjunction in each sentence.

1. Oceans and lakes have many things in common.
2. They are bodies of water, and they contain fish.
3. You can swim in an ocean or in a lake.
4. You can also go fishing in oceans and lakes.
5. The biggest difference is that lakes have fresh water, but oceans have salt water.

Directions: Finish each sentence by adding the conjunction **and, but,** or **or,** and more information. Write the conjunction on the line.

6. Last week my friends ______________________________
7. They were very excited ______________________________
8. My father said I could either ______________________________
9. I wanted to do both ______________________________
10. Today I am going to the park ______________________________

Write a Journal Entry

On a separate sheet of paper, write about a time you had to choose between doing two different things. Use at least three conjunctions.

Notes for Home: Your child identified conjunctions and wrote them in sentences. ***Home Activity:*** Have your child explain to you the job of each conjunction in a sentence (*and*—joins related ideas; *but*—joins contrasting ideas; *or*—shows a choice).

Name ____________________

Word Study: Syllabication

Directions: A **syllable** is an individual part of a word that you say or hear. For example, **syllable** has three syllables: **syl • la • ble.** When you add a prefix or a suffix to a word, you often add another syllable: **fast • er.** Read the words below. Separate each word into its syllables, using a dot (fast • er).

1. unsafe ____________________

2. partly ____________________

3. powerful ____________________

4. farthest ____________________

5. unless ____________________

6. quickly ____________________

7. disappoint ____________________

8. surface ____________________

Directions: Read the paragraph below. Say each underlined word to yourself. Count the number of syllables you hear. Write each word in the correct column.

If you could travel to another galaxy, what would you see? What information would you bring back? You would have to travel across the vast distances of space many times more swiftly than you do on Earth. What you'd see would probably be a combination of the beautiful and the incredible. The planets would look colorful against the darkness of space.

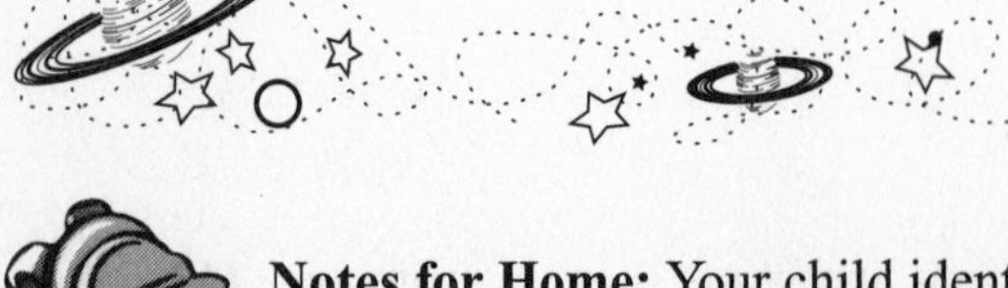

2 syllables

9. ____________________

10. ____________________

3 syllables

11. ____________________

12. ____________________

4 syllables

13. ____________________

14. ____________________

15. ____________________

Notes for Home: Your child identified syllables in words with prefixes such as *un* • *done* and suffixes such as *safe* • *ly*. ***Home Activity:*** When you read with your child, look for words with prefixes and suffixes. Ask your child to say the words and to clap to show each syllable.

Name ____________________

Spelling: Using Just Enough Letters

Pretest Directions: Fold back the page along the dotted line. On the blanks, write the spelling words as they are dictated. When you have finished the test, unfold the page and check your words.

1. ____________________
2. ____________________
3. ____________________
4. ____________________
5. ____________________
6. ____________________
7. ____________________
8. ____________________
9. ____________________
10. ____________________
11. ____________________
12. ____________________
13. ____________________
14. ____________________
15. ____________________
16. ____________________
17. ____________________
18. ____________________
19. ____________________
20. ____________________

1. I'm **coming** to watch the launch.
2. It **always** leaves on time.
3. We **almost** didn't make it.
4. The launch **didn't** take long.
5. Pebbles fell **upon** the surface.
6. He **wasn't** thinking clearly.
7. She waited **until** we came.
8. They cheered **during** liftoff.
9. We **want** to visit other planets.
10. My **father** was an astronaut.
11. This is a cute **hamster**.
12. We run around **a lot**.
13. Some people think eels are **ugly**.
14. I just **washed** up for dinner.
15. The **hotel** was full.
16. We **missed** the show.
17. Climb **eleven** steps to the top.
18. Are you **crazy**?
19. I'm feeling **lazy** today.
20. Don't ignore your **feelings**.

Notes for Home: Your child took a pretest on words with difficult vowel spellings. ***Home Activity:*** Help your child learn misspelled words before the final test. Your child should look at the word, say it, spell it aloud, and then spell it with eyes shut.

Name ______________________________

Spelling: Using Just Enough Letters

Word List				
coming	upon	want	ugly	eleven
always	wasn't	father	washed	crazy
almost	until	hamster	hotel	lazy
didn't	during	a lot	missed	feelings

Directions: Write the words from the box that have two syllables. Hint: Don't include the one two-word spelling word.

1. ____________________
2. ____________________
3. ____________________
4. ____________________
5. ____________________
6. ____________________
7. ____________________
8. ____________________
9. ____________________
10. ____________________
11. ____________________
12. ____________________
13. ____________________
14. ____________________
15. ____________________

Directions: Choose the word from the box that best matches each clue. Write the word in the puzzle.

Down

16. the opposite of *a little*

18. you're clean once you have done this

Across

17. the number just after ten

19. it means the same as *desire*

20. The batter swung and _____.

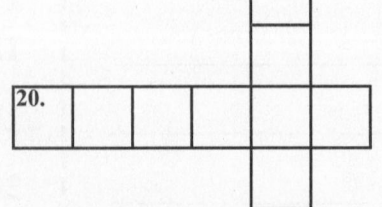

Notes for Home: Your child spelled words that are often misspelled by using too many letters. ***Home Activity:*** Write each word on separate index cards. Show your child the word for a few seconds. Have him or her say it aloud carefully and spell it.

Name ______________________________

Spelling: Using Just Enough Letters

Directions: Proofread this story about wishing to be an astronaut. Find five spelling mistakes. Use the proofreading marks to correct each mistake.

≡	Make a capital.
/	Make a small letter.
∧	Add something.
℘	Take out something.
⊙	Add a period.
¶	Begin a new paragraph.

Out of This World

I have allways wanted to be an astronaut. But until last year, I didn't realize that I could be one. My father told me about space camp. My sister thought it was a crazey idea, but I still went. During space camp I mised my hampster a lot—but not my sister! Yet when I knew my father was comming to pick me up, I wanted to stay longer.

Word List

coming	wasn't	hamster	missed
always	until	a lot	eleven
almost	during	ugly	crazy
didn't	want	washed	lazy
upon	father	hotel	feelings

Write a Short Story

On a separate sheet of paper, write a short story about traveling into space. Try to use at least five spelling words.

Spelling Tip

Pronouncing a word correctly and picturing how it looks can help you avoid writing too many letters.

Notes for Home: Your child spelled words that are often misspelled by using too many letters. ***Home Activity:*** Hold a spelling bee. Include the words on the list plus words from other lessons. Have your child invite classmates or other siblings to participate.

Name ____________________

REVIEW

Spelling: Using Just Enough Letters

Word List				
coming	upon	want	ugly	eleven
always	wasn't	father	washed	crazy
almost	until	hamster	hotel	lazy
didn't	during	a lot	missed	feelings

Directions: Write the word from the box that belongs with each group.

1. emotions, thoughts, __________

2. arriving, entering, __________

3. desire, need, __________

4. forever, all the time, __________

5. parent, mother, __________

6. thirteen, twelve, __________

7. gerbil, mouse, __________

8. unattractive, hideous, __________

9. nuts, loony, __________

10. atop, on, __________

11. about, approximately, __________

12. much, many, __________

13. inn, lodge, __________

14. cleaned, bathed, __________

Directions: Choose the word from the box that best completes each sentence. Write the word on the line to the left.

__________ **15.** When the spacecraft took off, it almost _____ go in the right direction.

__________ **16.** But the mission chief _____ too worried.

__________ **17.** That sort of thing often happens _____ the first minute.

__________ **18.** Still, he didn't relax _____ the problem was fixed.

__________ **19.** Space is lonely, and the astronauts _____ their families.

__________ **20.** But astronauts in space have to work hard, so there's no time to be _____.

Notes for Home: Your child spelled words that are often misspelled by using too many letters. ***Home Activity:*** For each spelling word, write a misspelling that includes extra letters. Have your child spell each word correctly.

Name ______________________________________

Take Notes/Record Findings

Taking notes and **recording findings** of what you have read can help you when you are collecting information for a report. It can also help you keep track of information in a story and remember what you have read for a test.

There is no right or wrong way to take notes, but keep these points in mind:

- When you take notes, put what you read into your own words.
- If you're taking notes about a story, include the main characters' names and what you learn about them.
- Include only important details. Use key words, phrases, or short sentences.
- If you're taking notes for a report, be sure to include the source of your information.
- Read over your notes immediately after writing them to make sure you understand them.

Directions: Read the following article about women in space. Record notes on the following page as you read. Then use your notes to summarize the article.

Women have made great contributions to our exploration of space. Did you know that the first woman in space was Valentina Tereshkova? Her flight was on June 16, 1963. She flew in the Soviet spacecraft *Vostok 6.* She spent three days orbiting Earth. Svetlana Savitskaya became the second woman in space in 1982. She was also part of the Soviet space program.

On June 18, 1983, Sally Kristen Ride became the first American woman into space. Sally Ride worked on the *STS-7* and *STS-41-G* space missions. These missions conducted experiments and worked on communication satellite systems.

Since Sally Ride's voyages into space, there have been many women to follow. Shannon Lucid is the woman who has spent the most time in space—more than 222 days. Her first flight was June 1, 1985. Her last flight was March 22, 1996. On this mission, Shannon Lucid spent 188 days in space. This is the longest flight for any U.S. astronaut. She spent this time on the Russian space station *Mir* conducting science experiments.

Name ______________________________

Notes

1. ______________________________

____

2. ______________________________

____

3. ______________________________

____

4. ______________________________

____

5. ______________________________

____

6. ______________________________

____

7. ______________________________

____

8. ______________________________

____

9. ______________________________

____

Summary

10. ______________________________

____

____

Notes for Home: Your child recorded notes about an article and used these notes to summarize it. ***Home Activity:*** Have your child take notes while reading a newspaper article or watching a TV program. Have your child use the notes to summarize the article or show.

Name ____________________

K-W-L Chart

Directions: Write your topic on the first line. In the chart, write what you know about it and what you want to know. As you research, write information to use in your report.

Topic ____________________

K What I Know	W What I Want to Know	L What I Learned (Information to Use in My Report)

Notes for Home: Your child has learned about finding information for a research report. ***Home Activity:*** Think of a topic, such as a planet or a space mission. Ask your child what kinds of books or other sources (such as the Internet) may offer information about the topic.

Name____

Elaboration

Prepositional Phrases

- You can add information to sentences or make sentences clearer by **using prepositional phrases.** Prepositional phrases begin with **prepositions**—words such as *about, before, from, in, of, on, through,* and *with.*

Directions: Complete each sentence by picking a prepositional phrase that tells more about the topic. Rewrite the sentence with the prepositional phrase at the end. More than one phrase may fit a sentence. Choose one that makes sense.

Prepositional Phrases		
about comets	from a launch pad	of the nine planets
around Saturn	in the night sky	with no moons

1. Circles made of rocks and ice are the rings _____.

____

2. My sister knows the names of seven _____.

____

3. A planet may look like a bright star _____.

____

4. Mercury and Venus are the two planets _____.

____

5. It takes power for a rocket to blast off _____.

____

6. In our classroom, there is a poster _____.

____

Notes for Home: Your child has added information to sentences by using prepositional phrases, such as *in the night sky. **Home Activity:*** Ask your child to describe various things in space, using prepositional phrases such as *around the Sun* or *on the moon.*

Name____

Self-Evaluation

Research Report

Directions: Think about the final draft of your research report. Then answer each question in the chart.

	Yes	No	Not sure
1. Did I find information about interesting questions or central ideas?			
2. Did I present the information from my research clearly?			
3. Did I keep my purpose and audience in mind?			
4. Did I identify sources of special information?			
5. Did I proofread and edit carefully to correct errors?			

6. What is the best part of my research report?

____

____

____

7. Write one thing that you would change about this research report if you had the chance to research or write it again.

____

____

____

Notes for Home: Your child answered questions about writing a research report. ***Home Activity:*** Ask your child what kinds of books or other sources gave the most useful information. Ask if it was hard to find information about the ideas and questions that he or she wanted to research.

Family Times

Name______________________________

Summary

Awesome Performance from Cousin Del!

Koya is thrilled about the visit of her cousin Del, who has become a major rock star. Even though the first part of Del's visit is supposed to be family only, the rest of the neighborhood finds out. Soon Del is surrounded by fans. The next day, Del visits Koya's school, where he gives a concert that everybody loves.

Activity

Write New Dialogue. Ask your child to imagine a conversation between Koya and Del, in which they talk about his music and the concert he gave. Let your child write or talk through the dialogue for you.

Reading Skills

Visualizing

Visualizing means forming a picture in your mind as you read. Forming pictures in your mind can help you "place" events and understand characters. Use what you already know, along with details from the story, to help you visualize scenes in a story.

In "Koya's Cousin Del," the author gives details about the crowd that gathers around Del at the airport. These details help readers picture what the scene was like.

Activity

Draw a Picture. Describe a place, without naming it. Have another person draw a picture of the place you describe. Switch roles. Then talk about how the drawings compare to what each person described.

Family Times

Tested Vocabulary

Words to Know

Knowing the meanings of these words is important to reading "Koya's Cousin Del." Practice using these words to learn their meanings.

applause clapping

auditorium large room for an audience in a theater or school

autographs people's signatures

imitation impersonation of another person or thing

impatient not willing to bear delay

microphones instruments for magnifying small sounds

performers persons who perform or entertain

Grammar

Review of Sentences/ Sentence Punctuation

A **sentence** is a group of words that makes a statement, a question, a command, a request, or an exclamation. A sentence begins with a capital letter and ends with a punctuation mark. A statement ends with a period. A question ends with a question mark. A command or a request usually ends with a period. A statement that expresses strong feeling ends with an exclamation point.

Statement: I play guitar.
Question: Do you play guitar?
Command: Please play for me.
Exclamation: I love playing the guitar!

Activity

Family Sentences. Take turns saying a sentence about a family member. Use expression to give clues about the kind of sentence it is. Have the listener tell what the end punctuation should be.

Tested Spelling Words

______	______	______	______
______	______	______	______
______	______	______	______
______	______	______	______
______	______	______	______

Name ________________________________

Visualizing

- **Visualizing** means forming a mental image as you read.
- To help visualize, look for details that tell how things look, smell, sound, taste, and feel.

Directions: Reread "Seeds." Then complete the word web. List sensory details from the story that help you imagine how things look, taste, and feel.

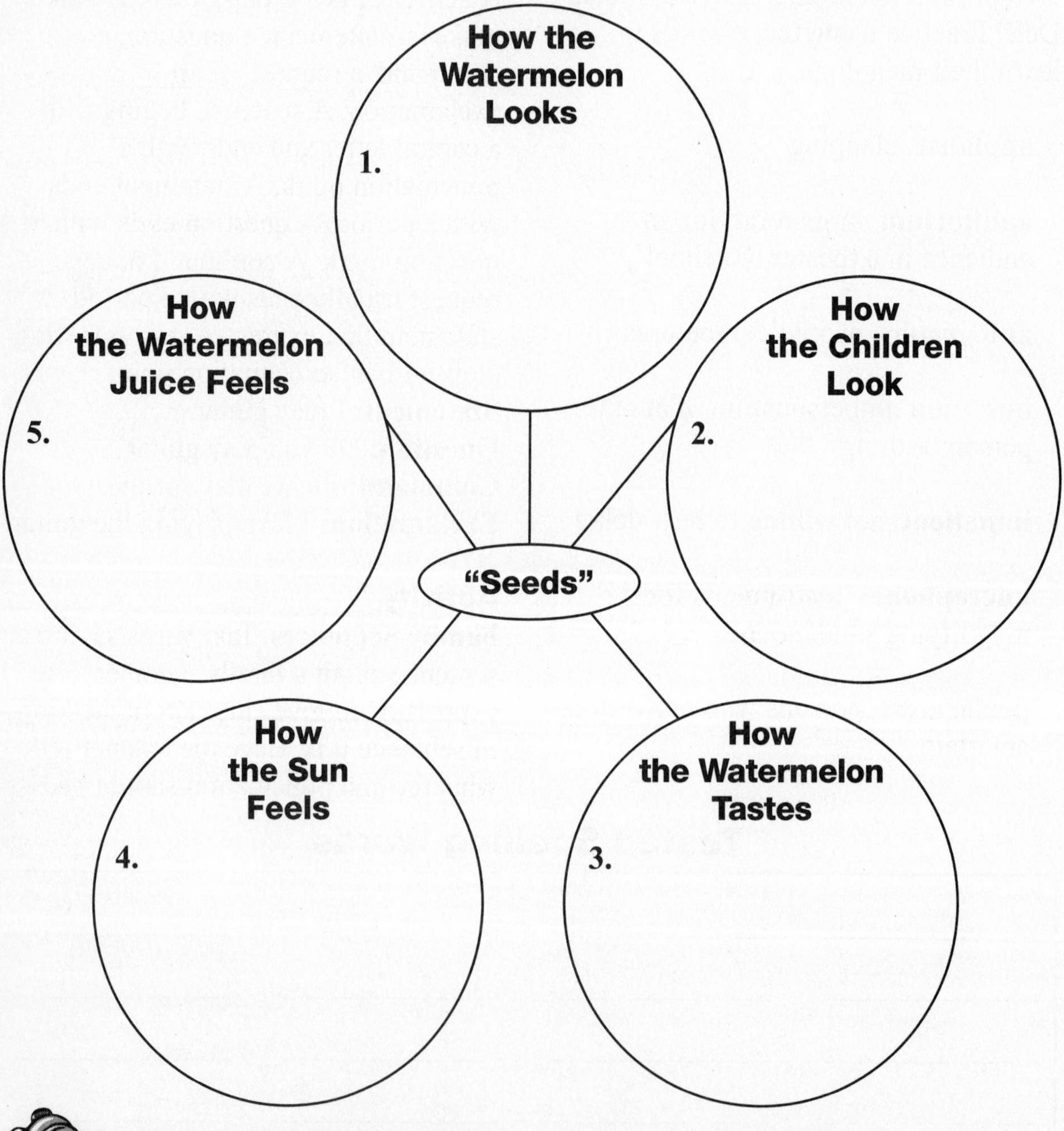

"Seeds"

How the Watermelon Looks

1.

How the Children Look

2.

How the Watermelon Tastes

3.

How the Sun Feels

4.

How the Watermelon Juice Feels

5.

Notes for Home: Your child read a story and visualized it. ***Home Activity:*** Ask your child to visualize a favorite person that you both know, such as a relative. Invite your child to tell sights, smells, sounds, tastes, and sensations that are associated with this person.

Name ______________________________

Vocabulary

Directions: Choose the word from the box that best matches each definition. Write the word on the line.

Check the Words You Know

- __ applause
- __ auditorium
- __ autographs
- __ imitation
- __ impatient
- __ microphones
- __ performers

________________ **1.** a copying or impersonation of another person or thing

________________ **2.** people's signatures

________________ **3.** people who perform or entertain

________________ **4.** not willing to bear delay

________________ **5.** instruments for magnifying small sounds

________________ **6.** large room for an audience in a theater or school

Directions: Choose the word from the box that best completes each sentence. Write the word on the line to the left.

________________ **7.** The _____ arrived ready to sing.

________________ **8.** The audience was _____ because they had been waiting a long time.

________________ **9.** The audience greeted the band's arrival with loud _____.

________________ **10.** Afterwards, people asked the band members for their _____.

Write a Music Review

On a separate sheet of paper, write about a concert, music video, or CD that you have enjoyed. Tell what you did and did not like about it. Use as many of the vocabulary words as you can.

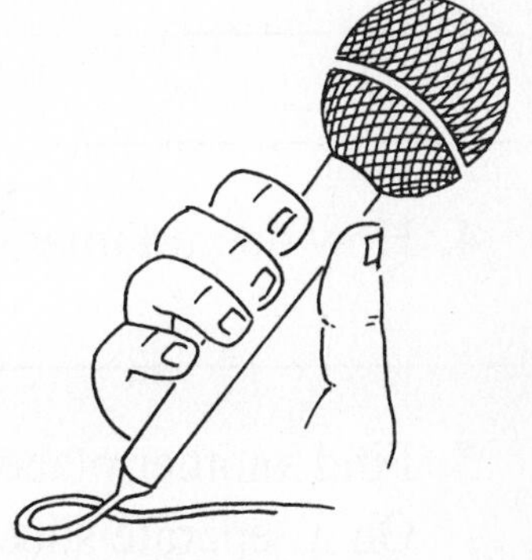

Notes for Home: Your child identified and used vocabulary words from the story "Koya's Cousin Del." ***Home Activity:*** Pretend that you and your child are radio announcers at a live concert. Use the vocabulary words to tell what you see and hear.

Name ______________________________

Visualizing

- **Visualizing** means forming a mental image as you read. To help visualize, look for details that tell how things look, smell, sound, taste, and feel.

Directions: Reread what happens in "Koya's Cousin Del." Then answer the questions below.

After dinner, the family gathered in the living room to listen to a tape of Delbert's next album. He had brought it to them as a gift.

"It won't be released until summer," he said. He got up and began dancing. "This is the latest thing from us folks up in the big city."

Koya glanced at her mother and was suprised to see that she was smiling. She never let them dance on the carpet. Whenever she caught them doing it, she would point toward the basement, and they knew they had better get down to the rec room, or they'd be sorry.

1. Picture the way the family looks as they gather in the living room. How do you think they look?

____

2. Picture Delbert's face as he begins to dance. Describe how you think his face appears.

____

____

3. What sounds can you imagine as Delbert dances?

____

____

4. How do you imagine the carpet looks in the living room?

____

5. Find another place in the story where you get a strong mental image of a scene. On a separate sheet of paper, write a paragraph describing what you visualize.

Notes for Home: Your child created a mental picture of the passage. ***Home Activity:*** Ask your child to picture a special place he or she has been. Invite your child to describe what he or she sees when imagining this place.

Name ______________________________

Selection Test

Directions: Choose the best answer to each item. Mark the letter for the answer you have chosen.

Part 1: Vocabulary

Find the answer choice that means about the same as the underlined word in each sentence.

1. The crowd is <u>impatient</u>.
- A. lively and loud
- B. not happy about waiting
- C. paying attention
- D. satisfied or content

2. We need <u>microphones</u>.
- F. written messages
- G. recordings of music
- H. musical instruments
- J. devices that make sounds louder

3. I collect <u>autographs</u>.
- A. books about cars
- B. old photographs
- C. people's signatures
- D. old records and tapes

4. The <u>performers</u> are here.
- F. people who entertain
- G. close relatives
- H. guests or visitors
- J. people who work at a school

5. The <u>applause</u> made me smile.
- A. joke or story
- B. clapping
- C. amusing event
- D. letter or note

6. That is a good <u>imitation</u>.
- F. hint or sign
- G. solution to a problem
- H. project or piece of work
- J. copy of someone or something

7. The <u>auditorium</u> is this way.
- A. test or tryout
- B. building with offices
- C. large room with a stage and seats
- D. public sale

Part 2: Comprehension

Use what you know about the story to answer each item.

8. Koya's cousin Del is a—
- F. builder.
- G. singer.
- H. governor.
- J. teacher.

GO ON

9. What did Del do at the airport?
- A. signed autographs
- B. sang a song
- C. gave tapes away
- D. danced with Koya

10. Who told the secret that Del was at Koya's house?
- F. Rodney
- G. Loritha
- H. Dr. Hanley
- J. Koya

11. How did most of the crowd outside Koya's house look and act when they saw Del?
- A. eager and happy
- B. hushed and shy
- C. rough and angry
- D. rude and loud

12. After Del's parents died, Koya's family helped him to—
- F. find a place to live.
- G. write a song about them.
- H. go back to his music.
- J. start a group with Sherita.

13. When Del sang the first song, he tried to—
- A. sing louder than the drums.
- B. make the students laugh.
- C. sing in his mother's voice.
- D. get the students to clap.

14. Which sentence helps you see in your mind what Del looked like as he arrived at the airport?
- F. "A man and a woman waiting at the gate had turned to look."
- G. "The young man looked at Delbert and back at the woman as if she were crazy."
- H. "'Del!' he said loudly. 'Your album is bad, man!'"
- J. "... a young man of medium height and build,... dressed in faded blue jeans and matching jacket."

15. What does Koya think about Del?
- A. She is jealous of him.
- B. She thinks he is vain.
- C. She worries about him.
- D. She is proud of him.

STOP

Name ____________________________________

Visualizing

- **Visualizing** means forming a mental image as you read. To help visualize, look for details that tell how things look, smell, sound, taste, and feel.

Directions: Read the story below.

Corey, Pam, Mei-Ling, and Tanya started a band together. Each girl played a different instrument. Corey, the leader, played guitar. She really had to stretch her arms to play the big instrument.

Pam played the clarinet. When she played, her eyes closed and her whole body swayed with the music.

Mei-Ling was the drummer. When Mei-Ling played, she seemed to be moving in all directions. Her hands flew, her elbows jiggled, her knees bounced, and her feet tapped.

Tanya played the bass. Tanya usually had a big, broad smile—except when she played. Then she looked very serious.

Directions: Complete the table. Fill in words from the story that help you picture each character. Then tell what you visualized as you read.

Characters	Descriptive Words from the Story
Corey	**1.**
Pam	**2.**
Mei-Ling	**3.**
Tanya	**4.**

5. What I Picture:

____

____

Notes for Home: Your child created mental images in his or her mind based on story details. ***Home Activity:*** Ask your child to think of a place he or she has been today. Suggest that your child picture the place in his or her mind. Then ask your child to describe it.

Name ______________________________

Setting

REVIEW

Directions: Read the story. Then read each question about the story. Choose the best answer to each question. Mark the letter for the answer you have chosen.

A Difficult Concert

Randall and his band got to the auditorium two hours later than planned. It was a cold day, and the roads were icy. Randall had to drive extra carefully to avoid an accident.

While they were driving, Randall had switched on the radio in the van. "Hello, out there!" said the disk jockey cheerfully. "We're going to start our countdown of the year's greatest hits!"

When the band finally got to the auditorium, the crowd was restless. They stamped so hard, the wooden bleachers shook. Even the basketball hoops were shaking. The band ran out onto the stage. "Greetings, everybody!" Randall shouted. "How are things here in Central Valley?"

The crowd cheered. "Are you ready for the year 2000?" he cried. "Here's a song to celebrate the last night of the old year!"

1. Based on the information in the story, what season is it?
- **A.** summer
- **B.** winter
- **C.** fall
- **D.** spring

2. How is Randall affected by the setting during the band's drive?
- **F.** He is shivering and uncomfortable.
- **G.** He puts on an extra sweater.
- **H.** He drives more slowly.
- **J.** He doesn't want to perform.

3. What else is the auditorium used for?
- **A.** a gym
- **B.** a cafeteria
- **C.** a town meeting hall
- **D.** school meetings

4. In what year does the story take place?
- **F.** 2001
- **G.** 1899
- **H.** 2000
- **J.** 1999

5. What holiday is coming up?
- **A.** Homecoming
- **B.** Presidents' Day
- **C.** Thanksgiving
- **D.** New Year's Day

Notes for Home: Your child identified a story's setting—the time and place where it occurs. ***Home Activity:*** Ask your child to identify a favorite book, movie, or television show. Then ask him or her to tell you when and where the story takes place and tell you how he or she knows.

Name ____________________

Writing Across Texts

Directions: Consider what you learned about how Delbert expressed his creativity in "Koya's Cousin Del." Think of people or characters from other stories in class and consider the ways they expressed themselves creatively. Complete the table below by listing the ways they expressed themselves.

Creativity
Delbert used music to tell others how he felt.
1.
2.
3.
4.
5.

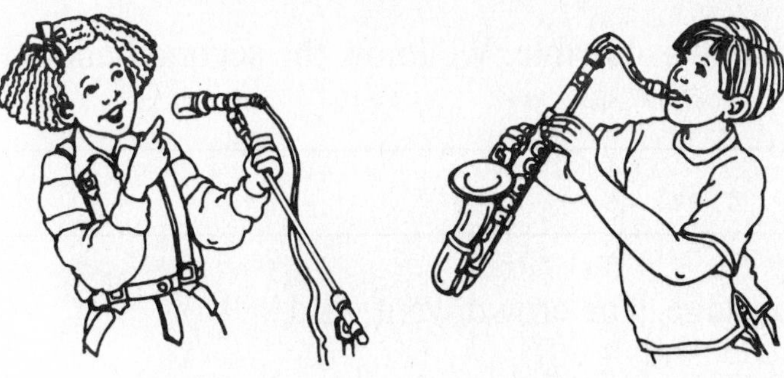

Write a Paragraph

On a separate sheet of paper, write a paragraph that tells about the ways in which people can express themselves creatively.

Notes for Home: Your child used information from many stories to write a paragraph about the ways people express themselves creatively. ***Home Activity:*** Use the creativity of family members as examples. Discuss with your child ways he or she has to express creativity.

Name ________________________________

Grammar: Conjunctions

REVIEW

Directions: Choose the correct conjunction in ( ) to complete each sentence. Write the conjunction on the line.

________ **1.** It is getting late, (but/or) I want to hear the next band.

________ **2.** The guitar player (and/but) the keyboard player walked onto the stage together.

________ **3.** Would the singer (and/or) the drummer be the next one onstage?

________ **4.** The group played two old hits (and/but) two brand-new songs.

________ **5.** Should we leave now (but/or) listen to another band?

Directions: Use the conjunction *and, but,* or *or* to combine each pair of sentences. Write your new sentence on the line.

6. The concert was almost sold out. We did get two tickets.

____

____

7. Can your brother drive us? Should we take the bus?

____

8. The opening band was terrible. We know the second band will be great.

____

____

9. The band ran onstage. The crowd went wild.

____

10. They opened with their biggest hit. The audience sang along.

____

Notes for Home: Your child used the conjunctions *and, but,* and *or* to complete or combine sentences. ***Home Activity:*** Give your child two words and a conjunction. Challenge your child to form a sentence. Repeat as many times as you like.

Grammar: Sentences and Punctuation

A **sentence** is a group of words that makes a statement, a question, a command, a request, or an exclamation. It begins with a capital letter and ends with a punctuation mark. One way to tell whether a group of words is a complete sentence is to check whether it expresses a complete thought.

A **declarative sentence** is a sentence that makes a statement. It ends with a period.

I love music.

An **interrogative sentence** asks a question. It ends with a question mark.

Do you love music too?

An **imperative sentence** gives a command or a request. It ends with a period. The first word is usually a verb or *please* followed by a verb. The subject *(you)* is not shown, but it is understood.

Listen to me play the guitar.

An **exclamatory sentence** shows strong feeling. It ends with an exclamation point.

That was so wonderful!

Directions: Match each group of words on the left with a group of words on the right to form complete sentences. Write the letter on the line.

________	**1.** Did you go	**a.** study for a long time.
________	**2.** At the concert,	**b.** was so talented!
________	**3.** The lead guitarist	**c.** to the concert last week?
________	**4.** I'm going	**d.** to start taking lessons next week.
________	**5.** Good musicians must	**e.** the singer sang a solo.

Directions: Write the correct end punctuation on the line after each sentence.

6. Martin was practicing piano all afternoon _____

7. Did you know he is playing in the concert _____

8. Wow, he is a great musician _____

9. Why didn't he send me an invitation _____

10. I hope I can go to the concert _____

Notes for Home: Your child reviewed sentences and their end punctuation. ***Home Activity:*** Say a sentence and have your child punctuate it with a gesture: pointing a finger for a period, shaking his or her head for a question mark, and clapping hands for an exclamation mark.

Name ______________________________________

Grammar: Sentences and Punctuation

Directions: Write **S** on the line if each group of words is a sentence. Write **NS** if the group of words is not a sentence.

_______________ **1.** I have been studying music since I was seven years old.

_______________ **2.** For three years!

_______________ **3.** The very first instrument I ever studied was.

_______________ **4.** Then I decided to learn piano, so that I could play by myself.

_______________ **5.** The reason I like to play solos?

Directions: Rewrite each sentence with correct capitalization and end punctuation.

6. do you think that it's better to play music by yourself

____

7. if you could play any instrument in the world, what would it be

____

8. my piano teacher wants me to study harder

____

9. come to my concert and watch me play

____

10. wow, I really love music

____

Write a Description of Music

On a separate sheet of paper, write a description of some music that you like. Explain why you like it and tell how the music makes you feel.

Notes for Home: Your child reviewed sentences and their end punctuation. ***Home Activity:*** Have your child read aloud from a favorite story. Encourage your child to use his or her voice to express statements, commands, questions, and exclamations.

Name ____

RETEACHING

Grammar: Sentences and Punctuation

A **sentence** is a group of words that makes a statement, a question, a command, a request, or an exclamation. It begins with a capital letter and ends with a punctuation mark.

Read each sentence. Write a punctuation mark that best completes each sentence.

1. Please bring me the book ______

2. I've never seen anything so amazing ______

3. Do you know what time it is ______

4. I am writing a report ______

An **imperative sentence** gives a command or makes a request and ends with a period. An **exclamatory sentence** shows strong feeling and ends with an exclamation point. An **interrogative sentence** asks a question and ends with a question mark. A **declarative sentence** makes a statement and ends with a period.

Directions: Read each sentence and identify which type it is. Write **declarative**, **exclamatory**, **imperative**, or **interrogative** on the line.

________________ **1.** What an exciting movie that was!

________________ **2.** Do you know the names of the actors?

________________ **3.** Yes, I do.

________________ **4.** Please tell me what they are.

________________ **5.** Can you wait until we get home?

________________ **6.** Tell me now.

________________ **7.** You are the most curious person I've ever met!

Notes for Home: Your child correctly punctuated four types of sentences. ***Home Activity:*** Write some sentences without end punctuation. Discuss with your child which punctuation mark (. or *!* or *?*) best ends each sentence.

Name ______________________________

Grammar: Sentences and Punctuation

Directions: Write the correct end punctuation on the line after each sentence.

1. Everyone loved the play _____
2. Did Sabrina remember all her lines _____
3. Did you help clean up after the show _____
4. What a mess it was _____
5. Hang your costume in the closet _____
6. Phil fixed a light _____
7. Wow, what bright lights they are _____
8. Please fold all those chairs _____
9. Did you check down that row _____
10. Brenda swept the stage _____
11. Does Mr. Carter think we did well _____
12. He took everyone out for a snack _____

Directions: Rewrite each sentence with correct capitalization and end punctuation.

13. did you get tickets to the baseball game

____

14. please get one for me too

____

15. it will be a fun game

____

16. what a great time we're going to have

____

Notes for Home: Your child correctly punctuated four types of sentences. **Home Activity:** Listen to a favorite song. Have your child write some of the words to the song and decide which type of punctuation mark (. or *!* or *?*) to use.

Name ____

Word Study: Complex Spelling Patterns

Word List				
steady	reindeer	niece	caught	said
again	veil	brought	piece	bread

Directions: Some letter combinations, such as **ei, ie, ai, ea,** and **gh,** are hard to remember and spell correctly. Read the words in the box. Listen and look for similar letter combinations. Write each word in the correct column.

Words with ei	Words with ie	Words with ai
1. ________________	3. ________________	5. ________________
2. ________________	4. ________________	6. ________________

Words with ea	Words with gh
7. ____________________________	9. ____________________________
8. ____________________________	10. ____________________________

Directions: Choose the word from the box that best completes each sentence. Write the word on the line to the left. Not all the words will be used.

________________ **11.** "The winter concert has started," _____ one parent.

________________ **12.** "I can hear the _____ beat of the school's drummer," the other parent agreed.

________________ **13.** Opening the door of the auditorium _____ the holiday music into the school corridor.

________________ **14.** The children came out singing, dressed as silly _____.

________________ **15.** "I think I can recognize my _____ under the horns and bright red nose," said the girl's uncle.

Notes for Home: Your child practiced words with complex spelling patterns. ***Home Activity:*** Encourage your child to keep a list of words he or she has trouble spelling correctly. Set aside time each week to practice spelling these words with your child.

Pretest

Spelling: Getting Letters in Correct Order

Pretest Directions: Fold back the page along the dotted line. On the blanks, write the spelling words as they are dictated. When you have finished the test, unfold the page and check your words.

1. ______	1. Would you like a **piece**?
2. ______	2. She's my best **friend**.
3. ______	3. There's wheat in that **field**.
4. ______	4. Do you **believe** me?
5. ______	5. They think my cousin is **weird**.
6. ______	6. That's what I **said**.
7. ______	7. I want to see the movie **again**.
8. ______	8. They **asked** many questions.
9. ______	9. We're not the **only** ones.
10. ______	10. Look what we **brought** for you.
11. ______	11. He grew in **height**.
12. ______	12. He has gained **weight**.
13. ______	13. I'm trying to be a good **neighbor**.
14. ______	14. Everyone has **heard** the secret.
15. ______	15. It nearly broke her **heart**.
16. ______	16. The soup burned his **tongue**.
17. ______	17. The baby is shaking the **rattle**.
18. ______	18. I will have a **pickle** with that.
19. ______	19. His **toes** were frostbitten.
20. ______	20. I was born in a **hospital**.

Notes for Home: Your child took a pretest on words with difficult letter combinations. ***Home Activity:*** Help your child learn misspelled words before the final test. See if there are any similar errors and discuss a memory trick that could help.

Name ____________________

Spelling: Getting Letters in Correct Order

Directions: Choose the words from the box that contain the letters **ie** and **ei.** Write the words in the correct column.

Words with ie	Words with ei
1. ____________	**5.** ____________
2. ____________	**6.** ____________
3. ____________	**7.** ____________
4. ____________	**8.** ____________

Word List	
piece	height
friend	weight
field	neighbor
believe	heard
weird	heart
said	tongue
again	rattle
asked	pickle
only	toes
brought	hospital

Directions: Choose the word from the box that best matches each clue. Write the word on the line to the left.

____________ **9.** The past tense of the verb *say*.

____________ **10.** Over and over, or more than once.

____________ **11.** If you had listened, you would have _____.

____________ **12.** It beats in your chest.

____________ **13.** If you hear a snake doing this, you're in trouble.

____________ **14.** This is tasty, but sometimes sour.

____________ **15.** Where you go when you're sick.

____________ **16.** If someone had _____, I would have answered.

____________ **17.** You are my one and _____.

____________ **18.** It rhymes with *sought*.

____________ **19.** They're the fingers of your feet.

____________ **20.** It should stay in your mouth.

Notes for Home: Your child spelled words with letter combinations that are often mixed up, such as *fr<u>ie</u>nd* and *h<u>e</u>ight.* ***Home Activity:*** Say each word twice, and have your child write it. Together, check and correct for any misspellings.

Proofread and Write

Spelling: Getting Letters in Correct Order

Directions: Proofread this review of a concert. Find five spelling mistakes. Use the proofreading marks to correct each mistake.

≡	Make a capital.
/	Make a small letter.
∧	Add something.
⅁	Take out something.
⊙	Add a period.
¶	Begin a new paragraph.

"COWBOY BLUES" ARE A GREAT GROUP

Last night, my friend and I haerd some of the best music I have heard in a long time. The "Cowboy Blues" concert was full of songs to touch the haert and set your tose tapping. At the end, the audience cheered wildly, so the group played their most famous song egain. I believe that hearing "Howdy, Nieghbor" was the best part of the evening!

Spelling Tip

Some letter combinations are especially hard to keep in order: **bel<u>ie</u>ve, h<u>ea</u>rt, s<u>ai</u>d.** Pay special attention to words with these combinations.

Word List

piece	said	height	tongue
friend	again	weight	rattle
field	asked	neighbor	pickle
believe	only	heard	toes
weird	brought	heart	hospital

Write a Music Review

On a separate sheet of paper, write your own review of a concert you have heard or of a favorite tape or CD. Tell what you did and didn't like about the music. Use at least five spelling words.

Notes for Home: Your child spelled words with letter combinations that are often mixed up, such as *fr<u>ie</u>nd* and *h<u>ei</u>ght*. ***Home Activity:*** Ask your child to name and spell as many words as he or she can think of with the letter combinations *ie* and *ei.*

Name ______________________________

Spelling: Getting Letters in Correct Order

REVIEW

Word List

piece	weird	only	neighbor	rattle
friend	said	brought	heard	pickle
field	again	height	heart	toes
believe	asked	weight	tongue	hospital

Directions: Choose the word from the box that begins and ends with the same letters as each word below. Write the word on the line.

1. beat ____________________ **7.** around ____________________

2. bone ____________________ **8.** never ____________________

3. filed ____________________ **9.** price ____________________

4. hall ____________________ **10.** true ____________________

5. officially ____________________ **11.** peace ____________________

6. apron ____________________ **12.** wrist ____________________

Directions: Choose the word from the box that best completes each sentence. Write the word on the line to the left.

____________________ **13.** We _____ a great concert last night!

____________________ **14.** At first, the music sounded a bit _____.

____________________ **15.** My best _____ was starting to get bored.

____________________ **16.** "This is no good!" she _____.

____________________ **17.** Then the lead singer shook a huge _____.

____________________ **18.** The guitarist stood up to his full _____.

____________________ **19.** My _____ began to beat faster.

____________________ **20.** My friend and I stood on our _____ and cheered.

Notes for Home: Your child spelled words with letters that are often mixed up. ***Home Activity:*** With your child, take turns choosing spelling words. Read a word and ask the other person to spell it. Without looking at the list, tell whether the word was spelled correctly.

Name ____________________

Poster/Advertisement

A **poster** is a kind of announcement that gives specific facts about an event. It usually answers the questions "Who?" "What?" "When?" "Where?" "Why?"

Directions: This poster gives information about a rock concert. Use the poster to answer the questions that follow.

Sunfruit Soft Drinks Present:
The Howling Wolf Pack
Friday, April 26th, 8:00 P.M.
The Whitamore Center, 125 Fairchild Ave.,
906 - 555 - 8364
Tickets cost $15 – $25
Opening performance will be
by the Rainbow Rockers.

1. What is the name of the main group performing? ____________________
2. What is the name of the group that will be performing first? ____________________
3. Where is the concert? ____________________
4. What date is the concert? ____________________
5. Which ticket do you think costs $25—a ticket for a seat close to the stage or far away from the stage? Explain.

Name ___________________________________

An **advertisement** is a kind of announcement that can be found in print or electronic media. The goal of an advertisement is to persuade readers, listeners, or viewers to do something, buy something, or feel a particular way about something.

Directions: Use the video game advertisement to answer the questions that follow.

6. What is the purpose of this advertisement? ___________________________________

____

7. How do the pictures support this purpose? ___________________________________

____

8. How do the words support this purpose? ___________________________________

____

____

9. What do you need to have to play this game? ___________________________________

____

10. Name one fact and one opinion from the advertisement. ___________________

____

Notes for Home: Your child answered questions about a poster and an advertisement. ***Home Activity:*** Choose an advertisement from the newspaper or a commercial on television. Ask your child to point out some facts and some opinions that the advertisement presents.

Family Times

Name

Summary

Pueblo Family Works with Clay

In Gia Rose's family, the children and grown-ups of the family work together to make things from clay. They coil clay to make bowls and figures of animals and people. They roll clay into slabs to make other things. As they work, Gia Rose tells everyone about Clay-Old-Woman, who helps them create beautiful things. When they finish forming the clay, they set the pieces aside to dry. Later, they will polish and paint the pieces they've made.

Activity

Symbols Tell Stories. Ask your child to tell you about the symbols painted on the pots, such as the bear paw (a reminder of the healing power of the bear), the lizard (respected for its quickness), and the clouds and mountains (symbols of rain). Choose a personal symbol—an animal, plant, or other image from nature. Draw and color the symbols on note paper to make stationery.

Reading Skills

Steps in a Process

Telling the **steps in a process** is telling the order of steps to complete an action.

Clue words like *first, next,* and *last* or numbers can show the order of the steps. Sometimes illustrations show the steps. At other times you have to picture the steps in your mind.

For example, in "Children of Clay," the author tells the steps in the process of making clay pots and figurines. Photographs help readers picture each step in the process.

Activity

Draw a Cartoon. Think of something you know how to do, such as make a special kind of sandwich. Make a series of cartoon pictures to show each step. Number the steps.

Family Times

Tested Vocabulary

Words to Know

Knowing the meanings of these words is important to reading "Children of Clay." Practice using these words to learn their meanings.

figures pieces of pottery

polish make smooth and shiny

pottery pots or dishes made from clay, hardened by heat

screens woven wire with small openings in between

symbols things that represent something else

Grammar

Capitalization

A **title** tells what a person is or does. Titles begin with a capital letter. Some examples of titles are: **Mr., Ms., Miss, Mrs., Dr.,** and **Capt.**.

Activity

A Title for Everyone. Take turns naming names of people you know. Have someone else tell the title of that person and what letter in the title would be capitalized.

Tested Spelling Words

Name ______________________________

Steps in a Process

- Telling the **steps in a process** is telling the order of steps to complete an action.
- Clue words like *first, next,* and *last* or numbers written by the steps can show when each step is done.

First → Next → Last

Directions: Reread "From Drawing to Carousel Critter." Then complete the flowchart. Put the steps listed in the box in the order they must be done to turn a drawing into a carousel critter.

Steps

Enlarge drawing.
Paint animal.
Carve foam animal.
Trace drawing onto foam.
Sand it smooth.
Cover with varnish.
Glue together to make "sandwich."
Add eyes, a mouth, and other details.
Fit pole between cutouts.
Add three coats of fiberglass.
Cut out shapes.

Enlarge drawing.
↓
1. ______
↓
2. ______
↓
3. ______
↓
4. ______
↓
5. ______
↓
6. ______
↓
7. ______
↓
8. ______
↓
9. ______
↓
10. ______

Notes for Home: Your child read a story and identified steps in a process—the steps needed to complete an action. ***Home Activity:*** Together, perform a simple household task, such as putting away groceries or washing dishes. Ask your child to identify each step as it is performed.

Name ____________________________________

Vocabulary

Directions: Choose the word from the box that best matches each clue. Write the word on the line.

Check the Words You Know
__ figures
__ polish
__ pottery
__ screens
__ symbol

____________________ **1.** You make this out of clay.

____________________ **2.** This is something you do to make things shiny.

____________________ **3.** People often put these on doors and windows.

____________________ **4.** This is used to represent something else.

____________________ **5.** These are small pieces of finished pottery.

Directions: Choose the word from the box that best completes each sentence. Write the word on the line to the left.

____________________ **6.** Tyrone is a skilled potter who makes and sells all different kinds of _____.

____________________ **7.** Tyrone picked up one of the many little clay _____ that he had made.

____________________ **8.** He began to _____ the object to give it a bright shine.

____________________ **9.** He placed the object next to a plate painted with a _____ representing the sun.

____________________ **10.** Outside, several children peered through the wire _____ to watch Tyrone at work.

Write an Art Review

On a separate sheet of paper, write about a piece of pottery or sculpture, either one you have seen or one you saw in a picture. Tell what the figure looks like and what you like about it. Use as many vocabulary words as you can.

Notes for Home: Your child identified and used vocabulary words from "Children of Clay." ***Home Activity:*** Invite your child to tell you what each vocabulary word means. Together, write a definition for each word. Take turns using these words in sentences.

Steps in a Process

- Telling the **steps in a process** is telling the order of steps to complete an action.
- Clue words like *first, next,* and *last* or numbers written by the steps can show when each step is done.

Directions: Reread what happens in "Children of Clay" when everyone finishes coiling and forming the clay. Then answer the questions below.

When they finish coiling and forming the clay, everyone carefully puts the pieces out of the way to dry. Big pieces like Nora's figures are wrapped in cloth so that they don't dry too fast and crack. The children know not to touch the clay pieces while they are drying because they are very fragile and will break easily.

A week later, it is time to smooth the pieces with sandpaper. Eliza is very careful as she helps to sand the hands that Devonna made. She sits working with her grandmother Rose, her aunt Rina, and her aunt Tessie, while the younger children play close by.

1. What is the first step after coiling and forming the clay?

____

2. What additional step is necessary if the clay pieces are big?

____

3. How long do the pieces need to dry?

____

4. What is the final step in the process described here?

____

5. Reread the part of the story that describes steps in finishing the clay pieces. On a separate sheet of paper, list these steps.

Notes for Home: Your child read a nonfiction passage and identified steps in a process. ***Home Activity:*** Invite your child to watch you perform a simple chore, such as washing the dishes. Ask him or her to list at least three steps in that process.

Name ______________________________

Selection Test

Directions: Choose the best answer to each item. Mark the letter for the answer you have chosen.

Part 1: Vocabulary

Find the answer choice that means about the same as the underlined word in each sentence.

1. We used the <u>screens</u>.

A. rolls of paper
B. large bottles or jugs
C. carving tools
D. wires woven with small openings

2. He showed us the <u>figures</u>.

F. forms or shapes
G. materials or supplies
H. large painted pictures
J. chips of broken clay

3. Now I will <u>polish</u> the dish.

A. harden by baking
B. make smooth and shiny
C. decorate with designs
D. show or display

4. These pictures are <u>symbols</u>.

F. hopes or dreams
G. ideas shared by many people
H. strong feelings
J. things that stand for something else

5. Show us the <u>pottery</u>.

A. glass dishes and plates
B. metal pieces of art
C. pots and dishes made of clay
D. objects carved from wood

Part 2: Comprehension

Use what you know about the selection to answer each item.

6. The family in this selection lives in a—

F. Pueblo village.
G. log cabin.
H. large city.
J. ranch house.

7. Which step happens first?

A. taking sticks out of the clay
B. soaking the clay in water
C. letting the clay dry
D. wrapping the clay in cloths

8. Sand is added to the clay to—

F. make the clay thicker.
G. keep the clay from cracking when it dries.
H. get rid of stones and twigs.
J. make the clay shiny.

GO ON

9. Who is Clay-Old-Woman?
   A. the children's grandmother
   B. a woman in the village
   C. a pottery teacher
   D. a spirit the people believe in

10. What step comes next after the clay is formed into pots and figures?
    F. They are left to dry.
    G. They are polished.
    H. They are washed.
    J. They are painted.

11. A good polishing stone must be—
    A. light.
    B. smooth.
    C. pointed.
    D. large.

12. When pottery is "fired," it is—
    F. covered with hot wax.
    G. dipped in boiling water.
    H. baked to make it hard.
    J. left out in the hot sun.

13. The author's main purpose in this selection is to—
    A. persuade people to make pottery.
    B. tell how to choose well-made pottery.
    C. explain how one family makes pottery.
    D. describe the village of Santa Clara.

14. What makes this pottery special to the people who buy it?
    F. It has been sanded.
    G. Some of it is plain.
    H. It is made completely by hand.
    J. Food can be cooked in it.

15. Which sentence best describes the family in this selection?
    A. They spoil the children.
    B. They like to play tricks on one another.
    C. They love to have fun.
    D. They work well together.

STOP

Name ________________________________

Steps in a Process

- Telling the **steps in a process** is telling the order of steps to complete an action.
- Clue words like *first, next,* and *last* or numbers written by the steps can show when each step is done.

Directions: Read the passage below. Then complete the flowchart.

Suppose you want to find out about Native American arts, especially pottery. The first thing to do when you are searching for a book is ask the librarian. He or she may have useful ideas.

Next, check the card catalog under the words *Native American* and *pottery.* In the catalog, there is a card for each book. Each card has a book title, a description of the book, and a call number that will help you find the book in the library. Read the descriptions to see which books will be helpful.

Write down the title, author, and number of each book that looks good. Then go find the book on the library shelves. If you can't find it, ask the librarian for help. The librarian can find out if your book has been checked out or is on a special shelf.

Finally, when you do find your book, and it seems to be helpful, check it out!

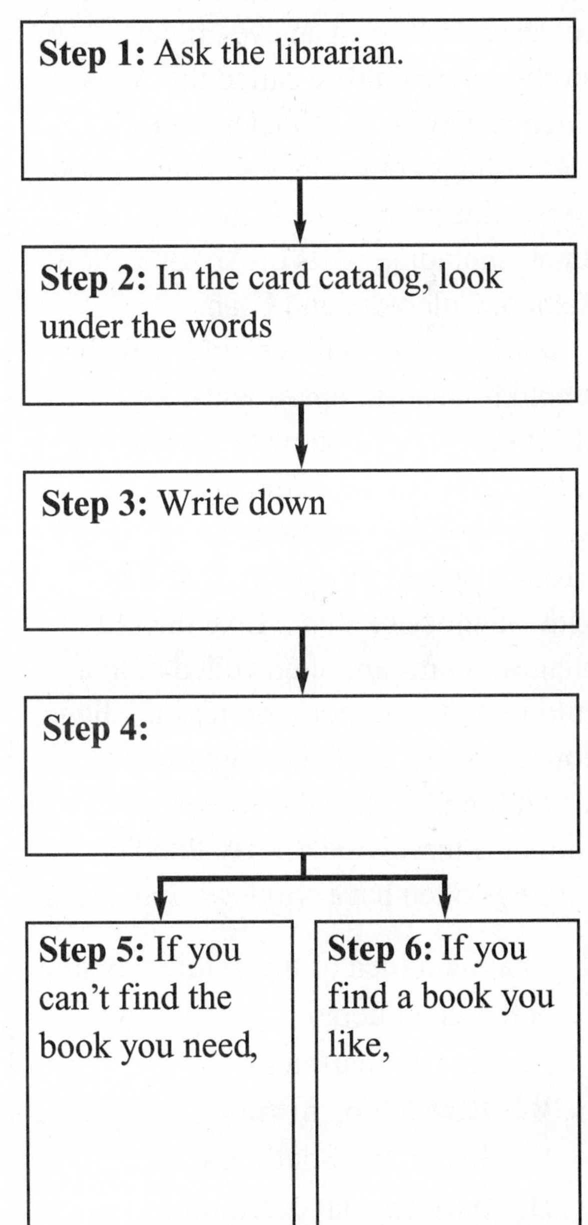

Step 1: Ask the librarian.
Step 2: In the card catalog, look under the words
Step 3: Write down
Step 4:
Step 5: If you can't find the book you need,
Step 6: If you find a book you like,

Notes for Home: Your child used a flowchart to help identify steps in a process. ***Home Activity:*** Ask your child to think of a task he or she usually does, such as making the bed. Invite him or her to tell you each step in that process.

Name ____

REVIEW

Main Idea and Supporting Details

Directions: Read the passage. Then read each question about the passage. Choose the best answer to each question. Mark the letter for the answer you have chosen.

The Pueblo People

The Pueblo are one of the oldest peoples in North America. The Pueblo are descended from an even older Southwestern culture called the Anasazi, which is Navajo for "ancient ones." Their villages developed in what is now the Southwestern area of the United States, including parts of Arizona, New Mexico, Colorado, and Utah.

Pueblo means "village" in Spanish. Pueblo homes are apartment-like buildings made of stone or adobe. An underground room, called a *kiva,* is used for special ceremonies.

Today, pueblo villages may still be made of adobe or stone. Like the old villages, rooms are often added onto a building to make more room as a village grows. An entire village might live in one building. Unlike the earlier buildings, these modern-day Pueblo buildings often have windows and doors.

1. The main idea of the whole passage is that the Pueblo—
- **A.** live in apartments.
- **B.** have a long history.
- **C.** live in the Southwest.
- **D.** have special ceremonies.

2. A key word to the main idea in the first paragraph is—
- **F.** oldest.
- **G.** developed.
- **H.** Arizona.
- **J.** Utah.

3. The second paragraph tells about the Pueblo's—
- **A.** homes.
- **B.** economy.
- **C.** religious beliefs.
- **D.** ancestors.

4. The last paragraph—
- **F.** describes the Anasazi.
- **G.** compares old and modern Pueblo villages.
- **H.** explains how to make adobe bricks.
- **J.** describes the Pueblo people.

5. Which of the following does **not** support the main idea of the passage?
- **A.** The Pueblo are one of the oldest peoples in North America.
- **B.** The Pueblo are descendents of the Anasazi.
- **C.** Modern Pueblo villages are similar to old villages.
- **D.** A kiva is a room used for special ceremonies.

Notes for Home: Your child identified the main idea and details of a passage. ***Home Activity:*** Read a brief newspaper article about a local person, place, or event. Ask your child to tell you the main idea. Take turns telling details from the story.

Name ____________________

Writing Across Texts

Directions: Using information from "Children of Clay" and "Clay Old Woman and Clay Old Man," fill in the five most important steps in the making of Pueblo pottery on the flowchart below.

How to Make Pueblo Pottery

↓

1.

↓

2.

↓

3.

↓

4.

↓

5.

Write a How-to List

Using information from "Children of Clay" and "Clay Old Woman and Clay Old Man," write a numbered how-to list on the making of Pueblo Indian pottery. Be sure to include the most important steps in the process. Write your list on a separate sheet of paper.

Notes for Home: Your child combined information from two selections to create a how-to list for making pottery. ***Home Activity:*** Ask your child to select an activity such as making a bed or riding a bicycle. Together, list the steps included in the process of doing the activity.

Name ______________________________

REVIEW

Grammar: Proper Nouns and Adjectives

Directions: Rewrite each sentence correctly. Capitalize the proper nouns and adjectives.

1. ms. sams talked about the art of native peoples of north america.

____

2. Groups in the great plains, such as the sioux, decorated with beads.

____

3. In the united states, ancient stone dwellings are found in the southwest.

____

4. Hundreds of families lived in these dwellings in arizona and new mexico.

____

5. The american museum of natural history has a fine collection of native art.

____

6. Have you seen any mexican art?

____

7. Mexican art is another kind of american art.

____

8. Many items show a spanish influence.

____

9. Art is important to canadian groups too.

____

10. For example, inuit sculptures are world famous.

____

Notes for Home: Your child capitalized proper nouns and proper adjectives. ***Home Activity:*** Ask your child to write a paragraph about a place he or she would like to visit. Encourage your child to use proper nouns and adjectives in the paragraph.

Grammar: Capitalization

Use these rules for **capitalization:**

- Capitalize the first word of a sentence.

  My friend is an artist.

- Capitalize the first word and every important word of a proper noun. Remember, proper nouns name particular people, places, or things.

  His name is Joseph Stephens. He wrote a book called *How to Paint*.

- Capitalize the first letter of an abbreviation. An abbreviation is a shortened form of a word. It usually ends with a period. State name abbreviations use two capital letters and no periods.

  He lives in Flagstaff, AZ. His address is 182 Cottonwood St.

- Capitalize titles before people's names.

  Capt. Alice Stephens is his wife.

Directions: Rewrite each sentence, using correct capitalization.

1. mrs. johnson is a very good artist.

____

2. she lives in phoenix, az, in a big house.

____

3. her address is 17 bluebird road.

____

4. she teaches a class called "drawing can be fun!"

____

5. she has visited all 50 states, including alaska and hawaii.

____

Notes for Home: Your child practiced capitalizing proper nouns, abbreviations, and titles. ***Home Activity:*** Write down the names and addresses of some of your child's friends and relatives, without capitalizing them. Help him or her to capitalize each word correctly.

Name ______________________________

Grammar: Capitalization

Directions: Write **C** on the line for each group of words that is correctly capitalized. If a group of words is not correctly capitalized, rewrite it on the line, using correct capitalization.

______________________________ **1.** she created a new painting.

______________________________ **2.** Capt. Martin Anderson

______________________________ **3.** yuma, az

______________________________ **4.** *The Life of the buffalo*

______________________________ **5.** mr. peter alvarez

______________________________ **6.** 1313 Blue View Terrace

______________________________ **7.** los angeles, ca

Directions: Rewrite each sentence on the line, using proper capitalization.

8. frank has been an artist all his life.

____

9. his best friend is dr. russell mears.

____

10. together they wrote a book called *we are native americans.*

____

Write a Review

On a separate sheet of paper, write a review of a movie, book, or video you liked. Compare it to at least two other works. Remember to capitalize each proper noun you use in your review.

Notes for Home: Your child practiced capitalizing proper nouns, abbreviations, and titles. ***Home Activity:*** Write down some silly titles for books, movies, or videos without capitalizing them. Have your child correct the capitalizations.

Name ______________________________

RETEACHING

Grammar: Capitalization

Underline the sentence that is capitalized correctly.

1. I live at 2121 Dobson Ave.

2. my favorite book is called *cats and dogs.*

Use a **capital letter** to begin a **sentence.** Capitalize the first word and every important word of a **proper noun.** Proper nouns can be people, places, or things. Capitalize the first letter of an **abbreviation.** Also capitalize **titles** before people's names.

Directions: Capitalize each sentence correctly and write it on the line.

1. i live at 1501 kenmore st.

____

2. my sister turned six years old on may 6, 2000.

____

3. dr. peter montgomery is my dentist.

____

Directions: Write **correct** on the line next to each group of words that is capitalized correctly. Rewrite the others on the line, using correct capitalization.

______________ **4.** mrs. joanna thornton

______________ **5.** December 31, 1902

______________ **6.** the book *How I learned italian*

______________ **7.** Boston, Massachusetts

______________ **8.** he likes to write songs.

Notes for Home: Your child practiced capitalizing proper nouns, abbreviations, and titles. ***Home Activity:*** Have your child explain rules for using capital letters when writing.

Name ______________________________

Grammar: Capitalization

Directions: Look at each underlined word or group of words. Some of them have mistakes. Find twelve capitalization mistakes in the paragraph. Rewrite the incorrect words, using capital letters correctly.

my friend mr. Applebee has lived on town square st. for a long time. He has been teaching me how to play the piano since last march. He teaches kids from other families in harpersville too. On september 12, we will have a recital. Everyone in the town will be there, including capt. Maria Lopez from the police department. I am a little nervous, but mrs. applebee told me not to be scared. she gave me a book called *Your first recital* by r. j. Martin. now I'm ready!

1. ______________________________
2. ______________________________
3. ______________________________
4. ______________________________
5. ______________________________
6. ______________________________
7. ______________________________
8. ______________________________
9. ______________________________
10. ______________________________
11. ______________________________
12. ______________________________

Directions: Rewrite each sentence, using correct capitalization.

13. rita and tony are going to visit their aunt and uncle.

____

14. aunt gina and uncle andrew live in atlanta, georgia.

____

15. they are planning to visit the fernbank museum of natural history.

____

16. they haven't seen their aunt and uncle since january two years ago!

____

Notes for Home: Your child corrected mistakes in capitalization. ***Home Activity:*** Write (without capital letters) a list of titles and authors of books your child has read. Have him or her capitalize the titles and authors correctly.

Name ______________________________

Word Study: Irregular Plurals

Directions: Most plurals are formed by adding **-s** or **-es.** Some words change their spelling to become plural. Some words have the same singular and plural form. Both of these types of words are called **irregular plurals.** Read each word below. Write the plural form of the word on the line.

1. child ______________________

2. deer ______________________

3. sheep ______________________

4. man ______________________

5. moose ______________________

6. person ______________________

7. foot ______________________

8. fish ______________________

9. woman ______________________

10. goose ______________________

Directions: Each sentence below has two plural nouns. Circle the plural nouns in each sentence. Then write just the irregular plurals on the lines.

One day last summer we went to a shop where two women make musical instruments. On Saturdays, visitors could make something to play too. We built shoe-box guitars, then tapped our feet to the music we made. We sang songs about fish swimming upstream and one funny song about a humpback whale. People listened and sang along, and the children had a lot of fun.

11. ______________________

12. ______________________

13. ______________________

14. ______________________

15. ______________________

Notes for Home: Your child wrote irregular plural words, such as *children, deer,* and *feet.* ***Home Activity:*** Write plural words on index cards. Include examples of irregular plurals. Ask your child to sort the words into two piles—regular and irregular.

Name ______________________________________

Pretest

Spelling: Capitalization and Abbreviation

Pretest Directions: Fold back the page along the dotted line. On the blanks, write the spelling words as they are dictated. When you have finished the test, unfold the page and check your words.

1. ______________________________
2. ______________________________
3. ______________________________
4. ______________________________
5. ______________________________
6. ______________________________
7. ______________________________
8. ______________________________
9. ______________________________
10. ______________________________
11. ______________________________
12. ______________________________
13. ______________________________
14. ______________________________
15. ______________________________
16. ______________________________
17. ______________________________
18. ______________________________
19. ______________________________
20. ______________________________

1. It's a **Memorial Day** picnic.
2. Will you be home for **Christmas**?
3. My birthday is in **May**.
4. They were married in **June**.
5. School starts in **September**.
6. **Hanukkah** candles are burning.
7. There's a **Kwanzaa** fest tonight.
8. **Chinese New Year** is coming up!
9. I got a card for **Valentine's Day**.
10. We will visit you in **November**.
11. Today is **Sun.**, March 8.
12. We fly out on **Dec.** 19.
13. This is my mom, **Dr.** Nunez.
14. She's also called **Mrs.** Nunez.
15. They live on Sheraton **Rd.**
16. It's on **Feb.** 14, I think.
17. The tickets say "**Wed.**, May 1."
18. My name is **Ms.** Wood.
19. His name is **Mr.** Delmar.
20. They live on Atlantic **Ave.**

Notes for Home: Your child took a pretest on words that are capitalized and abbreviated. ***Home Activity:*** Help your child learn misspelled words before the final test. Dictate the word and have your child write the word on paper, including the capital letter and/or a period.

Name ______________________________

Spelling: Capitalization and Abbreviation

Directions: Choose the words from the box that name holidays or months. Write the words in the correct columns.

Word List	
Memorial Day	Sun.
Christmas	Dec.
May	Dr.
June	Mrs.
September	Rd.
Hanukkah	Feb.
Kwanzaa	Wed.
Chinese New Year	Ms.
Valentine's Day	Mr.
November	Ave.

Holidays	Months
1. ____________	7. ____________
2. ____________	8. ____________
3. ____________	9. ____________
4. ____________	10. ____________
5. ____________	11. ____________
6. ____________	12. ____________

Directions: Choose an abbreviation from the box that best completes each sentence. Write the abbreviation on the line to the left. Use an abbreviation only once.

____________ **13.** If you're ill, we can go see _____ Levenson.

____________ **14.** We're going to meet Mr. Jones and his wife, _____ Jones.

____________ **15.** My neighbor, _____ Winston, says she doesn't want to get married.

____________ **16.** I live at 38 Kingston _____.

____________ **17.** My best friend lives at 857 Rushmore _____.

____________ **18.** _____ is a weekend day.

____________ **19.** _____ is in the middle of the week.

____________ **20.** Our plumber is _____ George Smith.

Notes for Home: Your child spelled abbreviations and words that are always capitalized. ***Home Activity:*** Make a list with your child of other abbreviations and proper nouns that require capital letters.

Name ______________________________

Spelling: Capitalization and Abbreviation

Directions: Proofread this letter. Find five spelling mistakes. Use the proofreading marks to correct each mistake.

≡ Make a capital.
/ Make a small letter.
∧ Add something.
Take out something.
⊙ Add a period.
¶ Begin a new paragraph.

Dear ms. Duke,

This coming may, on Memmorial Day, my family and I will be visiting your town. I would love to visit your pottery workshop. If you agree, please send directions to my mother, Mrs. Kim Lee, at 100 Coldfield rd., Denver, CO 35009. Thank you!

Sincerely,

Mr Vernon Lee

Spelling Tip

Holidays, days and months of the year, titles, and words that are part of an address are always capitalized: **Kwanzaa, November.** Abbreviations should be capitalized and followed by a period: **Dr., Mrs.**

Word List

Memorial Day	Sun.
Christmas	Dec.
May	Dr.
June	Mrs.
September	Rd.
Hanukkah	Feb.
Kwanzaa	Wed.
Chinese New Year	Ms.
Valentine's Day	Mr.
November	Ave.

Write a Letter

On a separate sheet of paper, write a reply from Ms. Duke, inviting Vernon Lee to visit her pottery workshop. Use at least four spelling words, including at least one abbreviation.

Notes for Home: Your child spelled abbreviations and words that are always capitalized. ***Home Activity:*** Say the full word for one of the abbreviations on the list and have your child write the abbreviation. Make sure he or she includes capital letters and periods.

Name ________________________________

REVIEW

Spelling: Capitalization and Abbreviation

Directions: Choose the word from the box that is an abbreviation for each word below. Write the word on the line.

Word List	
Memorial Day	Sun.
Christmas	Dec.
May	Dr.
June	Mrs.
September	Rd.
Hanukkah	Feb.
Kwanzaa	Wed.
Chinese New Year	Ms.
Valentine's Day	Mr.
November	Ave.

1. doctor ________

2. mister ________

3. avenue ________

4. road ________

5. Wednesday ________

6. Sunday ________

7. December ________

8. February ________

Directions: Choose the word from the box that best matches each clue. Write the word on the line.

9. fifth month ________________

10. sixth month ________________

11. ninth month ________________

12. eleventh month ________________

13. title for a married woman ________________

14. title for a married or unmarried woman ________________

15. February 14 ________________

16. holiday to remember soldiers who have died ________________

17. Jewish eight-day "festival of lights" ________________

18. December 25 ________________

19. African American celebration that starts on December 26 ________________

20. four-day festival that features dragons and firecrackers ________________

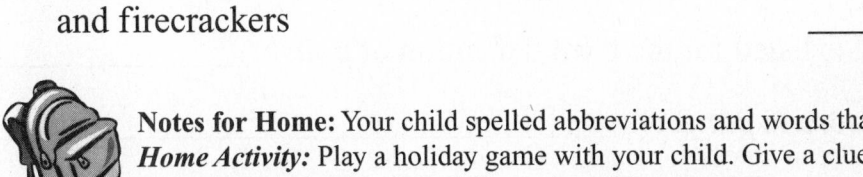

Notes for Home: Your child spelled abbreviations and words that are always capitalized. ***Home Activity:*** Play a holiday game with your child. Give a clue about a holiday and invite your child to identify the holiday and spell it correctly.

Dictionary

A **dictionary** is a book of words and their meanings. A **glossary** is a short dictionary at the back of some books that contain the definitions for words used in a specific book. You can use a **dictionary** or **glossary** to find a word's meaning.

Here are some things to know about using a dictionary:

- The words at the top of a dictionary page are called **guide words.** They show the first and last words on the page.
- If your word fits alphabetically between the two guide words, it is included on that page.
- When you find your word, you will see letters and symbols in parentheses. This **pronunciation key** tells how to say the word.
- The **definition** tells the meaning of the word. Choose the definition that makes the most sense in the sentence containing the word. Example sentences and illustrations may help define the word. Sometimes there is more than one meaning for a word.
- The **part of speech** tells how the word is used, such as a verb or noun.

Directions: Use these dictionary entries to answer the questions that follow.

polish/power

pol•ish (pol ´ ish), **1** to make or become smooth and shiny: *to polish shoes. The silverware polished beautifully.* **2** a substance used to give smoothness or shine: *silver polish.* **3** Smoothness or shininess: *The polish of the furniture reflected our faces like a mirror.* 1,2 *verb,* 2,3 *noun, plural* **po • lish • es.**

pot•ter•y (pot ´ ər ē), pots, dishes, or vases made from clay and hardened by heat. *noun.*

scrawl/script

scrawl (skrȯl), **1** to write or draw poorly or carelessly. **2** poor, careless handwriting. 1 *verb,* 2 *noun.*

scream (skrēm), **1** to make a loud, sharp, piercing cry. People scream in fright, in anger, and in excitement. **2** a loud, sharp, piercing cry. 1 *verb,* 2 *noun.*

1. What are the guide words for the page on which the entry word *scream* appears?

____

2. What part of speech is listed for the third definition of *polish?* ____________

3. How many syllables are in *pottery?* ______________________

4. What part of the entry for *polish* tells what the word sounds like? Write that part here.

____

5. Does the *e* in *pottery* sound like the *e* in *scream?* ___________

6. List one other word that might appear on a page that has *polish* and *power* as its guide words.

____

7. What is the plural form of *polish?* ___________

8. How many definitions does *scream* have? ___________

9. What part of speech is listed for the first definition of *scream?* ___________

10. How many definitions does *polish* have? ___________

11. Which of the four words listed is used as a noun only? ___________

12. List one word that might appear on the page just before the page with *scrawl.*

____

13. How is the word *scrawl* used in the following sentence? *He scrawled his signature on the check.*

____

14. Write the meaning of *scream* that is used in this sentence: *I scream every time I see a spider.*

____

____

15. Write a sentence using the third definition of *polish.*

____

____

Notes for Home: Your child practiced using a dictionary. ***Home Activity:*** Read a news article with your child and have him or her circle any unfamiliar words. Together, look up these words in a dictionary and discuss their meanings.

Family Times

Name____

Summary

Langston Hughes Finds "Home" at Last

Langston Hughes lived in Lawrence, Kansas, with his grandmother. Granma Mary Langston was poor, but she loved Langston and took care of him as best she could. Langston missed his mother and his father, who lived far away and rarely visited. Then one day, Langston went to live with Auntie and Uncle Reed. After being alone for many of his early years, Langston at last found a place that felt like home.

Activity

Home Is Where.... Let your child tell you more about what "home" meant to Langston Hughes. Then take turns completing the sentence "Home is where...." to tell about what home means to you.

Reading Skills

Fact and Opinion

A **statement of fact** tells something that can be proved true or false. A **statement of opinion** tells a person's ideas or feelings. It cannot be proved true or false, but it can be supported by facts and reasons.

In *Coming Home,* the author gives statements of fact about Langston Hughes that can be proved: where he lived, whom he lived with, and so forth. He also gives statements of opinion, such as "Langston never had a home like most people."

Activity

Play "Fact or Opinion?" Play this game with two or more people. One person talks. When he or she makes a statement of fact, the others stand up. When he or she makes a statement of opinion, the others stay seated.

Family Times

Tested Vocabulary

Words to Know

Knowing the meanings of these words is important to reading *Coming Home.* Practice using these words to learn their meanings.

dreamer someone who has a lot of dreams

drifted did not know or care where one was going

heroes people who are admired

librarians people who organize and run a library

rusty has a lot of rust

tremble shake with fear or excitement

Grammar

Commas

A **series** is a group of items. In a sentence, use commas to separate items in a series. An item can have more than one word, such as *beautiful poems.* No comma comes after the last word in a series.

Langston Hughes lived in Cleveland, Los Angeles, and New York City.

Activity

Make a List. Turn your grocery list into a way to practice using commas. Take turns writing sentences that tell three or more things that your family needs. For example: **We need milk, juice, and cereal.** Talk about where the commas go.

Tested Spelling Words

________	________	________	________
________	________	________	________
________	________	________	________
________	________	________	________
________	________	________	________

Name ______________________________

Fact and Opinion

- A **statement of fact** tells something that can be proved true or false.
- A **statement of opinion** tells your ideas or feelings. It cannot be proved true or false, but it can be supported by facts and reasons. Sometimes statements of opinion begin with clues such as *I believe.*

Directions: Reread the book review of *Naomi's Geese.* Then complete the tables. Identify statements of fact and statements of opinion from the review. Some have been done for you.

Fact
The book is about Naomi and two geese.
The reviewer's family moved to a lake in Maine.
1.
2.
3.

Opinion
I was worried about the loons.
I like how the geese called pieces of bread "fluffy white things."
4.
5.

Notes for Home: Your child read a book review and identified statements of fact and opinion. ***Home Activity:*** Choose a recent family event, such as a visit to a relative's house. Take turns telling statements of fact and opinion about the event.

Name ____________________

Vocabulary

Directions: Choose the word from the box that best matches each clue. Write the word on the line.

Check the Words You Know

- __ dreamer
- __ drifted
- __ heroes
- __ librarians
- __ rusty
- __ tremble

____________ **1.** It's what your bike will become if you leave it out in the rain.

____________ **2.** It's what you are if you spend more time asleep than awake.

____________ **3.** These are people who do things that other people admire.

____________ **4.** These are people who can't keep their hands off a good book.

Directions: Choose the word from the box that best replaces each underlined word or words. Write the word on the line.

____________ **5.** Traci had many people she admired.

____________ **6.** She loved books, and so she also admired people who ran libraries.

____________ **7.** Traci was a person who had a lot of dreams.

____________ **8.** One day in the attic, she found an old metal box that was covered in rust.

____________ **9.** She thought she had found a hidden treasure, and she began to shake with excitement.

____________ **10.** The box held old postcards of an uncle who had wandered from one interesting town to another.

Write a Poem

On a separate sheet of paper, write a poem about a wish or a dream. Use vocabulary words in your poem.

Notes for Home: Your child identified and used vocabulary words from *Coming Home: From the Life of Langston Hughes.* ***Home Activity:*** Ask your child to write six sentences, each one including a different vocabulary word.

Fact and Opinion

- A **statement of fact** tells something that can be proved true or false.
- A **statement of opinion** tells your ideas or feelings. It cannot be proved true or false.

Directions: Reread what happens in *Coming Home: From the Life of Langston Hughes* when Langston's mother comes to visit him. Then follow the instructions below.

Other times Langston's ma would come to Lawrence. Once it wasn't the best of times for her. Money was scarce. She snapped at Langston and it hurt.

Later that evening they went to St. Luke's Church where Langston's ma was giving a performance. She told him that she had a wonderful surprise for him. That he was going to be on the stage with her. That he was going to be a star, just like she was going to be.

Langston didn't like the surprise. That evening he was the one with the surprise. As his ma introduced him, behind her back Langston made faces: He crossed his eyes, stretched his mouth, and imitated her. Everyone burst out laughing.

1. Tell whether this statement is fact or opinion: "Once it wasn't the best of times for her." Explain your answer.

___

2. Tell whether this statement is fact or opinion: "Money was scarce." Explain your answer.

___

3. Give a statement of fact from the second paragraph.

___

4. Tell an opinion that Langston's mother expresses in the second paragraph.

___

5. Reread the story. On a separate sheet of paper, write three statements of fact about Langston Hughes and two statements of opinion about him.

Notes for Home: Your child read a biography and identified statements of fact and opinion. ***Home Activity:*** Think of a recent family event, such as a party or visit from a relative. Ask your child to tell two facts and two opinions about the event.

Name ________________________________

Selection Test

Directions: Choose the best answer to each item. Mark the letter for the answer you have chosen.

Part 1: Vocabulary

Find the answer choice that means about the same as the underlined word in each sentence.

1. The leaves began to <u>tremble</u>.
- A. move or shake
- B. grow quickly
- C. change color
- D. wither and die

2. The pot is <u>rusty</u>.
- F. large and heavy
- G. having many dents or bumps
- H. dripping or leaking
- J. covered with a reddish coating

3. Every child needs <u>heroes</u>.
- A. true friends
- B. people who are admired
- C. wise teachers
- D. thoughtful adults

4. He has always been a <u>dreamer</u>.
- F. one who is usually sad
- G. person who acts young
- H. one who imagines how things might be
- J. person who causes harm

5. The <u>librarians</u> can help us.
- A. ideas that are written down
- B. people who write books
- C. collections of things to read
- D. persons who work in libraries

6. People <u>drifted</u> through the park.
- F. moved easily or without care
- G. searched or looked about
- H. whispered or spoke softly
- J. rushed by

Part 2: Comprehension

Use what you know about the selection to answer each item.

7. Langston Hughes grew up in—
- A. Mexico.
- B. Kansas.
- C. Oklahoma.
- D. New York.

8. In his early years, Langston dreamed mostly of—
- F. becoming an actor.
- G. meeting famous people.
- H. learning to play jazz music.
- J. living with his pa and ma.

GO ON

9. You can tell from this selection that Langston's mother—
- A. cared a lot about her acting career.
- B. wanted Langston to be a dancer.
- C. liked living in different places.
- D. wanted Langston to be a writer.

10. How did Langston feel when he went to live with the Reeds?
- F. frightened and sad
- G. selfish and spoiled
- H. lonesome and bored
- J. happy and loved

11. Langston loved to tell his friends stories about—
- A. his mother and father.
- B. performing on stage.
- C. black people he admired.
- D. visiting the library.

12. Langston Hughes became a—
- F. writer.
- G. teacher.
- H. congressman.
- J. preacher.

13. Which sentence states a fact?
- A. "Living with Granma wasn't easy."
- B. "Auntie Reed's church was all right."
- C. "One day she took Langston all the way to Topeka to hear Booker T. Washington speak."
- D. "The singing and preaching felt so familiar."

14. Which sentence best describes Langston Hughes?
- F. He found home in his heart.
- G. He liked to be alone.
- H. He counted on other people to help him.
- J. He felt sorry for himself.

15. Which sentence states an opinion?
- A. Langston was chosen class poet.
- B. After school, he'd run and play with friends.
- C. Granma used to work on the Underground Railroad.
- D. Buffalo soldiers were the bravest of all.

STOP

Name ____________________

Fact and Opinion

- A **statement of fact** tells something that can be proved true or false.
- A **statement of opinion** tells ideas or feelings. It cannot be proved true or false.

Directions: Read the passage below.

Gwendolyn Brooks is one of the greatest poets of our time. She has won many awards. She was the first African American to receive the Pulitzer Prize, a famous prize for the best book of the year. She was also chosen *poet laureate* of Illinois. (A poet laureate is an honored and official poet.)

Brooks was born on June 7, 1917, in Topeka, Kansas. Her first books, *A Street in Bronzeville* and *Annie Allen,* are full of beautiful but sad poems.

Brooks taught poetry for many years. She believes children are important poets. She is a generous person. She has given her own money for poetry prizes to elementary and high school poets.

Brooks has also written books to help young people write poetry: *Young Poets' Primer* and *Very Young Poets.* She is an excellent teacher and a great writer.

Directions: Use statements from the passage to complete the table.

Statements of Fact (can be proved true or false)	Statements of Opinion (tells ideas and feelings)
She received a Pulitzer Prize.	She is one of the greatest poets of our time.
1.	She has written many beautiful poems.
2.	3.
4.	5.

Notes for Home: Your child has read a biography and identified statements of fact and opinion. ***Home Activity:*** Ask your child to think of the last time your family ate dinner together. Invite him or her to tell you two facts and two opinions about that dinner.

Name ______________________________

REVIEW

Paraphrasing

Directions: Read the passage. Then read each question about the passage. Choose the best answer to each question. Mark the letter for the answer you have chosen.

Carl Sandburg: American Poet

Carl Sandburg wrote poems that found the beauty in ordinary people. His poetry shows his belief in "the common folk" and in their power to make the world a better place.

Sandburg worked many different jobs. For a while, he was a soldier. He did hard physical labor. He wrote for a newspaper. All of these experiences helped shape his poetry.

In addition to his poetry, Sandburg wrote a famous biography of President Abraham Lincoln. He also wrote children's books. The most famous is called *Rootabaga Stories.*

1. Sandburg wrote—
- **A.** long poems.
- **B.** poems about nature.
- **C.** poems about ordinary people.
- **D.** poems about famous people.

2. Sandburg's work—
- **F.** helped him write his poetry.
- **G.** prevented him writing poetry.
- **H.** was separate from his poetry.
- **J.** paid a lot of money.

3. Complete this paraphrase of the last paragraph: Sandburg also wrote —
- **A.** children's stories.
- **B.** a biography of Lincoln and children's stories.
- **C.** a biography of Lincoln.
- **D.** *Rootabaga Stories.*

4. Which detail would probably not be part of a paraphrase of the passage?
- **F.** Sandburg wrote poems about ordinary people.
- **G.** He worked many different jobs.
- **H.** He wrote children's books and a biography.
- **J.** He wrote *Rootabaga Stories.*

5. Complete this paraphrase of the whole passage: Carl Sandburg was an American poet who—
- **A.** worked at different jobs and wrote books as well as poetry.
- **B.** showed his belief in ordinary people through his writing.
- **C.** wrote a famous biography.
- **D.** worked many hard jobs.

Notes for Home: Your child read a passage and identified statements that paraphrased the passage's main ideas. ***Home Activity:*** Tell your child about something you did together today. Ask your child to paraphrase your story by retelling it in his or her own words.

Name ______________________________

Writing Across Texts

Directions: Consider what you already know and what you read in the selections *Coming Home* and "Koya's Cousin Del." What did coming home mean to Del and Langston Hughes? Complete the table below to explain how each character felt about home.

Del's Feelings About Home	Langston Hughes's Feelings About Home
He loved spending time with his family.	He did not like how quiet it was.
1.	6.
2.	7.
3.	8.
4.	9.
5.	10.

Write a Paragraph

On a separate sheet of paper, write a paragraph that compares and contrasts what Koya's cousin Del and Langston Hughes felt about coming home. Use the information in your table to help you write your paragraph.

Notes for Home: Your child compared the feelings of characters in two different selections. ***Home Activity:*** Read other selections with your child and have your child find similarities and differences among the characters.

Name ___________________________

Grammar: Compound Subjects and Objects

REVIEW

Directions: Combine each set of sentences by using a compound subject. Write your new sentence on the lines. (Remember, verbs must agree with the subject.)

1. Harlem is located in New York City. Greenwich Village is located in New York City also.

____

____

2. Many workers settled in Harlem in the 1920s. Many artists settled there too.

____

____

3. Writers made Harlem the center of African American culture. Musicians and artists did too.

____

____

Directions: Combine each set of sentences by using a compound object. Write your new sentence on the lines.

4. Musicians from the South brought jazz to Harlem. They brought other exciting music as well.

____

____

5. People everywhere were reading novels about African American life. They also were reading poems and plays about African American life.

____

____

Notes for Home: Your child combined sentences by using compound subjects and objects. ***Home Activity:*** Challenge your child to make up sets of sentences for you to combine using compound subjects and compound objects.

Grammar: Commas

A **series** is a group of items. Items in sentences can be nouns, verbs, or other words. In a sentence, commas are used to separate items in a series.

Langston Hughes, Nella Larsen, and Zora Neale Hurston were all Harlem writers.

When you speak to, or address, a person by name, you are using a name in **direct address.** Commas are used when the name is at the beginning, in the middle, or at the end of a sentence.

Louis, have you read the biography of Langston Hughes?
No, Tanya, I haven't.
Why not, Louis?

Commas are also used in dates and addresses:

- between the day and the month: *Friday, June 4*
- between the date and the year: *Tanya was born on June 5, 1991.*
- between the city and the state: *Burlington, Vermont*
- after the street address, the city, and the Zip Code, if the address appears in the middle of a sentence: *She moved to 23 W. 5th St., Columbus, Ohio 43216, when she was five.*

Directions: Add commas as needed to each sentence.

1. Tanya is reading about writers painters and musicians who lived in Harlem.
2. Her favorite writers are Langston Hughes Richard Wright and Jessie Faucet.
3. Tanya what are you doing?
4. I am reading Mother.
5. I have to finish this book call Grandma and write my report.
6. Tanya's grandma lives in Marquette Michigan 49855 near a lake.
7. She was born on March 9 1942 and lived in Harlem for many years.
8. Tanya plans to do her research organize her notes and write her report.
9. Grandma have you ever read any books by Langston Hughes?
10. Yes Tanya he is one of my favorite writers.

Notes for Home: Your child used commas to separate items in a series, with names used in direct address, in dates, and in addresses. ***Home Activity:*** Look through a book with your child and ask him or her to explain why commas are used as they are.

Grammar: Commas

Directions: Add commas as needed to each sentence.

1. Keisha Jennifer and Otto had to choose a subject for a school report.
2. Keisha help us pick a famous writer.
3. Otto and Jennifer weren't sure if they wanted to write about an author a songwriter or a poet.
4. They knew that Langston Hughes wrote books stories poems and plays.
5. They began their research on Friday January 16.
6. Their report was due in two weeks on Friday January 30.
7. They went to the library bookstores and the school's computer lab.
8. Jennifer took lots of books home read them and returned them to the library.
9. Keisha even wrote to a library at 1185 6th Ave. New York New York 10036 to get more information.
10. The information arrived on Monday January 26.
11. Otto's mother sister and brother helped him do research on the Internet.
12. At last, the three friends finished their report on Thursday January 29.
13. They read the report to their teacher classmates and the school principal.
14. Everyone agreed it was the best report their school in Newark New Jersey had ever seen!
15. Class let's applaud these three students!

Write a Letter

Write a letter to a favorite author. List at least three of your favorite books by that author and describe some of the things you like about them. Remember to use commas in your letter.

Notes for Home: Your child used commas in a series, in direct address, and in dates and addresses. ***Home Activity:*** Ask your child to name three of something, such as three favorite colors. Then have him or her write the three in a list, using commas correctly.

Name ______________________________

RETEACHING

Grammar: Commas

Underline the sentence in which commas are used correctly.

1. He read many books, written in Chicago Illinois.
2. Laura, Danielle, and Sophie are going to the show.
3. Alicia are you, coming too?

Use **commas** to separate items in a **series.** Also use a comma to separate a name in **direct address** from the rest of the sentence. In a **date,** use commas between the day and the month, and between the date and the year. In an **address,** use a comma between the city and the state, and after the street address, the city, and the Zip Code if the address is in the middle of a sentence.

Directions: Add commas to each sentence as needed.

1. Andreas left Alaska on July 17 1996.
2. A book a game a rope and a box sat on the windowsill.
3. Bill do you know where your brother is?
4. Pants more socks and a shirt covered a chair.
5. Karen bring me the new blanket.
6. A bank another game and a horseshoe were on the rug.
7. His desk was dirty wobbly and messy.
8. Jeanne lives at 1002 Sue Parkway Ann Arbor MI 48103.
9. Some marbles a pencil and a sweater were under his bed.
10. José was born on October 1 1990.

Notes for Home: Your child corrected sentences by adding commas. ***Home Activity:*** Write a brief letter to your child, leaving out commas in dates, series, and addresses. Have your child correct the letter by adding commas where they belong.

Name ______________________________

Grammar: Commas

Directions: Add commas where they are needed in these sentences.

1. Puerto Rico Jamaica and Hispaniola are all Caribbean islands.

2. The weather in Puerto Rico is usually warm breezy and pleasant.

3. The beaches tropical forests and water attract many tourists.

4. Children play swim and build sand castles along the beaches.

5. Some of Puerto Rico's major products are milk eggs and coffee.

A GOOD PLACE TO BE

Write a Travel Brochure

Write a travel brochure to attract tourists to Puerto Rico. Describe what it's like there and what people can do to have fun. Include at least three sentences that use items in a series. Remember to separate the items with commas.

Notes for Home: Your child identified and wrote commas in a series of items in sentences. ***Home Activity:*** Have your child write sentences that list what he or she will do over the weekend. Remind your child to include commas between items in the list.

Name ______________________________________

Phonics: Consonant Sounds /k/ and /f/

Word List				
books	enough	America	trophy	kitchen
family	beautiful	Kansas	tracks	Buffalo

Directions: Read the words in the box. Listen for words that have the sound /k/ and words that have the sound /f/. Write each word in the correct column.

Words with the sound /k/	**Words with the sound /f/**
1. ______________	6. ______________
2. ______________	7. ______________
3. ______________	8. ______________
4. ______________	9. ______________
5. ______________	10. ______________

Directions: Read each sentence below. Listen for the word that has the sound /k/ or /f/. Circle the word and write it on the line. Underline the letters that stand for the sound /k/ or /f/.

______________ **11.** As he played in his backyard, the young boy heard the whistle of the passing train.

______________ **12.** He ran to the fence to watch the train go by.

______________ **13.** "Someday, I hope to ride on the train," he said to himself.

______________ **14.** He listened to the clickety-clack of the wheels.

______________ **15.** He laughed and waved at people in the train.

Notes for Home: Your child identified different letters that represent the sound /k/, *(c, k, ck)* and the sound /f/, *(f, ff, gh, ph)*. ***Home Activity:*** While reading with your child, take turns trying to find words with these two sounds.

Name ____________________________________

Pretest

Spelling: Words with /k/ and /f/

Pretest Directions: Fold back the page along the dotted line. On the blanks, write the spelling words as they are dictated. When you have finished the test, unfold the page and check your words.

1. ____________________
2. ____________________
3. ____________________
4. ____________________
5. ____________________
6. ____________________
7. ____________________
8. ____________________
9. ____________________
10. ____________________
11. ____________________
12. ____________________
13. ____________________
14. ____________________
15. ____________________
16. ____________________
17. ____________________
18. ____________________
19. ____________________
20. ____________________

1. Take **care** when you travel.
2. I'm going **because** I have to.
3. This blanket will **cover** me well.
4. His time broke the world **record**.
5. Hit the **brake**; we need to stop.
6. **Kansas** is a prairie state.
7. I can't keep **track** of all this.
8. Put this in your **pocket**.
9. She ate an apple for a **snack**.
10. The bear cubs will not **attack**.
11. Our hands are **stiff** and cold.
12. This **muffin** tastes good.
13. The **giraffe** ate its fill of leaves.
14. They have eaten **enough**.
15. We **laughed** at his joke.
16. The trail was **rough** to climb.
17. Who is that in the **photo**?
18. The **alphabet** soup is ready.
19. The **dolphin** swims quickly.
20. Look at the gray **elephant**.

Notes for Home: Your child took a pretest on words that have the /k/ and /f/ sound. ***Home Activity:*** Help your child learn misspelled words before the final test. Your child can underline the word parts that caused the problems and concentrate on those parts.

Name ________________________________

Spelling: Words with /k/ and /f/

Word List

care	brake	snack	giraffe	photo
because	Kansas	attack	enough	alphabet
cover	track	stiff	laughed	dolphin
record	pocket	muffin	rough	elephant

Directions: Choose the words from the box that have the consonant sound /f/. Write the words in the correct columns.

Spelled ph	Spelled ff	Spelled gh
1. ________	5. ________	8. ________
2. ________	6. ________	9. ________
3. ________	7. ________	10. ________
4. ________		

Directions: Choose the word from the box that best matches each clue. Write the word on the line.

________ **11.** Unlike golf, a hole in one of these isn't good.

________ **12.** It's something you eat between two meals.

________ **13.** You can run on one, or race a car on one.

________ **14.** Never say, "I don't ____ about you."

________ **15.** Ask why, and the answer may start with this word.

________ **16.** It's where Dorothy and Toto came from.

________ **17.** If you're going too fast, do this.

________ **18.** An animal might do this if cornered.

________ **19.** It wraps around the pages of a book.

________ **20.** If you set one of these, you should be proud.

Notes for Home: Your child spelled words with the consonant sounds /k/ and /f/. ***Home Activity:*** Read the words on the list aloud, one at a time. Ask your child to tell you the letters that represent either the sound /k/ or /f/ in each word.

Name ______________________________

Spelling: Words with /k/ and /f/

Directions: Proofread this invitation to a poetry reading. Find five spelling mistakes. Use the proofreading marks to correct each mistake.

- ≡ Make a capital.
- / Make a small letter.
- ∧ Add something.
- ⌇ Take out something.
- ⊙ Add a period.
- ¶ Begin a new paragraph.

You Are Invited

In honor of Animal Week, Kansis State University will hold a poetry contest on Friday night at the auditorium. Poems about dolfins, elephants, and girafes will be read. A snack will be served. A foto of the winner will appear on the kover of next month's poetry journal.

Spelling Tip

The sound /k/ can be spelled **c, k,** or **ck.** The sound /f/ can be spelled **ff, gh,** or **ph.** It's hard to tell when you have to use **ck** or when a simple **c** or **k** will do. Check the invitation to make sure words with these consonant sounds are spelled correctly.

Word List

care	brake	snack	giraffe	photo
because	Kansas	attack	enough	alphabet
cover	track	stiff	laughed	dolphin
record	pocket	muffin	rough	elephant

Write an Invitation

On a separate sheet of paper, write an invitation to a poetry reading. Try to use at least three spelling words.

Notes for Home: Your child spelled words with the consonant sounds /k/ and /f/. ***Home Activity:*** Have your child think of words that are similar to the spelling words (for example: *careful, snacking, pocketful),* and have him or her try to spell these longer words.

Name ______________________________

Spelling Words with /k/ and /f/ REVIEW

Word List				
care	brake	snack	giraffe	photo
because	Kansas	attack	enough	alphabet
cover	track	stiff	laughed	dolphin
record	pocket	muffin	rough	elephant

Directions: Choose the word from the box that rhymes with each word below. Write the word on the line. Use a word only once.

1. sack ______________________
2. fake ______________________
3. socket ______________________
4. sniff ______________________
5. puffin ______________________
6. raft ______________________
7. hover ______________________
8. stack ______________________
9. rack ______________________
10. pause ______________________
11. sword ______________________
12. staff ______________________

Directions: Choose the word from the box that best replaces each underlined word. Write the word on the line to the left.

________________ 13. Being a poet can be a little difficult.

________________ 14. Many people don't think about poetry.

________________ 15. But if you want it a lot, you can be a poet.

________________ 16. You might not have your picture in the paper.

________________ 17. People might not know your name in a Midwestern state.

________________ 18. But you'll make good use of the letters.

________________ 19. You can write about a big gray animal.

________________ 20. Or you can write about a porpoise, if you prefer.

Notes for Home: Your child spelled words with consonant sounds /k/ and /f/. ***Home Activity:*** Write the spelling words in a list, but spell some words incorrectly. Challenge your child to check the list and correct any misspellings.

Name ______________________________________

Organize and Present Information/Draw Conclusions

Before you prepare a report, you need to organize your information. For example, you might make a story map to record ideas about plot, setting, and characters in a story. You might use a cluster web to show facts and details about a person, place, or thing.

Directions: Reread *Coming Home.* Then complete the cluster web to give facts and details that you learned about Langston Hughes. Then answer the question that follows.

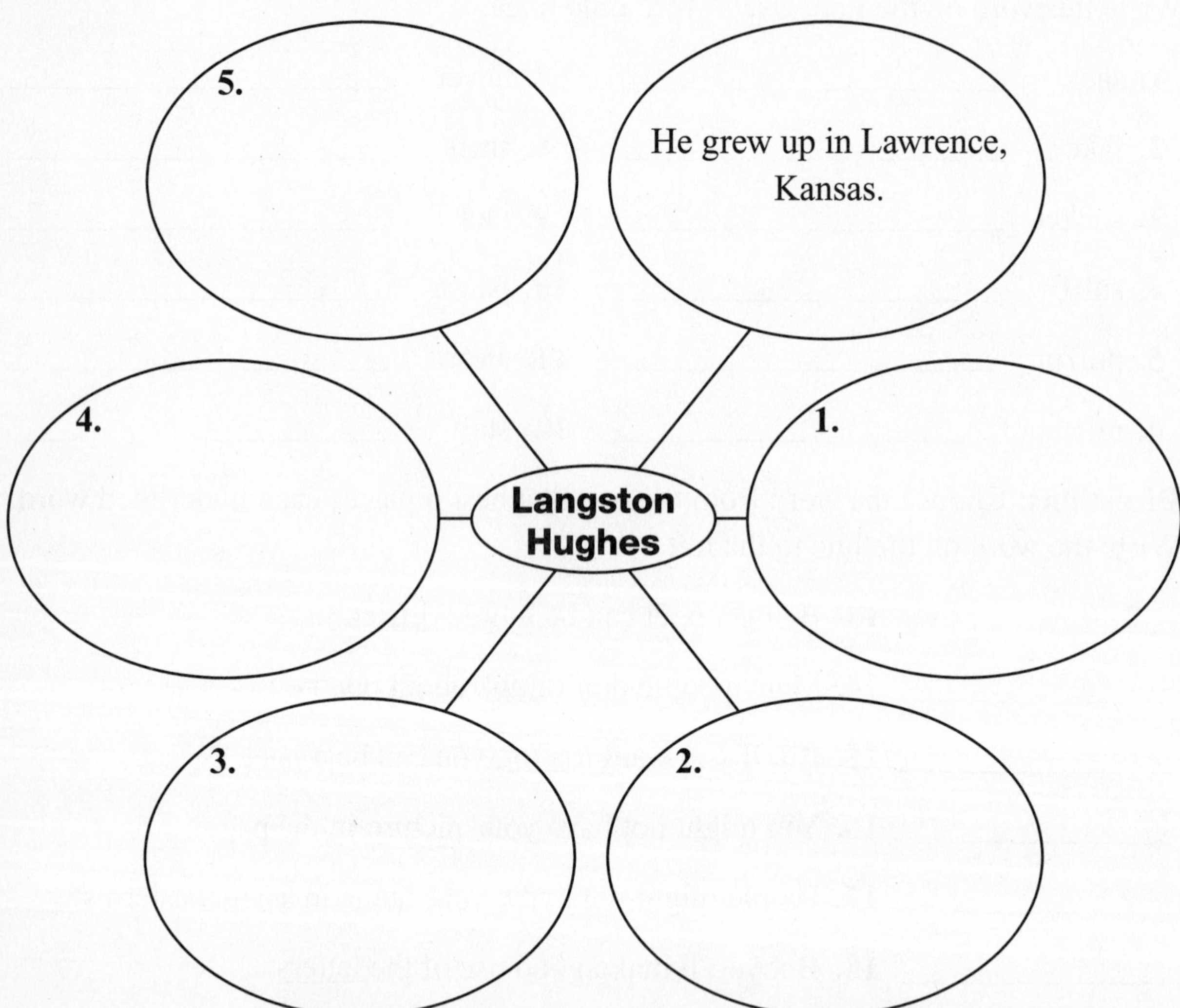

6. Did you find it helpful to organize information in a cluster web? Explain.

____

____

____

Name ______________________________

After you have collected information for a report, you have to present it to others. You could present your report orally, write a report or a story, draw a time line or make a drawing with captions. In your presentation, you should draw conclusions about the information you've organized to explain what it means.

Directions: Read each topic. Decide whether a written report, a time line, or a picture with captions would be the best method of presentation. Give an explanation to support each answer.

7. NASA space launches

____

____

____

8. poets of the 1950s

____

____

____

9. life cycle of a tree

____

____

____

10. Choose a strategy for organizing information, such as a story map, a time line, or a table. Explain why this strategy is useful for organizing information.

____

____

____

Notes for Home: Your child learned how to organize and present information. ***Home Activity:*** Work with your child to organize a story about his or her life. Use a time line to show important events. Have your child tell his or her story to family members or friends.

Family Times

Name ____

Summary

Inventor Ben Franklin Has Lots of Good Ideas!

Ben Franklin loved learning how to do things. As a young man in Philadelphia, he joined the Leather Apron Club, a group of people who liked to read and try out new ideas. Later, when he was 24, he married Debbie Read. Together, they ran a store. Though Ben Franklin was busy with the store and with a printshop, he never stopped thinking about and trying out new ideas. A big idea that made him famous was that electricity and lightning were the same.

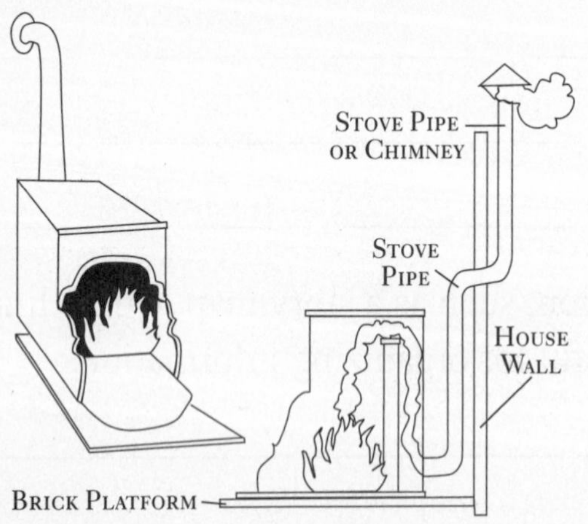

Activity
Talk About Ideas. Have your child tell you about some of the other creative ideas Ben Franklin had, such as a stove. Then talk about some of your own creative ideas. Which of those ideas could you try out?

Reading Skills

Main Idea and Supporting Details

A **topic** is what a story is about. The **main idea** is the most important idea about the topic. **Supporting details** are small pieces of information that tell more about the main idea.

In "Out of the Blue," the topic is Ben Franklin. The main idea is the fact that Ben Franklin was a creative person who had lots of useful and interesting ideas. Some supporting details are the names of the things that Benjamin Franklin invented.

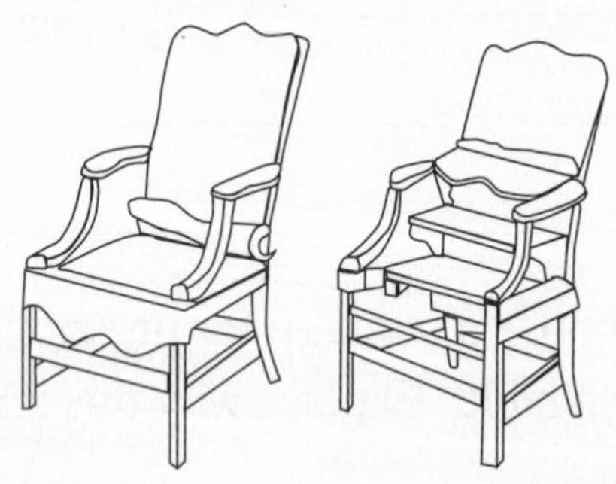

Activity
Share Ideas and Details. Try this with one or more people. One person tells a main idea, such as: **Our family takes fun trips.** The others share supporting details, such as names of places that you visited.

Family Times

Tested Vocabulary

Words to Know

Knowing the meanings of these words is important to reading "Out of the Blue." Practice using these words to learn their meanings.

almanac annual publication with information about many subjects

calendar chart showing months, weeks, days, and dates of a year

circulating distributing

electricity form of energy

experiment trial or test

inventions things invented

mysterious hard to explain or understand

theory explanation based on observation and reasoning

Grammar

Quotations/ Quotation Marks

A speaker's exact words are called a **quotation.** When you write a quotation, use quotation marks (" ") at the beginning and end of the speaker's words. Begin the quotation with a capital letter.

If the quotation comes first in a sentence, use a comma, question mark, or exclamation mark to separate it from the rest of the sentence: **"I have a great idea!" said the inventor.**

If the quotation comes last, use a comma to separate it: **He said, "I have a great idea!"**

Activity

TV Dialogue. Write dialogue for two characters on your favorite TV show. Write what each person says. Use quotation marks to show each person's exact words.

Tested Spelling Words

Name ________________________________

Main Idea and Supporting Details

- The **topic** is what a paragraph or article is all about.
- The **main idea** is the most important idea about the topic. Sometimes it is stated, and sometimes you have to figure it out and put it into your own words.
- **Supporting details** are small pieces of information that tell more about the main idea.

Directions: Reread "Working on the Railroad." Then complete the diagram by finishing the sentences that tell about the article's main idea and some of its supporting details.

Main Idea
1. Because railroad work was difficult and dangerous,

Supporting Details
2. The brakeman was in danger because
3. Andrew Beard created
4. Railroad firemen had to
5. Elijah McCoy invented

Notes for Home: Your child read an article and identified its main idea and some of its supporting details. ***Home Activity:*** Read a news article with your child. Together, identify the main idea of the article and take turns naming the supporting details.

Name ______________________________

Vocabulary

Directions: Choose the word from the box that best matches each definition. Write the word on the line.

Check the Words You Know
__ almanac
__ calendar
__ circulating
__ electricity
__ experiment
__ inventions
__ mysterious
__ theory

________________ **1.** chart showing months, weeks, days, and dates of a year

________________ **2.** form of energy that can produce light, heat, or motion

________________ **3.** hard to explain or understand

________________ **4.** explanation based on observation and reasoning

________________ **5.** a trial or a test to find out something

Directions: Choose the word from the box that best matches each clue. Write the word on the line.

________________ **6.** It has useful information.

________________ **7.** This is what library books are doing.

________________ **8.** These often become everyday tools, like toasters, automobiles, and computers.

________________ **9.** This runs your refrigerator and lights your house.

________________ **10.** Scientists use observation to help create this idea.

Write a Description

Imagine a new invention that would do some chore that you hate. On a separate sheet of paper, write a description of this invention and how it works. Use as many vocabulary words as you can.

Notes for Home: Your child identified and used vocabulary words from "Out of the Blue." ***Home Activity:*** Read each vocabulary word to your child and ask him or her to tell you what it means.

Name ______________________________

Main Idea and Supporting Details

- The **main idea** is the most important idea about the topic.
- **Supporting details** are small pieces of information that tell more about the main idea.

Directions: Reread the following passage in "Out of the Blue." Then answer the questions below.

Philadelphia suited young Benjamin perfectly. He lived on High Street, the busiest and noisiest street in town. On one end of the street was the Delaware River to jump into when he felt like a goat leap. On the other end of the street was Debbie Read, whom he courted and married.

Benjamin and Debbie were married in 1730. Benjamin was twenty-four years old now and getting ahead in the world. He had his own printshop, owned his own newspaper, and because he was such a good printer, he did the printing for the government of Pennsylvania. (He always used the blackest ink and the whitest paper he could find.) In addition, Debbie and Benjamin ran a store in the front of their house.

1. What is the main idea in the first paragraph?

____

2. Is the main idea in the first paragraph stated? Explain.

____

3. What is the main idea in the second paragraph?

____

4. What are two examples of supporting details in the second paragraph?

____

____

5. On a separate sheet of paper, tell the main idea of "Out of the Blue," and give two supporting details.

Notes for Home: Your child read a biography and identified its main ideas and supporting details. ***Home Activity:*** Read a newspaper article with your child. Ask your child to tell you the most important idea of the story. Take turns identifying supporting details.

Name ______________________________

Selection Test

Directions: Choose the best answer to each item. Mark the letter for the answer you have chosen.

Part 1: Vocabulary

Find the answer choice that means about the same as the underlined word in each sentence.

1. Where is the new <u>calendar</u>?
- A. large, heavy book
- B. chart of months and days
- C. list of places to see
- D. book of telephone numbers

2. There was no <u>electricity</u>.
- F. form of energy
- G. equipment used by scientists
- H. disagreement
- J. chance for people to vote

3. The <u>inventions</u> worked.
- A. wise sayings
- B. things created or thought up
- C. money set aside and saved
- D. builders or carpenters

4. We will do an <u>experiment</u>.
- F. trial or test
- G. report
- H. performance
- J. job or chore

5. The <u>almanac</u> is amusing.
- A. daily journal kept to record a person's ideas and activities
- B. postcard or letter
- C. yearly publication of brief information on many subjects
- D. storybook with pictures

6. She is a <u>mysterious</u> woman.
- F. very pretty
- G. old and wise
- H. highly skilled
- J. hard to understand

7. His <u>theory</u> interests me.
- A. training or education
- B. something made to be displayed
- C. way of behaving
- D. explanation based on observing

8. This is a <u>circulating</u> library book.
- F. popular or well liked
- G. passing from person to person
- H. easily torn or ripped
- J. uncommon or difficult to find

GO ON

Name ____________________

Part 2: Comprehension

Use what you know about the selection to answer each item.

9. In Philadelphia, Ben Franklin got a job with a—
- A. clothing maker.
- B. printer.
- C. watchmaker.
- D. sailor.

10. Members of the Leather Apron Club met every week to—
- F. talk about ideas.
- G. print newspapers.
- H. do experiments.
- J. make clothes.

11. You know that young Ben Franklin had many interests because he—
- A. went to work when he was 17.
- B. lived in Philadelphia.
- C. owned a printshop, a newspaper, and a store.
- D. made friends easily.

12. Publishing his almanac gave Ben Franklin a chance to—
- F. use his sense of humor.
- G. write about electricity.
- H. sell his inventions.
- J. tell how hurricanes move.

13. What is the main idea of this selection?
- A. Ben Franklin should have been a scientist.
- B. Ben Franklin improved the lives of people in Philadelphia.
- C. Most people liked Ben Franklin's ideas.
- D. Ben Franklin had many ideas, but his big one was that lightning is electricity.

14. Which sentence states an opinion?
- F. Electricity and lightning are the same.
- G. Lightning is as mysterious as heaven.
- H. Electricity is attracted to pointed iron rods.
- J. Ben Franklin felt an electric shock through a key tied to a kite.

15. In his lifetime, Ben Franklin was best known for his—
- A. magic squares.
- B. ideas about electricity.
- C. household inventions.
- D. writings about comets.

Name ____

Main Idea and Supporting Details

- The **main idea** is the most important idea about the topic.
- **Supporting details** are small pieces of information that tell more about the main idea.

Directions: Read the passage below.

Elijah McCoy was a famous inventor. He invented many things, including a folding ironing board, treads for tires, and a lawn sprinkler. He is best known for making different parts of a steam engine.

Elijah McCoy's inventions were popular. Because people wanted to be sure they were getting one of his inventions, not an imitation, they asked for "the real McCoy." This familiar phrase now means "the real thing" and not an imitation.

Elijah McCoy had a hard life before he became famous. His parents were slaves who had escaped from Kentucky to Canada. The McCoys had to work hard to take care of their twelve children.

Elijah McCoy first went to school in Canada. Later he learned to be an engineer in Edinburgh, Scotland. After Edinburgh, he went to Detroit. But he faced prejudice there. No one would hire him as an engineer, so he found work taking care of engines. That is when he invented better parts for steam engines.

Directions: Complete the diagram by telling the main idea of the passage. Then list supporting details that tell more about the main idea.

Main Idea
1. Elijah McCoy was

↓

Supporting Details
He made parts of a steam engine.
2.
3.
4.
5.

Notes for Home: Your child identified the main idea and supporting details in a passage. ***Home Activity:*** Tell your child about a place that you plan to visit. Give a few examples of things you will do. Ask your child to tell where you are going (main idea) and what you will do there (details).

Name ________________________________

REVIEW

Generalizing

Directions: Read the story. Then read each question about the story. Choose the best answer to each question. Mark the letter for the answer you have chosen.

Lydia LaRue: Great Inventor

Lydia LaRue wanted to be a great inventor. Her first invention was a new kind of alarm clock. A rooster crowed, which was supposed to wake up a mouse, who started running on a little wheel. The little wheel made a ball fall into a glass of water. Being splashed by the water woke the person up.

The first day Lydia tried out her invention, the rooster overslept. The second day, the mouse didn't wake up. By the third day, the water had dried up.

Lydia's second invention was a special kind of washing machine. In the bottom of the machine were three big fish. They were supposed to swim and splash, moving the water. However, the fish got sick from the laundry soap, so Lydia set them free.

"I'll never give up," Lydia vowed. "A person who works hard can always succeed."

1. Which generalization about Lydia's inventions is valid?

A. They are complicated.
B. They are simple.
C. They work well.
D. They are expensive.

2. Which generalization about Lydia's inventions is faulty?

F. They involve electricity.
G. They involve animals.
H. They involve water.
J. They imitate existing machines.

3. Which generalization about Lydia's first invention is valid?

A. Each part involved animals.
B. Each part involved water.
C. Each part involved electricity.
D. Each part failed to work.

4. Which of the following statements is a generalization?

F. Lydia has animals.
G. Lydia invents machines.
H. Lydia and Ben Franklin are both inventors.
J. Complicated ideas often do not work.

5. What clue word tells you that Lydia's last statement is a generalization?

A. I'll
B. works
C. hard
D. always

Notes for Home: Your child identified valid, or accurate, generalizations and faulty, or inaccurate, generalizations. ***Home Activity:*** Use the words *always, never, sometimes,* and *most* to make a broad statement about several things that is a valid generalization.

Name ______________________________

Writing Across Texts

Directions: Use information from "Out of the Blue" and "A Really Bright Idea" to compare the two inventors Benjamin Franklin and Thomas Edison. Fill in five facts about each inventor.

Benjamin Franklin	Thomas Edison
Born in 1706 in Boston.	His first invention was an electrical vote recorder in 1869.
1.	**6.**
2.	**7.**
3.	**8.**
4.	**9.**
5.	**10.**

Write a Comparison/Contrast Paragraph

On a separate sheet of paper, write a paragraph in which you compare and contrast the inventors Benjamin Franklin and Thomas Edison. Support your statements with information from "Out of the Blue" and "A Really Bright Idea."

Notes for Home: Your child combined and used information from two texts. ***Home Activity:*** As you read other stories and articles together, encourage your child to compare and contrast related information found in these reading materials.

Grammar: Commas

REVIEW

Directions: Add a comma where needed to each sentence.

1. The typewriter was invented in 1867 and this invention changed the world.
2. The typewriter seems old-fashioned now but it was an important invention.
3. The typewriter speeded up writing and it also brought more women into offices.
4. Was the telephone invented at the same time or did it come along later?
5. Alexander Graham Bell was the inventor and the first user of the telephone and he introduced it in 1876.
6. Tape recorders may seem modern but they first appeared in 1899.
7. Did Gabriel D. Fahrenheit invent the thermometer or was it invented by Anders Celsius?
8. Actually, Galileo invented the thermometer in 1593 and Gabriel D. Fahrenheit created the mercury thermometer.
9. An alcohol thermometer was invented in 1641 but Gabriel D. Fahrenheit's use of mercury in 1714 made it more accurate.
10. Anders Celsius developed a metric scale for the thermometer in 1742 and most thermometers today show both Fahrenheit and Celsius scales.
11. If you were around before 1849 you had trouble holding things together.
12. When the safety pin appeared in 1849 life became easier.
13. "After Velcro was invented in 1948" I said, "life became easier still."
14. If you wore a turtleneck sweater you didn't need either invention.
15. "Because humans are creative" my friend said, "new inventions appear every day."

Notes for Home: Your child used commas with compound sentences and complex sentences. ***Home Activity:*** Dictate sentences to your child from a book or a magazine. Challenge your child to add commas where needed.

Name ______________________________

Grammar: Quotations and Quotation Marks

A speaker's exact words are called a **quotation.** When you write a quotation, use **quotation marks (" ")** at the beginning and end of the speaker's exact words.

Ben Franklin said, "Early to bed and early to rise makes a man healthy, wealthy, and wise."

Rules:

- Begin the quotation with a capital letter.
- If the quotation comes last in a sentence, use a comma to separate it from the rest of the sentence.
- If the quotation comes first, use a comma, a question mark, or an exclamation mark to separate the quotation from the rest of the sentence.
- Periods and commas at the end of quotations appear before the quotation mark.
- If the quotation is a question or an exclamation, place the question mark or exclamation mark before the quotation marks at the end of the speaker's words.

"I like to experiment with my new science kit," said John.
"Don't blow up the house!" his sister joked.

Directions: Rewrite each sentence, adding quotation marks.

1. Have you seen the new invention Ben made? asked Letitia.

____

2. I haven't seen it yet, answered Thomas.

____

3. I can't wait to see it! said Letitia.

____

4. Thomas said, I heard it can light up a whole room!

____

5. Should I wear my sunglasses? asked Letitia.

____

Notes for Home: Your child used quotation marks to set off a speaker's exact words. ***Home Activity:*** Look at a favorite book with your child. Help him or her find examples of quotation marks. Talk about how they are used.

Name ________________________________

Extra Practice

Grammar: Quotations and Quotation Marks

Directions: Add quotation marks and the correct punctuation to each sentence.

1. Madeleine said I'm going to try my own experiment!
2. No you're not said her teacher.
3. Why not asked Madeleine.
4. Her teacher explained You have to do a lot of research before you try an experiment.
5. I guess I'd better think about it carefully said Madeleine.

Directions: Write sentences on the lines below to continue the conversation between Madeleine and her teacher. Use quotation marks in each sentence.

6. ________________________________
7. ________________________________
8. ________________________________
9. ________________________________
10. ________________________________

Write a Conversation

On a separate sheet of paper, write a conversation between two friends talking about a science experiment or an invention. Use quotation marks to show each speaker's exact words. Remember to put the punctuation that is part of a quotation *inside* the quotation marks.

Notes for Home: Your child practiced using quotation marks to enclose a speaker's exact words. ***Home Activity:*** Say three sentences and invite your child to record each one, using quotation marks, the proper punctuation, and the phrase: _____ *said.*

Name ____________________

RETEACHING

Grammar: Quotations and Quotation Marks

Read the sentences. Circle all the quotation marks. Underline all the periods, commas, question marks, and exclamation marks.

1. "I like to see the stars," Kirsten said.
2. "When should we look?" her brother asked.
3. Their mother called, "Come right now!"

Notice that a comma or an end mark always separates the quotation from the speaker.

Use **quotation marks** to show the exact words of a speaker. Place a comma, period, question mark, or exclamation mark just before the second quotation mark.

Directions: The exact words of the speaker are underlined. Write quotation marks where needed.

1. I found my telescope, called Kirsten.
2. Will you look at the stars tonight? asked her mother.
3. I will if the sky is clear, replied Kirsten.
4. Mars also will be in view, added her brother.
5. Her father asked, Are you excited?
6. I can't wait! cried Kirsten.

Directions: Write the correct punctuation marks in the spaces.

7. __ I'd love to travel in space __ __ exclaimed Kirsten __
8. __ Do you want to go to a certain planet __ __ asked her mother __

Notes for Home: Your child identified and punctuated quotations. ***Home Activity:*** Have your child interview you and summarize your responses to his or her questions. Remind your child to use quotation marks to show the exact words you used.

Name ________________________________

Grammar: Quotations and Quotation Marks

Directions: Write each sentence, adding quotation marks and other correct punctuation marks where needed.

1. I found a bird's nest in this tree said Scott.

____

2. What kind of nest is it asked Mark.

____

3. The nest has blue eggs in it replied Scott.

____

4. Don't touch the eggs Lea pleaded.

____

5. I would never do that Scott said.

____

Directions: Write the necessary four punctuation marks in each sentence.

6. __ I've read many books about bird nests __ __ said Scott __

7. __ Can you tell us an interesting fact __ __ asked Lea __

8. Scott said happily __ __ One kind of bird doesn't build a nest __ __

9. __ What does the bird do with its eggs __ __ asked Mary __

10. __ It lays one egg on a branch and sits on it __ __ stated Scott __

11. Lea exclaimed __ __ That's really amazing __ __

Write a Conversation

On a separate sheet of paper, write a conversation between you and a friend about a bird you have read about or seen. Include quotations in your conversation.

Notes for Home: Your child wrote and punctuated quotations—the exact words of a speaker. ***Home Activity:*** Have your child write an imaginary conversation between himself or herself and a famous person. Remind your child to use quotation marks.

Name ____________________

Word Study: Suffixes

Directions: Letters added to the end of base words are called **suffixes.** Suffixes can change the meaning of the base words. Add a suffix to each word below to make a new word. Write each new word on the line. Hint: You might need to change some letters in the base word.

1. bright + -en = ____________

2. creative + -ity = ____________

3. educate + -ion = ____________

4. bother + -some = ____________

5. pass + -ive = ____________

6. transport + -ation = ____________

7. divide + -sion = ____________

Directions: Read each sentence below. Look for words that use one of the suffixes listed above. Write the word on the line. Then circle the suffix.

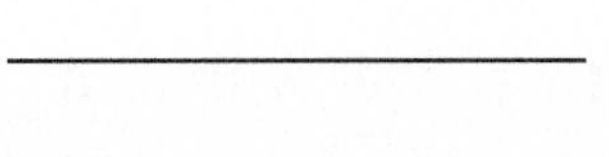

8. Electricity was an amazing discovery.

9. The need for a better source of energy was a strong motivation.

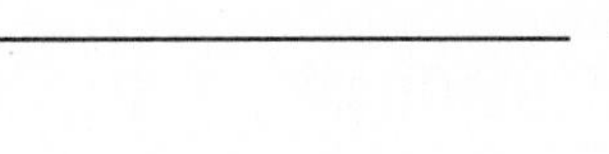

10. People tested their ideas to deepen their understanding of this new energy source.

11. An experiment was one way to test an invention.

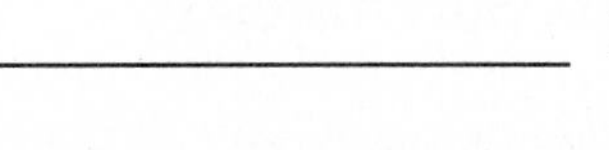

12. To be effective, an experiment must be carefully controlled.

____________ **13.** Much information can be gained by testing.

14. The creation of the first light bulb is a day to remember.

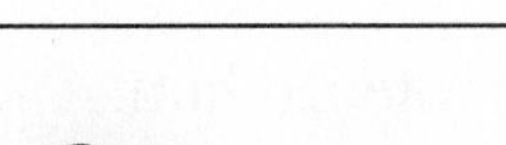

15. An inventor's hard work should never be viewed as troublesome.

Notes for Home: Your child built new words by adding suffixes such as *-en (lengthen)*. ***Home Activity:*** Challenge your child to find words in print with suffixes. Start a three-column chart to write the base word, the suffix, and the word with the suffix added.

Pretest

Spelling: Suffixes -less, -ment, -ness

Pretest Directions: Fold back the page along the dotted line. On the blanks, write the spelling words as they are dictated. When you have finished the test, unfold the page and check your words.

1. ______
2. ______
3. ______
4. ______
5. ______
6. ______
7. ______
8. ______
9. ______
10. ______
11. ______
12. ______
13. ______
14. ______
15. ______
16. ______
17. ______
18. ______
19. ______
20. ______

1. Don't look so **helpless**.
2. Don't be **careless** with the paint.
3. Things are not **hopeless**.
4. The room was **spotless**.
5. I was **breathless** from running.
6. That old rag is **worthless**.
7. The broken mop is **useless**.
8. I will use a check for **payment**.
9. I gave a **statement** to the press.
10. I saw **movement** in the grass.
11. The **pavement** was wet with rain.
12. The **treatment** was expensive.
13. What should be my **punishment**?
14. He was full of **goodness**.
15. I felt the **softness** of the pillow.
16. The **brightness** hurt his eyes.
17. What's your **business** here?
18. I see the **greatness** of the woods.
19. In all **fairness**, you're right.
20. The **darkness** frightened him.

Notes for Home: Your child took a pretest on words that include the suffixes *-less*, *-ment*, and *-ness*. ***Home Activity:*** Help your child learn misspelled words before the final test. Have your child divide misspelled words into parts (such as syllables) and concentrate on each part.

Name ______________________________

Spelling: Suffixes *-less*, *-ment*, *-ness*

Word List				
helpless	breathless	statement	punishment	business
careless	worthless	movement	goodness	greatness
hopeless	useless	pavement	softness	fairness
spotless	payment	treatment	brightness	darkness

Directions: Choose the word from the box that is formed by adding the suffix **-less** or **-ness** to each base word. Write the word on the line.

1. spot ____________________ **8.** busy ____________________

2. dark ____________________ **9.** help ____________________

3. breath ____________________ **10.** bright ____________________

4. fair ____________________ **11.** care ____________________

5. worth ____________________ **12.** soft ____________________

6. great ____________________ **13.** hope ____________________

7. use ____________________ **14.** good ____________________

Directions: Add the suffix **-ment** to each word in ( ) to form a word from the box and complete each sentence. Write the word on the line.

______________ **15.** The great inventor made a (state) to the press.

______________ **16.** She said, "I have invented a (treat) for colds and flu."

______________ **17.** "I did not do it for (pay)."

______________ **18.** Just then, there was a (move) in the crowd.

______________ **19.** Another woman ran in from the (pave) outside.

______________ **20.** "This impostor deserves (punish)," she cried, "because I am the true inventor!"

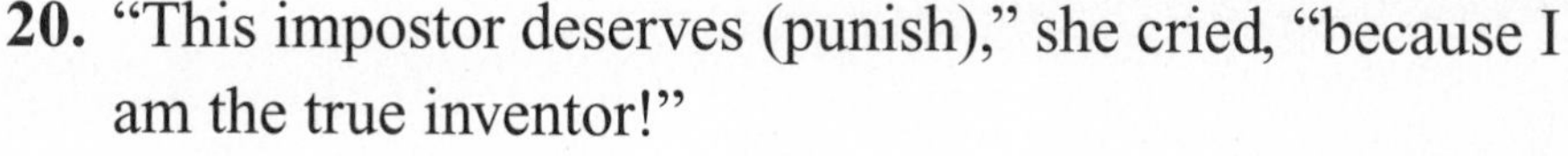

Notes for Home: Your child spelled words with the suffixes *-less, -ment,* and *-ness*. ***Home Activity:*** Help your child think of some other words with these suffixes, such as *fearless, refreshment,* and *heaviness.*

Name ___________________________________

Proofread and Write

Spelling: Suffixes -less, -ment, -ness

Directions: Proofread this news story about an inventor. Find five spelling mistakes. Use the proofreading marks to correct each mistake.

≡	Make a capital.
/	Make a small letter.
∧	Add something.
⅌	Take out something.
⊙	Add a period.
¶	Begin a new paragraph.

INVENTOR MAKES STATEMENT

Today Pete Vargas, inventor of a famous treatmen used to increase the softness and briteness of carpets, spoke at the Porta Linda City Business Center. "In all fairnes," said the inventor, "I owe much of my greatnesse to my colleagues. Without them, my own discoveries would have been worthless. Therefore, any paiment I receive, I always share with them."

Spelling Tip

When **-less, -ment,** or **-ness** is added to most base words, the base stays the same. If the base word ends in a **consonant** and **y,** change the **y** to **i** before adding the suffix: **business.**

Word List

helpless	payment	softness
careless	statement	brightness
hopeless	movement	business
spotless	pavement	greatness
breathless	treatment	fairness
worthless	punishment	darkness
useless	goodness	

Write a News Story

On a separate sheet of paper, write your own news story about an imaginary inventor's visit to your town. Use at least four spelling words.

Notes for Home: Your child spelled words with the suffixes *-less, -ment,* and *-ness.* ***Home Activity:*** Say some base words from the list, such as *good, punish,* and *use.* Ask your child to add one of the suffixes to make the whole word. Then have your child spell the word.

Name ______________________________

Spelling: Suffixes *-less*, *-ment*, *-ness*

REVIEW

Word List

helpless	breathless	statement	punishment	business
careless	worthless	movement	goodness	greatness
hopeless	useless	pavement	softness	fairness
spotless	payment	treatment	brightness	darkness

Directions: Unscramble the letters to form a word from the box. Write the word on the line.

1. neatresgs ______________
2. soognesd ______________
3. inesfars ______________
4. sinbuess ______________
5. nessfost ______________
6. sardknes ______________
7. muiphsnent ______________
8. tovemmen ______________
9. mavepent ______________
10. meattrent ______________
11. meanttest ______________
12. sbraleehts ______________

Directions: Choose the word from the box that has the same meaning as the underlined word or words. Write the word on the line to the left.

______________ **13.** "It's <u>without hope</u>!" Yoshi said.

______________ **14.** "This invention is <u>without worth</u>!"

______________ **15.** "I feel so <u>unable to do anything</u>."

______________ **16.** "It's not as though I have been <u>inattentive</u>."

______________ **17.** "I kept all my equipment <u>completely clean</u>."

______________ **18.** "Yet this <u>worthless</u> rocket won't fly!"

______________ **19.** Suddenly, a <u>strong light</u> filled the room.

______________ **20.** "This is the <u>reward</u> for all my hard work," he said . . .

Notes for Home: Your child spelled words with the suffixes *-less, -ment,* and *-ness*. ***Home Activity:*** Look at the words on the list that end with *-less*. Challenge your child to add the suffix *-ly* to each and use it in a sentence.

Name ________________________________

Study Strategies

Study Strategies help you focus on the most important parts of what you read. **Skimming and scanning** are two ways of looking at written materials quickly, focusing only on important parts.

Skimming is looking at a story or article quickly to find out what it is about. When skimming, you do not read the entire story. You look for highlights, such as titles and captions. Skimming helps you decide whether you want to read the text and whether it is useful for your research and study purposes.

Scanning is looking for key words or ideas. You can scan when you need to answer a specific question. Read the sentences around the key words to find the answer to your question.

Directions: Skim the article on the next page to answer the questions below.

1. Who is the article about? ________________________________
2. What can you learn by reading this article? ________________________________

____

____

3. How many different inventions are mentioned? What are they? ____________

____

____

4. Would you read this article if you needed information about things Thomas Jefferson did when he was the President of the United States? Explain.

____

____

5. Would you read this article if you needed information about important accomplishments Thomas Jefferson made in his lifetime? Explain.

____

____

Name ________________________________

Thomas Jefferson: Inventor

While Thomas Jefferson is mostly known for being a brilliant politician, he was also quite an inventor. Many of his inventions were items he used in his house. They were things that made life easier for him.

Revolving Closet
One of his inventions helped him get dressed in the morning. At the end of his bed he had a revolving closet. It was a long pole that reached from floor to ceiling. This pole had forty-eight arms. Each arm held one item of clothing. Jefferson could turn the arms with a long stick making it easier to find the clothes he wanted to wear.

Revolving Bookstand
Another item Jefferson is believed to have invented is a revolving bookstand. Jefferson joined five bookstands and placed them on a revolving platform. Using this device, he was able to review different books with ease.

The Great Clock
One of Jefferson's most impressive creations was his Great Clock. This clock had two faces. The outside face had only an hour hand. This, he felt, was all the information workers needed. Its gong chimed the hour loud enough to be heard from 3 miles away. The inside face had hour, minute, and second hands. The weights that moved the clock's hands also indicated the day of the week.

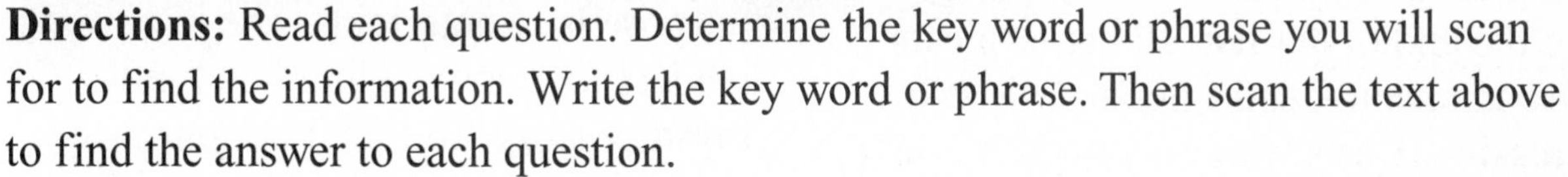

Directions: Read each question. Determine the key word or phrase you will scan for to find the information. Write the key word or phrase. Then scan the text above to find the answer to each question.

6. Which invention did Thomas Jefferson use to find clothes more easily?

____

7. From how many miles away could the Great Clock chime be heard?

____

8. Which invention did Thomas Jefferson use for reviewing several books at a time?

____

9. What portion of the Great Clock did Jefferson feel was most useful for workers?

____

10. What did the Great Clock's inside face show? ________________

____

Notes for Home: Your child skimmed and scanned an article to find necessary information quickly. ***Home Activity:*** Give your child a newspaper article you have read. Ask questions that can be answered by scanning (looking for key words) the article.

Family Times

Name____

Summary

Detective Lila Fenwick Solves the Mystery of Chocolate!

Lila Fenwick is a great detective. However, her skills are tested to the limit when the class guinea pig, Chocolate, is missing. Lila starts the way any good detective would: she makes a list of suspects and starts checking them out. Yet when she gets to the end of her list, all her suspects are innocent—and Chocolate is still missing. Lila's whole reputation is at stake—and she really wants to find Chocolate!

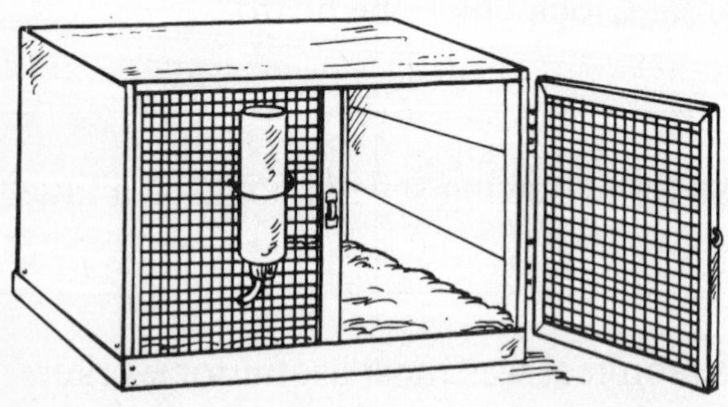

Activity

Finish the Story. Have your child tell you the rest of "Chocolate Is Missing," including how Lila finally finds Chocolate and what happens after that.

Reading Skills

Author's Purpose

An **author's purpose** is the reason for writing something. Some purposes for writing are to entertain, to inform, to express, and to persuade. Predicting an author's purpose can help you decide whether to read something slowly and carefully or just for fun.

In "Chocolate Is Missing," the author's purpose is to entertain—she just wants readers to enjoy reading this funny mystery story. To fulfill her purpose, the author has filled her story with interesting characters and exciting clues. You'll enjoy the story most if you notice these things.

Activity

Tell an Entertaining Story. Tell a story that you think will entertain someone. This can be a story you make up, such as other guinea pig adventures. It can also be a funny story about something that happened to you.

Family Times

Tested Vocabulary

Words to Know

Knowing the meanings of these words is important to reading "Chocolate Is Missing." Practice using these words to learn their meanings.

angle point of view

approach come near

brag boast

chocolate substance used to make foods like candy, fudge, or ice cream

poster large printed sheet or notice hung on a wall

presence ability to project a sense of ease or poise

Grammar

Review of Compound and Complex Sentences

A **compound sentence** contains two simple sentences joined by a comma and a conjunction such as *and, but,* or *or.*

Lila was going to find Chocolate, and she was going to find him soon!

A **complex sentence** is made up of a simple sentence and a sentence part. In a complex sentence, the sentence part cannot stand alone. It is joined to the sentence with a connecting word, such as *because* or *when.*

When Lila solved the mystery, she was more surprised than anyone!

Activity

Sentence Builders. Take turns! One person starts a compound or complex sentence, and the other person finishes it.

Tested Spelling Words

______	______	______	______
______	______	______	______
______	______	______	______
______	______	______	______
______	______	______	______

Author's Purpose

- An **author's purpose** is the reason for writing something.
- Some purposes for writing are to entertain, to inform, to express, and to persuade.

Directions: Reread "Breakfast with Brede." Then complete the web. Identify the author's purpose and give four clues that helped you decide.

2. Grandpa says scones are like

3. Brede says scones are like camels'

4. Brede says scones are like elephants'

Author's Purpose or Purposes

1.

5. Why isn't Andrew allowed to finish speaking?

Notes for Home: Your child identified the author's purpose in a story. ***Home Activity:*** Ask your child to pick a favorite story. Ask him or her to identify the author's purpose. Then have your child support his or her answer with examples from the story.

Name ______________________________

Vocabulary

Directions: Choose the word from the box that best matches each definition. Write the word on the line.

Check the Words You Know

__ angle
__ approach
__ brag
__ chocolate
__ poster
__ presence

__________ **1.** boast

__________ **2.** large printed sheet or notice on a wall

__________ **3.** point of view

__________ **4.** ability to project a sense of ease

__________ **5.** come near

Directions: Choose the word from the box that best completes each sentence. Write the word on the line to the left.

__________ **6.** Dottie is a detective who always has an interesting _____ on any problem.

__________ **7.** One day, Myron had lost a candy bar made from his favorite kind of _____.

__________ **8.** Right away, Dottie began to _____ to others that she could easily solve the mystery.

__________ **9.** Dottie's certainty and strong _____ made Myron believe that his candy bar would be found fast.

__________ **10.** "If you have seen the candy bar, come forward and _____ me," said Dottie. "There is a reward—another candy bar!"

Write a Detective Story

On a separate sheet of paper, tell the story of a classroom detective. Tell what the mystery is, who the detective is, and what he or she does to solve the mystery. Use as many vocabulary words as you can.

Notes for Home: Your child identified and used vocabulary words from "Chocolate Is Missing." ***Home Activity:*** With your child, act out the roles of a detective questioning a suspect. Try to use as many vocabulary words as you can.

Author's Purpose

- An **author's purpose** is the reason or reasons the author has for writing.
- Four common author's purposes are to entertain, to inform, to express, and to persuade.

1. Reread "Chocolate Is Missing." Tell what you think the author's purpose or purposes were for writing this story. Explain your answer.

____

Directions: Tell what the author's purpose or purposes were for writing each passage below. Explain your answer.

2. I love my cat, Tomiddy. He snuggles up next to me when I read and keeps me company. When I'm feeling blue, I pick Tomiddy up and give him a big hug. I push my face into his soft, comforting fur. He purrs and purrs. A Tomiddy hug is good for cheering me up.

____

3. Guinea pigs belong to a family of rodents that are native to South America. Other members of this family are rock cavies and mountain cavies. Rodents have unusually long, sharp front teeth that keep growing. Rodents' unusual ability to gnaw keeps their teeth sharp!

____

4. *All Creatures Great and Small* is a wonderful book about an English veterinarian and his animal cases. The stories are interesting, and the book is well written and easy to read. If you like reading about animals, you really should look at this fascinating book.

____

5. Think about other stories you have read in class. On a separate sheet of paper, name a story or article that was written for each of the four common purposes listed above. Explain your choices.

Notes for Home: Your child read several passages and identified the reason or reasons an author has for writing. ***Home Activity:*** Ask your child to think of a favorite book. Encourage him or her to tell you why the author wrote the book.

Selection Test

Directions: Choose the best answer to each item. Mark the letter for the answer you have chosen.

Part 1: Vocabulary

Find the answer choice that means about the same as the underlined work in each sentence.

1. Jay has a different <u>angle</u>.
- A. point of view
- B. troubled or worried feeling
- C. person who offers help
- D. notebook divider

2. The girls looked at the <u>poster</u>.
- F. open drawer
- G. small card sent by mail
- H. secret message
- J. printed notice hung on a wall

3. Mr. Jones changed his <u>approach</u>.
- A. way of working on a task
- B. tone of voice
- C. time and place for a meeting
- D. way a person looks

4. I tried not to <u>brag</u>.
- F. complain
- G. become confused
- H. boast
- J. worry

5. Here is some <u>chocolate</u>.
- A. dark-gray color
- B. strong, sweet odor
- C. small box or container
- D. substance used in candies and other foods

6. Rena has great <u>presence</u>.
- F. duties or jobs
- G. ability to imagine
- H. gift given to another person
- J. sense of being sure of oneself

Part 2: Comprehension

Use what you know about the story to answer each item.

7. How is Gayle different from Lila?
- A. Gayle is taller and wider.
- B. Gayle cares more about Chocolate.
- C. Gayle is a better writer.
- D. Gayle is not as logical.

8. In this story, Chocolate is a—
- F. cat.
- G. guinea pig.
- H. snake.
- J. rabbit.

GO ON

9. What happened next after the class found that Chocolate was gone?
A. Lila and Eddie looked for Chocolate.
B. Lila and Gayle made posters.
C. Lila realized Chocolate had escaped.
D. Lila and Gayle talked to Michael.

10. The author probably included Lila's list of suspects to show—
F. how smart Lila is.
G. that Chocolate was stolen.
H. that Lila was a bit silly.
J. which students could not be trusted.

11. Lila was not ready to do her oral report because she—
A. knew Mr. Sherman would understand how busy she was.
B. did not want to talk in front of the class.
C. forgot about it while searching for Chocolate.
D. did not want to learn about Brazil.

12. Chocolate probably hid in Mr. Sherman's desk because she—
F. found lots of food there.
G. was afraid of the children.
H. needed a safe place for her babies.
J. was sick.

13. The author's main purpose in this selection is to—
A. tell an amusing story.
B. explain how to solve mysteries.
C. describe a class of students.
D. give tips for keeping class pets.

14. Near the end of the story, it is suggested that Lila was jealous of—
F. Mr. Todd.
G. Rita Morgan.
H. Michael Watson.
J. Eddie English.

15. Mr. Sherman was probably most impressed that Lila—
A. pretended to be a detective.
B. worked so hard to find Chocolate.
C. knew so much about Brazil.
D. was Gayle's best friend.

STOP

Name ___________________________________

Author's Purpose

- An **author's purpose** is the reason or reasons the author has for writing.
- Four common author's purposes are to entertain, to inform, to express, and to persuade.

Directions: Read the story below.

You might think that a chicken is a funny kind of class pet to have. But I'm telling you, Cedric the Chicken is the best! He is a lot of fun to watch, and he is smart and loyal. I think every class should have a chicken as a class pet.

You might think chickens are boring, but you need to change your thinking on that! For example, did you know that new chicks can live for a week without eating? And while you may think chickens are as American as a certain fried chicken restaurant, they're originally from Asia.

Cedric can always tell when it's time for lunch. He lets us know by cackling until we notice. When there's chicken for lunch, he puts up a big fuss. He'd rather we ate peanut butter and jelly. We love our class pet—even if he's different from most!

Directions: Complete the table. Fill in a statement from the story for each purpose listed.

Author's Purpose	Statement from Story
To persuade	I think every class should have a chicken as a class pet.
To persuade	**1.**
To inform	**2.**
To inform	**3.**
To entertain	**4.**
To express	**5.**

Notes for Home: Your child identified statements that showed an author's reasons for writing a story. ***Home Activity:*** Look at a newspaper with your child. Discuss, for example, how the purpose for writing the comics may be different from writing an article.

Plot

REVIEW

Directions: Read the story. Then read each question about the story. Choose the best answer to each question. Mark the letter for the answer you have chosen.

Penny's Parrot

All her life, Penny had lived in sunny southern California. When she heard that her family was moving to Alaska, Penny felt sad.

However, Penny soon discovered that she liked sledding and skating. She also liked her new friends at school.

But Penny's parrot seemed very sad. It was home alone all day in Penny's house. Penny discovered that parrots like warm weather! Penny's house was too cold during the day when no one was home.

Penny decided to bring her parrot to school. The parrot was happy with the warm classroom—and Penny's class had a new pet!

1. What happens to Penny at the beginning of the story?
- **A.** She moves to Alaska.
- **B.** She moves to California.
- **C.** She learns to skate.
- **D.** She gets a parrot.

2. What problem does Penny have?
- **F.** She hates the cold.
- **G.** She has no friends.
- **H.** Her parrot is sad.
- **J.** Her parrot is noisy.

3. What causes Penny's problem?
- **A.** Alaska is not a good place to live.
- **B.** The parrot doesn't like the cold house.
- **C.** Alaska is a big state.
- **D.** Penny is very shy.

4. How does Penny solve her problem?
- **F.** She feeds her parrot.
- **G.** She gives her parrot away.
- **H.** She makes new friends.
- **J.** She brings her parrot to school.

5. Why does this action solve Penny's problem?
- **A.** The class likes her better now.
- **B.** She doesn't have to take care of her parrot anymore.
- **C.** The parrot has a warmer place to live.
- **D.** Her parrot makes less noise.

Notes for Home: Your child answered questions about a story's plot. ***Home Activity:*** Plan a story with your child. Describe when and where the story will take place, who the characters are, what problem they'll face, and how they'll solve it.

Name ______________________

Writing Across Texts

Directions: Use information from "Chocolate Is Missing" and *Komodo Dragons* in Unit 2 to fill in the table, using words and phrases from the box below.

are not social	are social
come from Indonesia	need a small cage
can eat a water buffalo	eat carrots, lettuce, apples, spinach
come from Brazil	makes an excellent classroom pet
would not be suitable as a classroom pet	have razor-sharp teeth

Guinea Pigs	Komodo Dragons
Traits have curly brown fur **1.** **2.** **3.** **4.**	**Traits** have leathery, scaly skin **6.** **7.** **8.** **9.**
What Kind of Class Pet Would a Guinea Pig Make? **5.**	**What Kind of Class Pet Would a Komodo Dragon Make?** **10.**

Write a Comparison/Contrast Paragraph

On a separate sheet of paper, write a comparison/contrast paragraph about guinea pigs and komodo dragons; conclude whether and why each animal would (or would not) be a good classroom pet. Refer to your table when writing. Remember to use descriptive details about each animal.

Notes for Home: Your child combined information from more than one reading selection. ***Home Activity:*** As you read other stories or articles about animals, encourage your child to identify the similarities and differences between animals.

Name ______________________________

Grammar: Quotations

REVIEW

Directions: Draw a circle around any letter that should be capitalized. If no letters need to be capitalized, write **N** on the line.

__________ **1.** "where's the white mouse?" Jenny asked.

__________ **2.** "The white mouse?" said Jamal. "it's in its cage."

__________ **3.** "If you look," replied Jenny, "you'll see it's not there."

__________ **4.** "That's not good. where could it be?" Jamal asked.

__________ **5.** Jenny answered, "we'd better start looking for it."

Directions: Each sentence is missing a punctuation mark—a comma, a period, or a question mark. Write the mark where it is needed. Use an insert symbol (∧) if necessary.

6. " I don't see the mouse anywhere " complained Jamal.

7. Jenny replied " Well, let's keep looking. "

8. " Could one of the kids have taken it home " asked Jamal.

9. " It's possible, " said Jenny " but the teacher didn't mention it. "

10. Jamal said, " I just hope it's all right "

11. Suddenly Jamal said " What's that? "

12. " What's what " asked Jenny.

Directions: Write a sentence that uses each group of words as a quotation.

13. what's that spot of white over there

____

14. it looks like a mouse to me

____

15. it looks okay!

____

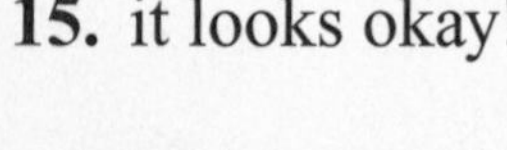

Notes for Home: Your child reviewed the use of capital letters and punctuation with quotations in sentences. ***Home Activity:*** Work with your child to write a short story about a pet and its owners. Include dialogue. Have your child write out the story.

Grammar: Review of Compound and Complex Sentences

A **compound sentence** contains two simple sentences. They are joined by a comma and a conjunction such as *and, but,* or *or.* The two sentences must have ideas that go together.

Two Sentences: Steve was a pet detective. He found my dog, Misty.
Compound Sentence: Steve was a pet detective, and he found my dog, Misty.

A **complex sentence** is made by combining a simple sentence with a group of words that cannot stand on its own as a sentence. The group of words is joined to the sentence with a word such as *because* or *when.*

He likes dogs because they are usually friendly.
When he feels sad, he takes his dog for a walk.

Directions: Write whether each sentence is **compound** or **complex.**

____________ **1.** Our cat was lost, and we didn't know where to look.

____________ **2.** The detective came, and she began looking for our cat.

____________ **3.** When she found our cat, we cheered loudly.

____________ **4.** The detective was smart, and she was good at her job.

____________ **5.** Because she knew just where to look, we found our cat!

Directions: Match each group of words on the left with a group on the right to make a compound or a complex sentence. Write the letter on the line.

______ **6.** Joe hired us to find his pet frog

______ **7.** We knew that the frog would be tired,

______ **8.** We looked outside for the frog,

______ **9.** We wanted to take a rest,

______ **10.** When we finally found the frog,

a. and it would be hungry too.

b. and we also looked inside.

c. because it was lost.

d. Joe was happy and relieved.

e. but we knew we had to keep looking.

Notes for Home: Your child reviewed compound and complex sentences. ***Home Activity:*** Look at a favorite book with your child. Invite him or her to find examples of compound and complex sentences.

Grammar: Review of Compound and Complex Sentences

Directions: Join the two sentences to form a compound sentence. Use *and* and a comma to combine them. Write the compound sentence on the line.

1. Being a detective is hard. It requires a lot of work.

____

____

2. I have a good memory. I never forget a face.

____

____

3. My teacher thinks I would be a good detective. Someday I might try to be one.

____

____

Directions: Add a simple sentence to each sentence part to form a complex sentence.

4. When I have a great idea, ___________________________

____

5. When I'm not sure that I'll remember my idea, ___________________

____

Write a What-If Story

What would happen if you had a really great idea? Write a story about it on a separate sheet of paper. Use at least two compound and two complex sentences.

Notes for Home: Your child reviewed compound and complex sentences. ***Home Activity:*** You can form complex sentences with your child by saying: "*If I were a* _____, *I would . . .*" Take turns filling in the blank and completing the sentence. *(If I were a dog, I would run around all day.)*

Name ______________________

RETEACHING

Grammar: Review of Compound and Complex Sentences

Combine the sentences to form a compound sentence.

1. Reading was his favorite subject. He read widely.

____

Combine the groups of words to form a complex sentence.

2. We wanted to leave. Because we were tired.

____

A **compound sentence** contains two simple sentences joined by a comma and a conjunction such as **and, but,** or **or.** The simple sentences must have ideas that go together. A **complex sentence** is made by combining a simple sentence with a group of words that cannot stand alone as a sentence.

Directions: Combine each pair of sentences to form a compound sentence. Use **and** and a comma to combine them. Write each new sentence on the line.

1. Ben lived a full life. His achievements were many.

____

2. His brother printed a newspaper. Ben wrote for it.

____

Directions: Write whether each sentence is **compound** or **complex.**

__________ **3.** Daniel missed the directions because he was late.

__________ **4.** Dori enjoyed singing, and she sang every day.

__________ **5.** When we walked outside, we noticed it was raining.

__________ **6.** We are going to Grandpa's house, and he will make us pancakes.

Notes for Home: Your child identified compound and complex sentences. ***Home Activity:*** Ask your child to give you an example of a compound sentence and a complex sentence. Challenge him or her to explain the differences between the two.

Name ____________________________________

Grammar: Review of Compound and Complex Sentences

Directions: Combine each pair of word groups to make a compound or a complex sentence. Write each sentence on the lines.

1. Many cartoonists begin with a pencil outline. They use a pen in a later step.

____

____

2. Movement is shown by using lines. Speech is shown by putting words in a balloon.

____

____

3. After drawings are scanned into a computer Computer operators can shade areas of the images.

____

____

4. The pictures can be seen on a computer screen. They can be sent to other computers.

____

____

5. When the pictures are placed in a form for a newspaper page The page is prepared for printing.

____

____

Notes for Home: Your child identified compound and complex sentences. ***Home Activity:*** Together, write a silly story about two animals. Use at least one compound sentence and one complex sentence in the story.

Name ____________________

Word Study: Word Building

Directions: Add a suffix to each word below to make a new word. Write each new word on the line. Hint: The spelling of some words may change slightly when the suffix is added. Use a dictionary if necessary.

1. explain + -ation = ____________________

2. imagine + -ation = ____________________

3. describe + -tion = ____________________

4. inform + -ation = ____________________

5. drama + -tic + -al + -ly = ____________________

Directions: Read each word below. Write each base word and suffix in the correct column. Remember to adjust the spelling of the base word if needed.

Word		Base Word		Suffix
6. interrogation	=	________________	+	________________
7. nomination	=	________________	+	________________
8. investigation	=	________________	+	________________
9. maintenance	=	________________	+	________________
10. rectangular	=	________________	+	________________

Directions: Sometimes when a suffix is added to a base word, some sounds in the word change. Read the pairs of words below. Listen for the syllable that is stressed. Underline the stressed syllable in each word, for example: **music** and **musician.**

11. nominate nomination

12. maintain maintenance

13. interrogate interrogation

14. rectangle rectangular

15. investigate investigation

Notes for Home: Your child listened for the ways in which words can change when a suffix is added. ***Home Activity:*** With your child, think of words that have suffixes. Clap each syllable as you say the word, clapping more loudly for the one that is stressed.

Name ____________________________________

Spelling: Related Words

Pretest Directions: Fold back the page along the dotted line. On the blanks, write the spelling words as they are dictated. When you have finished the test, unfold the page and check your words.

1. ____________________
2. ____________________
3. ____________________
4. ____________________
5. ____________________
6. ____________________
7. ____________________
8. ____________________
9. ____________________
10. ____________________
11. ____________________
12. ____________________
13. ____________________
14. ____________________
15. ____________________
16. ____________________
17. ____________________
18. ____________________
19. ____________________
20. ____________________

1. Are you **able** to understand?
2. I'm sure of your **ability**.
3. Please **sign** here.
4. What will be our **signal**?
5. I don't know what you **mean**.
6. That's what I **meant**.
7. All right, it's a **deal**.
8. He **dealt** me these cards.
9. The ice cream is **soft**.
10. Let the butter **soften** a little.
11. I can **relate** to that.
12. He is my oldest **relative**.
13. This will help it **heal** faster.
14. She's in very good **health**.
15. The desk is a **meter** long.
16. We will use the **metric** system.
17. Let her **compose** the note.
18. That was a fine **composition**.
19. There's hardly a **crumb** left.
20. First, we will **crumble** this bread.

Notes for Home: Your child took a pretest on related words that have parts spelled the same but pronounced differently. ***Home Activity:*** Help your child learn misspelled words before the final test by underlining the parts that are different in each pair and concentrating on those.

Name ______________________________

Spelling: Related Words

Word List				
able	mean	soft	heal	compose
ability	meant	soften	health	composition
sign	deal	relate	meter	crumb
signal	dealt	relative	metric	crumble

Directions: Choose the word from the box that has a related word part that is spelled the same but pronounced differently. Write the word on the line.

1. able ____________________

2. crumb ____________________

3. sign ____________________

4. compose ____________________

5. mean ____________________

6. meter ____________________

7. deal ____________________

8. heal ____________________

9. soft ____________________

10. relate ____________________

Directions: Choose the word from the box that best matches each clue. Write the word on the line.

11. the basic measurement of the metric system ____________________

12. capable or competent ____________________

13. not hard ____________________

14. an arrangement between two people ____________________

15. connect in thought or meaning ____________________

16. make better, like a wound ____________________

17. a billboard is an example ____________________

18. create a piece of music ____________________

19. not nice ____________________

20. a morsel, or a tiny piece ____________________

Notes for Home: Your child spelled related words that have parts that are spelled the same but are pronounced differently. ***Home Activity:*** Say one of the words on the list. Invite your child to say and spell the related word. Point out the differences in how the related words are said.

Name ___________________________________

Spelling: Related Words

Directions: Proofread this list of instructions for taking care of a class pet. Find five spelling mistakes. Use the proofreading marks to correct each mistake.

≡	Make a capital.
/	Make a small letter.
∧	Add something.
℘	Take out something.
⊙	Add a period.
¶	Begin a new paragraph.

Taking Care of "Hamlet," the Class Hamster

1. Look at the sine over his cage. It says, "Don't tease the hamster." That's what we say, and that's what we meen!
2. When Hamlet gets hungry, do not crumbel cookies or cupcakes into his cage. Cookie crumbs are not good for his helth!
3. When Hamlet is sleeping, you don't have to speak in a sofft voice. But please don't yell at him! He might get scared.

Spelling Tip

Pay close attention to related words. They often have parts that are spelled the same but pronounced differently: **sign, signal.**

Word List

able	mean	soft	heal	compose
ability	meant	soften	health	composition
sign	deal	relate	meter	crumb
signal	dealt	relative	metric	crumble

Write a List of Instructions

On a separate sheet of paper, write your own instructions for taking care of a class pet. Use at least two pairs of related spelling words.

Notes for Home: Your child spelled related words that have parts that are spelled the same but are pronounced differently. ***Home Activity:*** Write the shorter of a pair of related words. Then write an "equation" to show how to form the longer word *(relate – e + ive = relative).*

Name ____________________

Spelling: Related Words

REVIEW

Word List				
able	mean	soft	heal	compose
ability	meant	soften	health	composition
sign	deal	relate	meter	crumb
signal	dealt	relative	metric	crumble

Directions: Choose the word from the box that rhymes with each word below. Write it on the line to the right. Then, beside it, write the related word.

thumb **1.** ____________ **7.** ____________

often **2.** ____________ **8.** ____________

bean **3.** ____________ **9.** ____________

fine **4.** ____________ **10.** ____________

inflate **5.** ____________ **11.** ____________

heater **6.** ____________ **12.** ____________

Directions: Choose the word from the box that best completes each sentence. Write the word on the line to the left.

____________ **13.** One day our class rabbit was in poor _____.

____________ **14.** "The vet can _____ him," said our teacher.

____________ **15.** We knew the vet would be _____ to cure the rabbit.

____________ **16.** The vet has the _____ to cure most pet problems.

____________ **17.** The vet came and _____ with the problem.

____________ **18.** We decided to _____ a song in honor of the vet.

____________ **19.** The vet loved our _____.

____________ **20.** We made a _____ with the vet to call her for all our pet problems.

Notes for Home: Your child spelled related words that have parts that are spelled the same but are pronounced differently. ***Home Activity:*** Write each spelling word on separate index cards. Mix the cards. When a pair is drawn, the player must use one word in a sentence.

Technology: Electronic Media

There are many resources you can use to find information, such as books, newspapers, magazines, and people. You can also use **electronic media,** which include things such as audiotapes, videotapes, films, and computers. CD-ROM encyclopedias and the Internet are two ways to gather information using a computer.

Directions: Review the list of resources that give information about guinea pigs. Use the list to tell which resource you would choose for each situation described on the next page.

Books *(Nonfiction)*
Guinea Pigs: How to Care for Them, Feed Them, and Understand Them by Katrin Behrend
I Love Guinea Pigs by Dick King-Smith
The Guinea Pig, An Owner's Guide by Audrey Pavia

Books *(Fiction)*
Bedtime by Kate Duke
Olga De Polga by Michael Bond

Organizations
Guinea Pig Adoption Network
Home for Unwanted and Abandoned Guinea Pigs

Internet Web Pages
Todd's Guinea Pig Hutch
Carlo's Guinea Pig Site

Internet Mailing Lists*
Gpigs

Internet Newsgroups*
Pets: Guinea Pigs

Internet Sound Files*

"Need food" sound
Guinea pig's chuckle

Videos
Pocket Pet Series Featuring: Guinea Pigs

CD-ROMs
The ABC's of Caring for a Guinea Pig

*Mailing lists and newsgroups are discussions conducted on the Internet. People post questions and answers about a specific topic. You automatically receive mailing list posts in e-mail. You have to go to a newsgroup site to read news posted by other members of the newsgroup. An Internet sound file is a short audio recording of a specific sound. You can save the file and play the sound over and over again.

Name ____________________

1. You are giving a presentation on guinea pigs to your class. You want to let students know how to adopt a guinea pig.

____

____

2. Also as part of your presentation, you want the class to hear the sound guinea pigs make when they are hungry.

____

____

3. You are interested in receiving information through e-mail about the care of guinea pigs.

____

____

4. Your class is creating a Web page about your class pet—a guinea pig named Honey. You are responsible for finding out what kinds of information you should include in a web page.

____

____

5. Choose one of the electronic media resources from the list. Give an example of a research project where a student might use this resource. Tell why this resource best suits the purposes of the project.

____

____

____

____

____

Notes for Home: Your child chose resources for completing projects. ***Home Activity:*** Visit a library with your child. Many libraries have media centers that provide public access to electronic media. Discuss the resources available and how your child might use them for study or research.

Name ______________________________

Supporting an Opinion

Directions: Write your opinion in the top box. Then record facts, reasons and examples that support your opinion. Choose the most persuasive fact, reason, or example and write it on the lines at the bottom of the page.

I think that ______________________________

______________________________.

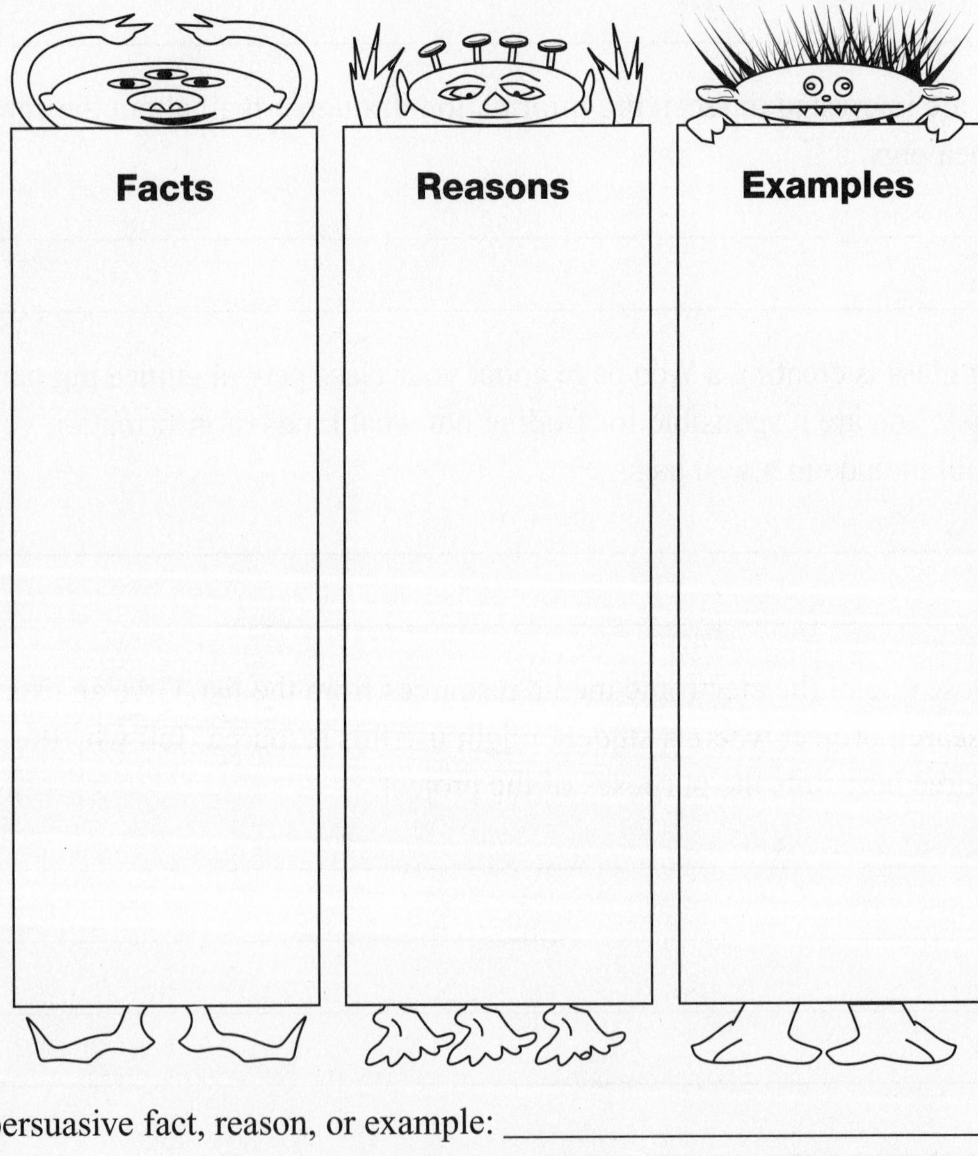

Facts	Reasons	Examples

Most persuasive fact, reason, or example: ______________________________

____

Notes for Home: Your child has been learning how to support an opinion in order to be persuasive. ***Home Activity:*** Ask your child to persuade you to try a certain kind of food.

Name______________________________

Elaboration

Combine Sentences

- When you write, you can elaborate by **combining short, choppy sentences** into one longer, more interesting sentence.
- You can make a compound sentence by joining sentences with *and, but,* or *or.*
- You can make a complex sentence by joining short sentences with words such as *when, if,* or *because*.

Directions: Use the word in parentheses to combine the sentences. Remember to capitalize the first word of your new sentence.

1. (because) Chocolate the guinea pig was missing. Lila began an investigation.

____

____

2. (or) Was Chocolate stolen? Did she escape from her cage?

____

3. (and) Lila made a list of suspects. She read the list to Gayle.

____

____

4. (if) Chocolate escaped from her cage. Where is she now?

____

5. (and) Lila searched the classroom. Eddie English helped her.

____

6. (when) Lila fell down. She saw Chocolate and her babies in the drawer.

____

Notes for Home: Your child combined short sentences into compound or complex sentences. ***Home Activity:*** To practice forming complex sentences, ask your child to think of sentences beginning with the words *when, if,* and *because* and say them to you.

Name ____________________

Self-Evaluation Guide

Persuasive Argument

Directions: Think about the final draft of your persuasive argument. Then answer each question below.

	Yes	No	Not sure
1. Did I state my opinion at the beginning of the argument?			
2. Did I use good reasons, facts, and examples to persuade my reader?			
3. Are my reasons organized in order of importance?			
4. Did I use persuasive words in my argument?			
5. Did I proofread and edit carefully to avoid errors?			

6. What is the best reason you used in your persuasive argument?

____

____

7. How would you change this persuasive argument if you were writing it for a different audience than your classmates? Explain.

____

____

____

Notes For Home: Your child has been learning to write a persuasive argument. ***Home Activity:*** Ask your child to think of a favorite leisure activity and give three reasons to persuade someone to try it.

Directions: Use the tables below to find the percentage score for the total number correct out of the total number of items. The last entry in each table shows the total number of items.

Number Correct	1	2	3	4	5
Percentage Score	20%	40%	60%	80%	100%

Number Correct	1	2	3	4	5	6	7	8	9	10
Percentage Score	10%	20%	30%	40%	50%	60%	70%	80%	90%	100%

Number Correct	1	2	3	4	5	6	7	8	9	10	11	12	13	14	15
Percentage Score	7%	13%	20%	27%	33%	40%	47%	53%	60%	67%	73%	80%	87%	93%	100%

Number Correct	1	2	3	4	5	6	7	8	9	10
Percentage Score	5%	10%	15%	20%	25%	30%	35%	40%	45%	50%
Number Correct	11	12	13	14	15	16	17	18	19	20
Percentage Score	55%	60%	65%	70%	75%	80%	85%	90%	95%	100%

Number Correct	1	2	3	4	5	6	7	8	9	10	11	12	13
Percentage Score	4%	8%	12%	16%	20%	24%	28%	32%	36%	40%	44%	48%	52%

Number Correct	14	15	16	17	18	19	20	21	22	23	24	25
Percentage Score	56%	60%	64%	68%	72%	76%	80%	84%	88%	92%	96%	100%

Number Correct	1	2	3	4	5	6	7	8	9	10	11	12	13	14	15
Percentage Score	3%	7%	10%	13%	17%	20%	23%	27%	30%	33%	37%	40%	43%	47%	50%
Number Correct	16	17	18	19	20	21	22	23	24	25	26	27	28	29	30
Percentage Score	53%	57%	60%	63%	67%	70%	73%	77%	80%	83%	87%	90%	93%	97%	100%

Name ____________________

1.	(A)	(B)	(C)	(D)
2.	(F)	(G)	(H)	(J)
3.	(A)	(B)	(C)	(D)
4.	(F)	(G)	(H)	(J)
5.	(A)	(B)	(C)	(D)
6.	(F)	(G)	(H)	(J)
7.	(A)	(B)	(C)	(D)
8.	(F)	(G)	(H)	(J)
9.	(A)	(B)	(C)	(D)
10.	(F)	(G)	(H)	(J)
11.	(A)	(B)	(C)	(D)
12.	(F)	(G)	(H)	(J)
13.	(A)	(B)	(C)	(D)
14.	(F)	(G)	(H)	(J)
15.	(A)	(B)	(C)	(D)

Practice Book 4.1, p. 1

Name______________________________ A Visit with Grandpa

Setting

- **Setting** is the time and place in which a story occurs. Sometimes the setting is important to the plot of a story. At other times, the setting is only background.
- Sometimes pictures show the setting, and sometimes you have to imagine it. Details that the author has written can help you see, hear, feel, and smell what it is like to be there.

Directions: Reread "The Red Fox." Fill in the word web with story details that would help you imagine the forest where the story takes place.
Possible answers given.

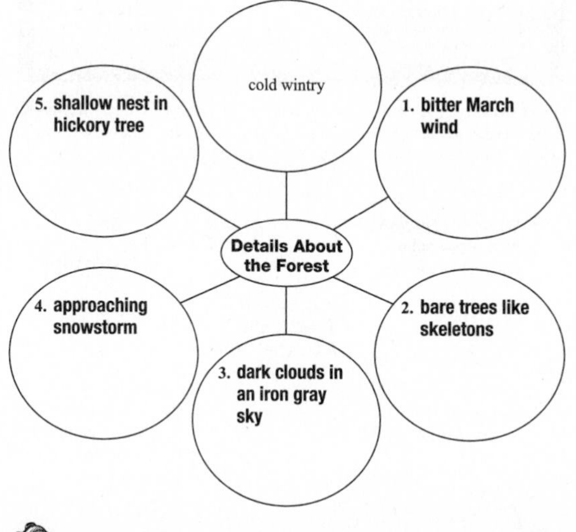

Notes for Home: Your child read a story and then identified details that helped in imagining the story's setting. ***Home Activity:*** Have your child choose a favorite room or place outdoors and give key details that would help someone who didn't know the place to imagine it.

Practice Book 4.1, p. 2

Name______________________________ A Visit with Grandpa

Vocabulary

Directions: Choose the word from the box that best completes each statement. For example, *Neat* is to *messy* as *smooth* is to *rumpled.* Write the word on the line to the left.

Check the Words You Know
__ biscuits
__ dough
__ prairie
__ raisins
__ rumpled
__ teasing
__ wrinkled

dough 1. *Pancakes* is to *batter* as *cookies* is to _____.
raisins 2. *Plums* is to *prunes* as *grapes* is to _____.
prairie 3. *Sheep* is to *meadow* as *buffalo* is to _____.
wrinkled 4. *Silky* is to *rough* as *unlined* is to _____.
teasing 5. *Happy* is to *praising* as *angry* is to _____.

Directions: Circle the word that has the same or nearly the same meaning as the first word in each group.

6. dough	(mixture)	pan	bacon
7. teasing	honking	(annoying)	singing
8. prairie	beach	forest	(field)
9. rumpled	steamed	(crushed)	pressed
10. biscuits	peanuts	fruit	(rolls)

Write an Experience Story

On a separate sheet of paper, write about an experience you had camping, on a picnic, or at some other outdoor event. Describe what you did and how you helped out. Use as many of the vocabulary words as you can. **Students' stories should tell about an outdoor experience and use vocabulary words correctly.**

Notes for Home: Your child identified and learned vocabulary words from "A Visit with Grandpa." ***Home Activity:*** With your child, go through the vocabulary words and make a list of all the things the two of you think of in connection with each word.

Practice Book 4.1, p. 3

Name______________________________ A Visit with Grandpa

Setting

- **Setting** is the time and place in which a story occurs.
- Sometimes pictures show the setting, and sometimes you have to visualize it from details the author has written.

Directions: Reread this passage from "A Visit with Grandpa" and try to visualize the scene it paints. Then answer the questions below.

> Now the sun heated up the morning. The foothills were now varying shades of green. Shadows dotted the plains. Among the blackish green trees on the rolling hills, fog still lingered like lazy clouds. Insects buzzed. A small cloud of mosquitoes swarmed just behind their heads, and beautiful cardinals splashed their redness on the morning air. Justin felt a surge of happiness and hugged Black with his knees and heels.
>
> From JUSTIN AND THE BEST BISCUITS IN THE WORLD by Mildred Pitts Walter. Text Copyright © 1986 by Mildred Pitts Walter. By permission of Lothrop, Lee & Shepard Books, a division of William Morrow & Company, Inc.

1. What season of the year do you think it is? Why?
Possible answer: It is probably spring or summer because the hills are green and there are insects and leaves on the trees.

2. What can you tell about the time in which the story takes place? Explain.
The phrase "in the morning" tells you the time of day, but you can't tell the specific year from the passage.

3. What colors and sounds does Justin see and hear?
He sees green hills, blackish green trees, and red cardinals. He hears insects buzzing.

4. Why do you think Justin feels a "surge of happiness"?
Justin feels happy because he is surrounded by nature's beauty.

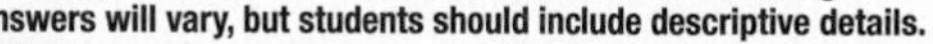

5. Use a separate sheet of paper to describe a place that makes you feel the way Justin does. Remember to include vivid details about the setting.
Answers will vary, but students should include descriptive details.

Notes for Home: Your child has read a story and used story details to visualize its setting. ***Home Activity:*** Have your child describe in detail a place both of you know well. Then try to guess the place. Take turns describing and guessing other places.

Practice Book 4.1, p. 5

Name______________________________ A Visit with Grandpa

Selection Test

Directions: Choose the best answer to each item. Mark the letter for the answer you have chosen.

Part 1: Vocabulary

Find the answer choice that means about the same as the underlined word in each sentence.

1. Kenyi had never seen the <u>prairie</u> before.
   - A. herd of cattle
   - (B.) large, open area with no trees
   - C. mountain range
   - D. show put on by cowboys

2. The boy was <u>teasing</u> his little brother.
   - (F.) joking with; making fun of
   - G. instructing; giving a lesson to
   - H. watching
   - J. waiting for

3. Jenny offered me some <u>biscuits</u>.
   - A. toast spread with jam or jelly
   - B. sandwiches served with tea
   - (C.) bread baked in small, round forms
   - D. servings of meat

4. The man's clothing was <u>rumpled</u>.
   - F. brightly colored
   - G. expensive
   - H. brand new
   - (J.) crushed and messy

5. The sheets are <u>wrinkled</u>.
   - A. torn in pieces
   - B. covered with stains or dirt
   - C. faded in color
   - (D.) having many small folds or creases

6. It's time to prepare the <u>dough</u>.
   - F. a box or trunk
   - G. a favorite family recipe
   - (H.) a mixture of flour, milk, fat, and other ingredients
   - J. a simple meal cooked over a campfire

7. Be sure to bring enough <u>raisins</u>.
   - A. fruit juices
   - (B.) dried grapes
   - C. sour apples
   - D. small candies

Part 2: Comprehension

Use what you know about the story to answer each item.

8. What was Grandpa doing when Justin woke up?
   - F. sleeping
   - (G.) cooking breakfast
   - H. fixing fences
   - J. feeding the cattle

GO ON

Practice Book 4.1, p. 6

Name__________________________________ **A Visit with Grandpa**

9. Grandpa expected Justin to—
   Ⓐ tidy up after himself.
   B. train the horses.
   C. wash his clothes.
   D. learn to rope.

10. At first, Justin thought that washing dishes was—
   F. a waste of time.
   G. an easy task.
   Ⓗ woman's work.
   J. a silly idea.

11. Where does Grandpa live?
   A. in the mountains
   Ⓑ on a prairie
   C. in a large town
   D. in a desert

12. Which sentence tells about the setting of this story?
   F. "He hoped the wrinkles would disappear in time for the festival."
   G. "Justin felt a surge of love for his grandpa."
   Ⓗ "The foothills were now varying shades of green."
   J. "Justin noticed that Grandpa had a map."

13. Justin was surprised to find out that Grandpa—
   A. liked the cowboy festival.
   B. had to mend the fences.
   Ⓒ was a good cook.
   D. enjoyed riding horseback.

14. What can you tell about Black cowboys from reading this story?
   F. There were only a few Black cowboys.
   G. Many books have been written about Black cowboys.
   H. There are no more Black cowboys today.
   Ⓙ Most people do not know about the greatest Black cowboys.

15. What was the most important thing Justin learned from Grandpa?
   A. Riding fence takes a great deal of a rancher's time.
   B. A mother deer will protect her fawn if she thinks people might hurt it.
   C. Good bread can be made with just a few ingredients.
   Ⓓ When a job needs to be done, it does not matter if a man or a woman does it.

Name__________________________________ **A Visit with Grandpa**

Setting

- **Setting** is the time and place in which a story occurs.
- Sometimes pictures show the setting, and sometimes you have to imagine it from details the author has written.

Directions: Read the story below.

It was the kind of day when you don't want to move an inch. The sun beat down on us through bare windows. The air conditioning wasn't working, and the fans were useless. We were sitting in our new apartment. There were so many boxes, we could hardly see the furniture.

The heat wave seemed to have come out of nowhere. The day before, the movers had brought our things over in their truck. The weather was cool then. I hoped it would get cool again by the next week, when school started.

"When it's this hot," Ma said, "there's only one thing to do. Let's go down to the corner for an ice-cream soda."

Directions: Complete the diagram. For each question, underline the correct answer. Write a detail or a clue in each circle that helped you decide. In the middle, write a new title that tells something about the story's setting.

1. Winter or Summer? heat wave, school starting in a week

2. Present Time or Long Ago? air conditioning, fans, truck

5. Title: Possible title: "A Summer Day in the City"

3. Day or Night? sun beating down

4. City or Country? apartment, go down to the corner for an ice-cream soda

Notes for Home: Your child has read a story and used story details and clues to identify the time and place in which the story takes place. ***Home Activity:*** With your child, make a list of details that would help someone visualize a room in your home.

Practice Book 4.1, p. 7

Name__________________________________ **A Visit with Grandpa**

Sequence

REVIEW

Directions: Read the story. Then read each question about the story. Choose the best answer to each question. Mark the letter for the answer you have chosen.

But What Can I Do?

When Joe was five, he decided it was time to help around the house. Greg had already been taking out the trash for a few years. Mollie had started to help Dad vacuum. But what could he do?

He tried carrying the trash. But it was too heavy. Then he tried to vacuum. But it was too hard. The dishes were too slippery, and the beds were too big.

"I know," Joe said. "I'll cook dinner."

Dad smiled. "How about if you put your toys away?"

"Aw, Dad," Joe said. "Do I have to?" Dad laughed.

1. Which story event happened first?
   Ⓐ Joe decided it was time to help.
   B. Mollie vacuumed.
   C. Dad cooked.
   D. Joe put his toys away.

2. Which list indicates the correct sequence of the tasks that Joe tried to do?
   F. dishes, beds, vacuum, trash
   G. vacuum, trash, beds, dishes
   Ⓗ trash, vacuum, dishes, beds
   J. beds, trash, vacuum, dishes

3. Which clue word in the second paragraph helps show the order of events?
   A. but
   Ⓑ then
   C. tried
   D. carrying

4. What is Joe most likely to do next?
   Ⓕ put his toys away
   G. eat dinner
   H. cry
   J. take out the trash

5. Which event took place years before Joe tried to take out the trash?
   A. Mollie began to help vacuum.
   Ⓑ Greg began to take out the trash.
   C. Joe started to wash dishes.
   D. Greg started to wash dishes.

Notes for Home: Your child has read a story and used story details to identify the order of story events. ***Home Activity:*** With your child prepare an item of food from a recipe. Go over the importance of the steps, or the sequence, of the recipe.

Name__________________________________ **A Visit with Grandpa**

Writing Across Texts

Directions: Skim through "A Visit with Grandpa" and "Understanding Horses." Make notes about horses. Include at least five details from each selection about how horses act and about the work they do. Then decide whether you would make a good cowhand. **Possible answers given.**

How Horses Act and the Work They Do	
A Visit with Grandpa	**Understanding Horses**
1. Cowboys use horses to ride fence.	6. Horses have sharp senses of hearing, smell, and sight.
2. Horses wear saddles when people ride them.	7. Horses cannot move their eyes up and down like we can.
3. Horses get tied up when people aren't riding them.	8. Horses can move their ears in all directions.
4. Horses get nervous when they see blood.	9. Young horses like to play.
5. When horses are nervous, running sometimes calms them.	10. Horses show how they feel by their behavior.

Write a Paragraph

You have learned a great deal about horses from reading "A Visit with Grandpa" and "Understanding Horses." Use information from both selections to write a paragraph telling about horses.

Paragraphs will vary. Be sure that students support their writing with details from the selections.

Notes for Home: Your child used information from different sources to write a paragraph. ***Home Activity:*** As you read a story or article with your child, discuss how its ideas connect to other reading your child has done.

Grammar Practice Book 4.1, p. 1

Name______________________ A Visit with Grandpa

Grammar: Statements and Questions

REVIEW

Directions: Write S if a group of words is a statement. Write **Q** if it is a question.

Q 1. Do you have a pet?

Q 2. What kind of pet do you have?

S 3. Cats and dogs are the most common pets.

S 4. Pets can be fun.

S 5. Pet owners also have many responsibilities.

S 6. Proper pet care takes time, effort, and money.

Q 7. Do you feed and exercise your pet every day?

Q 8. When did you last brush your cat or dog?

Q 9. Do you know the signs of a sick pet?

S 10. Libraries have many books on pet care.

Possible answers given.

Directions: Add a word or a group of words to complete each sentence or question.

11. The pet I want **is a horse**.
12. How do you know **how to take care of a horse**?
13. I would make sure **my horse had oats and water every day**.
14. My pet would **be great for taking long rides in the country**.
15. What animal do you **especially like**?

Notes for Home: Your child identified and wrote statements and questions. *Home Activity:* Take turns asking each other some simple questions and answering them using complete statements.

Grammar Practice Book 4.1, p. 2

Name______________________ A Visit with Grandpa

Grammar: Sentences

A **sentence** is a group of words that tells, asks, commands, or exclaims. It begins with a capital letter and ends with a punctuation mark. You can tell whether a group of words is a sentence by checking to see if it expresses a complete thought.

Sentence: My grandpa lives on a ranch.

Not a sentence: Lives on a ranch.

Directions: Read each group of words. Write **S** if it is a sentence. Write **NS** if it is not a sentence.

NS 1. Making the bed.

NS 2. Washing the dishes.

S 3. My grandpa taught me to enjoy cleaning.

NS 4. In the kitchen.

S 5. I like folding my clothes.

Directions: Choose the group of words in ( ) that will complete each sentence. Write the complete sentence on the line.

6. _____ helps your family. (All your hard work/Makes the bed)
All your hard work helps your family.

7. Do you do _____? (in the house/chores at home)
Do you do chores at home?

8. Which chores _____? (the dirty dishes/should you do)
Which chores should you do?

9. Someday I will have _____. (house a mess/my own house to clean)
Someday I will have my own house to clean.

10. A clean house _____. (is a happy house/without any dirt)
A clean house is a happy house.

Notes for Home: Your child identified groups of words that make complete sentences. *Home Activity:* Talk with your child about an event that occurred at school. Have him or her describe the event, using complete sentences.

Grammar Practice Book 4.1, p. 3

Name______________________ A Visit with Grandpa

Grammar: Sentences

Directions: Match each group of words on the left with a group of words on the right to make a sentence that makes the most sense. Write the matching letter on the line.

c 1. Have you ever gone — a. pancakes in the morning.

e 2. Wonderful things — b. the breakfast dishes.

a 3. First, we made — c. to visit your grandpa?

b 4. Then we washed — d. made the beds.

d 5. After doing the dishes, we — e. may be waiting for you at Grandpa's house.

Directions: Add a word or group of words to complete each sentence. Write the complete sentence on the line. **Possible answers given.**

6. _____ make my bed.
Each morning I make my bed.

7. The wrinkled shirt _____.
The wrinkled shirt should be ironed.

8. The house _____.
The house looked great after we cleaned.

9. My grandfather cleans _____.
My grandfather cleans the house every day.

10. Everyone _____.
Everyone helped with the chores.

Write a Paragraph

Do you help with cleaning and other chores at home? On a separate sheet of paper, describe any tasks or chores that you do. Use complete sentences. **Students' descriptions should use complete sentences.**

Notes for Home: Your child practiced completing sentences. *Home Activity:* Make a "To Do" list with your child of chores that need to be done. Be sure to use complete sentences.

Grammar Practice Book 4.1, p. 4

Name______________________ A Visit with Grandpa

Grammar: Sentences

RETEACHING

Look at the picture. Then underline the word group that describes it best.

All of the sheep.

<u>All of the sheep are eating grass.</u>

Is eating grass.

Did you underline the second group of words? It expresses a complete thought. It is a sentence.

A **sentence** is a group of words that tells, asks, commands, or exclaims. It begins with a capital letter and ends with a punctuation mark.

Directions: Underline the group of words in each pair that is a sentence.

1. The small brown cow. <u>The cow grazed in the pasture.</u>
2. <u>Frogs caught flies.</u> Their stomachs with insects.
3. Many bears in the cave. <u>Did one bear eat fresh fish?</u>
4. <u>A raccoon got into our tent.</u> Eating all our food.

Directions: Write complete sentences. Add your own words to each word group. **Possible answers given.**

5. many bears
Many bears lived in the cave.

6. one grasshopper
I saw one grasshopper in the garden.

7. chased a zebra
The lion chased a zebra.

Notes for Home: Your child identified and wrote complete sentences. *Home Activity:* Talk with your child about what you did today. Have him or her summarize your day, using complete sentences.

Grammar Practice Book 4.1, p. 5

Name ____________________ A Visit with Grandpa

Grammar: Sentences

Directions: Read the word group each animal is saying. Write each word group that is a sentence.

1. **My body stores fat for winter.**
2. **Many butterflies migrate with me.**
3. **My friends travel many miles.**

Directions: Underline each word group that is not a sentence. Add words to write a sentence of your own. **Possible answers given.**

4. Many birds travel south.
5. Build nests.
6. Some animals migrate to warm climates.
7. Gray squirrels.
8. Need food in winter.

9. **Birds build nests.**
10. **Gray squirrels climbed the tree.**
11. **Animals need food in winter.**

Notes for Home: Your child identified and wrote complete sentences. ***Home Activity:*** Have your child write five sentences about his or her favorite subject in school. Remind your child to use complete sentences.

Grammar: Sentences 15

Practice Book 4.1, p. 8

Name ____________________ A Visit with Grandpa

Phonics: Vowel Digraphs

Directions: Read the words in the box. Decide whether the underlined part of each word has a vowel sound like **tree, hay,** or **boat.** Write each word in the correct column. **Order may vary.**

stay	heated	soap
doe	receive	waited
slowly	feeling	plain

tree	hay	boat
1. **receive**	4. **stay**	7. **slowly**
2. **heated**	5. **waited**	8. **soap**
3. **feeling**	6. **plain**	9. **doe**

Directions: Underline the word in each sentence that has the same vowel sound as the boldfaced word to the left. Write the word on the line.

feeling 10. **tree** Eric had a good feeling about the day ahead.
today 11. **hay** He and his grandpa were going riding today.
meadow 12. **boat** They took the path through the meadow.
doe 13. **boat** They saw a doe coming out of the woods.
afraid 14. **hay** The doe was afraid of Eric and his grandpa.
easy 15. **tree** It is easy to frighten a doe.
field 16. **tree** Later, they rode home across the field.
slowly 17. **boat** Later, they watched as the sun slowly set.

Directions: For each word below, write three more words that have the same vowel sound spelled the same way. **Possible answers given**

18. nail	**tail**	**pail**	**fail**
19. need	**seed**	**sleeve**	**feed**
20. slow	**know**	**follow**	**shadow**

Notes for Home: Your child learned different spellings for the vowel sounds long *e* (*tree, eat, deceive, niece*), long *a* (*play, bait*), and long *o* (*boat, mow, toe*). ***Home Activity:*** Pick one of these vowel sounds. Make a list of words that use each spelling.

16 Phonics: Vowel Digraphs

Spelling Workbook 4.1, p. 1

Name ____________________ A Visit with Grandpa

Spelling: Vowel Sounds in *few* and *moon*

Pretest Directions: Fold back the page along the dotted line. On the blanks, write the spelling words as they are dictated. When you have finished the test, unfold the page and check your words.

1. **huge**	1. The volcano is **huge**.
2. **excuse**	2. **Excuse** me from the table.
3. **confuse**	3. Don't **confuse** me!
4. **few**	4. There are a **few** left.
5. **nephew**	5. Her **nephew** is seven.
6. **curfew**	6. What time is our **curfew**?
7. **usual**	7. This is my **usual** lunch.
8. **pupil**	8. He is a good **pupil**.
9. **fuel**	9. Gasoline is a **fuel**.
10. **menu**	10. Is soup on the **menu**?
11. **cool**	11. It is **cool** outside.
12. **mood**	12. I'm in a good **mood**.
13. **shoot**	13. **Shoot** the picture.
14. **school**	14. This is our **school**.
15. **shampoo**	15. I forgot my **shampoo**.
16. **fruit**	16. Pick **fruit** off the tree.
17. **suit**	17. She wore a blue **suit**.
18. **juice**	18. Drink some **juice**.
19. **bruise**	19. My **bruise** is healing.
20. **cruise**	20. **Cruise** down the river.

Notes for Home: Your child took a pretest on words that have vowel sounds such as those in *few* and *moon*. ***Home Activity:*** Help your child learn misspelled words before the final test. Your child should look at the word, say it, spell it aloud, and then spell it with eyes shut.

Spelling: Vowel Sounds in *few* and *moon* 17

Spelling Workbook 4.1, p. 2

Name ____________________ A Visit with Grandpa

Spelling: Vowel Sounds in *few* and *moon*

Word List

huge	nephew	fuel	shoot	suit
excuse	curfew	menu	school	juice
confuse	usual	cool	shampoo	bruise
few	pupil	mood	fruit	cruise

Directions: Write the words from the box that have the same vowel sound as **moon.** Sort the words according to how the vowel sound is spelled.

Order may vary.

Spelled oo	Spelled ui
1. **cool**	6. **fruit**
2. **mood**	7. **suit**
3. **shoot**	8. **juice**
4. **school**	9. **bruise**
5. **shampoo**	10. **cruise**

Directions: Choose the word from the box that best matches each clue. Write the word on the line.

confuse 11. to make unclear
nephew 12. opposite of *niece*
fuel 13. wood for a fire; food for your body
menu 14. a list of food you can order
curfew 15. the time at which you have to be home
excuse 16. your reason for not doing what you're supposed to
huge 17. immense; large
pupil 18. someone who studies something
few 19. not many
usual 20. ordinary

Notes for Home: Your child spelled words with the vowel sounds in *few* and *moon*. ***Home Activity:*** Together, write silly sentences that use two or more of the spelling words in each sentence.

18 Spelling: Vowel Sounds in *few* and *moon*

Spelling Workbook 4.1, p. 3
Name______________________ A Visit with Grandpa

Spelling: Vowel Sounds in *few* and *moon*

Directions: Proofread this list. Find five spelling mistakes. Use the proofreading marks to correct each mistake.

≡ Make a capital.
/ Make a small letter.
∧ Add something.
Take out something.
⊙ Add a period.
¶ Begin a new paragraph.

A Few Rules of the House

1. Curfuw: Schol nights 8:00. Weekends 9:00. (corrected: Curfew, School)
2. If you use up the soap or shampew, tell somebody. (corrected: shampoo)
3. Put your laundry in the basket. No exkuse will be accepted! (corrected: excuse)
4. If you drink all the jewce or milk, put the container in the recycling bin. (corrected: juice)
5. If you have a few extra minutes, pick up a few things.

Spelling Tip

exc<u>u</u>se f<u>ew</u> p<u>u</u>pil c<u>oo</u>l j<u>ui</u>ce

Watch for words that have the same vowel sounds but different spellings. The vowel sound in **few** can be spelled **u-consonant-e, ew,** or **u.** The vowel sound in **moon** can be spelled **oo** or **ui.**

Word List

huge	cool
excuse	mood
confuse	shoot
few	school
nephew	shampoo
curfew	fruit
usual	suit
pupil	juice
fuel	bruise
menu	cruise

Write Your Own Rules

On a separate sheet of paper, write your own list of rules. Try to use at least three spelling words.

Answers will vary, but each set of rules should include at least three spelling words.

Notes for Home: Your child spelled words with the vowel sounds in *few* and *moon*. ***Home Activity:*** Write a list of words with your child that rhyme with *few* and *moon*. Discuss the different spellings for these two vowel sounds.

Spelling Workbook 4.1, p. 4
Name______________________ A Visit with Grandpa

Spelling: Vowel Sounds in *few* and *moon*

REVIEW

Directions: Choose the word from the box that completes each comparison. Write the word on the line.

1. song and program, food and **menu**
2. aunt and uncle, niece and **nephew**
3. body and soap, hair and **shampoo**
4. hot and warm, cold and **cool**
5. tiny and little, big and **huge**
6. knife and cut, bump and **bruise**
7. sailboat and wind, car and **fuel**
8. football and toss, basketball and **shoot**
9. thinking and idea, feeling and **mood**
10. rare and uncommon, ordinary and **usual**

Word List: huge, excuse, confuse, few, nephew, curfew, usual, pupil, fuel, menu, cool, mood, shoot, school, shampoo, fruit, suit, juice, bruise, cruise

Directions: Choose the word from the box that best completes each statement. Write the word on the line to the left.

cruise 11. To see the world, be a waiter on a _____ ship.
school 12. To learn your job, go to a training _____.
pupil 13. If you do well, you are a good _____.
curfew 14. On work days, you will have an early _____.
confuse 15. Don't let the passengers _____ you with their orders.
suit 16. Try not to spill soup on a passenger's good _____.
fruit 17. Don't drop the bowl of _____ and bruise the apples.
juice 18. Don't bring tomato _____ if someone orders water.
excuse 19. If you forget an order, don't make an _____.
few 20. After work, you will have a _____ free hours.

Notes for Home: Your child spelled words with the vowel sounds in *few* and *moon*. ***Home Activity:*** Choose a word from the box. Then give clues about the word so your child can guess and spell the word. Let your child do the same for you.

Practice Book 4.1, p. 9
Name______________________ A Visit with Grandpa

Textbook/Trade Book

Textbooks usually teach about one subject, such as social studies or math. These books are organized to help you find information quickly. Each **chapter title** tells you about a main section of the book, and the **headings** and **subheadings** show what information you can find in a particular section. **Vocabulary words** are often printed in bold and included in the margin.

Directions: Use the textbook section to answer the questions that follow.

CHAPTER 8 American History 1865–1885

A Cowboy's Life

Chefs on the Prairie

A cowboy's job involved many hours of hard work, so when dinnertime finally arrived, he was ready for hearty meals. Since cowboys used the word "chuck" to mean food, the vehicle that carried the food around was called a **chuck wagon.** These wagons, which also served as kitchens, hotels, and ranch headquarters, were driven by the cook.

chuck wagon: vehicle that carried meals to cowboys

The cook's day began at about 3:00 A.M. He would wake up the crew to help him prepare breakfast. Some cowboys complained that they had to work from sunrise to sunset, or as they put it from "can't see to can't see." To bake the biscuits, the camp chefs used cast iron **Dutch ovens.** These ovens were used to bake biscuits, cornbread, fruit cobblers, and cakes. Popular cowboy meals around the campfire included beef, beans, biscuits, rice, and dried fruit. Cowboys rarely ate fresh vegetables, milk, or eggs.

Dutch oven: a large, heavy kettle

1. How could you quickly find the definitions for vocabulary words on this page?
Look in the left margin for the vocabulary words and definitions.

2. If you wanted to write an essay called "A Day in the Life of a Cowboy," do you think this textbook chapter would be helpful? Explain why or why not.
Yes, the heading tells you that the section is about a cowboy's life.

3. What part of the page tells you the time period this chapter covers?
The chapter title, American History 1865–1885, tells the time period covered.

Practice Book 4.1, p. 10
Name______________________ A Visit with Grandpa

A **trade book** is any book that is not a textbook, a periodical, or a reference book. The skills you use for understanding trade books are a lot like those you use when you read textbooks. When you choose a trade book, think about your purpose for reading, the same as you would for choosing a reference book.

Directions: Use the trade book excerpt to answer the questions that follow.

25

Chapter 3: If You Were a Wild West Wrangler

Q: Did cowboys travel with tables and chairs?
A: They usually ate their meals sitting or squatting on the ground.

Q: What other responsibilities did a cowboy cook have?
A: In addition to preparing food, it was not unusual for the cook to serve as the camp doctor and barber. The cook also drove the chuck wagon. Every night after dinner, the cook pointed the wagon toward the North Star, so he could head in the right direction the next day.

4. How is the information in this book organized? How might this be helpful for writing an essay about a cowboy's daily life?
The book is organized by question and answer. You can use the questions to quickly find information you need.

5. In addition to cooking meals, what other responsibilities did the cook have?
The cook might also serve as camp doctor and barber and drive the chuck wagon.

Notes for Home: Your child used a textbook and a trade book to locate information and draw conclusions. ***Home Activity:*** Discuss some other resources your child might use to find information about cowboys, such as history TV channels, history magazines, and so on.

Practice Book 4.1, p. 11

Name________________________ Train to Somewhere

Sequence

- **Sequence** means the order in which things happen. **Sequence** can also mean steps we follow to do something.
- Clue words such as *first, then, next,* and *finally* help you figure out the sequence of events.
- Some events in a story may take place at the same time. Authors may use words like *meanwhile, while,* or *during* to show this.
- Sometimes events are told out of order. Verb tenses or clue words can show this.

First → Next → Last

Directions: Reread "Will Sarah Return?" On the lines below, write the story events from the box in the order that they happened. Use the letter shown next to each event.

Story Events

a. Anna sweeps the porch.
b. Anna sweeps the porch again.
c. Caleb picks up Seal.
d. Seal jumps onto the porch.
e. Anna asks her father where Sarah has gone.
f. Caleb cleans out the stove.
g. Anna watches a wagon take Mama away.
h. Caleb spills the ashes.
i. Anna and Caleb watch Sarah.
j. Anna and Caleb take lunch to their father.

1. **g**
2. **i**
3. **d**
4. **c**
5. **a**
6. **f**
7. **h**
8. **b**
9. **j**
10. **e**

Notes for Home: Your child read a story and identified the order in which the story events occurred. ***Home Activity:*** Work with your child to create a "My Day" list that shows all your child's activities in order from waking up in the morning to the present time.

Practice Book 4.1, p. 12

Name________________________ Train to Somewhere

Vocabulary

Directions: Choose the word from the box that best completes each sentence. Write the word on the matching numbered line to the right.

Mr. and Mrs. Garcia are the **1.**_____ next door. Last month they told me they were going to **2.**_____ a daughter. Mrs. Garcia took out her **3.**_____ and showed me the country where the baby was born. She said that she would be very happy to end the **4.**_____ of waiting so long for the baby. Yesterday I saw Mr. Garcia happily pushing a **5.**_____ with a beautiful baby girl inside.

1. **couple**
2. **adopt**
3. **atlas**
4. **misery**
5. **carriage**

Check the Words You Know
__ adopt
__ atlas
__ carriage
__ couple
__ misery
__ platform

Directions: Choose the word from the box that best matches each clue. Write the word in the puzzle.

Down
6. accept a child of other parents and bring it up as your own
7. book of maps
9. great unhappiness

Across
8. a raised, level surface
10. a 4-wheeled vehicle that is pulled or pushed

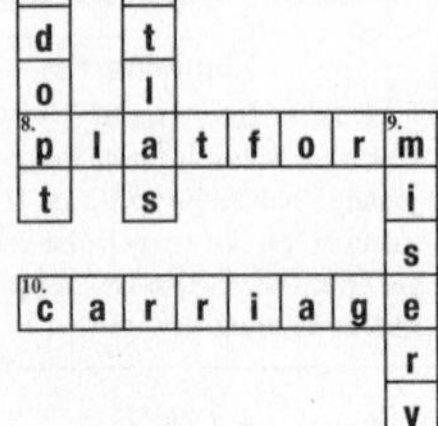

Write a Story

On a separate sheet of paper, write a story about a couple who think they are adopting a puppy, but get a very different kind of animal instead. Use as many of the vocabulary words as you can.
Students' stories should use vocabulary words correctly.

Notes for Home: Your child identified and used new vocabulary words from *Train to Somewhere. **Home Activity:*** With your child, make up a story about a child traveling to a new home. Encourage your child to use as many of the vocabulary words as possible.

Practice Book 4.1, p. 13

Name________________________ Train to Somewhere

Sequence

- **Sequence** means the order in which things happen. Clue words such as *first, then, next,* and *finally* help you figure out the sequence of events.
- Authors do not always use clue words to show sequence.

Directions: Reread what happens in *Train to Somewhere* after Marianne and eight other children leave the first stop, Porterville, Illinois. Then answer the questions below. Look for any clue words the author uses to show the sequence of events.

Nine of us are left to get back on the train. Miss Randolph says we're to keep on our good clothes. We'll be getting off again soon.

At Kilburn we are walked to a hardware store to stand in line.

"I expect they took all the biggest boys in Porterville," one man says. "But still. . . ."

Eddie Hartz, who is only seven, is taken. There's a boy who can stand on his hands and pretend to pull buttons out of people's ears. He makes the crowd laugh and he gets taken, too.

As soon as the train has loaded on wood and fresh water, the rest of us get back aboard.

1. What is the first event of this passage? **Nine children get back on the train.**
2. What is the last event of this passage? **The rest of the children get back on the train.**
3. Were the children wearing their good clothes before they got to Kilburn? How do you know?
Yes. Miss Randolph tells the children to keep their good clothes on.
4. How many children get back on the train? How do you know?
Seven; There were nine when they arrived and two are taken.
5. On a separate sheet of paper, write three sentences telling what happens next in the story. **Possible answer: First, they make another stop at Glover. Next, Susan is chosen. Then, three boys are chosen.**

Notes for Home: Your child has read a story and used story details to describe the order in which events occurred. ***Home Activity:*** Have your child make a list of tomorrow's activities. Then ask him or her to number the list in the order that the events are expected to happen.

Practice Book 4.1, p. 15

Name________________________ Train to Somewhere

Selection Test

Directions: Choose the best answer to each item. Mark the letter for the answer you have chosen.

Part 1: Vocabulary

Find the answer choice that means about the same as the underlined word in each sentence.

1. Wanda described her misery to me.
   A. way of doing things
   (B) great suffering or unhappiness
   C. adventure
   D. plans for the future
2. The platform is large and sturdy.
   F. a chest for clothing
   G. a wall made of stone
   H. a wooden box
   (J) a raised flat surface
3. The Lees will adopt a little boy.
   A. have happy memories of
   (B) raise a child of other parents as their own
   C. pay a visit to
   D. guide someone on a long trip
4. I borrowed this atlas from Arnie.
   F. small suitcase
   G. old-fashioned camera
   (H) book of maps
   J. heavy jacket
5. The carriage needs to be repaired.
   (A) something to carry passengers
   B. something to eat with
   C. something to train animals
   D. something to row with
6. The couple ate dinner at home.
   F. the children of a family
   G. several people who are traveling together
   H. a close relative
   (J) two people with a close relationship

Part 2: Comprehension

Use what you know about the story to answer each item.

7. What is the first thing Marianne does each time the train stops?
   A. has some cookies and milk
   B. changes into old clothes
   C. tries to look pleasant
   (D) looks for her mother in the crowd
8. Miss Randolph's feeling about the children is that they—
   F. are hard to care for.
   G. will all be happy in their new homes.
   H. are fussy and spoiled.
   (J) are very special and she will miss them.

GO ON

Practice Book 4.1, p. 16

Name ______ **Train to Somewhere**

9. Which event in this story happens before the train leaves New York?
   A. Nora and Marianne sit together on the train.
   B. Miss Randolph gives the children milk and cookies.
   (C.) Marianne's mother leaves her at St. Christopher's.
   D. The train stops at a town called Somewhere.

10. The feather Marianne carries in her pocket is a—
   (F.) reminder of her mother.
   G. gift from Nora.
   H. decoration for her hair.
   J. lucky charm.

11. How does Marianne feel when the train reaches Somewhere?
   A. peaceful and content
   B. tired and bored
   C. excited and hopeful
   (D.) hurt and unloved

12. What happens first when Marianne meets the Books?
   F. She gives Mrs. Book her feather.
   (G.) She notices that the Books are old.
   H. She agrees to go with the Books.
   J. She asks for a puppy.

13. Which sentence best describes the lesson in this story?
   A. Children should learn to do the things that please adults.
   B. Friends are usually more important than relatives.
   (C.) Sometimes what you get is better than what you wished for.
   D. Adults always know what is best for children.

14. Which sentence suggests that Marianne likes Mrs. Book?
   F. "She's wearing a heavy black dress and a man's droopy black hat."
   G. "The woman's holding a wooden toy locomotive."
   (H.) "Somehow this woman understands about me, how it felt that nobody wanted me."
   J. "She pats Mr. Book's hand and they smile at each other."

15. In this story, Marianne's biggest disappointment was—
   A. leaving Miss Randolph.
   B. leaving St. Christopher's.
   C. being taken by the Books.
   (D.) knowing her mother had not come for her.

Name ______ **Train to Somewhere**

Sequence

First → Next → Finally

- **Sequence** means the order in which things happen. Clue words such as *first, then, next,* and *finally* help you figure out the sequence of events.
- Authors do not always use clue words to show sequence.

Directions: Read the story below.

My great-grandmother Rose told me how she loved to visit her country cousins. It took all morning to go across town and a few miles into the next county. First, she walked to the corner of her block. There, she got on a trolley. Then, she took a train. Next, she rode a second trolley to the city limits. Finally, she took a bus out into the country!

Her uncle and cousins always picked up my great-grandmother in their buggy at the bus station. She was tired from the trip, but it was worth it. She would stay with her relatives for a few days. What fun they would have! Then, finally, it was time for her to make the long trip home.

Directions: Fill in the flowchart with the events in the order they happened.

Rose walked to the corner.
→ 1. **She got on a trolley.**
→ 2. **She took a train.**
→ 3. **She rode a second trolley to the city limits.**
→ 4. **She took a bus out into the country.**
→ She was picked up in a buggy.
→ She stayed with her relatives for a few days.
→ 5. **She had to make the long trip home.**

Notes for Home: Your child has read a story and used story details to fill in a flowchart showing the sequence of events. ***Home Activity:*** The next time you take a trip with your child, such as to the grocery store, take turns recalling the sequence of events of the trip.

Practice Book 4.1, p. 17

Name ______ **Train to Somewhere**

Cause and Effect

REVIEW

Directions: Read the story. Then read each question about the story. Choose the best answer to each question. Mark the letter for the answer you have chosen.

Leaving Time

Mom told me that her family was always late leaving on vacation. That's because they didn't like to get up early. Also, it took a long time to get ready.

Mom said Grandma had too many clothes. She could never decide what to pack.

Grandpa always spotted a chore he forgot to do. Mom usually found him cleaning or fixing something. Sometimes he couldn't find the map.

My uncle David had hair that wouldn't stay down. He would spend an hour combing it. Then it would pop up again.

Mom could never decide what books to take. So she had to start reading each one.

1. Which was **not** a cause of the family leaving late?
   A. getting up late
   (B.) the weather
   C. Grandma's packing
   D. Mom's reading

2. What was the effect of David's hair not staying down?
   F. He forgot to comb it.
   G. He had a cowlick.
   (H.) His combing made the family late.
   J. His hair popped up.

3. What might Grandpa do to make the family late?
   A. go to the park
   B. comb his hair
   (C.) fix the lawn sprinkler
   D. eat a big breakfast

4. What might have helped the family be on time?
   F. eat breakfast together
   (G.) pack the night before
   H. check the weather report
   J. get gas for the car

5. In the following sentence, which word gives a clue about why something happened?
   David's hair wouldn't stay down, so he took a long time combing it.
   A. wouldn't
   B. down
   C. time
   (D.) so

Notes for Home: Your child identified causes and effects in a story. ***Home Activity:*** Play a game of cause and effect. When something happens at home, look for causes and effects. For example, if the timer doesn't go off (cause), then dinner may burn (effect).

Name ______ **Train to Somewhere**

Writing Across Texts

Directions: The stories *Train to Somewhere* and "A Visit with Grandpa" show how an event in a person's life can have many effects. Complete the first two columns of the table by listing effects that Marianne and Justin had as a result of their experiences. Then, in the third column, list an important event in your own life and the multiple effects it has caused. **Possible answers given.**

Cause: Marianne was left in an orphanage. **Effect:** She was put on an orphan train.	**Cause:** Justin went to stay with Grandpa. **Effect:** He learned that making a bed was easy.	**Cause:** **Effect:** **Answers will vary.**
1. **She met Mrs. Randolph and many other orphans.**	6. **He learned how to fold clothes.**	11.
2. **She saw families who were looking for a child.**	7. **He learned about famous black cowboys.**	12.
3. **She learned that most people wanted only one child.**	8. **He learned that is all right for men to cry.**	13.
4. **She learned that some wanted a child for work.**	9. **He learned that men can be good cooks.**	14.
5. **She met and was adopted by Mr. and Mrs. Book.**	10. **He learned that it is important to do all work well.**	15.

Write a Cause and Effect Paragraph

On a separate sheet of paper, write a cause and effect paragraph that describes how an event in your life has caused multiple effects.
Check that students have created paragraphs that describe a cause and numerous effects.

Notes for Home: Your child listed details from two different selections. ***Home Activity:*** Talk with your child about someone who has had an effect on you in your lifetime. Share how that person has changed your life in some way.

Grammar Practice Book 4.1, p. 6

Name______________ Train to Somewhere

Grammar: Sentences

REVIEW

Directions: Read each group of words. Write **S** if it is a sentence. Write **NS** if it is not a sentence.

S 1. A big family has many benefits.

NS 2. Never lonely.

NS 3. Lots of help with homework.

S 4. You can meet the friends of your brothers and sisters.

S 5. Someone will always stick up for you.

Directions: Add a word or group of words to complete each sentence. Write the complete sentence on the line. Remember to begin each sentence with a capital letter and end each one with a punctuation mark. **Possible answers given.**

6. have fun together
The children in our family have fun together.

7. younger brothers and sisters
The older ones help the younger brothers and sisters.

8. share toys and games
Sometimes it's hard to share toys and games.

9. never quiet
Things are never quiet with so many voices speaking.

10. have responsibilities
We all have responsibilities.

Notes for Home: Your child identified and wrote complete sentences. ***Home Activity:*** Choose a picture in a magazine. Have your child write several sentences about the picture. Check that each sentence begins with a capital letter and ends with a punctuation mark.

Grammar Practice Book 4.1, p. 7

Name______________ Train to Somewhere

Grammar: Subjects and Predicates

The **subject** is the word or group of words about which something is said in the sentence. The **predicate** is the word or group of words that tells something about the subject. All the words in the subject are called the **complete subject.** All the words in the predicate are called the **complete predicate.**

All my friends love baseball.

The **simple subject** is the main noun or pronoun in the complete subject. It may be more than one word. The **simple predicate** is the verb in the complete predicate. Some simple predicates can be more than one word.

Peter Jones hit the ball hard. The fans were cheering loudly.

Directions: For each sentence, underline the complete subject once and underline the complete predicate twice.

1. A.J. is always picked last for baseball games.
2. The team captains pick all the best players first.
3. A.J. waits in the hot sun.
4. I may be team captain one day.
5. My friend A.J. will not be picked last then.

Directions: For each sentence, underline the simple subject once and the simple predicate twice.

6. I had a big surprise yesterday.
7. Ms. Martin chose A.J. as a team captain.
8. A.J. made many picks.
9. Believe it or not, I was the last one picked.
10. Suddenly, I have changed my mind about picking A.J.!

Notes for Home: Your child identified simple and complete subjects and simple and complete predicates in sentences. ***Home Activity:*** Ask your child to identify simple and complete subjects and predicates in a variety of sentences from a story or newspaper.

Grammar Practice Book 4.1, p. 8

Name______________ Train to Somewhere

Grammar: Subjects and Predicates

Directions: For each sentence, underline the complete subject once. Underline the complete predicate twice. Circle the simple subject and the simple predicate.

1. Trains were slower a hundred years ago.
2. The earliest models took a long time to get anywhere.
3. A family had no other good way to travel.
4. Cars were a new invention.
5. Few people had them.
6. Our lives were much slower then.
7. Many people traveled to see new places.
8. They liked to get off at a stop and look around.
9. Most families thought cross-country travel was amazing.
10. They tried to imagine faraway places.
11. Most people never went far from home.
12. Fancy new cars had changed people's ideas about travel.
13. They made it easier to travel farther and faster.
14. Roads were appearing everywhere.
15. Trains became less important.

Write a Letter

Imagine you're traveling somewhere on a train. On a separate sheet of paper, write a letter home, describing what you see. Identify the simple and complete subjects and predicates in each sentence.

Students should correctly identify the complete subjects and complete predicates in their sentences.

Notes for Home: Your child identified simple and complete subjects and predicates. ***Home Activity:*** Start with a sentence that has a simple subject and predicate. Take turns adding words to make the sentence longer, without losing the starting words or idea.

Grammar Practice Book 4.1, p. 9

Name______________ Train to Somewhere

Grammar: Subjects and Predicates

RETEACHING

Read the sentence about Ana. Then answer the questions.

Ana plays ball.

1. Write the one word that tells whom the sentence is about. **Ana**
That word is the subject of the sentence.

2. Write the words that tell what Ana does. **plays ball**
Those words are the predicate of the sentence.

A sentence has two parts. The **subject** is the word or group of words about which something is said in the sentence. The **predicate** tells about the subject.

Directions: Complete each sentence. Add a subject or a predicate from the lists.

Subjects	**Predicates**
You	make puppets for children
People in ancient times	are popular today

1. Puppet shows **are popular today**.
2. Some adults **make puppets for children**.
3. **You** can give your own puppet show.

Directions: Underline the subject and circle the predicate in each sentence.

4. Some children make puppets from old socks.
5. They put the socks on their hands.
6. Their fingers make the puppet move.
7. Some of the puppets look like real people.
8. Other puppets are very unusual.
9. This puppet wears a tall hat.

Notes for Home: Your child identified and wrote subjects and predicates of sentences. ***Home Activity:*** Look at a magazine or newspaper article with your child. Have him or her underline the subjects and circle the predicates of five sentences.

Grammar Practice Book 4.1, p. 10

Name________________________ Train to Somewhere

Grammar: Subjects and Predicates

Directions: Draw a line between the subject and the predicate of each sentence. Then write each simple subject and simple predicate below the correct heading.

1. Many people | live in Colorado.
2. The state | has many mountains.
3. Few trees | grow on the mountaintops.
4. The tall mountains | are beautiful.

Simple Subjects	Simple Predicates
1. people	1. live
2. state	2. has
3. trees	3. grow
4. mountains	4. are

Directions: Read each sentence. Draw one line under the subject. Draw two lines under the predicate. Circle the simple subject and the simple predicate.

5. Many **hikers** **climb** the mountains.
6. The **water** in the streams **is** clear.
7. The **birds** in the trees **sing** in the morning.
8. **Squirrels** **run** around the trees.
9. Groups of **campers** **look** for campsites.

Write a Speech

On a separate sheet of paper, write a speech about your state. Use complete sentences to communicate your ideas. **Students may write speeches describing your state. Make sure they use complete sentences.**

Notes for Home: Your child wrote subjects and predicates of sentences. ***Home Activity:*** Provide your child with two subjects (for example, *The huge basketball, My jeans*). Have him or her make up predicates to go with the subjects and write the complete sentences.

Grammar: Subjects and Predicates 37

Practice Book 4.1, p. 18

Name________________________ Train to Somewhere

Phonics: Vowel Digraphs

Directions: Read each sentence. Say the underlined word to yourself. Listen for the vowel sounds that the letters **ea** and **ou** represent in **feather, peak,** and **country.** Circle the word in ( ) that has the same vowel sound as the underlined word.

1. The steam train pulled into the station. (break/**beat**)
2. The train was taking orphan children to the country. (found/**tough**)
3. Many people had read about the children on the train. (sea/**dead**)
4. The train traveled in all kinds of weather. (**bread**/bead)
5. After four days, the children had had enough of riding the train. (though/**tough**)
6. Not knowing where their next home would be was tough on them. (fought/**rough**)
7. Instead of getting off the train, they waited until the next stop. (**head**/meat)
8. Only one couple came to meet the train at the stop. (**rough**/bought)
9. The woman had a white feather in her hat. (fear/**head**)
10. She quickly reached out to welcome the children. (**seat**/ready)

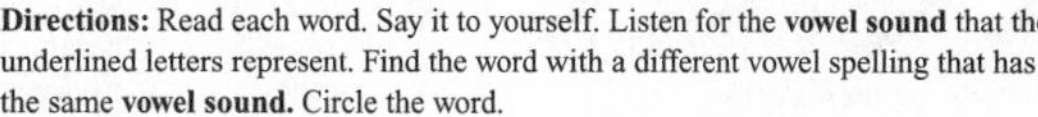

Directions: Read each word. Say it to yourself. Listen for the **vowel sound** that the underlined letters represent. Find the word with a different vowel spelling that has the same **vowel sound.** Circle the word.

11. country	cold	foul	**fun**
12. weather	**bed**	bath	bead
13. heat	height	**receive**	wait
14. couple	**cup**	cope	cop
15. heaven	heave	**seven**	haven

Notes for Home: Your child paired words with the same vowel sounds heard in *feather, peak,* and *country.* ***Home Activity:*** Help your child think of other words spelled with *ea* and *ou* that have these vowel sounds.

38 Phonics: Vowel Digraphs

Spelling Workbook 4.1, p. 5

Name________________________ Train to Somewhere

Spelling: Short e and Long e

Pretest Directions: Fold back the page along the dotted line. On the blanks, write the spelling words as they are dictated. When you have finished the test, unfold the page and check your words.

1. them	1. Have you seen **them**?
2. went	2. Morgan **went** ice-skating.
3. fence	3. Our **fence** needs fixing.
4. credit	4. He got **credit** for his deed.
5. engine	5. Turn the **engine** on.
6. contest	6. I will enter the **contest**.
7. speak	7. **Speak** up in class.
8. reason	8. What **reason** do you have?
9. beat	9. **Beat** the drum.
10. least	10. Which is the **least** full?
11. steal	11. Mice might **steal** cheese.
12. treat	12. We will have a **treat**!
13. season	13. It is the harvest **season**.
14. money	14. I save **money** in a jar.
15. valley	15. Look down in the **valley**.
16. honey	16. Bees make **honey**.
17. monkey	17. Watch the **monkey** climb.
18. hockey	18. Can you play **hockey**?
19. alley	19. The **alley** needs sweeping.
20. donkey	20. Quinn rode a **donkey**.

Notes for Home: Your child took a pretest on words with the short *e* and long *e* sounds. ***Home Activity:*** Help your child learn misspelled words before the final test. Your child can underline the word parts that caused the problems and concentrate on those parts.

Spelling: Short *e* and Long *e* 39

Spelling Workbook 4.1, p. 6

Name________________________ Train to Somewhere

Spelling: Short e and Long e

Word List

them	engine	beat	season	monkey
went	contest	least	money	hockey
fence	speak	steal	valley	alley
credit	reason	treat	honey	donkey

Directions: Write the words from the box with the **long e** vowel sound. Sort the words according to how the vowel sound is spelled. **Order may vary.**

Long e spelled ea	Long e spelled ey
1. speak	8. money
2. reason	9. valley
3. beat	10. honey
4. least	11. monkey
5. steal	12. hockey
6. treat	13. alley
7. season	14. donkey

Directions: Choose the word from the box that best completes each sentence. Write the word on the line to the left.

went 15. Yesterday we _____ to get a present for my cousin.

contest 16. We had a _____ to see who could find the best present.

engine 17. I picked a tiny train with a working _____.

fence 18. My mom picked a model farm surrounded by a white picket _____.

them 19. We took _____ both to the clerk.

credit 20. The clerk said, "Will that be cash or _____?"

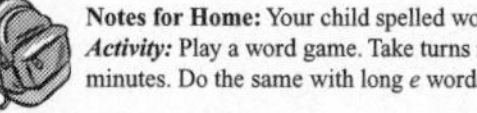

Notes for Home: Your child spelled words with short *e* and long *e* vowel sounds. ***Home Activity:*** Play a word game. Take turns naming words with a short *e (went)*. Play for three minutes. Do the same with long *e* words *(speak, money)*.

40 Spelling: Short *e* and Long *e*

Spelling Workbook 4.1, p. 7

Name________________

Train to Somewhere

Spelling: Short e and Long e

Directions: Proofread this letter. Find five spelling mistakes. Use the proofreading marks to correct each mistake.

≡	Make a capital.
/	Make a small letter.
∧	Add something.
℘	Take out something.
⊙	Add a period.
¶	Begin a new paragraph.

Dear Aunt Natalie,

Thanks for the birthday money. I used it to get a new field hock[e]y stick. We play after school in the field behind the fenc[e]. The grass is a little tall down there in the vall[e]y, especially this se[a]son, but at le[a]st we get to play!

Love,

Marcy

Spelling Tip

Short e is often spelled **e,** as in **went. Long e** can be spelled **ea,** as in **speak,** or **ey,** as in **money.**

Word List

them	steal
went	treat
fence	season
credit	money
engine	valley
contest	honey
speak	monkey
reason	hockey
beat	alley
least	donkey

Write Your Own Letter

Imagine you are Aunt Natalie. On a separate sheet of paper, write a letter back to Marcy. Try to use at least three spelling words.

Answers will vary, but each letter should include at least three spelling words.

Notes for Home: Your child spelled words with short *e (went)* and long *e (speak, money)* vowel sounds. ***Home Activity:*** Post paper on your refrigerator and invite your child to add words with short *e* and long *e* vowel sounds each day. Notice the different spellings for these sounds.

Spelling Workbook 4.1, p. 8

Name________________

Train to Somewhere

Spelling: Short e and Long e

REVIEW

Directions: Choose the word from the box that best matches each clue. Write the word on the line.

fence 1. You might hit the ball over it.

alley 2. narrow place between two buildings

season 3. It is a time of year.

honey 4. Bees are busy making this.

monkey 5. a long-tailed animal that likes bananas

donkey 6. long-eared animal that can carry things

reason 7. what you give when you tell why

beat 8. You do this to cake batter or on a set of drums.

least 9. This is the smallest amount.

engine 10. It is the part that makes a machine run.

money 11. It's green but doesn't grow on trees. Hint: You could buy a tree with it.

speak 12. You do this when you want to be heard.

Word List

them
went
fence
credit
engine
contest
speak
reason
beat
least
steal
treat
season
money
valley
honey
monkey
hockey
alley
donkey

Directions: Each of the words below is hidden in a word from the box. Write the word on the line. Hint: It won't be a word you've already used.

13. hock	**hockey**	17. we	**went**
14. test	**contest**	18. teal	**steal**
15. alley	**valley**	19. the	**them**
16. red	**credit**	20. eat	**treat**

Notes for Home: Your child spelled words with short *e* and long *e* vowel sounds. ***Home Activity:*** Hold a spelling bee for your child. Say each spelling word twice. Have your child spell it aloud.

Practice Book 4.1, p. 19

Name________________

Train to Somewhere

Research Process

Begin your research by asking yourself questions about your topic. Find resources, such as encyclopedias, that will help answer these questions. As you gather information, you can ask new questions. Summarize the information you find by taking notes or writing outlines. Then organize your information into a report.

Directions: Complete the table. For rows 1, 2, and 3, decide what key words would help you locate information in a reference source. For row 4, write a question based on the key word that you could answer in your research.

What I Want to Find Out	Key Words
What year did the first Orphan Train leave?	1. **Orphan Train**
How many people lived in New York City in 1880?	2. **New York City or population**
Are any orphan-train riders alive today?	3. **Orphan Train**
4. **Possible answer: How many people travel by railroad each year?**	railroad

Directions: Use the information on this set of encyclopedias to answer the questions that follow.

5. Which volume would help you find out what year the helicopter was invented? Explain.

Vol. 5 may have information about helicopters since it is the "G-H" volume.

Practice Book 4.1, p. 20

Name________________

Train to Somewhere

6. Which volume or volumes would help you find out more about the inventor of the steam locomotive, Richard Trevithick? Explain.

Volumes 12 and 13 would probably have this information since 12 is the "S" volume (steam locomotive) and 13 is the "T" volume (Trevithick).

7. Suppose you want to find information about "orphan trains." The library's encyclopedias are 10 years old. Will the information you find be useful to your research? Why or why not?

Yes, the information would still be useful because the event happened long ago.

Directions: Use the almanac table to answer the questions below.

State	Postal Abbreviation	Date Entered Union (United States)
Florida	FL	1845
Georgia	GA	1788
Hawaii	HI	1959
Idaho	ID	1890

8. Using this almanac table, how would you find out if Florida and Georgia were part of the United States in the year 1885?

Look under the third column for the date they entered the Union.

9. If you wanted to mail a letter to a friend in Atlanta, Georgia, how could this table help you?

This table lists each state's postal abbreviation.

10. Why is it important to ask questions about the topic before looking for resources?

Possible answer: You need to know what kind of information you are looking for before deciding which resources will be the most useful.

Notes for Home: Your child learned about conducting research. ***Home Activity:*** Name a topic. Have your child ask a question about this topic. Then switch and let your child name the topic. Talk about where you might find answers to your questions.

Practice Book 4.1, p. 21

Name________________

Yingtao's New Friend

Compare and Contrast

- To **compare** is to tell how two or more things are alike. To **contrast** is to tell how two or more things are different.
- Clue words such as *like* or *as* show comparisons. Clue words such as *but* or *unlike* show contrasts.
- Often authors don't use clue words, and readers have to compare and contrast things on their own.

Directions: Reread "Anna's New School." Then complete the table that shows the contrasts between Anna's new school and her old school. Some information has been filled in for you.

Items	New School	Old School
1. desks	in groups, hinges	**in rows, no hinges**
2. pencils	**bigger around than Anna's thumb**	smaller around than Anna's thumb
3. blackboards	**green**	**black**
4. chalk	**fat, yellow**	**thin, white**
5. children	**mostly older**	**same age**

Notes for Home: Your child read a story and made contrasts using word clues and their own inferences. ***Home Activity:*** Choose two objects (flowers, bowls, books, tables, and so on) and have your child list ways they are similar (comparisons) and ways they are different (contrasts).

Practice Book 4.1, p. 22

Name________________

Yingtao's New Friend

Vocabulary

Directions: Choose the word from the box that best completes each sentence. Write the word on the line to the left.

Check the Words You Know
- __ instrument
- __ measures
- __ orchestra
- __ rehearsal
- __ triangle

orchestra 1. The members of our school _____ began to go on stage.

rehearsal 2. It was their final _____ before the big performance.

instrument 3. Each student got an _____ ready to play.

triangle 4. From the giant tuba to the tiny _____, all the instruments were ready.

measures 5. As I heard the first few _____ of the music begin, I knew the concert would be a success.

Directions: Cross out the word that does not belong in each group.

6. band	~~stage~~	orchestra	group
7. measures	beats	bars	~~violins~~
8. performer	~~instrument~~	dancer	singer
9. rehearsal	practice	~~flute~~	warm-up
10. trumpet	triangle	~~conductor~~	drum

Write a Music Review

On a separate sheet of paper, tell about a concert you attended. Tell why you did or did not enjoy the concert. Use as many of the vocabulary words as you can.

Students' music reviews should use vocabulary words correctly.

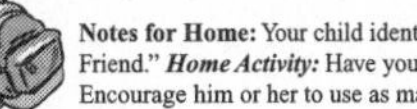

Notes for Home: Your child identified and used vocabulary words from "Yingtao's New Friend." ***Home Activity:*** Have your child talk about a piece of music he or she likes. Encourage him or her to use as many of the vocabulary words as possible.

Practice Book 4.1, p. 23

Name________________

Yingtao's New Friend

Compare and Contrast

- To **compare** is to tell how two or more things are alike. To **contrast** is to tell how two or more things are different. Clue words such as *like* or *as* show comparisons. Clue words such as *but* or *unlike* show contrasts.

Directions: Reread Yingtao's descriptions of his two older sisters in "Yingtao's New Friend." Then answer the questions below. **Possible answers given.**

I think Second Sister felt the loneliest. In China, people always said she would turn out to be a real beauty. She had been popular at school there, always surrounded by friends. But in America not many people told her she was beautiful. These days she was often cranky and sad. Mother told the rest of us that we just had to be patient with Second Sister.

Third Sister had no trouble at all making friends. Even before she could speak much English, she began chatting with other kids. She could always fill the gaps with laughter.

1. Is Second Sister the same in America as she was in China or is she different? What clue word in the passage tells you?

The word *but* suggests that she was different in America.

2. How do you think Second Sister felt in China? Explain.

In China she had had lots of friends, so she must have felt happy.

3. Does Third Sister act like Second Sister? Explain.

No; Third Sister has no trouble at all making friends.

4. Write a sentence contrasting the two sisters' behavior in America.

Second Sister acts cranky, but Third Sister is friendly.

5. Use a separate sheet of paper to tell how you think Yingtao feels in America compared with each of his sisters. Give examples from the story.

Yingtao may feel less lonely than Second Sister but less friendly and popular than Third Sister.

Notes for Home: Your child used story details to compare and contrast two characters. ***Home Activity:*** Work with your child to come up with a list of ways two people he or she knows well are similar (comparisons) and ways they are different (contrasts).

Practice Book 4.1, p. 25

Name________________

Yingtao's New Friend

Selection Test

Directions: Choose the best answer to each item. Mark the letter for the answer you have chosen.

Part 1: Vocabulary

Find the answer choice that means about the same as the underlined word in each sentence.

1. Play the first six <u>measures</u>.
   - A. places in line
   - B. tunes
   - **(C) bars of music**
   - D. numerals

2. Cecily is in the <u>orchestra</u>.
   - **(F) a group of musicians**
   - G. a music class
   - H. people who write music
   - J. a holiday parade

3. Matt put the <u>instrument</u> away.
   - A. a loud noise
   - **(B) a device for producing musical sounds**
   - C. a small container
   - D. a group of songs played together

4. The <u>rehearsal</u> will begin soon.
   - F. dinner
   - G. tryout
   - H. show
   - **(J) practice**

5. I borrowed the <u>triangle</u> from Keisha.
   - A. measuring tool
   - B. toy
   - **(C) musical device**
   - D. whistle

Part 2: Comprehension

Use what you know about the story to answer each item.

6. Yingtao's parents signed him up to—
   - F. take piano lessons.
   - G. play baseball.
   - **(H) join the orchestra.**
   - J. learn to cook.

7. What was Second Sister doing when Yingtao brought Matthew home with him?
   - A. making shelves
   - B. playing the viola
   - C. cooking dinner
   - **(D) cutting tea bags**

8. How was Matthew like Yingtao?
   - F. His family was Chinese.
   - **(G) His family did not have much money.**
   - H. He had many friends at school.
   - J. He loved to play the violin.

GO ON

Practice Book 4.1, p. 26

Name______________________ **Yingtao's New Friend**

9. How are Third Sister and Eldest Brother alike?
   - (A) They are talented musicians.
   - B. They enjoy cooking.
   - C. They like to cut tea bags
   - D. They are very fun loving.
10. When Matthew said he wanted to use chopsticks to eat his dinner, Yingtao most likely felt—
    - F. annoyed.
    - (G) pleased.
    - H. embarrassed.
    - J. amused.
11. Why did Yingtao slouch in his seat and interrupt his teacher?
    - (A) He wanted to fit in with the other students.
    - B. Matthew dared him to be impolite.
    - C. He was bored and unhappy in school.
    - D. He wanted to bother his teacher.
12. When Matthew called Yingtao "tough," he meant that Yingtao was—
    - F. mean and rude.
    - G. unlucky and sad.
    - (H) strong and determined.
    - J. cold and unfriendly.
13. After visiting Yingtao's home, Matthew could see that—
    - A. Yingtao's family did not get along well.
    - B. Yingtao's brothers and sisters were unfriendly.
    - C. Yingtao's parents did not work hard.
    - (D) Yingtao's family had some customs that were different from his.
14. Yingtao's parents were probably disappointed about—
    - F. his friendship with Matthew.
    - (G) the way he played the violin.
    - H. his poor manners.
    - J. how he did in school.
15. What is the most important thing that happened to Yingtao?
    - A. He tried out for the orchestra.
    - B. He had a chance to play the triangle.
    - (C) He became friends with Matthew.
    - D. He got better at spelling.

Name______________________ **Yingtao's New Friend**

Compare and Contrast

- To **compare** is to tell how two or more things are alike. To **contrast** is to tell how two or more things are different. Clue words such as *like* or *as* show comparisons. Clue words such as *but* or *unlike* show contrasts.

Directions: Read the story below.

Mr. Berg was our new music teacher. Unlike our old music teacher Mrs. Marsh, Mr. Berg let anybody join the orchestra. Some students, like my friend Jim, had taken music lessons. But some students, like my sister June and me, hadn't. That didn't matter to Mr. Berg. He told us all just to try our best.

He gave out instruments. I got a trumpet, and June got a violin. The first time she played, it sounded like a cat screeching. But at least she got her violin to do something. Jim blew a few notes on his trumpet, then asked me to try. But I couldn't make even a little squeak.

Mr. Berg wasn't upset. "You have only one way to go, Brian," he told me. "That's to get better. I'll teach you how."

Mr. Berg was right. With some lessons, I could play a few notes.

Directions: Complete the table. Use what you are told about the characters and what you can figure out to compare and contrast pairs of characters.

People	Alike	Different
Mrs. Marsh, Mr. Berg	Both are music teachers.	1. **Mr. Berg allows anybody to join, but Mrs. Marsh didn't.**
Brian, June	Neither has had any lessons.	2. **Brian: plays trumpet, no sounds; June: plays violin, sounds**
Brian, Jim	3. **Both play trumpets.**	Brian: no lessons, no sounds; Jim: lessons, sounds
June, Jim	4. **Both make sounds on their instruments.**	5. **June: plays violin, no lessons; Jim: plays trumpet, lessons**

Notes for Home: Your child has read a story and used details and what he or she knows to make comparisons and contrasts. ***Home Activity:*** With your child, choose two persons, places, or things that you both know. Take turns making comparisons and contrasts.

Practice Book 4.1, p. 27

Name______________________ **Yingtao's New Friend**

Sequence

REVIEW

Directions: Read the story. Then read each question about the story. Choose the best answer to each question. Mark the letter for the answer you have chosen.

Hard Choices!

My mom and I were at the music store looking at instruments. Last month Mom had promised she would buy me one. She said, "You can join the school orchestra this year, Ray."

"No way, Mom!" I replied. "I want to be in a rock band. Besides, orchestra rehearsal takes place while I have track practice."

A salesperson came over to us. "May I show you an instrument?" he asked.

"Violin! Guitar!" came our answers at the same time.

"I see," said the salesperson. "Let me show you both, and you can decide which one you want . . . I hope."

1. The first event that takes place during the story is—
   - **A.** Mom wanting Ray to play the violin.
   - **B.** Ray wanting to play the guitar.
   - **C.** Ray and his mom looking at instruments.
   - (D) Ray's mom agreeing to buy Ray an instrument.
2. Ray doesn't want to join the orchestra because it is at the same time as—
   - **F.** dinner.
   - **G.** math class.
   - (H) track practice.
   - **J.** guitar lessons.
3. While Ray and his mom were looking at instruments—
   - (A) a salesperson came over.
   - **B.** a salesperson ignored them.
   - **C.** Ray's mom wrote out a check.
   - **D.** Ray's mom called Ray's father.
4. While Ray asks to see a guitar, his mom—
   - **F.** starts to leave.
   - **G.** drops her wallet.
   - (H) asks to see a violin.
   - **J.** promises to buy him a guitar.
5. Which of these events did **not** happen in the store?
   - **A.** Ray said he would rather play in a rock band.
   - (B) Ray's mom said she would buy him an instrument.
   - **C.** Ray's mom asked a salesperson to show her a violin.
   - **D.** Ray's mom said he could join the orchestra.

Notes for Home: Your child answered questions to describe the order of events in a story. ***Home Activity:*** Have your child tell a story of something that happened recently. Try to have him or her use word clues to let you know the order of events.

Name______________________ **Yingtao's New Friend**

Writing Across Texts

Directions: Consider what you know about Justin from "A Visit with Grandpa" and Yingtao from "Yingtao's New Friend." Use the diagram below to compare the two boys. Think about what each boy does well. Consider how the background and family traditions of the boys are similar and different. Try to include at least ten entries. **Possible answers given.**

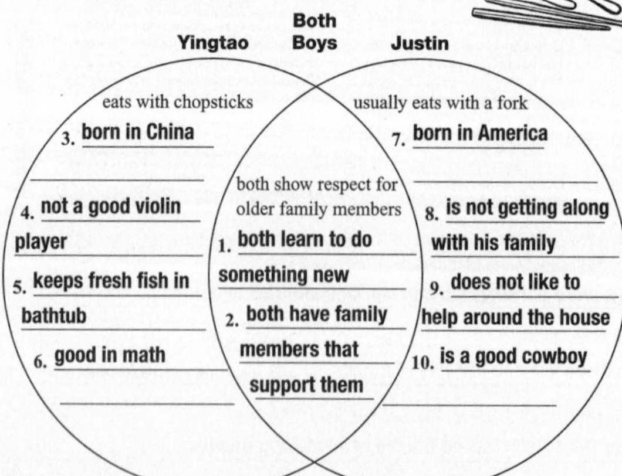

Write a Compare/Contrast Paragraph

Yingtao and Justin have very different backgrounds and abilities. On a separate sheet of paper, write a paragraph in which you compare and contrast the boys. Use the information from your diagram to help you. Then draw a conclusion telling whether or not you think the boys could be friends. **Paragraphs will vary. Students should use the boys' similarities and differences to write their paragraphs.**

Notes for Home: Your child used information from two reading selections to write a compare/contrast paragraph. ***Home Activity:*** As you read stories and articles with your child, talk about how ideas or characters are alike and different.

Grammar Practice Book 4.1, p. 11

Name______________________ Yingtao's New Friend

Grammar: Sentence End Punctuation

REVIEW

Directions: Add the correct punctuation mark at the end of each statement or question.

1. How many instruments are in a standard orchestra **?**
2. Usually most orchestras have about 100 instruments **.**
3. An orchestra is made up of four groups of instruments **.**
4. Do you know what they are **?**
5. The groups of instruments are strings, woodwinds, brass, and percussion **.**
6. What is the most common string instrument **?**
7. The violin is the most common string instrument **.**
8. Some orchestras have as many as 36 violins **.**
9. Can you name another string instrument **?**
10. Yes, a harp is a string instrument **.**

Directions: Write five sentences—four statements and one question. Write about a musical instrument you play or would like to play. Remember to begin each sentence with a capital letter and end each one with the correct punctuation. **Possible answers given.**

11. **I want to play the trumpet.**
12. **The trumpet is an important instrument in a band or orchestra.**
13. **Trumpets sound bright and strong in marches.**
14. **The trumpet can also play songs.**
15. **What instrument would you like to play?**

Notes for Home: Your child identified the correct end punctuation for sentences and wrote sentences. ***Home Activity:*** Say a statement or ask a question about music your child enjoys. Have him or her tell what punctuation mark should go at the end of each sentence.

Grammar: Sentence End Punctuation 55

Grammar Practice Book 4.1, p. 12

Name______________________ Yingtao's New Friend

Grammar: Declarative and Interrogative Sentences

A sentence that tells something is a statement. It ends with a period. Another name for a statement is a **declarative sentence.**

I play in the orchestra at school.

A sentence that asks something is a question. It ends with a question mark. Another name for a question is an **interrogative sentence.**

Does your school have an orchestra?

Directions: For each sentence, add the correct end punctuation. Then write **D** if the sentence is declarative. Write **I** if it is interrogative.

1. Do you play a musical instrument **?** **I**
2. How well do you play **?** **I**
3. The violin is a beautiful instrument **.** **D**
4. It isn't easy to play a violin **.** **D**
5. It is important to practice every day **.** **D**
6. Which musical instruments do you like **?** **I**
7. You could play more than one kind of instrument **.** **D**
8. Playing an instrument can make you feel proud **.** **D**
9. Would you like to play in a concert **?** **I**
10. Would you like to listen to some music **?** **I**
11. There are many different types of music **.** **D**
12. Some people don't listen to music **.** **D**
13. Your family could listen to music together **.** **D**
14. Everyone in my family likes music **.** **D**
15. Does music make you happy **?** **I**

Notes for Home: Your child identified declarative and interrogative sentences. ***Home Activity:*** Take turns making statements or asking questions about songs that you have listened to together.

56 Grammar: Declarative and Interrogative Sentences

Grammar Practice Book 4.1, p. 13

Name______________________ Yingtao's New Friend

Grammar: Declarative and Interrogative Sentences

Directions: For each sentence, add the correct end punctuation. Then write **D** if the sentence is declarative. Write **I** if it is interrogative. **Possible answers given.**

1. Will the orchestra start to play **?** **I**
2. The audience is eager to hear the musicians play **.** **D**
3. The music is soft and beautiful **.** **D**
4. How long do you think the concert will last **?** **I**
5. I am glad that we came tonight **.** **D**

Directions: Change each of these declarative sentences into an interrogative sentence. Be sure to use the correct end punctuation.

6. The orchestra played a piece by Beethoven.
Did the orchestra play a piece by Beethoven?

7. The drums are loud.
Why are the drums so loud?

8. The violin player can play very high notes.
Can the violin player play very high notes?

9. There is another concert next week.
Is there another concert next week?

10. We should go again.
Should we go again?

Write Questions

On a separate sheet of paper, write three questions about a musical instrument you like. Then answer each question with a declarative sentence. **Check that students write complete sentences and use correct end punctuation.**

Notes for Home: Your child changed statements (declarative sentences) into questions (interrogative sentences). ***Home Activity:*** To practice asking questions and making statements, take turns "interviewing" one another.

Grammar: Declarative and Interrogative Sentences 57

Grammar Practice Book 4.1, p. 14

Name______________________ Yingtao's New Friend

Grammar: Declarative and Interrogative Sentences

RETEACHING

Read the interrogative sentence below.

1. What do you like to ride?

Write a declarative sentence. Complete the statement below. **Possible answer given.**

2. I like to ride **a bike**.

A **declarative sentence** makes a statement. It begins with a capital letter and ends with a period. An **interrogative sentence** asks a question. It begins with a capital letter and ends with a question mark.

Directions: Decide what kind of sentence each one is. Draw a line from the sentence to **declarative** or **interrogative.**

1. His airplane just landed. — declarative
   Who was the pilot? — interrogative
2. Will he rent a car? — interrogative
   He can take a taxi to the boat. — declarative
3. I will ride my bicycle to the dock. — declarative
   How far away is it? — interrogative

Directions: Underline the capital letter. Write the correct punctuation mark at the end of each sentence. Then write each sentence correctly.

4. The man is going to the airport **.**
The man is going to the airport.

5. Will he arrive on time **?**
Will he arrive on time?

Notes for Home: Your child identified and wrote declarative and interrogative sentences. ***Home Activity:*** Have your child write one declarative sentence and one interrogative sentence and explain to you the difference between them.

58 Grammar: Declarative and Interrogative Sentences

Grammar Practice Book 4.1, p. 15

Name________________________ Yingtao's New Friend

Grammar: Declarative and Interrogative Sentences

Directions: Write each sentence under the correct heading. Begin each sentence with a capital letter. Use periods and question marks correctly.

1. plains are grassy lands **3.** do crops grow on these lands

2. are there trees on the plains **4.** cows graze on the plains

Declarative Sentences

Plains are grassy lands.

Cows graze on the plains.

Interrogative Sentences

Are there trees on the plains?

Do crops grow on these lands?

Directions: Change each sentence to the kind named in ( ).

5. Our country has flat land. (interrogative)

Does our country have flat land?

6. Do wheat fields grow here? (declarative)

Wheat fields grow here.

7. Is this the Central Plains? (declarative)

This is the Central Plains.

Write Sentences

On a separate sheet of paper, write interrogative sentences about your town or city. Write declarative sentences to answer your questions.

Check that students have capitalized and punctuated interrogative and declarative sentences correctly.

Notes for Home: Your child identified and wrote declarative and interrogative sentences. ***Home Activity:*** Have your child write four interrogative sentences—sentences that ask questions—and give them to you to answer.

Practice Book 4.1, p. 28

Name________________________ Yingtao's New Friend

Phonics: Vowel Digraphs

Directions: Read the words in the box. Say the words to yourself. Decide whether each word has a **vowel sound** like **cool** or like **book.** Write each word in the correct column.

pool	shook	soon	took	food
room	stood	look	good	mood

cool		book	
1.	**pool**	6.	**shook**
2.	**soon**	7.	**stood**
3.	**room**	8.	**look**
4.	**food**	9.	**good**
5.	**mood**	10.	**took**

Directions: Read each sentence. Say the underlined word to yourself. Circle the word in ( ) that has the same **vowel sound** as the underlined word.

11. Band practice was held Tuesday in the music building. (suit/**bin**)

12. The orchestra leader shook his head when the children played. (food/**good**)

13. The guilty children knew they should have practiced more. (fruit/**fin**)

14. Julie liked playing the guitar. (**build**/find)

15. Matthew thought playing the violin was cool. (stood/**food**)

16. Matthew wore his best suit for the concert. (**too**/should)

17. He stood and closed his eyes when he played. (**shook**/room)

18. When he was finished playing, he took a bow. (**look**/school)

19. They served apples, oranges, and juice after the concert. (guilty/**bruise**)

20. He was hungry after the concert, so he ate a piece of fruit. (build/**soon**)

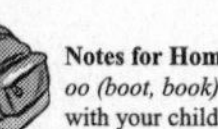

Notes for Home: Your child distinguished between the different vowel sounds for words with *oo (boot, book)* and *ui (fruit, build).* ***Home Activity:*** Read a newspaper or magazine article with your child to find words with *oo* and *ui.* Sort the words by their vowel sounds.

Spelling Workbook 4.1, p. 9

Name________________________ Yingtao's New Friend

Spelling: Short Vowels *a, i, o, u*

Pretest Directions: Fold back the page along the dotted line. On the blanks, write the spelling words as they are dictated. When you have finished the test, unfold the page and check your words.

1. **band**	**1.** Watch the marching **band.**
2. **cash**	**2.** Put your **cash** in the bank.
3. **January**	**3. January** is the first month.
4. **blanket**	**4.** I need a warm **blanket.**
5. **backpack**	**5.** This **backpack** is full.
6. **river**	**6.** Float a raft down the **river.**
7. **finger**	**7.** Point with your **finger.**
8. **build**	**8.** Let's **build** a tree house!
9. **guilt**	**9.** Can you prove his **guilt**?
10. **window**	**10.** Look out the **window.**
11. **pond**	**11.** This **pond** has tadpoles.
12. **block**	**12.** Don't **block** the exit.
13. **forgot**	**13.** Ariel **forgot** her lunch.
14. **closet**	**14.** Hang coats in the **closet.**
15. **chop**	**15. Chop** vegetables for stew.
16. **trouble**	**16.** The cat gets into **trouble.**
17. **young**	**17.** My kitten is very **young.**
18. **cousin**	**18.** Invite your **cousin** over.
19. **couple**	**19.** Bring a **couple** of cups.
20. **tough**	**20.** The nut is **tough** to crack.

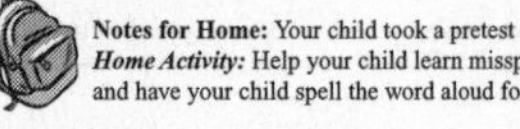

Notes for Home: Your child took a pretest on words that have the short vowels *a, i, o,* and *u.* ***Home Activity:*** Help your child learn misspelled words before the final test. Dictate the word and have your child spell the word aloud for you or write it on paper.

Spelling Workbook 4.1, p. 10

Name________________________ Yingtao's New Friend

Spelling: Short Vowels *a, i, o, u*

Word List

band	river	pond	trouble
cash	finger	block	young
January	build	forgot	cousin
blanket	guilt	closet	couple
backpack	window	chop	tough

Directions: Write the words from the box with **short a, short o,** and **short u** vowel sounds. Sort the words according to how the vowel sound is spelled. **Order may vary.**

Short a Spelled a		Short o Spelled o		Short u Spelled ou	
1.	**band**	6.	**pond**	11.	**trouble**
2.	**cash**	7.	**block**	12.	**young**
3.	**January**	8.	**forgot**	13.	**cousin**
4.	**blanket**	9.	**closet**	14.	**couple**
5.	**backpack**	10.	**chop**	15.	**tough**

Directions: Choose the word from the box that best completes each sentence. Write the word on the line to the left.

build **16.** Lucy and her mother decided to _____ their own guitar from scratch.

river **17.** They cut down a tree by the _____ to use for wood.

window **18.** Each day, they sat inside by the _____ and carved.

guilt **19.** Lucy felt some _____ because her mother did most of the work.

finger **20.** When the guitar was done, Lucy tried to play it, but she couldn't remember which _____ went where.

Notes for Home: Your child spelled words with short vowels *a, i, o,* and *u (band, river, build, pond, young).* ***Home Activity:*** Join your child on a walk around the house. Have your child point out objects that have these short vowel sounds.

Spelling Workbook 4.1, p. 11
Name________________ Yingtao's New Friend

Spelling: Short Vowels *a, i, o, u*

Directions: Proofread this concert ad. Find five spelling mistakes. Use the proofreading marks to correct each mistake.

- ≡ Make a capital.
- / Make a small letter.
- ∧ Add something.
- Take out something.
- ⊙ Add a period.
- ¶ Begin a new paragraph.

Concert Notice
Yung People's Jazz Baind
Wednesday, Jenuary 15
at 8 in the evening
River View Park by the pand
Bring a blanket or chairs
Admission $3 cashe only

Spelling Tip

Short a, i, o, and **u** are often spelled with one vowel letter: **band, river, pond.** But **short i** can also be spelled **ui** and **short u** can also be spelled **ou: build, cousin.**

Word List

band	pond
cash	block
January	forgot
blanket	closet
backpack	chop
river	trouble
finger	young
build	cousin
guilt	couple
window	tough

Write a Concert Review

Imagine that you attended the concert in the ad. On a separate sheet of paper, write a review. Try to use at least three spelling words.

Answers will vary, but each review should include at least three spelling words.

Notes for Home: Your child spelled words with the short vowels *a, i, o, u (band, river, build, pond, young). **Home Activity:*** Read a story with your child. Challenge your child to notice words in which the short *i* and short *u* sounds are spelled with two vowel letters: *build, cousin.*

Spelling Workbook 4.1, p. 12
Name________________ Yingtao's New Friend

Spelling: Short Vowels *a, i, o, u* REVIEW

Word List

band	river	pond	trouble
cash	finger	block	young
January	build	forgot	cousin
blanket	guilt	closet	couple
backpack	window	chop	tough

Directions: Choose the word from the box that best completes each sentence. Write the word on the matching numbered line to the right.

Lucy sat in the **1.** _____ room waiting for rehearsal to start. She felt a terrible sense of **2.** _____. It's not that she **3.** _____ to bring her flute. It was worse. She couldn't remember where she left it. She had looked in her **4.** _____ that she carried everywhere. She had looked in her bedroom, even in the back of her messy **5.** _____. She knew she was in big **6.** _____!

Suddenly, from her seat near the **7.** _____, she saw her first **8.** _____, Mary, outside. She was about a **9.** _____ away, but Lucy could see Mary had her flute. Lucy now remembered that she had left it at Mary's house a **10.** _____ of days ago.

1. **band**
2. **guilt**
3. **forgot**
4. **backpack**
5. **closet**
6. **trouble**
7. **window**
8. **cousin**
9. **block**
10. **couple**

Directions: Write the word from the box that best fits in each group.

11. ocean, lake, **pond**
12. strong, firm, **tough**
13. creek, stream, **river**
14. make, construct, **build**
15. cut, saw, **chop**
16. youthful, immature, **young**
17. quilt, comforter, **blanket**
18. November, December, **January**
19. arm, hand, **finger**
20. money, coins, **cash**

Notes for Home: Your child spelled words with the short vowels *a, i, o, u (band, river, build, pond, young). **Home Activity:*** Read the newspaper with your child. Have him or her point out words that have these short vowel sounds and spellings.

Practice Book 4.1, p. 29
Name________________ Yingtao's New Friend

Technology: Questions for Inquiry

You can learn about the traditions of another country by **asking questions** and doing research to find answers to your questions. The **Internet** is one place to find answers to your questions. You can use **search engines** to find information. After you type in key words from your questions, the search engine looks for Web sites that may have answers. A search engine home page may look something like this:

Directions: For each topic below, write a question that you could research to find out about life in China. **Possible answers given.**

1. types of food prepared **What foods are eaten in China?**
2. games children like to play **What games do children like to play in China?**
3. languages spoken **What languages are spoken by people who live in China?**

Practice Book 4.1, p. 30
Name________________ Yingtao's New Friend

Directions: A search engine may give you a list of Web sites that are related to your question or topic. Put an **X** in front of the Web site names listed below that you think may have answers to the question shown on the computer screen.

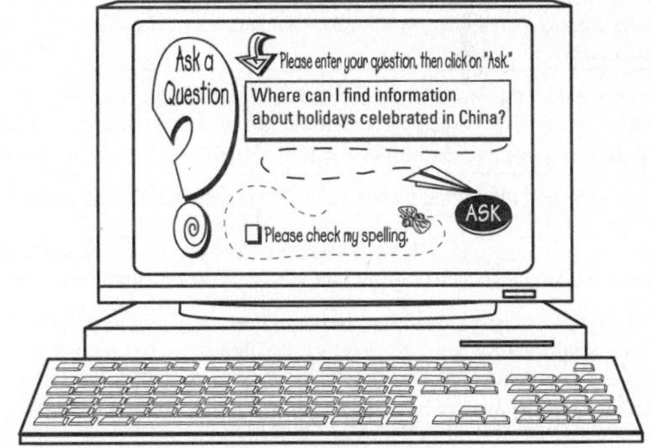

Where can I find information about holidays celebrated in China?

_____ 4. Folktales from China
X 5. Worldwide Holiday Calendar
X 6. China Travel and Tourism
_____ 7. Web site of Jamaica
X 8. Holidays and Festivals
_____ 9. Chinese Poetry
X 10. Holiday Traditions Around the World

Notes for Home: Your child wrote questions and identified possible Web sites that would be useful to find out more about China. ***Home Activity:*** Play a game in which you give the answer to a question, and your child asks the question that would produce that answer.

Practice Book 4.1, p. 31
Name______________________________ **Family Pictures**

Author's Purpose

- An **author's purpose** is the reason or reasons an author has for writing. Four common purposes are to inform, to entertain, to express, and to persuade.
- Often, people read more quickly when the author's purpose is to entertain, and more slowly and carefully when the author has another purpose.

Directions: Reread "Painting Mist and Fog." In the first row of the table, describe the author's purpose or purposes. Use the second row to give supporting reasons to explain why this is the author's purpose. In the last row, tell how quickly or slowly you read the article and why. **Possible answers given.**

Author's Purposes:	1. **The author's purpose is to inform.**
Supporting Reasons	2. **The author gives detailed instructions for making a painting of fog and mist.**
Read Quickly or Slowly?	3. **I read the article slowly because the article used many specific details to explain how to paint pictures of fog and mist.**

Directions: Think about the author's purpose for these types of writing. Write the purpose of each type in the table.

Comic book	**4. Purpose:** **to entertain**
How-to instruction book	**5. Purpose:** **to inform**

Some students may also note that the author of "Painting Mist and Fog" is persuading readers to try to make a painting because it is easy and they don't have to worry about streaks.

Notes for Home: Your child read a magazine article and identified the author's purpose in writing it. ***Home Activity:*** Read several different kinds of articles with your child. Have your child figure out the author's purpose for each and give supporting reasons.

Practice Book 4.1, p. 32
Name______________________________ **Family Pictures**

Vocabulary

Directions: Choose the word from the box that best completes each sentence. Write the word on the line to the left.

Check the Words You Know
__ border
__ future
__ handkerchief
__ inspired
__ involved
__ laundry
__ memories
__ scene

inspired 1. My grandfather makes paintings that are _____ by his childhood.

scene 2. Once he painted a _____ of children playing ball in a meadow.

involved 3. Another painting _______ the toys he had when he was little.

memories 4. From his paintings, I guess that Grandpa has happy ____ of his childhood.

future 5. People in the _____ will learn about life long ago from artwork like Grandpa's paintings.

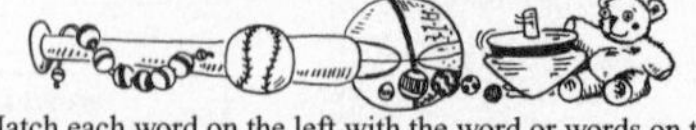

Directions: Match each word on the left with the word or words on the right that have a similar meaning. Write the letter of the similar word or words on the line.

d 6. handkerchief — a. washing
e 7. border — b. included
a 8. laundry — c. encouraged
c 9. inspired — d. soft cloth
b 10. involved — e. boundary

Write a Paragraph

On a separate sheet of paper, write a paragraph about artwork that you saw and liked. It could be a painting in a museum, a picture or photo in your reading book, or even something you made yourself. Tell what you liked and why. Use as many vocabulary words as you can.
Students' paragraphs should use vocabulary words correctly.

Notes for Home: Your child identified and used vocabulary words from *Family Pictures*. ***Home Activity:*** With your child, look at works of art in a book or magazine. Encourage him or her to talk about the artwork, using as many vocabulary words as possible.

Practice Book 4.1, p. 33
Name______________________________ **Family Pictures**

Author's Purpose

- An **author's purpose** is the reason or reasons an author has for writing. Authors often have more than one reason for writing.
- Four common purposes are to inform, to entertain, to express, and to persuade.

1. Reread *Family Pictures.* What do you think is the author's purpose? Write the reason or reasons for writing below. Explain your answer. **Possible answer: The author is informing the reader about her family's customs. She wants the reader to be entertained by her story. She is also expressing pride.**

Directions: Read each paragraph. Write whether the author's purpose is to inform, entertain, express, or persuade. Explain your answers. **Possible answers given.**

2. The best place to go on vacation is the beach. How can you go wrong with water, sand, and sky? There are people sunning themselves and swimming. There are boats and sand castles. You'll have so much fun. **The author is trying to persuade readers that beaches make the best vacation places.**
3. My favorite painting is of the beach. The colors of the water, sand, and sky make me remember all the happy times I had there last summer. **The author is expressing how a favorite place makes him or her feel.**
4. Seaweed is any type of plant that grows in the ocean. It can be both a place to live and a source of food for sea creatures. **The author is informing readers about seaweed.**
5. On a separate sheet of paper, write a short paragraph about something that happened to you today. You might inform readers about the day's events, entertain them with a funny story, express how you felt about your day, or try to convince others that it was the best or worst day ever. Below your paragraph, tell your purpose for writing. **Paragraphs and purposes will vary. Check that students' described purposes are appropriate for the kind of paragraphs they have written.**

Notes for Home: Your child has identified the author's purpose(s) in *Family Pictures* and several short paragraphs. ***Home Activity:*** Read a short story with your child. Talk about the author's reasons for writing the piece. Was it to inform, entertain, persuade, or express a feeling or mood?

Practice Book 4.1, p. 35
Name______________________________ **Family Pictures**

Selection Test

Directions: Choose the best answer to each item. Mark the letter for the answer you have chosen.

Part 1: Vocabulary

Find the answer choice that means about the same as the underlined word in each sentence.

1. Anna plans for the <u>future</u>.
   A. special friend
   B. favorite hobby
   C. problem or worry
   (D) time to come
2. Tell us what is happening in this <u>scene</u>.
   F. time of year; season
   G. place of work
   (H) a view or picture
   J. faraway land
3. The <u>border</u> is 100 miles from here.
   A. nearest neighbor
   (B) boundary of a country or state
   C. grandparent's house
   D. woods or forest
4. I bought a yellow <u>handkerchief</u>.
   (F) square cloth for wiping the nose
   G. colorful flag or banner
   H. pair of gloves
   J. large woolen blanket
5. Enrique shared some of his childhood <u>memories</u>.
   A. old toys
   (B) things that a person remembers
   C. songs that tell a story
   D. drawings or paintings
6. Grandpa <u>inspired</u> me to write a poem.
   F. allowed
   G. ordered
   (H) gave confidence to
   J. taught how
7. Please put the <u>laundry</u> away.
   A. dress-up clothes
   B. rags used for cleaning
   C. fabric to be cut and sewn
   (D) clothes that have been washed
8. The girls are <u>involved</u> in their chores.
   F. proud of
   (G) busy or occupied
   H. tired of
   J. skilled at

GO ON

Practice Book 4.1, p. 36

Name________________________

Family Pictures

Part 2: Comprehension

Use what you know about the selection to answer each item.

9. What did the author dream of being when she grew up?
   A. a poet
   Ⓑ an artist
   C. an actress
   D. a mother

10. What did the author do at her grandmother's house?
   F. hung laundry
   G. caught a shark
   Ⓗ picked oranges
   J. made tamales

11. Which step comes last when preparing a meal of nopal cactus?
   A. shaving off the needles
   B. boiling in hot water
   C. cutting into pieces
   Ⓓ frying with chili powder and eggs

12. Which of these was a frightening experience for the author?
   F. hitting a piñata
   Ⓖ seeing a hammerhead shark
   H. being up on the roof
   J. picking nopal cactus

13. The author probably included the part called "Beds for Dreaming" to—
   A. tell about a funny event.
   B. explain what her house was like.
   C. describe a holiday custom.
   Ⓓ express important feelings she had as a girl.

14. One of the author's main purposes for writing this selection was to—
   F. compare her family with other families.
   Ⓖ share special times she had with her family.
   H. tell how people in a family should behave.
   J. describe each member of her family.

15. Who does the author feel most grateful to for helping her make her dreams come true?
   A. her father
   B. her grandparents
   C. her sister
   Ⓓ her mother

Name________________________

Family Pictures

Author's Purpose

- An **author's purpose** is the reason or reasons an author has for writing. Authors often have more then one reason for writing.
- Four common purposes are to inform, to entertain, to express, and to persuade.

Directions: Read the story below.

My sister collects junk. I know that a lot of people do. But her junk is different. She uses it to make art. You might not think that's what it is. But if you spent as much time around it as I do, you would change your mind.

Monica takes the junk and makes scenes of our everyday life. Our family is sitting at an orange-crate table. Our heads are made of dried noodles inside plastic. There's a crushed milk carton. There's an empty cake box. Monica calls the work, "The Party's Over." You really have to see it sometime!

Directions: Read each statement in the first column. For each statement, tell whether its purpose is to inform, entertain, express feelings, or persuade.

Statement	Author's Purpose
Some of the text is funny.	1. **entertain**
The author sounds proud of Monica for being creative.	2. **express feelings**
The author tells the reader how to make one kind of "junk" sculpture.	3. **inform**
The author writes, "But if you spent as much time around it as I do, you would change your mind."	4. **persuade**
The author thinks you should see the art sometime.	5. **persuade**

Notes for Home: Your child has read a story and used story details to identify the author's purposes for writing it, such as to inform, to entertain, express feelings, and persuade. ***Home Activity:*** When you read with your child, identify together the author's purposes for writing.

Practice Book 4.1, p. 37

Name________________________

Family Pictures

Fact and Opinion

REVIEW

Directions: Read the story. Then read each question about the story. Choose the best answer to each question. Mark the letter for the answer you have chosen.

A Visit to the Museum

My class went to the art museum last month. I thought I would be bored, but I was in for a big surprise. We saw paintings by the artist Van Gogh. But his flowers were beautiful. One of the paintings was of a sunny field. In the art world, it is called a *landscape.*

We had pizza for lunch, which was OK. Then we saw paintings of laundry. I pass laundry every day, but I never look at it. I guess going to a museum can get a person to see things differently.

1. Which is a story fact?
   Ⓐ The class went to the museum.
   B. The narrator decided to become a painter.
   C. Van Gogh is a cool artist.
   D. The class went by bus.

2. Which sentence contains both fact and opinion?
   F. I thought I would be bored.
   G. Then we saw paintings of laundry.
   H. In the art world, it is called a *landscape.*
   Ⓙ We had pizza for lunch, which was OK.

3. Which sentence from this story states an opinion?
   A. I pass laundry every day, but I never look at it.
   Ⓑ I guess going to a museum can get a person to see things differently.
   C. We saw paintings by the artist Van Gogh.
   D. In the art world, it is called a *landscape.*

4. Which sentence states a fact about Van Gogh?
   F. Van Gogh made strange-looking sculptures.
   G. Van Gogh's paintings are boring.
   H. Van Gogh's flowers are cool.
   Ⓙ Van Gogh painted flowers and landscapes.

5. Which word or words in the last sentence are a clue that the sentence is an opinion?
   A. can
   B. differently
   C. museum
   Ⓓ I guess

Notes for Home: Your child has read a story and used story details to tell fact from opinion. ***Home Activity:*** Take turns with your child making statements that are either fact or opinion. Identify the type of statement the other person makes.

Name________________________

Family Pictures

Writing Across Texts

Directions: Consider what you learned about Yingtao's family in "Yingtao's New Friend" and Carmen Lomas Garza's family in *Family Pictures.* Complete the table by listing details about each family. **Possible answers given.**

Yingtao's Family	Carmen Lomas Garza's Family
His father must have been a good violinist because he gave lessons.	Her father played games with the children at birthday parties.
1. **Third Sister wanted an American name.**	6. **Carmen's mother liked to have big birthday parties.**
2. **Eldest Brother made furniture.**	7. **Carmen's grandfather took her to pick nopal leaves.**
3. **Mother put fish in the bathtub.**	8. **Her grandmother helped cook many meals.**
4. **Second Sister made tea.**	9. **Her brother picked oranges from the trees.**
5. **Third Sister was a good violinist.**	10. **Carmen's sister and she shared their dreams for their futures.**

Write a Compare/Contrast Paragraph

Think about these two families. How are they alike? How are they different? On a separate sheet of paper, write a paragraph comparing and contrasting Yingtao's family and Carmen Lomas Garza's family. Use the table you completed to help you.

Paragraphs will vary. Check that sentences in students' paragraphs contain a variety of structures, from simple to compound sentences.

Notes for Home: Your child analyzed information from two reading selections to write their own paragraph. ***Home Activity:*** As you read stories and articles with your child, discuss how ideas in these materials connect to other reading they have done.

Grammar Practice Book 4.1, p. 16
Name________________________

Family Pictures

Grammar: Subjects and Predicates

REVIEW

Directions: For each sentence, underline the complete subject once and the complete predicate twice.

1. Many pictures in a museum tell wonderful stories.
2. Pictures of things in nature are called *landscapes.*
3. Most paintings like these include water and trees.
4. Portraits show lifelike pictures of people.
5. I saw one that was a portrait of the artist's dog!

Directions: Write sentences that include the following simple subjects and predicates. Remember to begin each sentence with a capital letter and end each one with a punctuation mark. **Possible answers given.**

6. I enjoy
I enjoy visits to the art museum.

7. museums look
Museums look like interesting places.

8. painters use
Painters use different styles in their paintings.

9. people will pay
People will pay a lot of money for a famous painting.

10. Mrs. Andrews studied
My neighbor Mrs. Andrews studied art in college.

Notes for Home: Your child identified and used complete and simple subjects and predicates. ***Home Activity:*** Ask your child to point out the simple subject and predicate in several sentences that you find in a book, on a cereal box, or in a newspaper.

Grammar Practice Book 4.1, p. 17
Name________________________

Family Pictures

Grammar: Imperative and Exclamatory Sentences

A sentence that tells someone to do something is a command, or an **imperative sentence.** It usually begins with a verb. The subject of the sentence (*you*) is not shown, but it is understood. Imperative sentences end with periods.

Don't get wet. Please take an umbrella along.

An **exclamatory sentence** shows strong feeling or surprise. It ends with an exclamation mark.

What a day for walking the dog!

Directions: For each sentence, add the correct end punctuation. Then write **I** if the sentence is imperative. Write **E** if it is exclamatory.

1. Don't take too long getting ready **.** **I**
2. What a wonderful day to go to a museum **!** **E**
3. Leave your umbrella here **.** **I**
4. That's some big painting **!** **E**
5. Please follow the tour guide **.** **I**

Directions: Change each of these sentences into a command. Write your new sentence on the line. (Hint: You will not use all the words in each sentence.)

6. My art teacher says to try your best. **Try your best.**
7. He says we should work in pairs. **Work in pairs.**
8. I tell my partner to let me do some. **Let me do some.**
9. I tell my partner to keep helping me. **Keep helping me.**
10. My partner tells me to be quiet. **Be quiet.**

Notes for Home: Your child identified imperative and exclamatory sentences. ***Home Activity:*** To practice using commands and exclamations, make up funny dialogue in which one bossy character gives many orders that other characters don't like.

Grammar Practice Book 4.1, p. 18
Name________________________

Family Pictures

Grammar: Imperative and Exclamatory Sentences

Directions: For each sentence, add the correct end punctuation. Then write **I** if the sentence is imperative. Write **E** if it is exclamatory.

1. Let's learn to draw **.** **I**
2. Please be patient **.** **I**
3. I am *not* impatient **!** **E**
4. Please get some paper and a pencil **.** **I**
5. Watch what I do **.** **I**
6. Start with an outline of the face **.** **I**
7. Draw the nose next **.** **I**
8. Try going a little slower **.** **I**
9. Please get the brown pencil **.** **I**
10. Let me help you do that **.** **I**
11. How wonderful it turned out **!** **E**
12. I'm so excited about your drawing **!** **E**
13. Please draw a picture of me **.** **I**
14. Use all your talent **.** **I**
15. What fun we'll have **!** **E**

Write a Memo

Imagine you're in charge of getting a big mural made for school. On a separate sheet of paper, write a memo using commands and exclamations giving your friends instructions about how to get the job done. **Students might use exclamations such as "I'm so happy you're on the team!" and commands such as "Let me know if you have any questions."**

Notes for Home: Your child decided whether sentences were commands or exclamations. ***Home Activity:*** Name a strong feeling. Have your child make up an exclamatory sentence to match the feeling. Name a task. Have your child make up a command to tell someone to do it.

Grammar Practice Book 4.1, p. 19
Name________________________

Family Pictures

Grammar: Imperative and Exclamatory Sentences

RETEACHING

Look at the picture. Then follow these instructions.

1. Circle the end marks of each sentence in the picture.
2. Circle the command. It is an imperative sentence.
3. Underline the sentence that shows strong feeling. It is an exclamatory sentence.

An **imperative sentence** gives a command or makes a request. It begins with a capital letter and ends with a period. An **exclamatory sentence** shows strong feeling. It begins with a capital letter and ends with an exclamation mark.

Directions: Circle each imperative sentence. Underline each exclamatory sentence.

1. Pour water on the soil.
2. Find the seeds.
3. What a rare flower it is!
4. That flower smells wonderful!
5. Those flowers are amazingly tiny!
6. Please place the tree here.

Directions: Unscramble the words to make a sentence. Write each sentence. Use periods and exclamation marks correctly.

7. flowers away please put the
Please put the flowers away.

8. is so beautiful this garden
This garden is so beautiful!

Notes for Home: Your child identified and wrote imperative and exclamatory sentences. ***Home Activity:*** Together, write a short story about an exciting adventure. Make sure your child writes at least two imperative sentences and two exclamatory sentences.

Grammar Practice Book 4.1, p. 20

Name________________________

Family Pictures

Grammar: Imperative and Exclamatory Sentences

Directions: Look at the sentence in each space. Underline each imperative sentence. Shade each space with an exclamatory sentence.

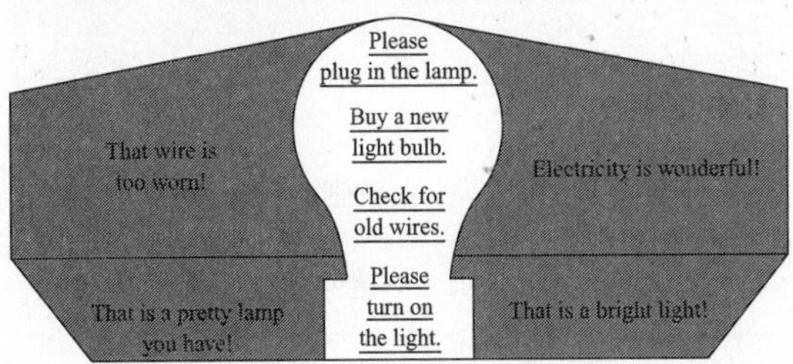

Please plug in the lamp.
Buy a new light bulb.
Check for old wires.
Please turn on the light.
That wire is too worn!
Electricity is wonderful!
That is a pretty lamp you have!
That is a bright light!

Directions: Decide if each sentence below is imperative or exclamatory. Write a period or an exclamation mark on the line. Then write **imperative** or **exclamatory.**

1. Pick up the lamp **.** **imperative**
2. It was so expensive **!** **exclamatory**
3. That old lamp still works great **!** **exclamatory**
4. Please change the bulb **.** **imperative**
5. What a cute cat he is **!** **exclamatory**
6. Turn on the light **.** **imperative**

Write Safety Rules

On a separate sheet of paper, write imperative and exclamatory sentences about how to use electricity safely. **Make sure students' imperative and exclamatory sentences are capitalized and punctuated correctly.**

Notes for Home: Your child identified imperative and exclamatory sentences. ***Home Activity:*** Have your child create a collage of imperative and exclamatory sentences, using words cut out from magazines. Have your child label them as *imperative* or *exclamatory.*

Grammar: Imperative and Exclamatory Sentences 81

Practice Book 4.1, p. 38

Name________________________

Family Pictures

Phonics: Common Word Patterns

Directions: Read each word below. Some words have a word pattern as in **home: consonant-vowel-consonant-e.** Other words have a word pattern as in **basket: vowel-consonant-consonant-vowel.** Write each word in the correct column.

rope	cactus	tale	same	summer	tender
brother	time	shelter	line	sister	make

CVCe home		VCCV basket	
1.	**rope**	7.	**brother**
2.	**time**	8.	**cactus**
3.	**tale**	9.	**shelter**
4.	**same**	10.	**summer**
5.	**line**	11.	**sister**
6.	**make**	12.	**tender**

Directions: Read each sentence. Find an example of each word pattern **(CVCe, VCCV)** in each sentence. Write the words in the correct columns.

CVCe	VCCV	
fine	**summer**	13. Our summer at the beach was fine.
made	**mother**	14. My mother made cookies.
rope	**sister**	15. My sister hung a rope from a tree for a bird feeder.
came	**shelter**	16. Birds came to the feeder and took shelter in a nearby tree.
gave	**oranges**	17. My aunt gave us oranges for lunch.
game	**funny**	18. We played a funny game later.
home	**brother**	19. Then my brother said we had to go home.
nine	**after**	20. It was after nine when we left.

Notes for Home: Your child learned to recognize two common word patterns: *CVCe (home)* and *VCCV (basket). **Home Activity:*** Say each word in the box. Have your child listen for the long vowel sounds in *CVCe* and the short vowel sounds in the first syllable of *VCCV* words.

82 Phonics: Common Word Patterns

Spelling Workbook 4.1, p. 13

Name________________________

Family Pictures

Spelling: Long Vowels *a, i, o*

Pretest Directions: Fold back the page along the dotted line. On the blanks, write the spelling words as they are dictated. When you have finished the test, unfold the page and check your words.

1. **station**	1. The fire **station** is close.
2. **danger**	2. Are you in **danger**?
3. **April**	3. It rained all **April**.
4. **vacation**	4. Our **vacation** was great!
5. **cable**	5. The **cable** pulled us up.
6. **bacon**	6. **Bacon** is greasy.
7. **wild**	7. Wolves are **wild** animals.
8. **behind**	8. Stand **behind** me.
9. **pint**	9. Measure a **pint** of water.
10. **lion**	10. The **lion** roared loudly.
11. **hide**	11. Where did you **hide** it?
12. **decide**	12. Let's **decide** on a plan.
13. **invite**	13. **Invite** her to come along.
14. **arrive**	14. When did you **arrive**?
15. **whole**	15. Bring your **whole** family.
16. **broke**	16. I **broke** a glass.
17. **drove**	17. He **drove** away quickly.
18. **smoke**	18. **Smoke** rose from the fire.
19. **remote**	19. This is a **remote** island.
20. **stole**	20. Who **stole** the treasure?

Notes for Home: Your child took a pretest on words that have the long vowels *a, i,* and *o*. ***Home Activity:*** Help your child learn misspelled words before the final test. Have your child divide misspelled words into parts (such as syllables) and concentrate on each part.

Spelling: Long Vowels *a, i, o* 83

Spelling Workbook 4.1, p. 14

Name________________________

Family Pictures

Spelling: Long Vowels *a, i, o*

Directions: Write the words from the box with the **long i** vowel sound. Sort the words according to how the vowel sound is spelled. **Order may vary.**

Word List
station
danger
April
vacation
cable
bacon
wild
behind
pint
lion
hide
decide
invite
arrive
whole
broke
drove
smoke
remote
stole

Long i spelled i		Long i spelled i-consonant-e	
1.	**wild**	5.	**hide**
2.	**behind**	6.	**decide**
3.	**pint**	7.	**invite**
4.	**lion**	8.	**arrive**

Directions: Choose the word from the box that best completes each tongue twister. Write the word on the line to the left.

broke	9. Bill _____ his blue bicycle.
whole	10. Who ate the _____ hog?
April	11. Apes ate eight acres of acorns in _____.
stole	12. Stuart _____ silently up the steep stairs.
cable	13. Curt's cousin's company sells computer _____.
smoke	14. Smedley's smock was smudged by smelly _____.
drove	15. Dave _____ drooling drummers to dinner.
bacon	16. Bailey the baker baked _____ by the bay.
danger	17. Doug didn't discuss the _____.
remote	18. Ron and Rick wrestled for the _____ control.
station	19. Steve stood still at the _____.
vacation	20. Vera vanished and went on _____ .

Notes for Home: Your child spelled words with long vowels *a, i,* and *o (station, wild, hide, whole). **Home Activity:*** Choose a word with one of these long vowel sounds. Write some of the letters, but leave spaces for the others. Have your child fill in the missing letters.

84 Spelling: Long Vowels *a, i, o*

Spelling Workbook 4.1, p. 15
Name________________________

Family Pictures

Spelling: Long Vowels *a, i, o*

≡ Make a capital.
/ Make a small letter.
∧ Add something.
Take out something.
⊙ Add a period.
¶ Begin a new paragraph.

Directions: Proofread this invitation. Find five spelling mistakes. Use the proofreading marks to correct each mistake.

The Old Fire Station Gallery and Danger Safaris invit^e you to a new show—A Walk On The Wilde Side—opening April 10 at 150 Bacon St. Come see exciting close-up photos taken from behinde tall grass as photographers h^i~~y~~de from a lion. Once you arriv^e be ready for anything!

Monday–Friday 11 A.M.–5 P.M.

Spelling Tip

Long Vowels

Words with long vowels are often spelled with one letter: **station, wild.** They can also be spelled **vowel-consonant-e: whole, hide.**

Word List

station	bacon	hide	broke
danger	wild	decide	drove
April	behind	invite	smoke
vacation	pint	arrive	remote
cable	lion	whole	stole

Write an Invitation

Imagine you're a photographer. On a separate sheet of paper, write an invitation to a showing of your work. Try to use at least three spelling words. **Answers will vary, but each invitation should include at least three spelling words.**

Notes for Home: Your child spelled words with long vowels *a, i,* and *o (station, wild, hide, whole). **Home Activity:*** When you are in a grocery store, have your child call words to your attention that have these long vowel sounds, such as *whole* milk and *wild* berry punch.

Spelling: Long Vowels *a, i, o* 85

Spelling Workbook 4.1, p. 16
Name________________________

Family Pictures

Spelling: Long Vowels *a, i, o*

REVIEW

Word List

station	cable	pint	invite	drove
danger	bacon	lion	arrive	smoke
April	wild	hide	whole	remote
vacation	behind	decide	broke	stole

Directions: Choose the word from the box that is the most opposite in meaning for each word below. Write the word on the line.

1. front **behind**
2. tame **wild**
3. fixed **broke**
4. part **whole**
5. leave **arrive**
6. seek **hide**
7. safety **danger**
8. work **vacation**
9. ignore **invite**

Directions: Choose the word from the box that matches each clue. Write the word on the line.

remote 10. This type of control lets you turn on a TV.
bacon 11. You can eat it with eggs instead of sausage.
stole 12. The baseball player did this to second base.
smoke 13. Where there's fire, there's this.
pint 14. Two cups make one of these.
cable 15. A ski lift runs on one.
drove 16. It's the past tense of *drive.*
April 17. It's the month before May.
station 18. Trains arrive here.
lion 19. This is a name for a very big cat.
decide 20. It's what you do when you make up your mind.

Notes for Home: Your child spelled words with long vowels *a, i,* and *o (station, wild, hide, whole). **Home Activity:*** Give your child a page of the newspaper and a highlighter. Ask your child to look for and highlight words with long vowels *a, i,* and *o.*

86 Spelling: Long Vowels *a, i, o*

Practice Book 4.1, p. 39
Name________________________

Family Pictures

Outline

Making an **outline** can help you organize information you read. Outlining helps you remember important points and understand what you read. Outlining information can also help you prepare for tests.

Directions: Read this article about flowers found in Texas. Then use the information in this article to complete the outline on the next page.

Texas Wildflowers

by William G. Morales

Mexican Hat

Texas Dandelion

Indian Paintbrush

Many people know the old folk song, "The Yellow Rose of Texas." Texas is home to many beautiful wildflowers too.

If you see a yellow-orange flower that looks like a sombrero, you probably have found a flower called a **Mexican Hat.** These pretty flowers are also called "coneflowers" and "thimbleflowers." Mexican Hat flowers can be used for making dye.

Another flower found in the Lone Star State is the **Texas Dandelion.** These members of the sunflower family are found in pastures, near roads, and on people's lawns. When the stems of these flowers are broken, they leak a kind of milky sap. When the seeds dry, children enjoy blowing them into the air.

One of the most beautiful flowers in Texas is the **Indian Paintbrush,** also known as the "scarlet paintbrush." The paintbrush plants use the roots of other plants to help them grow. They bloom from March to May, but are the prettiest in April.

Research and Study Skills: Outline 87

Practice Book 4.1, p. 40
Name________________________

Family Pictures

Texas Wildflowers

I. **Mexican Hat**
   A. Also called coneflowers and **thimbleflowers**
   B. Used for making dye

II. **Texas dandelion**
   A. When broken, they leak milky sap.
   B. Found near pastures, roads, and on **people's lawns**
   C. Children blow the seeds in the air.

III. Indian Paintbrush
   A. Also known as **scarlet paintbrush**
   B. Uses the roots of other plants to grow

Directions: Explain why an outline can be useful for researching and studying. Write your explanation on the lines below.

Possible answer: An outline can be useful for researching and studying because it helps you organize information. You can use an outline to group related ideas together. An outline lets you see at a glance the important information you have collected.

Notes for Home: Your child used an outline to organize information and understand what he or she read. ***Home Activity:*** Create an outline that organizes information about an interesting topic, such as your family history or wildlife in your area. Use the above outline as a model.

88 Research and Study Skills: Outline

Practice Book 4.1, p. 41

Name ________________________ **Addie in Charge**

Character

- **Characters** are the people or animals in a story or nonfictional article.
- You can learn about characters by what they think, do, and say.
- You can also learn about characters by seeing how other characters in the story treat them and what other characters say about them.

Directions: Reread "Ma on the Prairie." Fill in the word web with story details about Ma that help you learn about her. On the line at the bottom of the page, write your own description of this character. **Possible answers given.**

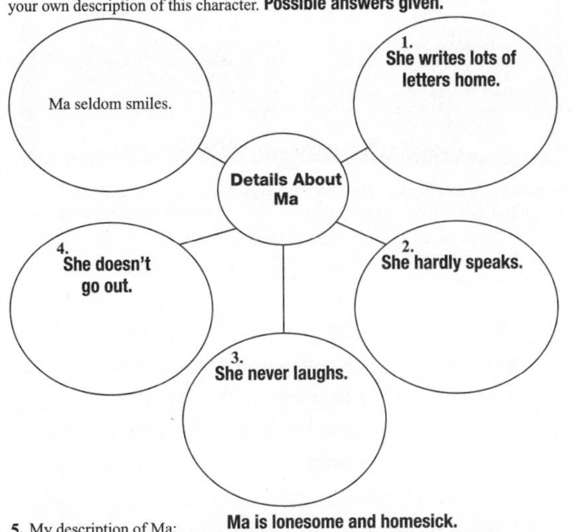

5. My description of Ma: **Ma is lonesome and homesick.**

Notes for Home: Your child read a story and identified details that helped her or him understand a main character. ***Home Activity:*** Have your child try to understand a person better by making a list of things that person does and says and what other people say about the person.

Character 91

Practice Book 4.1, p. 42

Name ________________________ **Addie in Charge**

Vocabulary

Directions: Draw a line to connect each word on the left with its definition on the right.

Check the Words You Know
- __ bellows
- __ billows
- __ crouched
- __ smarted
- __ tufts

Directions: Choose the word from the box that best matches each clue. Write the word on the line.

crouched 6. The cat did this before it jumped off the bookshelf.

billows 7. This word rhymes with soft things for your head on your bed.

bellows 8. This word rhymes with *fellows,* and one fellow does it when he's angry.

tufts 9. These can be made up of feathers, hair, or grass.

smarted 10. I yelled, "That ____!" when I sat on a pin, but it did not help my grades at school.

Write a Story

On a separate sheet of paper, write a made-up story about how someone solves a big problem. The problem can be serious, such as a fire, or funny, such as an incredibly bad day where everything goes wrong. Use as many vocabulary words as you can.

Students' stories should describe a problem and its solution and use vocabulary words correctly.

Notes for Home: Your child identified and used vocabulary words from "Addie in Charge." ***Home Activity:*** Say the vocabulary word *crouched* and have your child act out its meaning. Take turns saying other action words that can be acted out by the other person.

92 Vocabulary

Practice Book 4.1, p. 43

Name ________________________ **Addie in Charge**

Character

- **Characters** are the people or animals in a story.
- You can learn about characters by what they think, do, and say. You can also learn about characters by how other characters in the story treat them and what other characters say about them.

Directions: Reread what happens in "Addie in Charge" when she tries to save herself and her little brother from the fire. Then answer the questions below. Think about how you learn what Addie and Burt are like.

Still kneeling on the ground, Addie used one foot to carefully feel for the ladder's highest rung. Slowly, she lowered herself, balancing Burt with great effort. Down into the well she went, step over step. Now they were below ground level. It was pitch black, and the water felt cold around Addie's knees as she reached the bottom rung. "Don't let go, Burt. Don't let go," she told her brother, who buried his face into the back of her neck so that her necklace dug deep into her skin.

1. Is Addie sure of herself? How do you know?
No. She carefully feels for the ladder and slowly lowers herself.

2. How do you know Addie cares about her brother?
She says, "Don't let go, Burt. Don't let go."

3. How do you think Burt feels? How do you know?
Burt is frightened. He buries his face hard into Addie's neck.

4. Addie's parents left her in charge. How do you think they felt about her?
Possible answers: They trust her. They think she can manage it.

5. On a separate sheet of paper, describe Addie in your own words. Use details from the story to support your answers.
Possible answers: Addie was smart; she knew it was fire and not sunset from the direction. She also thought of a good place to go for shelter.

Notes for Home: Your child has read a story and used story details to understand characters. ***Home Activity:*** Help your child understand characters in books you read together by talking about the things they think, do, or say.

Character 93

Practice Book 4.1, p. 45

Name ________________________ **Addie in Charge**

Selection Test

Directions: Choose the best answer to each item. Mark the letter for the answer you have chosen.

Part 1: Vocabulary

Find the answer choice that means about the same as the underlined word in each sentence.

1. Stella <u>crouched</u> on the floor.
   - A. spun around quickly
   - (B) stooped low with bent legs
   - C. walked on tiptoes
   - D. pounded with the feet

2. I could hear the cow's <u>bellows</u>.
   - F. deep breaths
   - G. rings from a bell
   - H. sweet songs
   - (J) loud, deep noises

3. Grains of sand <u>smarted</u> my face.
   - (A) caused pain in
   - B. stuck to
   - C. blew around
   - D. covered

4. We pulled <u>tufts</u> of weeds from the garden.
   - F. seeds
   - G. roots
   - (H) bunches
   - J. flowers

5. <u>Billows</u> of smoke rose from the roof.
   - A. thin streams
   - B. large piles
   - (C) great waves
   - D. storm clouds

Part 2: Comprehension

Use what you know about the story to answer each item.

6. When the story begins, Addie's parents and brother were—
   - F. traveling to Iowa.
   - G. planting crops.
   - H. visiting neighbors.
   - (J) building a sod home.

7. Who was Ruby Lillian?
   - A. Addie's friend from Iowa
   - B. the Fencys' cow
   - C. Addie's little sister
   - (D) a doll

8. What clue shows that Addie was quite grown-up and dependable?
   - (F) She was left in charge of her little brother for two days.
   - G. She was making a sampler.
   - H. She saw a strange light in the sky.
   - J. She read Burt a story.

GO ON

94 Selection Test

Practice Book 4.1, p. 46

Name________________ Addie in Charge

9. What was the first sign of trouble that Addie noticed?
   A. The horizon was orange and yellow.
   B. Coyotes ran through the field.
   (C) The cows were making frightened noises.
   D. Ashes were flying in the air.

10. As the fire drew closer, Addie felt—
   F. sure the firebreak would stop the fire.
   (G) terrified but determined to stay safe.
   H. sure that she and Burt were going to die.
   J. nervous but certain that her parents would rescue her.

11. Why did Addie climb down into the well?
   (A) She knew fire could not go there.
   B. It was quiet and dark.
   C. She and Burt needed water to drink.
   D. It was far from the fire's path.

12. In the well, Addie felt—
   F. too afraid to do anything.
   (G) afraid, but responsible for her brother's safety.
   H. in control of the situation.
   J. angry that her parents had left her alone.

13. When George found a scrap of Addie's bonnet, he thought that Addie and Burt had—
   A. hidden in the well.
   B. run away from the fire.
   C. hidden in the root cellar.
   (D) died in the fire.

14. For Addie, what was the best thing to come out of her experience?
   F. She would never quarrel with George again.
   (G) She discovered that she was strong enough to be a pioneer.
   H. Her parents probably wouldn't leave her alone again.
   J. The Fencys would always be grateful to her.

15. What was the most important thing Addie did in this story?
   A. threw water on the Fencys' house
   B. put Anna Fency's trunk in the cellar
   (C) kept herself and her brother safe
   D. untied Bess and Missy

Name________________ Addie in Charge

Character

- **Characters** are the people or animals in a story.
- You can learn about characters by what they think, do, and say. You can also learn about characters by how other characters in the story treat them and what other characters say about them.

Directions: Read the story below.

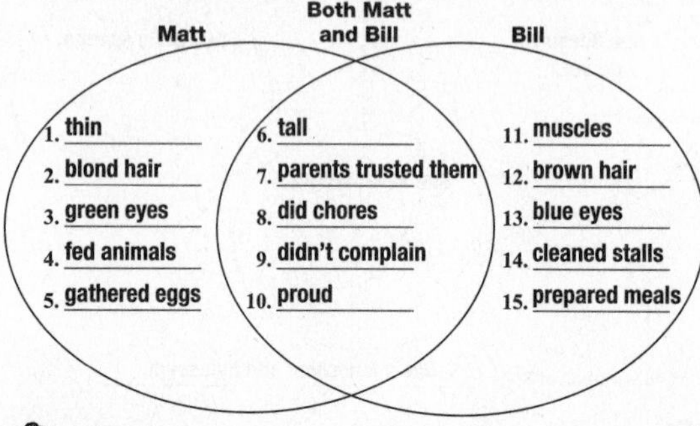

Matt and Bill were twins, but you couldn't tell from looking at them. They both were tall. Matt was thin, and Bill had lots of muscles. Matt had blond hair, but Bill's was brown. Matt had green eyes, and Bill's were blue.

What was important was that their parents could trust them both. When Matt and Bill's grandfather got sick, their parents had to take him in the wagon all the way to the doctor in Glenville. The twins' parents were counting on Matt and Bill to take care of things.

While they were away, Matt and Bill did the farm chores. Matt fed the animals, while Bill cleaned their stalls. Matt gathered eggs, and Bill prepared meals. Neither of them complained. They were just proud they could help out.

Directions: In the diagram below, list five things that are true of Matt, five that are true of Bill, and five that are true of both of them. **Possible answers given.**

Matt	Both Matt and Bill	Bill
1. **thin**	6. **tall**	11. **muscles**
2. **blond hair**	7. **parents trusted them**	12. **brown hair**
3. **green eyes**	8. **did chores**	13. **blue eyes**
4. **fed animals**	9. **didn't complain**	14. **cleaned stalls**
5. **gathered eggs**	10. **proud**	15. **prepared meals**

Notes for Home: Your child has read a story and used story details to describe two characters. ***Home Activity:*** With your child, fill out a diagram similar to the one above for two family members or friends.

Practice Book 4.1, p. 47

Name________________ Addie in Charge

Theme

REVIEW

Directions: Read the story. Then read each question about the story. Choose the best answer to each question. Mark the letter for the answer you have chosen.

Helping Hans

Ten-year-old Hans and his father were building a table. Hans was proud to be helping his father. Anna, his little sister, wanted to help too, but Hans said, "Go play with your dolls. You're too little to help."

When Hans and his father finished sawing, they began to put the table together. They pounded nail after nail. At last, just one leg was left, but there were no more nails.

Hans and his father searched everywhere, but they could not find any nails. Little Anna, playing quietly on the floor, suddenly pounced.

"Here they are!" she said. The nails had rolled across the floor to where she was playing.

"Thank you, Anna," said Hans. "You're a big help!"

1. A story's theme is—
   A. what happens.
   (B) its big idea.
   C. its ending.
   D. why something happens.

2. Which statement best describes this story's theme?
   F. Don't build anything unless you have all the pieces.
   (G) Even the littlest can help.
   H. Don't drop the nails before the table is finished.
   J. Children should be seen but not heard.

3. The theme of this passage is—
   A. stated by Hans.
   B. stated by Hans's father.
   C. stated by Anna.
   (D) Not stated directly by any one character.

4. A title that suggests the theme is—
   (F) Little Helpers.
   G. We Need Nails.
   H. Stop! Look! Listen!
   J. Table Building Long Ago.

5. Which statement from the story supports the theme?
   A. There were no more nails.
   B. They pounded nail after nail.
   (C) "You're a big help!"
   D. Ten-year-old Hans and his father were building a table.

Notes for Home: Your child has read a story and used story details to identify its theme. ***Home Activity:*** When you and your child are watching television together, suggest that he or she tell the theme of a story and give reasons to support his or her answer.

Name________________ Addie in Charge

Writing Across Texts

Directions: Consider what you know about Addie from "Addie in Charge" and Merle Block from the article "Merle Builds a Sod House." What pioneer-like qualities does each of them have? In the left-hand column, write traits that describe Addie. In the right-hand column, write traits that describe Merle Block.
Possible answers given.

Addie's Traits	Merle's Traits
She is brave and responsible.	He appreciates his ancestors.
1. **She works hard.**	6. **He works hard.**
2. **She is clever.**	7. **He is creative.**
3. **She is quick thinking.**	8. **He knows a lot about pioneer life.**
4. **She is determined.**	9. **He is handy.**
5. **She is strong and protective.**	10. **He is strong.**

Write a Character Description

Think about what you learned about Addie and Merle Block. What qualities would a pioneer need to survive on the prairie? On a separate sheet of paper, write a paragraph that describes the qualities of a good pioneer. Use the information you wrote in the table above to help you with ideas. **Description will vary, but they should reflect the information in the table and an understanding that successful pioneers are hard working and determined.**

Notes for Home: Your child used information from different sources to write a character description. ***Home Activity:*** As you read stories and articles with your child, compare and contrast the characters and people in these materials.

Grammar Practice Book 4.1, p. 21

Name________________ Addie in Charge

Grammar: Simple Sentences

REVIEW

Directions: Read each group of words. Write **S** if it is a sentence. Write **NS** if it is not a sentence. For each sentence, underline the simple subject once and the simple predicate twice.

S 1. Matthew will go to a new school in September.

S 2. He has worried about it all summer.

NS 3. Meeting new teachers and students.

S 4. This smart boy made some plans.

NS 5. Memorized a map of the school.

Directions: Think of a time you have been afraid of something. Write five sentences about that time. Underline each simple subject once and each simple predicate twice. **Possible answers given.**

6. Sometimes the darkness in my room scares me.

7. My mind imagines all kinds of things.

8. Monsters hide under the bed.

9. Then I turn on the light.

10. All scary things disappear immediately.

Notes for Home: Your child identified the subjects and predicates in simple sentences and wrote sentences. ***Home Activity:*** Look at comics in a newspaper. Have your child tell which statements the characters are saying are sentences that contain a subject and a predicate.

Grammar: Simple Sentences 99

Grammar Practice Book 4.1, p. 22

Name________________ Addie in Charge

Grammar: Compound and Complex Sentences

A **simple sentence** expresses one complete thought. A **compound sentence** contains two simple sentences joined by a comma and a connecting word such as *and, but,* or *or.*

Simple sentences: My mother went out. I was home alone.
Compound sentence: My mother went out, and I was home alone.

A **complex sentence** contains a simple sentence combined with a group of words that cannot stand on its own.

Complex sentence: When my mother left, I was home alone.
group of words — simple sentence

Directions: Write whether each sentence is **compound** or **complex.**

complex 1. When I turned the corner, I heard a strange noise.

compound 2. The noise grew louder, and I was scared.

complex 3. Before I knew it, I was running.

compound 4. I saw a police car, and I told the officer what I had heard.

complex 5. When we saw the garbage truck, we both laughed.

Directions: Write **Yes** if the underlined words can stand alone to make a sentence. Write **No** if they cannot stand alone.

Yes 6. You are not alone, but you wish you were.

No 7. Because you are scared, you run fast.

Yes 8. You fall, or you are knocked down.

No 9. When your face is licked, you start to laugh.

Yes 10. You hug your dog, and you give him a treat.

Notes for Home: Your child identified compound and complex sentences. ***Home Activity:*** Read a newspaper article. Challenge your child to find compound and complex sentences in it.

100 Grammar: Compound and Complex Sentences

Grammar Practice Book 4.1, p. 23

Name________________ Addie in Charge

Grammar: Compound and Complex Sentences

Directions: Make a compound sentence by joining the simple sentences with a comma and one of these words: *and, but,* or *or.*

1. We watched a TV movie. We didn't see the end.
We watched a TV movie, but we didn't see the end.

2. Something went wrong with the set. The picture disappeared.
Something went wrong with the set, and the picture disappeared.

3. The screen went dark. The sound stopped too.
The screen went dark, and the sound stopped too.

4. My dad would fix the set. We would replace it.
My dad would fix the set, or we would replace it.

5. My brother turned on the radio. We listened to the news.
My brother turned on the radio, and we listened to the news.

Directions: Write **Yes** if the underlined words can stand alone to make a sentence. Write **No** if they cannot stand alone.

No 6. Because my parents were at Open School Night, I was home alone.

Yes 7. I was reading, and the lights went out.

Yes 8. Was it just my house, or was it a neighborhood blackout?

No 9. When I looked outside, the whole neighborhood was dark.

Yes 10. Since all the electric power was off, I used my flashlight.

Write a Paragraph

Think of a problem you solved. On a separate sheet of paper, write a paragraph that tells how you solved it. Include compound and complex sentences. **Check that students have formed compound and complex sentences correctly.**

Notes for Home: Your child identified compound and complex sentences. ***Home Activity:*** Point to two objects in the room. Ask your child to make up a compound sentence (contains two simple sentences and a connecting word) that compares the objects.

Grammar: Compound and Complex Sentences 101

Grammar Practice Book 4.1, p. 24

Name________________ Addie in Charge

Grammar: Compound and Complex Sentences

RETEACHING

Read the compound sentence. It is made of two simple sentences. Circle the word **and** in the sentence.

1. The pitcher throws the ball, (and) the batter hits it.

Read the complex sentence. It is made up of a simple sentence and a group of words that cannot stand alone as a sentence.

2. When I threw it as hard as I could, the ball sailed away.

A **simple sentence** expresses one complete thought. It has one subject and one predicate. A **compound sentence** contains two simple sentences joined by the word **and.** A **complex sentence** contains a simple sentence and another group of words that cannot stand alone as a complete sentence.

Directions: Read each sentence. Then circle **compound** or **complex.**

1. The catcher crouches behind the plate, and the pitcher throws the first ball. (compound) complex

2. When the ball comes, the batter hits it solidly. compound (complex)

3. The shortstop runs toward the ball because that is his job. compound (complex)

4. The ball hops past the shortstop, and the batter runs to first base. (compound) complex

Directions: Complete each compound or complex sentence. **Possible answers given.**

5. When the game begins, the crowd cheers wildly.

6. A batter hits a high ball, and the pitcher catches it.

7. The home team wins, and the happy fans applaud.

Notes for Home: Your child identified compound and complex sentences. ***Home Activity:*** Have your child combine pairs of sentences to form compound sentences. Then write pairs of word groups for your child to combine to create complex sentences.

102 Grammar: Compound and Complex Sentences

Grammar Practice Book 4.1, p. 25

Name______________________ Addie in Charge

Grammar: Compound and Complex Sentences

Directions: Write **compound** or **complex** for each sentence.

1. Mozart was young, and he was famous. **compound**
2. When he was three, he played music. **complex**
3. Mozart read music, and he wrote it too. **compound**
4. He wrote melodies for many instruments because he enjoyed it. **complex**
5. He went on tours, and crowds cheered him. **compound**
6. If you say *The Magic Flute*, someone might think of Mozart. **complex**
7. Because of Mozart, more people were interested in the piano. **complex**
8. It was new, and few people played it. **compound**

Directions: Add a simple sentence or a group of words. Write each compound or complex sentence. **Possible answers given.**

9. Music makes me smile, because ______
   Music makes me smile, because it relaxes me.
10. I like to sing, and ______
    I like to sing, and I like to dance.
11. We can listen, and ______
    We can listen, and we can sing along.

Write a Story

On a separate sheet of paper, write a story about a musician you like. Use compound and complex sentences. Begin with a compound sentence that starts:

I have a favorite musician, and ______. **Make sure that students have used compound and complex sentences.**

Notes for Home: Your child identified and wrote compound and complex sentences. ***Home Activity:*** Read your child's story about a favorite musician. Have him or her point out to you which sentences are compound and which are complex.

Practice Book 4.1, p. 48

Name______________________ Addie in Charge

Phonics: Three-letter Blends

Directions: Read each short word. Make a longer word by following the first instruction. Take that longer word and make an even longer word by following the second instruction. Write each new word on the line.

1. sash
Add an **l** after the first **s.** **slash**
Add a **p** after the first **s.** **splash**

2. tee
Add an **r** after the **t.** **tree**
Add an **h** after the **t.** **three**

3. ream
Add a **c** before the **r.** **cream**
Add an **s** before the **c.** **scream**

4. sing
Add a **t** after the **s.** **sting**
Add an **r** after the **t.** **string**

Directions: The sentences below are part of a diary entry about solving a problem. Six words start with a three-letter blend. Write the six words on the lines.

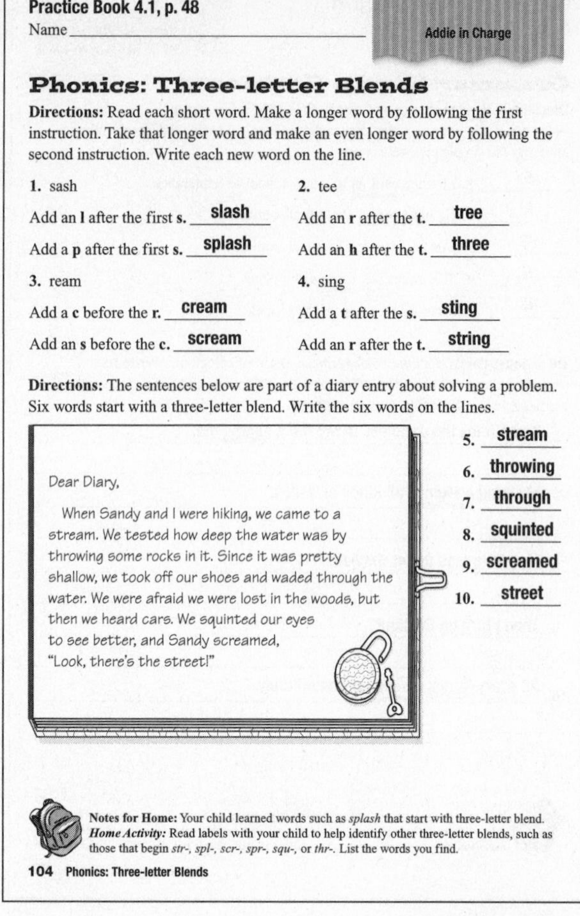

Dear Diary,
When Sandy and I were hiking, we came to a stream. We tested how deep the water was by throwing some rocks in it. Since it was pretty shallow, we took off our shoes and waded through the water. We were afraid we were lost in the woods, but then we heard cars. We squinted our eyes to see better, and Sandy screamed, "Look, there's the street!"

5. **stream**
6. **throwing**
7. **through**
8. **squinted**
9. **screamed**
10. **street**

Notes for Home: Your child learned words such as *splash* that start with three-letter blend. ***Home Activity:*** Read labels with your child to help identify other three-letter blends, such as those that begin *str-, spl-, scr-, spr-, squ-,* or *thr-*. List the words you find.

Spelling Workbook 4.1, p. 17

Name______________________ Addie in Charge

Spelling: Words with *thr, scr, str, squ*

Pretest Directions: Fold back the page along the dotted line. On the blanks, write the spelling words as they are dictated. When you have finished the test, unfold the page and check your words.

1. **throat**	1. My **throat** is sore.
2. **through**	2. Run **through** the field.
3. **screen**	3. The **screen** keeps out bugs.
4. **scratch**	4. My bike has a **scratch**.
5. **scream**	5. Did someone **scream**?
6. **strange**	6. It is a **strange** story.
7. **street**	7. The **street** is empty.
8. **strike**	8. **Strike** the piñata.
9. **square**	9. The windows are **square**.
10. **squeeze**	10. **Squeeze** the toothpaste.
11. **threat**	11. The bully made a **threat**.
12. **thrown**	12. The ball was **thrown** far.
13. **thrill**	13. Did the play **thrill** you?
14. **scrub**	14. **Scrub** the pots and pans.
15. **skyscraper**	15. Look up at the **skyscraper**!
16. **strawberry**	16. Is the **strawberry** ripe?
17. **strength**	17. Use **strength** to lift this.
18. **squeal**	18. Listen to the pig **squeal**.
19. **squirm**	19. Snakes make me **squirm**.
20. **squirt**	20. **Squirt** water on the plant.

Notes for Home: Your child took a pretest on words with *thr, scr, str,* and *squ*. ***Home Activity:*** Help your child learn misspelled words before the final test. See if there are any similar errors and discuss a memory trick that could help.

Spelling Workbook 4.1, p. 18

Name______________________ Addie in Charge

Spelling: Words with *thr, scr, str,* and *squ*

Word List			
throat	screen	strange	square
through	scratch	street	squeeze
threat	scream	strike	squeal
thrown	scrub	strawberry	squirm
thrill	skyscraper	strength	squirt

Directions: Write the words that have a three-letter **consonant blend** with **s.** Sort the words by the way they are spelled. **Order may vary.**

Spelled scr	Spelled str	Spelled squ
1. **screen**	6. **strange**	11. **square**
2. **scratch**	7. **street**	12. **squeeze**
3. **scream**	8. **strike**	13. **squeal**
4. **scrub**	9. **strawberry**	14. **squirm**
5. **skyscraper**	10. **strength**	15. **squirt**

Directions: Choose the word from the box that best matches each definition. Write the word on the line.

through 16. in one side and out the other
threat 17. a warning or promise to do harm
thrown 18. sent through the air forcefully
throat 19. the front of the neck
thrill 20. an exciting feeling

Notes for Home: Your child spelled words with *thr, scr, str,* and *squ*. ***Home Activity:*** Write *thr, scr, str,* and *squ* on index cards (one per card). On others write endings from spelling words. Let your child use the cards to build words *(str + ength = strength).*

Spelling Workbook 4.1, p. 19

Name________________________ **Addie in Charge**

Spelling: Words with *thr, scr, str,* and *squ*

Directions: Proofread this message. Find five spelling mistakes. Use the proofreading marks to correct each mistake.

≡	Make a capital.
/	Make a small letter.
∧	Add something.
℘	Take out something.
⊙	Add a period.
¶	Begin a new paragraph.

Thought for Today

Once you start to solve a problem, it's important to try to see it through. Sure, you might get stuck. At times you might even want to scream, "Enough!" But it's amazing and strange how much inner strength you can find. And the thrill of success is sweet.

Spelling Tip

Each spelling word has three letters that together represent a blended sound: **throat, scream, street, squeeze.**

Word List	
throat	strange
through	street
threat	strike
thrown	strawberry
thrill	strength
screen	square
scratch	squeeze
scream	squeal
scrub	squirm
skyscraper	squirt

Write About an Experience

On a separate sheet of paper, write about a problem you solved successfully. Try to use at least three spelling words.

Answers will vary, but each student should include at least three spelling words.

Notes for Home: Your child spelled words with consonant blends *thr, scr, str,* and *squ. Home Activity:* Say a word that starts with one of these blends. Have your child say that word plus a new word with that blend. You say both words and add a third word. Continue taking turns.

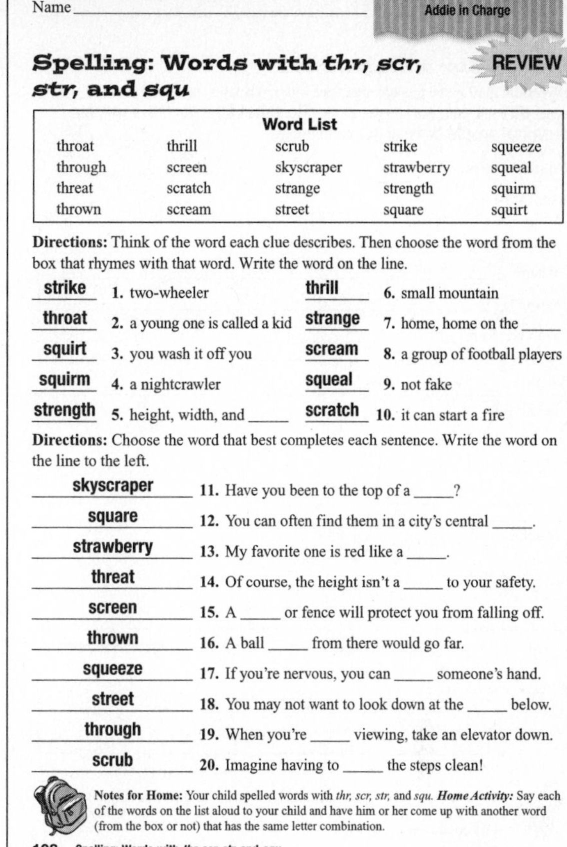

Spelling Workbook 4.1, p. 20

Name________________________ **Addie in Charge**

Spelling: Words with *thr, scr, str,* and *squ* REVIEW

Word List				
throat	thrill	scrub	strike	squeeze
through	screen	skyscraper	strawberry	squeal
threat	scratch	strange	strength	squirm
thrown	scream	street	square	squirt

Directions: Think of the word each clue describes. Then choose the word from the box that rhymes with that word. Write the word on the line.

strike 1. two-wheeler

throat 2. a young one is called a kid

squirt 3. you wash it off you

squirm 4. a nightcrawler

strength 5. height, width, and _____

thrill 6. small mountain

strange 7. home, home on the _____

scream 8. a group of football players

squeal 9. not fake

scratch 10. it can start a fire

Directions: Choose the word that best completes each sentence. Write the word on the line to the left.

skyscraper 11. Have you been to the top of a _____?

square 12. You can often find them in a city's central _____.

strawberry 13. My favorite one is red like a _____.

threat 14. Of course, the height isn't a _____ to your safety.

screen 15. A _____ or fence will protect you from falling off.

thrown 16. A ball _____ from there would go far.

squeeze 17. If you're nervous, you can _____ someone's hand.

street 18. You may not want to look down at the _____ below.

through 19. When you're _____ viewing, take an elevator down.

scrub 20. Imagine having to _____ the steps clean!

Notes for Home: Your child spelled words with *thr, scr, str,* and *squ. Home Activity:* Say each of the words on the list aloud to your child and have him or her come up with another word (from the box or not) that has the same letter combination.

Practice Book 4.1, p. 49

Name________________________ **Addie in Charge**

Parts of a Book

Knowing the **parts of a book** makes it easier to locate information. For example, a **table of contents** shows what a book is about and where to find each chapter.

Directions: Use the table of contents to answer the questions that follow.

American Pioneers of the Wild West

Table of Contents

CHAPTER 1 Introduction **3**
- Western Trails
- Prairie Life

CHAPTER 2 Famous Pioneers **10**
- Buffalo Bill
- Davy Crockett
- Kit Carson
- Wyatt Earp

CHAPTER 3 Women of the West **29**
- Calamity Jane
- Charley Parkhurst
- Narcissa Prentiss
- Belle Starr

1. What do the numbers shown on the right of the table of contents tell you?
They show on which page each chapter begins.

2. How do the topics under each chapter head help you? **The topics under the chapter heads give you a better idea of what you'll find on those pages.**

3. How many different people can you read about in Chapter 2? **four**

4. If you wanted to research American Pioneers who were women, which chapter should you read? On what page does this chapter begin?
Chapter 3; page 29

5. Which chapter should you read to learn more about Buffalo Bill?
Chapter 2

Practice Book 4.1, p. 50

Name________________________ **Addie in Charge**

An **index** is a list of the specific subjects covered in a book. It tells what pages have information about each subject.

Directions: Study this index from *American Pioneers of the Wild West.* Use it to answer the questions that follow.

Index

Americans, Native, 40, 51–65
- customs of, 40
- folk tales of, 60–65
- speeches, 51–59

Bill, Buffalo, 11–13

Buffaloes, 35–39
- herding of, 38
- near extinction, 36–37

Carson, Kit, 25–27

Cowboys (General), 8, 80–104
- daily life of, 101–104
- dude ranches, 81
- horse training, 98
- meals of, 8
- museums, 83

6. If you wanted to find information about a famous Native American speech, which pages would you read?
51–59

7. If you wanted to know what cowboys ate for dinner, which page would you read?
8

8. If you wanted to use an index to find information about a person, would you look under the first name or last name?
last name

9. If you looked on pages 25–27, what information would you expect to find?
information about Kit Carson

10. How does a table of contents and an index help you find information quickly?
Possible answer: They both show the subject covered at a glance and give page numbers so you can find the information quickly.

Notes for Home: Your child learned about the parts of a book, such as the table of contents and the index. *Home Activity:* Challenge your child to locate information in a nonfiction book, using the index and table of contents.

Name________________________________

Notes for a Narrative

Directions: Fill in the graphic organizer with information about the event or experience that you plan to write about. **The Notes for a Narrative graphic organizer should be filled out completely.**

Possible title: ________________________________

Summary

What happened? ________________________________

When? ________________________________

Where? ________________________________

Who was there? ________________________________

Details

Beginning

Middle

End

Notes for Home: Your child has been planning a personal narrative. ***Home Activity:*** Have your child tell you about the experience that he or she is writing about. Ask for details about what happened first, next, and last.

Name________________________________

Elaboration

Words That Show Emotion

- You can elaborate by adding vivid, precise **words to show emotion.**
- Adjectives can show emotion: He was *furious.* He was *annoyed.*
- Adverbs can show emotion: Clare paced *nervously.* Clare spoke *timidly.*
- Verbs can show emotion: They *waltzed* down the street. They *trudged* down the street.

Directions: Write a sentence about each scene below. Use vivid, precise words that show emotions. Use the words from the box as ideas for your sentences. **Answers will vary.**

Verbs	Adjectives	Adverbs
howled	worried	excitedly
stomped	terrified	hurriedly
ripped	frantic	worriedly
celebrated	astonished	cautiously

1. The mail arrives. Judy has a letter. **Judy excitedly ripped open the letter.**

2. Raul runs. He misses the bus. **A frantic Raul raced hurriedly for the bus, but he missed it.**

3. The poster contest winner is announced. Oliver wins. **Astonished and surprised, Oliver celebrated winning the poster contest.**

4. The toddler falls off of the swing. She is upset. **The terrified toddler howled when she fell off the swing.**

5. A puppy is lost. The owner is looking for it. **The worried owner hunted frantically for the lost puppy.**

6. Jack hears a noise in the old house. He investigates. **Jack cautiously searched the old house to find the cause of the frightening noise.**

Notes for Home: Your child has been learning to use vivid, precise words to show emotions. ***Home Activity:*** Ask your child to suggest an angry word, a sad word, and a happy word to use in place of the word *said.*

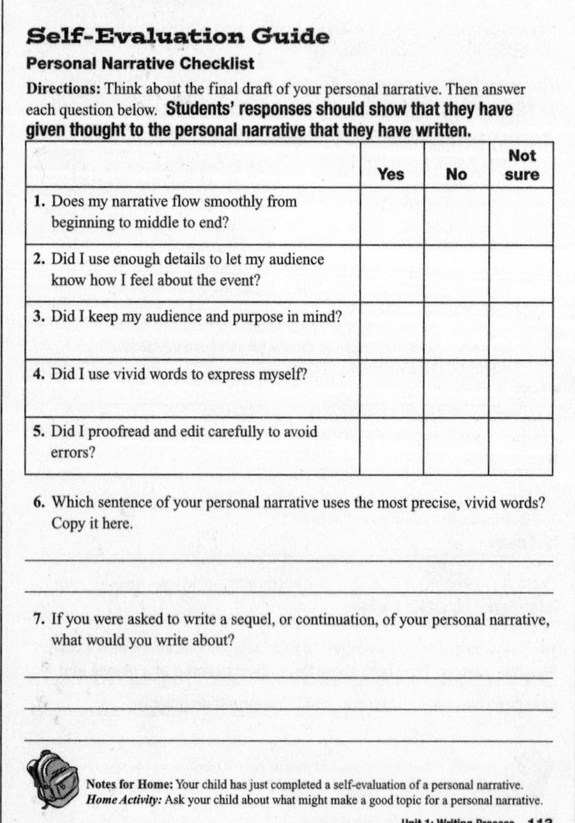

Name________________________________

Self-Evaluation Guide

Personal Narrative Checklist

Directions: Think about the final draft of your personal narrative. Then answer each question below. **Students' responses should show that they have given thought to the personal narrative that they have written.**

	Yes	No	Not sure
1. Does my narrative flow smoothly from beginning to middle to end?			
2. Did I use enough details to let my audience know how I feel about the event?			
3. Did I keep my audience and purpose in mind?			
4. Did I use vivid words to express myself?			
5. Did I proofread and edit carefully to avoid errors?			

6. Which sentence of your personal narrative uses the most precise, vivid words? Copy it here.

7. If you were asked to write a sequel, or continuation, of your personal narrative, what would you write about?

Notes for Home: Your child has just completed a self-evaluation of a personal narrative. ***Home Activity:*** Ask your child about what might make a good topic for a personal narrative.

Name________________________________

Visualizing

- To **visualize** means to form a picture in your mind as you read.
- As you read, look for details that tell how things look, smell, sound, taste, and feel.

Directions: Reread "Caught in the Kitchen." Then complete the web. Write details from the story that help you picture the characters and setting.
Possible answers given.

"Caught in the Kitchen"

Gertrude and Omeletta
1. **look like ghosts**
2. **sugar-coated**
3. **look like two speeding blobs of cotton**

Countertop
4. **dripping with streams of cream**

Kitchen
5. **white woodwork**

Notes for Home: Your child pictured events and characters in his or her mind while reading. ***Home Activity:*** Ask your child to visualize a favorite place. Invite him or her to tell you sights, smells, sounds, tastes, and sensations associated with that place.

Practice Book 4.2, p. 52

Name______________________________

from The Cricket in Times Square

Vocabulary

Directions: Choose the word from the box that best completes each sentence. Write the word on the line to the left.

Check the Words You Know

- _ chirp
- _ furiously
- _ melody
- _ occasion
- _ railroad
- _ subway
- _ traffic
- _ venturing

occasion 1. It is always a special _____ when my family goes to the city.

railroad 2. We take the train into the city because the _____ station is close by.

subway 3. Once we're in the city, we usually travel by underground _____.

traffic 4. Traveling underground gets us where we want to go faster than trying to drive through heavy _____.

chirp 5. Once, when we were at a concert in the park, I heard a cricket _____.

melody 6. It wasn't exactly singing a _____, but it sounded nice anyway.

Directions: Circle the word that has the same or nearly the same meaning as the first word in each group.

7. melody	words	(tune)	ringing
8. furiously	(wildly)	softly	lightly
9. chirp	bark	(tweet)	growl
10. venturing	frying	(risking)	staying

Write a Letter

On a separate sheet of paper, write a letter to a friend about a trip to a city. Use as many vocabulary words as you can.

Students' letters should have a friendly tone and use vocabulary words correctly.

Notes for Home: Your child identified and used new vocabulary from *The Cricket in Times Square. **Home Activity:*** With your child, make a list of imaginary, fun trips and describe how you would travel. Use the vocabulary words, such as *railroad* or *subway,* in your planning.

Practice Book 4.2, p. 53

Name______________________________

from The Cricket in Times Square

Visualizing

- **Visualizing** means creating a picture or pictures in your mind as you read.
- If you have trouble visualizing, you may want to reread parts of the story.

Directions: Reread about Tucker Mouse in *The Cricket in Times Square.* Then answer the questions below. Think about what it says in the story to help you visualize.

Tucker Mouse had been watching the Bellinis and listening to what they said. Next to scrounging, eavesdropping on human beings was what he enjoyed most. That was one of the reasons he lived in the Times Square subway station. As soon as the family disappeared, he darted out across the floor and scooted up to the newsstand. At one side the boards had separated and there was a wide space he could jump through. He'd been in a few times before—just exploring. For a moment he stood under the three legged stool, letting his eyes get used to the darkness. Then he jumped up on it.

1. Where is Tucker at the very beginning of the passage? How do you know?
Tucker is in a safe, hidden place—probably his mouse hole.

2. Where does Tucker go when the family leaves? Is he moving quickly or slowly?
He goes up to the newsstand. He moves quickly. He "darted" and "scooted."

3. How does Tucker get into the newsstand? Is it difficult or easy? Explain.
He goes through a wide space. It is easy. He could "jump through."

4. Is it easy or hard for Tucker to see? How do you know?
It is hard for Tucker to see. His eyes have to "get used to the darkness."

5. Pick another scene from the story. On a separate sheet of paper, tell what mental pictures you have as you read. Give examples of words or details that help you visualize the scene. **Answers will vary. Check that students include descriptive words or details.**

Notes for Home: Your child has read a story and used story details to visualize it by creating a mental picture of the story. ***Home Activity:*** With your child, look at a descriptive passage in a favorite book or story. Invite your child to tell you what he or she imagines while reading.

Practice Book 4.2, p. 55

Name______________________________

from The Cricket in Times Square

Selection Test

Directions: Choose the best answer to each item. Mark the letter for the answer you have chosen.

Part 1: Vocabulary

Find the answer choice that means about the same as the underlined word in each sentence.

1. The boys worked <u>furiously</u>.
   - A. without much interest
   - B. in a slow, careful way
   - **(C.) quickly and wildly**
   - D. in a cheerful way

2. The <u>chirp</u> came from inside that box.
   - **(F.) short sharp sound**
   - G. beat of a drum
   - H. loud flapping sound
   - J. low moan

3. The children were <u>venturing</u> into the woods.
   - A. shouting or calling
   - **(B.) daring to go**
   - C. hiking fast
   - D. staring

4. I have heard that <u>melody</u> before.
   - F. idea
   - G. joke or funny story
   - **(H.) tune**
   - J. signal or message

5. Everyone was there for the <u>occasion</u>.
   - A. talk or discussion
   - **(B.) special event**
   - C. lesson or class
   - D. small meal

6. We met at the <u>railroad</u> station.
   - F. taxi
   - G. police
   - H. bus
   - **(J.) train**

7. Watch out for the <u>traffic</u>.
   - **(A.) cars and buses moving along streets**
   - B. rules of safe driving
   - C. signs for drivers on highways
   - D. rest stop for travelers

8. We decided to take the <u>subway</u>.
   - F. ship that travels under water
   - G. bridge over a city street
   - **(H.) underground electric train**
   - J. train that travels at night

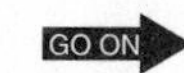

Practice Book 4.2, p. 56

Name______________________________

from The Cricket in Times Square

Part 2: Comprehension

Use what you know about the story to answer each item.

9. At the beginning of the story, Tucker Mouse is in a—
   - **(A.) subway station.**
   - B. tree stump.
   - C. bus station.
   - D. city apartment.

10. What did Tucker Mouse give Chester to eat?
    - F. roast beef
    - **(G.) liverwurst**
    - H. eggs
    - J. chocolate

11. At the beginning of the story, how did Chester feel about being in New York?
    - A. excited and amazed
    - B. bored and sleepy
    - C. surprised and glad
    - **(D.) nervous and uncomfortable**

12. Which words match your mental picture of Chester's journey inside the picnic basket?
    - **(F.) dark and cramped**
    - G. quiet and smooth
    - H. cozy and comfortable
    - J. smelly and dirty

13. Which detail from the story helps create a mental picture of New York City at night?
    - A. "And there he gasped, holding his breath and crouching against the cement."
    - B. "They were standing at one corner of the Times building."
    - **(C.) "Above the cricket, towers that seemed like mountains of light rose up into the night sky."**
    - D. "'Well—it's—it's quite something,' Chester stuttered."

14. What was the luckiest thing that Chester did in this story?
    - F. hopping into a picnic basket
    - G. riding in a subway
    - **(H.) meeting Tucker Mouse**
    - J. climbing up the pipe

15. At the end of the story, Chester has probably decided to—
    - A. move to New York for good.
    - B. find a way to escape from Tucker Mouse and Harry Cat.
    - C. return to Connecticut right away.
    - **(D.) let his new friends show him New York for a little while.**

Name

from The Cricket in Times Square

Visualizing

- To **visualize** means to create a picture or pictures in your mind as you read.
- If you have trouble visualizing, you may want to reread parts of the story.

Directions: Read the story below.

Marvin and Melissa Mouse lived in a small hole behind the kitchen wall. Their hole was right behind the stove, so it was warm and cozy in winter.

Both Marvin and Melissa liked to be comfortable, so they had been careful about what they took to make their nest. Marvin had found some pieces of cloth from an old T-shirt. Melissa had found some cotton balls. The cloth and cotton balls made a nice, soft place to sleep.

Sometimes it was hard to find food, so Marvin and Melissa stored as much as they could. Marvin found scraps of cheese and bacon on the kitchen floor. Melissa brought in pieces of popcorn. They kept their food in a neat pile in the corner.

Marvin and Melissa were very happy in their little mousehole. Both of them thought they had the coziest, most comfortable house in the world!

Directions: Complete the table. Use descriptive words from the story and draw pictures of what you imagine Marvin and Melissa's home is like.

Visualize	What the Story Says	What You Picture in Your Mind
Their mouse hole	small hole behind the stove	
Their nest	1. **comfortable bed made of cloth and cotton balls**	2. **Check that students' drawings reflect story details.**
Their food	3. **store food in their hole in a neat pile**	4.
The characters	Marvin and Melissa were very happy in their mouse hole.	5.

Notes for Home: Your child has read a story and used story details to create a mental picture of what is being described. ***Home Activity:*** Name one of your child's favorite places. Ask your child to visualize, or imagine, the place. Then invite him or her to tell you more about it.

Practice Book 4.2, p. 57

Name

from The Cricket in Times Square

Making Judgments

REVIEW

Directions: Read the story. Then read each question about the story. Choose the best answer to each question. Mark the letter for the answer you have chosen.

The Best Place to Live

Maria lives in the big city of Chicago. Jade lives in a little town called Gladstone. Maria says that Chicago is the best place to live in the whole world. Jade says that nobody should live in a big city because small towns are best!

When Maria went to visit Jade, Jade invited all her friends to meet Maria.

When Jade visited Maria, Maria took her to the top of Chicago's tallest building. Jade felt scared being so high up, so they went down right away. Then Jade started to have a good time. She began to think that big cities might be just as nice as small towns.

Maria wants to bring Jade back to the tall building again. She hopes they go there before it's time for Jade to leave.

1. A word that describes how Maria and Jade feel about where they live is—
   - **A.** embarrassed.
   - **(B.)** proud.
   - **C.** bored.
   - **D.** afraid.
2. When Jade invited all her friends to meet Maria, she was probably trying to make Maria feel—
   - **F.** lonely.
   - **(G.)** welcome.
   - **H.** confused.
   - **J.** angry.
3. When Maria took Jade to the top of Chicago's tallest building, she probably wanted Jade to feel—
   - **A.** scared.
   - **B.** sick.
   - **(C.)** excited.
   - **D.** angry.
4. Jade changed her mind about big cities because she was—
   - **F.** lonely.
   - **G.** wishy-washy.
   - **H.** confused.
   - **(J.)** open-minded.
5. Maria wants Jade to go back to the building so that Jade will—
   - **A.** feel scared again.
   - **(B.)** like being at the top.
   - **C.** get sick.
   - **D.** like Maria more.

Notes for Home: Your child made judgments about characters in a short story. ***Home Activity:*** Invite your child to share times when someone was a good friend and when someone was not a good friend.

Name

from The Cricket in Times Square

Writing Across Texts

Directions: Consider some of the likenesses and differences among animal characters in the excerpt from *The Cricket in Times Square* and "The Country Mouse and the City Mouse." Then complete the table.

	Chester	Tucker	City Mouse	Country Mouse
Types of Animals	1. **cricket**	4. **mouse**	mouse	8. **mouse**
Where They Live	tree stump in Connecticut	5. **drainpipe in the subway station**	house in city	hole in country
What They Eat	2. **liverwurst and chocolate**	liverwurst	6. **fine feasts**	9. **moldy crusts and celery**
Problems They Face	3. **trapped in picnic basket**	convincing a friend to stay in New York City	7. **scary servants and dogs**	10. **starving**

Write a Compare/Contrast Paragraph

On a separate sheet of paper, compare and contrast two characters from the table above. Include information about the likenesses and differences between the two characters. **Paragraphs will vary. Check that students have included information about the two characters' likenesses and differences.**

Notes for Home: Your child combined and used information from more than one source. ***Home Activity:*** As you read a story or an article with your child, discuss how its ideas connect to other stories or articles. Encourage your child to compare and contrast the stories or articles.

Grammar Practice Book 4.2, p. 26

Name

from The Cricket in Times Square

Grammar: Subjects

REVIEW

Directions: Underline the complete subject in each sentence. Then circle each simple subject. (There may be more than one in a sentence.)

1. My (cousin) visited New York City last week.
2. The busy, noisy (streets) frightened Andrew.
3. The (traffic) moved too fast.
4. (Andrew) and his (brother) preferred to see New York from their hotel window.
5. (Andrew) became braver after a few days, however.

Directions: Add a complete subject to each group of words to make your own sentence. Write your sentence on the line. Then circle the simple subject.

Possible answers given.

6. can be a good place to live
   A busy (city) can be a good place to live.
7. would be a wonderful place to visit
   A small (farm) would be a wonderful place to visit.
8. can usually be found in a big city
   (Crowds) of people can usually be found in a big city.
9. might be hard to find in the city
   (Peace) and (quiet) might be hard to find in the city.
10. might not be very happy in a city
    A (horse) might not be very happy in a city.

Notes for Home: Your child identified and used subjects in sentences. ***Home Activity:*** Have your child identify the subjects of some sentences in a favorite book or magazine. Suggest that your child create new sentences using the same subjects.

Grammar Practice Book 4.2, p. 27

Name________________________

from The Cricket in Times Square

Grammar: Nouns

A **noun** is a word that names one or more people, places, or things.

Persons: Many actors and musicians live in the city.
Places: Many actors live in the city and the suburbs.
Things: Tall buildings are part of a city's skyline.

Directions: One noun in each sentence is underlined. Circle the other noun or nouns.

1. I grew up in the city, near the river.
2. We lived on the first floor of a tall building.
3. Cars and buses rolled past my window.
4. A doctor and a plumber lived in two apartments down the hall.
5. My family went to see a house in the country.
6. I didn't want to move, but my parents and my brother did.
7. We left the city and drove in a big van.
8. I had never smelled such clean air or seen so many cows.
9. I thought my parents had decided to become farmers.
10. Then I heard them talking on the phone about their new store.

Directions: One of the underlined words in each sentence is a noun. Circle that noun.

11. I suppose I could get used to open spaces.
12. One problem is that it's hard to meet other people.
13. You can't just wait by your door.
14. I don't want my best friend to be a cow!
15. Where will I find new human friends?

Notes for Home: Your child identified nouns. ***Home Activity:*** Have your child look around the house and write names and other nouns for as many people, places, and things as possible.

Grammar: Nouns 125

Grammar Practice Book 4.2, p. 28

Name________________________

from The Cricket in Times Square

Grammar: Nouns

Directions: Circle all the nouns in the following sentences.

1. I grew up in the country, surrounded by farms and woods.
2. The closest village was five miles away.
3. Every single day I saw the same buildings, animals, and trees.
4. Then a letter came from my cousin.
5. He begged me to visit him at his house.
6. I couldn't make up my mind because I had never been in the city.
7. It sounded like a rough, tough place.
8. What if I didn't get another chance?
9. I packed my best clothes, my toothbrush, and my umbrella.
10. I left under a bright, sunny sky.

Directions: Add a noun that makes sense to complete each sentence. Write the noun on the line to the left. **Possible answers given.**

puddle 11. A car splashed through a _____, drenching me.

way 12. That was not a good _____ to begin my visit!

bed 13. In my cousin's big house, I slept on a very soft _____.

mouse 14. Still, there wasn't a single _____ for a country cat to eat.

home 15. I was happy to scamper back to my _____.

Write a Tale

On a separate sheet of paper, write your own tale about going somewhere new and strange. Use nouns to describe whom and what you see.

Students should include a variety of nouns in their tales.

Notes for Home: Your child found nouns in some sentences and supplied nouns in others. ***Home Activity:*** Take a walk or a ride around your neighborhood. Have your child make a list of as many nouns as possible. Nouns may include places, names on signs, products in stores, and so forth.

126 Grammar: Nouns

Grammar Practice Book 4.2, p. 29

Name________________________

from The Cricket in Times Square

Grammar: Nouns

RETEACHING

The nouns are underlined. Write one noun to answer each question. **Possible answers given.**

1. Are you a boy or a girl? **girl** (person)
2. Do you like a town or a city better? **city** (place)
3. Do you write with a pen or a pencil? **pencil** (thing)

A **noun** names a person, place, or thing. It gives information.

Directions: Write the three nouns in each sentence.

1. The girl threw the ball to the boy.
   girl, ball, boy
2. Many students play sports at school.
   students, sports, school
3. That girl kicked the ball over the tree.
   girl, ball, tree
4. Lin was a player on our team.
   Lin, player, team
5. The teacher took the class to the playground.
   teacher, class, playground

Directions: Circle the nouns in each sentence.

6. Some athletes wear uniforms.
7. Many swimmers have red suits.
8. Sue belonged to a good team.
9. The crowd cheered the divers.
10. A student on the bench was tired.

Notes for Home: Your child identified nouns in sentences. ***Home Activity:*** Together, think of two categories. (For example: *sports; foods*) Have your child list as many nouns as possible that fit in each category.

Grammar: Nouns 127

Grammar Practice Book 4.2, p. 30

Name________________________

from The Cricket in Times Square

Grammar: Nouns

Directions: On the lines below, write the three nouns that are in each sentence.

1. Chicago is a city with many fine museums.
2. Those paintings on the wall have bright colors.
3. Some of the artists drew with pencils on paper.
4. The sketches hang in frames around the room.
5. The statue in the hall is made of marble.

1.	**Chicago**	**city**	**museums**
2.	**paintings**	**wall**	**colors**
3.	**artists**	**pencils**	**paper**
4.	**sketches**	**frames**	**room**
5.	**statue**	**hall**	**marble**

Directions: Change one noun in each sentence. Write the new sentence.

6. Jorge drew a picture of the fruit. **Possible answers given.**
   Jorge drew a picture of the vegetable.
7. The colors in the painting catch my eye.
   The colors in the shirt catch my eye.
8. The artist used strong lines in this drawing.
   The artist used strong lines in this sketch.
9. The photograph shows the view from the window.
   The photograph shows the view from the roof.

Write a Poem **Make sure that students use nouns in their poems.**

Write a poem about a painting or a statue you have seen. Write on a separate sheet of paper. Use nouns in your sentences.

Notes for Home: Your child identified and wrote nouns in sentences. ***Home Activity:*** Have your child write sentences describing a room in your home. Make sure he or she uses at least two nouns in each sentence.

128 Grammar: Nouns

Practice Book 4.2, p. 58

Name________________

from The Cricket in Times Square

Phonics: Diphthongs

Directions: Read the words in the box. Say the words to yourself. Listen to the vowel sounds. Some words have the vowel sound in **found.** Other words have the vowel sound in **boy.** Write each word in the correct column.

scrounge	enjoyed	down	pointed	about
house	voice	noise	town	boiled

found		boy	
1.	scrounge	6.	enjoyed
2.	house	7.	voice
3.	down	8.	noise
4.	town	9.	pointed
5.	about	10.	boiled

Directions: Read each sentence. Say the underlined word to yourself. Then read the words in ( ). Circle the word that has the same vowel sound as the underlined word.

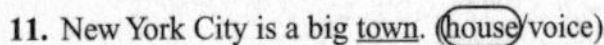

11. New York City is a big town. (house/voice)

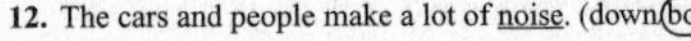

12. The cars and people make a lot of noise. (down/boy)

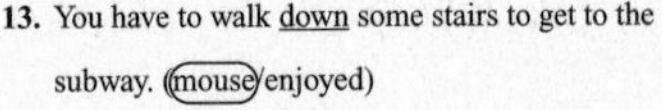

13. You have to walk down some stairs to get to the subway. (mouse/enjoyed)

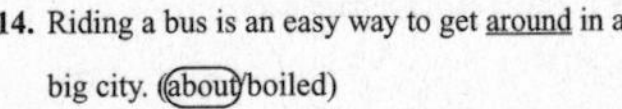

14. Riding a bus is an easy way to get around in a big city. (about/boiled)

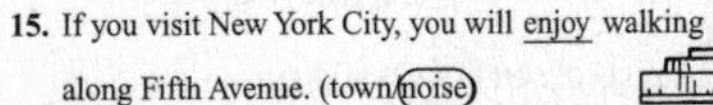

15. If you visit New York City, you will enjoy walking along Fifth Avenue. (town/noise)

Notes for Home: Your child distinguished different sounds and spellings for the vowel sounds in *town* and *noise*. ***Home Activity:*** Help your child list words with *oi* and *oy* that stand for the vowel sound in *noise* and with *ou* and *ow* that stand for the vowel sound in *town*.

Phonics: Diphthongs **129**

Spelling Workbook 4.2, p. 21

Name________________

from The Cricket in Times Square

Spelling: Vowel Sounds in *put* and *out*

Pretest Directions: Fold back the page along the dotted line. On the blanks, write the spelling words as they are dictated. When you have finished the test, unfold the page and check your words.

1. stood	1. She **stood** up tall.
2. took	2. Who **took** my book?
3. wood	3. Chop **wood** for the fire.
4. football	4. Throw me the **football**!
5. brook	5. Wade into the **brook**.
6. bush	6. The **bush** needs water.
7. July	7. **July** is hot in this city.
8. cushion	8. I need a seat **cushion**.
9. butcher	9. The **butcher** sells meat.
10. pudding	10. He served us **pudding**.
11. power	11. The **power** went out.
12. however	12. **However** did you find us?
13. shower	13. A **shower** of rain fell.
14. crowd	14. Push through the **crowd**.
15. loud	15. The music is too **loud**.
16. house	16. Welcome to my **house**.
17. outside	17. **Outside** it is windy.
18. mountain	18. The **mountain** has snow.
19. cloud	19. A **cloud** covered the sun.
20. proud	20. We are **proud** of her.

Notes for Home: Your child took a pretest on words with the vowel sounds in *put* and *out*. ***Home Activity:*** Help your child learn misspelled words before the final test. Your child should look at the word, say it, spell it aloud, and then spell it with eyes shut.

130 Spelling: Vowel Sounds in *put* and *out*

Spelling Workbook 4.2, p. 22

Name________________

from The Cricket in Times Square

Spelling: Vowel Sounds in *put* and *out*

Word List

stood	bush	power	house
took	July	however	outside
wood	cushion	shower	mountain
football	butcher	crowd	cloud
brook	pudding	loud	proud

Directions: Choose the word from the box that rhymes with each word. Use each word only one time. Write the word on the line.

1. mouse **house**
2. fountain **mountain**
3. flower **power (or shower)**
4. tower **shower (or power)**
5. book **brook (or took)**
6. look **took (or brook)**
7. good **stood (or wood)**
8. hood **wood (or stood)**

Directions: Write the word from the box that belongs in each group.

9. tree, shrub, **bush**
10. baseball, basketball, **football**
11. nature, outdoors, **outside**
12. but, nonetheless, **however**
13. May, June, **July**
14. baker, grocer, **butcher**
15. audience, mob, **crowd**
16. noisy, high-volume, **loud**
17. pillow, pad, **cushion**
18. fog, mist, **cloud**
19. pie, cake, **pudding**
20. happy, pleased, **proud**

Notes for Home: Your child spelled words with the vowel sounds in *put,* spelled *oo* and *u,* and *out,* spelled *ou* and *ow*. ***Home Activity:*** Make a list with your child of other words with these vowel sounds and spellings, such as *foot, soot, push,* and *mouse, how, now.*

Spelling: Vowel Sounds in *put* and *out* **131**

Spelling Workbook 4.2, p. 23

Name________________

from The Cricket in Times Square

Spelling: Vowel Sounds in *put* and *out*

Directions: Proofread this story about a city. Find five spelling mistakes. Use the proofreading marks to correct each mistake.

≡ Make a capital.
/ Make a small letter.
∧ Add something.
Take out something.
⊙ Add a period.
¶ Begin a new paragraph.

Odessa lived in a ho~~w~~se [u] on Orchard Street, between the bu[t]cher shop and the shoe store. On hot J~~oo~~ly [u] days, she and the other children on the block always went to the city swimming pool. "I like swimming better than taking a sho~~u~~er [w]!" Odessa thought. "I just wish there wasn't such a big cro~~u~~d [w] at the pool." However, that didn't stop her. It was more fun than the sprinkler!

Spelling Tip

The vowel sound in **put** can be spelled two different ways: **oo** in t**oo**k and **u** in b**u**sh. The vowel sound in **out** is also spelled two ways: **ow** in p**ow**er and **ou** in l**ou**d.

Word List

stood	power
took	however
wood	shower
football	crowd
brook	loud
bush	house
July	outside
cushion	mountain
butcher	cloud
pudding	proud

Write a Travel Brochure

Imagine that you are in charge of helping visitors to a city find sights to see. On a separate sheet of paper, write a travel brochure, a short pamphlet that tells visitors about something fun to do in a city. It could be your own city or a city you look up in a book or encyclopedia. Try to use at least four spelling words. **Answers will vary, but each brochure should include at least four spelling words.**

Notes for Home: Your child spelled words with the vowel sounds in *put,* spelled *oo* and *u,* and *out,* spelled *ou* and *ow*. ***Home Activity:*** Say a word with one of the two vowel sounds, like *loud* or *wood.* Ask your child to find as many rhymes for that word as possible.

132 Spelling: Vowel Sounds in *put* and *out*

Spelling Workbook 4.2, p. 24

Name__________

from The Cricket in Times Square

Spelling: Vowel Sounds in *put* and *out*

REVIEW

Word List				
stood	brook	butcher	shower	outside
took	bush	pudding	crowd	mountain
wood	July	power	loud	cloud
football	cushion	however	house	proud

Directions: Choose the word from the box that has the same or nearly the same meaning as each word or words below. Write the word on the line.

1. noisy **loud**
2. outdoors **outside**
3. seventh month **July**
4. strength **power**
5. pillow **cushion**
6. but **however**
7. creek **brook**
8. shrub **bush**
9. lumber **wood**
10. a huge hill **mountain**

Directions: Choose the word from the box that best completes each sentence. Write the word on the line to the left.

stood 11. Ana _______ in front of the department store.

football 12. In the window was a TV showing the _______ game.

cloud 13. It was a great day for the game, not a _______ in the sky.

crowd 14. There was a big _______ of people watching.

butcher 15. But Ana had to go buy meat at the _______ shop.

took 16. If she _______ too long, dinner would be late.

house 17. Then she went back home to her _______.

pudding 18. Her mother had made chocolate _______ for dessert.

proud 19. "Good job!" her mother said, "I'm _______ of you."

shower 20. Since she was dirty, Ana went to take a _______.

Notes for Home: Your child spelled words with the vowel sounds in *put*, spelled *oo* and *u*, and *out*, spelled *ou* and *ow*. ***Home Activity:*** Write *put* and *out* on separate sheets of paper. Encourage your child to add words to each sheet that have the same vowel sound.

Practice Book 4.2, p. 59

Name__________

from The Cricket in Times Square

Newspapers/Magazines/Periodicals

Newspapers are published daily or weekly and contain news, advertisements, feature stories, editorials, and other useful, current information.

Directions: Read the front page headlines of these newspapers. Use the information to answer the questions that follow.

1. Would you expect to find an article on how to make and use skateboards in the *New York City Business News Today?* Explain.
Possible answer: No, it is unlikely that a story about making and using skateboards would be in a business paper.

2. Is the headline for *The New York City Daily Reporter* the beginning of a news story, an editorial, or an advertisement?
a news story

3. A well-known actor is coming to New York City to film a movie. Which paper is most likely to cover this story?
The New York Entertainment News

4. Why are newspapers helpful sources of information? **Possible answer: Newspapers give current information.**

5. Would you use last week's newspaper to find out about the original construction of Times Square? Explain.
Possible answer: No, last week's newspaper would probably not have information on something that happened long ago.

Practice Book 4.2, p. 60

Name__________

from The Cricket in Times Square

Magazines, also called **periodicals,** are published at set intervals (weekly, monthly, quarterly, and so on). They may contain news articles, opinion columns, advertisements, cartoons, reports, and other current information. They often focus on a particular subject. The name of the magazine will usually tell you what subject is covered.

Directions: Use information from the magazine covers here to answer the questions that follow.

6. Which magazine might have useful information about baseball?
New York Sports Magazine

7. Will you find stories about snakes in *Dogs & Cats?* Explain. **No, the name tells you it is just about dogs and cats.**

8. Which magazine will tell you about theater shows?
Broadway Bonanza

9. If you are doing a report on nutrition and want to find some healthful snacks to suggest, what magazine might have an article of interest?
New York Sports Magazine

10. If you needed to find out about a concert that took place in Central Park yesterday, would you look in a newspaper or a magazine? Explain.
Possible answer: A newspaper published daily is more likely to have information about an event that happened yesterday than a magazine.

Notes for Home: Your child learned about using newspapers and magazines as resources. ***Home Activity:*** Look at newspapers and magazines together. What does the name of the publication tell you? Use headlines or a table of contents to scan for articles of interest.

Practice Book 4.2, p. 61

Name__________

A Big-City Dream

Cause and Effect

- A **cause** is why something happened. An **effect** is what happened.
- Sometimes a cause can have more than one effect.
- Sometimes there are clue words like *because, so, if, then,* or *since* to help you figure out what happened and why.

Cause → Effect

Directions: Reread "Super Cooper Scoopers." Then complete the table. Write the effect or effects for each cause given.

Cause (Why did it happen?)	Effect (What happened?)
Because the creek was dirty,	1. **salmon stopped coming to Longfellow Creek.**
	2. **salmon had nowhere to lay their eggs.**
	3. **students and teachers started a super cleanup.**
Because garbage gets ripped apart in creeks and spreads,	4. **the kids had to use nets and shovels to get trash out of the creek.**
Because the creek is now clean,	5. **salmon are swimming in the creek again.**

Notes for Home: Your child read a news article and explained the effects of events. ***Home Activity:*** Talk about a recent happy family event, such as a pleasant dinner together or a special trip. Help your child identify the reasons that caused the event to be so enjoyable.

Practice Book 4.2, p. 62

Name______________ A Big-City Dream

Vocabulary

Directions: Choose the word from the box that best completes each sentence. Write the word on the line to the left.

Check the Words You Know
- __ blisters
- __ catalog
- __ celebrate
- __ impressed
- __ padlock

catalog 1. The garden _____ arrived in the mail yesterday.

impressed 2. We were _____ by how many seeds and plants it showed.

blisters 3. When we shovel dirt in the garden, we'll wear gloves so we don't get _____ on our hands.

celebrate 4. We will _____ our beautiful garden by having a garden party when we're done.

padlock 5. We will have to remember to put a _____ on the gate to keep our dogs out of the garden.

Directions: Choose the word from the box that best matches each clue. Write the letters of the word on the blanks. The boxed letters spell something found near a garden.

6. illustrated list 6. c a t a l o [g]

7. have a party 7. c e l e b [r] a t e

8. lock you can remove 8. p [a] d l o c k

9. sores on your skin 9. b l i [s] t e r s

10. influenced deeply 10. i m p r e [s] s e d

Something found near a garden: g r a s s

Write Instructions

On a separate sheet of paper, give instructions for growing flowers or vegetables. Use as many of the vocabulary words as you can. **Students' instructions should use vocabulary words correctly.**

Notes for Home: Your child identified and used vocabulary words from "A Big-City Dream." ***Home Activity:*** Create a picture catalog with your child. It can show flowers, vegetables, or any items that your child can identify. Write a caption for each picture drawn.

Practice Book 4.2, p. 63

Name______________ A Big-City Dream

Cause and Effect

- A **cause** is why something happens. An **effect** is what happens.
- A cause may have more than one effect. An effect may have more than one cause.
- Sometimes a clue word such as *because* or *since* signals a cause-effect relationship. Sometimes there is no clue word.

Directions: Reread what happens in "A Big-City Dream" when Rosie appears. Then answer the questions below. Think about what it says in the story to help you identify causes and effects.

Lots of people walk past. Most of them don't even notice what we're doing. And nobody offers to help.

Then, all of the sudden, I see Rosie and her mom turn the corner. My heart rises straight up in my chest.

Yay! I want to shout. You're coming after all!

I wipe my sweaty face on my sleeves. I get ready to run over and open the gate extra wide to let her in. But Rosie doesn't even look at me. My heart falls down, hard, when she walks right past without even turning her head.

1. What causes the narrator's heart to rise "straight up in her chest"?
She is happy that Rosie is coming.

2. Why does the narrator want to shout "Yay! You're coming after all!"
She thought Rosie wasn't coming, and no one else was offering to help.

3. Why do you think Rosie walks right past "without even turning her head"?
Possible answer: Rosie is still angry at the narrator.

4. How does the narrator feel when Rosie walks past her? How do you know?
She is very disappointed. The narrator's "heart falls down, hard."

5. On a separate sheet of paper, tell two things that cause the narrator to feel happy and two things that cause her to feel sad. **Check that students support their answers.**

Notes for Home: Your child has read a story and used story details to understand cause and effect. ***Home Activity:*** Play a cause and effect game with your child. You name a cause *(It started to rain.)* and invite your child to name an effect *(We got our umbrellas.)*.

Practice Book 4.2, p. 65

Name______________ A Big-City Dream

Selection Test

Directions: Choose the best answer to each item. Mark the letter for the answer you have chosen.

Part 1: Vocabulary

Find the answer choice that means the same as the underlined word in each sentence.

1. We will need a padlock.
   - A. area enclosed with a fence
   - B. gardening tool
   - (C) lock that can be put on and removed
   - D. set of keys

2. I noticed Nell's blisters.
   - (F) sores on the skin
   - G. small bandages
   - H. rips or tears in clothing
   - J. deep wrinkles

3. Mike looked at the catalog.
   - A. finished project
   - B. list of jobs to be done
   - C. people working together
   - (D) book of things for sale

4. The teacher was impressed.
   - (F) strongly affected
   - G. treated in a mean way
   - H. remembered with fondness
   - J. entertained or amused

5. The parents and children will celebrate together.
   - A. solve a problem by talking
   - (B) have activities for a special day
   - C. share work equally
   - D. learn new skills

Part 2: Comprehension

Use what you know about the story to answer each item.

6. On Saturday morning, Luz hurried to meet—
   - (F) Ms. Kline.
   - G. Papi.
   - H. Rosie.
   - J. Mami.

7. When Luz got to the corner on the first day, the first thing she looked for was—
   - A. Rosie.
   - B. the Green Giants.
   - (C) the red tulip.
   - D. a rake.

8. Rosie probably did not help Luz because—
   - F. she was too busy.
   - G. her mother would not let her.
   - (H) she was upset with Luz.
   - J. she didn't have work clothes.

GO ON

Practice Book 4.2, p. 66

Name______________ A Big-City Dream

9. Luz worked without complaining because she—
   - A. was so happy with the way the lot looked.
   - B. needed the exercise.
   - C. did not want to be scolded.
   - (D) wanted to show Ms. Kline that she could do the job.

10. How did Luz feel about the Dream Garden at the end of the first day?
    - (F) not willing to give up on it
    - G. relieved that it was almost done
    - H. ready to give up
    - J. happy to have so much help

11. What happened at the lot just before Ms. Kline came back to check Luz's progress?
    - A. Luz saw Rosie walk by.
    - B. Someone planted a tulip.
    - C. The neighbors had a party.
    - (D) Someone dumped garbage.

12. Which sentence shows how the neighbors felt about Luz when she gave Ms. Kline a dollar?
    - F. "I figure lots of people will stop by and help."
    - (G) "Everybody crowds around, shaking my hands and clapping me on the back."
    - H. "Ms. Kline sounds like she can hardly believe it."
    - J. "Everybody laughs, and the man looks a little confused."

13. The hardest part about getting the garden started was—
    - (A) cleaning up the trash.
    - B. ordering from the catalog.
    - C. planting seeds and trees.
    - D. finding water.

14. When did most people in this story become truly interested in helping with the garden?
    - F. on the first Saturday that Luz got started
    - G. when Ms. Kline warned Luz to find more help
    - (H) when someone dropped garbage in the cleaned lot
    - J. after the truck delivered the plants and supplies

15. Which is the best reason to think that the garden will be a success?
    - A. Officers Ramirez and Carter will go to the celebration.
    - B. Ali will let the group use his water.
    - C. Rosie didn't join the group.
    - (D) The people in the neighborhood believe in it.

Name ______________________ A Big-City Dream

Cause and Effect

- A **cause** is why something happens. An **effect** is what happens.
- A cause may have more than one effect. An effect may have more than one cause.
- Sometimes a clue word such as *because* or *since* signals a cause-effect relationship. Sometimes there is no clue word.

Directions: Read the story below.

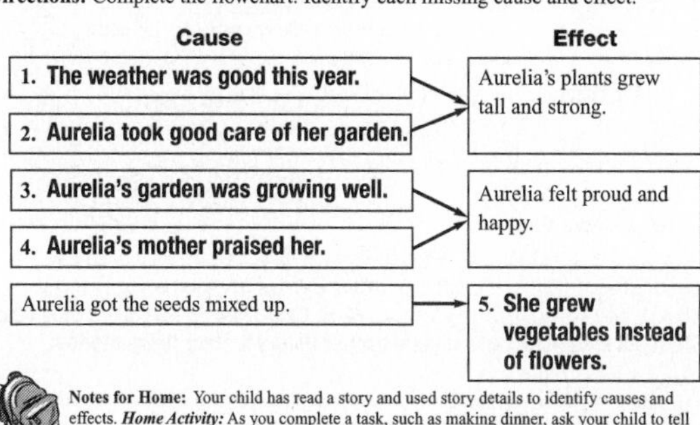
Aurelia was very excited. This year, she had her very first garden. Aurelia had decided to plant flowers. She had chosen and planted the seeds all by herself. The weather was good that year, and the plants grew tall and strong.

"You've done a good job, Aurelia," said her mother. "Because you have taken good care of your garden, you have three rows of beautiful, healthy plants."

Aurelia felt proud when she heard her mother's praise. She was glad her garden was growing so well. Then she looked more closely at her plants. What she saw made her feel very upset.

"Mama!" she cried. "I don't see any flowers blooming. In fact, *my* plants look just like *your* plants." She pointed to some feathery leaves growing in her mother's garden—and in Aurelia's garden too.

Aurelia's mother grabbed the leaves in Aurelia's garden and pulled up—a carrot! "Oh, no!" said Aurelia. "I must have gotten the seeds mixed up. I grew vegetables instead of flowers!"

Directions: Complete the flowchart. Identify each missing cause and effect.

Cause	Effect
1. **The weather was good this year.**	Aurelia's plants grew tall and strong.
2. **Aurelia took good care of her garden.**	
3. **Aurelia's garden was growing well.**	Aurelia felt proud and happy.
4. **Aurelia's mother praised her.**	
Aurelia got the seeds mixed up.	5. **She grew vegetables instead of flowers.**

Notes for Home: Your child has read a story and used story details to identify causes and effects. ***Home Activity:*** As you complete a task, such as making dinner, ask your child to tell what would happen if you did something differently, for example, used salt instead of sugar.

Name ______________________ A Big-City Dream

Compare and Contrast REVIEW

Directions: Read the story. Then read each question about the story. Choose the best answer to each question. Mark the letter for the answer you have chosen.

Flowers and Vegetables

A famous poet once said, "My love is like a red, red rose."

I enjoy that poem because I also think red roses are beautiful. That's why I grow them in my garden.

My brother, Jesse, doesn't like flowers. He grows vegetables in *his* garden—peas, carrots, lettuce, and string beans. Jesse says that vegetables growing in a garden are the most beautiful sight on Earth.

Both Jesse and I enjoy working in our gardens. Our favorite time is early in the morning, when the weather is cool and dew covers every leaf.

This summer, I will enter my roses in the flower show. Maybe I'll win first place! Jesse doesn't like to enter contests, but he's just as proud of his peas and carrots as I am of my roses.

1. In the line, "My love is like a red, red rose," the poet compares—
   - (A) love to a flower.
   - B. love to a garden.
   - C. a rose to a garden.
   - D. flowers to vegetables.
2. Both the narrator and the poet quoted—
   - (F) like roses.
   - G. don't like roses.
   - H. grow vegetable gardens.
   - J. write poems.
3. One thing the narrator and Jesse have in common is that they both—
   - A. like vegetables.
   - B. like flowers.
   - (C) grow gardens.
   - D. enter contests.
4. The clue word in the fourth paragraph that shows a comparison is—
   - F. favorite.
   - (G) both.
   - H. early.
   - J. gardens.
5. One word that describes both Jesse and the narrator is—
   - (A) hard-working.
   - B. lazy.
   - C. foolish.
   - D. cruel.

Notes for Home: Your child compared and contrasted elements in a short story. ***Home Activity:*** Think of two favorite activities that your child enjoys doing. Ask him or her to tell you some ways they are alike and ways that they are different.

Name ______________________ A Big-City Dream

Writing Across Texts

Directions: Refer to the excerpt from *The Cricket in Times Square* and "A Big-City Dream" to write sentences about the help Chester and Luz received from the other characters in the stories. **Possible answers given.**

Help for Luz
Mrs. Kline brings rakes, brooms, plastic bags, and work gloves.
1. **Papi measures, saws, and hammers benches.**
2. **Lorenzo helps pick up trash.**
3. **Mrs. Chapman and Ms. Kline help Luz measure the flower beds.**

Help for Chester
Tucker gives Chester a piece of liverwurst.
4. **Harry and Tucker show Chester how to get along in New York.**
5. **Tucker helps Chester understand how people talk in the city.**

Write a Comparative Essay

Write an essay in which you tell how the other characters in the stories helped Chester and Luz. Compare and contrast the kinds of help they received.
Essays will vary. Check that students' essays contain accurate information from the stories and include both likenesses and differences.

Notes for Home: Your child combined and used information from more than one source. ***Home Activity:*** As you read a story or an article with your child, discuss how its ideas connect to other stories or articles read. Encourage your child to make comparisons.

Name ______________________ A Big-City Dream

Grammar: Nouns REVIEW

Directions: Circle all the nouns in the following sentences.

1. My (family) lives on the fifteenth (floor) of a (building) in the (city).
2. (Visitors) to our (apartment) take the (elevator) to the top (floor).
3. Although our (dad) loves the (city), he misses his (garden).
4. My (father) appeared one (day) with huge (bags), tiny (plants), (shovels), and other (tools).
5. That amazing (man) had decided to grow (vegetables) on the (roof)!
6. My (mother) and (sister) helped him carry the (things) up the (stairs).
7. Our (farmer) poured (dirt) from the (bags) into big (pots) and set the (plants) into the (soil).
8. The (days) were hot and sunny, and we kept pouring (water) on our little (farm).
9. When the (summer) ended, we invited (friends) for a (dinner) of (beans), (tomatoes), and (broccoli).
10. Our (family) and (guests) finished our whole (crop) in just one (meal)!

Directions: Fill in each blank with a noun that makes sense in the sentence. Write each noun on the line to the left. **Possible answers given.**

flowers 11. If I had a garden, I would grow _____.

sun 12. A garden needs lots of _____ if the plants are to grow.

shovel 13. A _____ is a tool that gardeners are likely to use often.

supermarkets 14. City people usually get their food from _____.

vegetables 15. Some people, however, grow their own _____, even in the city.

Notes for Home: Your child identified nouns. ***Home Activity:*** Read a story to your child. Then go back and ask your child to pick out words that name people, places, and things.

Grammar Practice Book 4.2, p. 32

Name__________ A Big-City Dream

Grammar: Proper Nouns

A **proper noun** names a particular person, place, or thing. The words *Carmen, Florida,* and *April* are proper nouns. Begin proper nouns with capital letters. Nouns that are not proper nouns are called **common nouns.** The words *girl, state,* and *month* are common nouns.

Common nouns: We walked down the street.
At the corner, an officer was directing traffic.

Proper nouns: We walked down Third Street.
At the corner, Officer Ortiz was directing traffic.

Directions: Read the following paragraph. Each underlined noun has a number next to it. Write **C** if the underlined noun is a common noun. Write **P** if the underlined noun is a proper noun. Rewrite the proper nouns correctly.

Do you love **1.** nature but live in a **2.** city? If you look carefully, you'll see plenty of natural **3.** life. You don't need to go to **4.** yellowstone national park or the **5.** florida everglades. You don't need a large outdoor place like **6.** central park in **7.** new york city. On your own **8.** block there may be a **9.** crack in the **10.** sidewalk. Start there.

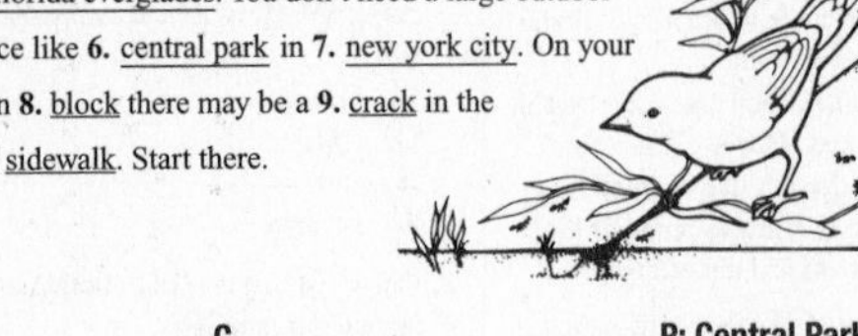

1. C
2. C
3. C
4. P; Yellowstone National Park
5. P; Florida Everglades
6. P; Central Park
7. P; New York City
8. C
9. C
10. C

Notes for Home: Your child identified common and proper nouns and used capital letters to write proper nouns. ***Home Activity:*** Ask your child to use common nouns to identify persons, places, and things in your home. Then ask your child to replace each noun with a proper noun.

Grammar Practice Book 4.2, p. 33

Name__________ A Big-City Dream

Grammar: Proper Nouns

Directions: Write a proper noun to replace the underlined words in the following sentences. **Possible answers given.**

Tonia 1. One day my friend and I had a real adventure.

Third Street 2. We were walking on our street.

Mr. Frank 3. We saw our neighbor and some other people standing around.

Officer Washington 4. Just then, a police officer drove up.

Ms. Perez 5. "What's this?" he asked one woman, who was holding something.

Prospect Park 6. "I was in the park and found this injured bird," she answered.

Sewell Animal Hospital 7. "I can't bring a bird all the way to the animal hospital," she continued.

Dr. Ross 8. "No, but a veterinarian has a clinic around the corner," I said.

National Savings Bank 9. "I have to be at a downtown building in ten minutes," the woman said. "Could someone else take the bird to the clinic?"

Mr. Rizzo 10. "We'll go," I told her. "Great!" said a man who had been listening to us.

Write a News Story

On a separate sheet of paper, write a news story about an interesting event that happened near where you live. Think about these reporter questions as you write: Who? What? When? Where? Why? and How? Use as many proper nouns as possible.
Students should include several proper nouns in their news stories.

Notes for Home: Your child substituted proper nouns for common nouns. ***Home Activity:*** Encourage your child to tell you about the day's events, substituting proper nouns *(Jefferson Elementary School)* for common nouns *(school).*

Grammar Practice Book 4.2, p. 34

Name__________ A Big-City Dream

Grammar: Proper Nouns RETEACHING

Match the nouns. Draw a line from a common noun to the proper noun that matches it.

Common Noun	Proper Noun
1. man	Kennedy Parkway
2. country	George Washington
3. road	United States

A **common noun** names any of a kind or group of persons, places, or things. A **proper noun** names a particular person, place, or thing. Each important word in a proper noun begins with a capital letter.

Directions: Write each underlined noun in the correct column.

Laura Salerno visited her cousins in Brooklyn. The whole family rode a boat around Manhattan. They met some Italians there. Laura liked her trip.

Common Nouns	Proper Nouns
1. cousins	5. Laura Salerno
2. family	6. Brooklyn
3. boat	7. Manhattan
4. trip	8. Italians

Directions: Circle the proper noun or proper nouns in each sentence.

9. The (Statue of Liberty) has many visitors.
10. The statue is on (Liberty Island) in (New York Harbor).
11. (France) gave this gift to the (United States).
12. People can climb it for a view of (New York).

Notes for Home: Your child identified proper nouns. ***Home Activity:*** List familiar places or people. *(park, store, neighbor, friend)* Have your child write a proper noun for each noun you wrote. *(Lee Park, Northbrook Foods, Mrs. Washbein, Lizzie Webster)*

Grammar Practice Book 4.2, p. 35

Name__________ A Big-City Dream

Grammar: Proper Nouns

Possible answers given.

Directions: Write a proper noun for each common noun. Use capital letters.

1. a state Hawaii
2. a neighbor Mrs. J. Lee
3. a day Saturday
4. a doctor Dr. Smith
5. a river Mississippi River
6. a dog Sparky
7. a date July 4
8. a city Asheville

Directions: Write each sentence. Replace the underlined noun with a proper noun. **Possible answers given.**

9. Jack sails on a lake in Ohio.
Jack sails on Lake Erie in Ohio.
10. Jack also fishes in a lake.
Jack also fishes in Lake Huron.
11. A man sails with Jack on weekends.
Captain Joe sails with Jack on weekends.
12. Jack wants to sail on an ocean someday.
Jack wants to sail on the Atlantic Ocean someday.
13. Mrs. Wright will sail there on a holiday.
Mrs. Wright will sail there on Memorial Day.

Write a List of Proper Nouns

On a separate sheet of paper, write a list of proper nouns. Write the names of a river, a president, a date, a doctor, a park, and a country.
Make sure students correctly capitalize proper nouns on their lists.

Notes for Home: Your child identified and wrote proper nouns in sentences. ***Home Activity:*** Have your child write a description of your neighborhood, using at least five proper nouns.

Practice Book 4.2, p. 68
Name____________________ **A Big-City Dream**

Phonics: Consonant Sounds for *c* and *g*

Directions: Read the words in each box. Follow the instructions below.

celebrate community nice panic

1. Write the two words with the **hard-c** sound like **cat.**
   community, **panic**
2. Write the two words with the **soft-c** sound like **cell.**
   celebrate, **nice**

practice convince

3. Write the part of each word that has the **hard-c sound.**
   prac, **con**
4. Write the part of each word that has the **soft-c sound.**
   tice, **vince**

giant garden vegetable big

5. Write the two words with the **hard-g** sound like **get.**
   garden, **big**
6. Write the two words with the **soft-g** sound like **gym.**
   giant, **vegetable**

garage garbage

7. Write the part of each word that has the **hard-g** sound.
   ga, **gar**
8. Write the part of each word that has the **soft-g** sound.
   rage, **bage**

grocery courage

9. Write the part of each word that has a hard consonant sound.
   gro, **cour**
10. Write the part of each word that has a soft consonant sound.
   cery, **age**

Notes for Home: Your child practiced distinguishing between hard and soft sounds for the letters *c* and *g*. ***Home Activity:*** Play a game of "I Spy." For example, say, "I spy something that begins with a hard *c*, as in *cat*." Have your child find the object and say the name.

Spelling Workbook 4.2, p. 25
Name____________________ **A Big-City Dream**

Spelling: Including All the Letters

Pretest Directions: Fold back the page along the dotted line. On the blanks, write the spelling words as they are dictated. When you have finished the test, unfold the page and check your words.

1.	often	1.	We play here **often**.
2.	might	2.	He **might** visit us soon.
3.	known	3.	I wish I had **known** her!
4.	they	4.	**They** are riding bikes.
5.	remember	5.	Do you **remember** me?
6.	surprised	6.	We **surprised** them!
7.	caught	7.	Flora **caught** two fish.
8.	island	8.	The **island** is deserted.
9.	finally	9.	It **finally** stopped raining.
10.	really	10.	I **really** missed you.
11.	several	11.	**Several** friends came by.
12.	everyone	12.	Serve food to **everyone**.
13.	everybody	13.	**Everybody** brought games.
14.	interesting	14.	This story is **interesting**.
15.	swimming	15.	I go **swimming** in summer.
16.	camera	16.	The **camera** has film.
17.	December	17.	Will it snow in **December**?
18.	evening	18.	It will be **evening** soon.
19.	beginning	19.	Start at the **beginning**.
20.	February	20.	We leave in **February**.

Notes for Home: Your child took a pretest on words that have difficult letter combinations. ***Home Activity:*** Help your child learn misspelled words before the final test. Have your child divide misspelled words into parts (such as syllables) and concentrate on each part.

Spelling Workbook 4.2, p. 26
Name____________________ **A Big-City Dream**

Spelling: Including All the Letters

Word List

often	surprised	several	camera
might	caught	everyone	December
known	island	everybody	evening
they	finally	interesting	beginning
remember	really	swimming	February

Directions: Choose the words from the box that have three syllables. Write the words on the lines. **Order may vary.**

1. **remember**
2. **finally**
3. **really**
4. **several**
5. **everyone**
6. **camera**
7. **December**
8. **beginning**

Directions: Choose the word from the box that best matches each clue. Write the word on the line.

9. not boring **interesting**
10. moving through water **swimming**
11. second month **February**
12. early part of the night **evening**
13. land surrounded by water **island**
14. captured **caught**
15. astonished **surprised**
16. many times **often**
17. opposite of *nobody* **everybody**
18. understood **known**
19. possibly would **might**
20. a plural pronoun **they**

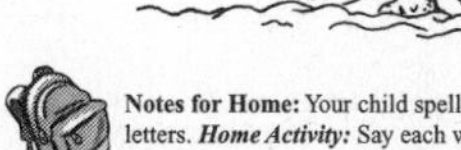

Notes for Home: Your child spelled words that are often misspelled by leaving out certain letters. ***Home Activity:*** Say each word syllable by syllable. Have your child write each word. Together, correct any misspellings.

Spelling Workbook 4.2, p. 27
Name____________________ **A Big-City Dream**

Spelling: Including All the Letters

Directions: Proofread this letter written to a pen pal. Find five spelling mistakes. Use the proofreading marks to correct each mistake.

Proofreading marks
≡ Make a capital.
/ Make a small letter.
∧ Add something.
Take out something.
⊙ Add a period.
¶ Begin a new paragraph.

Dear Richard,

Remember how I wrote you that I wanted my own garden? Well, I fin^al^ly have one! I'm real^l^y excited about it! There are sev^e^ral kinds of vegetables I'd like to plant there. Ev^e^rybody says that flowers are more int^e^resting, but I don't care—I like vegetables! Are you surprised?

Love,
Yoshi

Spelling Tip

Some words have more letters than you might expect. To spell these words, pronounce each syllable carefully.

Word List

often	several
might	everyone
known	everybody
they	interesting
remember	swimming
surprised	camera
caught	December
island	evening
finally	beginning
really	February

Write a Letter

Imagine you are Richard. On a separate sheet of paper, write a letter back that tells what you would grow in a garden. Use at least three spelling words in your letter.
Answers will vary, but each letter should include at least three spelling words.

Notes for Home: Your child spelled words that are often misspelled by leaving letters out. ***Home Activity:*** Write some of the words listed, leaving out some letters. Ask your child to be a letter detective who finds the missing letters and tells you what they are.

Spelling Workbook 4.2, p. 28
Name___________________ A Big-City Dream

Spelling: Including All the Letters

REVIEW

Word List

often	surprised	several	camera
might	caught	everyone	December
known	island	everybody	evening
they	finally	interesting	beginning
remember	really	swimming	February

Directions: Choose the word from the box that is the most opposite in meaning for each word below. Write the word on the line.

1. few **several**
2. ending **beginning**
3. morning **evening**
4. forget **remember**
5. no one **everyone**
6. nobody **everybody**
7. boring **interesting**
8. rarely **often**

Directions: Write the word from the box that belongs in each group.

9. actually, truly, **really**
10. she, he, **they**
11. unexpected, astonished, **surprised**
12. snorkeling, diving, **swimming**
13. at last, in conclusion, **finally**
14. may, could, **might**
15. October, November, **December**
16. captured, seized, **caught**
17. Valentine's Day, President's Day, **February**
18. photographs, film, **camera**
19. tropical, deserted, **island**
20. familiar, recognized, **known**

Notes for Home: Your child spelled words that are often misspelled by mispronouncing and then leaving out letters. ***Home Activity:*** Slowly sound out the syllables, or word parts, for each word while your child spells it. Discuss how saying words this way makes spelling them easier.

Spelling: Including All the Letters 155

Practice Book 4.2, p. 69
Name___________________ A Big-City Dream

Technology: Locate/Collect Information/Telephone Directory

A **telephone directory** lists phone numbers and addresses for individual people and businesses. The **white pages** list entries for individuals and businesses in alphabetical order. The **yellow pages** list entries for businesses and advertisements by category or type of business.

You can also find phone numbers and addresses in "yellow pages" on the Internet. You can search for businesses on the Internet by category, such as garden supplies.

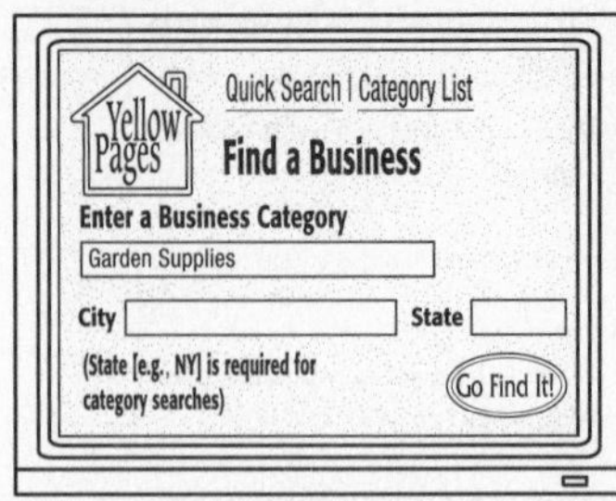

Directions: Write the category you would use to search the Internet for each store.

Possible answers given for questions 1–4.

toys 1. a store that sells games and jump ropes

grocery stores 2. a store that sells food

building materials 3. a store that sells windows, doors, and lumber

sporting goods 4. a store that sells baseball bats, basketballs, and sneakers

5. Look at the following categories. Write an **X** next to the category you would search to find a store that sells seeds, potting soil, and a spray to control weeds.

_____ Lawn Mowing Equipment

_____ Lawn and Garden Decorations

X Lawn and Garden Supplies

156 Research and Study Skills: Technology: Locate/Collect Information/Telephone Directory

Practice Book 4.2, p. 70
Name___________________ A Big-City Dream

When you choose a category on the Internet Yellow Pages, a listing is displayed. For gardening supplies, it might look like this:

Directions: Use the listings above to answer these questions.

6. You want to find out if a store sells what you are looking for without going there. What information could you use?
phone number
7. Which store is in Roxbury? **Scooper Gardening**
8. Which store is on Silver Rd.? **Greenfield Field and Grain**
9. On the Internet, you can click on underlined words to get more information. What do you think you will get when you click on "map"?
You would probably see a map that shows the store's location.
10. How is searching the Internet Yellow Pages similar to searching the yellow pages in a phone book?
Possible answer: You use categories to search for businesses in both kinds of yellow pages.

Notes for Home: Your child learned how to find a business on a yellow pages Web site. ***Home Activity:*** Ask your child to find a specific local store on a yellow pages Web site or in the yellow pages of a phone book.

Research and Study Skills: Technology: Locate/Collect Information/Telephone Directory 157

Practice Book 4.2, p. 71
Name___________________ I Love Guinea Pigs

Text Structure

- **Text structure** is the way a piece of writing is organized. The two main kinds of writing are fiction and nonfiction.
- **Fiction** tells stories of imaginary people and events. Events are often told in the order in which things happen.
- **Nonfiction** tells of real people and events or tells information about the real world. One way to organize nonfiction is to have a main idea followed by supporting details. Other ways to organize nonfiction are cause and effect, problem and solution, and comparison and contrast.

Directions: Reread "Your Best Friend." Then complete the table. Tell what kind of writing it is, list details from the piece, and determine how the piece is organized.
Possible details given.

Title	"Your Best Friend"
Fiction or Nonfiction?	1. **nonfiction**
1st Heading	2. **Wild Wolves**
Detail	3. **Thousands of years ago, some wolves settled with humans.**
Detail	4. **Dogs are related to wolves.**
2nd Heading	5. **Dogs Today**
Detail	6. **Dogs behave like wolves.**
Detail	7. **You are the leader of your dog's pack.**
3rd Heading	8. **Perfect Pals**
Detail	9. **Your dog will defend its home.**
Method of Organization	10. **main idea and supporting details**

Notes for Home: Your child read an article and identified text structure. ***Home Activity:*** Ask your child about some favorite books. Encourage him or her to identify text structure by telling you whether the material is fiction or nonfiction and by saying how it is organized.

160 Text Structure

Practice Book 4.2, p. 72

Name____________________ I Love Guinea Pigs

Vocabulary

Directions: Choose the word from the box that best completes each sentence. Write the word on the matching numbered line below.

Check the Words You Know
- __ boars
- __ fond
- __ gnawing
- __ sow
- __ varieties

There are many different **1.** _____ of pigs. Many people are **2.** _____ of the small ones because they make good pets. Unlike guinea pigs, real pigs aren't seen **3.** _____ on everything in sight. A mother pig is called a **4.** _____, and father pigs are called **5.** _____.

1. **varieties**
4. **sow**
2. **fond**
5. **boars**
3. **gnawing**

Directions: Choose the word from the box that best matches each clue. Write the word in the puzzle.

Down
6. kinds
7. female pig
9. liking

Across
8. male pigs
10. biting away

				6. v		
		7. s		a		
	8. b	o	a	r	s	
		w		i		
	9. f			e		
	o			t		
10. g	n	a	w	i	n	g
	d			e		
				s		

Write an Animal Care List

Imagine you are the proud owner of a guinea pig. On a separate sheet of paper, make a list of things you need to know to take care of your guinea pig. Use as many of the vocabulary words as you can. **Students may need to do some research before writing their lists. Students' lists should use vocabulary words correctly.**

Notes for Home: Your child has learned new vocabulary words from *I Love Guinea Pigs.* ***Home Activity:*** Talk with your child about the fun and responsibilities of having a pet. Encourage him or her to use the vocabulary words.

Practice Book 4.2, p. 73

Name____________________ I Love Guinea Pigs

Text Structure

- **Text structure** is the way a piece of writing is organized.
- Fiction tells stories of imaginary people and events. They are usually told in the order in which things happen. Nonfiction tells of real people and events or tells information about the real world. Some ways to organize nonfiction are cause and effect, problem and solution, or comparison and contrast.

Directions: Reread the part of *I Love Guinea Pigs* where the author explains why guinea pigs are "sensible animals." Then answer the questions below.

They don't like the cold, of course, or the damp, any more than you would, and they're not happy living in a poky little place, any more than you would be. But as long as they have a comfortable, warm, dry place to live, guinea pigs are as happy as can be.

They're hardy animals and don't often get sick. Properly cared for, they can live a long time.

I once had a crested sow named Zen. She lived two years with me and then eight more with one of my daughters. People's hair grows whiter as they age, but Zen's grew darker.

Guinea pigs need plenty of food. They love eating, just like you do. . . .

1. Is this text fiction or nonfiction? Tell why you think so.
Nonfiction. It tells facts about guinea pigs, which are real animals.

2. Name three ways that guinea pigs are compared to humans.
Like humans, guinea pigs don't like to be cold or damp, they don't like living in a small place, and they love eating.

3. Name one way that guinea pigs are contrasted to humans.
People's hair turns white as they age, but Zen's hair got darker.

4. Tell two things that make guinea pigs happy.
They are happy when they have a warm, dry place and when they eat.

5. On a separate sheet of paper, tell how the author organized the text. Give another example from the story of how he used this text structure. **Comparison and contrast; He compares guinea pigs to mice, rats, and squirrels.**

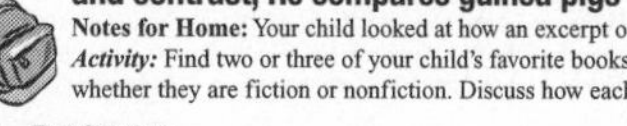

Notes for Home: Your child looked at how an excerpt of a larger text was organized. ***Home Activity:*** Find two or three of your child's favorite books and ask your child to tell you whether they are fiction or nonfiction. Discuss how each book is organized.

Practice Book 4.2, p. 75

Name____________________ I Love Guinea Pigs

Selection Test

Directions: Choose the best answer to each item. Mark the letter for the answer you have chosen.

Part 1: Vocabulary

Find the answer choice that means about the same as the underlined word in each sentence.

1. There are many <u>varieties</u> of cats.
   - A. problems or fears
   - B. habits or ways
   - C. favorite foods or treats
   - (D) kinds or sorts

2. Henry counted seven <u>boars</u>.
   - F. nests made by animals
   - (G) male pigs or hogs
   - H. sounds made by pigs
   - J. pens for small pets

3. The dog was <u>gnawing</u> on a box.
   - (A) biting and wearing away
   - B. burrowing into
   - C. batting or hitting lightly
   - D. sniffing at

4. Liam decided to take the <u>sow</u>.
   - F. smallest piglet in a litter
   - G. piglet born in the winter
   - (H) fully grown female pig
   - J. pig with several colors

5. The pet is <u>fond</u> of its owner.
   - A. free or without need
   - (B) having a liking for
   - C. growing tired or bored
   - D. seeming afraid

Part 2: Comprehension

Use what you know about the selection to answer each item.

6. Guinea pigs belong to the same family as—
   - F. horses.
   - G. humans.
   - H. pigs.
   - (J) mice.

7. The first guinea pigs came from—
   - A. Australia.
   - (B) South America.
   - C. Africa.
   - D. Asia.

8. The author thinks that guinea pigs are—
   - F. loud and active.
   - G. shy and nervous.
   - (H) chubby and cuddly.
   - J. fussy and messy.

9. How does the author know so much about guinea pigs?
   - (A) He had them as pets for much of his life.
   - B. He studied them in pet shops.
   - C. He read many books about guinea pigs.
   - D. He is an animal doctor.

GO ON

Practice Book 4.2, p. 76

Name____________________ I Love Guinea Pigs

10. Which sentence tells how this selection is written?
    - F. It explains how someone solved a problem.
    - (G) It gives facts and opinions.
    - H. It lists many events in the order they happened.
    - J. It describes imaginary people and animals.

11. A guinea pig will become friendly and tame if its owner—
    - (A) holds and pets it often.
    - B. keeps it in a cool, dry place.
    - C. lets it go outdoors often.
    - D. feeds it many different foods.

12. How were the guinea pigs named Beach Boy and King Arthur alike?
    - F. They were both a bright golden color.
    - G. They both lived to an old age.
    - (H) They were both buried in the yard.
    - J. They both loved dandelions and clover.

13. Most of the details given in this selection are used to—
    - A. compare baby and adult guinea pigs.
    - B. describe the author's favorite guinea pig.
    - C. explain how to feed a guinea pig that won't eat.
    - (D) tell what it is like having guinea pigs for pets.

14. Which detail is an opinion?
    - F. A guinea pig sow carries her litter for about seventy days.
    - G. The guinea pigs are born with their eyes open.
    - H. Their mouths are already filled with teeth.
    - (J) Newborn guinea pigs are a funny sight.

15. What does the author want you to remember most about guinea pigs?
    - A. how long they have been kept as pets
    - (B) how much pleasure they can give
    - C. how much they are like other rodents
    - D. how hard they are to care for

STOP

Name________________________ I Love Guinea Pigs

Text Structure

- **Text structure** is the way a piece of writing is organized.
- Fiction tells stories of imaginary people and events. They are usually told in the order in which things happen. Nonfiction tells of real people and events or tells information about the real world. Some ways to organize nonfiction are cause and effect, problem and solution, or comparison and contrast.

Directions: Read the passage below.

Which is a better pet—a fluffy rabbit or a colorful bird? Both rabbits and birds need food, water, a safe place to live, and exercise. They are both easy to take care of and are good pets.

A rabbit eats carrots, lettuce, and other green vegetables, as well as commercial rabbit food. It nibbles with its long front teeth. A bird eats birdseed of different kinds. You can watch it crack the seed with its beak and drop the husk.

Rabbits are furry and cuddly. You can take a rabbit out of the cage to hold and stroke it. You can even let it hop around. Birds' colorful feathers may be beautiful, but they aren't so cuddly. Birds fly around and dart quickly from place to place.

Rabbits are usually silent; you could say they are good listeners! Birds are noisier. Some birds talk or sing a lot during the day.

Now that you know all this, which pet would you choose?

Directions: List things that are true about only rabbits, things that are true about only birds, and the things that are true about both of them. Then tell whether this story is fiction or nonfiction.

Rabbits	Rabbits and Birds	Birds
are furry and cuddly	are easy to take care of	fly around quickly
1. **nibble food with their long front teeth**	2. **make good pets**	4. **crack and eat seeds with their beaks**
	3. **need food, water, safe place, and exercise**	

5. Is the passage fiction or nonfiction? **nonfiction**

Notes for Home: Your child has read a passage, identified whether it is fiction or nonfiction, and used a diagram to examine the way it is organized. *Home Activity:* Read a story together. Ask your child to tell you whether it is fiction or nonfiction and how it is organized.

Practice Book 4.2, p. 77

Name________________________ I Love Guinea Pigs

Fact and Opinion

REVIEW

Directions: Read the passage. Then read each question about the passage. Choose the best answer to each question. Mark the letter for the answer you have chosen.

Down with Cats!

Cats make terrible pets!

First of all, as everyone knows, cats are hunters. They are related to lions and tigers. Today's house cats hunt mice, birds, and lizards just the way big cats hunt bigger animals.

Some people think this is a good quality. But I definitely do not. I feel sorry for the mice that my brother's cat tries to catch. Of course, my brother's cat has never yet caught a single mouse. But someday I believe he might!

Finally, dogs are much nicer than cats. That is not just my opinion. It's a fact!

1. In the first sentence, the writer gives—
   - A. an order.
   - B. a question.
   - C. a statement of fact.
   - **(D)** a statement of opinion.
2. Which clue word in this sentence signals that it is an opinion? "Some people think this is a good quality."
   - **(F)** think
   - G. good
   - H. some
   - J. is
3. A statement from the story that cannot be proved true or false is—
   - A. cats are hunters.
   - B. they are related to lions and tigers.
   - **(C)** dogs are much nicer than cats.
   - D. house cats hunt mice, birds, and lizards.
4. The third paragraph includes—
   - F. only statements of fact.
   - **(G)** statements of both fact and opinion.
   - H. only statements of opinion.
   - J. statements of fact that cannot be proved.
5. Which is **not** a good way to prove that one of the facts is true or false?
   - A. Check an encyclopedia.
   - B. Check a book about animals.
   - **(C)** Ask a friend.
   - D. Ask an animal expert.

Notes for Home: Your child identified statements of opinions and facts in a passage. *Home Activity:* Ask your child to explain the difference between opinion and fact. Then take turns making statements about a subject, such as the weather, and identifying it as opinion or fact.

Name________________________ I Love Guinea Pigs

Writing Across Texts

Directions: Refer to *I Love Guinea Pigs* and the excerpt from *The Cricket in Times Square* to fill in the table below. Write the sentences about guinea pigs in the left column, and the sentences about mice in the right column. The sentences that apply to both animals should be written in each column.

They like to live in a pen on the grass.
They love to eat.
They can make purring sounds.
They have teeth for gnawing.
They are chubby.
They are very often messy.
They are usually skinny.
Their teeth keep growing.
They may live in drainpipes.

Possible answers given.

Guinea Pigs	Mice
1. **They love to eat.**	6. **They are very often messy.**
2. **They are chubby.**	7. **They are usually skinny.**
3. **They can make purring sounds.**	8. **They may live in drainpipes.**
4. **They like to live in a pen on the grass.**	9. **They have teeth for gnawing.**
5. **They have teeth for gnawing.**	10. **Their teeth keep growing.**

Write a Comparison/Contrast Essay

Think about what you learned about mice and guinea pigs in the excerpt from *The Cricket in Times Square* and *I Love Guinea Pigs.* On a separate sheet of paper, write an essay discussing the likenesses and differences between these animals. Use the table you created to help you. **Essays will vary. Check that students have used information from both stories and from the table.**

Notes for Home: Your child combined information from more than one source. *Home Activity:* As you read stories and articles, encourage your child to discuss the likenesses and differences between two things or characters.

Grammar Practice Book 4.2, p. 36

Name________________________ I Love Guinea Pigs

Grammar: Common and Proper Nouns

REVIEW

Directions: Read the nouns in the box. Write each noun in the correct column. Capitalize the proper nouns.

kangaroo	circus
debby's pet store	dr. ruiz
new england dog show	veterinarian
elephant	harold
puppy	reed animal hospital

Common Nouns	Proper Nouns
1. **kangaroo**	6. **Debby's Pet Store**
2. **elephant**	7. **New England Dog Show**
3. **puppy**	8. **Dr. Ruiz**
4. **circus**	9. **Harold**
5. **veterinarian**	10. **Reed Animal Hospital**

Directions: Replace the underlined words in each sentence with a proper noun. Write each proper noun on the line. **Possible answers given.**

Alfredo 11. I was surprised when <u>our neighbor</u> got a new pet.

Daisy 12. I was even more surprised when <u>the pet</u> turned out to be a little duckling.

Bedford Animal Shelter 13. Our neighbor got the duckling from the <u>animal shelter</u>.

Minerva Lake 14. Someone had found it quacking and alone near <u>the town lake</u>.

Shade Street 15. The duckling loved to visit people and soon learned to fly across <u>the street</u> to avoid cars.

Notes for Home: Your child identified and wrote common and proper nouns. *Home Activity:* Encourage your child to name people, animals, and places he or she knows, using common nouns first and then proper nouns.

Grammar Practice Book 4.2, p. 37

Name________________________ I Love Guinea Pigs

Grammar: Regular Plural Nouns

Nouns that name one person, place, or thing are **singular nouns. Plural nouns** name more than one person, place, or thing.

- Add **-s** to form the plural of most nouns.
  monkey/monkeys pig/pigs cat/cats snake/snakes
- Add **-es** to form the plural of nouns that end in **ch, sh, s, ss,** or **x.**
  bunch/bunches wish/wishes gas/gases fox/foxes glass/glasses
- To form the plural of nouns that end in a **consonant** and a **y,** change the **y** to **i** and add **-es.**
  penny/pennies baby/babies party/parties lady/ladies

Directions: Write the plural form of each underlined noun on the line.

friends 1. My friend says that I live in a zoo.

dogs 2. It all started with a stray dog.

puppies 3. Soon after she came to live with us, she had a puppy.

dishes 4. Yes, that means getting another animal dish.

hamsters 5. Then my friend Mel was moving to Mexico, so she gave me her hamster.

lizards 6. Next, my little brother wanted a lizard.

tadpoles 7. My sister brought home a tadpole from the lake.

frogs 8. Before long, it turned into a frog.

pigeons 9. My older brother decided to raise a racing pigeon.

ponies 10. "What's next?" my friend asked me. "A pony?"

Notes for Home: Your child added *-s* or *-es* to nouns to show more than one person, place, or thing. ***Home Activity:*** Take a walk through your house. Have your child name the nouns he or she sees using singular and plural nouns *(one sofa, two chairs).*

Grammar Practice Book 4.2, p. 38

Name________________________ I Love Guinea Pigs

Grammar: Regular Plural Nouns

Directions: Write **P** if the noun is plural. Write **S** if the noun is singular. Then, write the plural form of each singular noun.

1. rabbits **P**
2. pellet **S; pellets**
3. tails **P**
4. family **S; families**
5. kitten **S; kittens**
6. stripes **P**
7. monkey **S; monkeys**
8. circus **S; circuses**
9. snake **S; snakes**
10. tanks **P**

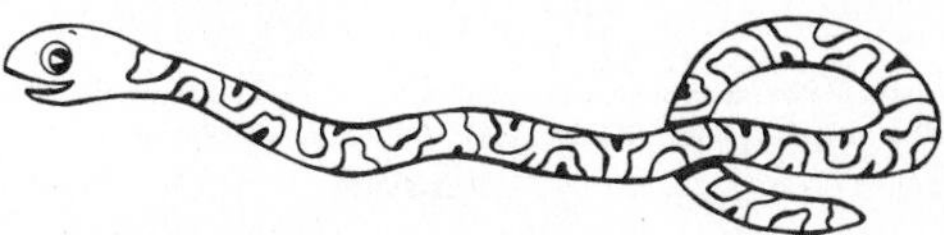

Directions: Write the plural forms of the nouns in each sentence.

ferrets; pets 11. A ferret can be a great pet.

ferrets; balls; bells 12. My ferret likes to play with a ball and a bell.

beds; floors; tanks 13. It likes to sleep in a special bed and on the floor of its tank.

rats; ferrets; rodents 14. Unlike a rat, a ferret is not a rodent.

ferrets; skunks; ocelots 15. Having a ferret is not as strange as having a skunk or an ocelot.

Write About a Pet

On a separate sheet of paper, write about a pet you have or would like to have. Describe where it lives, what it eats, and what things it likes to play with. Circle all the regular plural nouns. **Students should include several regular plural nouns spelled correctly.**

Notes for Home: Your child wrote regular plural nouns. ***Home Activity:*** Write pairs of singular and plural nouns on index cards, one word per index card. Use nouns whose plurals are formed by adding *-s* or *-es*. Mix the cards and draw two at a time to try to match pairs.

Grammar Practice Book 4.2, p. 39

Name________________________ I Love Guinea Pigs

Grammar: Regular Plural Nouns

RETEACHING

Read the chart. Circle the **-s** or **-es** ending in each plural noun.

add **-s**	days cups boys paths seas
add **-es**	riches dishes dresses boxes buses

A **singular noun** names one person, place, or thing. A **plural noun** names more than one person, place, or thing. Add **-s** or **-es** to spell the plural forms of most nouns.

Directions: Complete the chart. Write each noun in the correct column.

axes cobra desert goats
brushes colts eagles house
banana couches ferns peaches

Singular Nouns	Plural Nouns	
1. **cobra**	5. **axes**	9. **eagles**
2. **desert**	6. **goats**	10. **couches**
3. **house**	7. **brushes**	11. **ferns**
4. **banana**	8. **colts**	12. **peaches**

Directions: Write the plural of each noun in ( ).

13. Those (store) sell (pet). **stores, pets**
14. The (dog) saw the (bone). **dogs, bones**
15. Some (boy) sat on the (box). **boys, boxes**
16. (Student) rode the (bus). **Students, buses**

Notes for Home: Your child identified regular plural nouns. ***Home Activity:*** Name objects in your home. Have your child write the plural forms of the names of the objects.

Grammar Practice Book 4.2, p. 40

Name________________________ I Love Guinea Pigs

Grammar: Regular Plural Nouns

Directions: Replace each underlined singular noun with a plural noun. Write the plural noun on the line.

1. The student saw a movie in the morning.
   students
2. The girl liked the actor in the movie.
   actors
3. The class rode the bus to the movie.
   buses
4. The movie held my attention.
   movies
5. Judy made lunch for the group.
   lunches

Directions: Complete each sentence with a plural noun. **Possible answers given.**

6. The actors studied their **parts** for the play.
7. The performers gave two **performances** each day.
8. Even **parents** attended the show at school.
9. Some friends sent **flowers** to the actors.
10. Some people sat on **benches** .
11. The actor said his **lines** to the audience.

Write a Review

Write a review of a play or movie you enjoyed. Use plural nouns. Write on a separate sheet of paper. **Students should spell plural nouns correctly in their reviews.**

Notes for Home: Your child wrote plural nouns in sentences. ***Home Activity:*** Have your child choose nouns from a page of a favorite story. Then have him or her write sentences, using plural forms of those nouns.

Practice Book 4.2, p. 78

Name________________________ **I Love Guinea Pigs**

Word Study: Compound Words

Directions: Compound words are words made by joining two words, such as **sun + shine = sunshine.** Some compound words have a hyphen. Read this paragraph. Circle each compound word. Then write the word on the line.

(Throughout) history, people have had dogs as pets. Some dogs have long fur. They are called (long-coated.) Others have short fur. They are called (smooth-coated.) (Newborn) puppies have very little fur, so it is hard to tell how long their fur will be when they are (grown-up) dogs.

1. **throughout**
2. **long-coated**
3. **smooth-coated**
4. **newborn**
5. **grown-up**

Directions: Match each word in the first column with a word in the second column to make a compound word that makes sense. Write the word on the line.

6.	snow	–legged	**snowstorm**
7.	four	storm	**four-legged**
8.	any	times	**anyway**
9.	what	born	**whatever**
10.	new	out	**newborn**
11.	some	–haired	**sometimes**
12.	through	ever	**throughout**
13.	long	way	**long-haired**

Directions: Choose two of the compound words you made. Write a sentence using each of your words. **Possible answers given.**

14. **It can be hard to see a white dog in a snowstorm.**

15. **Dogs are four-legged animals.**

Notes for Home: Your child wrote compound words. ***Home Activity:*** Look for compound words on directions that come with toys or games. Write each part of the word on separate slips of paper, then have your child put the words together.

Spelling Workbook 4.2, p. 29

Name________________________ **I Love Guinea Pigs**

Spelling: Compound Words

Pretest Directions: Fold back the page along the dotted line. On the blanks, write the spelling words as they are dictated. When you have finished the test, unfold the page and check your words.

1. **baseball**	**1.** Michelle loves **baseball**!
2. **basketball**	**2.** Our **basketball** team won.
3. **upstairs**	**3.** My bedroom is **upstairs**.
4. **myself**	**4.** I baked this **myself**.
5. **highway**	**5.** Drive down the **highway**.
6. **classroom**	**6.** Our **classroom** is huge.
7. **anyway**	**7.** Will you come **anyway**?
8. **newspaper**	**8.** Recycle the **newspaper**.
9. **something**	**9.** Bring **something** warm.
10. **sometimes**	**10. Sometimes** we visit her.
11. **chalkboard**	**11.** Write on the **chalkboard**.
12. **earrings**	**12.** Those **earrings** are shiny.
13. **nighttime**	**13.** Watch stars at **nighttime**.
14. **motorcycle**	**14.** She rode a **motorcycle**.
15. **downstairs**	**15.** Come **downstairs** with me.
16. **softball**	**16.** Do you play **softball**?
17. **weekend**	**17.** We leave this **weekend**.
18. **classmate**	**18.** Study with a **classmate**.
19. **doorbell**	**19.** The **doorbell** rang.
20. **driveway**	**20.** Hose down the **driveway**.

Notes for Home: Your child took a pretest on compound words. ***Home Activity:*** Help your child learn misspelled words before the final test. Dictate the word and have your child spell the word aloud for you or write it on paper.

Spelling Workbook 4.2, p. 30

Name________________________ **I Love Guinea Pigs**

Spelling: Compound Words

Word List

baseball	highway	something	nighttime	weekend
basketball	classroom	sometimes	motorcycle	classmate
upstairs	anyway	chalkboard	downstairs	doorbell
myself	newspaper	earrings	softball	driveway

Directions: Add a word to each word below to form a compound word from the box. Write the compound word on the line.

1. up	**upstairs**	**8.** door	**doorbell**
2. cycle	**motorcycle**	**9.** rings	**earrings**
3. down	**downstairs**	**10.** any	**anyway**
4. basket	**basketball**	**11.** base	**baseball**
5. drive	**driveway**	**12.** paper	**newspaper**
6. high	**highway**	**13.** soft	**softball**
7. night	**nighttime**	**14.** end	**weekend**

Directions: Choose the words from the box that best complete the story. Write each word on the matching numbered line to the right.

At school, we have a wonderful pet in our **15.** _____. It's a gerbil named Max. Before we got Max, our teacher wrote a list of class rules on the **16.** _____ so we'd know how to take care of Max. I take care of two gerbils by **17.** _____ at home, and I know that **18.** _____ you can forget what they need.

With Max, there's always **19.** _____ interesting to see. My **20.** _____, Lesley, says that Max is more fun than her pet goldfish!

15. **classroom**
16. **chalkboard**
17. **myself**
18. **sometimes**
19. **something**
20. **classmate**

Notes for Home: Your child spelled compound words in which two words are joined to make a new word. ***Home Activity:*** Together, write sentences using each part of a compound word and then the whole word. For example: *A room where you have a class is a classroom.*

Spelling Workbook 4.2, p. 31

Name________________________ **I Love Guinea Pigs**

Spelling: Compound Words

Directions: Proofread this entry from a journal. Find five spelling mistakes. Use the proofreading marks to correct each mistake.

- ≡ Make a capital.
- / Make a small letter.
- ∧ Add something.
- Take out something.
- ⊙ Add a period.
- ¶ Begin a new paragraph.

Dear Diary,

This weekkend I had fun with my cat Saucy. I chased her dowstairs and back upstairs until we both got tired of running. Then I rolled up some old newpaper and tied it to a string. She pounced on it, pretending it was a mouse. Suddenly, the dorbell rang. My friend Jaime wanted to play baskeball or softball. I told him I did, too, but first I had to feed Saucy!

Spelling Tip

baseball

A compound word is made of two or more words. Keep all the letters when spelling compounds.

Word List

baseball	highway	something	nighttime	weekend
basketball	classroom	sometimes	motorcycle	classmate
upstairs	anyway	chalkboard	downstairs	doorbell
myself	newspaper	earrings	softball	driveway

Write a Diary Entry

Imagine that you have a new pet. On a separate sheet of paper, write a diary entry telling about your pet. Include how you care for it, what it likes to eat, and how the two of you have fun. Try to use at least three spelling words. **Answers will vary, but each diary entry should include at least three spelling words.**

Notes for Home: Your child spelled compound words in which two words are joined to make a new word. ***Home Activity:*** With your child, think of some other compound words, such as *mailbox, stairway,* and *daylight.*

Spelling Workbook 4.2, p. 32
Name____________________ I Love Guinea Pigs

Spelling: Compound Words

REVIEW

Word List				
baseball	highway	something	nighttime	weekend
basketball	classroom	sometimes	motorcycle	classmate
upstairs	anyway	chalkboard	downstairs	doorbell
myself	newspaper	earrings	softball	driveway

Directions: Choose the word from the box that shares a word part with the word shown. Use each word only once. Write the word on the line.

1. motorboat **motorcycle**
2. daytime **nighttime**
3. everything **something**
4. somewhere **sometimes**
5. weekday **weekend**
6. earache **earrings**
7. anyone **anyway**
8. herself **myself**
9. basement **baseball**
10. downtown **downstairs**
11. uptown **upstairs**
12. newscast **newspaper**

Directions: Choose the word from the box that best completes each sentence. Write the word on the line to the left.

highway 13. My dog Simon loves to go outside, even though we live near a busy _____.

driveway 14. But we only let him go to the end of our _____.

basketball 15. We also let him play with us on the _____ court.

softball (or baseball) 16. When I play _____, he barks when I hit the ball!

classroom 17. I would love to take Simon to my _____ at school.

classmate 18. My _____, Luis, would just love him.

chalkboard 19. But on the _____ at school is written, "No Pets!"

doorbell 20. So Luis is coming here now to play with Simon— and I think I just heard the _____ ring!

Notes for Home: Your child spelled compound words in which two words are joined to make a new word. ***Home Activity:*** Play "word toss." You "toss" a word part at your child, who "tosses back" a compound word. For example, you say *every,* and he or she says *everyone!*

Spelling: Compound Words 177

Practice Book 4.2, p. 79
Name____________________ I Love Guinea Pigs

Chart/Table

A **chart** organizes information in a way that is easy to follow. A **table** is a kind of chart that presents information in rows and columns.

Directions: Use the table to answer the questions that follow.

GUIDE TO GUINEA PIG CARE

Topics	What You Need to Know
Food and Water	Guinea pigs should eat a diet of hay, pellets, fresh fruit, and vegetables such as broccoli, cauliflower, carrots, and peas. Guinea pigs need lots of fresh water daily.
Bedding	Put some shredded newspaper at the bottom of the cage. Replace with fresh newspapers daily. You can also use towels and blankets but these have to be washed every day.
Vet Visits	Guinea pigs should have a physical exam twice a year. They should also see a vet if they have a loss of appetite, bleeding, diarrhea, hair loss, or show strange behavior.
Safety	Don't put plastic toys in a guinea pig's cage. It will chew them and could choke on the pieces.

1. Which row would you look at to find out what a guinea pig needs for sleeping?
Look in the row under the topic of "Bedding."

2. How can you use the table to find out if plastic toys are safe for guinea pigs?
Look in the row under the topic of "Safety."

3. What four vegetables are good for a guinea pig's diet? **broccoli, cauliflower, carrots, and peas**

4. What information can you learn by reading the section on Vet Visits?
You find out when to take your guinea pig to the vet.

5. Suppose you were going to add another row to the table on what a guinea pig's sounds mean. What words would you use to label this topic?
Possible answers: Guinea Pig Language, Communication

178 Research and Study Skills: Chart/Table

Practice Book 4.2, p. 80
Name____________________ I Love Guinea Pigs

Directions: Study the table below. Use the table to answer the questions that follow.

"WHAT IS MY GUINEA PIG TRYING TO SAY TO ME?"

Guinea Pig Sounds	What It Probably Means
gurgles, grunts	comfort, happiness
squeaks, squeals	fear, in pain, hungry
cooing	calm, relaxed
hisses, teeth clacking	fighting, warning

6. If your guinea pig was grunting and cooing, what "Sounds" would you look under to learn more?
Look under "gurgles, grunts" and "cooing."

7. If you saw a guinea pig clacking its teeth, how could you use this table to figure out what this means?
Look under "hisses, teeth clacking" to see what this sound means.

8. What sound could you expect from a guinea pig that does not want to be disturbed?
hissing or teeth clacking

9. Suppose you are adding a third column to this chart. It will tell how to respond to a guinea pig's sounds. What heading could you give this column?
Possible answers: What to Do, How to Respond, Taking Action

10. Why are headings in a table useful? **Possible answer: Headings tell you at a glance what the information will be about.**

Notes for Home: Your child used tables to answer questions about pet care. ***Home Activity:*** Create a table with your child to keep track of weekly activities. For example, on Monday, your child might play soccer; on Tuesday, your child may watch a specific TV program, and so on.

Research and Study Skills: Chart/Table 179

Practice Book 4.2, p. 81
Name____________________ The Swimming Hole

Theme

- **Theme** is the underlying meaning of a story—a big idea that stands on its own outside the story.
- Sometimes an author states the theme directly. Sometimes readers have to figure out the theme on their own, using evidence from the text to support their big idea.

Directions: Reread "Ant and Dove." Then complete the chart. Tell what the theme is and give supporting evidence from the story. Some sentences have been started for you. **Possible answers given.**

Theme

1. **If you help others, they will help you.**

Supporting Evidence

The ant was in trouble.
2. The dove helped the ant by: **dropping her a leaf.**
3. The ant felt: **grateful.**

The dove was in trouble.
4. The ant: **helped the dove by biting the birdcatcher.**
5. The ant did this because: **the dove had helped her.**

Notes for Home: Your child read a fable and identified its theme, or "big idea." ***Home Activity:*** Invite your child to tell you a favorite story. Then ask your child to identify the story's big idea and what lesson about life might be learned from it.

182 Theme

Practice Book 4.2, p. 82
Name________________________ The Swimming Hole

Vocabulary

Directions: Choose the word from the box that best matches each definition. Write the word on the line.

Check the Words You Know
__ bristled
__ dugout
__ jointed
__ naughty
__ punish
__ rushes
__ shallow

shallow 1. not deep

bristled 2. made hair stand up straight

rushes 3. hollow-stemmed plants

jointed 4. having places where two parts join together

dugout 5. shelter formed by hole in hillside

naughty 6. not well-behaved

Directions: Choose the word from the box that best completes each sentence. Write the word on the matching numbered line to the right.

I waded out into the **7.** _____ water near where the **8.** _____ grew. I knew it was **9.** _____ of me to go into the deeper water. My mother saw what I did, and she will now **10.** _____ me. I won't do that again now that I know.

7. **shallow**
8. **rushes**
9. **naughty**
10. **punish**

Write a Description

On a separate sheet of paper, write a paragraph describing what you might see if you lived in the prairie long ago. Use as many vocabulary words as you can. **Students' descriptions should use vocabulary words correctly.**

Notes for Home: Your child identified and used new words from "The Swimming Hole." ***Home Activity:*** Imagine you and your child are pioneers living in a house on the prairie. Use the vocabulary words to help you talk about what life would have been like.

Practice Book 4.2, p. 83
Name________________________ The Swimming Hole

Theme

- **Theme** is the underlying meaning of a story—a "big idea" that stands on its own outside the story.

1. Reread "The Swimming Hole." Write its theme on the line below.
Possible answer: It's hard to win back trust.

Directions: Read the story. Then answer the questions below.

Ever since Malcolm could remember, Uncle Dave had kept his promises. One day, Uncle Dave broke a promise. He said he would come visit on Malcolm's birthday, and he didn't. Malcolm felt terrible. "I can never trust him again," he thought. The next time Uncle Dave visited, he said he was sorry. He had written down the wrong date on his calendar.

Malcolm thought he could never trust Uncle Dave again. But his mother said, "Sometimes people do mean things, but sometimes they just make mistakes."

"I guess he just made a mistake," said Malcolm. "So I guess I will try trusting him again."

2. Why did Malcolm always trust Uncle Dave?
Uncle Dave always kept his promises.

3. What does Uncle Dave do to make Malcolm stop trusting him?
He misses Malcolm's birthday and breaks his promise.

4. What does Uncle Dave do to show that Malcolm can trust him again?
He says he's sorry and explains what happened.

5. Use what you know about the events and characters of the story above to write about its theme. Below the theme, list all the details in the story that support this big idea. Use a separate sheet of paper. **Possible answer: Theme: You can lose trust and then win it back. Supporting Details: Uncle Dave misses Malcolm's birthday. Malcolm stops trusting him. Uncle Dave apologizes and explains. Malcolm decides to trust him again.**

Notes for Home: Your child has read a story and identified its theme, or big idea, as well as some details that support that theme. ***Home Activity:*** Talk together about a favorite book, movie, or television show. Invite your child to explain its theme, or "big idea."

Practice Book 4.2, p. 85
Name________________________ The Swimming Hole

Selection Test

Directions: Choose the best answer to each item. Mark the letter for the answer you have chosen.

Part 1: Vocabulary

Find the answer choice that means about the same as the underlined word in each sentence.

1. The wind blew the rushes.
   A. tall shrubs or bushes
   B. largest branches of a tree
   C. pale blue flowers
   Ⓓ grasslike plants that grow in wet soil

2. We stood in the shallow water.
   F. dark
   G. very cold
   Ⓗ not deep
   J. still

3. The doll's arms and legs are jointed.
   A. soiled or stained
   Ⓑ having places where parts join together
   C. stiff or unable to move
   D. made from cloth filled with padding

4. Trees grew around the dugout.
   F. valley between two mountains
   G. soil or gravel taken from the ground
   H. deepest part of a pond
   Ⓙ shelter formed by digging into the side of a hill

5. Jenna's parents will punish her.
   Ⓐ cause pain for doing something wrong
   B. give a reward to
   C. show her a lot of love and affection
   D. send away to somewhere else

6. The cat's coat bristled.
   F. became tangled
   G. trembled or shook
   Ⓗ stood up straight
   J. gleamed or shone

7. The mother spoke to the naughty child.
   A. worn out
   Ⓑ badly behaved
   C. lonesome
   D. confused or puzzled

Part 2: Comprehension

Use what you know about the story to answer each item.

8. Laura and her family lived near—
   F. the ocean.
   Ⓖ a creek.
   H. a lake.
   J. a river.

GO ON

Practice Book 4.2, p. 86
Name________________________ The Swimming Hole

9. Laura and Mary discovered many things they could make with—
   A. flowers.
   B. rocks.
   Ⓒ rushes.
   D. mud.

10. Pa and Ma did not want the girls to go to the swimming hole because—
    Ⓕ it was not safe for them to swim there alone.
    G. they had too many chores to do.
    H. it was too far from home.
    J. wild animals lived near it.

11. What does this story suggest about the outdoors?
    A. Children do not enjoy the outdoors.
    Ⓑ The outdoors is full of fun and wonder.
    C. People spend too much time outdoors.
    D. The outdoors is a dark, bad place.

12. The badger probably flattened itself because it—
    F. was getting ready to sleep.
    Ⓖ was afraid.
    H. liked Laura.
    J. was thirsty.

13. What is the theme of this story?
    A. Sisters are best friends.
    Ⓑ Children earn freedom when they can be trusted.
    C. Growing up is fun.
    D. Parents make many mistakes.

14. What bothered Laura most when she returned to the dugout after going near the swimming hole?
    F. running home without getting a cool drink
    G. remembering the badger she had seen
    H. worrying that Ma and Pa would find out
    Ⓙ knowing that she had broken a promise to Pa

15. Laura probably felt that her parents—
    A. thought only of themselves.
    B. should have had more rules.
    C. made her work too hard.
    Ⓓ tried to do what was best for her.

Name________________________ The Swimming Hole

Theme

- **Theme** is the underlying meaning of a story—a "big idea" that stands on its own outside the story.

Directions: Read the story below.

Beth and Rosa were best friends. Beth looked forward to starting the fourth grade together. Having a friend makes everything more fun.

Then Rosa found a new best friend! She stopped walking home with Beth. She stopped having lunch with her. She stopped playing with Beth on Saturdays. Beth felt awful.

One day at lunch, Mei-Ling came over to Beth's table. "Can I sit here?" she asked shyly. The two girls had a good time. The next day, they ate together again. On Saturday, Mei-Ling came over to play. Beth began to feel much better.

It seemed as though Mei-Ling wanted to be best friends, but Beth wasn't sure she wanted a new best friend. What if Mei-Ling stopped being her friend too?

Finally, Beth decided to take a chance. She decided it was better to have a friend and lose her than not to have any friends at all. She and Mei-Ling became good friends and stayed that way for a long time.

Directions: Complete the diagram. In the first box, write the theme of the story. In each of the other boxes, write a detail that supports the theme.

1. Theme: It is better to have a friend and lose her than not to have any friends at all.

2. Supporting Detail:
Having a friend makes everything more fun.

3. Supporting Detail:
It felt awful not to have a friend.

4. Supporting Detail:
Beth felt better after making friends with Mei-Ling.

5. Supporting Detail:
Beth and Mei-Ling became good friends for a long time.

Notes for Home: Your child read a story, identified its theme, and gave details that support the theme. ***Home Activity:*** Talk together with your child about a book you've read together. Ask your child to describe the underlying meaning of the story.

Practice Book 4.2, p. 87

Name________________________ The Swimming Hole

Cause and Effect

REVIEW

Directions: Read the story. Then read each question about the story. Choose the best answer to each question. Mark the letter for the answer you have chosen.

House Rules

We have several rules in our house. My parents say that's because rules help us all get along better.

Once my sister broke the rule about calling home if you're going to be late. Dad got worried. Mama called many of my sister's friends. When my little sister saw how worried everyone was, she started to cry.

When the baby heard my sister cry, he started crying too. Mama rushed to pick him up and tripped on the rug. She hurt her leg. Just then, my sister walked in.

"I'm sorry," my sister said. "I was with Diana, and we took her dog for a long walk. I didn't realize how late it was."

When she saw what had happened, my sister was very sorry. Now she never forgets to call!

1. One clue word that signals a cause-effect relationship in the first paragraph is—
   - **A.** several.
   - **B.** that's.
   - **C.** help.
   - **(D.)** because.
2. This family's rules—
   - **F.** make the baby cry.
   - **(G.)** help everyone get along better.
   - **H.** make the older sister sorry.
   - **J.** make Dad worry.
3. Mama hurt her leg because
   - **A.** Dad got worried.
   - **B.** the baby was crying.
   - **(C.)** she tripped on a rug.
   - **D.** the telephone rang.
4. The sister didn't call because—
   - **F.** she didn't think the rule was important.
   - **(G.)** she didn't know how late it was.
   - **H.** there wasn't a phone around.
   - **J.** Diana wouldn't let her.
5. Why does the sister remember to call now?
   - **(A.)** She was sorry for the trouble she caused.
   - **B.** She got a better watch.
   - **C.** She doesn't go to Diana's any more.
   - **D.** She got punished for not calling.

Notes for Home: Your child identified causes and effects in a story. ***Home Activity:*** Play "Cause-Effect Chain." Name a cause *(I was late starting dinner.)*. Ask your child to name an effect *(We ate late.)*. You name an effect of *that* effect. *(We were late washing dishes.)*, and so on.

Name________________________ The Swimming Hole

Writing Across Texts

Directions: Consider what you know about taking risks and what you learned from "The Swimming Hole" and "A Big-City Dream." Is it usually a good idea to take risks? Think of examples from the stories to support each of the sentences below.
Possible answers given.

Taking a risk is usually a good idea. You can enjoy new adventures.	Taking a risk is usually not a good idea. If you fail, people may not trust you.
1. **You earn the respect of others.**	6. **Some risks can be dangerous.**
2. **You learn new things.**	7. **Unexpected things happen.**
3. **Your life is exciting.**	8. **You can get punished if you take a risk without permission.**
4. **You can help make the world a better place.**	9. **Once you have broken a promise with someone, it is hard to regain their trust.**
5. **Other people may want to be part of what you are doing, and that is fun.**	10. **Sometimes you have to take a risk by yourself, which is not much fun.**

Write a Letter of Advice

On a separate sheet of paper, write a letter of advice about taking risks. Explain whether it is a good idea to take risks or not. Support your letter with information from "The Swimming Hole" and "A Big-City Dream." Use the table you created to help you.
Letters will vary. Check that students based their letters on details from the two stories.

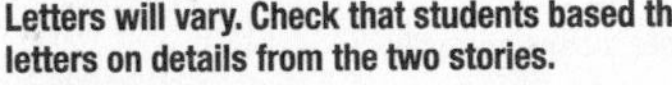

Notes for Home: Your child combined and used information from more than one fictional story. ***Home Activity:*** As you read stories to your child, discuss the actions of the characters. Discuss with your child whether those actions are advisable in real life.

Grammar Practice Book 4.2, p. 41

Name________________________ The Swimming Hole

Grammar: Singular and Plural Nouns

REVIEW

Directions: Write **S** for nouns that are singular. After the **S**, write the plural form of the noun. Write **P** for nouns that are plural.

1. mess **S; messes**
2. penny **S; pennies**
3. movies **P**
4. crash **S; crashes**
5. unicorn **S; unicorns**
6. glass **S; glasses**
7. boxes **P**
8. desks **P**
9. treasures **P**
10. hole **S; holes**
11. tray **S; trays**
12. hearts **P**
13. turkey **S; turkeys**
14. lady **S; ladies**

Directions: Write the plural form of each underlined noun on the line.

classes 15. Ronald was on a trip with his <u>class</u>.

ferries 16. The group was crossing the river in a <u>ferry</u>.

quarters 17. Ronald wanted to buy a drink, but he had only a <u>quarter</u>.

benches 18. He noticed some money a man had dropped under a <u>bench</u> nearby.

minutes 19. He picked up the money, thought for a <u>minute</u>, and went to look for the man.

drinks 20. The man thanked Ronald and gave him some change to buy a <u>drink</u>.

Notes for Home: Your child identified singular and plural nouns and wrote the plural form for singular nouns. ***Home Activity:*** Have your child identify singular nouns in a book or a magazine and write the plural form for each noun.

Grammar Practice Book 4.2, p. 42

Name____________________________________ **The Swimming Hole**

Grammar: Irregular Plural Nouns

Some plural forms of nouns do not end in **-s** or **-es.** To form these **irregular plurals,** you may have to change the spelling of the word.

Singular/Plural	
child/children	mouse/mice
foot/feet	ox/oxen
goose/geese	tooth/teeth
leaf/leaves	wolf/wolves
man/men	woman/women

A few nouns have the same form for both singular and plural.

deer	moose	sheep

Directions: Circle the correct plural noun in ( ) to complete each sentence.

1. Jenny wanted to go swimming with the other (childs/**children**).
2. First, she had to help the (**women**/womans) with chores on the farm.
3. The (sheeps/**sheep**) had to be brought in from the field.
4. The (**oxen**/oxes) had to be fed.
5. The (gooses/**geese**) needed more water.
6. There were (leafs/**leaves**) to be raked.
7. The dogs were let out to keep watch for (**wolves**/wolfs).
8. Jenny helped her aunt set traps for the (mouse/**mice**).
9. Finally, she ran to the water and jumped in with both (**feet**/foots).
10. The splash startled two (**deer**/deers) that were drinking at the stream.

Notes for Home: Your child identified irregular plural nouns that do not end in *-s* or *-es,* such as *children.* ***Home Activity:*** Take turns naming irregular plural nouns. Use these words to tell a story about a country adventure.

Grammar Practice Book 4.2, p. 43

Name____________________________________ **The Swimming Hole**

Grammar: Irregular Plural Nouns

Directions: Circle the correct plural noun in ( ) to complete each sentence.

1. Of all the (childs/**children**) at Olive Tree High School, Tanya was the most adventurous.
2. Every winter, she was first on the pond, her skates gleaming on her (foots/**feet**).
3. One day, Tanya looked up from skating and saw two big (**moose**/mooses).
4. She was so scared, her (teeths/**teeth**) started to chatter.
5. She thought, "I'm not afraid of (meece/**mice**), but I feel scared now!"

Directions: Write the plural form of each noun in ( ) to complete each sentence. Be careful. Don't let the rhymes fool you!

oxen 6. What would happen if foxes were friends with (ox)?

geese 7. If (goose) travel on trains, do they ride in the cabooses?

wolves 8. Those three (wolf) like to loaf.

men 9. The (man) were cooking flapjacks in big pans.

feet 10. These boots are too small for my (foot).

Write an Adventure Story

On a separate sheet of paper, write a short adventure story that involves different animals. It can be a funny story, if you wish. Use at least five irregular plural nouns.

Check that each story includes at least five irregular plural nouns.

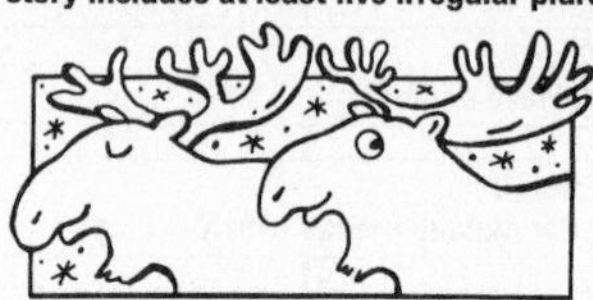

Notes for Home: Your child identified and wrote irregular plural nouns such as *mice.* ***Home Activity:*** Make up rhymes that use irregular plural nouns such as those listed above.

Grammar Practice Book 4.2, p. 44

Name____________________________________ **The Swimming Hole**

Grammar: Irregular Plural Nouns

RETEACHING

Read the chart. Underline each singular noun. Circle each plural noun.

Singular Nouns		Plural Nouns
1. loaf	(the spelling changes)	loaves
2. mouse	(the spelling changes)	mice
3. sheep	(the spelling does not change)	sheep

Some plural nouns are formed in special ways. They are called **irregular plural nouns.** Pay attention to the spelling of irregular plural nouns.

Directions: Write the plural form of each noun.

1. man **men**
2. wolf **wolves**
3. life **lives**
4. person **people**
5. leaf **leaves**
6. deer **deer**
7. moose **moose**
8. shelf **shelves**

Directions: Circle each plural noun that is not formed correctly. There is one in each sentence. Then write that plural noun correctly.

9. Grandma makes us **scarfs.** **scarves**
10. She makes up stories about **deers.** **deer**
11. She reads about kinds of **fishs.** **fish/fishes**
12. She tells tales of ancient **womans.** **women**
13. She also tells stories about **gooses.** **geese**
14. Some tales are about **childrens.** **children**
15. Their **foots** take them far. **feet**

Notes for Home: Your child wrote irregular plural nouns correctly. ***Home Activity:*** Write irregular nouns, such as *thief* or *deer,* and have your child write the plural forms of the nouns.

Grammar Practice Book 4.2, p. 45

Name____________________________________ **The Swimming Hole**

Grammar: Irregular Plural Nouns

Directions: Write the plural form of each noun.

1. moose **moose**
2. tooth **teeth**
3. calf **calves**
4. hoof **hooves/hoofs**
5. self **selves**
6. sheep **sheep**
7. deer **deer**
8. woman **women**
9. wife **wives**
10. ox **oxen**
11. wolf **wolves**
12. goose **geese**
13. man **men**
14. foot **feet**
15. mouse **mice**
16. child **children**

Directions: Write the plural form of the right noun on the line. Then choose two nouns from the list and use their plural forms in two sentences. Use one plural in each sentence.

child deer mouse wolf

17. He saw two tiny **mice** in the bushes.
18. The **children** ate three bowls of fruit.
19. Several swift **deer** ran by the house.
20. Two gray **wolves** howled at the moon.
21. **Sentences will vary.**
22. ______________________________

Write a Silly Story

Write a silly story about what happened when two mice explored a library. Use plural nouns. Write on a separate sheet of paper.

Make sure students spell plural nouns correctly.

Notes for Home: Your child wrote irregular plural nouns. ***Home Activity:*** Have your child circle irregular plural nouns in a newspaper or magazine article. Then challenge him or her to use three of the irregular plural nouns in sentences.

Practice Book 4.2, p. 88
Name________________________________ **The Swimming Hole**

Phonics: Vowel Digraphs

Directions: Read the letter below. Find words that have the vowel sound in **paw, thought,** and **author.** The vowel sound in each word is the same, but the sound has three different spellings. Write the words on the lines.

Dear Billy,

I was late for school today, but it wasn't really my fault! Okay, maybe I am to blame. I guess I was naughty and slept too late. Anyway, I thought I'd ride my bike to get to school quickly. Then guess what happened! I saw this awful dog! Then I realized that it was friendly. On my way back, I brought the dog home. We are going to keep it as a pet. I ought to get up earlier, but this time I'm glad I didn't!

Your friend,
Kezia

1. **fault**
2. **naughty**
3. **thought**
4. **saw**
5. **awful**
6. **brought**
7. **ought**

Directions: Read these sentences. Say the underlined words to yourself. Circle the word in ( ) that has the same vowel sound as the underlined word.

8. When it is too hot outside, most people feel awful. (April/**(thoughtful)**)
9. So the family thought a trip to the river would be cool. (**(taught)**/though)
10. They brought a picnic basket for lunch. (browse/**(pause)**)
11. The children fought about who could wade deepest. (fight/**(caught)**)
12. The parents warned the children not to be naughty. (note/**(bought)**)
13. As they were eating, the family saw dark clouds in the sky. (**(straw)**/sew)
14. Now the children are arguing about whose fault it is that everything got wet in the rain. (**(flaw)**/flower)

Directions: Choose one of the words you circled. Write a sentence for it.

15. **Possible answer: I bought an apple at the store.**

Notes for Home: Your child learned three spellings for the vowel sound in *paw, thought,* and *author. Home Activity:* Read a newspaper story with your child. Help your child recognize this vowel sound. Ask your child to write the words in three groups: *aw, ou,* and *au.*

Phonics: Vowel Digraphs 195

Spelling Workbook 4.2, p. 33
Name________________________________ **The Swimming Hole**

Spelling: Homophones

Pretest Directions: Fold back the page along the dotted line. On the blanks, write the spelling words as they are dictated. When you have finished the test, unfold the page and check your words.

1. **wood**	1. Gather **wood** for the fire.
2. **would**	2. **Would** you help me?
3. **too**	3. I want some **too**!
4. **to**	4. Come **to** my house.
5. **two**	5. **Two** birds flew by.
6. **there**	6. I will meet you **there**.
7. **their**	7. This is **their** garden.
8. **they're**	8. **They're** going to town.
9. **your**	9. Where is **your** puppy?
10. **you're**	10. **You're** late today.
11. **beat**	11. **Beat** the rug clean.
12. **beet**	12. Add a **beet** to the stew.
13. **break**	13. Did you **break** a bone?
14. **brake**	14. Use the **brake** to stop.
15. **clothes**	15. Hang the **clothes** to dry.
16. **close**	16. **Close** the window.
17. **piece**	17. Cut off a **piece** for me.
18. **peace**	18. Let me read in **peace**!
19. **thrown**	19. The ball was **thrown** far.
20. **throne**	20. She sat on her **throne**.

Notes for Home: Your child took a pretest on homophones, words that sound alike but are spelled differently and have different meanings. ***Home Activity:*** Help your child learn to connect the spelling of the word with its meaning.

196 Spelling: Homophones

Spelling Workbook 4.2, p. 34
Name________________________________ **The Swimming Hole**

Spelling: Homophones

Word List

wood	two	your	break	piece
would	there	you're	brake	peace
too	their	beat	clothes	thrown
to	they're	beet	close	throne

Directions: Choose the word from the box that best matches each clue. Write the word on the line.

1. lumber **wood**
2. will **would**
3. opposite of *war* **peace**
4. one part **piece**
5. chair for a king **throne**
6. form of *throw* **thrown**
7. red vegetable **beet**
8. hit **beat**
9. come apart **break**
10. can slow a car **brake**
11. shut **close**
12. things you wear **clothes**

Directions: Choose the words from the box that best complete each sentence. Write each word on the matching numbered line to the right.

13. _____ friend Dylan just called you. **14.** _____ invited to a party at his house next week!

I have **15.** _____ wonderful friends, Deedee and Sam. I trust them always **16.** _____ be there when I need them. They trust me **17.** _____.

Deedee and Sam are brother and sister—in fact, **18.** _____ twins. Today I'm going to **19.** _____ house after school. I'll go **20.** _____ as soon as my last class is over.

13. **Your**
14. **You're**
15. **two**
16. **to**
17. **too**
18. **they're**
19. **their**
20. **there**

Notes for Home: Your child practiced spelling homophones, words that sound alike but are spelled differently and have different meanings. ***Home Activity:*** Write one of the homophones from the box and have your child use it in a sentence. Switch roles and repeat.

Spelling: Homophones 197

Spelling Workbook 4.2, p. 35
Name________________________________ **The Swimming Hole**

Spelling: Homophones

Directions: Proofread this letter from one friend to another. Find five spelling mistakes. Use the proofreading marks to correct each mistake.

≡ Make a capital.
/ Make a small letter.
∧ Add something.
Take out something.
⊙ Add a period.
¶ Begin a new paragraph.

Dear Tammy,

I want you too [to] know that I'm glad you're my best friend. I know I can trust you, no matter what! You can always trust me, to [too]. You never brake [break] you're [your] promises, and you always are their [there] when I need a friend.

Your friend,
Anya

Spelling Tip
A **homophone** is a word that sounds exactly like another word but has a different spelling and meaning. Try to think of memory tricks to help you spell, such as: I'd like a **piece** of **pie**.

Word List

wood	two	your	break	piece
would	there	you're	brake	peace
too	their	beat	clothes	thrown
to	they're	beet	close	throne

Write a Friendly Letter

Imagine you are Tammy. On a separate sheet of paper, write a letter back to Anya about the trust you have for her. Use at least three spelling words in your letter.

Answers will vary, but each letter should include at least three spelling words.

Notes for Home: Your child learned to spell homophones, words that sound alike but are spelled differently and have different meanings. ***Home Activity:*** Work with your child to write sentences for each set of homophones. Discuss ways to remember the meaning and spelling of each word.

198 Spelling: Homophones

Spelling Workbook 4.2, p. 36
Name______________________

The Swimming Hole

Spelling: Homophones

REVIEW

Word List				
wood	two	your	break	piece
would	there	you're	brake	peace
too	their	beat	clothes	thrown
to	they're	beet	close	throne

Directions: Use the words in ( ) to complete each sentence. Write the words on the matching numbered lines to the right.

There once was a queen who was **1.**_____ from her **2.**_____. (throne/thrown)
The queen did not know what **3.**_____ do, so she called her **4.**_____ advisors, and her jester **5.**_____. (to/too/two)
"**6.**_____ all very smart," the queen thought, "and once I see them sitting **7.**_____ in front of me, I know I'll take **8.**_____ advice." (there/their/they're)
When they arrived, the queen said, "**9.**_____ here because I want **10.**_____ opinion. How can I regain my people's trust?" (your/you're)
"It's very simple," they all said. "Bring **11.**_____ to the kingdom—and give everyone a big **12.**_____ of pie to celebrate!" (peace/piece)

1. **thrown**
2. **throne**
3. **to**
4. **two**
5. **too**
6. **They're**
7. **there**
8. **their**
9. **You're**
10. **your**
11. **peace**
12. **piece**

Directions: Unscramble each set of letters below to form a word from the box. Write the word on the line.

13. solec **close**
14. hotcels **clothes**
15. odow **wood**
16. ludow **would**
17. tabe **beat**
18. ebet **beet**
19. kareb **brake (or break)**
20. kerab **break (or brake)**

Notes for Home: Your child spelled homophones, words that sound alike but are spelled differently and have different meanings. ***Home Activity:*** Play a homophone game. Take turns making up sentences that use at least two homophones, such as: *The king was thrown from his throne.*

Spelling: Homophones 199

Practice Book 4.2, p. 89
Name______________________

The Swimming Hole

Following Directions

Following directions means doing or making something in a certain order. Be sure to:
- Read all directions carefully so you know what you need to do.
- Gather any items needed to complete the directions.
- Follow the directions in the order they are given.

Directions: Read the directions given in this recipe carefully. Then answer the questions that follow.

Apple Crisp

1. Preheat the oven to 375°F. (Ask a grown-up to help you.)
2. Peel 6 apples, and then core and slice them.
3. Mix together in a bowl:
   $\frac{1}{2}$ cup sugar
   2 tbsp. cinnamon
4. Mix together in a different bowl:
   1 cup flour
   $\frac{1}{2}$ cup sugar
   2 eggs
   $\frac{1}{2}$ cup butter, melted
   1 tsp. vanilla extract
   $2\frac{1}{2}$ tbsp. lemon juice
5. Grease a 9-by-9-inch baking pan. Put the apple slices in the pan.
6. Sprinkle half the sugar and cinnamon mixture over the apples.
7. Pour the mixture from step 4 over the apples. Make sure to cover the whole surface.
8. Cut about 1 tbsp. of butter into tiny bits. Add these bits of butter to the other half of the sugar and cinnamon mixture. Use your fingers to mush the butter into the sugar until crumbs form.
9. Sprinkle these crumbs over the top of the apple mixture.
10. Place the pan in the oven and bake the mixture for 45 minutes, or until the batter on the top is golden brown.
11. Cool for about 5 minutes, and then cut the apple crisp into squares.

200 Research and Study Skills: Following Directions

Practice Book 4.2, p. 90
Name______________________

The Swimming Hole

1. When using a recipe, why is it important to read all the directions first before starting the first step?
Possible answer: Reading all the directions helps you get organized. It tells you what you will need to make the food.
2. What is the first step you do? **Preheat the oven.**
3. How many apples are needed? **6 apples**
4. How many ingredients get mixed in step 3? What are they? **two; sugar and cinnamon**
5. How many ingredients get mixed in step 4? What are they? **six; flour, sugar, eggs, butter, vanilla extract, lemon juice**
6. How much sugar is needed? **1 cup**
7. What abbreviations are used for teaspoon and tablespoon? **tsp. and tbsp.**
8. If you didn't time the apple crisp cooking, what is another way to tell if it is done? What step gives you this information?
Check to see if it is golden brown on top; step 10.
9. Why do you think many cookbooks include pictures? **Possible answer: The pictures show how to do a step or what the food should look like.**
10. What might happen if you didn't follow the steps for making apple crisp in the order given in the recipe?
Possible answer: The apple crisp might not turn out correctly.

Notes for Home: Your child used a recipe to practice following directions. ***Home Activity:*** Show your child a recipe for a favorite family dish. Discuss the steps and write a list of what is needed to make the dish.

Research and Study Skills: Following Directions 201

Practice Book 4.2, p. 91
Name______________________

Komodo Dragons

Context Clues

- When you are reading and you see an unfamiliar word, use **context clues,** or words around the unfamiliar word, to figure out its meaning.
- The context may give a definition or an explanation. Often the definition or explanation comes just before or just after the word. Sometimes a synonym, a word with nearly the same meaning as another word, is used as a context clue.

Directions: Reread "Crocodilians." Then complete the table. Use the context clues in the article to figure out the meaning of each word in the table.
Possible answers given.

Word	Meaning
osteoderms	1. **bony plates**
hides	2. **skins**
amphibious	3. **can live both on land and in water**
ripple	4. **movement of water**
ectothermic	5. **cold-blooded; having body temperatures that change**

Notes for Home: Your child used context clues to figure out the meanings of five words. ***Home Activity:*** Encourage your child to use context clues to figure out the meanings of unfamiliar words as you read together.

204 Context Clues

Practice Book 4.2, p. 92

Name ____________________

Komodo Dragons

Vocabulary

Directions: Cross out the word that does not belong in each group.

1. roam wander ~~dash~~ travel

2. armor shell scales ~~elbow~~

3. reptile snakes ~~chickens~~ alligators

Check the Words You Know

- __ armor
- __ fierce
- __ harshest
- __ lizards
- __ prey
- __ reptiles
- __ roam

Directions: Choose the word from the box that best completes each sentence. Write the word on the matching numbered line to the right.

My friend Carrie told me a story about some **4.** _____ and scary dragons. She said that the climate where they live is one of the **5.** _____ in the world. The dragons have hard scales, like **6.** _____, to protect them. They **7.** _____ the land in search of animals to eat. The dragons are strong and swift, so they almost always catch their **8.** _____.

"I bet they are not even dragons. I bet they are only **9.** _____," I said.

"Well, maybe not," said Carrie. "But some **10.** _____ are lizards that are so large that they look like dragons."

4. **fierce**
5. **harshest**
6. **armor**
7. **roam**
8. **prey**
9. **lizards**
10. **reptiles**

Write a Science Log

Imagine you are a scientist who studies reptiles. Write an entry in your log describing one of the reptiles you are studying. What does it look like? How does it act? What foods does it eat? Use as many vocabulary words as you can in your logs. **Students may need to do some research before writing. Science logs should use vocabulary words correctly.**

Notes for Home: Your child identified and used new words from *Komodo Dragons*. ***Home Activity:*** Talk with your child about different types of reptiles, such as snakes, lizards, turtles, or alligators. Create a picture encyclopedia. Write captions for each picture.

Practice Book 4.2, p. 93

Name ____________________

Komodo Dragons

Context Clues

- When you are reading and see an unfamiliar word, use **context clues,** or words around the unfamiliar word, to figure out its meaning.
- **Context clues** include definitions, explanations, and synonyms (words that have the same or nearly the same meaning as other words).

Directions: Reread the part of *Komodo Dragons* that talks about where Komodo dragons live. Then answer the questions below. Look for context clues as you read.

Komodo dragons are a type of lizard called a *monitor.* They come from the Komodo Island area of Indonesia, near the northwest shore of Australia. It is one of the harshest and hottest places in the world. Often, the temperature is over 100° F. Sometimes it even gets as hot as 110° F.

On the hottest days, dragons escape the heat by getting out of the sun. They rest in underground burrows. But in the morning, when they first wake up, they lie in the sun to warm up. They do that on cooler days, too. That is because, like all lizards, they are **reptiles.** Reptiles are **cold-blooded** animals. They need outside heat (like sunlight) to warm them up.

1. What is a *monitor?* **A *monitor* is a kind of lizard.**

2. What sentence in the passage contains a clue to the meaning of *monitor?*
"Komodo dragons are a type of lizard called a *monitor.*"

3. What does *cold-blooded* mean?
It means an animal needs outside heat to keep warm.

4. What sentence in the passage contains a clue to the meaning of *cold-blooded?*
"Reptiles are cold-blooded animals. They need outside heat (like sunlight) to warm them up."

5. Read the section called "What Do Komodo Dragons Eat?" Find an unfamiliar word in that section and define it on a separate sheet of paper. Tell what context clue helped you figure out the word's meaning. **Check that definitions make sense and are based on context clues.**

Notes for Home: Your child practiced using context clues in a story. ***Home Activity:*** Think of a difficult word, and tell your child a sentence that makes its meaning clear ("Today I saw a bird called a *flamingo.*"). Ask your child to tell you what the word means.

Practice Book 4.2, p. 95

Name ____________________

Komodo Dragons

Selection Test

Directions: Choose the best answer to each item. Mark the letter for the answer you have chosen.

Part 1: Vocabulary

Find the answer choice that means about the same as the underlined word in each sentence.

1. Scott wrote a report on <u>reptiles</u>.
- A. plants found in the desert
- B. mammals of South America
- C. types of building materials
- (D) cold-blooded animals

2. The lion followed its <u>prey</u>.
- (F) an animal hunted for food
- G. an animal's parents
- H. the way an animal behaves
- J. a smell left behind by an animal

3. Jamal caught two <u>lizards</u>.
- A. common illnesses
- B. hard balls used in a game
- (C) kinds of reptiles with four legs
- D. insects with wings

4. Talia's cat likes to <u>roam</u>.
- (F) wander
- G. hunt
- H. sleep
- J. hide

5. Tigers are <u>fierce</u> hunters.
- A. patient
- (B) savage; wild
- C. restless
- D. skillful; clever

6. This has been the <u>harshest</u> winter ever.
- F. warmest
- G. mildest; most pleasant
- H. longest
- (J) roughest; most difficult

7. That animal's skin is like <u>armor</u>.
- A. a thick hairy coat
- B. a band worn around the waist
- (C) a covering worn to protect the body
- D. a kind of saddle

Part 2: Comprehension

Use what you know about the selection to answer each item.

8. Komodo dragons are—
- F. make-believe animals.
- G. alligators.
- H. birds.
- (J) lizards.

9. Where do Komodo dragons live?
- A. Australia
- B. India
- (C) Indonesia
- D. Africa

Practice Book 4.2, p. 96

Name ____________________

Komodo Dragons

10. Komodo dragons swish their tails back and forth to—
- F. show they like something.
- G. smell the air around them.
- H. hold on to their prey.
- (J) help them balance.

11. How is the female Komodo dragon different from the male?
- (A) She is usually smaller.
- B. She is not as strong.
- C. She digs burrows.
- D. She is active during the day.

12. What word is being defined in this sentence? "That's why the tongue is forked, or shaped like a Y."
- F. shaped
- (G) forked
- H. tongue
- J. why

13. Because Komodo dragons are cold-blooded, they—
- A. prefer to eat warm food.
- B. must escape the heat by getting out of the sun.
- (C) need outside heat to warm them up.
- D. can easily live in very cold places.

14. You can tell that Komodo dragons are—
- (F) well suited to their surroundings.
- G. very particular about what they eat.
- H. not very intelligent animals.
- J. lazy because they sleep all day.

15. Which sentence states an opinion?
- A. Dragon eggs have a soft, smooth shell.
- B. Hatching takes about eight months.
- C. Komodo dragons live on only a few islands.
- (D) Komodo dragons are very interesting creatures.

STOP

Name________________ Komodo Dragons

Context Clues

- When you are reading and you see an unfamiliar word, use **context clues,** or words around the unfamiliar word, to figure out its meaning.
- **Context clues** include definitions, explanations, and synonyms (words with the same or nearly the same meaning as other words).

Directions: Read the article below.

Do you know what a lemming is? It is a kind of small rodent that lives in the Arctic—the region around the North Pole.

Lemmings eat grass and plants. Lemmings produce many offspring—having up to 10 babies at a time and producing up to 30 in a year. When there are too many lemmings, reindeer, caribou (large animals that look like reindeer), and other plant-eaters begin to go hungry. However, when there are lots of lemmings, predators, or hunting animals, have plenty. The hunting animals eat the lemmings—and the lemming population goes down. When there are fewer lemmings, hunting animals have less to eat and have fewer babies—so the lemming population goes back up.

The ups and downs of the lemming population is called a *cycle.* A cycle is a process that repeats itself over and over again.

Directions: Complete the table. Find the unfamiliar words in the article. Figure out what they mean, using clues from the article. Write the missing meanings or words.
Possible definitions given.

Unfamiliar Words	What It Means
lemming	1. **small rodent**
Arctic	2. **region around the North Pole**
caribou	3. **large animal like a reindeer**
predators	hunting animals
offspring	4. **babies**
5. **cycle**	process that repeats itself

Notes for Home: Your child used context clues in a story to figure out the meanings of unfamiliar words. ***Home Activity:*** Find a difficult word on a label, a videotape box, or in a favorite book. Help your child use context clues to figure out what the word means.

Practice Book 4.2, p. 97

Name________________ Komodo Dragons

Main Idea and Supporting Details

REVIEW

Directions: Read the passage. Then read each question about the passage. Choose the best answer to each question. Mark the letter for that answer.

Animals of the Arctic

Animals that live in the Arctic have found many ways to cope with the cold.

Polar bears have two main guards against the cold: extra fur and a layer of fat. These things help keep bears warm in below-freezing temperatures.

Some animals have other ways of handling the cold. Hares and reindeer can run quickly across the snow. That's because their wide "snowshoe" feet don't break through the snow's crust.

Hares in the Arctic also have very small ears. That's because body heat escapes through the ears, cooling the body down. Smaller ears allow less heat to escape.

Some animals, such as whales, birds, and caribou, handle the cold by heading south. They live in the Arctic in the summer, when temperatures are higher.

1. A key word to the main idea in the second paragraph is—
   - **A.** fat.
   - **B.** fur.
   - **(C.)** guards.
   - **D.** layer.
2. A detail in the third paragraph is—
   - **F.** whales head south.
   - **(G.)** snowshoe feet don't break through the crust.
   - **H.** hares and reindeer.
   - **J.** hares have small ears.
3. A key word to the main idea of the third paragraph is—
   - **A.** hares.
   - **B.** reindeer.
   - **(C.)** run.
   - **D.** break.
4. A key word to the main idea in the last paragraph is—
   - **(F.)** south.
   - **G.** whales.
   - **H.** birds.
   - **J.** caribou.
5. The main idea of the whole passage is that Arctic animals—
   - **A.** get cold.
   - **B.** leave during the winter.
   - **C.** have small ears.
   - **(D.)** find ways to cope with cold.

Notes for Home: Your child practiced identifying the main idea and its supporting details in a story. ***Home Activity:*** Ask your child to name an important family rule (main idea), such as washing hands before dinner. Have him or her give examples of why the rule is important.

Name________________ Komodo Dragons

Writing Across Texts

Directions: Consider what you learned about the lizards from reading *Komodo Dragons* and "Two Uncommon Lizards." What are some of the characteristics of each lizard? Add five characteristics to each column in the table.

Facts About the Komodo Dragon
It is ten feet long.
1. **It can be found on Komodo Island, near Australia.**
2. **It is covered with scales.**
3. **It has long claws.**
4. **It can use its tongue to smell.**
5. **It has sharp teeth.**

Facts About the Horned Lizard
It is 3–5 inches long.
6. **It has spines on the back of its head.**
7. **It can be found in the United States.**
8. **It eats a lot of ants.**
9. **It has a wide, flat body.**
10. **It sprays from its eyes for protection.**

Facts About the Glass Lizard
It is over three feet long.
11. **It has no legs.**
12. **It has movable eyelids.**
13. **It can be different colors.**
14. **It moves its tail for protection.**
15. **It is found in Eurasia and the Americas.**

Write a Compare/Contrast Paragraph

Look at the characteristics of each lizard and decide how they are alike and different. On a separate sheet of paper, write a paragraph comparing and contrasting the three kinds of lizards. Support your paragraph with facts from the boxes.

Paragraphs will vary. Check that students base their paragraphs on details from the two stories.

Notes for Home: Your child compared and contrasted information about lizards. ***Home Activity:*** Read a story or article with your child and discuss how characters, events, and place descriptions are the same and different.

Grammar Practice Book 4.2, p. 46

Name________________ Komodo Dragons

Grammar: Irregular Plural Nouns

REVIEW

Directions: Read each singular noun. Then circle the correct plural form for each one.

Singular	Plural
1. deer	(deer) / deers
2. wolf	wolfs / (wolves)
3. foot	(feet) / foots
4. tooth	tooths / (teeth)
5. woman	(women) / womans
6. ox	oxes / (oxen)
7. mouse	mices / (mice)
8. goose	(geese) / gooses
9. child	childrens / (children)
10. man	mans / (men)

Directions: Use the plural form of the noun in ( ) to complete each sentence. Write the plural noun on the line to the left.

leaves 11. The path through the woods was covered with _____. (leaf)

feet 12. One hiker put her _____ down on something hard. (foot)

teeth 13. Bending down to look, she picked up some large _____. (tooth)

women 14. Two other _____ suggested an explanation. (woman)

wolves 15. They had heard _____ howling in the night. (wolf)

Notes for Home: Your child chose and wrote nouns that change form in the plural, such as *children.* ***Home Activity:*** Encourage your child to make up a short story with the irregular plural nouns that she or he circled and wrote above.

Grammar Practice Book 4.2, p. 47

Name______________________ Komodo Dragons

Grammar: Possessive Nouns

A noun that shows who owns, or possesses, something is a **possessive noun.**

- Add an **apostrophe (')** and **-s** to a singular noun to make it a possessive noun.
  the **bear**'s claws the **fish**'s eggs
- Add just an **apostrophe (')** to a plural noun that ends in **-s** to make it a possessive noun.
  the two **girls**' mother these **families**' homes
- Add an **apostrophe (')** and **-s** to a plural noun that does not end in **-s** to make it a possessive noun.
  the **mice**'s nest the **men**'s caps

Directions: Circle the possessive noun in ( ) to complete each sentence.

1. The (scientist's/scientists) work was hard, but she would not stop.
2. The (county's/counties) new road would go through the middle of the forest.
3. She had to find the four (bears/bears') den before the road was built.
4. Then she noticed a clue in a (tree's/trees') huge trunk.
5. She had discovered the (den's/dens') location!

Directions: Write the possessive form of the noun in ( ) to complete each sentence.

cubs' 6. The three (cubs) first days were cold and snowy.

bears' 7. The (bears) mother was sleepy, but she took good care of her babies.

sun's 8. In the spring, the (sun) rays made the cubs feel warm and frisky.

bees' 9. Once they heard bees humming and found the (bees) hive.

honey's 10. The (honey) flavor was delicious!

Notes for Home: Your child formed possessive nouns to show ownership, such as *the tree's leaves. **Home Activity:*** Ask your child to describe some favorite possessions. Then help your child make labels that use the possessive form, such as *Rosa's hat.*

Grammar: Possessive Nouns 213

Grammar Practice Book 4.2, p. 48

Name______________________ Komodo Dragons

Grammar: Possessive Nouns

Directions: Circle the possessive noun in ( ) to complete each sentence.

1. Many (visitors/visitors') love of animals grows at Yosemite National Park.
2. A (park's/parks) wildlife includes bears, badgers, otters, and moose.
3. A (badgers/badger's) way of doing things is stubborn and fearless.
4. An (otters'/otter's) playfulness is wonderful to watch!
5. Don't you admire the (moose/moose's) huge antlers?

Directions: Write the possessive form of the noun in ( ) to complete each sentence. Then, circle **S** if the possessive noun is singular. Circle **P** if the possessive noun is plural.

hikers' 6. The two (hikers) trip to the forest had seemed dull. S (P)

birds' 7. True, they had found three (birds) nests. S (P)

rabbits' 8. Malcolm had even discovered some (rabbits) tracks. S (P)

forest's 9. For most of the day though, the (forest) sights were fairly ordinary. (S) P

grizzly's 10. Then Keisha saw a (grizzly) paw prints in the mud by a creek! (S) P

Write a Fantasy

Write a fantasy story about an animal family with human qualities. Use at least five possessive nouns in order to tell about the family members.

Students should use at least five possessive nouns, correctly spelled, to describe the members of the animal family.

Notes for Home: Your child identified and wrote possessive nouns—nouns that show ownership, such as *the bear's claws. **Home Activity:*** Invite your child to make a list of favorite things or qualities that belong to friends and family *(my grandparents' house, Aunt Joyce's smile).*

214 Grammar: Possessive Nouns

Grammar Practice Book 4.2, p. 49

Name______________________ Komodo Dragons

Grammar: Possessive Nouns RETEACHING

Study the chart. Then complete the rules for making the possessive forms of singular and plural nouns.

Singular Noun	Singular Possessive Noun
parent / lady	parent's / lady's
man / deer	man's / deer's
Plural Noun	**Plural Possessive Noun**
parents / ladies	parents' / ladies'
men / deer	men's / deer's

1. If the noun is singular, add **'s** .
2. If the plural noun ends in **-s**, add **'** .
3. If the plural noun does not end in **-s**, add **'s** .

Singular and plural nouns can show ownership. To make the possessive form of a singular noun, add an **apostrophe (')** and **-s.** To make the possessive form of a plural noun that ends in **-s,** add an **apostrophe (').** To make the possessive form of a plural noun that does not end in **-s,** add an **apostrophe (')** and **-s.**

Directions: Add an apostrophe or an apostrophe and **-s** to each noun.

1. (plural) sheep **'s** wool
2. mouse **'s** holes
3. cat **'s** meows
4. foxes **'** dens
5. trucks **'** wheels
6. driver **'s** maps
7. dog **'s** barks
8. (plural) elk **'s** horns
9. (plural) deer **'s** coats
10. birds **'** nests
11. roads **'** signs
12. whistles **'** blasts

Notes for Home: Your child identified and wrote singular and plural possessive nouns. ***Home Activity:*** Have your child write a story about animals and their qualities. (For example: *Once there was a giraffe with a long neck.*) Remind your child to use possessive nouns.

Grammar: Possessive Nouns 215

Grammar Practice Book 4.2, p. 50

Name______________________ Komodo Dragons

Grammar: Possessive Nouns

Directions: Use the possessive form of each noun to fill in the blanks.

children trees birds gardener flowers park goose

1. The **park's** gates were opened for the children.
2. The children liked the **flowers'** bright colors.
3. The **trees'** leaves were beginning to turn.
4. Fall flowers were the **gardener's** favorites.
5. The **birds'** nests were filled with eggs.
6. The **children's** trip to the park was fun.
7. The **goose's** honking made them laugh.

Directions: Underline the correct form of the noun in parentheses.

8. Our (gardens/garden's) flowers are beautiful.
9. Few flowers can survive most (deserts/deserts') hot temperatures.
10. People admire open (prairies/prairies') bright flowers.
11. A (ponds/pond's) flowers have roots in the mud bottom.
12. The (flowers/flowers') heads are lifted to the sun.
13. (Sunflowers/Sunflowers') grow very tall.
14. (Gardeners/Gardeners') flowers are carefully tended.

Write a Song

On a separate sheet of paper, write a song about a garden. Write possessive forms of nouns in your song.

Make sure students spell possessive forms of nouns correctly in their songs.

Notes for Home: Your child wrote and identified singular and plural possessive nouns in sentences. ***Home Activity:*** Have your child use his or her song about a garden to explain to you how to make the possessive forms of singular and plural nouns.

216 Grammar: Possessive Nouns

Practice Book 4.2, p. 98

Name

Komodo Dragons

Phonics: r-Controlled Vowels

Directions: Many vowels have a different sound when they are followed by the letter **r.** Listen to the difference in **cat** and **cart.** Read each sentence below. Each sentence has a word with a vowel followed by the letter **r.** Write the word on the line. Underline the **r-controlled vowel** you hear and see in the word.

sharp 1. Many animals in the wild have sharp claws.

fur 2. An animal's fur protects it from the cold.

survive 3. Many wild animals today have to fight against human progress to survive.

near 4. It is sometimes not wise to live too near wild animals.

birth 5. The birth of a wild animal in captivity is often a great accomplishment.

curious 6. One should be cautious around wild animals who seem curious about people.

dark 7. Some animals come out at night, protected by the dark.

deer 8. The deer come out at night to eat the leaves off low-hanging trees.

hours 9. I could sit and watch these animals for hours.

Directions: Read the words in the box. Some words have the same vowel sound as **for.** Other words have the same vowel sound as **word.** Write each word in the correct column. **Order may vary.**

north
armor
shore
born
predator
monitor

for	word
10. north	13. armor
11. shore	14. predator
12. born	15. monitor

Notes for Home: Your child listened for words where the letter *r* changes the sound of the vowel that precedes it, such as *start, morning, shirt,* and *curious. Home Activity:* Read a book about animals with your child. Have your child look for words with these sounds.

Spelling Workbook 4.2, p. 37

Name

Komodo Dragons

Spelling: Vowels with r

Pretest Directions: Fold back the page along the dotted line. On the blanks, write the spelling words as they are dictated. When you have finished the test, unfold the page and check your words.

1. storm	1. A **storm** is brewing.
2. morning	2. It is chilly this **morning**.
3. forest	3. The **forest** is lush.
4. Florida	4. Oranges grow in **Florida.**
5. form	5. **Form** the clay into a bird.
6. pour	6. **Pour** milk on the cereal.
7. fourteen	7. We saw **fourteen** lizards.
8. court	8. The judge is in **court**.
9. fourth	9. I am **fourth** in line.
10. course	10. This **course** is rocky.
11. serve	11. **Serve** them lemonade.
12. herself	12. She made it **herself.**
13. certain	13. Are you **certain** he's here?
14. nerve	14. A pinched **nerve** hurts.
15. perfect	15. What a **perfect** day!
16. dirty	16. The dishes are **dirty**.
17. first	17. This is my **first** pet.
18. girlfriend	18. Invite your **girlfriend** along too!
19. thirsty	19. Is the baby **thirsty**?
20. skirt	20. Her **skirt** is bright red.

Notes for Home: Your child took a pretest on words that have vowel sounds with the letter *r*. *Home Activity:* Help your child learn misspelled words before the final test. See if there are any similar errors and discuss a memory trick that could help.

Spelling Workbook 4.2, p. 38

Name

Komodo Dragons

Spelling: Vowels with r

Word List			
storm	pour	serve	dirty
morning	fourteen	herself	first
forest	court	certain	girlfriend
Florida	fourth	nerve	thirsty
form	course	perfect	skirt

Directions: Write the words that have the same vowel sound as **for.** Sort the words according to the way the vowel sound is spelled. **Order may vary.**

Spelled our	Spelled or
1. pour	6. storm
2. fourteen	7. morning
3. court	8. forest
4. fourth	9. Florida
5. course	10. form

Directions: Write the word from the box that belongs in each group.

11. skin, bone, nerve

12. offer, provide, serve

13. positive, definite, certain

14. blouse, dress, skirt

15. filthy, sloppy, dirty

16. hungry, dry, thirsty

17. myself, himself, herself

18. third, second, first or fourth

19. ideal, excellent, perfect

20. boyfriend, buddy, girlfriend

Notes for Home: Your child spelled words where the letter *r* changes the way the vowel sounds *(storm, fourth, serve, first). Home Activity:* Help your child think of other words with these vowel sounds and spellings.

Spelling Workbook 4.2, p. 39

Name

Komodo Dragons

Spelling: Vowels with r

Directions: Proofread this entry from an explorer's log. Find five spelling mistakes. Use the proofreading marks to correct each mistake.

≡	Make a capital.
/	Make a small letter.
∧	Add something.
↝	Take out something.
⊙	Add a period.
¶	Begin a new paragraph.

Everglades, Flodrida

Today I saw my first baby alligator! Since this is my forth (u added) day here, I had almost given up hope. I was not cirtain (corrected to er) whether I would ever see the wildlife I was looking for. And of corse (u added), yesterday, we had a huge storm, and I couldn't see anything then.

Then I saw a dark fourm (u taken out) coming out of the swamp. Was it an alligator? Yes! Hurray!

Spelling Tip

The vowel sounds in **fourth** and **storm** sound the same, but are spelled differently. The same is true of **serve** and **dirty.** Check the log entry to see if the vowels with **r** have been spelled correctly.

Word List	
storm	serve
morning	herself
forest	certain
Florida	nerve
form	perfect
pour	dirty
fourteen	first
court	girlfriend
fourth	thirsty
course	skirt

Write a Log Entry

Imagine that you are exploring a part of the world where you can see animals in the wild. On a separate sheet of paper, describe an experience. Use at least three spelling words.

Answers will vary, but each log should include at least three spelling words.

Notes for Home: Your child spelled words where the letter *r* changes the way the vowel sounds *(storm, fourth, serve, first). Home Activity:* Help your child divide the words on the list into four columns: words with *or, our, ir,* and *er.* Then take turns making up sentences with each word.

Spelling Workbook 4.2, p. 40

Name

Komodo Dragons

Spelling: Vowels with *r*

REVIEW

Word List				
storm	form	fourth	certain	first
morning	pour	course	nerve	girlfriend
forest	fourteen	serve	perfect	thirsty
Florida	court	herself	dirty	skirt

Directions: Choose the word from the box that rhymes with each word. Write the word on the line. Use a word only once.

1. thirst **first**
2. north **fourth**
3. dirt **skirt**
4. short **court**
5. more **pour**
6. horse **course**
7. dorm **storm (or form)**
8. norm **form (or storm)**
9. verve **serve (or nerve)**
10. swerve **nerve (or serve)**

Directions: Choose the word from the box that best replaces the underlined word or words. Write the word on the line.

girlfriend 11. One day my female friend, Malika, and I went out.

morning 12. It was still the early part of the day.

forest 13. We were on vacation in a cabin in the woods.

Florida 14. The cabin was in a southern state.

fourteen 15. We were going to stay one more than thirteen days.

certain 16. Malika was sure that we would see interesting wildlife.

dirty 17. "Everything is so dusty and filthy!" I complained.

perfect 18. "No, it's faultless," said Malika.

thirsty 19. I was in need of a drink, so we went to the store.

herself 20. Malika bought some gum for her own use.

Notes for Home: Your child spelled words where the letter *r* changes the way the vowel sounds (*storm, fourth, serve, first*). ***Home Activity:*** Have your child say one of the words on the list. Together, think of other words that rhyme. Challenge your child to spell some of the rhyming words.

Spelling: Vowels with *r* 221

Practice Book 4.2, p. 99

Name

Komodo Dragons

Encyclopedia

An **encyclopedia** gives general information about many different subjects. Encyclopedias are organized in a set of **volumes,** or books, usually in alphabetical order. An **entry** is an encyclopedia article. Entries are listed in alphabetical order. An **entry word** is the word or phrase that begins each entry and tells its subject. To find information in an encyclopedia, use a **key word** that identifies the information you are trying to find.

Directions: Use this encyclopedia entry about Komodo Island to answer the questions that follow.

> KOMODO ISLAND has only one village and fewer than 500 people. The Komodo Island National Park takes up most of the space on Komodo Island.
>
> Many of the mountains on the island were formed by volcanoes. These volcanic mountains are usually brown and lifeless. Every year, however, during monsoon season, these mountains appear green. This color comes from small tropical plants that grow on the hill slopes.
>
> Komodo Island is one of the few places left on Earth where the Komodo dragon can be found. About 1,000 Komodo dragons live there. Komodo dragons are giant monitor lizards that run wild on the island. They can grow to up to 10 feet long, weigh up to 300 pounds, and live for 100 years.

1. What key word would someone have looked up to find this article?
Komodo Island

2. Would the entry above appear before or after an entry on Koala bears? Explain.
It would appear after the entry on Koala bears because entries are listed in alphabetical order. "Komodo" comes alphabetically after "Koala."

3. What key word would you use to find more information about monsoons?
monsoons

4. What key word would you use to find information about volcanoes?
volcanoes

5. Suppose you have a volume of an encyclopedia marked "M." Name two entry words you might find in this volume.
Check that answers begin with the letter *m*.

222 Research and Study Skills: Encyclopedia

Practice Book 4.2, p. 100

Name

Komodo Dragons

Directions: Read the encyclopedia entry about reptiles. Use the entry to answer the questions that follow.

> **REPTILES** are a group of animals that include snakes, lizards, turtles, crocodiles, the tuatara, and many extinct creatures. The bodies of many snakes are covered with scales. Reptiles can be found in temperate and tropical climates around the world. They are cold-blooded animals, so most of them cannot live in polar regions.
>
> **Reptile behavior.** Most reptiles lay eggs, but many lizards and snakes give birth to live offspring. When the winter is cold, some reptiles *estivate*—this means they become inactive. Most reptiles rely on the sun's heat to stay warm.

6. Would you expect to find an article about tigers before or after the reptiles entry in the encyclopedia? Explain.
An article on tigers would come after the reptiles entry because the entries are listed in alphabetical order.

7. What key word would you use to find out more about snakes?
snakes

8. What section of the entry contains information about how reptiles act?
Reptile behavior

9. What letter would likely be on the volume of the encyclopedia that contains this entry on reptiles?
R

10. If you wanted to get information about the reptile exhibit at your local zoo, would an encyclopedia be a good reference source? Explain.
Possible answer: No, an encyclopedia only gives general information about a subject.

Notes for Home: Your child read encyclopedia entries and answered questions about them. ***Home Activity:*** Brainstorm questions about related topics. Ask your child to tell the key words he or she would use to look up more information in an encyclopedia.

Research and Study Skills: Encyclopedia 223

Name

Description Web

Directions: Write your topic (the person you will describe) on the line in the Topic circle. Then organize details about this person by writing them in the Details circles.

Answers will vary. The Description Web should be filled out completely.

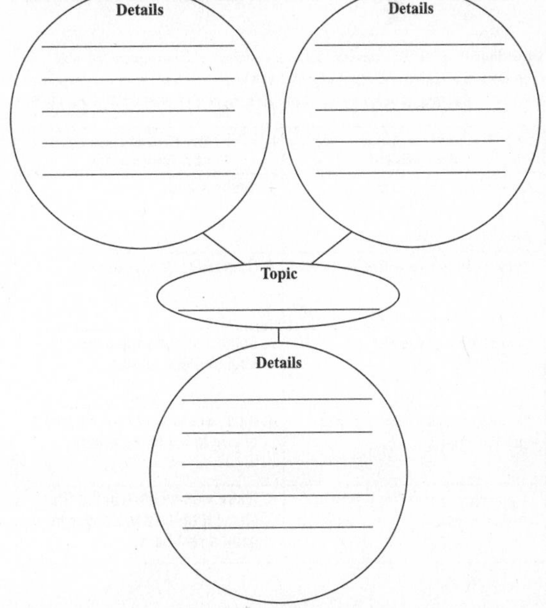

Notes for Home: Your child recently organized information for a description. ***Home Activity:*** Have your child describe a quality of a family member in time order. *Grandma's hair was blond when she was born. It was brown when she got married. Now it's white.*

224 Unit 2: Writing Process

Name______________________________

Elaboration

Sense Words

- One way to elaborate is by adding **sense words** that help readers picture things clearly.
- You can provide vivid images by telling how things look, sound, feel, taste, and smell.

Directions: Choose words from the box to make each sentence below more interesting. Write your new sentence on the line.

fragrant	warm	tasty	hurriedly	red	rickety
smoky	cluttered	bright	sparkling	wooden	excitedly
burned	frequently	noisy	messy	black	friendly

Possible answers given.

1. Our kitchen is where we get together.
Our smoky, warm kitchen is where we get together.

2. We all sit around a table and talk.
We all sit around a cluttered table and talk excitedly.

3. We take turns cooking meals.
We take turns cooking tasty meals.

4. Smells fill other rooms.
Fragrant smells fill other rooms.

5. Friends come for dinner.
Noisy friends join us for dinner at the rickety, wooden table.

6. We often fill all eight chairs.
We often fill all eight sagging chairs.

Notes for Home: Your child recently expanded sentences by adding sense words. ***Home Activity:*** Ask your child to describe the looks, smells, and tastes of lunch today. For example: *The warm, noisy cafeteria smelled like pizza.*

Name______________________________

Self-Evaluation Guide

Descriptive Paragraph

Directions: Think about the final draft of your description. Then answer each question below. **Answers will vary. Students' responses should show that they have given thought to the description that they have written.**

	Yes	No	Not sure
1. Does my description tell about a person that is special to me?			
2. Did I use descriptive words and images to give readers a good picture of this person?			
3. Did I keep my audience and purpose in mind?			
4. Did I present my ideas in an organized way?			
5. Did I proofread and edit carefully to avoid errors?			

6. What part of your description do you think gives the best picture of your special person?

____

____

7. Write one thing that you could change to make this description even better (a word, phrase, or sentence).

____

____

____

Notes for Home: Your child recently wrote a description. ***Home Activity:*** Encourage your child to tell you one way he or she tried to make this description vivid.

Practice Book 4.3, p. 101

Name______________________ John Henry

Making Judgments

- **Making judgments** means thinking about and deciding how to react toward people, situations, and ideas in stories and articles that you read.
- Use what you know and your experience as you make judgments.

Directions: Reread "Welcome to McBroom's Farm." Then complete the table. For each story event, give evidence from what you know and from your own experience that makes a judgment about how realistic each event is. **Possible answers given.**

Story Event	My Knowledge and Experience
Seeds burst in the ground.	1. **Seeds sprout.**
Crops shoot right up before your eyes.	2. **Crops take weeks to grow.**
A nickel grew to a quarter.	3. **Coins can't change from one kind into one another.**
The hat would take a day or two to reach the ground.	4. **A hat would only take a second or two to fall to the ground.**
The stranger painted the no-barn in less than a second.	5. **There was no barn in the first place. It takes a lot longer to paint a real barn.**

Notes for Home: Your child read a story and used his or her knowledge, story details, and life experience to make judgments. ***Home Activity:*** Read a tall tale with your child. Ask him or her to find places where the author has exaggerated in order to make a funny story.

Practice Book 4.3, p. 102

Name______________________ John Henry

Vocabulary

Directions: Read the story about Paul Bunyan. Choose the word from the box that best completes each sentence. You will use some words more than once. Write the word on the matching numbered line below.

Check the Words You Know
- __ boulder
- __ glimpse
- __ hollered
- __ horizon
- __ rhythm
- __ shivered
- __ tunnel

A gusty wind blew into the **1.** _____ that ran through the mountain. Paul Bunyan **2.** _____ with cold. Moving outside, he caught a **3.** _____ of a log cabin with smoke coming out its chimney. The cabin was far off on the **4.** _____. Quickly, Paul Bunyan stepped over a huge **5.** _____ and was soon on his way to getting warm.

Paul walked on with a steady, quick **6.** _____. He was getting warmer, so he no longer **7.** _____. When he **8.** _____ from a hilltop, he heard his echo. He remembered how dark it had been inside that **9.** _____. But the sun on the **10.** _____ made everything look brighter.

1. **tunnel**
2. **shivered**
3. **glimpse**
4. **horizon**
5. **boulder**
6. **rhythm**
7. **shivered**
8. **hollered**
9. **tunnel**
10. **horizon**

Write a Tall Tale

On a separate sheet of paper, create a tall tale about an amazing hero—real or imaginary. Tell how your hero gets out of a difficult situation. Use as many of the vocabulary words as you can. **Students' tall tales should use vocabulary words correctly.**

Notes for Home: Your child identified and used words from *John Henry*. ***Home Activity:*** With your child, make up your own tale about an amazing person who can do incredible things. Include the vocabulary words whenever you can.

Practice Book 4.3, p. 103

Name________________________ **John Henry**

Making Judgments

- **Making judgments** means thinking about and deciding how to react to people, situations, and ideas in a story.

Directions: Reread this description of John Henry smashing the boulder. Then answer the questions below. Support each answer with story details.

"Don't see how you can do what dynamite couldn't," said the boss of the crew.

John Henry chuckled. "Just watch me." He swung one of his hammers round and round his head. It made such a wind that leaves blew off the trees and birds fell out of the sky.

RINGGGGGG!

The hammer hit the boulder. That boulder shivered like you do on a cold winter morning when it looks like the school bus is never going to come.

RINGGGGGG!

The boulder shivered like the morning when freedom came to the slaves.

Possible answers given.

1. What do you think the crew boss thinks of John Henry?
The crew boss doubts John Henry. He says, "Don't see how you can do what dynamite couldn't."

2. How do you think John Henry feels about his own abilities?
He's confident. He says, "Just watch me."

3. What is one way you can tell that *John Henry* is a legend?
You can tell by statements such as, "It made such a wind that leaves blew off the trees and birds fell out of the sky."

4. Do you think the comparison, "That boulder shivered like you do on a cold winter morning when it looks like the school bus is never going to come" is a good one?
Yes, it helps readers vividly picture John Henry hitting the boulder.

5. On a separate sheet of paper, write a description of the kind of person you think John Henry is. Include details from the story.
He has a good sense of humor. He sits in a chair during a race.

Notes for Home: Your child used story details to make judgments about a story and its characters. ***Home Activity:*** Have your child choose a character from a book or a TV show and make judgments about the character's behavior, using details from the work.

Making Judgments 231

Practice Book 4.3, p. 105

Name________________________ **John Henry**

Selection Test

Directions: Choose the best answer to each item. Mark the letter for the answer you have chosen.

Part 1: Vocabulary

Find the answer choice that means about the same as the underlined word in each sentence.

1. The young boy shivered.
   A. fell asleep
   (B) shook
   C. fainted
   D. disappeared

2. Tanya got a glimpse of the car.
   F. bad smell
   G. honking noise
   (H) short look
   J. long report

3. The men dug a tunnel.
   (A) underground passage
   B. shallow ditch
   C. canal for water
   D. deep well

4. There was a boulder in the road.
   (F) large rock
   G. bump
   H. red light
   J. yellow line

5. The captain searched the horizon.
   A. forward part of a ship
   B. deepest part of the ocean
   C. person who hides on a ship
   (D) line where earth and sky seem to meet

6. That song has a nice rhythm.
   F. pleasing sound
   (G) regular beat
   H. musical note
   J. piano part

7. Josie hollered at us.
   A. laughed
   B. threw things
   (C) yelled
   D. blew bubbles

Part 2: Comprehension

Use what you know about the story to answer each item.

8. This story is mostly about—
   F. the meanest man in the state.
   G. unicorns living in the woods.
   H. people building a railroad.
   (J) the adventures of John Henry.

GO ON

232 Selection Test

Practice Book 4.3, p. 106

Name________________________ **John Henry**

9. What happened when John Henry was born?
   A. The sun did not shine that day.
   (B) Birds and animals came to see him.
   C. His parents threw him a birthday party.
   D. A rainbow shined in the sky.

10. As everyone admired the new baby, he suddenly began to—
    (F) grow.
    G. cry.
    H. smile.
    J. blush.

11. How was John Henry different from other newborn babies?
    A. He was quite small for his age.
    B. He liked to sleep all day.
    (C) He was fully grown in one day.
    D. He was born at night.

12. Ferret-Faced Freddy became Frederick the Friendly after John Henry—
    (F) beat him in a race.
    G. gave him a soda.
    H. beat him in a fight.
    J. asked for his help.

13. John Henry was like a steam drill in that he—
    A. was taller than most men.
    B. produced smoke and steam when he hammered.
    (C) could hammer faster and harder than ten men.
    D. wore a rainbow on his shoulders.

14. How did John Henry feel about his special strength?
    F. He was embarrassed by it.
    (G) He was happy to have it.
    H. He was ashamed of it.
    J. He felt the need to work harder because of it.

15. The author of this story would most likely agree that John Henry—
    A. did not live his life to the fullest.
    B. was an angry man who always needed to prove his strength.
    C. was foolish for racing a steam drill and dying because of it.
    (D) was a hero to the people who knew him.

Selection Test 233

Name________________________ **John Henry**

Making Judgments

- **Making judgments** means thinking about and reacting to people, situations, and issues in a story or an article.

Directions: Read the story below.

Mr. Jackson took care of everything in the apartment house. But the first day he was on vacation, a pipe leaked in Mrs. Dahl's kitchen. Her one-year-old son, Carl, calmly tied one of his diapers around the pipe. It stopped leaking. The amazed Mrs. Dahl told the story to Mrs. Noah.

The second day Baby Dahl unstuck a window in Mrs. Noah's apartment with baby lotion. By evening he was a legend among the neighbors. They called him Super Duper Baby.

By the end of the week he had fixed the washing machine, patched the roof, and gotten the weeds to leave and promise never to return.

Mr. Jackson decided to retire. Super Duper Baby took care of everything from then on—except at nap time.

Directions: Complete the table by making judgments and using story details to support them. **Possible answers given.**

Questions	Judgment
What do you think was Mrs. Dahl's opinion of her baby?	1. **She thought it was amazing that he could fix her pipe.**
Why do you think Mrs. Noah had Baby Dahl fix her window?	2. **She heard of his amazing deed from his mother.**
What do you think the neighbors thought of Baby Dahl?	3. **They thought he was incredible and called him Super Duper Baby.**
Do you think Baby Dahl could do all those things?	4. **No, his actions are all unbelievable for a one-year-old child.**
How do you think the author expects you to react to the story?	5. **The author means it to be funny by having the baby do unbelievable tasks.**

Notes for Home: Your child used story details to make judgments about characters, actions, and the author's purpose. ***Home Activity:*** Tell a story about something that happened today. Exaggerate some details. Ask your child to make judgments about what could or couldn't be true.

234 Making Judgments

Practice Book 4.3, p. 107

Name______________________ John Henry

Character

REVIEW

Directions: Read the story. Then read each question about the story. Choose the best answer to each question. Mark the letter for the answer you have chosen.

Paul Bunyan Travels the Country

Paul Bunyan swung his ax through the forest. "Timber!" he hollered to make sure people got out of the way safely. The forest was gone in minutes. The loggers who needed wood to build houses waved happily. They shouted good-by as he left for another forest.

At the next forest, farmers were clearing the land. At first, they trembled at the sight of Paul. Then they cheered as they saw how fast he could clear their farmland.

Paul moved from forest to forest until he got tired. "I need to find other people who can clear trees and haul logs," he thought. But he never did find anyone with his size and strength. To this day, Paul Bunyan is remembered across the country for what happened when he yelled "Timber!"

1. Why did Paul holler "Timber!" to the loggers?
   A. to tease them
   B. to entertain them
   C. to confuse them
   (D) to warn them

2. How did the loggers feel when Paul cut the trees?
   F. angry
   G. disgusted
   (H) grateful
   J. sad

3. When the farmers first saw Paul, how did they feel?
   (A) frightened
   B. mean
   C. rude
   D. quiet

4. Paul wanted to find people to help him so he could—
   F. plant more trees.
   G. be remembered.
   (H) rest his body.
   J. build houses.

5. In the end, how did people treat Paul?
   A. They ignored him.
   B. They mocked him.
   C. They forgot him.
   (D) They remembered him.

Notes for Home: Your child identified a character's traits through his words and actions. ***Home Activity:*** With your child, read newspaper articles about people. Take turns telling what you think the people in the story are like, based on what they did or said.

Name______________________ John Henry

Writing Across Texts

Directions: Think about the two versions of the legend of John Henry that you read. In many ways they are alike, but there are ways in which they differ. Fill in the boxes below with information from each version.

John Henry The Story	John Henry The Poem
John Henry's size when he was a baby	
1. **He was normal baby size in the story.**	2. **In the poem, he could fit on the palm of your hand.**
How fast he grew	
3. **In the story, he grew overnight.**	4. **In the poem, he grew gradually.**
What his parents thought he would do	
5. **In the story, his dad gave him sledgehammers that belonged to his grandfather to make his way in the world.**	6. **In the poem, his mom said he would be a steel drivin' man.**
How John Henry died	
7. **In the story, he beat the steam drill and then died.**	8. **In the poem, he died when he hammered in the Big Bend Tunnel.**
Where John Henry was buried	
9. **In the story, he was buried on the White House lawn.**	10. **In the poem, he was buried by the railroad track.**

Write a Comparison/Contrast

On a separate sheet of paper, write a paragraph in which you say what is the same and what is different about the two versions of the legend of John Henry. Use the information from the boxes above. **Essays will vary. Check that students use**

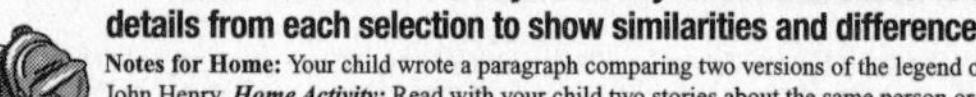

details from each selection to show similarities and differences.

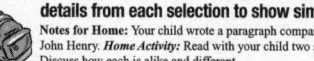

Notes for Home: Your child wrote a paragraph comparing two versions of the legend of John Henry. ***Home Activity:*** Read with your child two stories about the same person or topic. Discuss how each is alike and different.

Grammar Practice Book 4.3, p. 51

Name______________________ John Henry

Grammar: Predicates

REVIEW

Directions: Underline the complete predicate in each sentence. Then circle each simple predicate. (There may be more than one in a sentence.)

1. Paul Bunyan **found** Babe the Blue Ox during the winter of the blue snow.
2. Babe **fell** into a frozen river.
3. The icy water **caused** the ox's blue color.
4. Paul Bunyan **rescued** Babe and **carried** him back to the logging camp.
5. This famous logger **built** Babe a big barn.

Directions: Think about the life of a logger and his pet ox. Add a word or words to each subject below to form a sentence. Write the complete sentence on the line. **Possible answers given.**

6. The big logger _____.
   The big logger chopped trees faster than anyone else.
7. The strong ox _____.
   The strong ox helped haul the logs to town.
8. The logger and his ox _____.
   The logger and his ox worked long and hard.
9. The other loggers _____.
   The other loggers were amazed at how fast the two worked.
10. The cook at the logging camp _____.
    The cook at the logging camp made pancakes every day.

Notes for Home: Your child identified simple and complete predicates. ***Home Activity:*** Play a simple alphabet game with your child. Take turns thinking of a simple predicate, or verb, that starts with each letter of the alphabet.

Grammar Practice Book 4.3, p. 52

Name______________________ John Henry

Grammar: Verbs

Action verbs are words that show what action someone or something does.

The crew built the railroad tracks. The train raced down the tracks.

Every sentence has a subject and a predicate. The main word in the subject is often a noun. The verb is the main word in the predicate.

The people cheered at the sight of the train.
Subject Predicate

Linking verbs link, or join, the subject to a word in the predicate. The word helps tell what the subject is or what the subject is like. *Am, is, are, was,* and *were* are often used as linking verbs.

The train was noisy. I was surprised at its size and speed.

Directions: Read the paragraph. Underline the verb in each sentence below.

1. The old train left the station. **2.** At first, it moved slowly. **3.** The engineer rang the bell. **4.** The wheels of the train rolled faster and faster. **5.** Smoke poured from the smokestack. **6.** The rumbling wheels sounded loud. **7.** The train's whistle was a warning. **8.** The train sped down the tracks. **9.** Then the old locomotive slowed its speed. **10.** It stopped at the station exactly on time.

Directions: Add a verb to complete each sentence. The verb should tell what Maria does or what Maria is like. Write the verb on the line to the left. **Possible answers given.**

jumps 11. Maria _____ out of bed early.
walks 12. She _____ quickly into the kitchen.
cooks 13. Next, Maria _____ a huge breakfast.
is 14. She _____ a skilled carpenter.
builds 15. Today, she _____ a cradle for a baby.

Notes for Home: Your child wrote action verbs and linking verbs. ***Home Activity:*** Play an action words game with your child. Say, for example, *Mrs. West [pause] the school bus.* Ask your child to supply the missing verb *(drives).* Switch roles and play again.

Grammar Practice Book 4.3, p. 53
Name___________________ John Henry

Grammar: Verbs

Directions: Circle the verb in each sentence. Write **A** on the line if the verb is an action verb. Write **L** if it is a linking verb. Keep in mind that some action verbs such as *know* or *decide* show actions you cannot see.

A 1. The construction crew (worked) very hard that hot summer day.
A 2. Frederick (wanted) a cold drink of water and a rest.
L 3. Susannah (is) tired and hungry.
A 4. Finally, the crew (finished) the new road.
L 5. They (are) proud of their smooth, gray highway.

Directions: Choose a verb from the box to complete each sentence. Write the verb on the line to the left.

build	grew	felt	looks	was

build 6. Didn't Lydia's family _____ their own mountain cabin?
felt 7. At first, they _____ nervous about doing the work themselves.
grew 8. After a while, they _____ more confident about their skills!
was 9. Pale green paint _____ their choice for the outside walls.
looks 10. The finished cabin now _____ great!

Write a How-To Paragraph

On a separate sheet of paper, write a paragraph telling how to do a simple task, such as tying a small child's shoelaces. Tell the reader what to do: *First, untangle any knots in the shoelaces. Next, . . .* Use at least three verbs. **Each paragraph should describe a task in sequence, using at least three verbs.**

Notes for Home: Your child identified and wrote verbs—words like *build* that show action, or words like *is* that tell what the subject is or is like. ***Home Activity:*** Take turns describing a character and telling what he or she did or is like.

Grammar Practice Book 4.3, p. 54
Name___________________ John Henry

Grammar: Verbs

RETEACHING

Read each sentence. Complete each one with a verb from the list.

am is are tame tames

1. She **is** a clown. 2. They **tame** the lion.

A **linking verb** shows being. It tells what the subject is or was. The forms of the verb **be** are often used as linking verbs. An **action verb** is a word that shows what action someone or something does.

Directions: Read each underlined verb. Circle **action verb** or **linking verb** to describe it.

1. The parade was colorful. action verb (linking verb)
2. Jan admires the costumes. (action verb) linking verb
3. The horses were graceful. action verb (linking verb)
4. Tiny dogs danced happily. (action verb) linking verb
5. I am a tumbler. action verb (linking verb)
6. I jump high into the air. (action verb) linking verb

Directions: Circle each linking verb. Underline each action verb.

7. I like the circus.
8. P. T. Barnum (was) the most famous circus owner.
9. His circus delighted huge crowds everywhere.
10. Circuses (were) small long ago.
11. A modern circus often (is) big.
12. Circus people (are) skillful performers.
13. They invent new tricks all the time.

Notes for Home: Your child identified action and linking verbs in sentences. ***Home Activity:*** Have your child look at a favorite book. Have him or her make a list of all the verbs on one page and say whether they are action or linking verbs.

Grammar Practice Book 4.3, p. 55
Name___________________ John Henry

Grammar: Verbs

Directions: Write an action verb to replace the underlined linking verb in each sentence. The new verb may change the meaning of the sentence. If you need ideas, pick a verb from the box. Remember to write the form of the verb that fits the subject and tense of the sentence.

float	shine	dance	wave	walk	play	howl

Possible answers given.

1. The pencil is on the page. **dances**
2. The sun's rays are in the air. **shine**
3. A cloud is in the sky. **floats**
4. The wind was outside all night. **howled**
5. The waves were along the shore. **played**

Directions: Imagine that one of the sentences above is the beginning of a story. Using action and linking verbs, write the next two or three sentences of the story.
Make sure students use linking and action verbs in their sentences.

Notes for Home: Your child changed sentences by adding interesting verbs. ***Home Activity:*** Say simple sentences to your child. *(I walked down the street. I went there.)* Have your child replace the verbs with more interesting verbs.

Practice Book 4.3, p. 108
Name___________________ John Henry

Word Study: Inflected Forms with -er and -est

Directions: When you add an ending to some words, you might need to drop an **e**, change **y** to **i**, or double the final consonant. Read each word below. Change the word by adding **-er** or **-est.** Write the new word on the line.

1. fast + -er = **faster**
2. white + -er = **whiter**
3. pretty + -est = **prettiest**
4. mean + -er = **meaner**
5. big + -er = **bigger**
6. funny + -est = **funniest**
7. straight + -est = **straightest**

Directions: Read each sentence. Write the base word of each underlined word on the line.

fast 8. Martha was the fastest worker on the road crew.
large 9. Even though Joe was larger, he couldn't beat her record.
long 10. Bill worked the longest hours of all the crew.
noisy 11. Tom was the noisiest of the bunch.
loud 12. He could yell "Let's move it!" louder than anyone else.
nice 13. Despite his huge size, Anthony was one of the nicest people in the group.
happy 14. I couldn't be happier than to be working with this crew.
smart 15. Taking this job was one of my smarter ideas.

Notes for Home: Your child added *-er* and *-est* to base words to create longer words and identified base words in words ending in *-er* and *-est*. ***Home Activity:*** List some describing words, such as *tall, small, smooth.* Take turns adding *-er* and *-est* to each word.

Spelling Workbook 4.3, p. 41

Name________________________ **John Henry**

Spelling: Adding *-er* and *-est*

Pretest Directions: Fold back the page along the dotted line. On the blanks, write the spelling words as they are dictated. When you have finished the test, unfold the page and check your words.

1. **smaller**	**1.** My shovel is **smaller** than yours.
2. **larger**	**2.** Your truck is **larger** than mine.
3. **happier**	**3.** Tom is **happier** than Anne.
4. **hotter**	**4.** Today is **hotter** than yesterday.
5. **sadder**	**5.** My story is **sadder** than yours.
6. **deeper**	**6.** His hole is **deeper**.
7. **closer**	**7.** Come **closer** to the window.
8. **scarier**	**8.** Which noise is **scarier**?
9. **funnier**	**9.** Whose joke is **funnier**?
10. **fatter**	**10.** That dog looks **fatter** today.
11. **smallest**	**11.** He has the **smallest** feet.
12. **largest**	**12.** Her truck has the **largest** engine.
13. **happiest**	**13.** He's **happiest** when he's outside.
14. **hottest**	**14.** August is the **hottest** month.
15. **saddest**	**15.** Whose story is **saddest**?
16. **deepest**	**16.** Whose hole is **deepest**?
17. **closest**	**17.** Which house is **closest** to town?
18. **scariest**	**18.** I know the **scariest** story of all.
19. **funniest**	**19.** That's the **funniest** joke ever!
20. **fattest**	**20.** I want the **fattest** apple.

Notes for Home: Your child took a pretest on adding *-er* and *-est* to words. ***Home Activity:*** Help your child learn misspelled words before the final test. Your child should look at the word, say it, spell it aloud, and then spell it with eyes shut.

Spelling Workbook 4.3, p. 42

Name________________________ **John Henry**

Spelling: Adding *-er* and *-est*

Word List

smaller	happier	sadder	closer	funnier
smallest	happiest	saddest	closest	funniest
larger	hotter	deeper	scarier	fatter
largest	hottest	deepest	scariest	fattest

Directions: Choose the words from the box in which the spelling of the base word changed before **-er** or **-est** was added. Write each word in the correct column.

Order may vary.

Final Consonant Doubled	y changed to i
1. **hotter**	7. **happier**
2. **hottest**	8. **happiest**
3. **sadder**	9. **scarier**
4. **saddest**	10. **scariest**
5. **fatter**	11. **funnier**
6. **fattest**	12. **funniest**

Directions: Add **-er** or **-est** to each word in ( ) to form a word from the box that completes each sentence. Write the word on the line.

largest **13.** Gerry liked to climb the (large) tree in his yard.
larger **14.** He had never climbed a tree that was (large).
smallest **15.** His sister would climb to the (small) branch.
smaller **16.** It was (small) than a baseball bat.
closest **17.** Gerry and his sister were the (close) of friends.
closer **18.** They were (close) than anyone thought possible.
deepest **19.** They would go exploring in the (deep) caves.
deeper **20.** "The (deep), the better," they would say.

Notes for Home: Your child spelled words that end in *-er* and *-est.* ***Home Activity:*** Have fun playing "Can You Top This?" Write, for example, *Monday was hot.* Ask your child to write, for example, *Tuesday was hotter.* Then you write, *Wednesday was the hottest.*

Spelling Workbook 4.3, p. 43

Name________________________ **John Henry**

Spelling: Adding *-er* and *-est*

Directions: Proofread this diary entry. Find five spelling mistakes. Use the proofreading marks to correct each mistake.

≡ Make a capital.
/ Make a small letter.
∧ Add something.
Take out something.
○ Add a period.
¶ Begin a new paragraph.

April 1
Dear Diary,
The scar~~r~~iest thing happened to me. I was kidnapped by space pigs! They were the smal[l]est, funniest creatures I've ever seen. They were no large~~e~~r than mice. They took me to their spaceship, which was hot[t]er than a rain forest. Then I was saved by a superhero. I don't know his name, but he was the strongest person I've ever seen. When he flew me back to Earth, it was almost scar[i]~~y~~er than being kidnapped!

Spelling Tip

Some base words change their spelling before the endings **-er** and **-est** are added. You may need to drop a final **e** as in **larger,** double a final consonant as in **saddest,** or change **y** to **i** as in **funnier.**

Word List

smaller	deeper
smallest	deepest
larger	closer
largest	closest
happier	scarier
happiest	scariest
hotter	funnier
hottest	funniest
sadder	fatter
saddest	fattest

Write a Diary Entry

Imagine you are a larger-than-life hero. On a separate sheet of paper, write a diary entry describing one of your incredible acts of heroism. Try to use at least three spelling words. **Answers will vary, but each diary entry should include at least three spelling words.**

Notes for Home: Your child spelled words that end in *-er* and *-est.* ***Home Activity:*** Help your child think of other base words to which he or she could add the endings *-er* and *-est,* such as *big, soft, white, fluffy.*

Spelling Workbook 4.3, p. 44

Name________________________ **John Henry**

Spelling: Adding *-er* and *-est* REVIEW

Word List

smaller	happier	sadder	closer	funnier
smallest	happiest	saddest	closest	funniest
larger	hotter	deeper	scarier	fatter
largest	hottest	deepest	scariest	fattest

Directions: Add **-er** and **-est** to each base word below to form a word from the box.

Base Word	Add -er	Add -est
happy	1. **happier**	2. **happiest**
sad	3. **sadder**	4. **saddest**
close	5. **closer**	6. **closest**
fat	7. **fatter**	8. **fattest**
large	9. **larger**	10. **largest**

Directions: Choose the word from the box that completes each statement. Write the word on the line to the left.

smaller **11.** *Taller* is to *shorter* as *bigger* is to _____.
hotter **12.** *Cool* is to *cooler* as *hot* is to _____.
deepest **13.** *Longest* is to *shortest* as *shallowest* is to _____.
scarier **14.** *Weird* is to *weirder* as *scary* is to _____.
funnier **15.** *Small* is to *smaller* as *funny* is to _____.
funniest **16.** *Sad* is to *saddest* as *funny* is to _____.
hottest **17.** *Wet* is to *wettest* as *hot* is to _____.
smallest **18.** *Big* is to *biggest* as *small* is to _____.
scariest **19.** *Funny* is to *funniest* as *scary* is to _____.
deeper **20.** *Shallow* is to *shallower* as *deep* is to _____.

Notes for Home: Your child spelled words that end in *-er* and *-est.* ***Home Activity:*** Say the base word for each spelling word, such as *sad* for *sadder* and *saddest.* Have your child add *-er* and *-est* to each base word and spell the new words aloud.

Practice Book 4.3, p. 109
Name____________________ **John Henry**

Technology: Card Catalog/Library Database

To find books in the library, you can use the **card catalog** or **library database.** You can search for a book by author, title, or subject. When searching by author, always use the last name first.

Directions: The computer screen shows how to search a library database. Tell how you would search to find each of the following books. Write **A** for author, **T** for title, or **S** for subject.

A 1. a book by Kathryn Lasky

S 2. a book about tall tales

T 3. a book titled *Me and My Hero*

S 4. a book about steam drills

A 5. a book by Julius Lester

Practice Book 4.3, p. 110
Name____________________ **John Henry**

Library books are sorted by call numbers, usually based on the Dewey Decimal System. Books of fiction have call numbers that use letters from the last names of the authors. They are sorted alphabetically. Books that are nonfiction are sorted by numbers and appear in a different section from fiction books.

Directions: The computer screen shows the results of a subject search on *tall tales.* Use the results to answer the questions that follow.

Subject/Titles	Call Number
Tall Tales—Fiction	
1) Paul and Babe	EAT
2) The Great North Wind	THR
Tall Tales—Characters	
3) Paul Bunyan and Other Tall Tale Heroes	839.1
Tall Tales—Authors	
4) Julius Lester: A Master Storyteller	860.8

Type a number to find out more about each title. ☐

Type **A, T,** or **S** to begin a new search. ☐

6. Which books listed are books of fiction? ***Paul and Babe* and *The Great North Wind***

7. What does the call number THR represent? **It represents letters of the author's last name.**

8. Will *Paul and Babe* be on the shelf before or after *The Great North Wind?* Explain. **before; Its call number EAT will come before the call number THR.**

9. Which of the two nonfiction books listed would be first on a shelf? Explain. **Paul Bunyan and Other Tall Tale Heroes; Its call number 839.1 will come before 860.8.**

10. Which book will be about someone who writes and tells tall tales? **Julius Lester: A Master Storyteller**

Notes for Home: Your child answered questions about a card catalog/library database. ***Home Activity:*** Take your child to the library. Have your child show how to use the card catalog or library database to find a book he or she might like to read.

Practice Book 4.3, p. 111
Name____________________ **Marven of the Great North Woods**

Drawing Conclusions

- Authors don't always tell you everything. Instead, they may give you a few details about what happens or about characters.
- You can use the details and what you know to **draw conclusions,** or figure out things about people or animals and what they do.

Directions: Reread "Winter of the Snowshoe Hare." Then complete the table. Write a conclusion for each piece of evidence given. Write evidence that supports each conclusion drawn. **Possible answers given.**

Evidence (Story Details and What I Know)	Conclusions
The sounds of paws and breathing are louder.	1. **The dog is getting closer to the hare.**
The master blew the whistle.	2. **He wanted the dog to stop chasing the hare.**
The dog turned and trotted back to the master.	3. **The dog knew what the whistle meant. The dog usually obeyed its master.**
4. **The hare kept running.**	The hare didn't know the dog had turned back.
5. **The dog had stopped chasing the hare.**	The hare was safe.

Notes for Home: Your child read a story and used story details and life experience to draw conclusions. ***Home Activity:*** Watch a television show or a movie with your child. Discuss what conclusions you can draw about how the characters feel or why they behave as they do.

Practice Book 4.3, p. 112
Name____________________ **Marven of the Great North Woods**

Vocabulary

Directions: Choose the word from the box that best matches each definition. Write the word on the line.

Check the Words You Know
__ cord
__ depot
__ flapjacks
__ grizzly
__ snowshoes

grizzly 1. large, fierce, North American bear

flapjacks 2. pancakes

cord 3. a measure of wood

depot 4. railroad or bus station

snowshoes 5. wooden-framed shoes

Directions: Read the letter. Choose the word from the box that best completes each sentence. Write the word on the matching numbered line to the right.

Dear Charlie,

We have just arrived at the train **6.** _____ in the mountains. The snow is so deep we might need **7.** _____ to get around! Grandma says we get to stack a whole **8.** _____ of wood. Then we'll be hungry for her great **9.** _____! I hope we get to see a **10.** _____ bear on this trip. That would be amazing!

Love,
Beth

6. **depot**
7. **showshoes**
8. **cord**
9. **flapjacks**
10. **grizzly**

Write a Letter

On a separate sheet of paper, write a letter to a friend—real or imaginary—who lives in the Great North Woods. Show your excitement about going to visit your friend. Use as many vocabulary words as you can. **Students' letters should use vocabulary words correctly.**

Notes for Home: Your child identified and used vocabulary words from *Marven of the Great North Woods.* ***Home Activity:*** With your child, use the vocabulary words to make up an adventure story about camping in the woods.

Practice Book 4.3, p. 113

Name

Marven of the Great North Woods

Drawing Conclusions

• As you read, use story details and what you know to **draw conclusions,** or make a sensible decision, about the characters and what they do.

Directions: Reread this passage from *Marven of the Great North Woods* in which Marven is becoming used to the logging camp. Then answer the questions below.

> Every day Marven worked until midday, when he went into the cookhouse and ate baked beans and two kinds of pie with Mr. Murray and the cook. After lunch he returned to his office and worked until the jacks returned from the forest for supper.
>
> By Friday of the second week, Marven had learned his job so well that he finished early. He had not been on his skis since he had arrived at camp. Every day the routine was simply meals and work, and Marven kept to his office and away from the lumberjacks as much as he could. But today he wanted to explore, so he put on his skis and followed the sled paths into the woods.

Possible answers given.

1. Why don't Marven and Mr. Murray eat with the lumberjacks?
because the lumberjacks eat in the woods

2. Why do you think Marven could learn his job so well in so little time?
Marven was bright and worked hard.

3. Why do you think Marven kept away from the lumberjacks?
He didn't have anything in common with them.

4. How does Marven feel about his daily routine? How do you know?
He gets bored. He finishes early and wants to explore.

5. How do you think Marven feels about the lumberjacks by the end of the story? On a separate sheet of paper, explain your answer.
He begins to feel comfortable with them. He hums along as they sing, speaks French to wake them up, and goes to the woods where they work.

Notes for Home: Your child drew conclusions about characters and their actions. ***Home Activity:*** Have your child draw conclusions by playing a game of "If". For example: *If your dog whines by the front door, what do you think it wants? (to go outside)*

Practice Book 4.3, p. 115

Name

Marven of the Great North Woods

Selection Test

Directions: Choose the best answer to each item. Mark the letter for the answer you have chosen.

Part 1: Vocabulary

Find the answer choice that means about the same as the underlined word in each sentence.

1. The hunters saw a grizzly.
   - A. kind of tree
   - B. large, fish-eating bird
   - C. kind of wild cat
   - **(D)** large, fierce kind of bear

2. Do you like flapjacks?
   - **(F)** pancakes
   - G. a game played with cards
   - H. tools for lifting
   - J. rabbits

3. Grant bought a cord of logs.
   - A. a long flat-bottomed sled
   - **(B)** a certain amount of cut wood
   - C. a thin, strong rope
   - D. a box used to store things

4. The hikers wore snowshoes.
   - F. heavy boots lined with fur
   - G. long, narrow runners for gliding on snow
   - H. skates with metal blades
   - **(J)** light frames worn on the feet for walking in deep snow

5. Tom met us at the depot.
   - A. small restaurant
   - B. camp
   - **(C)** train station
   - D. hotel

Part 2: Comprehension

Use what you know about the selection to answer each item.

6. Marven spent four months at a—
   - F. music camp.
   - G. sports camp.
   - **(H)** logging camp.
   - J. hunting camp.

7. Marven's job was to—
   - **(A)** keep the payroll.
   - B. stack wood in the office.
   - C. ring the morning bell.
   - D. make breakfast.

8. On the first morning, Marven ran to the bunkhouse to—
   - F. find an overcoat to wear.
   - G. talk with Jean Louis.
   - H. light the lamps.
   - **(J)** make sure the men were up.

Practice Book 4.3, p. 116

Name

Marven of the Great North Woods

9. In this selection, you can tell that "*Lève-toi!*" means—
   - **(A)** Get up!
   - B. You're lazy!
   - C. It's time for breakfast!
   - D. Good morning!

10. You can tell that Marven was—
    - F. glad to be away from his family.
    - G. stronger than Jean Louis.
    - **(H)** good with numbers.
    - J. afraid of snow.

11. Which word best describes Marven in his job?
    - A. bored
    - **(B)** organized
    - C. lazy
    - D. patient

12. When he skied across the lake, Marven began to cry because—
    - F. the rest of his family had died.
    - G. Jean Louis was laughing at him.
    - H. his hands and feet were frozen.
    - **(J)** he felt alone and afraid.

13. How did Jean Louis feel about Marven?
    - A. He thought Marven was a pest.
    - B. He did not like taking care of him.
    - **(C)** He came to love him almost as a son.
    - D. He thought Marven acted like a baby.

14. When Marven didn't see his family at the train station, he probably thought that—
    - F. he was at the wrong stop.
    - G. they had forgotten him.
    - H. he should go back to the woods.
    - **(J)** everyone had died from the flu.

15. How did Marven's experience away from home change him?
    - **(A)** He was forced to grow up faster than most children his age.
    - B. He began to depend on others to take care of him.
    - C. He became afraid to get close to others because they would die.
    - D. He realized he didn't really need his family.

Name

Marven of the Great North Woods

Drawing Conclusions

• As you read, use story details and what you know to **draw conclusions,** or make sensible decisions, about the characters and what they do.

Directions: Read the story below.

> Paul and Rick did everything together. They rode bikes, played ball, hiked, and fished.
>
> One winter there was a huge snowstorm. The next day, Paul shoveled a path to Rick's house to see if he wanted to go sledding. But when Rick came to the door, he wasn't his usual cheerful self. His mom's leg ached and was swollen. Rick's dad was out of town.
>
> "Here's what we'll do," Paul said. "We'll tie our sleds together and pull your mom to my house. After all, my mom's a doctor."

Directions: Complete the table by drawing conclusions from what you have read.

Possible answers given.

Story Details	Conclusions I Can Draw
Paul and Rick ride bikes, play ball, hike, and fish together.	1. **Paul and Rick are good friends.**
Paul shovels a path to Rick's house.	2. **Paul and Rick live close to each other.**
Rick isn't his usual cheerful self.	3. **Rick is worried about something.**
Rick's mom's leg ached and was swollen.	4. **His mother has hurt herself.**
Paul's mom is a doctor.	5. **Paul's mom probably knows how to help Rick's mom.**

Notes for Home: Your child read a story and used story details and what he or she knows to draw conclusions. ***Home Activity:*** Tell your child a story about a friend of yours. Ask your child to draw conclusions about your friend from details in your story.

Practice Book 4.3, p. 117
Name

Marven of the Great North Woods

Context Clues

REVIEW

Directions: Read the story. Then read each question about the story. Choose the best answer to each question. Mark the letter for the answer you have chosen.

A Friend to Many

Frank Benson wanted to improve life for everyone in Hillsdale. His many projects helped countless people he never even met. Because Frank felt that everyone should be literate, he started a program to teach people who couldn't read. He also founded a Library on Wheels program that brought books to people living out in the country. It was the first program of its kind in the state.

When Frank passed away at the age of 92, a memorial service was held at the town's main library. Many family members and friends told stories about all the good things Frank had done in his life. Later, the town voted to rename the library after Frank. The brass plaque on the front door reads, "Frank Benson: A Friend to Many."

1. The word countless in this passage means—
- **(A.)** many.
- **B.** few.
- **C.** poor.
- **D.** mean.

2. The word literate in this passage means able to—
- **F.** make money.
- **(G.)** read.
- **H.** litter.
- **J.** teach.

3. The word founded in this passage means—
- **A.** find.
- **B.** purchased.
- **(C.)** started.
- **D.** approved.

4. The word memorial in this passage means something done to—
- **F.** get a person elected to office.
- **G.** raise funds for a good cause.
- **H.** make people happy.
- **(J.)** remember a person who has died.

5. The word plaque in this passage means—
- **A.** a door.
- **(B.)** a sign.
- **C.** a wooden board.
- **D.** a book.

Notes for Home: Your child defined words in a story using context clues. ***Home Activity:*** Give your child a list of unfamiliar words. Use each word in a sentence and challenge your child to use context clues to figure out the meaning of each unfamiliar word.

Name

Marven of the Great North Woods

Writing Across Texts

Directions: Consider what you learned about working with money in the selections *Marven of the Great North Woods* and "Counting Money." Complete each list by recording the steps for figuring out amounts of money that were described in the selections. **Possible answers given.**

How Marven Did His Job
List the lumberjacks' names alphabetically.
Write the symbol for those who could not write.
1. List the dates of a single pay period.
2. Code each chit with a date.
3. Use a ruler to make a chart.

How to Subtract Money
Line up the decimals.
4. Subtract as you would with whole numbers.
5. Write the decimal point and dollar sign in the difference.

Writing About Money

Use the information you gathered from above and your own experiences to write a paragraph about a time when you have used money. What steps did you follow in dealing with money? Write about your experience on a separate sheet of paper.
Stories will vary. Check that students have related personal experiences about using money in the classroom or at home.

Notes for Home: Your child listed details from a nonfiction story and an excerpt from a mathematics textbook. ***Home Activity:*** Play games with your child that offer him or her the opportunity to count change, add money, or calculate amounts in some way.

Grammar Practice Book 4.3, p. 56
Name

Marven of the Great North Woods

Grammar: Verbs

REVIEW

Directions: Write the verb in each sentence on the line. Remember that some verbs show what action someone or something does. Other verbs link, or join, the subject to a word in the predicate. A linking verb helps to tell what the subject is or what the subject is like.

wanted **1.** Once a lonely pig wanted a friend very much.
appeared **2.** Then one day a spider appeared in the barn.
was **3.** The spider's name was Charlotte.
shared **4.** Soon the pig and the spider shared a wonderful friendship.
felt **5.** The pig Wilbur felt so happy.

Directions: Use each of the following words as the verb in a sentence. Write the sentence on the line. **Possible answers given.**

6. laughed
I laughed very hard at her joke.

7. wrote
I wrote a long report.

8. am
I am sleepy now.

9. *felt* as an action verb
I felt the sheep's woolly coat.

10. *felt* as a linking verb
The sheep's woolly coat felt soft.

Notes for Home: Your child identified action and linking verbs. ***Home Activity:*** Go back over items 3 and 5 in this activity that use linking verbs. Ask your child to circle each subject and the word in each sentence that renames or describes the subject.

Grammar Practice Book 4.3, p. 57
Name

Marven of the Great North Woods

Grammar: Verbs in Sentences

The subject and the verb in a sentence must work together, or **agree.** Decide whether a noun subject is singular (one) or plural (more than one). Then use the verb form that agrees with it: Jay works. Lumberjacks work.

If the verb shows action that is occurring now, or if it tells what the subject is like now, follow these rules:

- Add **-s** or **-es** to many verbs to make them agree with singular noun subjects. For verbs that end in a **consonant** and **y,** change the **y** to **i** before adding **-es.**

  This hot breakfast looks good!
  The cook fries more eggs.

- For the verb **be,** use *is* to agree with singular noun subjects and *are* to agree with plural noun subjects.

  The temperature outside the cabin is cold.
  The lumberjacks are warm from the hot food.

Directions: Circle the correct form of the verb in ( ) to complete each sentence. Write **S** if the subject is singular. Write **P** if the subject is plural.

S **1.** The snow (fall/(falls)) on the woods.
S **2.** Ice (freeze/(freezes)) on the lake.
P **3.** Rabbits ((run)/runs) across the snow.
P **4.** Their tracks ((lead)/leads) to their burrows.
P **5.** Meanwhile, the bears ((sleep)/sleeps) in their den.
P **6.** All winter, the woods (is/(are)) very quiet.
S **7.** A person (hear/(hears)) only the sound of the wind.
S **8.** In spring, the ice ((melts)/melt).
P **9.** Animals (wakes/(wake)) from their long sleep.
S **10.** Life ((returns)/return) to the woods.

Notes for Home: Your child used the correct form of verbs with singular or plural noun subjects. ***Home Activity:*** Offer some sentences in which the subjects need verbs ("The boy [work/works] hard"), and ask your child to choose the right verb for each sentence.

Grammar Practice Book 4.3, p. 58

Name________________

Marven of the Great North Woods

Grammar: Verbs in Sentences

Directions: Circle the correct form of the verb in ( ) to complete each sentence. Write **S** if the subject is singular. Write **P** if the subject is plural. Remember that a verb must agree with its subject.

P 1. Logging camps (supplies/supply) wood to paper mills and furniture companies.

P 2. Paper mills (makes/make) paper out of wood pulp from trees.

S 3. That carpenter in the blue overalls (is/are) also an instructor.

S 4. Her helper (saw/saws) the wood carefully.

P 5. The customers (like/likes) their sturdy furniture.

Directions: Use the correct form of the verb in ( ) to complete each sentence. Write the verb on the line.

appears 6. Every morning, the sun (appear) over the frozen lake.

get 7. Slowly, the lumberjacks (get) out of bed.

eats 8. Marc (eat) the smallest breakfast.

eats 9. His sister, Marcia, (eat) much more than he does!

need 10. These people (need) a good meal to handle the morning's work.

Write a Description

On a separate sheet of paper, write a description of people doing hard work. Use at least five verbs. Be sure your verbs agree with their subjects. Under your description, list each verb you have used, and write whether its subject is singular or plural.

Check that students have used the correct verb forms and have correctly identified the verbs as used with singular or plural nouns.

Notes for Home: Your child identified the forms of verbs for singular and plural subjects: *the dog barks, the dogs bark.* ***Home Activity:*** Name some verbs about sounds for your child *(growl, squeak, hum).* Have your child use each verb in a sentence.

Grammar: Verbs in Sentences 261

Grammar Practice Book 4.3, p. 59

Name________________

Marven of the Great North Woods

Grammar: Verbs in Sentences

RETEACHING

Complete each sentence with the verb from the box that makes sense.

1. The girl **holds** a flute.
2. She **turns** the music pages.
3. The boys **play** the violins.
4. They **perform** at concerts.

perform
holds
turns
play

Notice that when a singular noun or pronoun is the subject of a sentence, the verb is written with **-s** or **-es**. When a plural noun or plural pronoun is the subject of a sentence, the verb is written without **-s** or **-es**.

A verb in the present tense must agree with the subject of the sentence. With **he, she, it,** or a singular noun, add **-s** or **-es** to the verb.

Directions: Draw a line to connect each subject and verb that go together.

1. The flute	plays the trumpet.
2. We	sounds like a bird.
3. Jamal	take our music lessons.

Directions: Write the correct form of each verb in ( ).

4. Ms. Ames **teaches** (teach/teaches) music.
5. The girls **dance** (dance/dances) well.
6. They **practice** (practice/practices) every day.

Notes for Home: Your child used verbs that agreed with the subjects of sentences. ***Home Activity:*** Write three subjects, such as *the cats, our house, you and I,* and have your child write sentences, using the subjects you wrote and verbs that agree.

262 Grammar: Verbs in Sentences

Grammar Practice Book 4.3, p. 60

Name________________

Marven of the Great North Woods

Grammar: Verbs in Sentences

Directions: Write the verb in ( ) that agrees with each subject.

1. The children **sing** a song. (sing/sings)
2. Asako **plays** the piano. (play/plays)
3. The director **leads** the singers. (lead/leads)
4. The audience **watches** the musical. (watch/watches)
5. We **clap** for the children. (clap/claps)
6. The music **sounds** beautiful. (sound/sounds)

Directions: Write each sentence using the verb in ( ) correctly.

7. The singers (prepare) a song.
8. The director (train) them.
9. They (work) together.
10. The students (learn) quickly.
11. Asako (wish) for a solo.
12. Audiences (like) Asako.

7. **The singers prepare a song.**
8. **The director trains them.**
9. **They work together.**
10. **The students learn quickly.**
11. **Asako wishes for a solo.**
12. **Audiences like Asako.**

Write About a Song

Use verbs in the present tense to write about a song you recently learned. Be sure the verbs agree with the subjects. Write on a separate sheet of paper.

Check that students have used verbs and subjects that agree.

Notes for Home: Your child wrote verbs in sentences correctly. ***Home Activity:*** Have your child write sentences with blanks instead of verbs. Then fill in verbs. Have your child check to make sure the verbs you wrote agree with the nouns in the sentences.

Grammar: Verbs in Sentences 263

Practice Book 4.3, p. 118

Name________________

Marven of the Great North Woods

Word Study: Regular Plurals

Directions: To make most nouns plural, add the letter **-s**. For nouns that end in **x, s, ss, ch,** or **sh**, add **-es**. For nouns that end in **consonant** and y, add **-es**. Read the paragraph below. Make each word in ( ) plural. Write the plural word on the line.

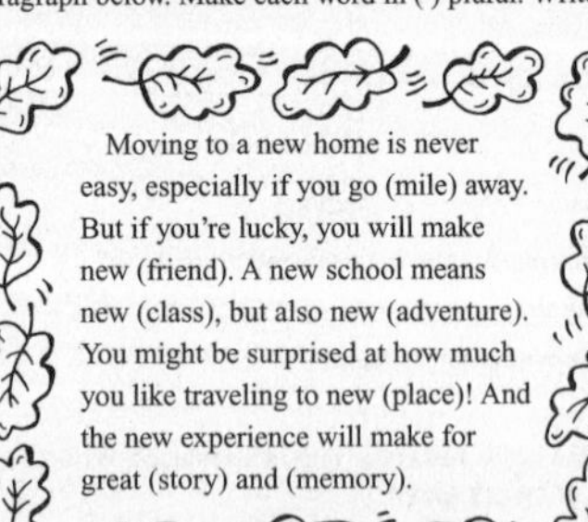

Moving to a new home is never easy, especially if you go (mile) away. But if you're lucky, you will make new (friend). A new school means new (class), but also new (adventure). You might be surprised at how much you like traveling to new (place)! And the new experience will make for great (story) and (memory).

1. **miles**
2. **friends**
3. **classes**
4. **adventures**
5. **places**
6. **stories**
7. **memories**

Directions: Write the plural form for each word. For some words, you will add **-s**. For some you will add **-es**. You may need to change some letters before adding **-es**.

8. pencil	**pencils**	17. bush	**bushes**
9. candy	**candies**	18. tree	**trees**
10. ax	**axes**	19. star	**stars**
11. city	**cities**	20. fox	**foxes**
12. monkey	**monkeys**	21. horse	**horses**
13. lunch	**lunches**	22. flapjack	**flapjacks**
14. paper	**papers**	23. beard	**beards**
15. tower	**towers**	24. shadow	**shadows**
16. glass	**glasses**	25. pony	**ponies**

Notes for Home: Your child changed singular nouns into plurals by adding *-s* or *-es* to create words such as *tigers, babies,* and *boxes.* ***Home Activity:*** Read some coupons with your child. Look for plural words. Talk about how the singular noun changed to become a plural noun.

264 Word Study: Regular Plurals

Spelling Workbook 4.3, p. 45

Name________________________________

Marven of the Great North Woods

Spelling: Adding *-s* and *-es*

Pretest Directions: Fold back the page along the dotted line. On the blanks, write the spelling words as they are dictated. When you have finished the test, unfold the page and check your words.

1. **monkeys** — 1. The **monkeys** swung from trees.
2. **holidays** — 2. **Holidays** are happy days.
3. **delays** — 3. There were **delays** in the march.
4. **flowers** — 4. The field was full of **flowers**.
5. **friends** — 5. We all rely on our **friends**.
6. **tigers** — 6. Grass hid the **tigers** from view.
7. **supplies** — 7. The **supplies** were running out.
8. **enemies** — 8. Tex had no **enemies**.
9. **hobbies** — 9. Hiking is one of her **hobbies**.
10. **memories** — 10. My **memories** of him are cloudy.
11. **mysteries** — 11. Life holds great **mysteries**.
12. **eyelashes** — 12. His **eyelashes** were long.
13. **ashes** — 13. The wind blew the fire's **ashes**.
14. **beaches** — 14. **Beaches** have sand and stones.
15. **bunches** — 15. The fruit grew in **bunches**.
16. **circuses** — 16. Horses perform in **circuses**.
17. **glasses** — 17. His **glasses** were broken.
18. **classes** — 18. All **classes** of people come here.
19. **taxes** — 19. The country had high **taxes**.
20. **suffixes** — 20. Add the **suffixes** now.

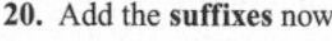

Notes for Home: Your child took a pretest on adding *-s* and *-es* to nouns. ***Home Activity:*** Help your child learn misspelled words before the final test. Your child can underline the word parts that caused the problems and concentrate on those parts.

Spelling Workbook 4.3, p. 46

Name________________________________

Marven of the Great North Woods

Spelling: Adding *-s* and *-es*

Word List				
monkeys	friends	hobbies	ashes	glasses
holidays	tigers	memories	beaches	classes
delays	supplies	mysteries	bunches	taxes
flowers	enemies	eyelashes	circuses	suffixes

Directions: Choose the words from the box in which **-es** has been added to the base word without any spelling changes. Write the words on the lines. **Order may vary.**

1. **eyelashes** 4. **bunches** 7. **classes**
2. **ashes** 5. **circuses** 8. **taxes**
3. **beaches** 6. **glasses** 9. **suffixes**

Directions: Write the word from the box that belongs in each group.

10. festivals, celebrations, **holidays**
11. equipment, provisions, **supplies**
12. puzzles, secrets, **mysteries**
13. rivals, opponents, **enemies**
14. interests, pastimes, **hobbies**
15. remembrances, recollections, **memories**
16. plants, trees, **flowers**
17. waits, pauses, **delays**
18. lions, cougars, **tigers**
19. pals, buddies, **friends**
20. chimpanzees, apes, **monkeys**

Notes for Home: Your child spelled words that end in *-s* and *-es*. ***Home Activity:*** Write the singular form of each spelling word, such as *supply* for *supplies*. Have your child write the plural form by adding *-s* or *-es* to each word.

Spelling Workbook 4.3, p. 47

Name________________________________

Marven of the Great North Woods

Spelling: Adding *-s* and *-es*

Directions: Proofread this description of a friend. Find five spelling mistakes. Use the proofreading marks to correct each mistake.

Proofreading marks
≡ Make a capital.
/ Make a small letter.
∧ Add something.
Take out something.
⊙ Add a period.
¶ Begin a new paragraph.

Best Freinds [corrected: Friends]

We were always in the same clases [corrected: classes]. We both had dark hair and wore wire-rimmed glasses. One of our favorite hobbys [corrected: hobbies] was woodworking. We used to go to the crafts store for suplies [corrected: supplies]. We also liked to read misteries [corrected: mysteries] together. Then my friend moved across town. Now we can see each other only on vacations and holidays.

Spelling Tip

monkeys **supplies**

If a word ends in a **vowel** and **y**, add **-s** to make it plural. If a word ends in a **consonant** and **y**, change the **y** to **i** and add **-es.**

Word List	
monkeys	mysteries
holidays	eyelashes
delays	ashes
flowers	beaches
friends	bunches
tigers	circuses
supplies	glasses
enemies	classes
hobbies	taxes
memories	suffixes

Write a Description

On a separate sheet of paper, write a description of one of your best friends. Try to use at least three spelling words.

Answers will vary, but each description should include at least three spelling words.

Notes for Home: Your child spelled words that end in *-s* and *-es*. ***Home Activity:*** Have your child make a list of the things in his or her room. Have him or her use as many words ending in *-s* and *-es* as possible.

Spelling Workbook 4.3, p. 48

Name________________________________

Marven of the Great North Woods

Spelling: Adding *-s* and *-es* REVIEW

Word List				
monkeys	friends	hobbies	ashes	glasses
holidays	tigers	memories	beaches	classes
delays	supplies	mysteries	bunches	taxes
flowers	enemies	eyelashes	circuses	suffixes

Directions: Write the plural form of each word below to form a word from the box.

1. friend **friends** 5. holiday **holidays** 9. mystery **mysteries**
2. memory **memories** 6. beach **beaches** 10. ash **ashes**
3. hobby **hobbies** 7. glass **glasses** 11. tax **taxes**
4. class **classes** 8. enemy **enemies** 12. suffix **suffixes**

Directions: Choose the word from the box that answers each rhyme. Write the word on the line to the left.

monkeys 13. We have long tails. We are not donkeys. We like to play. Yes, we are _____.

delays 14. They could take days, those shipping _____.

Tigers 15. _____ have stripes, leopards have spots, but both of them could scare me lots.

flowers 16. Stones and wood build castle towers, but gardens grow with grass and _____.

eyelashes 17. Below your forehead, above your cheek, raise your _____ and take a peek.

circuses 18. Into the big top, everyone, _____ are so much fun.

bunches 19. You can have _____ of flowers, bananas, or grapes, but never camels, iguanas, or apes.

supplies 20. If _____ are low, you must get more. Get on your bike and ride to the store.

Notes for Home: Your child spelled words that end in *-s* and *-es*. ***Home Activity:*** Work together to write an adventure story about monkeys and tigers. Use as many spelling words as possible.

Practice Book 4.3, p. 119
Name________________________

Marven of the Great North Woods

Locate/Collect Information

To find out information about a subject, you can use resources such as books, magazines, newspapers, dictionaries, encyclopedias, videotapes, audiotapes, CD-ROMs, Internet Web sites, photographs, drawings, and diagrams. You can also talk to a reference librarian or an expert in the field.

Directions: Review these resources for information on lumberjacking. Use the resources to answer the questions that follow.

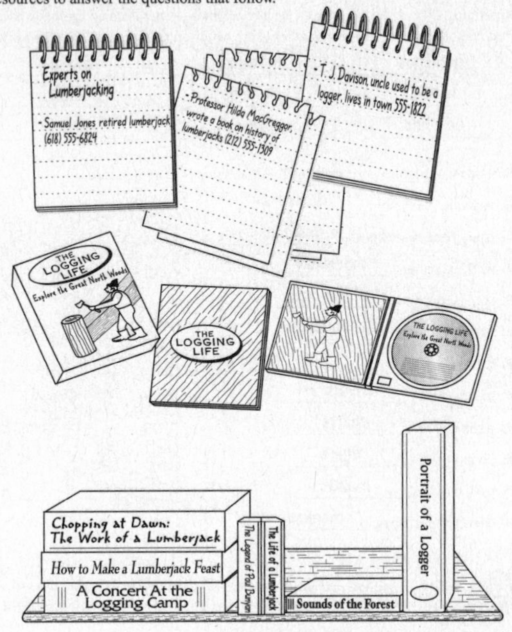

Practice Book 4.3, p. 120
Name________________________

Marven of the Great North Woods

1. If you wanted to find out what the lumberjacks ate for dinner, which resources do you think would be most helpful?

Possible answers: The video called "How to Make a Lumberjack Feast," the audiotape "The Life of a Lumberjack," and the retired lumberjack

2. What is one advantage of getting information by interviewing an expert?

Possible answer: Interviewing an expert lets you ask the questions to which you want answers without sifting through a lot of other information.

3. Which expert would probably have the most information about logging in the 1800s? Explain.

Possible answer: Professor MacGreggor; She wrote a book on the history of logging.

4. What is one question you might ask expert Samuel Jones?

Possible answer: What did you like most/least about your job?

5. From looking at the titles, which of the audiotapes probably contains the least factual information? Explain.

The Legend of Paul Bunyan; It's a "legend," which means the facts are exaggerated.

Notes for Home: Your child learned about using different resources. ***Home Activity:*** List five adults your child knows. Ask your child to tell you on what subject each person could be interviewed as an expert, such as Louisa—flowers, Chico—biology.

Practice Book 4.3, p. 121
Name________________________

On the Pampas

Generalizing

- A **generalization** is a broad statement or rule that applies to many examples.
- Often clue words like *all, most, many, some, sometimes, usually, seldom, few,* or *generally* signal generalizations. A **valid generalization** is supported by facts and your own knowledge. A **faulty generalization** is not.

Directions: Reread "Salmon for All." Write **V** if the generalization is valid. Write **F** if it is faulty. Give evidence from the text to support your choices.

Possible answers given.

Generalization	V or F	Evidence
Many animals eat salmon.	V	Bears, foxes, birds, and people all eat salmon.
Foxes sometimes feed their pups salmon.	1. **V**	2. **A mother fox takes scraps back to her den for the pups.**
Bears never eat salmon.	3. **F**	4. **A Kodiak bear feeds a king salmon to her two cubs.**
Bears always hide their tracks.	5. **F**	6. **Alex sees a bear's claw tracks in the sand.**
There is seldom enough salmon for everyone.	7. **F**	8. **There's an abundance of salmon for all.**
Not everyone can catch salmon.	9. **V**	10. **Alex gives salmon to the people in town who are too old to fish.**

Notes for Home: Your child identified valid and faulty generalizations. ***Home Activity:*** Take turns using the clue words listed above to make generalizations. (*I seldom am wrong.*) Determine whether each generalization is valid (accurate) or faulty (not accurate).

Practice Book 4.3, p. 122
Name________________________

On the Pampas

Vocabulary

Directions: Choose the word from the box that best completes each sentence. Write the word on the line to the left.

Check the Words You Know
__ brand
__ bridles
__ calves
__ corral
__ herd
__ initials
__ manes
__ reins

initials 1. Did you know that a ranch is often known by a set of _____, or letters?

herd 2. Every steer in the ranch's whole _____ is marked with these letters.

calves 3. The young _____ are separated from the mother cows to be marked.

corral 4. Even the horses standing in the _____ have been marked.

manes 5. Cowboys groom their horses by brushing their _____.

Directions: Choose the word from the box that best matches each clue. Write the word in the puzzle.

Down

6. to mark with a hot iron
7. straps held by a horse's rider
8. pen where horses or cattle are kept

Across

9. large number of one kind of animal
10. straps that fit on horses' heads

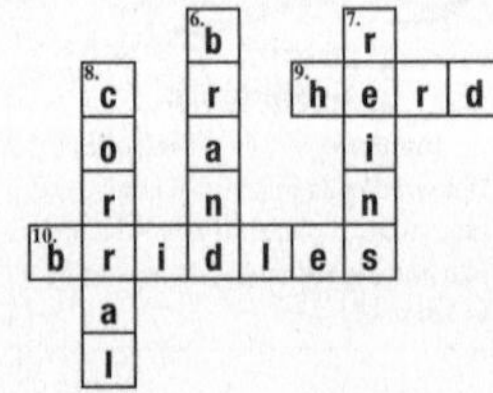

Write a Postcard

On a separate sheet of paper, write a short postcard to a friend telling about a visit to a ranch. Use as many of the vocabulary words as you can.

Students' postcards should use vocabulary words correctly.

Notes for Home: Your child identified and used vocabulary words from *On the Pampas.* ***Home Activity:*** With your child, find out more about life on a modern ranch. Use as many of the vocabulary words as possible as you and your child discuss what you have learned.

Practice Book 4.3, p. 123

Name________________________________ **On the Pampas**

Generalizing

- Sometimes when you read, you are given ideas about several things or people. When you make a statement about all of them together, you are making a **generalization.**
- A **valid generalization** is accurate. A **faulty generalization** is not accurate.

Directions: Reread this passage from *On the Pampas*. Then make generalizations based on what you read.

> At noon, everybody would sit down around one big table and eat together. I was always hungry. Grandma, Susanita's mother, and María the cook had been working hard all morning too. They would make soup, salad, and lamb stew or pot roast, or my favorite, *carbonada*, a thick stew made of corn and peaches.
>
> After lunch the grown-ups took a *siesta*, but not us. We liked to stay outdoors. Some afternoons, when it was too hot to do anything else, we rode out to a eucalyptus grove that was nice and cool, and stayed there until it got dark, reading comic books or cowboy stories.
>
>

1. What was true of mornings on the ranch? **Possible answers given.**
   Many people worked hard in the mornings.
2. What usually happened at noon?
   Everybody sat down and ate together.
3. What did all the grown-ups do after lunch?
   The grown-ups took a *siesta* after lunch.
4. What did the children do after lunch?
   They stayed outdoors.
5. On a separate sheet of paper, write a valid generalization about life on the *pampas.*
   The author always enjoys her summers on the *pampas.*

Notes for Home: Your child used details to make generalizations about a story. ***Home Activity:*** Read a story or newspaper article with your child. Together, make generalizations—statements about several things or people in the story.

Practice Book 4.3, p. 125

Name________________________________ **On the Pampas**

Selection Test

Directions: Choose the best answer to each item. Mark the letter for the answer you have chosen.

Part 1: Vocabulary

Find the answer choice that means about the same as the underlined word in each sentence.

1. Helen walked to the corral.
   A. building for storing hay
   B. piece of land planted with crops
   C. small country store
   (D) pen where animals are kept
2. Marco grabbed the reins.
   F. seat for a rider
   (G) straps used to guide a horse
   H. loops for a rider's foot
   J. long rope with a loop on the end
3. The herd headed west.
   (A) group of animals of one kind
   B. great mass of clouds
   C. group of sailing ships
   D. line of covered wagons
4. Where are the bridles stored?
   F. hats with wide brims
   G. strong leather pants
   (H) part of a harness for a horse
   J. metal shoes for horses
5. She brushed the horses' manes.
   A. back part of a horse's body
   B. parts of the mouth
   (C) long heavy hair on a horse's neck
   D. place for an animal in a barn
6. María helped brand the cattle.
   (F) mark by burning with a hot iron
   G. move to another location
   H. gather into a group
   J. give food and water to
7. The boys saw some calves.
   A. plants with no leaves
   B. large, flat rocks
   C. dark storm clouds
   (D) young cows or bulls
8. Whose initials are these?
   (F) first letters of a person's names
   G. coverings for the hands
   H. marks made by the tip of a finger
   J. sets of funny drawings

GO ON

Practice Book 4.3, p. 126

Name________________________________ **On the Pampas**

Part 2: Comprehension

Use what you know about the selection to answer each item.

9. The ranch where the author spent the summer was called—
   A. San Enrique.
   (B) La Carlota.
   C. Buenos Aires.
   D. La Gauchita.
10. Susanita is the author's—
    (F) cousin.
    G. grandmother.
    H. horse.
    J. friend.
11. What is a *ñandú?*
    A. a horse
    B. a herd of cattle
    (C) a kind of bird
    D. a fancy belt
12. Based on this selection, which generalization is most likely true?
    F. All horses are friendly.
    G. Few cattle live on the pampas.
    H. Girls always learn faster than boys.
    (J) Most gauchos work very hard.
13. What can you tell about the author of this story?
    (A) She is willing to try new things.
    B. She doesn't really have what it takes to be a gaucho.
    C. She is secretly jealous of Susanita.
    D. She likes to call attention to herself.
14. The author's grandmother expects her to—
    F. write to her during the winter.
    G. take her horse home with her.
    (H) come back the next summer.
    J. share her horse with Susanita.
15. The author probably feels proudest that she—
    A. stole a bird's egg.
    (B) had become a gaucho.
    C. baked a birthday cake for Grandma.
    D. escaped from the ñandú.

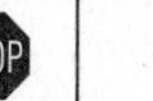

Name________________________________ **On the Pampas**

Generalizing

- Sometimes when you read, you are given ideas about several things or people. When you make a statement about all of them together, you are making a **generalization.**
- A **valid generalization** is accurate. A **faulty generalization** is not accurate.

Directions: Read the story below.

> Dad said it would be great to live on a real ranch for a week. "None of that dude ranch stuff," he said. "This is the real thing." When I didn't look excited, he looked hurt. "Every kid wants to be a cowboy."
>
> We were treated like the cowboys the whole time. We ate the same terrible food, did the same hard work, and slept in the same hard bunks. We were always up by dawn. I was so tired. Dad was too, but he wouldn't admit it.
>
> Home never looked so good. When we stumbled into the house, Mom took one look at us and knew we needed sleep. But all she said was, "How did it go?"
>
> "Wonderful," said Dad. "It was just wonderful!"

Directions: Complete the table by filling in details from the story and making generalizations. **Possible answers given.**

From the Story	Generalizations
1. **The father says the ranch is the real thing.**	Dude ranches aren't for people who really want to live like cowboys.
Cowboys eat bad food, work hard, sleep in hard bunks, and get up early.	2. **A cowboy's life isn't as exciting as we think.**
3. **I was so tired. Dad was tired too.**	Vacations can be tiring.
4. **Home never looked so good.**	It feels good to be home after a long trip.
Dad said the trip was wonderful.	5. **You can have a good time in spite of hard work.**

Notes for Home: Your child read the story and used ideas from it to make generalizations. ***Home Activity:*** Discuss with your child a trip you took together. From things that happened, try to make generalizations about people, places, and events.

Practice Book 4.3, p. 127
Name______________________ **On the Pampas**

Context Clues

REVIEW

Directions: Read the story. Then read each question about the story. Choose the best answer to each question. Mark the letter for the answer you have chosen.

Life on a TV Ranch

I've never set foot on an actual ranch, but I've traveled to many in my mind. That's because TV shows made life on a ranch so enticing. It looks like so much fun.

One thing confused me about cowboy shows. I wasn't sure of the era when they were taking place.

They all showed herds of cattle and corrals. But in one they got water from a well and cooked on a wood-burning stove. In another there was a modern kitchen. In one there were cars. In another, there were only horses.

It took me a while to realize the obvious truth: Some cowboy shows took place in the Old West. Some took place in the present.

1. The word actual in the story means—
   A. working.
   B. nasty.
   C. make-believe.
   (D.) real.

2. The word enticing in the story means—
   F. dangerous.
   (G.) appealing.
   H. uninviting.
   J. boring.

3. The word confused in the story means—
   (A.) puzzled.
   B. dazzled.
   C. angered.
   D. entertained.

4. Which phrase gives a clue to the meaning of era?
   F. wasn't sure
   (G.) when they were taking place
   H. one thing confused me
   J. they all showed

5. An obvious truth is—
   A. sad.
   B. unclear.
   (C.) clear.
   D. whole.

Notes for Home: Your child defined words using context clues. ***Home Activity:*** Read a magazine or newspaper article with your child. Discuss which words are unfamiliar and what context clues can be used to figure out their meanings.

Name______________________ **On the Pampas**

Writing Across Texts

Directions: Consider what you learned from reading *Marven of the Great North Woods* and *On the Pampas.* Think about the ways that the great north woods and the pampas are alike. Think about ways they are different. Use the table below to organize your thoughts. **Possible answers given.**

The North Woods and the Pampas	
How They Are Alike	**How They Are Different**
They are both in remote areas.	The pampas are in Argentina; the north woods are in Minnesota.
1. **A lot of animals live there.**	6. **The setting on the pampas is a ranch; in the north woods, it is a logging camp.**
2. **There is much work to be done.**	7. **The pampas are plains; the north woods is a forest.**
3. **Both places are exciting.**	8. **The pampas have warm weather; the north woods has cold weather.**
4. **People live and work there.**	9. **The pampas have birds; the north woods has grizzlies.**
5. **There are interesting foods to eat.**	10. **On the pampas, people travel on horses; in the great north woods, they travel on skis.**

Write a Comparison

On a separate sheet of paper, write a paragraph that tells how the pampas and the great north woods are either alike or different. Support your paragraph with information from each selection that you have listed in the table above.

Paragraphs will vary. Check that students have supported their comparisons with accurate information from both texts.

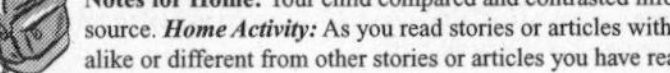

Notes for Home: Your child compared and contrasted information from more than one source. ***Home Activity:*** As you read stories or articles with your child, discuss how they are alike or different from other stories or articles you have read.

Grammar Practice Book 4.3, p. 61
Name______________________ **On the Pampas**

Grammar: Subject-Verb Agreement

REVIEW

Directions: Circle the action verb in ( ) that agrees with the subject in each sentence. Write the verb on the line.

visit 1. Today some people (visits/(visit)) a ranch during their vacations.
wakes 2. A loud bell ((wakes)/wake) everyone early in the morning.
makes 3. The cook ((makes)/make) a hearty breakfast.
tells 4. A ranch manager ((tells)/tell) the workers their chores for the day.
help 5. Sometimes grown-ups (helps/(help)) the ranch hands.
brand 6. Occasionally they even (brands/(brand)) cattle.
ride 7. Children often (rides/(ride)) horses out to the range.
echoes 8. At night, music ((echoes)/echo) across the ranch.
practice 9. Visitors (practices/(practice)) square dances.
fall 10. Soon people of all ages quickly (falls/(fall)) asleep.

Directions: Circle the linking verb in ( ) that agrees with the subject in each sentence. Write the verb on the line.

are 11. Many ranches (is/(are)) located in the Southwest.
has 12. The Double X Ranch ((has)/have) been in Arizona for almost 300 years.
was 13. Luis Martinez ((was)/were) the original owner.
have 14. His ancestors (has/(have)) raised cattle there ever since.
is 15. Martinez's great-grandson ((is)/are) in charge there today.

Notes for Home: Your child identified verbs that agree with their subjects. ***Home Activity:*** Because oral repetition helps students become familiar with the sound of correct agreement between subjects and verbs, have your child read the sentences in this activity aloud to you.

Grammar Practice Book 4.3, p. 62
Name______________________ **On the Pampas**

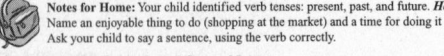

Grammar: Verb Tenses: Present, Past, and Future

The tense of a verb is a form that tells about time. It lets you know *when* something happens. A verb in the **present tense** shows action that is happening now. A verb in the **past tense** shows action that has already happened. A verb in the **future tense** shows action that will happen.

Present Tense: My horse gallops quickly.
Past Tense: My horse galloped quickly.
Future Tense: My horse will gallop quickly.

Verbs in the past tense often end in *-ed.* Verbs in the future tense include the helping verb *will.*

Directions: Write **present, past,** or **future** to tell the tense of each underlined verb.

past 1. The horses whinnied.
present 2. The gauchos ride well.
future 3. They will tell us stories later.
present 4. Now they rope calves.
past 5. Yesterday, I roped a calf by myself!

Directions: Underline the verb in each sentence. Then write **present, past,** or **future** to tell the tense of the verb.

present 6. On the pampas, the grass looks very green.
future 7. After the rain, the air will seem damp.
past 8. We visited one very large farm.
past 9. We admired the herd of cows and the big flock of sheep.
present 10. I love the pampas!

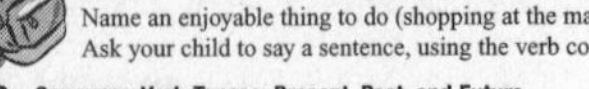

Notes for Home: Your child identified verb tenses: present, past, and future. ***Home Activity:*** Name an enjoyable thing to do (shopping at the market) and a time for doing it (tomorrow). Ask your child to say a sentence, using the verb correctly.

Grammar Practice Book 4.3, p. 63
Name____________________ On the Pampas

Grammar: Verb Tenses: Present, Past, and Future

Directions: Use the correct form of the verb in ( ) to complete each sentence. Use the verb tense named in ( ). Write the verb on the line to the left.

need **1.** We _____ ostrich eggs to make a birthday cake for Julia. (need—present)

baked **2.** Last year, we _____ her a beautiful huge cake. (bake—past)

will chase **3.** We know the ostrich _____ us through the grass. (chase—future)

will like **4.** Julia _____ her cake very much. (like—future)

expected **5.** Last time we threw her a party, Julia never _____ it. (expect—past)

Directions: Choose a verb from the box that best completes each sentence. On the line to the left, write the verb in the tense named in ( ).

eat
help
herd
show
stay

herd **6.** The gauchos _____ the cattle into a large group. (present)

helped **7.** I _____ the gauchos on the ranch last summer. (past)

showed **8.** My cousin _____ me how to ride. (past)

eat **9.** Every night, we _____ a delicious dinner with her family. (present)

will stay **10.** Next summer, she and I _____ at her ranch again. (future)

Write a Journal Entry

Imagine you are spending the summer on a ranch. On a separate sheet of paper, write a journal entry telling what you did today and yesterday, and what you will do tomorrow. Use different verb tenses. **Check that students have used the correct verb tense.**

Notes for Home: Your child identified verb tenses: present *(cook)*, past *(cooked)*, and future *(will cook)*. ***Home Activity:*** Invite your child to write the present, past, and future tense forms of such verbs as *play (play, played, will play)* and use them in a story or a rhyme.

Grammar Practice Book 4.3, p. 64
Name____________________ On the Pampas

Grammar: Verb Tenses: Present, Past, and Future

RETEACHING

These sentences use the verb **bake** in three ways. Write the underlined verb in each sentence.

1. She bakes apples. bakes (present tense)
2. She baked apples. baked (past tense)
3. She will bake apples. will bake (future tense)

The **tense** of a verb shows the time of the action. A verb may be written in the **present tense, past tense,** or **future tense.**

Directions: Write **present, past,** or **future** beside each verb.

1. helps present
2. enjoyed past
3. will roll future
4. learns present
5. will want future
6. walk present
7. roasted past
8. will boil future

Directions: Complete each sentence. Write the past-tense verb in ( ).

9. Dad peeled the tomatoes. (peeled/will peel)
10. Pat and I prepared the salad. (prepare/prepared)
11. Tony served fresh bread. (served/will serve)
12. Mom carved the meat. (carves/carved)
13. The family worked together. (will work/worked)
14. People helped themselves. (helped/help)
15. Guests enjoyed the dinner. (enjoy/enjoyed)

Notes for Home: Your child wrote verbs in the present, past, and future tenses. ***Home Activity:*** Listen to a favorite song together. Have your child point out verbs in the song and tell whether they are in the present, past, or future tense.

Grammar Practice Book 4.3, p. 65
Name____________________ On the Pampas

Grammar: Verb Tenses: Present, Past, and Future

Directions: Underline the verb in each sentence. Then write **present, past,** or **future** to show the tense.

1. Serge drilled a hole in the tree. past
2. He pushes a peg into the hole. present
3. The sap will drip into a bucket. future
4. We will take it to the sugarhouse. future
5. Max pulls it on a sled. present
6. We boiled it for a long time. past
7. The water turned to steam. past
8. Pure maple syrup remains. present
9. We will pour it on pancakes. future

Directions: Complete each sentence. Write the past-tense form of each verb in ( ).

10. Northern Native Americans discovered maple syrup. (discover)
11. Pioneers traded some for clothes. (trade)
12. Traders liked the "sweet water." (like)
13. People wanted more. (want)
14. The syrup tasted sweet. (taste)
15. Children enjoyed it. (enjoy)

Write a Description

On a separate sheet of paper, write a description of your favorite breakfast. Use future-tense verbs in your sentences. **Check that students have used future-tense verbs correctly.**

Notes for Home: Your child identified and wrote verbs in the present, past, and future tenses. ***Home Activity:*** Have your child write about thoughts he or she had today. Remind your child to use verbs in the present, past, and future tenses.

Practice Book 4.3, p. 128
Name____________________ On the Pampas

Word Study: Inflected Forms with *-ed, -ing, -es*

Directions: You can change a verb by adding endings, such as **-ed, -ing,** or **-es.** For some verbs, you don't need to change the base word when you add these endings. For other verbs, you might need to drop the final **e,** change a **y** to **i,** or double the final consonant. Add **-ed** and **-ing** to each base word. Write the new words on the lines.

Verbs That Don't Change	-ed	-ing
stay	1. stayed	2. staying
turn	3. turned	4. turning
Verbs That Drop the Final e	**-ed**	**-ing**
chase	5. chased	6. chasing
graze	7. grazed	8. grazing
Verbs That Double the Final Consonant	**-ed**	**-ing**
stop	9. stopped	10. stopping
drag	11. dragged	12. dragging

Directions: If the verb ends in **consonant** and **y,** change the **y** to **i** before adding **-ed** or **-es.** Keep the **y** before adding **-ing.** Add **-ed, -ing,** and **-es** to the word **try.**

13. try + -ed = tried
14. try + -ing = trying
15. try + -es = tries

Notes for Home: Your child added *-ed, -ing,* and *-es* to verbs. ***Home Activity:*** Read a story with your child. Help your child find verbs with these endings.

Spelling Workbook 4.3, p. 49

Name______________________ On the Pampas

Spelling: Adding *-ed* and *-ing*

Pretest Directions: Fold back the page along the dotted line. On the blanks, write the spelling words as they are dictated. When you have finished the test, unfold the page and check your words.

1. happened — 1. I wonder what **happened** to it.
2. opened — 2. She **opened** the door slowly.
3. danced — 3. They **danced** all night.
4. studied — 4. He **studied** very hard.
5. stopped — 5. We finally **stopped** running.
6. chased — 6. The cat **chased** its prey.
7. worried — 7. He wears a **worried** look.
8. dried — 8. He likes **dried** flowers.
9. robbed — 9. The snake **robbed** the nest.
10. slipped — 10. The jewels **slipped** off her neck.
11. happening — 11. What's **happening**?
12. opening — 12. It's **opening** night at the theater.
13. dancing — 13. We were **dancing** at the party.
14. studying — 14. Are you **studying** for your test?
15. stopping — 15. Why are we **stopping**?
16. chasing — 16. The dog's **chasing** his tail.
17. worrying — 17. Stop **worrying**!
18. drying — 18. The clothes are **drying** in the sun.
19. robbing — 19. Those men are **robbing** the store.
20. slipping — 20. I feel my foot **slipping**.

Notes for Home: Your child took a pretest on adding *-ed* and *-ing* to words. ***Home Activity:*** Help your child learn misspelled words before the final test. Have your child divide misspelled words into parts (such as base words and endings) and concentrate on each part.

Spelling: Adding *-ed* and *-ing* 287

Spelling Workbook 4.3, p. 50

Name______________________ On the Pampas

Spelling: Adding *-ed* and *-ing*

Word List

happened	danced	stopped	worried	robbed
happening	dancing	stopping	worrying	robbing
opened	studied	chased	dried	slipped
opening	studying	chasing	drying	slipping

Directions: Choose the words from the box in which the spelling of the base word changed before **-ed** and **-ing** was added. Write each word in the correct category.

Order may vary.

Final Consonant Doubled		Final e Dropped
1. stopped	4. robbing	7. danced
2. stopping	5. slipped	8. dancing
3. robbed	6. slipping	9. chased
		10. chasing

Directions: Choose the word from the box that best completes each sentence. Write the word on the line to the left.

happened **11.** What _____ today at the ranch?

dried **12.** After the rain stopped, the ground _____ up.

opened **13.** It was time for the dude ranch gates to be _____.

happening **14.** But it was too wet for anything to be _____ outside.

opening **15.** Inside, there was an _____ in one of the classes.

studied **16.** I _____ how to build a campfire.

drying **17.** Other people were _____ their laundry.

studying **18.** That night I spent time _____ how to rope.

worrying **19.** It sounded fun, but I began _____ about doing it right.

worried **20.** The other people told me that I _____ too much.

Notes for Home: Your child spelled words ending in *-ed* and *-ing*. ***Home Activity:*** Together, write each spelling word on an index card. Take turns drawing two cards at a time to try to match pairs of words with the same base word.

288 Spelling: Adding *-ed* and *-ing*

Spelling Workbook 4.3, p. 51

Name______________________ On the Pampas

Spelling: Adding *-ed* and *-ing*

Directions: Proofread this section of a travel brochure. Find four spelling mistakes. Use the proofreading marks to correct each mistake.

≡ Make a capital.
/ Make a small letter.
∧ Add something.
Take out something.
⊙ Add a period.
¶ Begin a new paragraph.

Stop worr~~i~~ying about having nothing to do. The Busy Bee Ranch will soon have you riding, roping, chas~~e~~ing cattle, and square danc~~e~~ing with real ranch folk.

Been working too hard? Been stud^y^ing too hard? It's time you tried something exciting and new. Come visit the Busy Bee Ranch—you'll be glad you did!

Word List

happened	chased
happening	chasing
opened	worried
opening	worrying
danced	dried
dancing	drying
studied	robbed
studying	robbing
stopped	slipped
stopping	slipping

Spelling Tip

chasing **studied** **worrying**

With words that end in a **consonant** and **e,** the **e** is dropped before adding the ending **-ing** or **-ed.** In words that end in a **consonant** and **y,** the **y** is changed to **i** when adding **-ed.** The **y** is kept when adding **-ing.**

Write a Travel Brochure

On a separate sheet of paper, write a paragraph for a travel brochure. Describe a place that you know or have read about. Make it sound like a great place to visit. Try to use at least four spelling words. **Answers will vary, but each paragraph should include at least four spelling words.**

Notes for Home: Your child spelled words ending in *-ed* and *-ing*. ***Home Activity:*** Have your child write a paragraph about a trip he or she took that was fun. Together, underline the words your child used that end in *-ed* and *-ing*.

Spelling: Adding *-ed* and *-ing* 289

Spelling Workbook 4.3, p. 52

Name______________________ On the Pampas

Spelling: Adding *-ed* and *-ing* REVIEW

Word List

happened	danced	stopped	worried	robbed
happening	dancing	stopping	worrying	robbing
opened	studied	chased	dried	slipped
opening	studying	chasing	drying	slipping

Directions: Add **-ed** and **-ing** to each base word below to form a word from the box.

Base Word	Add -ed	Add -ing
happen	1. happened	2. happening
dance	3. danced	4. dancing
study	5. studied	6. studying
worry	7. worried	8. worrying
rob	9. robbed	10. robbing
slip	11. slipped	12. slipping
chase	13. chased	14. chasing

Directions: Choose the word from the box that is the most opposite in meaning for each word below. Write the word on the line.

15. closed opened
16. starting stopping
17. wetting drying
18. shutting opening
19. began stopped
20. soaked dried

Notes for Home: Your child spelled words that end in *-ed* and *-ing*. ***Home Activity:*** Together, write the base word for each spelling word, such as *study* for *studying* and *studied*. Take turns flipping a coin. Add *-ed* to the base word if the coin shows "heads." Add *-ing* if it shows "tails."

290 Spelling: Adding *-ed* and *-ing*

Practice Book 4.3, p. 129

Name__________________ On the Pampas

Evaluate Information/Draw Conclusions

When you research information, you need to **evaluate** it to see if the information is accurate and up-to-date. You also need to make sure it meets the needs of your project. For example, a newspaper article might be up-to-date, but it may not have the information you need. When you find information you can use, you need to **draw conclusions** about it by deciding for yourself what the information means.

Directions: Read this encyclopedia entry about cattle. Use the information to answer the questions that follow.

Cattle: The Global Picture

In 1995, there were about $1\frac{1}{4}$ billion beef and dairy cattle in the world. More than one third of the cattle are raised in Asia. Many millions more are raised in South America. India has more cattle than any other country in the world, but the demand for meat in India is low because many people there believe that the cow is a sacred animal.

A century ago, there were 60 million cattle in the United States. In the early 1990s, the U.S. Department of Agriculture estimated that this number had grown to close to 100 million. During this same time period, each American ate about 67 pounds of beef a year and drank about 100 quarts of milk.

Practice Book 4.3, p. 130

Name__________________ On the Pampas

1. If you wanted to find information about the topic "Life on the Range," would this encyclopedia article be useful? Explain.
No, the entry only gives general information about cattle, not about life on the range.

2. Would this encyclopedia article be considered "up-to-date" if you were trying to find out about the number of cattle in the world currently? Explain.
No, the latest date mentioned in this article is 1995. For a report on cattle populations today, you would need more up-to-date information.

3. About how many pounds of beef does an American eat each year? About how much milk does an American drink each year? Why do you think data about milk consumption was given?
about 67 pounds of beef each year; about 100 quarts of milk each year; Since milk comes from cows, this data helps explain the increased number of cows in the U.S. in this century.

4. According to the entry, in which country are cows treated as sacred animals? Where did you find this information?
India; first paragraph

5. Would you say that the information presented would help you prepare a report on fast food in America? Why?
Possible answer: No. Though consumption of meat in the U.S. is mentioned, the information in this article is not specifically about fast food consumption.

Notes for Home: Your child read an encyclopedia entry to gather information and draw conclusions about it. ***Home Activity:*** Discuss with your child ways to find out more information about a particular topic. Talk about what resources would have useful content.

Practice Book 4.3, p. 131

Name__________________ The Storm

Predicting

- To **predict** means to tell what you think might happen next in a story or article based on what has already happened. Your prediction is what you say will happen next.
- Predicting is a process of checking and changing your predictions as you read, based on new information.

Directions: Reread "Summer Surfers." Fill in the prediction table. For each story event, tell what logical predictions can be made based on what you have read up to that point in the story. One prediction has been done for you. **Possible predictions given.**

What Happened	What Might Happen
Ben and the seal surfed side by side.	Ben and the seal will become friends.
Ben couldn't take his eyes off the seal.	1. **Ben will forget what he is doing and have an accident.**
Ben fell off his board and struck a rock.	2. **Ben will become unconscious and drown.**
Ben was forced upward and saw sunlight again.	3. **Ben will be rescued by a friend. The seal will rescue Ben.**
The seal flipped Ben onto his board.	4. **Ben will float to shore on his surfboard.**
Once he caught his breath, Ben felt fine.	5. **Ben will enjoy surfing with friends for the rest of the summer. Ben will surf with the seal for the rest of the summer.**

Notes for Home: Your child read a story and used story details and life experience to make predictions about what will happen next in a story. ***Home Activity:*** Watch a favorite TV show with your child. During the commercial breaks, predict what will happen next.

Practice Book 4.3, p. 132

Name__________________ The Storm

Vocabulary

Directions: Choose the word from the box that best completes each sentence. Write the word on the matching numbered line to the right.

Check the Words You Know
- __ accident
- __ coaxed
- __ nuzzled
- __ soothing
- __ tornado
- __ wail

One of the worst kinds of storms is a **1.** _____. When a bad storm is coming, the long, loud **2.** _____ of an alarm sounds a warning. During the last storm, we hid in the cellar. My dog Floppy pressed close and **3.** _____ me the whole time. He was scared too! Having him near me was **4.** _____ and comforting. After the storm passed, I **5.** _____ him to come out of the cellar by offering him a biscuit.

1. **tornado**
2. **wail**
3. **nuzzled**
4. **soothing**
5. **coaxed**

Directions: Cross out the word that does not belong in each group.

6. accident	disaster	~~plan~~	crash
7. wail	shout	scream	~~whisper~~
8. tornado	hurricane	~~breeze~~	storm
9. soothing	calming	quieting	~~annoying~~
10. coaxed	~~demanded~~	begged	asked

Write a TV Weather Report

On a separate sheet of paper, write a TV weather report telling listeners that a big storm is coming their way. Tell people what they should do to stay safe. Use as many of the vocabulary words as you can. **Students' reports should predict a big storm and use vocabulary words correctly.**

Notes for Home: Your child identified and used vocabulary words from *The Storm*. ***Home Activity:*** Talk with your child about bad storms and what to do in order to stay safe during one. Use as many vocabulary words as possible.

Practice Book 4.3, p. 133

Name ____________________ **The Storm**

Predicting

- **Predicting** means telling what you think might happen next in a story or article, based on what has already happened.
- Your prediction can change as you read, based on new information.

Directions: Reread the passage from *The Storm*. Think about the predictions you made while reading. Answer the questions below based on reading this passage.

> It was so incredible that for a moment he simply stared. From the rise of the farmyard he watched the snakelike funnel slowly twist across the distant fields and broaden into a larger blackness. Before his eyes it became a black wall headed straight for the farm. Fear replaced amazement. He hurried back across the lot. The wind was shrieking now. But before he could get to the house, he heard horses.
>
> Looking back, there were Buster and Henry tearing madly around the inner lot. How could they have gotten out? He didn't know. And not just Buster, but Henry, pride and joy of his father. Jonathan couldn't think if he had time or not, if it was safe or not.

Possible answers given.

1. Does it seem likely that the tornado will strike the farm?
Yes. It is a black wall headed straight for the farm.

2. Do you think Buster and Henry will go back into the barn by themselves?
No. They are too scared, which is why they're running around outside.

3. What might Jonathan do to help save Buster and Henry?
He could try to calm them down and take them back to the barn.

4. What do you think might happen if Jonathan gets Buster and Henry back into the barn?
They might be protected from the storm because they'll be inside.

5. As you read *The Storm,* what predictions did you make? Did any of your predictions change as you continued reading? Explain.
Answers will vary. Students should describe how new information caused them to adjust their predictions.

Notes for Home: Your child used story details to predict what will happen next. ***Home Activity:*** Name a situation (such as forgetting to turn off the bath water). Ask your child to predict what might happen next.

Practice Book 4.3, p. 135

Name ____________________ **The Storm**

Selection Test

Directions: Choose the best answer to each item. Mark the letter for the answer you have chosen.

Part 1: Vocabulary

Find the answer choice that means about the same as the underlined word in each sentence.

1. That was a coyote's <u>wail</u>.
   - A. baby animal
   - (B.) long, sad call
   - C. wild animal's home
   - D. mark made by a foot or paw

2. I <u>coaxed</u> the horse into the barn.
   - F. trapped
   - G. pushed from behind
   - H. tied with a rope
   - (J.) persuaded gently

3. We were caught in a <u>tornado</u>.
   - A. fast-moving water
   - B. trap for catching animals
   - (C.) destructive, whirling wind
   - D. sudden attack

4. Gus was in a bicycle <u>accident</u>.
   - (F.) something harmful that happens unexpectedly
   - G. important race
   - H. parade
   - J. repair shop

5. Alan was <u>soothing</u> the animals.
   - A. exciting
   - (B.) calming
   - C. feeding
   - D. gathering

6. The dog <u>nuzzled</u> Laura's hand.
   - (F.) rubbed with the nose
   - G. pushed away roughly
   - H. took quick small bites
   - J. looked at in a fearful way

Part 2: Comprehension

Use what you know about the story to answer each item.

7. What did Jonathan love?
   - A. street noise
   - B. trucks
   - C. hot weather
   - (D.) watching thunderstorms

8. How did Jonathan lose the use of his legs?
   - (F.) He was hit by a truck.
   - G. He was born that way.
   - H. A tree fell on his legs.
   - J. He fell off his bicycle.

GO ON

Practice Book 4.3, p. 136

Name ____________________ **The Storm**

9. Jonathan's mom left the house to—
   - A. buy a new car.
   - (B.) have her car fixed.
   - C. pick up Jonathan's dad.
   - D. go food shopping.

10. When the wind rose and the sky turned a green-yellow color, you could predict that—
    - F. the house would be ruined.
    - G. there would be no storm.
    - H. it would soon be night.
    - (J.) a tornado was coming.

11. During the tornado, where was the safest place for Jonathan?
    - (A.) in the root cellar
    - B. inside the house
    - C. outside in the yard
    - D. under a tree

12. Jonathan probably cried when he found the rooster because he—
    - F. had loved that bird.
    - G. was worried about his parents.
    - (H.) suddenly realized the same thing could have happened to him.
    - J. knew his parents would be angry at him for leaving the animals.

13. You can tell from this story that tornadoes are—
    - A. similar to snowstorms.
    - (B.) very powerful and dangerous.
    - C. impossible to escape from.
    - D. nothing to be afraid of.

14. What bothered Jonathan most about being in a wheelchair?
    - F. He could not play games.
    - (G.) People saw his "condition" rather than the person he was.
    - H. He could not feed the horses.
    - J. He disliked having to ask other people for help.

15. As a result of his experience in the storm, Jonathan felt—
    - A. guilty that he was not able to save the rooster.
    - B. angry at his parents for leaving him alone during a storm.
    - C. afraid that his parents would leave him alone again.
    - (D.) better about himself and how others would see him.

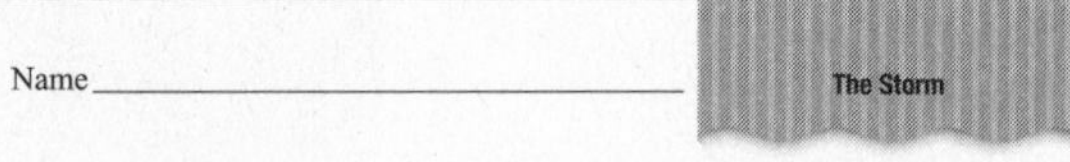

Name ____________________ **The Storm**

Predicting

- **Predicting** means telling what you think might happen next in a story, based on what has already happened.
- Your prediction can change as you read, based on new information.

Directions: Read the story below.

> When the hurricane watch came, Mom and I were on the hotel porch drinking lemonade. But the sky was blue and the water was calm. Mom just laughed and said we'd beat the storm home.
>
> When the hurricane warning came, we were gathering shells on the beach. The sky was gray, and the water was rough. People were pulling boats out of the water. Mom said we'd be safer inside.
>
> We sat with fifty other people in the hotel living room, behind strong shutters. We could only wait to see if the hurricane would hit. I felt calm, but Mom acted nervous. Suddenly, the wind picked up. Then came a bang at the door.

Directions: Fill in the boxes by predicting two events that could happen after each event listed. One has been done for you. **Possible answers given.**

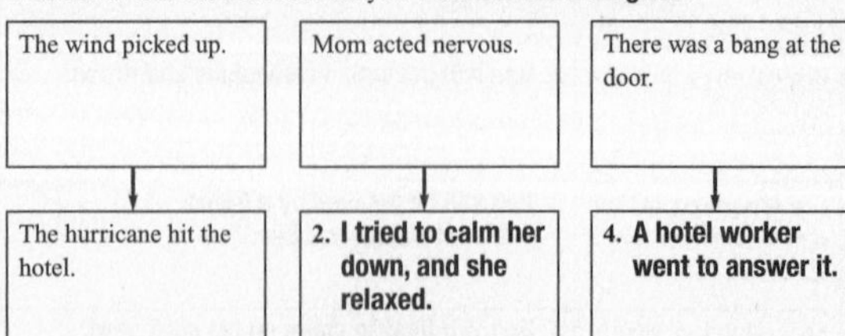

The wind picked up.	Mom acted nervous.	There was a bang at the door.
The hurricane hit the hotel.	2. **I tried to calm her down, and she relaxed.**	4. **A hotel worker went to answer it.**
Or	Or	Or
1. **We just got a bad windstorm.**	3. **Mom just got more nervous.**	5. **It was only the wind.**

Notes for Home: Your child has read a story and predicted two possible events that might happen. ***Home Activity:*** Read a story with your child, pausing at various places to predict what will happen next. Continue reading, pausing to check and change predictions.

Practice Book 4.3, p. 137

Name ______________________ The Storm

Drawing Conclusions and Character

REVIEW

Directions: Read the story. Then read each question about the story. Choose the best answer to each question. Mark the letter for the answer you have chosen.

What You're Made Of

Jane's English cousins were visiting. When Jane said there was a tornado watch, Will asked if they'd watch it on TV.

"No, we have to watch *out* for one," Jane said gently.

"Should I stay by the window?" asked Violet.

"No," said Jane just as gently. But she frowned. "If it becomes a warning, then we have to go down to the shelter."

Two hours later, Jane led her cousins down to the shelter. "We'll wait out the storm here," she said. Will looked afraid. Jane put an arm around him.

"You'll be okay," she said in a soothing voice. "Show us what you're made of."

1. Will asked if he would watch the tornado on TV because—
   - **A.** he was bored.
   - **(B.)** he thought that's what Jane meant.
   - **C.** nothing else was on.
   - **D.** he was joking.

2. Why didn't Violet's idea make sense?
   - **F.** It would be boring.
   - **G.** Violet was too young to be the look-out.
   - **(H.)** It would be dangerous.
   - **J.** She wouldn't be able to see the tornado.

3. Why did Jane lead her cousins into the shelter?
   - **A.** She was showing it off.
   - **(B.)** The danger of the tornado had increased.
   - **C.** The tornado hit the house.
   - **D.** Everyone was bored.

4. When Jane answers gently, she shows she is—
   - **F.** making fun of her cousins.
   - **G.** insecure.
   - **H.** afraid.
   - **(J.)** kind.

5. Jane puts her arm around Will to try to—
   - **(A.)** help him be less afraid.
   - **B.** keep him from falling.
   - **C.** make him go to the shelter.
   - **D.** keep him from leaving.

Notes for Home: Your child drew conclusions about the characters in a story. ***Home Activity:*** Read or tell a story about someone who was brave. Ask your child to draw conclusions about the character and the character's actions.

Drawing Conclusions and Character **301**

Name ______________________ The Storm

Writing Across Texts

Directions: Consider what the scene looked like after the tornado hit in *The Storm.* Then recall what you learned about the effects of a tornado in "Tornado Tales." Record your ideas in the table below. **Possible answers given.**

The Storm	Tornado Tales
The barn was full of litter and debris.	Stalks of straw were driven through poles.
1. **A feed bucket was on the roof.**	6. **A card was driven into a wooden door.**
2. **A wheel from a haywagon was in a tree.**	7. **Bark was stripped from trees.**
3. **The hay barn and other buildings were gone.**	8. **Feathers were plucked from chickens.**
4. **It looked as if someone had cut down the trees in the woods with a scythe.**	9. **Trains were lifted off their tracks.**
5. **A slat from a picket fence was driven into a door of a house.**	10. **Refrigerators were moved.**

Write a Descriptive Paragraph

Write a news story describing the scene after a tornado has hit. Use some of the details that you have recorded above. Make sure that all of the details have to do with the effects of the tornado. **News stories will vary. Check that students used information from each selection.**

Notes for Home: Your child used information from two reading selections to report on the effects of a tornado. ***Home Activity:*** Discuss severe weather that is likely to occur in your area. Help your child make a list of family safety rules in case of such an emergency.

302 Writing Across Texts

Grammar Practice Book 4.3, p. 66

Name ______________________ The Storm

Grammar: Verb Tenses: Past, Present, and Future

REVIEW

Directions: Circle the verb in each sentence. Write **past, present,** or **future** on the line to name the tense of each verb.

present 1. Forecasters on TV (predict) an approaching tornado.

future 2. Sometimes tornadoes (will catch) people outside.

past 3. Last year a man (saved) himself.

past 4. He (jumped) into a ditch.

present 5. Tornado warnings (save) many lives.

Directions: Follow the directions below. Write each new sentence on the line.

6. Rewrite sentence 1 in the past tense.
   Forecasters on TV predicted an approaching tornado.

7. Rewrite sentence 2 in the present tense.
   Sometimes tornadoes catch people outside.

8. Rewrite sentence 3 in the present tense.
   A man saves himself.

9. Rewrite sentence 4 in the future tense.
   He will jump into a ditch.

10. Rewrite sentence 5 in the future tense.
    Tornado warnings will save many lives.

Notes for Home: Your child identified the three main tenses of a verb. ***Home Activity:*** Ask your child to say the following verbs in all three tenses: *talk, want, laugh, watch,* and *walk.* Have your child create sentences that use each of the three tenses of *talk.*

Grammar: Verb Tenses: Past, Present, and Future **303**

Grammar Practice Book 4.3, p. 67

Name ______________________ The Storm

Grammar: Using Correct Verb Tenses

To form the **present tense** of most verbs, add **-s** or **-es** if a subject is a singular noun or is *he, she,* or *it:* A baby bird chirps. The mother watches.

Do not add an ending to the verb if the subject is plural: Birds live in nests.

To form the **past tense** of most verbs, add **-ed: raked, tasted, walked.**

When a one-syllable verb ends in a single vowel followed by a single consonant, double the final consonant before adding **-ed: hugged.**

When a verb ends in a **consonant** and **y,** change the **y** to **i** before adding **-ed: copied.**

A verb whose past tense does not end in **-ed** is called an **irregular verb.** You will need to remember how to form the past tense of irregular verbs: **held, drew, sang.**

Directions: Circle the correct verb form in ( ) to complete each sentence. Use a dictionary if you need help with irregular verbs.

1. Every year my friends (**watch**/watches) *The Wizard of Oz* on TV.
2. Last weekend they (see/**saw**) the movie again.
3. L. Frank Baum (writes/**wrote**) the original book.
4. Yesterday, I (asks/**asked**) them about the movie.
5. Tina said her favorite part (**was**/were) when the tornado took Dorothy to the land of Oz.
6. In Oklahoma, where we all (**live**/lived), we get tornadoes too.
7. Last year, a tornado (sweeps/**swept**) through our town.
8. We (go/**went**) to the cellar and stayed there for hours.
9. At first the noise of the tornado was very loud, but then suddenly it (**stopped**/stops).
10. After a while, we (**heard**/hear) the "all clear" signal and left our shelter.

Notes for Home: Your child identified verb tenses. ***Home Activity:*** Use four or five sentences to tell your child a story. Use the present tense *(A baby robin falls from its nest).* Then, have your child retell it using the past tense verbs.

304 Grammar: Using Correct Verb Tenses

Grammar Practice Book 4.3, p. 68

Name ______

The Storm

Grammar: Using Correct Verb Tenses

Directions: Use the correct form of the verb in ( ) to complete each sentence. Write the verb on the line to the left. Use a dictionary if you need help with irregular verbs.

move 1. Usually, tornadoes (move) very swiftly.

destroys 2. Often, the powerful wind (destroy) things in its path.

appeared 3. Yesterday, a strange whirling cloud (appear).

noticed 4. I was walking home when I (notice) it.

ran 5. I (run) to a safe place as fast as I could!

Directions: Use a verb from the box to complete each sentence. Write the verb in the correct tense on the line to the left. Use a dictionary if you need help with irregular verbs.

cry	fall	place	plant	snap

fell 6. Last year my favorite tree _____ in a bad storm.

snapped 7. The strong wind _____ it in two.

cried 8. I was so sad that I _____ for days.

planted 9. An hour ago, we _____ a new tree in the yard.

placed 10. My father dug the hole, and I _____ the tree in it.

Write a Letter to a Friend

Were you ever caught in a bad storm? Was the experience scary? What did you do? On a separate sheet of paper, write a letter to a friend about your experience. You can describe a real experience, or you can make one up. Try to use verbs in different tenses.

Students' letters should include a variety of verbs in the correct tenses and forms.

Notes for Home: Your child wrote verbs in different tenses to show when something occurred. ***Home Activity:*** Play a verb game with your child. Take turns naming a verb and naming that verb's past tense.

Grammar Practice Book 4.3, p. 69

Name ______

The Storm

RETEACHING

Grammar: Using Correct Verb Tenses

Read each sentence. Write the correct form of the verb in ( ) on the line.

1. The bright sun (shine—present tense) shines .
2. Yesterday I (cook—past tense) cooked soup.
3. Then I (dip—past tense) dipped berries in chocolate.
4. I was late for school, so I (hurry—past tense) hurried .
5. I could not read what he (write—past tense) wrote .

Add **-s** or **-es** to form the present-tense form of most verbs if the subject is singular. Add **-ed** to form the past-tense form of most verbs. When a one-syllable verb ends in a single vowel followed by a single consonant, double the final consonant before adding **-ed**. When a verb ends in a consonant and **y**, change the **y** to **i** before adding **-ed**. A verb whose past-tense form does not end in **-ed** is an irregular verb. You will need to remember the forms of these verbs.

Directions: Underline the correct verb form in ( ) to complete each sentence. Use a dictionary if you need help with irregular verbs.

1. Usually my family (<u>likes</u>/liked) to eat dinner together.
2. Although we were busy, we (eat/<u>ate</u>) together every night last week.
3. Sometimes my mom (<u>makes</u>/make) dinner, and sometimes my dad does.
4. Last night my dad (hurry/<u>hurried</u>) home to make dinner.
5. Then my mom and I (<u>jogged</u>/jogs) after dinner.
6. When we got home, my stepbrother (ask/<u>asked</u>) for help with math.
7. I was tired, but I (finish/<u>finished</u>) my homework by eight o'clock.
8. Then I finally (<u>went</u>/go) to bed!

Notes for Home: Your child identified correct verb tenses in sentences. ***Home Activity:*** Have your child point out verbs in a story and tell what tense they are. Then have him or her write new sentences, using the verbs from the story. Challenge him or her to change the tenses of the verbs.

Grammar Practice Book 4.3, p. 70

Name ______

The Storm

Grammar: Using Correct Verb Tenses

Directions: Use a verb from the box to complete each sentence. Write the verb in the correct tense on the line. Use a dictionary if you need help with irregular verbs.

bake call decide dry earn give hug lick make start tell wag wash worry write

Possible answers given.

gives (present) 1. My teacher _____ us a week to do an assignment.

wrote (past) 2. I _____ about a kite on a string.

wagged (past) 3. Our dog _____ his tail.

called (past) 4. I wanted to play with him, so I _____ him.

licked (past) 5. He came over to me and he _____ my hand.

makes (present) 6. My older sister _____ dinner on Monday nights.

washed (past) 7. After dinner, Sam _____ the dishes and I _____

dried them.

worried (past) 8. He _____ that he wouldn't have time to play.

told (past) 9. I _____ him he had an hour left before his bedtime.

hugged (past) 10. Sam was so happy that he _____ me.

bakes (present) 11. Renee _____ brownies and muffins to raise money for her club.

started (past) 12. She and Shaunna _____ the club a year ago.

earned (past) 13. They _____ twenty dollars in one weekend.

decided (past) 14. But the club hasn't _____ what to do with the money!

Notes for Home: Your child wrote verb tenses in sentences. ***Home Activity:*** Make flashcards with your child. Help your child identify which verbs he or she has trouble remembering how to write in the present and past tenses. Then make flashcards for the difficult verbs.

Practice Book 4.3, p. 138

Name ______

The Storm

Phonics: Consonant Sounds /j/, /ks/, /kw/

Directions: The sound /j/ can be spelled **dge** or **ge** as in **ledge** or **change.** The sound /ks/ can be spelled **x** or **xc** as in **fox** or **except.** The sound /kw/ can be spelled **qu** as in **quick.** Read each word below. Sort each word by the sounds you hear. Write each word in the correct column.

fidget	box	quiet	coaxed	huge
quite	sixty	ledge	explore	quilt

/j/	/ks/	/kw/
1. fidget	4. box	8. quiet
2. huge	5. coaxed	9. quite
3. ledge	6. sixty	10. quilt
	7. explore	

Directions: Read each sentence. Listen for the word that has the consonant sounds /j/, /ks/, or /kw/. Write the word on the line. Circle the letters that represent that sound.

changed 11. The weather forecaster changed her report to include a tornado warning.

edge 12. The storm hit the edge of town.

exciting 13. It was exciting to see the storm, but frightening too.

quickly 14. Just as quickly as it had come up, the storm died out.

explain 15. People who saw the tornado tried to explain what it was like.

Notes for Home: Your child practiced identifying consonant sounds: /j/ in *ledge* and *change,* /ks/ in *fox* and *except,* and the /kw/ in *quick.* ***Home Activity:*** Read a newspaper story with your child. Challenge your child to listen for words with these sounds and point them out.

Spelling Workbook 4.3, p. 53

Name ______________________ The Storm

Spelling: Words with /j/, /ks/, /kw/

Pretest Directions: Fold back the page along the dotted line. On the blanks, write the spelling words as they are dictated. When you have finished the test, unfold the page and check your words.

1. **change**	1. There's a **change** in the weather.
2. **village**	2. The **village** is not far away.
3. **edge**	3. I live at the **edge** of town.
4. **except**	4. I know them all **except** her.
5. **excited**	5. He's very **excited** about the party.
6. **explain**	6. She can **explain** how it works.
7. **expect**	7. We don't **expect** much trouble.
8. **Texas**	8. **Texas** is a large state.
9. **quick**	9. The train was **quick** and noisy.
10. **equal**	10. The two pies are **equal**.
11. **charge**	11. I'm in **charge** of this project.
12. **bridge**	12. The **bridge** was his only shelter.
13. **fudge**	13. The **fudge** is still cooking.
14. **excellent**	14. That meal was **excellent**.
15. **relax**	15. Now, we can **relax**.
16. **extra**	16. Do you have any **extra** sugar?
17. **queen**	17. The **queen** was in her palace.
18. **quart**	18. Please buy a **quart** of milk.
19. **liquid**	19. What's the **liquid** in that cup?
20. **quilt**	20. This was my mother's **quilt**.

Notes for Home: Your child took a pretest on words that have the sounds /j/, /ks/, and /kw/. ***Home Activity:*** Help your child learn misspelled words before the final test. Dictate the word and have your child spell the word aloud for you or write it on paper.

Spelling Workbook 4.3, p. 54

Name ______________________ The Storm

Spelling: Words with /j/, /ks/, /kw/

Word List

change	bridge	explain	relax	queen
village	fudge	expect	extra	quart
edge	except	Texas	quick	liquid
charge	excited	excellent	equal	quilt

Directions: Choose the words from the box that have the sound /ks/ as in e**x**pert and e**xc**use. Write the word on the line. **Order may vary.**

1. **except** 4. **expect** 7. **relax**
2. **excited** 5. **Texas** 8. **extra**
3. **explain** 6. **excellent**

Directions: Choose the word from the box that best matches each clue. Write the word on the line.

equal 9. This means "the same as."
edge 10. A building ledge is one kind of this.
quick 11. Jack be nimble, Jack be _____.
bridge 12. Trolls live under it.
fudge 13. This chocolate treat is very sweet.
queen 14. A princess might become this.
village 15. It's smaller than a city.
change 16. Everyone needs some of this, or life becomes boring.
liquid 17. Water is this, and so is milk.
quart 18. It's one-fourth of a gallon.
charge 19. Wild animals sometimes do this when they're scared.
quilt 20. This covering keeps you warm at night.

Notes for Home: Your child spelled words with the sounds /j/ spelled *ge* or *dge*, /ks/ spelled *x* and *xc*, and /kw/ spelled *qu*. ***Home Activity:*** Have your child list more words with these sounds and spellings. Ask for which sound he or she can list the most words.

Spelling Workbook 4.3, p. 55

Name ______________________ The Storm

Spelling: Words with /j/, /ks/, /kw/

Directions: Proofread this weather report. Find five spelling mistakes. Use the proofreading marks to correct each mistake.

≡ Make a capital.
/ Make a small letter.
∧ Add something.
Take out something.
⊙ Add a period.
¶ Begin a new paragraph.

Report for Central Texas

Two counties in central Tex~~x~~as were hit by a tornado yesterday afternoon. Residents in the whole area were told to e~~s~~[x]pect high winds and heavy rain. The storm was qui[c]k, though, and there wasn't much damage. Fortunately, the storm did not hit each county with e~~kwe~~[qua]l force. One villa~~d~~ge did report the loss of the main bridge.

Word List

change	fudge	Texas	equal
village	except	excellent	queen
edge	excited	relax	quart
charge	explain	extra	liquid
bridge	expect	quick	quilt

Spelling Tip

change edge
except explain
quick

The sound /j/ can be spelled **ge** or **dge.** The sound /ks/ can be spelled **xc** or **x.** The sound /kw/ can be spelled **qu.**

Write a Weather Report

On a separate sheet of paper, write a short weather report for your area. Try to use at least three spelling words. **Answers will vary, but each weather report should include at least three spelling words.**

Notes for Home: Your child spelled words with the sounds /j/, /ks/, and /kw/. ***Home Activity:*** Write a list of these spelling words, but deliberately misspell some of them. Challenge your child to check the list and correct any misspellings.

Spelling Workbook 4.3, p. 56

Name ______________________ The Storm

Spelling: Words with /j/, /ks/, /kw/

REVIEW

Word List

change	bridge	explain	relax	queen
village	fudge	expect	extra	quart
edge	except	Texas	quick	liquid
charge	excited	excellent	equal	quilt

Directions: Write the word from the box that belongs in each group.

1. superb, great, **excellent**
2. princess, king, **queen**
3. same, identical, **equal**
4. Utah, Oklahoma, **Texas**
5. eager, thrilled, **excited**
6. blanket, comforter, **quilt**
7. calm down, rest, **relax**
8. fast, swift, **quick**
9. cookies, cake, **fudge**
10. tunnel, ferry, **bridge**
11. cliff, ledge, **edge**
12. cup, pint, **quart**

Directions: Choose the word from the box that best completes each sentence. Write the word on the line to the left.

expect 13. The weatherman said to _____ a tornado.
explain 14. He started to _____ what would happen.
village 15. The _____ where we lived was put on alert.
change 16. He said the sky would start to _____.
extra 17. He said everyone should be _____ careful.
liquid 18. He suggested we go into our cellars with enough _____ to drink.
charge 19. The store owners were not allowed to _____ any more than usual.
except 20. That was all we could do, _____ hope for the best.

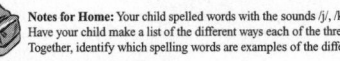

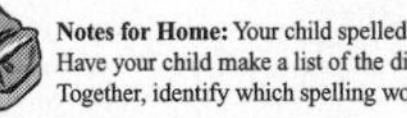

Notes for Home: Your child spelled words with the sounds /j/, /ks/, and /kw/. ***Home Activity:*** Have your child make a list of the different ways each of the three sounds can be spelled. Together, identify which spelling words are examples of the different spellings for these sounds.

Practice Book 4.3, p. 139
Name______________________ **The Storm**

Almanac

An **almanac** is a book that is published every year. It contains calendars, weather information, and dates of holidays. It also contains many charts and tables of current information about subjects such as city population and recent prize winners in science, literature, or sports.

Directions: Review this information from an almanac. Use the information to answer the questions that follow.

Tornado Facts

- The width of a tornado can vary from a few meters to a kilometer.
- Their "funnels" are made visible by dust that they suck up from the ground.
- Most tornadoes spin counterclockwise in the northern hemisphere and clockwise in the southern hemisphere.
- Tornado damage is caused by winds that often move at speeds of more than 300 miles per hour.

Notable U.S. Tornadoes Since 1980

Date	Location	Deaths
June 3, 1980	Grand Island, NE	4
March 2–4, 1982	South, Midwest	17
May 29, 1982	Southern IL	10
May 18–22, 1983	Texas	12
March 28, 1984	N. Carolina, S. Carolina	57
April 21–22, 1984	Mississippi	15

Measuring Tornadoes

Tornadoes are measured by the Fujita (or F) scale, created by T. Theodore Fujita. The F scale rates tornadoes on a scale of 0–5.

Rank	Wind Speed (mi/hr)	Damage	Strength
F-0	Up to 72 mi/hr	Light	Weak
F-1	73–112 mi/hr	Moderate	Weak
F-2	113–157 mi/hr	Considerable	Strong
F-3	158–206 mi/hr	Severe	Strong
F-4	207–260 mi/hr	Devastating	Violent
F-5	More than 261 mi/hr	Incredible	Violent

Practice Book 4.3, p. 140
Name______________________ **The Storm**

1. If you wanted to know if a strong wind where you live was tornado strength, what section of the almanac page would you look at?

Measuring Tornadoes

2. Which notable tornado caused the greatest number of deaths? Give the date and location of this tornado. How is this information presented in the almanac?

March 28, 1984; North Carolina and South Carolina; This information is presented in a table.

3. What information can you find about the size of tornadoes?

Possible answer: According to "Tornado Facts," the width of a tornado can be as small as a few meters to as large as a kilometer.

4. If a tornado's wind speed is 200 mi/hr, what would the damage level be according to the Fujita scale?

Possible answer: A speed of 200 mi/hr falls under an F-3 rank, which means the damage would be severe.

5. When might you want to use an almanac as a resource instead of an encyclopedia? Explain.

Possible answer: You would use an almanac when you want specific and current information about a subject. An encyclopedia gives general information that may not be as up-to-date.

Notes for Home: Your child read and interpreted information about tornadoes found in an almanac. ***Home Activity:*** Look at an almanac together. Take turns sharing interesting and/or useful information you find.

Practice Book 4.3, p. 141
Name______________________ **Rikki-tikki-tavi**

Drawing Conclusions

- As you read, look at the details and make decisions about the characters and what happens in the story or article.
- When you make decisions about the characters or events, you are **drawing conclusions.**

Directions: Reread "Another Death on the Ranch." Then complete the table. Write a conclusion for each piece of evidence given. Write evidence that supports each conclusion drawn. **Possible answers given.**

Evidence (Story Details and What I Know)	Conclusions
1. **Hank compares his job to those of people in high places. He says it's a great honor.**	Hank is proud of his job.
Hank doesn't consider the milk cow a suspect.	2. **The milk cow had no reason for wanting to kill a chicken.**
3. **Hank has too many suspects.**	It will be difficult for Hank to solve the crime.
Hank goes to the chickenhouse and is deep in thought about the murder.	4. **Hank takes his responsibility seriously. He is good at his job.**
5. **The chicken pecks him on the tail.**	Hank feels unappreciated.

Notes for Home: Your child read a story and used story details and life experience to draw conclusions. ***Home Activity:*** Have your child observe a pet or a neighborhood animal and draw conclusions about the animal's behavior based on observation and experience.

Practice Book 4.3, p. 142
Name______________________ **Rikki-tikki-tavi**

Vocabulary

Directions: Cross out the word that does **not** belong in each group.

1. cobra rattlesnake ~~alligator~~ garden snake
2. coiled ~~straight~~ curled looped
3. lame hurt ~~sure-footed~~ limping
4. plunged dipped dived ~~floated~~
5. triumph success victory ~~loss~~

Check the Words You Know
- __ cobra
- __ coiled
- __ lame
- __ plunged
- __ triumph

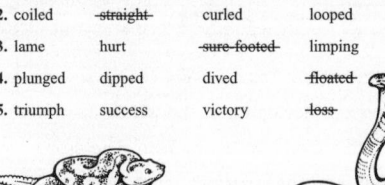

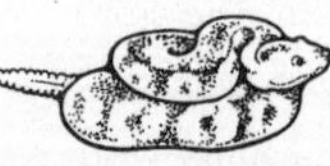

Directions: Choose the word from the box that best matches each clue. Write the letters of the word on the blanks. The boxed letters spell something that is given as an award.

6. success — t r i u [m] p h
7. unable to walk properly — l a m [e]
8. wound around into a pile — c o i l e [d]
9. big, scary snake — c o b r [a]
10. threw with force — p [l] u n g e d

Something that is given as an award: m e d a l

Write an Animal Story

On a separate sheet of paper, write a story in which the main character is an animal. Tell what problem your character faces and solves. Use as many vocabulary words as possible. **Students' stories should focus on an animal character. Check that included vocabulary words are used correctly.**

Notes for Home: Your child identified and used vocabulary words from *Rikki-tikki-tavi.* ***Home Activity:*** With your child, recall stories you have read or seen on TV about animals that have helped humans. Try to use vocabulary words as part of your discussion.

Drawing Conclusions

- When you use details from the story and what you know to make decisions about the characters or events, you are **drawing conclusions.**

Directions: Reread this passage from *Rikki-tikki-tavi*. It takes place the morning after Rikki-tikki helped kill Nag. Then answer the questions below.

> When morning came, Rikki-tikki was very stiff but well pleased with himself. "Now I have Nagaina to deal with, and she will be worse than five Nags. And there's no knowing when the eggs will hatch. I must go see Darzee," he said.
>
> Without waiting for breakfast, Rikki-tikki ran to the thornbush where Darzee was singing a song of triumph at the top of his voice. The news of Nag's death was all over the garden, because his body had been put on the garbage heap.
>
> "Oh, you stupid tuft of feathers!" said Rikki-tikki. "Is this the time to sing?"

Possible answers given.

1. Why does Rikki-tikki expect Nagaina to "be worse than five Nags"?
She's angry that Rikki-tikki helped kill Nag.

2. What eggs is Rikki-tikki talking about? What will happen when they hatch?
They are Nagaina's eggs. If they hatch, there will be more cobras.

3. Why does Rikki-tikki say, "I must go see Darzee"?
Rikki-tikki has a plan in mind that includes Darzee.

4. Why doesn't Rikki-tikki think this is the time to sing?
Their work is not done as long as Nagaina and the eggs are still around.

5. On a separate sheet of paper, write a description of Rikki-tikki. Use details from the story to support your answer.
He's patient and smart, and he doesn't give up. He waits for Nag in the bathroom. He tricks Nagaina. He follows her down the hole.

Notes for Home: Your child used story details to draw conclusions. ***Home Activity:*** Share events from work, a trip, and so on with your child. Provide details so your child can draw conclusions about why things happened or why somebody acted a certain way.

Selection Test

Directions: Choose the best answer to each item. Mark the letter for the answer you have chosen.

Part 1: Vocabulary

Find the answer choice that means about the same as the underlined word in each sentence.

1. The man caught a <u>cobra</u>.
   - A. bad illness
   - B. large cat with spots
   - C. songbird
   - Ⓓ poisonous snake

2. Art <u>plunged</u> into the lake.
   - F. opened
   - G. looked
   - H. walked
   - Ⓙ dived

3. Our game ended in <u>triumph</u>.
   - Ⓐ victory or success
   - B. loss or defeat
   - C. a tie score
   - D. sadness

4. The snake <u>coiled</u> itself.
   - F. shed its skin
   - Ⓖ wound around something
   - H. unfolded
   - J. slid away slowly

5. Terri's dog is <u>lame</u>.
   - A. having fleas
   - B. bad-tempered
   - Ⓒ not able to walk right
   - D. expecting puppies soon

Part 2: Comprehension

Use what you know about the story to answer each item.

6. What kind of animal is Chuchundra?
   - F. a rat
   - Ⓖ a muskrat
   - H. a mongoose
   - J. a snake

7. Nag believes that if he can rid the house of people, then—
   - A. he and Nagaina can move in.
   - Ⓑ Rikki-tikki will leave.
   - C. a mongoose can live in the garden again.
   - D. he can be crowned king.

8. Nag waits by the water jar to—
   - F. take a drink.
   - Ⓖ attack the man.
   - H. catch Rikki-tikki.
   - J. save the eggs.

GO ON

9. Darzee's wife pretends her wing is broken in order to—
   - A. make Nagaina angry.
   - B. lead the boy into a trap.
   - C. save Rikki-tikki.
   - Ⓓ trick Nagaina.

10. What can you tell about cobras from this story?
    - Ⓕ Cobras are very dangerous.
    - G. Most cobras can sing.
    - H. Baby cobras like to eat melon.
    - J. Adult cobras don't bite children.

11. How is Darzee's wife different from Darzee?
    - A. She is a better singer.
    - B. She has a broken wing.
    - Ⓒ She is smarter.
    - D. She is not as brave.

12. When Nagaina goes up on the porch, Rikki-tikki is—
    - F. waiting by the bathroom drain.
    - G. eating melons.
    - Ⓗ destroying her eggs.
    - J. looking for Nag.

13. Which word best describes Nagaina?
    - Ⓐ hateful
    - B. stupid
    - C. careless
    - D. shy

14. What was most important to Rikki-tikki?
    - F. having a friend
    - Ⓖ keeping Teddy safe
    - H. sleeping in the house
    - J. playing tricks on snakes

15. What part of this story could **not** really happen?
    - A. A cobra lays her eggs in the garden.
    - B. A bird sings loudly.
    - C. A mongoose kills a snake.
    - Ⓓ Animals talk to people.

Drawing Conclusions

- When you use details from the story and what you know to make decisions about the characters or events, you are **drawing conclusions.**

Directions: Read the story below.

> Once there was an old couple who lived in a forest. They feared that a wolf or a thief might get into their house at night, so they got a dog.
>
> The dog thought about how to keep the couple safe. While he was chasing one wolf or thief away, another might come and attack the old couple. He couldn't do the job all by himself.
>
> So the dog went out and brought back a stout stick. "Oh!" said the man. "This will make a bar for our door."
>
> Then the dog went out and brought back some boards. "Oh!" said the woman. "These will make perfect shutters for the windows."
>
> That night they all slept soundly. And they never worried about a wolf or a thief again!

Possible answers given.

Directions: Complete the table by drawing conclusions about what you have read.

What Happens in the Story	What Conclusions I Can Draw
The couple worry about a wolf or a thief breaking in.	1. **They have no locks on the door or the windows.**
They get a dog.	2. **They think a dog will protect them.**
The dog understands what needs to be done.	3. **The dog is smarter than the couple.**
That night everyone sleeps soundly.	4. **The couple made the bar and shutters.**
They never worried about a wolf or a thief again.	5. **The barred door, the shutters, and the dog kept the couple safe.**

Notes for Home: Your child read a story and used story details and what he or she knows to draw conclusions about the characters or events. ***Home Activity:*** Watch a TV show or a movie with your child. Draw conclusions about what happens and the characters' actions and feelings.

Practice Book 4.3, p. 147

Name______________________ Rikki-tikki-tavi

Making Judgments

REVIEW

Directions: Read the story. Then read each question about the story. Choose the best answer to each question. Mark the letter for the answer you have chosen.

Flo and Bob

"'Do this!' 'Don't do that!' That's all you say," cackled Flo the hen crossly to Bob the dog.

"Someday your life may depend on it," said Bob as he went to check on the ducks.

One day a fox appeared. Flo said, "Can I help you?"

"Just looking for now," answered the fox.

That night there was a loud squawking in the henhouse. Bob ran to see what was the matter. A fox!

"Help!" cried Flo. "What should we do?"

"Join wings so the fox can't grab any one of you," said Bob. "Leave him to me."

The hens did what Bob said. Bob chased the fox away. Flo never again complained about Bob's orders.

1. Bob is—
   A. mean.
   B. angry.
   (C.) careful.
   D. silly.

2. Flo is—
   F. helpful.
   (G.) annoyed.
   H. gentle.
   J. strong.

3. When the fox says "Just looking," he means that—
   A. he is not sure what he wants.
   B. he wants to find Bob.
   (C.) he is figuring a way into the henhouse.
   D. he wants to make friends with the hens.

4. In the story, Bob—
   F. is afraid.
   G. is mean.
   H. ignores the chickens.
   (J.) knows that there are dangers in the world.

5. By the end of the story, Flo has—
   A. decided to leave the henhouse.
   (B.) learned her lesson.
   C. lost a friend.
   D. complained to the fox.

Notes for Home: Your child made judgments about characters and events in a story. ***Home Activity:*** Watch a TV show with your child. Invite him or her to make judgments about events and characters. Prompt your child by asking, *Is that a nice way to act? Was that smart?*

Name______________________ Rikki-tikki-tavi

Writing Across Texts

Directions: In this unit, you read the stories *Rikki-tikki-tavi* and *John Henry.* Each selection featured main characters who did their jobs very well. They were heroes in different ways. Think about Rikki-tikki-tavi and John Henry. Use the lists below to record details about how or why they were heroes. **Possible answers given.**

Rikki-tikki-tavi	John Henry
Rikki-tikki-tavi stayed guard at night and overheard the plan to kill Karait.	John Henry helped his father rebuild and improve his house.
1. **He killed Nag in the bathroom.**	4. **He turned Ferret-Faced Freddy into a nice person.**
He devised a plan to distract Nagaina.	5. **He moved the boulder from the road.**
2. **He destroyed Nagaina's cobra eggs.**	
3. **He went into the cobra nest and killed Nagaina.**	

Write a Descriptive Paragraph

Each character described above was a hero to the people he helped. Use the information in your lists to write a paragraph that describes some of the qualities of a hero. Write your paragraph on a separate sheet of paper. **Paragraphs will vary. Check that students draw conclusions from both selections about heroic qualities.**

Notes for Home: Your child listed details about fantasy characters in two different stories. ***Home Activity:*** Discuss some movies that you have seen with your child. Discuss the lead character. Ask the child if this character is a hero in some way.

Grammar Practice Book 4.3, p. 71

Name______________________ Rikki-tikki-tavi

Grammar: Using Verb Tense Correctly

REVIEW

Directions: Use the correct form of the verb in ( ) to complete each sentence. Write the verb on the line.

helped 1. Special dogs have (help) blind people for many years.

trained 2. These Seeing Eye dogs have (train) at special schools.

used 3. Over the years, many people have (use) German shepherds as Seeing Eye dogs.

working 4. These dogs are always (work) hard for their owners.

offered 5. They have (offer) independence to many.

getting 6. My friend Jenna is (get) a Seeing Eye dog.

picked 7. Last month, she (pick) out a young dog she liked.

is 8. It (be) a German shepherd.

waiting 9. Jenna is (wait) for the dog to finish its training.

take 10. She will (take) the dog to school every day.

Directions: Circle the correct verb form in ( ) in each sentence.

11. Some special monkeys are (gave/**given**) other duties.
12. They are (teached/**taught**) special skills.
13. Many of these monkeys have (**gone**/went) to the homes of deaf people.
14. These monkeys are always (drew/**drawing**) their owner's attention to sounds such as a doorbell.
15. Getting one of these monkeys will (**make**/making) a big difference in a person's life.

Notes for Home: Your child practiced using the correct tense of verbs. ***Home Activity:*** Have your child make up sentences using the following tenses of the verb *eat: eat, am eating, ate, have eaten.*

Grammar Practice Book 4.3, p. 72

Name______________________ Rikki-tikki-tavi

Grammar: Review of Verbs

A word that shows action is a **verb.** Use the proper verb form to agree with a singular noun subject or with *he, she,* or *it* and use the proper verb form to agree with a plural subject.

Verbs in the **present tense** show action that is happening now. Verbs in the **past tense** show action that has already happened. Verbs in the **future tense** show action that will happen in the future.

Present: Our dog barks at strangers.
Past: Last night the dog barked once.
Future: He will bark when you ring the bell.

A verb in the past tense often ends with **-ed.** A verb whose past tense does *not* end in **-ed** is called an **irregular verb.** Since it doesn't follow a pattern, you have to remember its past tense form.

Directions: Circle the correct form of verb in ( ) to complete each sentence.

1. Some dogs (makes/**make**) noise when strangers appear.
2. Sometimes a cat's behavior (provide/**provides**) a warning.
3. Other animals (offers/**offer**) other kinds of protection for their young.
4. Geese (honks/**honk**) loudly at strangers.
5. An angry goose (**looks**/look) quite dangerous.

Directions: Use the correct form of the verb in ( ) to complete each sentence. Use the verb tense named in ( ). Write the verb on the line to the left.

sat 6. Freckles the dog _____ on the front porch. (sit—past)

will guard 7. He _____ the house all day. (guard—future)

caught 8. Last year, he _____ a burglar. (catch—past)

came 9. That burglar never _____ again! (come—past)

will worry 10. No one _____ with Freckles around. (worry—future)

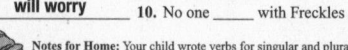

Notes for Home: Your child wrote verbs for singular and plural subjects and to show present, past, and future actions. ***Home Activity:*** Name a verb. Have your child give its past, present, and future tenses.

Grammar Practice Book 4.3, p. 73

Name______________________ Rikki-tikki-tavi

Grammar: Review of Verbs

Directions: Circle the correct form of verb in ( ) to complete each sentence.

1. Mosquitoes (flyed/flew) freely in the summer night.
2. Then the spider (catched/caught) one in her web.
3. Spiders (protect/protects) people from harmful insects.
4. Our mosquito bites (itch/itched) all last night!
5. Right now, all of us (hope/will hope) that the spider will catch more mosquitoes!

Directions: Add a verb to complete each sentence. Write the verb in the correct tense on the line to the left. **Possible answers given.**

stood 6. Yesterday, the sheep _____ peacefully in the meadow.

drank 7. They ate the grass that grew there and _____ the water from the stream.

guard 8. They are safe because our dogs _____ them every day.

keep 9. Sheepdogs _____ the sheep of a flock from wandering away.

were 10. The sheep _____ asleep, but now they are awake.

Write an Animal Story

Have you ever wondered what animals would say to each other if they could talk? On a separate sheet of paper, write a story about two animal friends. Use different verbs, including two irregular verbs. Be sure to use correct verb tenses. Underline your verbs. **Check that all verbs are underlined and that students have used the correct verb form and tense.**

Notes for Home: Your child circled and wrote verbs to complete each sentence. ***Home Activity:*** Name some "fun" action verbs, such as *smile, clap, cheer, jump, spin.* Invite your child to tell you the present, past, and future tense of each verb.

Grammar Practice Book 4.3, p. 74

Name______________________ Rikki-tikki-tavi

Grammar: Review of Verbs

RETEACHING

Complete each sentence. Write the correct form of the verb **walk** on the line.

Present: He **walks** to the playground.

Past: Yesterday he **walked** to school.

Future: Tomorrow he **will walk** to Jeremy's house.

Verbs in the **present tense** show action that is happening now. Verbs in the **past tense** show action that has already happened. Verbs in the **future tense** show what will happen.

Complete each sentence. Write the correct form of the verb **eat** on the line.

Present: Lorna **eats** lunch at home.

Past: Yesterday Lorna **ate** lunch at school.

Future: Tomorrow she **will eat** lunch at her grandparents' house.

Often a verb in the past tense ends with **-ed**. A verb whose past-tense form does not end in **-ed** is called an **irregular verb.**

Directions: Use the correct form of the verb in ( ) to complete each sentence. Use the verb tense named in ( ). Write the verb on the line to the left.

whispers 1. Celia _____ an answer to her friend. (whisper—present)

waved 2. I _____ my hands. (wave—past)

called 3. Bruce _____ on me. (call—past)

will know 4. "You _____ the answer," he said. (know—future)

think 5. "I _____ it is forty-two." (think—present)

are 6. "You _____ smart," he said. (be—present)

Notes for Home: Your child wrote verbs for singular and plural subjects and in different tenses. ***Home Activity:*** Talk about what you did for fun when you were your child's age and about what you would like to do together. Use verbs in the present, past, and future tenses.

Grammar Practice Book 4.3, p. 75

Name______________________ Rikki-tikki-tavi

Grammar: Review of Verbs

Directions: Circle the correct form of the verb in ( ) to complete each sentence. Use a dictionary if you need help with irregular verbs.

1. Our neighbors (gives/gave) us an empty box.
2. We (decides/decided) to make a rocket ship.
3. The box (were/was) so big we couldn't fit it into the house.
4. Mom (tell/told) us to leave it in the backyard.
5. All of us (played/will play) with it next weekend.
6. We (put/puts) stickers on the outside of the ship.
7. Mike (run/ran) to his house to get markers.
8. Then he and Joe (drawn/drew) windows and a door.
9. Steve (will cut/cut) a hole in the top before we can climb inside.
10. I (am/will be) the first one to sit in the ship tomorrow.
11. John (was/is) finishing the decorations inside the ship right now.
12. We (is/are) very excited about our ship!

Possible answers given.

Directions: Write sentences, using the verbs and verb tenses in ( ).

(draw—future) 13. **We will draw funny faces at the fair tomorrow.**

(move—past) 14. **Last year we moved to a new city.**

(fly—present) 15. **He flies airplanes on TV.**

Notes for Home: Your child identified and wrote verbs with singular and plural subjects and in present, past, and future tenses. ***Home Activity:*** Read a magazine or newspaper article with your child. Have him or her find one example each of present, past, and future-tense verb forms.

Practice Book 4.3, p. 148

Name______________________ Rikki-tikki-tavi

Word Study: Base Words

Directions: Many words are made by adding letters to the beginning or end of a word. The word you start with is called the **base word.** Read each word below. Find the base word for each word. Write it on the line.

1. hidden **hide**
2. sensible **sense**
3. emptied **empty**
4. frightened **fright**
5. forgotten **forgot**
6. mournful **mourn**
7. tingled **tingle**
8. gently **gentle**
9. lowered **low**
10. misspelled **spell**
11. beautifully **beauty**
12. recalled **call**

Directions: Base words can help you figure out the meaning of new words. Read each sentence. Think about the base word for the underlined word. Then read the two definitions in ( ). Circle the correct definition.

13. The small animals were frightened by the snake. (awakened/scared)
14. The sensible thing for a hunted animal to do is to stay with a group. (foolish/smart)
15. The bird searched for hidden dangers. (out of sight/out in the open)
16. But the animals had forgotten about the family in the house. (kept in mind/not remembered)
17. They let out a mournful cry as they thought about the family's fate. (bright/sad)
18. The boy tingled with fear as he faced the snake. (a stinging feeling/a sleepy feeling)
19. The mongoose told the snake he had emptied the nest of all its eggs. (left nothing/filled up)

Directions: Write a sentence using the word **courageous.** If you're not sure what the word means, use the base word to help you.

20. **Possible answer: It was courageous of the mongoose to try to kill the cobra.**

Notes for Home: Your child found base words in longer words, such as *care* in *carefully.* ***Home Activity:*** Read a magazine article with your child. As you spot longer words with base words, say, for example, "I spy the base word *near.*" Have your child find the longer word.

Spelling Workbook 4.3, p. 57

Name______________ Rikki-tikki-tavi

Spelling: Vowels in Final Syllables

Pretest Directions: Fold back the page along the dotted line. On the blanks, write the spelling words as they are dictated. When you have finished the test, unfold the page and check your words.

1. other — **1.** Help me find my **other** shoe.
2. number — **2.** We saw a **number** of birds.
3. October — **3.** **October** is a cool month.
4. another — **4.** Have **another** slice of cake.
5. color — **5.** What **color** are your eyes?
6. doctor — **6.** The **doctor** hasn't come yet.
7. motor — **7.** This car has a noisy **motor**.
8. people — **8.** How many **people** are here?
9. simple — **9.** The solution is **simple**.
10. angle — **10.** The owl chose an **angle** of attack.
11. title — **11.** I've forgotten the book's **title**.
12. model — **12.** She is a **model** citizen.
13. barrel — **13.** The rain **barrel** is getting full.
14. angel — **14.** He was an **angel** of mercy.
15. broken — **15.** Her wing looks **broken**.
16. sudden — **16.** The attack was **sudden**.
17. oven — **17.** Be careful, the **oven** is hot.
18. common — **18.** It's for the **common** good.
19. gallon — **19.** I need a **gallon** of water.
20. button — **20.** He needs a new **button**.

Notes for Home: Your child took a pretest on how to spell the vowel sound in final syllables. ***Home Activity:*** Help your child learn misspelled words before the final test. Your child should look at the word, say it, spell it aloud, and then spell it with eyes shut.

Spelling Workbook 4.3, p. 58

Name______________ Rikki-tikki-tavi

Spelling: Vowels in Final Syllables

Word List			
other	doctor	title	sudden
number	motor	model	oven
October	people	barrel	common
another	simple	angel	gallon
color	angle	broken	button

Directions: Choose the words from the box that end with **le** or **el.** Write each word in the correct column. Draw lines between the syllables.

Order may vary.

Ends with le	Ends with el
1. peo/ple	5. mod/el
2. sim/ple	6. bar/rel
3. an/gle	7. an/gel
4. ti/tle	

Directions: Write the word from the box that belongs in each group. Draw lines between the syllables.

8. different, separate, oth/er
9. quantity, amount, num/ber
10. additional, added, an/oth/er
11. snap, zipper, but/ton
12. pint, quart, gal/lon
13. unexpected, quick, sud/den
14. average, ordinary, com/mon
15. stove, burner, ov/en
16. busted, cracked, bro/ken
17. shade, hue, col/or
18. August, September, Oc/to/ber
19. dentist, veterinarian, doc/tor
20. engine, machine, mo/tor

Notes for Home: Your child spelled words with vowels in final syllables that sound alike but are spelled differently, such as *peopl<u>e</u>* and *mod<u>el</u>*. ***Home Activity:*** Work with your child to come up with more words that end similarly to the words in the box.

Spelling Workbook 4.3, p. 59

Name______________ Rikki-tikki-tavi

Spelling: Vowels in Final Syllables

Directions: Proofread this news story. Find five spelling mistakes. Use the proofreading marks to correct each mistake.

≡ Make a capital.
/ Make a small letter.
∧ Add something.
Take out something.
⊙ Add a period.
¶ Begin a new paragraph.

Dog Saves Boy

It was the first week of Octobor (er), and the leaves on the trees were all changing coler (o). A local boy, Jeff Blitz, went for a walk in the woods with his dog, Breck. All of a suden (d), Jeff realized that he was lost. There were a numbr (e) of ways to go, and he didn't know the right one. He turned to Breck, and said, "Home." And Breck led him home. Jeff declared there was not anothor (er) dog that was smarter than Breck!

Word List				
other	color	simple	barrel	oven
number	doctor	angle	angel	common
October	motor	title	broken	gallon
another	people	model	sudden	button

Write a News Story

On a separate sheet of paper, write a short news story about an animal who makes a heroic rescue. Try to use at least three spelling words.

Answers will vary, but each news story should include at least three spelling words.

Spelling Tip

The vowels in final syllables often sound alike but are spelled differently: **peopl<u>e</u>, mod<u>el</u>; brok<u>en</u>, comm<u>on</u>; anoth<u>er</u>, mot<u>or</u>.** Check the story to make sure the vowels in the final syllables are spelled correctly.

Notes for Home: Your child spelled words with vowels in final syllables that are pronounced the same but are spelled differently, such as *peopl<u>e</u>* and *mod<u>el</u>*. ***Home Activity:*** With your child, read stories in the newspaper. Look for words with the same final syllables as those in the box.

Spelling Workbook 4.3, p. 60

Name______________ Rikki-tikki-tavi

Spelling: Vowels in Final Syllables

REVIEW

Word List				
other	color	simple	barrel	oven
number	doctor	angle	angel	common
October	motor	title	broken	gallon
another	people	model	sudden	button

Directions: Unscramble the letters to form a word from the box. Write the word on the line.

barrel **1.** rrable — people **4.** pepleo — common **7.** monmco
sudden **2.** nedusd — number **5.** munreb — other **8.** hoter
broken **3.** korbne — October **6.** ctObreo — another **9.** arethon

Directions: Choose a word from the box that best matches each clue. Write the word on the line.

doctor **10.** It's who you go see when you are sick.
button **11.** It holds your clothes together.
color **12.** It's what leaves change in the fall.
gallon **13.** It is the same as four quarts.
angel **14.** It's a figure with wings often hung on Christmas trees.
angle **15.** It's one of four inside a square.
title **16.** It's the name of a book.
simple **17.** It's another word for *easy.*
model **18.** It's an airplane you can build at home.
motor **19.** It's the part of a car that makes it go.
oven **20.** It's where you bake a pie.

Notes for Home: Your child spelled words with vowels in final syllables that are pronounced the same but are spelled differently, such as *peopl<u>e</u>* and *mod<u>el</u>*. ***Home Activity:*** Have your child think of words that rhyme with words in the box. Check to see if the endings are spelled alike.

Practice Book 4.3, p. 149
Name________________ Rikki-tikki-tavi

Schedule

A **schedule** is a special kind of chart that tells you when events take place. For example, arrival and departure times for buses and trains are often organized in schedules.

Directions: Read the schedule. Use it to answer the questions that follow.

The Sun Prairie News is proud to sponsor:
Animal Rescue Stories
Meet the animals who saved their owners' lives.
Hear the amazing tales by the animals' owners.

Schedule of Presentations
(Each presentation will last 45 minutes.)

Saturday, October 3	9:00 A.M.	Mark and his dog, Pudding
	11:00 A.M.	Tonya and her cat, Pink Paws
	3:00 P.M.	J.T. and his monkey, Tippy
Sunday, October 4	11:00 A.M.	Miguel and his ferret, Freddy
	2:00 P.M.	Mark and his dog, Pudding
	3:30 P.M.	Carla and her cat, Detour

Program held in the F.W. Richey Auditorium,
100 State St., Sun Prairie, WI (920) 555-2304

Practice Book 4.3, p. 150
Name________________ Rikki-tikki-tavi

1. What are the names of the animals who are part of the first and last presentations of the weekend? List the times and dates when these two animals will appear.
The first animal is the dog Pudding at 9:00 A.M. on Saturday, October 3.
The last animal is the cat Detour at 3:30 P.M. on Sunday, October 4.

2. Which owner and animal will be presenting twice? What are your choices in dates and times to see them?
Mark and his dog, Pudding, will be presenting twice, once on Saturday at 9:00 A.M. and again on Sunday at 2:00 P.M.

3. What two owners will be presenting at 11:00 A.M. each day?
Tonya will be presenting at 11:00 A.M. on Saturday, and Miguel will be presenting at 11:00 A.M. on Sunday.

4. If you arrived at the auditorium at 2:00 P.M. on Saturday, October 3, which presentations could you see that day? Explain.
The only presentation you could see would be J.T. and his monkey, Tippy.
All the other presentations would be over by then.

5. How long will Tonya and Pink Paws' presentation be? How do you know?
45 minutes; All the presentations are that long.

Notes for Home: Your child used a schedule to find dates and times of special presentations. *Home Activity:* Find examples of schedules you and your child use often, such as TV listings or a bus schedule. Take turns asking each other questions about the schedule.

Name________________

Comparison/Contrast Organizer

Directions: Fill in the chart first. Then write your title, introductory sentence, topic sentences, and conclusion sentence. **Students' charts should be filled in completely.**

Title ________________

Introductory Sentence ________________

Topic Sentence ________________

Same

Food:	Food:
1.	1.
2.	2.

Topic Sentence ________________

Different

Food:	Food:
1.	1.
2.	2.

Conclusion Sentence ________________

Notes for Home: Your child recently completed a graphic organizer to plan a comparison/contrast essay. *Home Activity:* Ask your child to tell you how he or she decided upon the above similarities and differences for the essay.

Name________________

Elaboration

Adding Details

- When you write, you can elaborate by **adding details** to your examples. This will help your reader understand more clearly.

Directions: Read each sentence below. Answer the question to add details to make each sentence clearer.

Answers will vary. Example:
The children played. (Where did they play?)
The children played in the yard.

1. Marta worked very hard. (She worked hard by doing what?)
Marta worked very hard by scrubbing the floor.

2. I borrowed her book about plants. (Whose book was it?)
I borrowed Pat's book about plants.

3. Maria played hopscotch. (When did she play?)
Maria played hopscotch yesterday afternoon.

4. Jacob studied hard last night. (Why did he study hard?)
Jacob studied hard last night because he had a test today.

5. The five tired hikers rested. (Where did they rest?)
The five tired hikers rested by the pond.

6. Juan broke the vase. (How did he break it?)
Juan broke the vase by hitting it with his baseball by mistake.

7. Brad made sandwiches for lunch. (What kind did he make?)
Brad made peanut butter sandwiches for lunch.

8. Ilene helped her friend. (She helped her friend by doing what?)
Ilene helped her friend by explaining the assignment.

Notes for Home: Your child recently elaborated sentences by adding details. *Home Activity:* Think of activities you do at home related to mealtime. First ask your child to tell about one of these activities using simple details. Then have your child elaborate by adding more details.

Name________________________________

Self-Evaluation

Comparison/Contrast Essay

Directions: Think about the final draft of your comparison/contrast essay. Then answer each question below. **Answers will vary depending on each student's work.**

	Yes	No	Not sure
1. Is my topic sentence clear?			
2. Are my ideas organized well so they flow smoothly?			
3. Did I use transition words when I compared and contrasted the two characters?			
4. Did I use different kinds of sentences that are easy to understand?			
5. Are there any mistakes that could make it hard for the reader to understand my paragraph?			

6. What do you think you did best in your comparison/contrast essay?

____

____

7. Write one mistake you made this time that you will avoid the next time.

____

____

Notes for Home: Your child wrote and evaluated a comparison/contrast essay. ***Home Activity:*** Ask your child to explain one new writing skill that he or she learned during this project.

Practice Book 4.4, p. 151

Name________________________________ Half-Chicken

Paraphrasing

- **Paraphrasing** is explaining something in your own words. A paraphrase should keep the author's meaning.
- A paraphrase should include all of the author's ideas, but it should be easier to read than the original.

Directions: Reread "Blue Jay Takes the Heat." Then complete the table. Paraphrase the sentence or sentences from the story that are listed in the first column. Write your paraphrase of the text in the second column. **Possible answers given.**

Author's Sentences	My Paraphrase
Paragraph 1, Sentence 2	1. **Firekeeper didn't like Alcee Lingo because Alcee always tried to warm his hands at the fire and then ran away before Firekeeper could catch him.**
Paragraph 1, Last two sentences	2. **Firekeeper was a terrible person who wouldn't have liked any child.**
Paragraph 4, First sentence	3. **Bruh Blue Jay had to be fast to get safely away with the fire.**
Paragraph 4, Sentences 2–5	4. **Firekeeper had good eyes and saw what was happening. He was furious and chased Bruh Blue Jay. Bruh Blue Jay was terrified.**
Last paragraph, Last sentence	5. **Even today, you can often see Bruh Blue Jay taking little bits of wood over to Sis Squatty, Firekeeper's wife.**

Notes for Home: Your child read a story and paraphrased parts of it in his or her own words. ***Home Activity:*** Give your child some directions, such as asking for a particular can from a cupboard. Ask your child to restate the directions simply, using his or her own words.

Practice Book 4.4, p. 152

Name________________________________ Half-Chicken

Vocabulary

Directions: Choose the word from the box that best matches each definition. Write the word on the line.

Check the Words You Know
- __ farewells
- __ flung
- __ suggested
- __ tangled
- __ uniforms
- __ vain

suggested 1. proposed

farewells 2. good-bys

vain 3. too proud of one's own looks or abilities

flung 4. threw with force; past tense of *fling*

uniforms 5. worn by members of a group on duty

tangled 6. confused, twisted

Directions: Choose the word from the box that best completes each sentence. You will use some words more than once. Write the word on the line to the left.

flung 7. Last night's wind had _____ leaves and branches all around the yard.

suggested 8. Lydia _____ that we check the weather report to see if it would rain today.

uniforms 9. "This afternoon is our band concert, and our _____ might get wet," she said.

farewells 10. Just to be safe, Lydia grabbed her umbrella as she said her _____.

Write a Description

On a separate sheet of paper, write a description of a storm. Use as many vocabulary words as you can. **Students' descriptions should use vocabulary words correctly.**

Notes for Home: Your child identified and used vocabulary words from *Half-Chicken*. ***Home Activity:*** Have your child give a synonym (a word with the same or nearly the same meaning as another word) for each vocabulary word *(good-bys, farewells)*.

Practice Book 4.4, p. 153

Name________________________________ Half-Chicken

Paraphrasing

- **Paraphrasing** is explaining something in your own words. A paraphrase should include all of the author's ideas, but it should be easier to read than the original.

Directions: Reread what happens in *Half-Chicken* when the half-chicken hatches out of the egg. Then follow the instructions below.

> Finally there was a tiny sound. The baby chick was pecking at its egg from the inside. The hen quickly helped it break open the shell, and at last the thirteenth chick came out into the world.
>
> Yet this was no ordinary chick. He had only one wing, only one leg, only one eye, and only half as many feathers as the other chicks.
>
> It was not long before everyone at the ranch knew that a very special chick had been born.
>
> The ducks told the turkeys. The turkeys told the pigeons. The pigeons told the swallows. And the swallows flew over the fields, spreading the news to the cows. . . .

Possible answers given.

1. Paraphrase the first paragraph.
Once the chick started to peck, the hen helped it break open its shell.

2. Paraphrase the second paragraph.
This chick had only half of what the other chicks had.

3. Paraphrase the third paragraph.
Word about the special chick spread quickly.

4. Paraphrase the fourth paragraph.
All the birds told one another, and they told the cows.

5. Reread the passage. Then, on a separate sheet of paper, paraphrase the entire passage in your own words. **A special chick was born. It had only one wing, leg, and eye. It had half of its feathers. Soon, all the animals were talking about this chick.**

Notes for Home: Your child paraphrased several paragraphs. ***Home Activity:*** With your child, find a favorite part of a book, no more than a page or two. Read the passage. Ask your child to tell you what happens in his or her own words.

Practice Book 4.4, p. 155

Name________________ **Half-Chicken**

Selection Test

Directions: Choose the best answer to each item. Mark the letter for the answer you have chosen.

Part 1: Vocabulary

Find the answer choice that means about the same as the underlined word in each sentence.

1. The ropes were tangled.
   A. tied in a bow
   B. cut by something sharp
   C. worn along the edge
   Ⓓ twisted in a confused mass

2. The cousins said their farewells.
   Ⓕ good-bys
   G. prayers
   H. names
   J. speeches

3. Dad suggested a new plan.
   A. refused to allow
   B. got ready
   Ⓒ put forward the idea
   D. forced to do

4. Ben flung his cards on the table.
   F. dropped
   G. set
   H. matched
   Ⓙ threw

5. Cassie's sister is vain.
   Ⓐ having too much pride
   B. showing feelings freely
   C. hard to understand
   D. having good manners

6. Someone stole our uniforms.
   F. things that bring good luck
   Ⓖ clothes worn by members of a group
   H. small copies of something
   J. directions for doing something

Part 2: Comprehension

Use what you know about the story to answer each item.

7. Which birds on the ranch had been to Mexico City before?
   A. the chickens
   B. the ducks
   Ⓒ the swallows
   D. the turkeys

8. Half-Chicken was an unusual chick because he—
   Ⓕ had only one wing, one leg, and one eye.
   G. was born thirteenth.
   H. was the last chick born.
   J. wanted to leave the ranch.

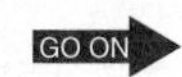

Practice Book 4.4, p. 156

Name________________ **Half-Chicken**

9. Because of the attention he got, Half-Chicken became very—
   A. shy.
   B. worried.
   C. spoiled.
   Ⓓ vain.

10. Half-Chicken left his home because he wanted to—
    F. be a weather vane.
    Ⓖ see the court of the viceroy.
    H. meet the wind.
    J. do good deeds.

11. What is another way to say, "I have no time to lose"?
    Ⓐ "I'm in a hurry."
    B. "I forgot my watch."
    C. "I have plenty of time."
    D. "I've lost track of time."

12. When Half-Chicken presented himself at the kitchen door of the palace, he—
    F. hoped to be invited in to dinner.
    G. gave the cook a chicken he had brought with him.
    Ⓗ didn't realize he was about to become dinner.
    J. was surprised to see his friends were there.

13. What is another way of saying, "This chicken has been more trouble than he's worth"?
    A. "This chicken is too wild to be used in soup."
    Ⓑ "This chicken is not worth all the work I've done trying to cook him."
    C. "Now I know why I didn't have to pay for this chicken."
    D. "The trouble is that everything tastes like chicken."

14. What lesson can be learned from this story?
    F. Good things come to those who wait.
    G. People should stay home instead of traveling to see the world.
    H. A bird in the hand is worth two in the bush.
    Ⓙ It's good to help others because someday you might need their help.

15. The author was probably trying to be funny when she wrote about a "vain" rooster that—
    A. talked to the wind.
    Ⓑ became a weather vane.
    C. was flung out the window.
    D. spoke to the palace guards.

Name________________ **Half-Chicken**

Paraphrasing

- **Paraphrasing** is explaining something in your own words.
- A paraphrase should include all of the author's ideas, but it should be easier to read than the original.

Directions: Read the story below.

One day, Fire, Water, and Wind decided to have a contest to see who was strongest. Fire went first. It burned very brightly. The flames went higher and higher into the sky. They gleamed like orange jewels. Everyone who was watching said, "Ooh!" and "Aah!" Everyone said, "Fire must be the strongest!"

Then Water came along and went, "Splash! Splash!" Pretty soon, Fire was gone. All that was left was a big, wet puddle! "Ha, ha, ha!" laughed Water. "I put out Fire! I am the strongest!"

"You are not the strongest," said Wind. Wind began to blow and blow. It blew the water into a million droplets scattered over the earth. "Ha, ha, ha!" laughed Wind. "I am the strongest!"

Then Fire came back. Fire can't burn in water, but it burns in air. So when Wind blew Water away, Fire came back, stronger than ever. Again, Water put out Fire, Wind blew away Water, and Fire ate up Wind. Who do *you* think was the strongest?

Directions: Complete the table. Use your own words to retell what happens in this story. **Possible answers given.**

Paragraph	Character	What Happens?
One	Fire	burns very brightly, looks like the strongest
Two	Water	1. **puts out fire, looks like the strongest**
Three	2. **Wind**	3. **scatters the water, looks like the strongest**
Four	4. **Fire**	5. **burns brightly again, looks like the strongest**

Notes for Home: Your child used his or her own words to explain what happens in a story. ***Home Activity:*** Tell your child a familiar story, like "The Tortoise and the Hare." Then ask him or her to tell *you* the story in his or her own words.

Practice Book 4.4, p. 157

Name________________ **Half-Chicken**

Predicting

REVIEW

Directions: Read the story. Then read each question about the story. Choose the best answer to each question. Mark the letter for the answer you have chosen.

What Will the Weather Be?

Miriam and her family were on a camping trip. Miriam had just felt a few drops of rain.

"Are you sure that was rain?" Miriam's mother asked. She pointed to the nearby lake, where Miriam's brother was swimming. "Maybe Josh splashed you."

Miriam shook her head. "Look at our campfire," she said. The wind made the flames flicker weakly. "I think that wind means a storm," said Miriam.

Miriam's father looked up at the sky. Overhead, the clouds were dark gray. But way over in the west, the sky was blue and clear. "Maybe the rain clouds will blow over," he said.

Miriam shook her head again. "No," she said. "The wind is blowing in the wrong direction." Then she heard thunder.

1. Based on what you've read, what kind of weather do you predict?
   A. a hurricane
   Ⓑ a rainstorm
   C. bright blue skies
   D. a few drops of rain

2. What is the first clue that helps you make your prediction?
   F. Miriam gets splashed by her brother.
   G. Miriam puts out the campfire.
   H. Miriam sees dark gray clouds.
   Ⓙ Miriam feels a few raindrops.

3. What is the second clue that helps you make your prediction?
   Ⓐ The campfire flickers.
   B. The wind blows leaves into the fire.
   C. Josh splashes Miriam.
   D. The rain starts.

4. Which clue might lead you to predict *good* weather?
   F. The wind is blowing.
   Ⓖ Part of the sky is blue.
   H. Dark gray clouds are overhead.
   J. The air is warm.

5. Which clue would lead you to change your "good-weather" prediction?
   A. The wind has died down.
   B. The fire goes out.
   Ⓒ Miriam hears thunder.
   D. Josh gets out of the lake.

Notes for Home: Your child made predictions about a story and identified the clues used to make the predictions. ***Home Activity:*** As you complete a task, such as preparing a meal, ask your child to predict what you will do next. Then ask how your child came up with that prediction.

Name______________________________ Half-Chicken

Writing Across Texts

Directions: Think about the chicken in the story *Half-Chicken*. How is he alike and different from the chickens in the selection "Chicken Farming"? Read the five statements in the box and use them to complete the table. Write the statements that are true of Half-Chicken, "real" chickens, and both in the correct places in the table. Add other information you have read to the table.

Statements

goes to visit the viceroy
probably lives on a "factory" farm
has only one leg, one wing, and one eye
says "Cock-a-doodle-do!"
produces one or more eggs a day

Half-Chicken	Real Chicken	Both
1. **goes to visit the viceroy** **has only one leg, one wing, and one eye**	2. **probably lives on a "factory farm"** **produces one or more eggs a day**	3. **say "Cock-a-doodle-do!"**

Write a Story

On a separate sheet of paper, write a story about Half-Chicken living on a factory farm. Would he find it difficult? How might he change? **Stories will vary. Check that students tell the story in a logical order and that they use clue words and transitional words and phrases to help explain the sequence of events.**

Notes for Home: Your child wrote a story about a character in a folk tale living in the real world. ***Home Activity:*** Read a folk tale with your child that features animal characters. Discuss how those animal characters are similar to and different from real animals.

Grammar Practice Book 4.4, p. 76

Name______________________________ Half-Chicken

Grammar: Complete Subjects REVIEW

Directions: Underline the complete subject in each sentence.

1. Many folk tales use animals as characters.
2. These make-believe animals talk, cry, and act just like human beings.
3. Natural events become characters in folk tales too.
4. A good storyteller can make the forces of nature seem alive.
5. The mighty wind might decide to show off its power, for example.
6. A strong, fast stream is able to float a child to safety.
7. A soft breeze grows angry and turns into a raging windstorm.
8. A thunderstorm gets tired and dozes off as a gentle drizzle.
9. Some animals persuade a little spark to grow into a dangerous fire.
10. Anything can take on human qualities in a folk tale.

Directions: Add a complete subject to each predicate to create a sentence. Your subject should have at least three words. Write your sentence on the line. **Possible answers given.**

11. became angry and roared down from the mountain
The mighty wind became angry and roared down from the mountain.

12. warmed all the people sitting around it
A glowing fire warmed all the people sitting around it.

13. ruined the picnic for everyone
The sudden rainstorm ruined the picnic for everyone.

14. came running out of the cabin
Seven squeaking mice came running out of the cabin.

15. appeared in the sky and frightened us
A huge black cloud appeared in the sky and frightened us.

Notes for Home: Your child identified and used complete subjects in sentences. ***Home Activity:*** Collect four or five things from around the house. Ask your child to write a sentence about each item and underline the complete subject.

Grammar Practice Book 4.4, p. 77

Name______________________________ Half-Chicken

Grammar: Adjectives

A word that describes a person, place, or thing is called an **adjective.** An adjective often comes before a noun, but it also can follow a noun or pronoun.

- Some adjectives tell what kind. They describe color, shape, size, sound, taste, touch, or smell: The little donkey trotted under its load of hay.
- Some adjectives tell how many: Are two men needed for the job?
- Some adjectives tell which one: Walk toward that restaurant.

Directions: Write the adjective or adjectives that describe each underlined noun.

irritable 1. The wind and the sun felt irritable.
short 2. They had a short argument.
This 3. This quarrel was about who had more strength.
strong; cold 4. A strong, cold wind blew across the field.
bright; hot 5. The bright, hot sun beat down on the land.
Each; fierce 6. Each fierce competitor was determined to win.

Directions: Use the adjectives in the box to write four sentences. **Possible answers given.**

cold hot this bright

7. **I hate cold weather.**
8. **This snowstorm will bring lots of snow.**
9. **I hope to see some bright sunshine soon.**
10. **Until then, I'll drink hot cider by the fire!**

Notes for Home: Your child identified adjectives, words that describe persons, places, or things in sentences. ***Home Activity:*** Point to objects and ask your child to describe them, using as many different adjectives as possible.

Grammar Practice Book 4.4, p. 78

Name______________________________ Half-Chicken

Grammar: Adjectives

Directions: Underline the adjective or adjectives in each sentence.

1. On a beautiful morning, a kind old woman decided to bake cookies.
2. She mixed ginger with the rest of the fresh ingredients and divided the sweet dough into pieces.
3. She rolled out one piece, then carefully cut it into the shape of a little man.
4. The old woman placed her special cookie in a large pan and slid it into the hot oven.
5. After a short time, the woman smelled ginger and heard a strange sound inside the oven.
6. When she opened the door, the surprised woman couldn't believe her eyes.
7. The crispy cookie-man sat up and said, "Thank you."
8. He jumped down and ran across the kitchen as fast as his little legs could go.
9. The old woman ran after him.
10. The clever cookie-man called out in a squeaky voice, "Run, run, as fast as you can. You can't catch me—I'm the cookie-man!"

Write a Folk Tale

On a separate sheet of paper, retell a folk tale or fairy tale that you know. Use at least one adjective in each sentence to describe the characters, things, and places in the story. Underline all the adjectives you use. **Check to make sure that students have correctly underlined each adjective they used.**

Notes for Home: Your child identified adjectives—words that describe persons, places, or things—in sentences. ***Home Activity:*** Describe objects in your child's room, using only adjectives, such as *blue, fluffy, soft,* and have him or her guess what you are describing. (*a pillow*)

Grammar Practice Book 4.4, p. 79

Name ____________ Half-Chicken

Grammar: Adjectives

RETEACHING

Connect the words that describe the picture.

Adjectives	Adjectives	Nouns
1. six	hard	rocks
2. some	little	turtles

Write the words you connected to complete each sentence.

3. I see **six** (adjective) **little** (adjective) **turtles** (noun).

4. I see **some** (adjective) **hard** (adjective) **rocks** (noun).

An **adjective** describes a person, place, or thing. Adjectives can answer the questions **How many?, What kind?,** and **Which one?**

Directions: Tell more about each noun with two adjectives. **Possible answers given.**

1. **some** **slow** snails
2. **this** **red** fox

Directions: Circle the adjectives that tell **what kind, how many,** and **which one.**

3. (Many) leaves lay on the (cold) ground.
4. (Two) woodchucks crawled in (long) tunnels.
5. (Ten) bats stayed in (dark) caves.
6. (One) deer searched for (some) food.

Notes for Home: Your child identified adjectives. ***Home Activity:*** Have your child write a description of a perfect day. Challenge your child to use six adjectives in his or her description.

Grammar Practice Book 4.4, p. 80

Name ____________ Half-Chicken

Grammar: Adjectives

Circle the adjectives that tell **what kind, how many,** and **which one.** Then write each adjective in the correct column.

1. (Many) craters are on (this) (dusty) moon.
2. (Those) (pointy) rocks are in (several) areas.
3. (Deep) valleys are in (some) places.
4. (Twelve) astronauts landed on its (rough) surface.

What Kind	How Many	Which One
5. **dusty**	9. **Many**	13. **this**
6. **pointy**	10. **several**	14. **Those**
7. **Deep**	11. **some**	
8. **rough**	12. **Twelve**	

Directions: Follow the correct path through the puzzle. Find the adjectives that tell **what kind.** Then write each one to tell more about a noun.

Possible answers given.

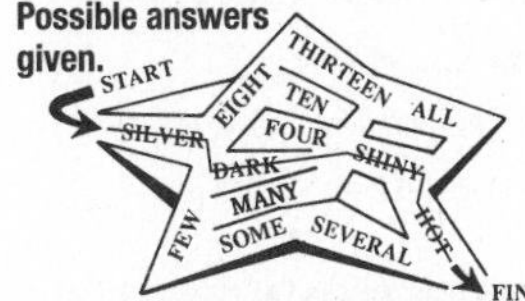

15. **shiny** star
16. **hot** sun
17. **silver** planets
18. **dark** sky

Write a Poem

On a separate sheet of paper, write a poem about the night sky. Tell what you see. Use adjectives that tell what kind and how many. **Check that students use adjectives that tell what kind and how many.**

Notes for Home: Your child identified adjectives that tell *what kind, how many,* and *which one.* ***Home Activity:*** Have your child look at a magazine article and find an example of each kind of adjective. Then have him or her use them to write new sentences.

Practice Book 4.4, p. 158

Name ____________ Half-Chicken

Word Study: Inflected Forms with -es

Directions: Add **-es** to base words ending in **sh, ch, s, ss,** and **x**. Read the paragraph below. Look for words where **-es** has been added. Circle each word and write it on the line.

A mother bird (perches) on her nest, until one day, a baby bird (hatches). A strong wind (brushes) through the trees. Out falls the baby bird! It (passes) right through the leafy greenery to the ground. A cat nearby (reaches) for the baby bird.

"Please don't hurt my baby!" says the mother.

"Why not?" asks the cat.

The mother thinks, then says, "Because one day I will do you a favor."

So the cat lets the baby bird go. A dog sitting nearby (watches) the cat and (catches) it. The mother bird sees what has happened. She swoops down and sits on the dog's nose, causing the dog to sneeze and drop the cat. And the cat never bothered another bird again.

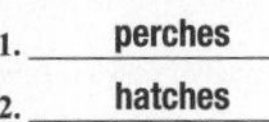

1. **perches**
2. **hatches**
3. **brushes**
4. **passes**
5. **reaches**
6. **watches**
7. **catches**

Directions: Add **-es** to each base word make a new word. Write the new word on the line.

8. fetch	**fetches**	12. toss	**tosses**
9. wash	**washes**	13. relax	**relaxes**
10. wish	**wishes**	14. teach	**teaches**
11. match	**matches**	15. confess	**confesses**

Notes for Home: Your child added *-es* to words such as *reach (reaches)* and *pass (passes).* ***Home Activity:*** Read a short story with your child. Take turns writing down words you find that end with *-es.*

Spelling Workbook 4.4, p. 61

Name ____________ Half-Chicken

Spelling: Words with *sh, ch, tch, wh*

Pretest Directions: Fold back the page along the dotted line. On the blanks, write the spelling words as they are dictated. When you have finished the test, unfold the page and check your words.

1. **shown**	1. They were **shown** into the parlor.
2. **short**	2. Hurry, time is **short**.
3. **punish**	3. Don't be quick to **punish** him.
4. **shelter**	4. They looked for **shelter**.
5. **flashlight**	5. Here's the **flashlight**.
6. **trash**	6. I put it in the **trash**.
7. **March**	7. **March** winds can be strong.
8. **chapter**	8. I read the first **chapter**.
9. **chocolate**	9. She likes **chocolate** milk.
10. **church**	10. The **church** is on the hill.
11. **watch**	11. Will you **watch** them for me?
12. **kitchen**	12. The cook's in the **kitchen**.
13. **pitcher**	13. The **pitcher** threw the ball.
14. **catcher**	14. The **catcher** wore a face mask.
15. **whatever**	15. I'll do **whatever** it takes.
16. **anywhere**	16. Dreams can take you **anywhere**.
17. **whenever**	17. Come **whenever** you want.
18. **wheat**	18. See the **wheat** in that field?
19. **awhile**	19. Sit and talk **awhile**.
20. **somewhere**	20. It's here **somewhere**.

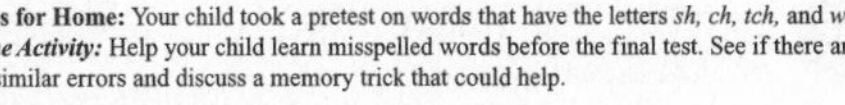

Notes for Home: Your child took a pretest on words that have the letters *sh, ch, tch,* and *wh.* ***Home Activity:*** Help your child learn misspelled words before the final test. See if there are any similar errors and discuss a memory trick that could help.

Spelling Workbook 4.4, p. 62

Name_______________________ **Half-Chicken**

Spelling: Words with *sh, ch, tch, wh*

Word List				
shown	flashlight	chocolate	pitcher	whenever
short	trash	church	catcher	wheat
punish	March	watch	whatever	awhile
shelter	chapter	kitchen	anywhere	somewhere

Directions: Choose the word from the box that is formed by adding **sh, ch, tch,** or **wh** at the beginning or end of each group of letters below. Write the word on the line.

1. own **shown** **7.** ocolate **chocolate**
2. tra **trash** **8.** Mar **March**
3. puni **punish** **9.** wa **watch**
4. elter **shelter** **10.** eat **wheat**
5. ort **short** **11.** enever **whenever**
6. apter **chapter** **12.** atever **whatever**

Directions: Choose the word from the box that best completes each sentence. Write the word on the line to the left.

kitchen **13.** The baseball team's cook was working in the _____.
church **14.** He had returned from a Sunday service at _____.
pitcher **15.** He poured a huge _____ of water.
catcher **16.** The team's _____ had asked the cook to make soup.
anywhere **17.** The cook looked to see if there was any chicken _____.
flashlight **18.** The electricity went out, so he got a _____.
awhile **19.** The catcher would have to wait _____ for the soup.
somewhere **20.** Maybe the catcher would have to eat _____ else.

Notes for Home: Your child spelled words with *sh, ch, tch,* and *wh.* ***Home Activity:*** Write *sh, ch, tch,* and *wh* in four columns on a sheet of paper. Have your child sort the spelling words, writing each word in the correct column.

Spelling Workbook 4.4, p. 63

Name_______________________ **Half-Chicken**

Spelling: Words with *sh, ch, tch, wh*

Directions: Proofread this beginning of a spooky book. Find five spelling mistakes. Use the proofreading marks to correct each mistake.

- ≡ Make a capital.
- / Make a small letter.
- ∧ Add something.
- Take out something.
- ⊙ Add a period.
- ¶ Begin a new paragraph.

Chapter 1

It was a dark and stormy night in March. The wind blew. The rain fell. The ocean waves crashed against the rocky shore. Somewere [h] an owl hooted, alert during his nightly whatch [h deleted]. Lightning flashed, and wenever [h] it did, the owl hooted louder.

Suddenly, the lightning struck an old, dead tree. The tree burst into flames. It burned awile [h], until the rain put it out. Just as darkness returned, a flachlight [c → s] beam gleamed brightly in the distance.

Spelling Tip

Words can have two or three consonants together that are pronounced as one sound, like **punish, chapter, watch,** and **whenever.**

Word List	
shown	watch
short	kitchen
punish	pitcher
shelter	catcher
flashlight	whatever
trash	anywhere
March	whenever
chapter	wheat
chocolate	awhile
church	somewhere

Write a Spooky Story

Write your own spooky story. On a separate sheet of paper, write a story that takes place during a storm, in a scary place, or with spooky characters. Use at least three spelling words. **Answers will vary, but each story should include at least three spelling words.**

Notes for Home: Your child spelled words with *sh, ch, tch,* and *wh.* ***Home Activity:*** Go on a word search hunt. Check a variety of print materials in the house (videos, food labels, magazines, books), looking for more words with *sh, ch, tch,* and *wh.*

Spelling Workbook 4.4, p. 64

Name_______________________ **Half-Chicken**

Spelling: Words with *sh, ch, tch, wh*

REVIEW

Word List				
shown	flashlight	chocolate	pitcher	whenever
short	trash	church	catcher	wheat
punish	March	watch	whatever	awhile
shelter	chapter	kitchen	anywhere	somewhere

Directions: Choose the word from the box that best completes each statement. Write the word on the line to the left.

short **1.** *Big* is to *little* as *tall* is to _____.
shelter **2.** *Trumpet* is to *instrument* as *house* is to _____.
whatever **3.** *Where* is to *wherever* as *what* is to _____.
March **4.** *Week* is to *Thursday* as *month* is to _____.
church **5.** *Skyscraper* is to *building* as *cathedral* is to _____.
watch **6.** *Finger* is to *ring* as *wrist* is to _____.
kitchen **7.** *Learn* is to *classroom* as *cook* is to _____.
chapter **8.** *Song* is to *verse* as *book* is to _____.

Directions: Choose the word from the box that contains each word below. Write the word on the line.

9. flash **flashlight** **15.** when **whenever**
10. how **shown** **16.** any **anywhere**
11. pitch **pitcher** **17.** late **chocolate**
12. cat **catcher** **18.** eat **wheat**
13. ash **trash** **19.** some **somewhere**
14. while **awhile** **20.** pun **punish**

Notes for Home: Your child spelled words with *sh, ch, tch,* and *wh.* ***Home Activity:*** Pick one of the letter combinations. Have a contest to see who can write the greatest number of words with that combination in two minutes.

Practice Book 4.4, p. 159

Name_______________________ **Half-Chicken**

Thesaurus

A **thesaurus** is a kind of dictionary that contains antonyms, synonyms, and other related words. Like a dictionary, the words are listed alphabetically. You can look up words in a thesaurus to better understand what you read and to find new ways of saying something.

Suppose you wanted to find a new word to replace *peaceful* in the following sentence: *News of the strange Half-Chicken spread quickly to the peaceful cows, grazing with their calves, the fierce bulls, and the swift horses.* First you look up *peaceful* in the index, and then find the entry.

> **peaceful** *(adjective)*
> *Synonyms:* nonviolent, calm, peaceable
> *Cross-reference:* cool, unruffled, steady
> *Antonyms:* disturbed, perturbed, upset

Here is what each part of the entry tells you:

- Part of speech—how a word is used
  Peaceful is an adjective. It is a word that describes nouns.
- Synonyms—words that have the same or similar meanings
  Peaceful means the same or nearly the same as *nonviolent, calm, peaceable.*
- Cross-reference—words that are related to the word you looked up
  You can look up *cool* in the thesaurus for more words with meanings similar to *peaceful.*
- Antonyms—words that have opposite meanings
  Disturbed, perturbed, and *upset* are opposite to *peaceful.*

Practice Book 4.4, p. 160

Name________________________________ **Half-Chicken**

Directions: The thesaurus entries below give you information about two more words in the sentence on the previous page about Half-Chicken. Use these entries to answer the questions that follow.

spread *(verb)*	swift *(adjective)*
Synonyms: circulate, distribute *Cross-reference:* broadcast, communicate, pass (on), transmit, scatter, sow, peddle *Antonyms:* hold (in), contain	*Synonyms:* fast, quick, rapid, snappy, speedy *Cross-reference:* sudden, double-quick *Antonyms:* sluggish

1. What word is opposite in meaning to *swift?* **sluggish**
2. What part of speech is *spread?* **verb**
3. What part of speech is *swift?* **adjective**
4. What words are synonyms for *spread?* **circulate, distribute**
5. Which related words could you look up to find more words similar in meaning to *swift?*
sudden, double-quick
6. Name one antonym for *spread.* **hold in or contain**
7. Which entry word has *pass (on)* as a related word? **spread**
8. Which entry word is similar in meaning to *speedy?* **swift**
9. Rewrite the sentence about Half-Chicken. Replace at least one word in the sentence. Use one of the three thesaurus entries shown.
Sentences will vary. Check that students have logically replaced *peaceful, spread,* or *swift* with one of the synonyms given.
10. Why would a thesaurus be helpful to writers? **Possible answer: Writers can use a thesaurus to find new ways of saying something.**

Notes for Home: Your child used thesaurus entries to locate synonyms, antonyms, and related words. ***Home Activity:*** If you have a thesaurus, have your child find a synonym for *fierce.* Or, ask your child to tell you what synonyms and antonyms are.

Research and Study Skills: Thesaurus 361

Practice Book 4.4, p. 161

Name________________________________ **Blame It on the Wolf**

Compare and Contrast

- To **compare** is to tell how two or more things are alike. To **contrast** is to tell how two or more things are different.
- Clue words such as *like* or *as* show comparisons. Clue words such as *but, instead,* and *unlike* show contrasts.

Directions: Reread "Wolves." Then complete the diagram below. List things that are true about gray wolves on the left, things that are true about red wolves on the right, and things that are true about both kinds of wolves in the middle.

Possible answers given.

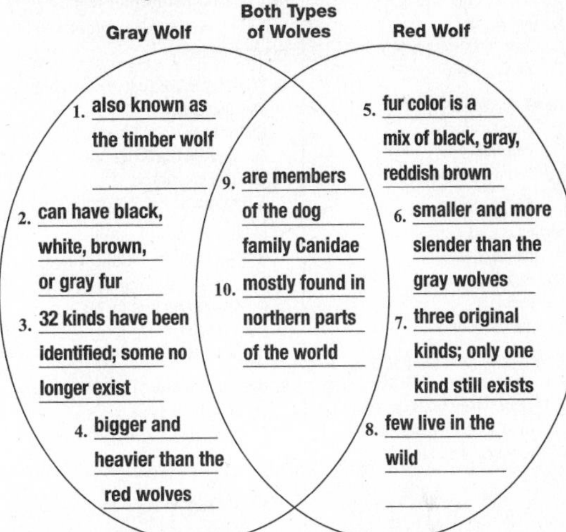

Notes for Home: Your child read a nonfiction text and told how the wolves are alike and different. ***Home Activity:*** Ask your child to identify a favorite dessert and a favorite main dish. Then ask him or her to tell how these foods are alike and different.

364 Compare and Contrast

Practice Book 4.4, p. 162

Name________________________________ **Blame It on the Wolf**

Vocabulary

Directions: Choose the word from the box that best matches each definition. Write the word on the line.

Check the Words You Know
__ character
__ courtroom
__ evidence
__ guilty
__ rescued

character 1. person in a story

evidence 2. facts; proof

guilty 3. having done wrong

rescued 4. saved

courtroom 5. room in which a court of law meets

Directions: Choose the word from the box that best completes each sentence. Write the word on the line to the left.

courtroom 6. The story about the trial took place in a _____.

character 7. My favorite _____ was the lawyer, Gary the Gorilla.

evidence 8. He presented _____ that the chimpanzees had stolen three bunches of bananas.

guilty 9. A jury of leopards, lions, and panthers had to decide whether the chimps were _____.

rescued 10. At the last minute, the chimps were _____ by a surprise witness.

Write a Journal Entry

On a separate sheet of paper, write a journal entry as if you were the judge in the case of the chimps who stole the bananas. Use as many of the vocabulary words as you can to describe the judge's reaction to the trial. **Students' journal entries should be written from the judge's point of view and use vocabulary words correctly.**

Notes for Home: Your child identified and used vocabulary words from *Blame It on the Wolf.* ***Home Activity:*** Ask your child to tell you what he or she knows about trials. If necessary, ask questions such as: *Where does a trial take place? (courtroom)*

Vocabulary 365

Practice Book 4.4, p. 163

Name________________________________ **Blame It on the Wolf**

Compare and Contrast

- To **compare** is to tell how two or more things are alike. To **contrast** is to tell how two or more things are different.
- Clue words such as *like* or *as* show comparisons. Clue words such as *but, instead,* and *unlike* show contrasts.

Directions: Reread what happens in *Blame It on the Wolf* when the Wolf questions the three little pigs. Then, follow the instructions below.

Wolf: What do you think I said outside your brick house? On the day in question?
Iggie: I thought you said, "I'll huff and I'll puff and blow you into another galaxy!"
Squiggy: I thought he said, "My hands are rough. Can I borrow some moisturizing lotion?"
Moe: I thought he said, "I'll have a BLT on whole wheat—hold the mayo!"
Wolf: So you admit that you really aren't sure what I said. *(to Jury)* I intend to prove that sometimes we don't hear everything clearly. Some people don't pay attention …
Judge *(trying to get Wolf's attention):* Mr. Wolf …
Wolf *(continuing without hearing the Judge):* Some people hear only what they want to hear …

Possible answers given.

1. What is one way in which the pigs' answers are different?
Only one pig thinks the wolf said he was going to blow down the house.
2. What is one way in which Squiggy's and Moe's answers are alike?
Neither Moe nor Squiggy remember the wolf threatening them.
3. How is Wolf's opinion different from Iggie's opinion?
Wolf thinks he is innocent; Iggie thinks Wolf is guilty.
4. In what way does the wolf in the courtroom act like the pigs at their house?
None of them listens very well.
5. On a separate sheet of paper, compare and contrast the wolf in this story to the wolf in other stories you know, such as "The Three Little Pigs" and "Little Red Riding Hood." **Check that students explain their comparisons and contrasts.**

Notes for Home: Your child compared and contrasted characters in stories to show how they are alike and different. ***Home Activity:*** Find a favorite story. Ask your child how two of the characters in it are alike, and how they are different.

366 Compare and Contrast

Practice Book 4.4, p. 165

Name______________________________ **Blame It on the Wolf**

Selection Test

Directions: Choose the best answer to each item. Mark the letter for the answer you have chosen.

Part 1: Vocabulary

Find the answer choice that means about the same as the underlined word in each sentence.

1. The young woman was <u>guilty</u>.
   - (A) having done wrong
   - B. not polite
   - C. away on vacation
   - D. feeling sick
2. I was a <u>character</u> witness.
   - F. about a place
   - G. colorful
   - (H) about a person
   - J. short
3. Susie <u>rescued</u> a kitten.
   - A. patted
   - (B) saved from harm
   - C. grabbed
   - D. gave food to
4. Everyone left the <u>courtroom</u>.
   - F. place where people play tennis
   - (G) place where trials are held
   - H. food court in a large mall
   - J. room where a king sits
5. We need more <u>evidence</u>.
   - A. lessons
   - B. good ideas
   - C. time to rest
   - (D) facts; proof

Part 2: Comprehension

Use what you know about the play to answer each item.

6. Where does the first scene of this play take place?
   - F. at Iggie's brick house
   - G. outside Big Red's house
   - (H) in a courtroom
   - J. at Auntie Pot Pie's house
7. In this play, Wolf wants to—
   - A. eat Little Red Riding Hood.
   - (B) tell his side of the story.
   - C. blame Old Red for his problems.
   - D. meet Hansel and Gretel.
8. Who gets to decide if Wolf is guilty of eating Grandma?
   - F. the judge
   - G. Iggie
   - H. Moe
   - (J) the jury

Practice Book 4.4, p. 166

Name______________________________ **Blame It on the Wolf**

9. Wolf's story is different from the pigs' story because he says that he—
   - (A) asked the pigs for help.
   - B. wanted to eat the pigs.
   - C. blew their house down.
   - D. wanted to take them out for supper.
10. Hansel and Gretel got lost in the woods because—
    - F. they didn't leave a trail.
    - G. they followed the wrong trail.
    - (H) animals ate their bread crumbs.
    - J. it was dark out.
11. Which character doesn't seem to fit in with the rest of the story?
    - A. Wolf
    - (B) Chicken Little
    - C. Little Red Riding Hood
    - D. Grandma
12. How are Auntie Pot Pie and Old Red alike?
    - F. They are both evil.
    - G. They are both sweet and kind.
    - H. They both dislike the wolf.
    - (J) They are twin sisters.
13. Why was Auntie Pot Pie angry at Wolf?
    - A. Wolf ate Little Red Riding Hood's grandma.
    - B. He scared Little Red.
    - (C) Wolf took Hansel and Gretel away from her.
    - D. He ate her candy house.
14. Which is the best proof that Wolf was not guilty?
    - (F) Little Red's grandma returned.
    - G. The three pigs told three different stories.
    - H. Hansel and Gretel said that Wolf was nice to them.
    - J. Auntie Pot Pie wanted to eat Hansel and Gretel.
15. This play suggests that if you think someone has done something wrong, it is wise to—
    - A. take a trip far away.
    - (B) listen to both sides of the story.
    - C. put wax in your ears.
    - D. keep children away from the forest.

Name______________________________ **Blame It on the Wolf**

Compare and Contrast

- To **compare** is to tell how two or more things are alike. To **contrast** is to tell how two or more things are different.
- Clue words such as *like* or *as* show comparisons. Clue words such as *but, instead,* and *unlike* show contrasts.

Directions: Read the play below.

LAWYER: Ms. Hogg, do you promise to tell the truth?
MS. HOGG: Yes.
LAWYER: You were at the store the day of the robbery. Did you see my client there?
MS. HOGG: I think I did, but I'm not sure. It might have been somebody else.
LAWYER: Then you can't tell us what happened. Next witness! Mr. Pigg! Do you promise to tell the truth?
MR. PIGG: Yes.
LAWYER: You were also at the store the day of the robbery. Did you see my client there?
MR. PIGG: Yes. I'm sure I did.
LAWYER: Good. What was he doing?
MR. PIGG: I think I saw him buying some socks—but I'm not sure. It might have been somebody else.
LAWYER: If you're not sure, you can't tell us what happened, either.
MR. PIGG: Yes, I can. Because *I'm* the one who robbed the store!

Directions: Complete the diagram. On the left, write words that describe Ms. Hogg. On the right, write words that describe Mr. Pigg. Where the circles overlap, write things both these characters have in common. **Possible answers given.**

Only Ms. Hogg	Both Ms. Hogg and Mr. Pigg	Only Mr. Pigg
1. not sure she saw client	3. were at store that day	5. sure he saw client robbed the store
2. did not rob the store	4. promised to tell the truth	

Notes for Home: Your child compared and contrasted characters in a play to show how the characters are alike and how they are different. ***Home Activity:*** Name two people that you and your child know well. Take turns telling how they are alike and how they are different.

Practice Book 4.4, p. 167

Name______________________________ **Blame It on the Wolf**

Theme

REVIEW

Directions: Read the play. Then read each question about the play. Choose the best answer to each question. Mark the letter for the answer you have chosen.

Who Was Right?

LAWYER: Mr. Gomez, are you absolutely sure of what you heard?
MR. GOMEZ: Yes, I'm sure. The man on trial said, "I'll kill you!"
LAWYER: Did you see him?
MR. GOMEZ: No. I didn't see him. But I heard him.
LAWYER: And you're sure of what you heard?
MR. GOMEZ: Yes. He said, "I'll kill you."
LAWYER: Next witness! Ms. Blanco, were you at the same gas station?
MS. BLANCO: Yes, I was there.
LAWYER: What did you hear and see?
MS. BLANCO: The man on trial didn't say, "I'll *kill* you." He said, "I'll *fill* you—up!" He was helping me get gas.
LAWYER: Members of the jury, now you know that my client is innocent!

1. Which statement could be the theme of the play?
   - **A.** Never believe a witness.
   - **B.** Witnesses always make mistakes.
   - **C.** Never believe a lawyer.
   - (D) Make sure you have all the facts.
2. Which statement supports the theme?
   - **F.** Mr. Gomez lied.
   - (G) Ms. Blanco explains how Mr. Gomez was mistaken.
   - **H.** The lawyer makes a mistake.
   - **J.** Ms. Blanco was frightened.
3. Which statement is **not** a theme of the play?
   - **A.** People often make mistakes.
   - **B.** People see things differently.
   - **C.** A small detail can change a lot.
   - (D) Guilty people should be punished harshly.
4. What did this story suggest about telling the truth?
   - **F.** Always tell the truth.
   - **G.** Some people lie.
   - (H) You might be mistaken about what you think is the truth.
   - **J.** The truth is the same for everyone.
5. What does Mr. Gomez learn?
   - (A) Don't be so sure you know everything.
   - **B.** Don't go to court.
   - **C.** Don't trust a lawyer.
   - **D.** Don't ever lie.

Notes for Home: Your child identified the theme, or "big idea," of a play. ***Home Activity:*** Reread a favorite story with your child. Ask your child to identify the story's theme. Discuss what events and details from the story help support the story's "big idea."

Name________________________ Blame It on the Wolf

Writing Across Texts

Directions: Consider what you know about Half-Chicken from the selection *Half-Chicken* and Wolf from *Blame It on the Wolf.* Write some of the things you learned about each character in the table below. **Possible answers given.**

Half-Chicken	Wolf
Half-Chicken was proud of the way he looked.	Wolf decided to be his own lawyer.
1. **He took a trip on his own.**	6. **The wolf speaks up for himself.**
2. **He stopped to help the stream, fire, and wind.**	7. **He is polite in the court of law.**
3. **He did not waste time after he helped.**	8. **He saves the lives of Hansel and Gretel.**
4. **He was polite to everyone he met.**	9. **He teaches people to look at both sides of a story.**
5. **Now he watches the wind for everyone.**	10. **He accepts everyone's apology.**

Write a Letter

Use the information in your table to compose a letter from one character to another. Think about how the character would talk and the kinds of things he would say. Write your letter on a separate sheet of paper. **Letters will vary. Check that students' lists included details from the notes they made.**

Notes for Home: Your child listed details from two different stories. ***Home Activity:*** With your child, read a fairy tale. Before you finish, have your child predict how the story will end. Check his or her predictions by reading to the end of the story.

Grammar Practice Book 4.4, p. 81

Name________________________ Blame It on the Wolf

REVIEW

Grammar: Adjectives

Directions: Draw two lines under the articles **a, an,** and **the** in the sentences below. Then draw a circle around each adjective that describes the underlined noun.

1. Many animals were gathered for an important trial.
2. The noisy crowded courtroom grew quiet when the judge entered.
3. Everyone admired this strong smart crow in the black robe.
4. Chester Cow was an eager witness.
5. When some young calves waved to Chester, the judge frowned.
6. "We are here for a serious trial," he declared. "No waving."
7. The cows and the sheep sat on different sides of the courtroom.
8. The two groups glared at one another.
9. Who had the right to graze on the beautiful green meadow near the lake?
10. That important question would be decided here today.

Directions: Complete each sentence with an article or with an adjective that tells how many or how much. Choose a word from the box, and write it on the line to the left.

more many an fifty few

fifty 11. In the crowded courtroom sat at least _____ sheep and cows.

many 12. Joining them were _____ chickens, goats, pigs, and others.

an 13. They had waited more than _____ hour to get a seat.

few 14. There were very _____ animals that were not interested in today's trial.

more 15. The winner of the trial would have _____ grass to eat and would rule the barnyard.

Notes for Home: Your child identified and used adjectives—words that describe persons, places, or things—in sentences. ***Home Activity:*** Ask your child to name five favorite people, places, and things, and then have your child write a sentence describing each one.

Grammar Practice Book 4.4, p. 82

Name________________________ Blame It on the Wolf

Grammar: Using Adjectives to Improve Sentences

The sentence below does not paint a clear picture. It needs descriptive details.

Sentence: The king wanted clothes.

One way to revise it is by adding adjectives.

Adjectives Added: The wealthy king wanted colorful clothes.

Don't use more adjectives than necessary to express your ideas clearly.

Overuse of Adjectives: The wealthy, worldly, old king wanted elegant, fancy clothes.

Directions: Choose an adjective in ( ) to complete each sentence. Write it on the line.

unkind 1. Once upon a time, two (unkind/nice) men played a cruel trick on their king.

royal 2. Someone from the (royal/tiny) palace told them the king was tired of his suits.

other 3. The king wanted suits that were better than any (all/other) suits in the kingdom.

these 4. (These/This) two men opened a tailoring business.

eager 5. The (eager/stingy) king ordered a new suit.

ordinary 6. The tailors said they used cloth that was so unusual that (marvelous/ordinary) people couldn't see it.

vain 7. The (vain/humble) king ordered a suit made of this cloth.

unsuspecting 8. The (dishonest/unsuspecting) king put on his "invisible suit."

greedy 9. He paid the (greedy/golden) men with gold coins.

foolish 10. A boy on the street saw the (little/foolish) ruler and exclaimed, "His Majesty forgot to put on a suit!"

Notes for Home: Your child used adjectives, words that describe nouns or pronouns, to make sentences more interesting. ***Home Activity:*** Have your child tell you about his or her day, using adjectives to give an interesting description.

Grammar Practice Book 4.4, p. 83

Name________________________ Blame It on the Wolf

Grammar: Using Adjectives to Improve Sentences

Directions: Add an adjective to improve each sentence. Write the adjective on the line to the left. **Possible answers given.**

little 1. "But I can explain!" insisted the _____ girl known as Goldilocks.

dear 2. "I was sent by my _____ grandmother to the bears' house."

trusted 3. "My grandmother is the bears' _____ housekeeper."

empty 4. "When I arrived at the _____ house, no one came to the door."

unlocked 5. "I walked in the _____ door and looked around."

awful 6. "I didn't sit in their chairs, and I didn't eat any of their _____ porridge either."

warm 7. "I just put it in the _____ oven so it wouldn't get cold."

messy 8. "I didn't really sleep in their _____ beds either."

clean 9. "I was just putting on some _____ sheets."

true 10. "I hope you think this _____ story is interesting."

Write an Explanation

Pretend you are a character from a folk tale or fairy tale you have read, such as "Goldilocks" or "Jack and the Beanstalk." On a separate sheet of paper, write an explanation for something you did in the tale, such as wander into the three bears' cottage or buy a hatful of beans. Use colorful adjectives to help you write vivid, interesting sentences. **Check to make sure that students have not overused adjectives.**

Notes for Home: Your child improved sentences by adding adjectives. ***Home Activity:*** Play a game of "Finish the Sentence," adding adjectives to each other's sentences.

Grammar Practice Book 4.4, p. 84

Name________________

Blame It on the Wolf

Grammar: Using Adjectives to Improve Sentences

RETEACHING

The sentences below do not have descriptive details. Add an adjective to each sentence. Write it on the line. **Possible answers given.**

1. The person ate **chocolate** cake.
2. Manuel put on **brown** shoes.

This sentence has too many adjectives. Draw lines through adjectives that aren't necessary.

3. My favorite, ~~best-liked, wonderful, nice,~~ blue sweater was in the wash.

Adding an **adjective** to a sentence is one way to add descriptive detail. Using adjectives also helps you to express your ideas more clearly.

Directions: The story below is not very descriptive or clear. Choose an adjective from the box that best fits each sentence. Write the adjective on the line. Some adjectives will not be used. **Possible answers given.**

afraid brave bright colorful dark empty gray happy heavy huge lonely long musty new old tall

Darron walked down the 1. **empty** sidewalk. He had never seen the street so 2. **dark**. He was a little 3. **afraid**. The streetlights were 4. **bright**, but it was still hard to see clearly. When he got to the 5. **tall** building, he stopped. The 6. **old** windows looked like rectangles. The doors were 7. **huge**. Darron closed his eyes. "I am 8. **brave**," he said. Then he went inside. The library smelled 9. **musty**. He reached the highest shelf and took down a 10. **heavy** book.

Notes for Home: Your child added adjectives to a story to make it more vivid and interesting. ***Home Activity:*** Read a page from a favorite story to your child, leaving out the adjectives. Have your child add adjectives of his or her choosing.

Grammar Practice Book 4.4, p. 85

Name________________

Blame It on the Wolf

Grammar: Using Adjectives to Improve Sentences

Directions: Change seven adjectives in the story to make the mood even scarier. Use the words in the idea bank, or make up words of your own.

1.–6. **Possible answers given.**

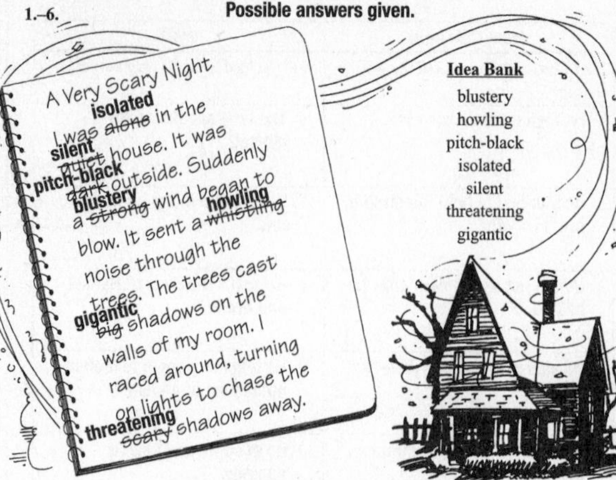

A Very Scary Night
I was ~~alone~~ **isolated** in the ~~quiet~~ **silent** house. It was ~~dark~~ **pitch-black** outside. Suddenly a ~~strong~~ **blustery** wind began to blow. It sent a ~~whistling~~ **howling** noise through the trees. The trees cast ~~big~~ **gigantic** shadows on the walls of my room. I raced around, turning on lights to chase the ~~scary~~ **threatening** shadows away.
Idea Bank
blustery
howling
pitch-black
isolated
silent
threatening
gigantic

Directions: Write three sentences that create a different mood of your choice. Remember to use adjectives that help create your mood.

Check that students have used appropriate adjectives.

Notes for Home: Your child replaced words in a story with more interesting adjectives. ***Home Activity:*** Have your child write a story about an exciting event. Challenge him or her to use descriptive adjectives in the story.

Practice Book 4.4, p. 168

Name________________

Blame It on the Wolf

Word Study: Contractions

Directions: Some contractions are formed by joining a verb and the word **not.** An **apostrophe (')** takes the place of the **o** in **not.** Form a contraction from each pair of words below. Write the contraction on the line.

1. did + not = **didn't**
2. do + not = **don't**
3. does + not = **doesn't**
4. was + not = **wasn't**
5. could + not = **couldn't**
6. have + not = **haven't**
7. are + not = **aren't**
8. had + not = **hadn't**

Directions: Other contractions are formed by joining a word and a verb such as **has, is, will, have,** and **are.** Read the paragraph below. Circle each contraction. Write the two words that each contraction combines on the line.

Favorite stories, such as fairy tales and folk tales, traditionally have some things in common. (They're) often about good people versus bad people. (There's) often some sort of magical element. (You'll) probably also read about people (who've) learned a lesson. The lesson could be something (they've) learned by doing a tremendous deed. Besides the hero and the villain, (you're) certain to meet some silly characters too. (What's) your favorite fairy tale or folk tale?

9. **They are**
10. **There is**
11. **You will**
12. **who have**
13. **they have**
14. **you are**
15. **What is**

Notes for Home: Your child made contractions using an apostrophe to join two words. ***Home Activity:*** Work with your child to write contractions and the word pairs they represent on separate slips of paper. Take turns matching a contraction with its word pair.

Spelling Workbook 4.4, p. 65

Name________________

Blame It on the Wolf

Spelling: Contractions

Pretest Directions: Fold back the page along the dotted line. On the blanks, write the spelling words as they are dictated. When you have finished the test, unfold the page and check your words.

1. **we'll**	1. I know **we'll** have fun.
2. **I'm**	2. **I'm** going to tell you.
3. **I'd**	3. **I'd** like to know.
4. **you'd**	4. I think **you'd** better tell me.
5. **I'll**	5. **I'll** have to find out later.
6. **we've**	6. I think **we've** already been there.
7. **it's**	7. I know **it's** a hard thing to do.
8. **that's**	8. Yes, **that's** what I said.
9. **what's**	9. He knows **what's** wrong.
10. **doesn't**	10. It **doesn't** make any sense.
11. **he'll**	11. I bet **he'll** win the case.
12. **she'll**	12. I know **she'll** tell the truth.
13. **they'll**	13. Are you sure **they'll** come?
14. **they'd**	14. They said **they'd** come.
15. **he'd**	15. He could make it if **he'd** hurry up.
16. **would've**	16. We **would've** been here sooner.
17. **could've**	17. We **could've** run faster.
18. **wouldn't**	18. I **wouldn't** do that if I were you.
19. **shouldn't**	19. It **shouldn't** make a difference.
20. **let's**	20. I say **let's** give him a chance.

Notes for Home: Your child took a pretest on words that are contractions. ***Home Activity:*** Help your child learn misspelled words before the final test. Your child can underline the word parts that caused the problems and concentrate on those parts.

Spelling Workbook 4.4, p. 66
Name______________________

Blame It on the Wolf

Spelling: Contractions

Word List				
we'll	I'll	what's	they'll	could've
I'm	we've	doesn't	they'd	wouldn't
I'd	it's	he'll	he'd	shouldn't
you'd	that's	she'll	would've	let's

Directions: Choose the contraction from the box that is formed by combining each pair of words below. Write the contraction on the line.

1. I would **I'd**
2. you would **you'd**
3. he would **he'd**
4. they would **they'd**
5. would have **would've**
6. could have **could've**
7. would not **wouldn't**
8. should not **shouldn't**
9. does not **doesn't**
10. I will **I'll**
11. he will **he'll**
12. she will **she'll**
13. we will **we'll**
14. they will **they'll**

Directions: Choose the word from the box that best completes each sentence. Write the word on the line to the left.

I'm **15.** Lawyer: _____ going to ask the witness another question.
What's **16.** Judge: _____ this all about? I thought you had finished.
We've **17.** Lawyer: _____ all been wondering where the witness was during the crime.
That's **18.** Witness: _____ what I've been telling you! I was home with two friends!
let's **19.** Lawyer: Well, _____ hear from these friends. I'll call them to testify.
It's **20.** Judge: Agreed. _____ important that we hear their testimony.

Notes for Home: Your child spelled contractions. ***Home Activity:*** Write each spelling word without the apostrophe. Have your child rewrite the word correctly.

Spelling Workbook 4.4, p. 67
Name______________________

Blame It on the Wolf

Spelling: Contractions

Directions: Proofread this dialogue from a trial. Find five spelling mistakes. Use the proofreading marks to correct each mistake.

≡ Make a capital.
/ Make a small letter.
∧ Add something.
Take out something.
⊙ Add a period.
¶ Begin a new paragraph.

Judge: I'm not happy with the way this trial is going. I'll have you know that this is a serious matter, and we'll proceed in a serious way!

Lawyer: Your honor, what did I do?

Judge: You have been making jokes! You shouldn't do that!

Lawyer: Your honor, I'am just naturally funny. If I could've been born different, I would have.

Spelling Tip
Contractions use an apostrophe to take the place of letters that have been left out: **we've** is the contraction for **we have.** The letters **h** and **a** are left out. Check the dialogue to make sure that each contraction is spelled correctly.

Word List				
we'll	I'll	what's	they'll	could've
I'm	we've	doesn't	they'd	wouldn't
I'd	it's	he'll	he'd	shouldn't
you'd	that's	she'll	would've	let's

Write a News Story

On a separate sheet of paper, write a news story about the trial above. Tell what you think of the characters' behavior. Use at least five contractions from the box.

Answers will vary, but each story should include at least five contractions from the box.

Notes for Home: Your child spelled contractions. ***Home Activity:*** Say some or all of the contractions from the list. Have your child tell you what two words each contraction combines. Have your child spell the contraction and use it in a sentence.

Spelling Workbook 4.4, p. 68
Name______________________

Blame It on the Wolf

Spelling: Contractions

REVIEW

Word List				
we'll	I'll	what's	they'll	could've
I'm	we've	doesn't	they'd	wouldn't
I'd	it's	he'll	he'd	shouldn't
you'd	that's	she'll	would've	let's

Directions: Choose the contraction from the box that is formed by combining each pair of words below. Write the contraction on the line.

1. does not **doesn't**
2. would not **wouldn't**
3. should not **shouldn't**
4. we have **we've**
5. would have **would've**
6. could have **could've**
7. she will **she'll**
8. he had **he'd**
9. we will **we'll**
10. let us **let's**
11. they will **they'll**
12. they had **they'd**

Directions: Choose the contraction from the box that best replaces the underlined words. Write the contraction on the line.

I'd **13.** Judge: I would like to think you respect me, sir.
I'm **14.** Lawyer: Of course I do. I am your biggest fan.
that's **15.** Judge: If that is true, why is there a pig in this court?
It's **16.** Lawyer: It is here for a good reason, sir.
what's **17.** Judge: And what is that reason?
He'll **18.** Lawyer: He will testify, if you don't mind.
I'll **19.** Judge: I will have to think about that.
you'd **20.** Lawyer: I knew you would say that.

Notes for Home: Your child spelled contractions. ***Home Activity:*** Say a sentence that includes two words that can be combined to form one of the contractions listed. Have your child repeat the sentence, replacing the two words with the contraction. Repeat for other contractions.

Practice Book 4.4, p. 169
Name______________________

Blame It on the Wolf

Evaluate Reference Sources

There are many sources you can use to find information. You can use books, magazines, encyclopedias, videotapes, audiotapes, CD-ROMs and even the Internet. When you **evaluate reference sources,** you decide which sources are reliable and up-to-date, and which are most useful for your purpose.

Directions: The table of contents can tell you at a glance what kind of information is in a book. Read the table of contents from two books. Use them to answer the questions that follow.

Wolves
Chapter 1 What do wolves look and sound like?
Chapter 2 What do wolves eat?
Chapter 3 Where do wolves live?

Stories About Wolves
Chapter 1 Little Red Riding Hood
Chapter 2 The Boy Who Cried Wolf
Chapter 3 The Three Little Pigs

1. Which book will give you factual information about how wolves live?
Wolves

2. Which book will have fictional stories about wolves?
Stories About Wolves

3. Suppose you want to write a report about stories that have wolves as main characters. Will *Stories About Wolves* give you useful information? Explain.
Yes; the stories in this book have wolves as main characters.

4. Suppose you want to write a report about wolves in the wild and how they live. Will *Wolves* give you useful information? Explain.
Yes; this book tells all about wolves and how they live.

Practice Book 4.4, p. 170

Name______________________________ **Blame It on the Wolf**

Directions: A copyright page tells when a book was written. Knowing this information can help you evaluate how up-to-date a source is. Read the copyright pages for two books. Use the copyright information to answer the questions that follow.

Wolves Copyright © 1972 by Animal Press All rights reserved. Animal Press, 537 W. 68th St., New York, NY 10015 Fifth Edition	Stories About Wolves Copyright © 1982 by Children's Book Publisher All rights reserved. Children's Book Publisher, 239 Red Rd., San Diego, CA 98716 First Edition

5. In what year was *Wolves* published? **1972**
6. In what year was *Stories About Wolves* published? **1982**
7. Which book is the oldest? ***Wolves***
8. Suppose you were writing about the number of wolves that exist today. Would you need a book about wolves published more recently than *Wolves?* Explain.
Possible answer: Yes, *Wolves* was published in 1972, so more current facts about today's wolf population would probably be needed.
9. If you were comparing *Blame It on the Wolf* to the story "The Three Little Pigs," would you need a book published more recently than *Stories About Wolves?* Explain.
Possible answer: No, "The Three Little Pigs" is an old story, so you wouldn't need to find it in a more recently published book.
10. Is it important to think about the purpose of your research before evaluating a reference source? Explain.
Yes, it's important to think about your research purpose first, so you can choose reference sources that are most useful for your purpose.

Notes for Home: Your child evaluated reference sources, based on their contents and when they were published. ***Home Activity:*** Discuss different reference sources available in your home or at the library. Talk about how each source could be used for different kinds of research projects.

Practice Book 4.4, p. 171

Name______________________________ **Lou Gehrig: The Luckiest Man**

Text Structure

- **Text structure** is the way a piece of writing is organized.
- One way to organize writing is to put events in **chronological,** or time, order.

Directions: Reread "Cal Ripken, Jr." Then complete the time line by listing the important events in Cal Ripken, Jr.'s life.

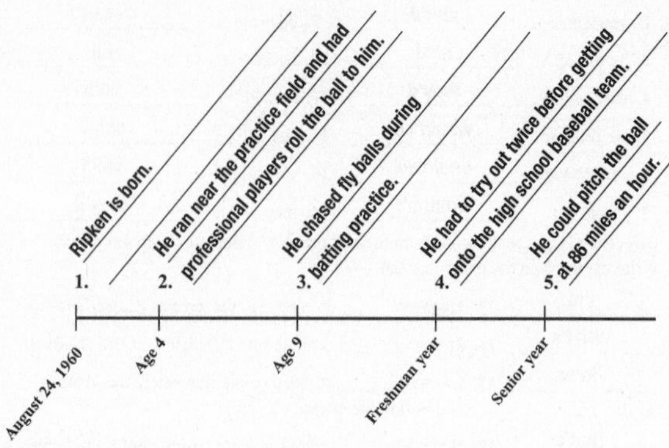
1. Ripken is born.
2. He ran near the practice field and had professional players roll the ball to him.
3. He chased fly balls during batting practice.
4. He had to try out twice before getting onto the high school baseball team.
5. He could pitch the ball at 86 miles an hour.
August 24, 1960
Age 4
Age 9
Freshman year
Senior year
Cal Ripken, Jr.

Notes for Home: Your child read a biography and used a time line to show events in the order in which they happened. ***Home Activity:*** Ask your child to tell the story of his or her life, by telling one memory each from preschool, first grade, second grade, third grade, and so on, in that order.

Practice Book 4.4, p. 172

Name______________________________ **Lou Gehrig: The Luckiest Man**

Vocabulary

Directions: Choose the word from the box that best matches each definition. Write the word on the line.

Check the Words You Know
__ convinced
__ courageous
__ engineer
__ gradually
__ immigrants

immigrants 1. people who come from a foreign country to live

convinced 2. caused to believe

courageous 3. brave

engineer 4. expert in engineering

gradually 5. slowly over a period of time

Directions: Choose the word from the box that the best completes each sentence. Write the word on the line.

courageous 6. You could see the _____ baseball player practicing in all kinds of weather.

Gradually 7. _____ Marta improved her game over the summer.

immigrants 8. She had come from a family of _____ and they were used to working hard.

engineer 9. Her brother was studying hard to become an _____.

convinced 10. Finally, the coach was _____ that Marta deserved a place on the team.

Write a Journal Entry

Imagine you are an immigrant who has recently arrived in this country. On a separate sheet of paper, write a journal entry about your hopes and dreams for your future. Use as many vocabulary words as possible. **Students' articles should use vocabulary words correctly.**

Notes for Home: Your child identified and used vocabulary words from *Lou Gehrig: The Luckiest Man.* ***Home Activity:*** Ask your child to use each vocabulary word in a sentence. If necessary, show your child how to make up a sentence that includes one of the words.

Practice Book 4.4, p. 173

Name______________________________ **Lou Gehrig: The Luckiest Man**

Text Structure

- **Text structure** is the way a piece of writing is organized.
- **Fiction** tells stories of imaginary people and events. They are usually told in chronological, or time, order. **Nonfiction** tells of real people and events or tells information about the real world. Some ways to organize nonfiction are chronological order, cause and effect, problem and solution, or comparison and contrast.

Directions: Reread what happens in *Lou Gehrig: The Luckiest Man* when Lou Gehrig becomes a successful ballplayer. Then answer the questions below.

After high school Lou Gehrig went to Columbia University. He was on the baseball team there, too, and on April 26, 1923, a scout for the New York Yankees watched him play. Lou hit two long home runs in that game. Soon after that he was signed to play for the Yankees.

The Yankees offered Lou a $1,500 bonus to sign plus a good salary. His family needed the money. Lou quit college and joined the Yankees. Lou's mother was furious. She was convinced that he was ruining his life.

On June 1, 1925, the Yankee manager sent Lou to bat for the shortstop. The next day Lou played in place of first baseman Wally Pipp.

Possible answers given.

1. What happens before Lou is signed to play for the Yankees?
He goes to college, plays baseball there, and a scout sees him play.
2. What happens after Lou is offered a $1,500 bonus to sign with the Yankees?
He quits college and joins the Yankees.
3. What happens on June 1, 1925?
Lou bats for the shortstop.
4. How are events in this passage organized?
Events are presented in chronological order.
5. On a separate sheet of paper, tell whether this text is fiction or nonfiction. Then tell how the author organizes his writing. Do you think this is a good way to organize it? Explain. **nonfiction; chronological order**

Notes for Home: Your child looked at the way a text is organized, for example, noticing that events in stories are often told in chronological order. ***Home Activity:*** Ask your child to tell you a story about his or her day, telling about events in the order in which they happened.

Practice Book 4.4, p. 175

Name____________________ Lou Gehrig: The Luckiest Man

Selection Test

Directions: Choose the best answer to each item. Mark the letter for the answer you have chosen.

Part 1: Vocabulary

Find the answer choice that means about the same as the underlined word in each sentence.

1. Dana gradually got better.
   A. suddenly
   B. at the end
   C. never
   (D) slowly
2. Lee is convinced that he's right.
   (F) sure
   G. worried
   H. sorry
   J. aware
3. Are they immigrants?
   A. birds that fly south
   (B) persons who come to a foreign country to live
   C. persons who teach others
   D. unusual animals
4. You are very courageous.
   F. clever
   G. popular
   H. special
   (J) brave
5. Kyle's mom is an engineer.
   A. one who knows the laws
   B. pilot of an airplane
   (C) one who plans and builds things such as bridges
   D. person who plays sports

Part 2: Comprehension

Use what you know about the selection to answer each item.

6. Lou Gehrig was born in—
   F. Baltimore.
   G. Germany.
   (H) New York City.
   J. Boston.
7. While Lou Gehrig was in college, he—
   A. became ill.
   B. had to quit school.
   C. gave a speech.
   (D) signed to play for the Yankees.
8. Lou's mother was angry when he decided to play baseball because she—
   F. wanted him to be happy.
   (G) thought he was ruining his life.
   H. knew he was sick.
   J. needed him to make money.

Practice Book 4.4, p. 176

Name____________________ Lou Gehrig: The Luckiest Man

9. Lou Gehrig was known as "Iron Horse" because he—
   (A) never missed a game.
   B. hit many home runs.
   C. broke his fingers.
   D. complained often.
10. The text in this selection is organized by—
    (F) time order.
    G. causes and effects.
    H. problems and solutions.
    J. how things are alike or different.
11. Which of these events happened first?
    A. Babe Ruth hit 60 home runs.
    B. Gehrig was named MVP.
    C. Babe Ruth hugged Lou Gehrig.
    (D) Gehrig got a $1,500 bonus.
12. During the 1938 baseball season, Lou Gehrig's playing got steadily worse because he—
    F. was getting old.
    G. was tired from playing so many games.
    H. stopped believing in himself.
    (J) became ill.
13. At the end of his career, Gehrig considered himself lucky because he—
    A. could finally quit baseball.
    B. got a new job right away.
    (C) was surrounded by so many caring people.
    D. was voted into the Hall of Fame.
14. The most amazing thing about Lou Gehrig is that he—
    F. was named MVP twice.
    (G) never felt sorry for himself.
    H. gave a speech to his fans.
    J. did not know anything was wrong.
15. Which sentence gives an opinion?
    A. Lou's hair was turning gray.
    B. On June 13, 1939, Lou went to the Mayo Clinic.
    C. Lou Gehrig walked to the microphone.
    (D) The 1927 Yankees were the best baseball team ever.

Name____________________ Lou Gehrig: The Luckiest Man

Text Structure

- **Text structure** is the way a piece of writing is organized.
- **Fiction** tells stories of imaginary people and events. They are usually told in chronological, or time, order. **Nonfiction** tells of real people and events or tells information about the real world. Some ways to organize nonfiction are chronological order, cause and effect, problem and solution, or comparison and contrast.

Directions: Read the passage below.

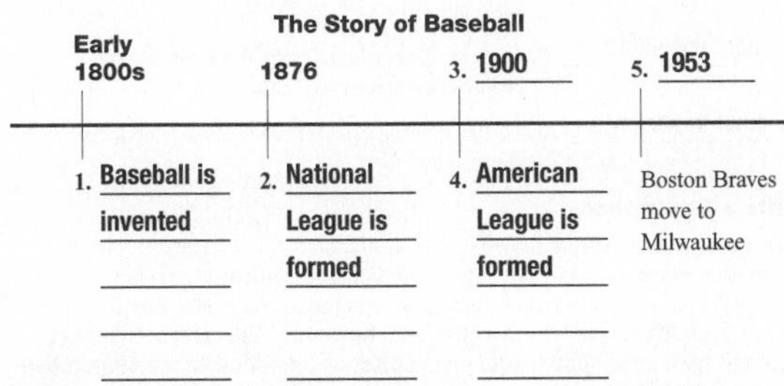

There wasn't always a game called baseball! It probably grew out of cricket and rounders, games Americans had learned from the English long ago.

Nobody knows exactly when baseball was invented, but it began in the 1800s. In 1876, a group of baseball teams organized themselves as the National League. In 1900, the American League was formed.

For many years, most baseball teams were located in the eastern part of the United States. Then, slowly, teams began to move west. The first team to move, the Boston Braves, went to Milwaukee, Wisconsin, in 1953. Gradually, baseball became a truly national sport, played from coast to coast.

Directions: This passage organized its information in chronological order. Complete the time line. Think about the order in which events happened. Write dates above the horizontal line. Describe events for that date below the line.

The Story of Baseball

Early 1800s	1876	3. 1900	5. 1953
1. Baseball is invented	2. National League is formed	4. American League is formed	Boston Braves move to Milwaukee

Notes for Home: Your child used a time line to show the text's chronological organization. ***Home Activity:*** Take turns with your child telling a story of your day. Tell events in the order in which they happened. Challenge your child to write a story of your day using chronological order.

Practice Book 4.4, p. 177

Name____________________ Lou Gehrig: The Luckiest Man

Paraphrasing

REVIEW

Directions: Read the passage. Then read each question about the passage. Choose the best answer to each question. Mark the letter for the answer you have chosen.

Satchel Paige: Baseball Hero

One of the greatest baseball players was the pitcher Satchel Paige.

For most of Paige's life, only white players were allowed in the Major Leagues. So Paige, who was African American, played in the Negro Leagues from the mid-1920s to the mid-1940s.

Paige's fast ball was legendary. Sometimes white players arranged to play against him. He pitched against the famous pitcher Dizzy Dean—and won.

In 1947, Jackie Robinson became the first African American to play in the Major Leagues. In 1948, Paige also joined the Major Leagues.

By then he was in his mid-forties—old for a ballplayer. But he still led his team to the top of the American League. Four years later, he was chosen as an American League All Star.

1. Which statement best paraphrases the first two paragraphs?
   A. Paige played ball for 20 years.
   B. Paige was a great ballplayer.
   (C) Paige, a star player, was in the Negro Leagues for 20 years.
   D. Paige was one of the greatest baseball players ever.
2. Which statement does **not** paraphrase the third paragraph?
   (F) Paige played in the Majors.
   G. Paige played against great white players.
   H. Paige was a legend in baseball.
   J. Paige attracted great competition.
3. Which phrase best completes this paraphrase of the fourth paragraph? Robinson and Paige both
   A. were stars.
   (B) joined the Major Leagues.
   C. were African American.
   D. were great players.
4. Which statement best paraphrases the last paragraph?
   F. Paige still pitched at forty.
   G. Paige was not a young player.
   (H) Despite his age, Paige led his team to the top.
   J. Paige was often tired.
5. Which detail does **not** belong in a paraphrase of the last paragraph?
   A. Paige was in his mid-forties.
   (B) Robinson joined the Major Leagues.
   C. Paige led his team to the top.
   D. Paige won honors playing.

Notes for Home: Your child paraphrased—restated in his or her own words—a nonfiction passage. ***Home Activity:*** Tell your child a story about a family member. Then ask your child to retell the story in his or her own words. The paraphrase should keep the story's important ideas.

Name________________________________ Lou Gehrig: The Luckiest Man

Writing Across Texts

Directions: Consider what you learned about baseball from reading about Lou Gehrig and other players mentioned in *The Baseball Hall of Fame.* What would you teach young children about this game? List five reasons the game is enjoyable and five ways people can show they like the game. **Possible answers given.**

Why Baseball Is Enjoyable	How to Show That You Like Baseball
You can play baseball just about anywhere.	You can collect baseball cards.
1. **Playing baseball is good exercise.**	6. **You can play Little League.**
2. **You can learn about teamwork by playing or watching.**	7. **You can visit the Baseball Hall of Fame.**
3. **You can play or watch baseball from the time you are young until you are old.**	8. **You can collect autographs from baseball players.**
4. **Playing baseball gives you something to do after school besides watching TV.**	9. **You can wear favorite baseball caps and jerseys.**
5. **If you're good, you can play in college or even in the pros.**	10. **You can go to baseball games.**

Write a Pamphlet

Create a pamphlet designed to encourage young children to develop an interest in playing or watching baseball. Include in the pamphlet reasons the game is enjoyable. **Pamphlets will vary. Check that pamphlets contain persuasive language and ideas as well as supporting details.**

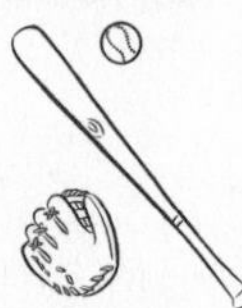

Notes for Home: Your child used information from two different selections to create a pamphlet. ***Home Activity:*** Choose a favorite sport that you and your child enjoy. Help your child make a poster about the sport to hang in his or her room.

Grammar Practice Book 4.4, p. 86

Name________________________________ Lou Gehrig: The Luckiest Man

Grammar: Using Adjectives to Improve Sentences

REVIEW

Directions: Add one or more adjectives to improve each sentence. Write your new sentence on the line. Underline your adjectives. **Possible answers given.**

1. The game of baseball is my favorite sport.
The exciting game of baseball is my favorite sport.

2. Baseball players must be athletes.
Baseball players must be trained athletes.

3. They have to be runners as well as hitters.
They have to be fast runners as well as strong hitters.

4. The pitcher is a player in baseball games.
The pitcher is an important player in all baseball games.

5. Crowds help players do their best.
Cheering crowds help most players do their best.

Directions: Cross out unneeded adjectives in each sentence below. Cross out any other words as needed so the revised sentences make sense. **Possible answers given.**

6. My sister and I went to an exciting, ~~wonderful, and thrilling~~ baseball game.
7. The packed, ~~crowded~~ stands were filled with loud, ~~noisy,~~ screaming fans.
8. Everyone cheered for his or her ~~best-liked and~~ favorite team.
9. By the seventh inning, the tired ~~and weary~~ pitcher was becoming sloppy ~~and weak~~.
10. The next batter hit a ~~strong,~~ soaring, ~~terrific~~ home run over the wall.

Notes for Home: Your child improved sentences by adding adjectives to give more detail and removing unnecessary adjectives. ***Home Activity:*** Have your child write sentences about something that happened today. Help your child add, take away, or replace some of the adjectives.

Grammar Practice Book 4.4, p. 87

Name________________________________ Lou Gehrig: The Luckiest Man

Grammar: Comparative and Superlative Adjectives

Adjectives are often used to tell how people, places, and things are alike or different. In the sentence below, the **-er** ending in **newer** shows that two things are being compared.

Comparative: Your bat is newer than mine.

The **-est** ending of **newest** in the next sentence shows that three or more things are being compared.

Superlative: Carlos's bat is the newest of all.

Here are some patterns you can use to write comparative and superlative adjectives.

- For most adjectives that end with a consonant and **y**, change the **y** to **i** before you add **-er** or **-est: dry, drier, driest.**
- For most adjectives that end in a single consonant after a vowel, double the final consonant before adding **-er** or **-est: flat, flatter, flattest.**
- If an adjective ends with **e**, drop the final **e** before you add **-er** or **-est: safe, safer, safest.**

If you use a long adjective such as **terrific,** use **more** to compare two nouns. Use **most** to compare three or more. Never use **more** or **most** with the endings **-er** or **-est.**

The other team is more terrific than ours.
Carlos's team is the most terrific of all.

Directions: Add **-er** or **-est,** or use **more** or **most** to form comparative and superlative adjectives.

Adjective	Comparative Adjectives	Superlative Adjectives
early	1. **earlier**	2. **earliest**
late	3. **later**	4. **latest**
low	5. **lower**	6. **lowest**
thin	7. **thinner**	8. **thinnest**
successful	9. **more successful**	10. **most successful**

Notes for Home: Your child wrote comparative and superlative forms of adjectives that compare people, places, and things. ***Home Activity:*** Play "Can You Top This?" Take turns. One person names an adjective, and the other person gives its comparative and superlative forms.

Grammar Practice Book 4.4, p. 88

Name________________________________ Lou Gehrig: The Luckiest Man

Grammar: Comparative and Superlative Adjectives

Directions: Complete each sentence by writing the correct form of the adjective in ( ).

most exciting 1. Some people think that baseball is the (exciting) sport.

more exciting 2. They think it is (exciting) than football, even though it is not as rough.

slower 3. Baseball is (slow) than basketball, but these fans still prefer it.

most enjoyable 4. They think that going to a baseball game is the (enjoyable) way to spend an afternoon.

strongest 5. They love to watch a player who is the (strong) hitter on the team.

faster 6. They like to argue about which runner is (fast) than another.

greatest 7. They think the players on their favorite teams are the (great) players of all.

happier 8. If your team wins a game it's a (happy) day than if the team loses.

more enjoyable 9. But even if they lose, seeing the game is still (enjoyable) than staying home.

most important 10. For the players, sportsmanship is the (important) thing of all.

Write a Description

On a separate sheet of paper, describe your favorite sport. Use comparative adjectives to compare your sport with another sport. Use superlative adjectives to compare three or more things in your description. Circle each comparative and superlative adjective you used. **Check to see whether students have used the correct adjective forms in their descriptions and have correctly identified each comparative or superlative form.**

Notes for Home: Your child used the comparative and superlative forms of adjectives. ***Home Activity:*** Have your child tell you about an exciting day, using as many comparative and superlative adjectives as possible.

Grammar Practice Book 4.4, p. 89

Name________________________ Lou Gehrig: The Luckiest Man

Grammar: Comparative and Superlative Adjectives

RETEACHING

Which dog won first prize in the dog show? Solve the riddle below.

bulldog

poodle

Irish setter

Riddle: The winner's tail is longer than the bulldog's tail. The winner does not have the longest tail of all. Circle the winner.

The words **longer** and **longest** are adjectives. The adjective **longer** compared two things. The adjective **longest** compared three things.

An adjective has two different forms that are useful in making comparisons. Use the **-er** form to compare two persons, places, or things. Use the **-est** form to compare three or more persons, places, or things.

Directions: Write the missing **-er** or **-est** form of each adjective.

1. clean, cleaner, **cleanest**
2. strong, **stronger**, strongest
3. bright, **brighter**, **brightest**

Directions: Complete each sentence with an adjective that compares. **Possible answers given.**

4. Bill's poodle is **smaller** than my dog.
5. Your collie is **taller** than his collie.
6. My dog has the **loudest** bark of all.

Notes for Home: Your child wrote comparative and superlative adjectives. ***Home Activity:*** Have your child choose three characters from a book, TV show, or movie, and use comparative and superlative adjectives to compare the characters.

Grammar: Comparative and Superlative Adjectives 397

Grammar Practice Book 4.4, p. 90

Name________________________ Lou Gehrig: The Luckiest Man

Grammar: Comparative and Superlative Adjectives

Directions: Write the missing **-er** or **-est** form of each adjective.

1. busy busier **busiest**
2. fat **fatter** fattest

Directions: Use one adjective from the list to complete each sentence.

small smaller smallest large larger largest

3. An ant is very **small**.
4. A lion is **larger** than a mouse.
5. A robin is **smaller** than an elephant.
6. The **largest** animal of all is a whale.

Directions: Complete each comparison. Write the correct form of an adjective in the list. Then write a noun. **Possible answers given.**

big slow thin noisy busy large

7. Chipmunks are **bigger** than **mice**.
8. Frogs are **noisier** than **rabbits**.
9. Snails are the **slowest** **animals** of all.
10. Worker bees are the **busiest** of all **insects**.

Write a Story

Write a story about a pet or a wild animal you like. Describe it well by using adjectives that compare. Write on a separate sheet of paper.

Check that students have used and spelled comparative and superlative adjectives correctly.

Notes for Home: Your child wrote comparative and superlative adjectives in sentences. ***Home Activity:*** Find pictures of three animals in books or magazines. Have your child label the pictures with comparative and superlative adjectives.

398 Grammar: Comparative and Superlative Adjectives

Practice Book 4.4, p. 178

Name________________________ Lou Gehrig: The Luckiest Man

Word Study: Possessives

Directions: Possessive nouns are words that show ownership. Rewrite each phrase below to show possession. For example, **the scores that the players have** can be written as **the players' scores.** Write the new phrase on the line.

the school's ball field 1. the ball field that the school has

Lou's dream 2. the dream that Lou has

the cities' buildings 3. the buildings that cities have

the schools' rules 4. the rules that schools have

Directions: Read the paragraph below. Several words have apostrophes, but they are not all possessive nouns. Circle each possessive noun. Write the word on the line.

Heroes and heroines in the world of sports make wonderful characters for stories. In such stories, the (athletes') goal is usually to overcome an obstacle. For example, they're trying to get along with their teammates. Or a (fan's) rudeness makes them feel that they'd rather be doing something else. The (league's) rules might make it impossible for the player to try new things. It's as if the (player's) own skills aren't good enough for others to believe in. But true athletes are not stopped by other (people's) fears. Over time, everyone's learned that a strong will and an (athlete's) dream turn winning into a reality.

5. **athletes'**
6. **fan's**
7. **league's**
8. **player's**
9. **people's**
10. **athlete's**

Notes for Home: Your child identified possessive nouns, such as *Chris's* and *players'*. ***Home Activity:*** Read a newspaper article with your child. Together, look for words that have apostrophes. Ask your child to decide whether or not these words show possession.

Word Study: Possessives 399

Spelling Workbook 4.4, p. 69

Name________________________ Lou Gehrig: The Luckiest Man

Spelling: Easily Confused Words

Pretest Directions: Fold back the page along the dotted line. On the blanks, write the spelling words as they are dictated. When you have finished the test, unfold the page and check your words.

1. **set**	1. Please **set** the table for dinner.
2. **sit**	2. Go ahead and **sit** down.
3. **off**	3. Tanika turned **off** the light.
4. **of**	4. Jack reads a lot **of** books.
5. **when**	5. I don't know **when** we'll be there.
6. **win**	6. I hope our team will **win**.
7. **our**	7. That's **our** house.
8. **are**	8. **Are** you going to the party?
9. **than**	9. I like carrots better **than** peas.
10. **then**	10. First I'll wash, **then** I'll dry.
11. **lose**	11. He hopes his team won't **lose**.
12. **loose**	12. Oops, this button is **loose**.
13. **were**	13. What **were** you saying?
14. **we're**	14. I hope **we're** going to have fun.
15. **where**	15. I know **where** it is.
16. **quiet**	16. This is a **quiet** neighborhood.
17. **quite**	17. Wow, that's **quite** a bike!
18. **quit**	18. He says he won't **quit** trying.
19. **whose**	19. **Whose** jacket is this?
20. **who's**	20. **Who's** that standing by the door?

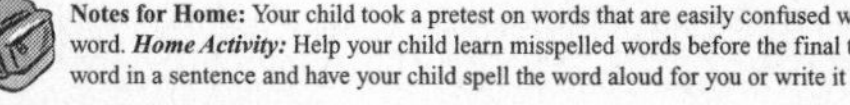

Notes for Home: Your child took a pretest on words that are easily confused with another word. ***Home Activity:*** Help your child learn misspelled words before the final test. Dictate the word in a sentence and have your child spell the word aloud for you or write it on paper.

400 Spelling: Easily Confused Words

Spelling Workbook 4.4, p. 70

Name ______________ **Lou Gehrig: The Luckiest Man**

Spelling: Easily Confused Words

Word List

set	when	than	were	quite
sit	win	then	we're	quit
off	our	lose	where	whose
of	are	loose	quiet	who's

Directions: Choose the word or words from the box that have a similar pronunciation or spelling as each word below. Write the word on the line.

1. win **when**
2. are **our**
3. whose **who's**
4. sit **set**
5–6. quit **quiet/quite** **quite/quiet**
7. off **of**
8. than **then**
9. lose **loose**
10–11. where **were/we're** **we're/were**

Directions: Choose the word in ( ) that best completes each sentence. Write the word on the line.

sit 12. Tim asked me to (set/sit) with him and watch TV.
Where 13. "(Where/We're) should I sit?" I asked.
are 14. We watched the Yankees, who (our/are) my favorite team.
quit 15. They try hard, and never (quite/quit).
win 16. They (when/win) almost every game.
lose 17. They never seem to (lose/loose).
than 18. They're better (then/than) they were last year.
Whose 19. "(Whose/Who's) feet are on the couch?" Tim said.
off 20. "Mine," I said. "I'll take them (off/of)."

Notes for Home: Your child spelled words that are easily confused because they have similar pronunciations or spellings. ***Home Activity:*** Pick a pair or trio of words that are easily confused. Have your child spell each word and use it correctly in a sentence.

Spelling Workbook 4.4, p. 71

Name ______________ **Lou Gehrig: The Luckiest Man**

Spelling: Easily Confused Words

Directions: Proofread this article about a baseball game. Find five spelling mistakes. Use the proofreading marks to correct each mistake.

≡ Make a capital.
/ Make a small letter.
∧ Add something.
Take out something.
○ Add a period.
¶ Begin a new paragraph.

SPORTS

The crowd was quit[e] as Darryl Benton picked up the bat. They were all hoping that he would hit a home run and wh~~e~~[i]n the game for his team. Benton swung his bat a few times. Then he nodded. He looked like a man who would never quit~~e~~ until he had reached his goal. And today his goal was to win the game. "It's ~~are~~ [our] turn now," he said. Th~~a~~[e]n he stepped up to the plate.

Spelling Tip

Some words are easily confused because they have similar pronunciations, such as **when** and **win.** Other words have similar spellings, like **quite, quiet,** and **quit.** Check the story to make sure that these words are used and spelled correctly.

Word List

set	when	than	were	quite
sit	win	then	we're	quit
off	our	lose	where	whose
of	are	loose	quiet	who's

Write a Sports Story

On a separate sheet of paper, write your own story about a sporting event. You could write about what happened during the event, or you could tell about a specific athlete or coach. Use at least five spelling words. **Answers will vary, but each story should include at least five spelling words.**

Notes for Home: Your child spelled words that are easily confused because they have similar pronunciations or spellings. ***Home Activity:*** Say a spelling word, and use it in a sentence. Have your child spell the word.

Spelling Workbook 4.4, p. 72

Name ______________ **Lou Gehrig: The Luckiest Man**

Spelling: Easily Confused Words REVIEW

Word List

set	when	than	were	quite
sit	win	then	we're	quit
off	our	lose	where	whose
of	are	loose	quiet	who's

Directions: Choose the word from the box that is the most opposite in meaning for each word below. Write the word on the line.

1. start **quit**
2. on **off**
3. loud **quiet**
4. stand **sit**
5. lose **win**
6. tight **loose**
7. win **lose**
8. now **then**
9. aren't **are**
10. weren't **were**

Directions: Look at the underlined word in each sentence. If it is the correct choice, write it on the line. If it is not the correct choice, write the word from the box that belongs there instead.

Our 11. Our coach called the team for a meeting.
set 12. She had us sit down our gloves.
we're 13. "I want to talk about what were doing tomorrow."
Who's 14. "Whose ready to go on a trip?" she asked.
Where 15. "Were to?" we asked.
of 16. "To the Baseball Hall off Fame!" she announced.
When 17. "When are we leaving?" we asked.
Quite 18. "Quit early in the day," she replied.
than 19. "Early is better than late," I said.
Whose 20. Who's coach is better than ours?

Notes for Home: Your child spelled words that are easily confused because of similar pronunciations or spellings. ***Home Activity:*** Think of other easily confused words, such as *its* and *it's* or *pin* and *pen.* Ask your child to spell each word and use it in a sentence.

Practice Book 4.4, p. 179

Name ______________ **Lou Gehrig: The Luckiest Man**

Technology: Order Form

An **order form** is a chart with spaces that need to be filled with specific information. You can use an order form to purchase merchandise from catalogs or to order publications, such as pamphlets, magazines, or newspapers. It is important to follow directions on order forms so that you get what you want.

Print sources, such as catalogs, have order forms that you complete by hand. Electronic sources, such as the Internet, also have order forms. Many companies have Web sites with electronic catalogs. You order items from these catalogs by clicking on pictures or descriptions. The items are automatically listed on an order form and totals are calculated for you. It is important to be careful when using online catalogs and order forms. You may accidentally click on an item you do not want.

Directions: Review these collectors' items available for sale on a baseball Web site. Use the information to answer the questions that follow.

Practice Book 4.4, p. 180

Name______________ Lou Gehrig: The Luckiest Man

1. Mr. Jonas wants to order a 1927 Yankees Baseball Cap. His order form is below. What mistake did he make?

Mr. Jonas chose the bat not the cap.

2. Draw a line through the information that Mr. Jonas mistakenly used in the order form above. Write in the item Mr. Jonas meant to order in the row underneath. Add to the order form the Unit Price, Quantity, and Total for this item.

3. Mr. Jonas wants to add to his order. He wants two Lou Gehrig Baseball Cards. Enter this item in the order form.

4. Find the grand total of Mr. Jonas' order. Write it in the order form.

5. How is ordering electronically different from using a printed order form?

Possible answer: When ordering electronically, the computer will fill in an order form and calculate costs for you. With a printed order form, you have to complete the form by hand.

Item	Unit Price	Quantity	Total
~~1927 Yankees Baseball Bat~~	~~$72.97~~	~~1~~	~~$72.97~~
1927 Yankees Baseball Cap	**$25.95**	**1**	**$25.95**
Lou Gehrig's Baseball Card	**$48.89**	**2**	**$97.78**
		Grand Total	**$123.73**

Notes for Home: Your child completed an order form. *Home Activity:* Have your child complete an order form from a catalog. Have him or her select several items. Challenge your child to make the grand total as close to $50 as possible.

Practice Book 4.4, p. 181

Name______________ The Disguise

Summarizing

- A **summary** is a short statement, no more than a few sentences, that tells the main idea of a selection.
- A **summary of an article** should tell the main idea, leaving out unnecessary details.

Directions: Reread "Korean Food." Then complete the web. Write a sentence summarizing the main idea for each topic given. **Possible answers given.**

Korean Food

- *Kimch'i* — 1. ***Kimch'i* is a spicy national dish served at most meals.**
- Rice — 2. **Rice is the main food, eaten at most meals.**
- Preparing Rice — 3. **Rice is cooked carefully with water in an iron pot.**
- Summer Food — 4. **In summer, many fruits and vegetables are eaten.**
- Fish, Meat, Eggs — 5. **Fish is eaten often, but meat and eggs are rarely eaten.**

Notes for Home: Your child read and summarized the main ideas in an article. *Home Activity:* Ask your child to identify a favorite story, movie, or television episode. Ask your child to summarize its events in no more than a few sentences.

Practice Book 4.4, p. 182

Name______________ The Disguise

Vocabulary

Directions: Choose the word from the box that best matches each definition. Write the word on the line.

Check the Words You Know
- __ cautious
- __ chanting
- __ dangerous
- __ disguise
- __ principal
- __ recite
- __ squatted
- __ suspected

chanting 1. singing in one tone
suspected 2. believed to be guilty without proof
principal 3. head of a school
disguise 4. make a thing seem like something else
squatted 5. crouched on the heels
cautious 6. very careful

Directions: Choose the word from the box that best completes each sentence. Write the word on the line.

dangerous 7. When Hector was little, he liked to do _____ things like sliding down stairs on his tummy.
suspected 8. He played so many tricks that people once _____ that Hector had put salt in the punch bowl!
recite 9. "How could I do that?" said Hector. "I was asked to _____ a poem while everyone else was drinking punch."
cautious 10. Now that he is older, Hector has become a lot more _____.

Write an Adventure Story

On a separate sheet of paper, write a story about two children who have an adventure. You might describe how they face danger and then tell what they do to save themselves. Use as many vocabulary words as you can.

Students' stories should use vocabulary words correctly.

Notes for Home: Your child identified and used vocabulary words from "The Disguise." *Home Activity:* Play a sentence game with your child. Taking turns, use a vocabulary word in a sentence. The other person has to then use the same word in a different sentence.

Practice Book 4.4, p. 183

Name______________ The Disguise

Summarizing

- A **summary** is a short statement that tells the main ideas of a selection.
- A **story summary** should tell the goals of the characters, how they try to reach them, and whether they reach them. A **summary of an article** should tell the main idea, leaving out unnecessary details.

Directions: Reread what happens in "The Disguise" when Imduk and her mother move to their new home. Then follow the instructions below.

Mother's work-worn hands smoothed the fabric of her black skirt as it lay on the floor. Quickly she began cutting it.

We were in our new home, a single room, in the village of Dukdong. We had planned to live with Mother's brother, but they had quarreled.

He said Mother's idea to educate me was ridiculous. A girl couldn't learn! Where did she get such wild ideas from? No one in their family had such crazy notions!

Stubbornly, Mother clung to her plans and decided to make her own home. This decision took tremendous courage. I knew of no other woman who lived without at least one male relative in her home. By doing this, she was breaking yet another rule of our culture.

Possible answers given.

1. What is Mother's goal?

Her goal is to educate her daughter.

2. Does Mother's brother help her reach that goal?

He tells her it's a crazy idea because girls can't learn.

3. Why did Mother's decision to make her own home take great courage?

It breaks another tradition in their culture.

4. Write a summary of this passage.

Mother will do whatever it takes to educate her daughter.

5. Write a summary of "The Disguise" on a separate sheet of paper.

Check that summaries focus on the story's main ideas.

Notes for Home: Your child summarized a story. *Home Activity:* Reread a familiar story with your child. Ask him or her to summarize it for you. Remind your child to think of the main characters, what they want, and how they try to get it.

Practice Book 4.4, p. 185

Name____________________

The Disguise

Selection Test

Directions: Choose the best answer to each item. Mark the letter for the answer you have chosen.

Part 1: Vocabulary

Find the answer choice that means about the same as the underlined word in each sentence.

1. You must <u>disguise</u> yourself.
- A. bring shame upon
- B. become pretty
- C. save from harm
- (D) dress to look like someone else

2. Who is the <u>principal</u>?
- F. person who studies
- (G) the head of a school
- H. person who swims
- J. member of the police

3. People say I'm too <u>cautious</u>.
- A. polite
- (B) very careful
- C. nervous
- D. very smart

4. Everyone <u>suspected</u> that he would be last.
- (F) thought it likely
- G. feared
- H. argued
- J. thought well of

5. That sounds <u>dangerous</u>.
- A. comfortable
- B. unusual
- (C) unsafe
- D. difficult

6. Can you <u>recite</u> a poem?
- F. explain the meaning of
- G. write over and over
- (H) repeat from memory
- J. read from a book

7. The boys were <u>chanting</u>.
- (A) singing in one tone
- B. running and shouting playfully
- C. fighting one another
- D. speaking with too much pride

8. Nadine <u>squatted</u> by the fire.
- F. got down on one's knees
- G. fell asleep standing up
- H. lay down
- (J) crouched on one's heels

Practice Book 4.4, p. 186

Name____________________

The Disguise

Part 2: Comprehension

Use what you know about the story to answer each item.

9. An old man came to Imduk's home to—
- A. make a pink shirt for her.
- (B) teach her the Korean alphabet.
- C. show her Chinese characters.
- D. see if she could paint.

10. Imduk's mother decided to move to Dukdong because—
- (F) a relative ran a school there.
- G. everyone in their town knew that Imduk was a girl.
- H. there were no teachers nearby.
- J. Dukdong was in China.

11. How were Imduk and the Chinese girl in Mother's story alike?
- A. Both fell in love.
- B. Both liked to swim.
- C. Both knew the alphabet.
- (D) Both dressed as boys.

12. Imduk's mother believed that—
- (F) Imduk would succeed in school.
- G. girls could not learn.
- H. her husband would return.
- J. going to school was silly.

13. Which sentence best summarizes what happens in this story?
- A. A girl pretended to be a soldier in the army.
- (B) Imduk dressed herself as a boy so she could go to school.
- C. Boys in the school wore black ribbons in their hair.
- D. Imduk's mother would not let her swim with the boys.

14. Imduk's mother is the kind of person who—
- F. likes to make people angry.
- G. does not value education.
- (H) does what she thinks is right.
- J. will never be happy.

15. Which sentence about the story includes a generalization that is faulty?
- A. Most people did not think a girl could be taught to read.
- B. Pink was a color worn by boys.
- (C) All Korean girls wanted to lead an exciting life.
- D. There is a risk in swimming without adults nearby.

Name____________________

The Disguise

Summarizing

- A **summary** is a short statement that tells the main ideas of a selection.
- A **story summary** should tell the goals of the characters, how they try to reach them, and whether they reach them. A **summary of an article** should tell the main idea, leaving out unnecessary details.

Directions: Read the story below.

Learning English was hard, but soon Li Chen spoke it quite well. Everyone else in her family spoke only Chinese. Li Chen felt proud. She spoke two languages! That meant she could help her family. Helping others is important to Li Chen.

Li Chen's parents were proud too. They were glad to have her help. When Li Chen's mother went shopping, she took Li Chen with her to ask questions for her. At a restaurant, Li Chen could order food for the family. Li Chen liked helping her family.

One day, a new girl who spoke only Chinese came to Li Chen's school. Li Chen could help the new girl understand the teacher. She could help the teacher understand the new girl. Sometimes helping out was a lot of work. But most of the time, Li Chen felt good that she could help.

Directions: Complete the table. Think about Li Chen's goal and how she tries to accomplish it. Then write a summary of the story.

Li Chen speaks	Chinese and English
Li Chen helps her mother by:	1. **asking questions when they shop or ordering food when they eat out.**
Li Chen helps the new girl by:	2. **telling her what the teacher says.**
Li Chen helps the teacher by:	3. **helping her understand the new girl.**
Li Chen feels:	4. **proud to be able to help others.**

5. Summary: **Li Chen is proud to use her ability to speak Chinese and English to help others.**

Notes for Home: Your child gave details about a character's goals and actions and wrote a summary of a story. ***Home Activity:*** Take turns summarizing stories you and your child both know. Have the listener tell the book title, based on the summary.

Practice Book 4.4, p. 187

Name____________________

The Disguise

Predicting

REVIEW

Directions: Read the story. Then read each question about the story. Choose the best answer to each question. Mark the letter for the answer you have chosen.

In a New Country

Marc was with his family in Paris, France! Marc could hardly wait to get out and see the sights.

Marc's parents were resting in the next room. But Marc was too excited to rest.

Suddenly, there was a knock on the hotel room door. A voice said something in French. Marc didn't know what to do.

Then Marc remembered that his parents had ordered breakfast. His mother had said that breakfast was brought right to your room.

Marc went to get his parents, and they opened the door. A waiter came in with a tray with three cups of a creamy, brown liquid and a covered dish.

1. Which clues helped you predict who was at the door?
- **A.** Marc hears a knock.
- (B) Marc's mother ordered breakfast at the hotel.
- **C.** Marc is in Paris, France.
- **D.** Marc's parents are next door.

2. Which of the following is most likely to be in the three cups?
- **F.** soup
- **G.** orange juice
- (H) coffee or hot chocolate
- **J.** gravy

3. Which of the following is most likely to be under the covered dish?
- **A.** roast beef
- **B.** ham sandwiches
- **C.** ice cream
- (D) rolls and butter

4. What do you predict Marc will do after breakfast?
- **F.** He will take a nap.
- **G.** He will make a phone call.
- (H) He will go sightseeing.
- **J.** He will read a book.

5. Which clue helped you predict what Marc will do next?
- **A.** Marc hears a knock at the door.
- **B.** Marc and his parents are staying in a hotel.
- **C.** Marc hears some French.
- (D) Marc can hardly wait to get out and see the sights.

Notes for Home: Your child made predictions based on information read in a story. ***Home Activity:*** Play a "prediction game" with your child. Take turns giving each other clues and making predictions. For example: *I'm at the gas station. What do you predict I'll do next?* (buy gas)

Name______________________________ The Disguise

Writing Across Texts

Directions: Consider what you learned about Imduk in the story "The Disguise" and Lou Gehrig in the story *Lou Gehrig: The Luckiest Man.* How are they alike? How are they different? Use the Venn Diagram to record your answers.

Possible answers given.

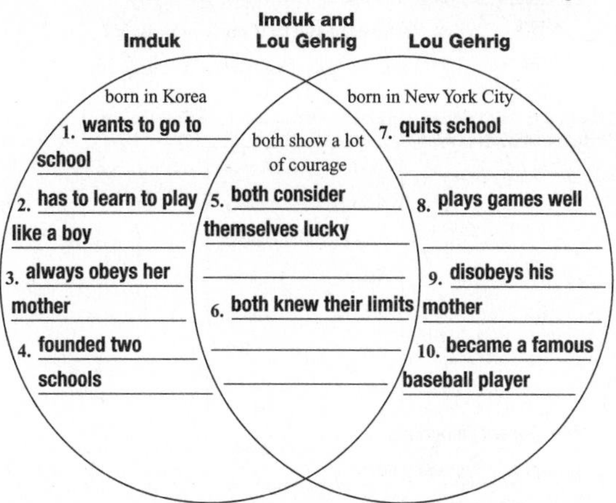

Write a Compare/Contrast Paragraph

Imduk and Lou Gehrig come from very different backgrounds and have different strengths. Both characters are very successful, but they achieve success in different ways. Write a paragraph in which you compare and contrast these two characters. Use information from your diagram to help you with ideas. Write your paragraph on a separate sheet of paper. **Paragraphs will vary. Students should use the similarities and differences as details in their paragraphs.**

Notes for Home: Your child used information from two reading selections to write a compare/contrast paragraph. ***Home Activity:*** As you read stories and articles with your child, talk about how the ideas in the reading materials connect to other reading you have done.

Writing Across Texts 415

Grammar Practice Book 4.4, p. 91

Name______________________________ The Disguise

Grammar: Comparative and Superlative Adjectives

REVIEW

Directions: Add **-er, -est, more,** or **most** to the adjectives to form comparative and superlative adjectives.

Adjective	Comparative Adjectives	Superlative Adjectives
funny	1. funnier	2. funniest
pale	3. paler	4. palest
high	5. higher	6. highest
big	7. bigger	8. biggest
wonderful	9. more wonderful	10. most wonderful

Directions: Write the correct form of the adjective in ( ) to complete each sentence.

more exciting 11. Few things are (exciting) than learning about other cultures.

most important 12. Food is one of the (important) parts of any culture.

largest 13. Yesterday I went to the (large) International Fair I have ever seen.

greatest 14. It had the (great) variety of food I have ever eaten.

spicier 15. The Mexican tacos seemed (spicy) than usual.

hotter 16. Indian food is often (hot) than Mexican food.

more delicious 17. The Chinese spring rolls were (delicious) than others I have eaten elsewhere.

tastier 18. The Russian beet salad was (tasty) than I had expected.

most incredible 19. The Italian gelato was the (incredible) ice cream I've ever tasted.

fuller 20. I have never felt (full) in my entire life!

Notes for Home: Your child used comparative forms of adjectives to compare two things and superlative forms to compare three or more things. ***Home Activity:*** Look through pictures in magazines. Use comparative and superlative forms of adjectives to compare the pictures.

416 Grammar: Comparative and Superlative Adjectives

Grammar Practice Book 4.4, p. 92

Name______________________________ The Disguise

Grammar: Adverbs

An **adverb** tells how, when, or where something happens. Most adverbs tell about verbs. An adverb can appear either before or after the verb. Many adverbs that tell how end in **-ly**.

How: The dancer performed gracefully.
(Other examples: beautifully, slowly, carefully)

Adverbs can also tell when or where an action happens.

When: Your new costume arrived today.
(Other examples: always, first, last)

Where: Don't leave it lying around.
(Other examples: far, out, through)

Directions: Underline the adverb in each sentence.

1. Frank was doing poorly in school.
2. Then he suddenly improved.
3. In class, he always paid attention.
4. Frank waited hopefully for Awards Day.
5. He excitedly claimed his award as the Most Improved Student.

Directions: Write the adverb that describes each underlined verb.

quickly 6. That day, Frank quickly ran home.

never 7. He said he would never forget how much his parents had helped him.

immediately 8. Then he immediately began his homework.

first 9. Frank would work first.

later 10. He would have fun later.

Notes for Home: Your child identified adverbs, words that tell how, when, or where an action happens. ***Home Activity:*** Ask your child questions about the day's events. Invite your child to use adverbs in his or her answers.

Grammar: Adverbs 417

Grammar Practice Book 4.4, p. 93

Name______________________________ The Disguise

Grammar: Adverbs

Directions: Write whether each underlined adverb tells **when, where,** or **how.**

when 1. My brother and I always enjoyed old family stories.

how 2. We eagerly listened to tales about Korea.

how 3. My brother sincerely wanted to visit Korea.

where 4. Our parents said he could study there.

how 5. My brother nervously boarded the plane.

Directions: Write an adverb for each sentence that tells whatever is named in ( ). Write your adverb on the line to the left. **Possible answers given.**

sometimes 6. John's uncle _____ told him tales from Ireland. (when)

best 7. John liked _____ the stories about leprechauns. (how)

gladly 8. "If you leave milk for a leprechaun," one story said, "the grateful creature will _____ work for you." (how)

often 9. The Irish _____ call leprechauns "the little people." (when)

here 10. John thinks we could use some grateful leprechauns _____! (where)

Write a Letter

On a separate sheet of paper, write a letter to a pen pal that tells about your family's culture. Describe an everyday event or a special holiday tradition. Use at least one adverb in each sentence. **Students should use a variety of adverbs.**

Notes for Home: Your child identified adverbs telling how, when, or where something happened. ***Home Activity:*** Tell your child a story about something that happened in your family. Have your child identify each adverb and say which it tells: how, when, or where.

418 Grammar: Adverbs

Grammar Practice Book 4.4, p. 94

Name________________ **The Disguise**

Grammar: Adverbs

RETEACHING

Circle the adverb that tells **how.**

1. My brother ate (slowly).

Circle the adverb that tells **when.**

2. He finished dinner (last).

Circle the adverb that tells **where.**

3. He left his dishes sitting (out).

An **adverb** tells how, when, or where something happens. Most adverbs tell about verbs. An adverb can appear before or after the verb. Many adverbs that tell how end in **-ly.**

Directions: Underline the adverb in each sentence.

1. Today the bears explore their surroundings.
2. One cub runs outside.
3. The bear family plays happily.
4. They always leave their home.
5. They travel around.
6. The three cubs never leave their mother's side.

Directions: Write an adverb that tells more about each underlined verb. **Possible answers given.**

always 7. The bears hunt for food.

quickly 8. Salmon are swimming toward their destination.

slowly 9. The mother steps into the stream.

Notes for Home: Your child identified and wrote adverbs in sentences. *Home Activity:* Talk with your child about what you did today. Have your child point out adverbs you use to describe how, when, or where.

Grammar: Adverbs 419

Grammar Practice Book 4.4, p. 95

Name________________ **The Disguise**

Grammar: Adverbs

Directions: Write whether each underlined adverb tells when, where, or how.

where 1. Snakes don't come here.

how 2. It is hard to find them easily in our town.

where 3. You have to travel far if you want to see one.

how 4. When you do spot one, you must walk quietly.

Directions: Write sentences, using a verb and an adverb from the box. **Possible answers given.**

Verbs	Adverbs
move	quickly
run	slowly
talk	hard
eat	loudly
melt	last
try	silently

5. **Bob can eat dinner last.**
6. **He will run the race quickly.**
7. **The snow melts slowly.**
8. **I will try hard to remember her name.**
9. **He talks loudly at the concert.**
10. **We move silently through the crowd.**

Notes for Home: Your child wrote adverbs in sentences. *Home Activity:* Have your student read a favorite story and look for adverbs. Then have him or her write new sentences with the adverbs from the story.

420 Grammar: Adverbs

Practice Book 4.4, p. 188

Name________________ **The Disguise**

Word Study: Suffixes

Directions: Suffixes are letters we add to the end of base words. Some suffixes are **-ful, -ly, -ion, -ous, -less, -ness,** and **-ment.** Read the journal entry below. Find each word that has one of these suffixes and write it on a line.

Dear Diary,

Today was a wonderful day! I wanted to see if a girl could join the boys' basketball team. I know it may not be a wise decision. It might even be dangerous. Some might even say my case was hopeless. But I had to try, even if it was only to make a statement about girls being good sports. Quickly I donned my disguise. I walked uneasily onto the court. I was careful to make sure no one recognized me. As the game started, I knew that the team was about to get an education it would never forget. In all fairness, it's a lesson they need to learn.

1. **wonderful**
2. **decision**
3. **dangerous**
4. **hopeless**
5. **statement**
6. **Quickly**
7. **uneasily**
8. **careful**
9. **education**
10. **fairness**

Directions: Each word below has a base word and one or two suffixes. Write the base word in the first column. Then write the suffix or suffixes in the second column.

	Base Word	Suffix or Suffixes
11. beautifully	**beauty**	**ful, ly**
12. pollution	**pollute**	**ion**
13. carelessly	**care**	**less, ly**
14. encouragement	**encourage**	**ment**
15. joyously	**joy**	**ous, ly**

Notes for Home: Your child identified suffixes, and added them to the ends of words. *Home Activity:* Play a game with your child. Write a word like *encourage.* Then write some suffixes, like *-ly, -ous,* and *-ment.* Have your child choose a suffix to make a new word.

Word Study: Suffixes 421

Spelling Workbook 4.4, p. 73

Name________________ **The Disguise**

Spelling: Suffixes *-ful, -ly, -ion*

Pretest Directions: Fold back the page along the dotted line. On the blanks, write the spelling words as they are dictated. When you have finished the test, unfold the page and check your words.

1. **powerful**	1. She's a **powerful** leader.
2. **peaceful**	2. This is a **peaceful** garden.
3. **beautiful**	3. What a **beautiful** place!
4. **cheerful**	4. What a **cheerful** baby!
5. **painful**	5. It was a **painful** situation.
6. **thoughtful**	6. She was a **thoughtful** girl.
7. **slowly**	7. He walked **slowly** to the garden.
8. **safely**	8. He was **safely** in her arms.
9. **daily**	9. They took a **daily** walk.
10. **suddenly**	10. The sun disappeared **suddenly**.
11. **carefully**	11. Please hold it **carefully**.
12. **weekly**	12. We have a **weekly** meeting.
13. **lately**	13. He hasn't been around **lately**.
14. **truthfully**	14. I hope you spoke **truthfully**.
15. **hopefully**	15. She looked at him **hopefully**.
16. **action**	16. What **action** would you take?
17. **location**	17. This is an interesting **location**.
18. **invention**	18. The zipper was a good **invention**.
19. **correction**	19. We need to make a **correction**.
20. **pollution**	20. **Pollution** made this place dirty.

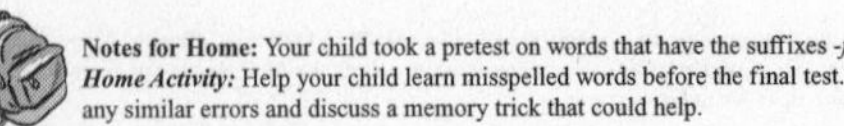

Notes for Home: Your child took a pretest on words that have the suffixes *-ful, -ly,* and *-ion.* *Home Activity:* Help your child learn misspelled words before the final test. See if there are any similar errors and discuss a memory trick that could help.

422 Spelling: Suffixes *-ful, -ly, -ion*

Spelling Workbook 4.4, p. 74

Name ______________________

The Disguise

Spelling: Suffixes *-ful*, *-ly*, *-ion*

Word List

powerful	painful	daily	lately	location
peaceful	thoughtful	suddenly	truthfully	invention
beautiful	slowly	carefully	hopefully	correction
cheerful	safely	weekly	action	pollution

Directions: Choose the word from the box that is formed by adding **-ful** or **-fully** to each base word. Write the complete word on the line.

1. power **powerful**
2. pain **painful**
3. cheer **cheerful**
4. thought **thoughtful**
5. peace **peaceful**
6. truth **truthfully**
7. hope **hopefully**
8. care **carefully**
9. beauty **beautiful**

Directions: Add the suffix **-ly** or **-ion** to each word in ( ) to form a word from the box and complete each sentence. Write the word on the line.

weekly 10. We have a (week) meeting in our class.
lately 11. (Late) it has been very interesting!
daily 12. We talk about what (day) life is like for each of us.
slowly 13. Achmed talks (slow), but he has a lot to say.
pollution 14. He is very concerned about (pollute).
safely 15. "How can we live (safe)?" he asks.
action 16. "We must take (act) to protect our planet!"
suddenly 17. Sladka came to this country very (sudden).
location 18. This was the best (locate) for her family's business.
invention 19. They sell an (invent) that her mother created.
correction 20. After much (correct), I know how to pronounce it.

Notes for Home: Your child spelled words with the suffixes *-ful*, *-ly*, and *-ion*. ***Home Activity:*** Have your child make a list of spelling words that end in *-ly*. Help your child think of additional words that end in *-ly*, such as *quickly, happily, sadly,* and *sweetly* and add them to the list.

Spelling Workbook 4.4, p. 75

Name ______________________

The Disguise

Spelling: Suffixes *-ful*, *-ly*, *-ion*

Directions: Proofread this letter to a friend back home. Find five spelling mistakes. Use the proofreading marks to correct each mistake.

≡ Make a capital.
/ Make a small letter.
∧ Add something.
Take out something.
⊙ Add a period.
¶ Begin a new paragraph.

Dear Hakim,

It was very thoughtfull of you to write me so soon. I miss you and all of my friends back home. I think of you dayly. We look hopefuly to a visit next summer. But this is a beautyful country too! Maybe you can come visit me. Correcttion, maybe you'll visit me soon!

Love,

Yacob

Spelling Tip

When you add **-ful, -ly,** or **-ion** to most base words, the base stays the same: **power<u>ful</u>.** For words ending in **y**, change the **y** to **i** before adding the suffix: **dail<u>y</u>.** For words ending in **e**, drop the **e: locat<u>ion</u>.**

Word List

powerful	carefully
peaceful	weekly
beautiful	lately
cheerful	truthfully
painful	hopefully
thoughtful	action
slowly	location
safely	invention
daily	correction
suddenly	pollution

Write a Letter

Find out something about a culture that is different from your own. Then, on a separate sheet of paper, write a letter to a friend about what you found out. Try to use at least three spelling words. **Students may need time for research before writing their letters. Answers will vary, but each letter should include at least three spelling words.**

Notes for Home: Your child spelled words with the suffixes *-ful*, *-ly*, and *-ion*. ***Home Activity:*** Look at the words on the list that end in *-ful*. Ask your child to add *-ly* to each word and use it in a sentence.

Spelling Workbook 4.4, p. 76

Name ______________________

The Disguise

Spelling: Suffixes *-ful*, *-ly*, *-ion* REVIEW

Word List

powerful	painful	daily	lately	location
peaceful	thoughtful	suddenly	truthfully	invention
beautiful	slowly	carefully	hopefully	correction
cheerful	safely	weekly	action	pollution

Directions: Choose the word from the box that is the most opposite in meaning for each word or words below. Write the word on the line.

1. unthinking **thoughtful**
2. falsely **truthfully**
3. pleasant **painful**
4. warlike **peaceful**
5. weak **powerful**
6. rest **action**
7. carelessly **carefully**
8. quickly **slowly**
9. error **correction**
10. pure environment **pollution**

Directions: Choose the word from the box that best replaces the underlined word or words. Write the word on the line.

weekly 11. We have a <u>once-a-week</u> culture fair in our class.
location 12. It is a good <u>place</u> to learn about other cultures.
invention 13. Often, people show a <u>creation</u> from their culture.
Lately 14. <u>Recently</u>, class has been very interesting.
beautiful 15. Today, Yoshi brought in some <u>very pretty</u> rice bowls.
safely 16. "I hope they have traveled <u>in a safe way</u>," he said.
hopefully 17. We all looked <u>with hope</u> at the box.
Suddenly 18. <u>All of a sudden</u>, Yoshi smiled.
cheerful 19. It was a big, <u>happy</u> smile.
daily 20. "They're fine," he said, "and now I can tell you about the way we use these bowls <u>every day</u>."

Notes for Home: Your child spelled words with the suffixes *-ful*, *-ly*, and *-ion*. ***Home Activity:*** Say one of the suffixes *-ful*, *-ly*, or *-ion*. Your child can respond by saying a spelling word that uses that suffix, spelling the word, and using it in a sentence. Switch roles and repeat.

Practice Book 4.4, p. 189

Name ______________________

The Disguise

Alphabetical Order

The words in glossaries and indexes are organized in **alphabetical order** to make them easier to find. To find an entry in an alphabetical list, start by looking for the first letter of the word you wish to find. If there are multiple entries with the same first letter, look for the second letter. If there are multiple entries with the same first and second letters, look for the third letter, and so on.

You can use alphabetical order to get information from a telephone book, a dictionary, and an encyclopedia too. You'll also find fiction books in a library organized on shelves by alphabetical order using the authors' last names.

Directions: Use this index listing from an almanac to find each topic listed below. Write the page number or numbers where information about this topic can be found.

A
Abbreviations, 112
Acid rain, 44
Afghanistan, 36
Africa
  Facts, 98
  History, 104, 216–217
  Map, 398
Alabama, 235
Alaska, 389
Angola, 67
Animals, 46–50
  Classifying, 46
  Endangered species, 87
  Fastest and largest, 50
Antarctica, 77
Antigua, 32–33
Arctic Ocean, 80
Argentina, 36–37
  Map, 398
Arizona, 135
Arkansas, 136
Armenia, 38–39
Art, 79–83

1. Alabama **235**
2. Arizona **135**
3. Antigua **32–33**
4. a map of Africa **398**
5. endangered animals **87**
6. largest animal **50**
7. African history **104, 216–217**
8. Arctic Ocean **80**
9. map of Argentina **398**
10. snakes **46–50**

Practice Book 4.4, p. 190

Name ____________________ **The Disguise**

Directions: Some of the words from the glossary below are missing. Choose the best word from the box to complete each glossary entry. Hint: The list should be in alphabetical order.

principal	chanting	disguise
dangerous	cautious	recite

11. **cautious**, very careful

chanting, singing in one tone

12. **dangerous**, likely to cause harm
13. **disguise**, make it seem like something else

principal, head of a school

14. **recite**, say over; repeat

15. Why is alphabetical order a useful way to organize information? Give an example of a reference source that uses alphabetical order to support your answer.

Possible answer: Alphabetical order makes it easier to sort through information quickly. A telephone directory lists the names and phone numbers of people and businesses in alphabetical order. You can look up a phone number quickly using the last name of the person or the name of the business.

Notes for Home: Your child learned ways to use alphabetical order. ***Home Activity:*** Take turns challenging each other to find names in a phone book or topics in an encyclopedia. Or, have your child list favorite television shows in alphabetical order.

Practice Book 4.4, p. 191

Name ____________________ **Keepers**

Plot

- Stories have **plot,** or a series of events that center on a problem, or conflict.
- A conflict can be a problem between two people or groups, between a person and nature, or within a character.
- The climax is the place where the action builds, and the conflict must be faced. The resolution is where the conflict is solved.

Directions: Reread "One Particular Small, Smart Boy." Then complete the plot map. Use the questions to help you describe the conflict, events that lead to the climax, and how the conflict is resolved. **Possible answers given.**

What is the problem?
1. **The giant wants to eat the boy.**

What does the boy do first to solve the problem?
2. **He squeezes the egg.**

What does the boy do next?
3. **He squeezes the salt.**

What does the boy do last to confront the problem?
4. **He threatens to squeeze the giant's hand.**

What finally happens?
5. **The giant runs away forever.**

Notes for Home: Your child read a story and described its plot. ***Home Activity:*** Ask your child to tell you the plot of a favorite story. Make sure your child tells you the main problem, the events that lead up to the problem being solved, and the way the problem is solved.

Practice Book 4.4, p. 192

Name ____________________ **Keepers**

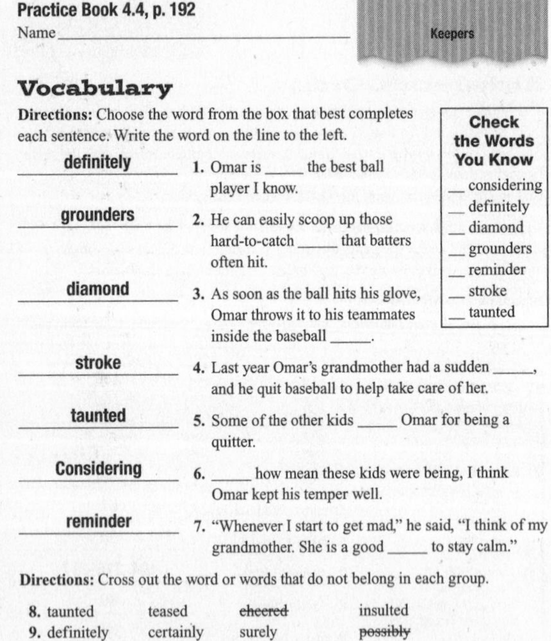

Vocabulary

Directions: Choose the word from the box that best completes each sentence. Write the word on the line to the left.

Check the Words You Know
- __ considering
- __ definitely
- __ diamond
- __ grounders
- __ reminder
- __ stroke
- __ taunted

definitely 1. Omar is _____ the best ball player I know.

grounders 2. He can easily scoop up those hard-to-catch _____ that batters often hit.

diamond 3. As soon as the ball hits his glove, Omar throws it to his teammates inside the baseball _____.

stroke 4. Last year Omar's grandmother had a sudden _____, and he quit baseball to help take care of her.

taunted 5. Some of the other kids _____ Omar for being a quitter.

Considering 6. _____ how mean these kids were being, I think Omar kept his temper well.

reminder 7. "Whenever I start to get mad," he said, "I think of my grandmother. She is a good _____ to stay calm."

Directions: Cross out the word or words that do not belong in each group.

8.	taunted	teased	~~cheered~~	insulted
9.	definitely	certainly	surely	~~possibly~~
10.	considering	~~forgetting~~	thinking about	keeping in mind

Write a Thank-You Note

On a separate page, write a letter to a relative saying "thank you" for something special he or she did for you. Use as many vocabulary words as you can.

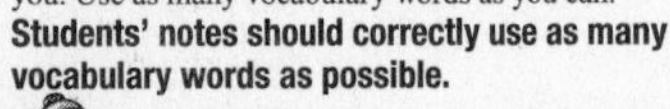

Students' notes should correctly use as many vocabulary words as possible.

Notes for Home: Your child identified and used vocabulary words from *Keepers.* ***Home Activity:*** Play a definition game with your child. You say a vocabulary word, and he or she tells you its definition. For extra fun, have your child give a definition and you guess the word.

Practice Book 4.4, p. 193

Name ____________________ **Keepers**

Plot

- A story's **plot** is the important parts of the story. The parts of a plot are the conflict, or problem, the rising action, the climax, and the resolution, or outcome.

Directions: Reread what happens in *Keepers* when Little Dolly tells her grandson, Kenyon, what a Keeper is. Then answer the questions below.

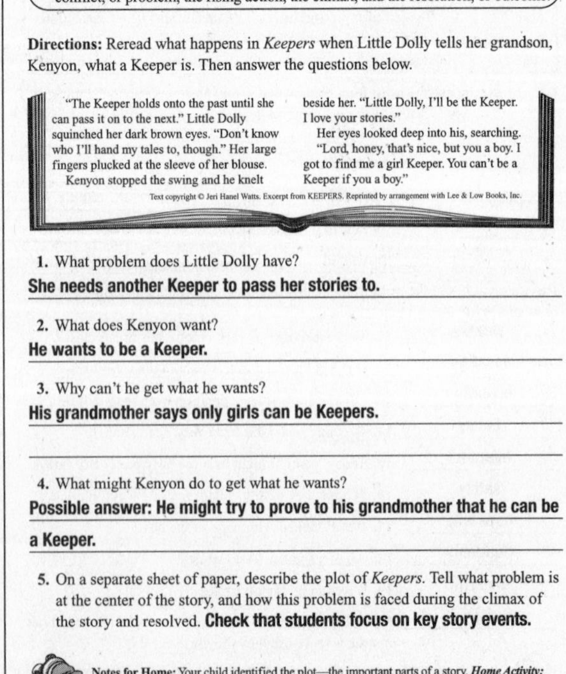

"The Keeper holds onto the past until she can pass it on to the next." Little Dolly squinched her dark brown eyes. "Don't know who I'll hand my tales to, though." Her large fingers plucked at the sleeve of her blouse.

Kenyon stopped the swing and he knelt beside her. "Little Dolly, I'll be the Keeper. I love your stories."

Her eyes looked deep into his, searching. "Lord, honey, that's nice, but you a boy. I got to find me a girl Keeper. You can't be a Keeper if you a boy."

1. What problem does Little Dolly have?
She needs another Keeper to pass her stories to.

2. What does Kenyon want?
He wants to be a Keeper.

3. Why can't he get what he wants?
His grandmother says only girls can be Keepers.

4. What might Kenyon do to get what he wants?
Possible answer: He might try to prove to his grandmother that he can be a Keeper.

5. On a separate sheet of paper, describe the plot of *Keepers.* Tell what problem is at the center of the story, and how this problem is faced during the climax of the story and resolved. **Check that students focus on key story events.**

Notes for Home: Your child identified the plot—the important parts of a story. ***Home Activity:*** Reread a favorite story with your child. Ask him or her to tell you the plot, including the main problem, or conflict, in the story and how this problem is resolved by the end.

Practice Book 4.4, p. 195

Name

Keepers

Selection Test

Directions: Choose the best answer to each item. Mark the letter for the answer you have chosen.

Part 1: Vocabulary

Find the answer choice that means about the same as the underlined word in each sentence.

1. The team left the diamond.
   - A. dugout
   - (B) baseball field
   - C. bus
   - D. place where fans sit

2. Marc taunted his brother.
   - F. greeted in a friendly way
   - G. surprised
   - (H) teased in a mean way
   - J. honored

3. Patti caught some grounders.
   - (A) baseballs hit along the ground
   - B. small animals with bushy tails
   - C. birds that cannot fly
   - D. balls hit high into the air

4. Today is definitely a good day.
   - F. probably
   - G. usually
   - H. fortunately
   - (J) certainly

5. Will you need a reminder?
   - A. permit to build something
   - (B) something to help one remember
   - C. set of instructions
   - D. written statement that money has been received

6. Fiona is considering buying a new coat.
   - (F) thinking seriously about
   - G. trying to keep away from
   - H. making a habit of
   - J. taking pleasure in

7. Terry's uncle had a stroke.
   - (A) illness caused by a broken or blocked blood vessel
   - B. pain in a tooth
   - C. long talk about something
   - D. time of good luck

Part 2: Comprehension

Use what you know about the story to answer each item.

8. Kenyon's grandmother is a Keeper of—
   - F. birthday presents.
   - G. homework.
   - (H) stories and legends.
   - J. chocolates.

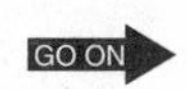

Practice Book 4.4, p. 196

Name

Keepers

9. Kenyon is not allowed to go out and play baseball until—
   - (A) he finishes his homework.
   - B. he gets a new glove.
   - C. his grandmother falls asleep.
   - D. his friends call for him.

10. Little Dolly tells Kenyon that he can't be a Keeper because he—
    - F. doesn't know enough stories.
    - (G) is a boy.
    - H. plays too much baseball.
    - J. can't remember things.

11. What is Kenyon's main conflict?
    - A. He can't get his homework done.
    - B. He can't hit Mo Davis's fastball.
    - C. He doesn't want to take care of his grandmother.
    - (D) He buys a new glove and has no money left for a present.

12. You can tell that a "wallop-bat day" is a day when—
    - F. Kenyon plays baseball.
    - (G) everything goes well.
    - H. Kenyon forgets something.
    - J. someone makes a mistake.

13. The climax of the story comes when—
    - A. Kenyon goes shopping.
    - B. Mrs. Montgomery walks up to the house.
    - (C) Kenyon gives the book to his grandmother.
    - D. Little Dolly gets some chocolates.

14. Mrs. Montgomery and the others come to the house to—
    - F. see Kenyon's baseball glove.
    - (G) surprise Little Dolly with her favorite things.
    - H. see what Kenyon gives to his grandmother.
    - J. show Kenyon that they know he has made a book.

15. This story shows that—
    - A. baseball gloves made of real leather are expensive.
    - B. few people live to be ninety.
    - C. a birthday should be a big event.
    - (D) some of the best presents don't cost anything.

Name

Keepers

Plot

- A story's **plot** is the important parts of the story. The parts of a plot are the conflict, or problem, the rising action, the climax, and the resolution, or outcome.

Directions: Read the story below.

Lucia loved her Uncle Harry. She wanted to get him the best present in the world. But what? Lucia thought hard. She remembered all the nice things Uncle Harry had done for her. He took her to the zoo. He came to her school play. He even gave her his old clarinet.

Suddenly, Lucia had a wonderful idea. She got out markers and paper and went to work.

The next day, Lucia gave Uncle Harry a huge envelope. He opened it—and there was a card with a drawing of the zoo, a ticket from the school play, and sheet music from a song Lucia played on her clarinet. "Do you see?" she said. "I'm giving you the wonderful memories I have of you!"

"It's the best present in the world," said Uncle Harry.

Directions: Complete the table by answering each question about the story's plot.
Possible answers given.

Characters Who is the main character?	1. **Lucia**
Conflict or Problem What problem does this character have?	2. **She can't decide what to get her uncle for a present.**
Rising Action How does this character try to solve the problem?	3. **She thinks hard about what to get and remembers nice things her uncle has done for her.**
Climax What happened that helped solve the problem?	4. **She makes him a card.**
Resolution or Outcome How does the story end?	5. **He loves the card.**

Notes for Home: Your child described the plot of a story by telling about the story's most important parts. ***Home Activity:*** Read a book or watch a movie with your child. Discuss what the main problem of the story is, what happens because of the problem, and how the problem is solved.

Practice Book 4.4, p. 197

Name

Keepers

Steps in a Process

REVIEW

Directions: Read the passage. Then read each question about the passage. Choose the best answer to each question. Mark the letter for the answer you have chosen.

Making a Family Album

Have you ever thought of making a family album? The first thing to do is to find an album. A nice, big sturdy album is best. Make sure that the album has pages made out of paper, not plastic. It's hard to paste things onto plastic.

The next thing to do is collect family treasures to go in the album. Some treasures you might collect are photographs, tickets or programs from special events, or postcards.

After that, you'll want to organize the treasures. You could give each family member a page or try to put things in chronological order.

Finally, label each treasure and write something about it. Ask family members to help.

1. What is the first step in the process?
   - **A.** putting things in order
   - **B.** talking to the family
   - (C) finding an album
   - **D.** pasting things onto paper

2. What clue word tells you what the second step is?
   - **F.** second
   - **G.** after
   - **H.** finally
   - (J) next

3. What is the third step in the process?
   - (A) organizing the treasures
   - **B.** asking for treasures
   - **C.** collecting treasures
   - **D.** labeling each treasure

4. What clue word or words tells you what the third step is?
   - (F) after that
   - **G.** could give
   - **H.** organize
   - **J.** chronological order

5. What clue word tells you what the last step is?
   - (A) finally
   - **B.** after that
   - **C.** next
   - **D.** share

Notes for Home: Your child identified steps in a process that tell the order of steps to be done to complete an action. ***Home Activity:*** Choose a familiar activity, such as making a sandwich. Have your child tell you four or five steps in the process of that activity. The steps should be told in order.

Name________________________ Keepers

Writing Across Texts

Directions: In the story *Keepers*, Little Dolly's family celebrates her birthday with a strawberry shortcake. Kenyon might prefer the cake featured in "Have-a-Ball! Cake" on his birthday. Compare Little Dolly's party with your predictions of the kind of party Kenyon might like on his birthday. Put your ideas in the boxes below.

Little Dolly's party	Your predictions of Kenyon's party
the cake	
1. **strawberry shortcake**	2. **possible answer: Have-a-Ball! cake**
the guests	
3. **friends and family that she has known for years**	4. **possible answer: friends from school and the ball team, family**
where the party is held	
5. **the front porch**	6. **possible answer: the ball field**
gifts	
7. **chocolates, a book of her stories**	8. **possible answer: things having to do with baseball**
party activities	
9. **telling stories, talking with friends and family**	10. **possible answer: games, a baseball game**

Write a Recipe **Recipes will vary. Students should list proper ingredients and write the steps in sequence.**
Think about a food you like to make or help make. On a separate sheet of paper, write the recipe. List the ingredients first, then tell the steps involved in making the dish.

Notes for Home: Your child wrote the recipe of a favorite food. ***Home Activity:*** Invite your child to help you in preparing dinner. Give him or her practice in measuring and combining ingredients.

Grammar Practice Book 4.4, p. 96
Name________________________ Keepers

Grammar: Adverbs

REVIEW

Directions: Identify the adverb that tells about the underlined verb in each sentence. Write the adverb on the line.

often 1. When I was little, my father often told me stories.
eagerly 2. I got into bed and waited eagerly for my story.
softly 3. My father sat on my bed and spoke softly.
Sometimes 4. Sometimes he told me made-up stories.
usually 5. As I got older, though, he usually told real stories.
really 6. The stories I really liked were about my father as a boy.
there 7. As I lay there, I tried to picture him at that age.
outside 8. Once, as a little boy, he looked outside and saw a red glow in the sky.
downstairs 9. Thinking the world was on fire, he ran downstairs.
gently 10. "You've seen your first sunset," his mother said to him gently.

Directions: Write the comparative or superlative form of the adverb in ( ) to complete each sentence.

faster 11. "Please walk (fast)," said my brother.
earlier 12. We wanted to get to our grandparents' house (early) than our parents.
sooner 13. We arrived (soon) than anyone else, and we listened eagerly to my grandfather's wonderful stories.
most loudly 14. I laughed (loudly) of all when he told us about our father's adventures as a boy.
later 15. When our parents arrived (late), we looked at my father and giggled.

Notes for Home: Your child identified adverbs—words that tell how, where, or when something happens—and wrote comparative and superlative adverbs. ***Home Activity:*** Talk with your child about a TV show. Ask questions using *how, when,* and *where.*

Grammar Practice Book 4.4, p. 97
Name________________________ Keepers

Grammar: Using Adverbs to Improve Sentences

The sentence below does not paint a clear picture. It needs descriptive details.

The storyteller spoke.

One way to revise the sentence is by adding an adverb.

The storyteller spoke quietly. (tells how)
The storyteller spoke later. (tells when)
The storyteller spoke outside. (tells where)

Never use more adverbs than you need for expressing ideas clearly.

The storyteller spoke confidently, strongly, easily, and fast.

Directions: Add adverbs to make the sentences more interesting. For each sentence, supply the kind of adverb named in ( ). Write the adverb on the line to the left. **Possible answers given.**

especially 1. There is someone in our family who _____ likes telling family stories. (how)
gladly 2. Uncle Bruce will _____ tell a good story. (how)
always 3. I _____ like the stories about me as a baby. (when)
often 4. He _____ tells about our visit to the country. (when)
there 5. We rented a little house on a lake, and I learned to swim _____. (where)
firmly 6. My uncle used to hold me _____ in the water. (how)
gently 7. One day he _____ let go of me in the water. (how)
Suddenly 8. _____ I was swimming! (when)
well 9. He enjoys seeing how _____ I swim now. (now)
Someday 10. _____ I will teach others how to swim. (when)

Notes for Home: Your child added adverbs to make sentences more interesting. ***Home Activity:*** Have your child tell you about his or her day. Ask questions your child can answer using adverbs.

Grammar Practice Book 4.4, p. 98
Name________________________ Keepers

Grammar: Using Adverbs to Improve Sentences

Directions: Add an adverb to improve each sentence. Remember that an adverb can tell how, when, or where the action takes place. Write the new sentence with the adverb on the line. **Possible answers given.**

1. Nellie's girlfriend wanted to go to a sleep over.
Nellie's girlfriend wanted to go to a sleep over soon.

2. She explained, "My parents think I am too young."
She explained, "My parents still think I am too young."

3. Nellie told her parents she wanted to join her friends.
Nellie told her parents she really wanted to join her friends.

4. Nellie's mother answered her daughter.
Nellie's mother answered her daughter calmly.

5. She told Nellie, "Act grown-up, and we will allow you to go."
She told Nellie quietly, "Act grown-up, and we will allow you to go."

Write a Diary Entry

On a separate sheet of paper, write a diary entry. Tell about a time when you showed your family that you were grown-up enough to do something new. Use adverbs to tell how, when, or where things happened.

Students' writing should include adverbs that tell how, when, and where actions take place.

Notes for Home: Your child added adverbs to sentences. ***Home Activity:*** Play "Who Am I?" by taking turns describing familiar people, using adverbs to describe how they perform actions.

Grammar Practice Book 4.4, p. 99

Name________________ Keepers

Grammar: Using Adverbs to Improve Sentences

RETEACHING

Choose a word from the box to finish each sentence.

now	outside	happily

Add an adverb that tells **how.**

1. The young cub played **happily** .

Add an adverb that tells **when.**

2. He wanted to eat **now** .

Add an adverb that tells **where.**

3. Then he took a nap **outside** .

One way to add descriptive detail to a sentence is by using an **adverb.** Adverbs can tell more about **how, when,** or **where** something happens. Do not use more adverbs than you need. Too many adverbs can make a sentence confusing.

Directions: Add descriptive detail to each sentence by choosing an adverb from the box. Write the adverb on the line. **Possible answers given.**

later	quickly	gently	quietly	down

1. Water filled the cold pool **gently** .
2. The bright sun melted the ice **quickly** .
3. Magda whispered **quietly** to her mother.
4. The trees bent **down** in the wind.
5. Our brown horse took us home **later** .

Notes for Home: Your child wrote adverbs in sentences. *Home Activity:* Write five verbs on cards. Have your child choose a card and write a sentence using that verb and any adverb that he or she would like to use.

Grammar: Using Adverbs to Improve Sentences 441

Grammar Practice Book 4.4, p. 100

Name________________ Keepers

Grammar: Using Adverbs to Improve Sentences

Directions: The verb is underlined in each sentence. Write the adverb that tells more about it.

1. The run rises first. **first**
2. A bird sings clearly. **clearly**
3. Next, the waves break. **Next**
4. The boat sails smoothly. **smoothly**
5. Sails flap slowly. **slowly**
6. The wind blows there. **there**
7. Sailors work carefully. **carefully**

Directions: Find the adverb in each sentence. Then write it in the spaces next to the sentence.

8. The scientists work hard. h a [r] d
9. The boat moves fast. f [a] s t
10. The team works well. w e l [l]
11. The gulls dive quickly. q u i [c] k l y
12. The scientists watch quietly. q u i [e] t l y

Unscramble the letters in the squares and write the word that completes the sentence.

The captain speaks c l e a r l y.

Write a Deep-Sea Tale

On a separate sheet of paper, write about a sea creature. Use abverbs to give details about how the creature might move. **Check that students' tales include descriptive adverbs.**

Notes for Home: Your child identified and wrote adverbs in sentences. *Home Activity:* Have your child explain to you the role of adverbs in sentences. (Adverbs tell more about the action named by the verb.)

442 Grammar: Using Adverbs to Improve Sentences

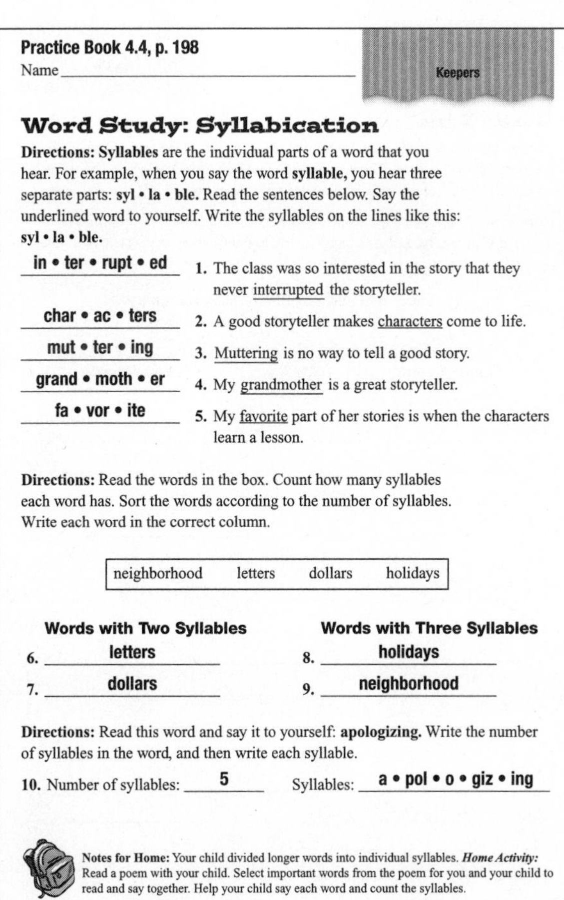

Practice Book 4.4, p. 198

Name________________ Keepers

Word Study: Syllabication

Directions: Syllables are the individual parts of a word that you hear. For example, when you say the word **syllable,** you hear three separate parts: **syl • la • ble.** Read the sentences below. Say the underlined word to yourself. Write the syllables on the lines like this: **syl • la • ble.**

1. **in • ter • rupt • ed** The class was so interested in the story that they never interrupted the storyteller.
2. **char • ac • ters** A good storyteller makes characters come to life.
3. **mut • ter • ing** Muttering is no way to tell a good story.
4. **grand • moth • er** My grandmother is a great storyteller.
5. **fa • vor • ite** My favorite part of her stories is when the characters learn a lesson.

Directions: Read the words in the box. Count how many syllables each word has. Sort the words according to the number of syllables. Write each word in the correct column.

neighborhood	letters	dollars	holidays

Words with Two Syllables	Words with Three Syllables
6. letters	8. holidays
7. dollars	9. neighborhood

Directions: Read this word and say it to yourself: **apologizing.** Write the number of syllables in the word, and then write each syllable.

10. Number of syllables: **5** Syllables: **a • pol • o • giz • ing**

Notes for Home: Your child divided longer words into individual syllables. *Home Activity:* Read a poem with your child. Select important words from the poem for you and your child to read and say together. Help your child say each word and count the syllables.

Word Study: Syllabication 443

Spelling Workbook 4.4, p. 77

Name________________ Keepers

Spelling: Words with Double Consonants

Pretest Directions: Fold back the page along the dotted line. On the blanks, write the spelling words as they are dictated. When you have finished the test, unfold the page and check your words.

1. tomorrow	1. We will come again **tomorrow**.
2. borrow	2. May I **borrow** your gloves?
3. different	3. That's a **different** story!
4. supper	4. We're having **supper** now.
5. matter	5. What's the **matter**?
6. written	6. I should have **written** sooner.
7. bottle	7. The **bottle** is almost empty.
8. ridden	8. He's **ridden** many trails today.
9. odd	9. This cold makes me feel **odd**.
10. bubble	10. Can you blow a **bubble**?
11. offer	11. What do you have to **offer**?
12. suffer	12. I don't want her to **suffer**.
13. slipper	13. Where is the other **slipper**?
14. grasshopper	14. The **grasshopper** jumped away.
15. worry	15. Don't **worry**, we'll find it.
16. current	16. What is your **current** address?
17. lettuce	17. My rabbit likes to eat **lettuce**.
18. paddle	18. The boy dropped his **paddle**.
19. shudder	19. He gave a **shudder** of fright.
20. hobby	20. Reading is a good **hobby**.

Notes for Home: Your child took a pretest on words with double consonants. *Home Activity:* Help your child learn misspelled words before the final test. Have your child divide misspelled words into parts (such as syllables) and concentrate on each part.

444 Spelling: Words with Double Consonants

Spelling Workbook 4.4, p. 78

Name ______________________ Keepers

Spelling: Words with Double Consonants

Word List

tomorrow	matter	odd	slipper	lettuce
borrow	written	bubble	grasshopper	paddle
different	bottle	offer	worry	shudder
supper	ridden	suffer	current	hobby

Directions: Choose the words in the box with **rr, ff,** or **dd.** Write each word in the correct column. **Order may vary.**

Words with Double r	Words with Double f	Words with Double d
1. tomorrow	5. different	8. ridden
2. borrow	6. offer	9. odd
3. worry	7. suffer	10. paddle
4. current		11. shudder

Directions: Choose a word from the box that best matches each clue. Write the word on the line.

hobby 12. a word with two *b*'s that is what you do for fun

supper 13. a word with two *p*'s that is the name of a meal

lettuce 14. a word with two *t*'s that you eat in a salad

slipper 15. a word with two *p*'s that you wear on your foot

grasshopper 16. a word with two double consonants

bottle 17. a word with two *t*'s that holds liquid

written 18. a word with two *t*'s that is the opposite of *spoken*

bubble 19. a word with two *b*'s that you might find in a bathtub

matter 20. a word with two *t*'s that means "problem or trouble"

Notes for Home: Your child spelled words with double consonants. **Home Activity:** Play a doubles game with your child. Choose a consonant and ask your child to say and spell as many words as he or she can think of that have that double consonant.

Spelling Workbook 4.4, p. 79

Name ______________________ Keepers

Spelling: Words with Double Consonants

≡ Make a capital.
/ Make a small letter.
∧ Add something.
Take out something.
⊙ Add a period.
¶ Begin a new paragraph.

Directions: Proofread this journal entry that tells a family history. Find five spelling mistakes. Use the proofreading marks to correct each mistake.

Our family comes from Puerto Rico. My grandparents grew letuce and other vegetables in their garden. They made wonderful food for super, and they taught my father how to make those dishes too. But when Papa makes them, they always taste a little different! Papa used to wery about that, but now he just laughs. "It doesn't mater," he says. "Maybe tomorow I'll get it right."

Spelling Tip

supper

Sometimes double consonants stand for one sound. For example, you hear the sound /p/ one time in supper. To help you remember to use a double consonant, think: I like **peas** for **supper.**

Word List

tomorrow	offer
borrow	suffer
different	slipper
supper	grasshopper
matter	worry
written	current
bottle	lettuce
ridden	paddle
odd	shudder
bubble	hobby

Write a Journal Entry

Think of an interesting story about your family's history. On a separate sheet of paper, write a journal entry telling the story. Try to use at least three spelling words.

Answers will vary, but each journal entry should include at least three spelling words.

Notes for Home: Your child spelled words with double consonants. **Home Activity:** Write each spelling word, but leave out the second letter of the double consonant. Ask your child to tell you which consonant should be doubled for each word.

Spelling Workbook 4.4, p. 80

Name ______________________ Keepers

Spelling: Words with Double Consonants

REVIEW

Word List

tomorrow	matter	odd	slipper	lettuce
borrow	written	bubble	grasshopper	paddle
different	bottle	offer	worry	shudder
supper	ridden	suffer	current	hobby

Directions: Unscramble the letters to form a word from the box. Write the word on the line.

1. tulcete	lettuce	7. trenruc	current
2. rwobor	borrow	8. tiferdenf	different
3. uedrhsd	shudder	9. termat	matter
4. prepils	slipper	10. lettob	bottle
5. fuserf	suffer	11. belbub	bubble
6. prasghorpes	grasshopper	12. lepadd	paddle

Directions: Choose the word from the box that best completes each sentence. Write the word on the line to the left.

tomorrow 13. I can't wait for the day after _____!

supper 14. That's when we'll eat _____ with my aunt.

written 15. She has _____ a book about our family history.

odd 16. She has done many _____ and unusual things.

ridden 17. For example, she has _____ on a camel in Egypt.

offer 18. I always _____ to help her cook when we visit.

worry 19. "Don't _____," she will say. "I like to cook!"

hobby 20. "In fact, it's my favorite _____."

Notes for Home: Your child spelled words with double consonants. **Home Activity:** With your child, think of some other words with double consonants, such as *coffee, lobby, add,* and *rubber.*

Practice Book 4.4, p. 199

Name ______________________ Keepers

Time Line

A **time line** is a special kind of chart that shows events in the order in which they happened or will happen. The bar of a time line is divided into units of time, such as months, years, or decades. It is labeled with the event.

Directions: Think of ten events that have become often-told family stories about you and your family, such as a camping trip to the Rockies or the birth of a little sister. Describe the events on the lines below. Tell how old you were for each event. Then figure out the year each event took place. Record the month the event took place, if you can. **Check that students have listed ten events with corresponding ages and dates.**

Family Events	My Age	Year/Month

Practice Book 4.4, p. 200

Name______________________________ Keepers

Directions: Use the bar below to make a time line of your family events. First, divide the bar into equal parts to show the number of years your time line will cover. For example, if your events cover a 10-year period, divide the bar into 10 equal parts. Then write the year (and month if you know it) that each event took place above the line. Write a short description of each event below the line. Draw lines connecting the labels to the bar. Make sure that the events and years match and that events are listed in the order in which they happened. **Check that dates and events are written in order on the time line.**

Notes for Home: Your child made a time line of family events. ***Home Activity:*** Tell your child some of your favorite family stories about special events. Together, make a time line of these events.

Name______________________________

How-to Chart

The How-to Chart should be filled out completely, although students may complete the Introduction and Conclusion at a later date.

Directions: Fill in the how-to chart with information about your project.

Explain task. ____________________

Materials ____________________

Introduction ____________________

Steps ____________________

Conclusion ____________________

Notes for Home: Your child has been preparing to write a how-to report. ***Home Activity:*** Ask your child to outline the steps in the process of a regular home activity, such as preparing for bed or playing a video game. Try it out. Are there any steps missing?

Name______________________________

Elaboration

Add Details

- When you write, you can elaborate by **adding vivid and specific** details that help readers picture your subject clearly.
- You can provide vivid and specific details by telling how things look, sound, feel, taste, and smell.

Directions: Read each sentence below. Pick words from the box to tell more about the process of making a book. Write your new sentences using the details.

unique	felt-tip	creative	wrapping
unusual	interesting	thick	special
hand-drawn	decorate	large	bright
cloth adhesive	small	thin	hard

Responses will vary. Reasonable answers are given.

1. You need paper for the pages.
You need thick paper for the pages.

2. Some cardboard will do for the covers.
Some hard cardboard will do for the covers.

3. You can cover your book with paper.
You can cover your book with wrapping paper.

4. Pictures will add life to your cover.
Hand-drawn pictures will add life to your cover.

5. Use pens to add different colors.
Use felt-tip pens to add different colors.

6. Hide the staples with tape.
Hide the staples with cloth adhesive tape.

Notes for Home: Your child expanded sentences by adding vivid and specific details. ***Home Activity:*** Discuss with your child how-to steps that occur in everyday life. Take turns giving examples and elaborating on the steps to make them as clear as possible.

Name______________________________

Self-Evaluation Guide

How-to Report

Students' responses should show that they have given thought to the how-to reports they have written.

Directions: Think about the final draft of your how-to report. Then answer each question below.

	Yes	No	Not sure
1. Are there any steps missing?			
2. Are all the steps in the right order?			
3. Are the steps clearly written and easy to follow?			
4. Did I provide all of the necessary information?			
5. Did I use words like *first* to indicate order?			
6. Did I proofread carefully for spelling, capitalization, and punctuation?			
7. Did I accomplish what I set out to accomplish?			
8. Did I learn anything new from this report?			

9. In what way would you improve your report if you rewrote it?

Notes for Home: Your child recently completed a self-evaluation of a writing assignment. ***Home Activity:*** Discuss the how-to report with your child. Consider the following questions: *What did you learn from the exercise? Are there other areas where this experience is applicable?*

Practice Book 4.5, p. 201

Name______

Amazing Alice!

Summarizing

- A **summary** gives the main ideas of an article, or it tells what happens in a story.
- A summary is short, and it doesn't include unimportant details.

Directions: Reread "Stagecoaches Then . . . and Now." Then complete the table. List details that belong with each topic. Then write a sentence summarizing the article. **Possible answers given.**

Topic	Summary
Movie image of stages vs. reality	Movie Image: exciting, almost always ambushed by robbers 1. Reality: **uneventful, dusty, tiring**
How stages began	2. **way to get mail and people from place to place**
How stages got name	3. **routes in "stages;" horses replaced about every 12 miles**
How stages made money	4. **mainly from mail; extra money from passengers**

Summary of Article

5. **Stagecoaches were an important means of transportation and mail delivery in the newly settled West, even if they weren't as exciting as modern movies make them look.**

Notes for Home: Your child read an article and summarized its main idea. ***Home Activity:*** Read an article from a children's magazine or watch a TV documentary with your child. Ask him or her to summarize the main idea.

Practice Book 4.5, p. 202

Name______

Amazing Alice!

Vocabulary

Directions: Choose the word from the box that best matches each definition. Write the word on the line.

Check the Words You Know
- __ blacksmith
- __ crank
- __ dependable
- __ forge
- __ ravines
- __ telegraph

ravines 1. deep, narrow valleys

telegraph 2. a way of sending coded messages over wires

crank 3. part of a machine that sets it in motion

blacksmith 4. ironworker

forge 5. blacksmith's shop

dependable 6. reliable

Directions: Read the help wanted ad. Choose the word from the box that best completes each sentence. Write the word on the matching numbered line.

Blacksmith Needed

We need a **7.** _____ person that can be trusted to work hard. The new blacksmith would work in the **8.** _____ with five other workers. You must be willing to travel across two deep **9.** _____ to get to work each day. If interested, please use a **10.** _____ to send your response because we don't have a telephone.

7. **dependable**
8. **forge**
9. **ravines**
10. **telegraph**

Write Dictionary Entries

Make dictionary entries for three of the vocabulary words. Each dictionary entry should have the word, a definition, and a picture. You may wish to look at pictures in a history book or encyclopedia. Pictures make the words easier to understand!
Students may need to do some research to find appropriate illustrations. They should define each vocabulary word correctly.

Notes for Home: Your child identified and used new vocabulary words from "Amazing Alice!" ***Home Activity:*** Work with your child to write a story about hiring a blacksmith to fix something for you.

Practice Book 4.5, p. 203

Name______

Amazing Alice!

Summarizing

- A **summary** is a short statement that tells the main idea of a selection, leaving out unimportant details.

Directions: Reread this passage from "Amazing Alice!" Then answer the questions below. Use what you know about summarizing.

There were only 20 more miles to go until we reached the ferry house at Oakland, where we would board a boat taking us across the wide, blue bay to San Francisco. Time sped by too quickly. We arrived at the Oakland boat dock within an hour after breakfast. Once on the ferry, we set the Maxwell's brakes and raced to the front end of the boat to watch San Francisco bobbing in the water. Great golliwogs! To think that those same Pacific Ocean waves touch the shores of the Chinese Empire!

Our ferry slid out into the bay. Gulls were squawking like New York street vendors. Buoys were clanging. We heard foghorns hoot, though there was no fog. The other passengers seemed very excited to get a look at the Maxwell and us. Who told them I don't know, but everyone knew where we were from and what Alice had done. We did not have a single quiet moment, as every rider wanted to congratulate us.

Possible answers given.

1. Why isn't the following sentence a good example of a summary for the first paragraph? *It was 20 more miles to the ferry house.*
It tells a detail, but it does not tell the main idea.

2. Write a summary of the first paragraph.
In Oakland, the women boarded a ferry for San Francisco.

3. Is the following sentence a good summary of the second paragraph? Explain. *The ferry boat ride was noisy.*
No. It does not give the main idea.

4. What is the main idea of the second paragraph?
The other passengers wanted to congratulate the Maxwell's passengers.

5. On a separate sheet of paper, write a summary of "Amazing Alice!"
Students' summaries should focus on the main ideas of the selection.

Notes for Home: Your child used story details to summarize a passage. ***Home Activity:*** Take turns with your child reading short articles from a newspaper or magazine and summarizing them. Decide what is the main idea of each article and what are unimportant details.

Practice Book 4.5, p. 205

Name______

Amazing Alice!

Selection Test

Directions: Choose the best answer to each item. Mark the letter for the answer you have chosen.

Part 1: Vocabulary

Find the answer choice that means about the same as the underlined word in each sentence.

1. He will telegraph his answer.
   - (A) send a message by wire
   - B. look for
   - C. watch from a distance
   - D. join

2. Joan is a dependable person.
   - F. interesting
   - (G) able to be counted on
   - H. clever
   - J. funny or amusing

3. This is the crank.
   - A. sheet of metal
   - B. type of map
   - C. a narrow bridge
   - (D) handle on a machine

4. He found a blacksmith.
   - (F) ironworker
   - G. storyteller
   - H. driver
   - J. news reporter

5. Tell us about the ravines.
   - A. strong winds
   - B. small streams
   - C. words of praise
   - (D) deep, narrow valleys

6. The forge is open now.
   - F. place to cross a river
   - G. shelter or station
   - (H) shop for metal work
   - J. place for meetings

Part 2: Comprehension

Use what you know about the selection to answer each item.

7. Alice was the first woman to—
   - (A) drive across the country.
   - B. own a car.
   - C. fix cars for a living.
   - D. enter a contest.

8. This selection is written as if it were told by—
   - F. Alice.
   - (G) Minna.
   - H. Maggie.
   - J. Nettie.

GO ON

Practice Book 4.5, p. 206
Name ____________________ **Amazing Alice!**

9. How did Minna feel about Alice?
   A. She was jealous of her.
   B. She thought she was strange.
   (C) She admired her.
   D. She thought she was bossy.
10. What did the women learn about the "Blue Book"?
   F. It was easy to use.
   (G) Parts of it were out of date.
   H. It had very good maps.
   J. Most of it was about the West.
11. Which sentence best summarizes what happened in Wyoming?
   (A) The women walked across a railroad bridge to get a permit to drive across it.
   B. The bridge across the river had been washed away.
   C. A train came along while the women were crossing the trestle bridge.
   D. Alice got a case of "jolt-itis."
12. The entries in this journal tell mostly about—
   F. what Alice was like.
   G. how the women got along.
   (H) the challenges of the trip.
   J. how homesick Minna felt.
13. Which sentence best summarizes this selection?
   A. Alice drove over a prairie dog hole and broke an axle.
   (B) Alice Ramsey and three other women drove across the United States in 59 days.
   C. Alice and her friends drove all day and stayed in a different hotel every night.
   D. Alice drove the car and told Minna what to write in her journal.
14. Which sentence gives an opinion?
   F. "There were only 20 more miles to go."
   (G) "Time sped by too quickly."
   H. "We arrived at the Oakland boat dock."
   J. "Our ferry slid out into the bay."
15. What made Alice an unusual woman for her time?
   A. She was smart.
   B. She had a good friend.
   C. She liked traveling.
   (D) She was an expert driver.

Name ____________________ **Amazing Alice!**

Summarizing

- A **summary** is a short statement that tells the main idea of a selection, leaving out unimportant details.

Directions: Read the passage below.

In the summer of 1899, William K. Vanderbilt and his new bride arrived in Newport, Rhode Island. But the Vanderbilts did not stay long in Newport. It was all because of William K. Vanderbilt's motor car. The people of Newport didn't like it. That's because he liked to drive fast. Sometimes he drove as fast as a train, people said.

Newport leaders set speed limits. Did that slow Vanderbilt down? Not a chance. The wealthy Vanderbilt was willing to pay the fines for going fast.

Vanderbilt and his wife left Newport in 1901 for Long Island. Here, Vanderbilt came up with the idea for the nation's first international auto race and also built a road especially for cars.

Directions: Complete the table by listing important details for each paragraph. Then write a summary of the passage. **Possible answers given.**

Paragraph	Story Details
Paragraph 1	**1. The people of Newport didn't like Vanderbilt's car.**
Paragraph 2	**2. Newport leaders set speed limits.**
	3. Vanderbilt was willing to pay the fines.
Paragraph 3	**4. The Vanderbilts moved to Long Island where Vanderbilt held auto races.**

Summary
5. William K. Vanderbilt liked to drive fast. The people in Newport, where he lived, didn't like it and set speed limits. Vanderbilt just paid the fines. Then he and his wife moved to Long Island, where he held auto races.

Notes for Home: Your child identified important details of a passage and used them to write a summary of the passage's main idea. ***Home Activity:*** With your child, read a short article from a newspaper or magazine. Underline important details and use them to write a short summary.

Practice Book 4.5, p. 207
Name ____________________ **Amazing Alice!**

Graphic Sources

REVIEW

Directions: Read the passage and look at the bar graph. Then read each question about the passage and the bar graph. Choose the best answer to each question. Mark the letter for the answer you have chosen.

Henry Ford's Car

In 1903, Ford Motor Company sold its first car. But real success came in 1908, with the Model T car.

Then in 1913, Ford's assembly line greatly cut the time it took to make a Model T car. The price also kept coming down. By the mid-1920s, many working people could afford a Model T car and the company's sales soared.

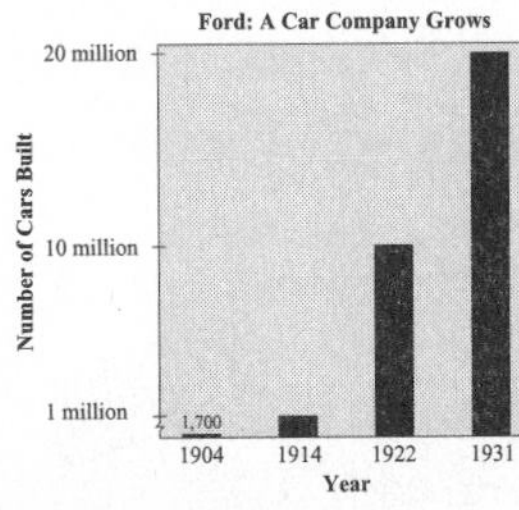

1. Ford Motor Company built its millionth car in—
   (A) 1914.
   B. 1922.
   C 1908.
   D. 1931.
2. About how many cars did Ford build in 1922?
   F. 1,000
   G. 1 million
   (H) 10 million
   J. 20 million
3. The price of the Model T car dropped because of—
   (A) the assembly line.
   B. the Depression.
   C. cheaper materials.
   D. their bumpy ride.
4. How long after it built its 10 millionth car did Ford build its 20 millionth car?
   F. about 20 years
   (G) about 10 years
   H. only one year
   J. 31 years later
5. In what year did the Ford Motor Company build its 30 millionth car?
   A. 1933
   B. 1943
   C. 1922
   (D) can't tell from facts given

Notes for Home: Your child read a passage and interpreted a bar graph. ***Home Activity:*** Look for graphs in the newspaper with your child. Take turns asking one another questions based on information in the graph. Discuss how you used the graph to answer each question.

Name ____________________ **Amazing Alice!**

Writing Across Texts

Directions: Think about the journal entries in *Amazing Alice!* Take the information from one day of Hermine's journal of her trip with Alice Ramsey and put it onto a journal page similar to one from "Keeping a Road Journal."

Possible Answers

1. Date: **June 24, 1909**
2. Time: **9:00 PM**
3. Location: **Mechanicsville, Iowa**
4. Weather: **rainy**
5. What happened today: **It started to rain hard this afternoon. We spent time in a livery stable with the horses, while waiting for the rain to stop. This evening, Alice has been entertaining the hotel guests with her piano playing.**

Write an Essay

On a separate sheet of paper, write an essay describing the kinds of things you can learn from reading stories that are set in other times and places. Use details from your road journal entry and other stories you've read as examples. **Essays will vary. Check that students use details from their road journal entries as examples.**

Notes for Home: Your child thought about how the details in a story tie to the unit's theme, "Journeys in Time and Space." ***Home Activity:*** When watching television shows or movies set in other times and places, talk about things you can learn from these shows and movies.

Grammar Practice Book 4.5, p. 101

Name______________________ Amazing Alice!

Grammar: Possessive Nouns and Pronouns

REVIEW

Directions: Make each underlined noun possessive. Write the possessive noun on the line.

1. that car color **car's**
2. the people choice **people's**
3. Bess bicycle **Bess's**
4. his parents automobile **parents'**
5. the child tricycle **child's**

Directions: Underline each possessive pronoun. Write **S** above the pronoun if it is singular. Write **P** if it is plural.

6. Rosa, do you have your (S) ticket to the car show?
7. My (S) family drove there in our (P) old jalopy.
8. Many people showed off their (P) antique cars.
9. Tina found the car of her (S) dreams.
10. Bryan, however, preferred his (S) motorcycle.

Directions: Circle the correct word in ( ) to complete each sentence.

11. Does that red car belong to (you're/**your**) parents?
12. No, that is my cousin (Iris/**Iris's**) car.
13. She set up her (**baby's**/babies) car seat in the back.
14. The dog lies on (it's/**its**) pillow in the front.
15. Her passengers will have to look around for (they/**their**) own place to sit.

Notes for Home: Your child used possessive nouns and pronouns—nouns and pronouns that show ownership. ***Home Activity:*** Point to things around the house. Have your child use possessive nouns and pronouns to tell who owns each object.

Grammar: Possessive Nouns and Pronouns 463

Grammar Practice Book 4.5, p. 102

Name______________________ Amazing Alice!

Grammar: Pronouns

Pronouns are words that replace nouns or noun phrases. *I, you, he, she, it, me, him,* and *her* are singular pronouns. *We, you, they, us,* and *them* are plural pronouns. The singular pronoun *I* is always capitalized.

Scruffy likes to ride in the car.
She is the first to jump into it when we go for a drive.

Directions: Underline each singular pronoun once and each plural pronoun twice.

1. Jane said she wanted to bike all the way to Maine.
2. We told Jane the idea was foolish and dangerous.
3. Jane said it wasn't dangerous; five other high school students and two gym teachers would be in the group.
4. "Just call us if you find the trip too hard," Mom told Jane.
5. "Call me collect anytime," Dad added.
6. Jane just smiled. "I won't need to do it," she said.
7. "You say so *now*," Dad pointed out.
8. "I know you all mean well," Jane said.
9. "However, I am a big girl now, and we will be careful."
10. "Well, stay alert and be sure you call home every night," Mom directed.

Directions: Choose a pronoun in ( ) to replace each underlined noun or noun phrase. Write the pronoun on the line.

She 11. Jane did call us every night. (She/I)
them 12. She spoke to Mom and Dad. (us/them)
her 13. They gave Jane advice. (her/it)
her 14. Jane listened to Mom. (her/me)
him 15. Jane listened to Dad too. (them/him)

Notes for Home: Your child identified singular and plural pronouns and wrote pronouns. ***Home Activity:*** Name objects and people and have your child suggest pronouns for them.

464 Grammar: Pronouns

Grammar Practice Book 4.5, p. 103

Name______________________ Amazing Alice!

Grammar: Pronouns

Directions: Choose a pronoun in ( ) to replace each underlined noun or noun phrase. Write the pronoun on the line.

it 1. I couldn't wait to go on vacation in our new mobile home. (it/them)
They 2. Our next-door neighbors had fun going on a trip last year. (We/They)
them 3. Somebody had given our neighbors many good suggestions. (us/them)
us 4. They passed the suggestions on to my family and me. (it/us)
We 5. My family and I made sure we didn't drive too far in a single day. (We/They)
It 6. The trip was very interesting. (I/It)
She 7. Mom found some shorter routes. (She/They)
He 8. My brother found campsites. (He/They)
She 9. My sister just had fun. (She/We)
They 10. Mom and Dad say that next year we'll feel like expert travelers. (We/They)

Write a Postcard

On a separate sheet of paper, write a postcard to a friend about a trip you have taken. The trip can be a real one or one you have imagined. Make sure you use some pronouns as well as nouns. Circle all the pronouns you use.

Students should use pronouns as well as nouns in writing about their real or imaginary travels. Check to be sure that each pronoun is circled.

Notes for Home: Your child used pronouns to replace nouns. ***Home Activity:*** Think of one or more people or objects in the room. Give a pronoun, such as *they,* and play a questions game with your child to identify those people or objects.

Grammar: Pronouns 465

Grammar Practice Book 4.5, p. 104

Name______________________ Amazing Alice!

Grammar: Pronouns

RETEACHING

Read the sentences. Arrows connect each pronoun with a noun.

Eli plants seeds. He likes to plant them.

1. Write the pronoun that stands for the noun Eli. **He**
2. Write the pronoun that stands for the noun seeds. **them**

A **pronoun** takes the place of a noun or nouns. Singular pronouns are **I, you, she, he, it, me, her,** and **him.** Plural pronouns are **we, you, they, us,** and **them.**

Directions: Circle the pronoun in each sentence.

1. (**I**) carry some tools for Flo.
2. (**We**) ask the teacher for the small rake.
3. (**She**) does not have the rake.
4. Flo asks (**her**) for the vegetable seeds.
5. The teacher gives (**them**) to Flo.

Directions: Write the correct pronoun to stand for each underlined noun.

he you they them her

6. Eli planted seeds. **He** enjoyed the work.
7. Janet wanted to help. Eli gave **her** pepper seeds.
8. Janet took the seeds. She planted **them** in the ground.
9. Bill and Tanya watched. **They** held water buckets.
10. Eli said to Tanya, "Now **you** can water the plants."

Notes for Home: Your child identified and wrote pronouns in sentences. ***Home Activity:*** Read a news article with your child. Have him or her point out the pronouns and use three of them in new sentences.

466 Grammar: Pronouns

Grammar Practice Book 4.5, p. 105

Name______________________________ Amazing Alice!

Grammar: Pronouns

Directions: Circle six pronouns in the puzzle. Then write the pronouns in the sentences to replace the words in ( ).

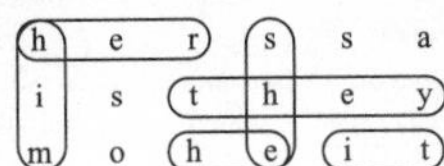

1. (Marla and Joe) live in the Painted Desert. **They**
2. (The Painted Desert) is beautiful. **It**
3. (Marla) likes the colors of the desert. **She**
4. I bring (Marla) colored sand. **her**
5. (Joe) likes the weather in the desert. **He**
6. We ask (Joe) questions. **him**

Directions: Write a pronoun to complete each sentence.

My family traveled to the Painted Desert. 7. **We** marveled at the animal life. Lizards and toads moved along the ground near 8. **us**. 9. **They** are strange creatures. My father spotted some bats high above 10. **us** last night. 11. **He** exclaimed, 12. "**I** watched 13. **them**. 14. **They** can fly very fast!"

Write a Short Description

On a separate sheet of paper, write a short description of a place you have read about. Use pronouns in your sentences to avoid repeating nouns.

Check that students use correct pronouns in their descriptions.

Notes for Home: Your child identified and wrote pronouns in sentences. ***Home Activity:*** Have your child write about a trip your family has taken. Challenge him or her to use pronouns to avoid repeating nouns.

Practice Book 4.5, p. 208

Name______________________________ Amazing Alice!

Word Study: Prefixes

Directions: Letters added to the beginning of words are called **prefixes.** Prefixes can change the meaning of the base word. Add the prefix to each word below to make a new word. Write each new word on the line.

	Prefix		Base Word		New Word
1.	dis	+	obey	=	**disobey**
2.	re	+	paint	=	**repaint**
3.	mis	+	lead	=	**mislead**
4.	un	+	hooked	=	**unhooked**
5.	il	+	logical	=	**illogical**

Directions: Read the journal entry below. Look for words with the prefix: **dis-, re, mis-, un-, il-, sub-, en-,** or **in-.** Circle each word and write it on the line.

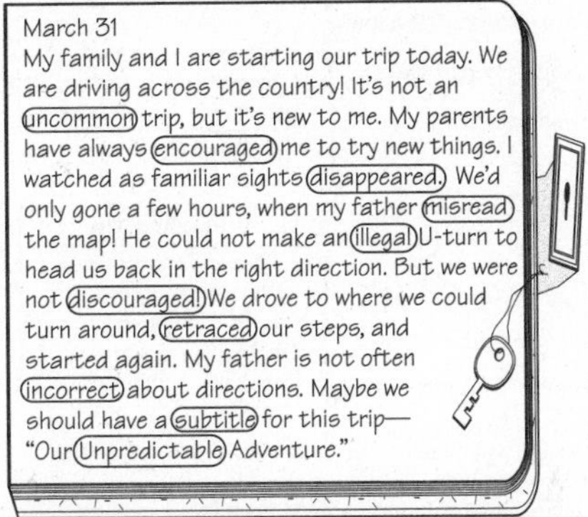

March 31
My family and I are starting our trip today. We are driving across the country! It's not an uncommon trip, but it's new to me. My parents have always encouraged me to try new things. I watched as familiar sights disappeared. We'd only gone a few hours, when my father misread the map! He could not make an illegal U-turn to head us back in the right direction. But we were not discouraged! We drove to where we could turn around, retraced our steps, and started again. My father is not often incorrect about directions. Maybe we should have a subtitle for this trip— "Our Unpredictable Adventure."

6. **uncommon**
7. **encouraged**
8. **disappeared**
9. **misread**
10. **illegal**
11. **discouraged**
12. **retraced**
13. **incorrect**
14. **subtitle**
15. **Unpredictable**

Notes for Home: Your child wrote and identified words with prefixes, such as *disappear (dis + appear).* ***Home Activity:*** Read a newspaper story with your child. Work together to find words with the prefixes listed above.

Spelling Workbook 4.5, p. 81

Name______________________________ Amazing Alice!

Spelling: Prefixes *dis-, in-, mis-, re-*

Pretest Directions: Fold back the page along the dotted line. On the blanks, write the spelling words as they are dictated. When you have finished the test, unfold the page and check your words.

1. **dislike**	1. She doesn't **dislike** anyone.
2. **disappear**	2. He made the food **disappear**.
3. **distrust**	3. Don't **distrust** people too much.
4. **dishonest**	4. Lying is **dishonest**.
5. **disagree**	5. I **disagree** with that.
6. **incomplete**	6. This collection is **incomplete**.
7. **independent**	7. She is an **independent** girl.
8. **incorrect**	8. This answer is **incorrect**.
9. **invisible**	9. The crack is almost **invisible**.
10. **inactive**	10. The volcano is **inactive** now.
11. **misplace**	11. I never **misplace** my homework.
12. **misspell**	12. Did I **misspell** your name?
13. **misled**	13. Their lies **misled** the jury.
14. **mistreat**	14. Don't **mistreat** the dog.
15. **misbehave**	15. Babies, don't **misbehave**!
16. **rebuild**	16. We need to **rebuild** our house.
17. **reuse**	17. I can **reuse** this jar.
18. **react**	18. How should you **react** to that?
19. **replace**	19. Please **replace** the light bulb.
20. **recall**	20. He can't **recall** what happened.

Notes for Home: Your child took a pretest on words that begin with *dis-, in-, mis-,* and *re-.* ***Home Activity:*** Help your child learn misspelled words before the final test. Your child should look at the word, say it, spell it aloud, and then spell it with eyes shut.

Spelling Workbook 4.5, p. 82

Name______________________________ Amazing Alice!

Spelling: Prefixes *dis-, in-, mis-, re-*

Word List

dislike	incomplete	misplace	rebuild
disappear	independent	misspell	reuse
distrust	incorrect	misled	react
dishonest	invisible	mistreat	replace
disagree	inactive	misbehave	recall

Directions: Add the prefix **dis-, in-, mis-,** or **re-** to each base word to form a word from the box. Write the word on the line.

1. appear **disappear**
2. call **recall**
3. place **misplace**
4. active **inactive**
5. visible **invisible**
6. like **dislike**
7. correct **incorrect**
8. honest **dishonest**
9. dependent **independent**
10. use **reuse**
11. build **rebuild**
12. spell **misspell**
13. treat **mistreat**
14. complete **incomplete**

Directions: Choose the word from the box that best replaces the underlined word or words. Write the word on the line.

distrust 15. I <u>don't trust</u> Billy.

replace 16. Why didn't he <u>put back</u> the toy car that he broke?

misled 17. I don't know why he <u>deceived</u> us.

misbehave 18. Why does he always <u>behave badly</u>?

react 19. Maybe I shouldn't <u>respond</u> so strongly.

disagree 20. After all, he and I always <u>think different things</u>.

Notes for Home: Your child spelled words with the prefixes *dis-, in-, mis-,* and *re-.* ***Home Activity:*** Make up a matching game. Write the prefixes from the lesson on one set of cards and the base words on another. Have your child match the cards to make words *(dis- + like = dislike).*

Spelling Workbook 4.5, p. 83

Name______________________________ Amazing Alice!

Spelling: Prefixes *dis-*, *in-*, *mis-*, *re-*

Directions: Proofread this ad for car repair. Find five spelling mistakes. Use the proofreading marks to correct each mistake.

- ≡ Make a capital.
- / Make a small letter.
- ∧ Add something.
- Take out something.
- ⊙ Add a period.
- ¶ Begin a new paragraph.

Joseph's Complete Auto Repair

Don't be missled by other repair shops. Don't distrust us just because you have had bad service elsewhere. Don't settle for inncomplete work. We will rplace any bad part at a low cost. We will rebild any part we can. We will make your worries dissappear.

Word List

dislike	misplace
disappear	misspell
distrust	misled
dishonest	mistreat
disagree	misbehave
incomplete	rebuild
independent	reuse
incorrect	react
invisible	replace
inactive	recall

Spelling Tip

When prefixes **dis-**, **in-**, **mis-**, and **re-** are added to words, make no change in the spelling of the base word: **dis-** + **like** = **dislike.**

Write an Ad

On a separate sheet of paper, write your own ad for a car dealership, repair shop, car wash, or other car-related business. Try to use at least three spelling words.

Answers will vary, but each ad should include at least three spelling words.

Notes for Home: Your child spelled words with the prefixes *dis-*, *in-*, *mis-*, and *re-*. ***Home Activity:*** Give your child clues about the meaning of each spelling word. Have him or her guess the word as quickly as possible.

Spelling Workbook 4.5, p. 84

Name______________________________ Amazing Alice!

Spelling: Prefixes *dis-*, *in-*, *mis-*, *re-* REVIEW

Word List

dislike	disagree	invisible	misled	reuse
disappear	incomplete	inactive	mistreat	react
distrust	independent	misplace	misbehave	replace
dishonest	incorrect	misspell	rebuild	recall

Directions: Choose the word from the box that is the most opposite in meaning for each word or words below. Write the word on the line.

1. appear **disappear**
2. treat well **mistreat**
3. find **misplace**
4. successfully guided **misled**
5. relying on someone **independent**
6. agree **disagree**
7. complete **incomplete**
8. easily seen **invisible**
9. write correctly **misspell**
10. active **inactive**
11. act properly **misbehave**
12. like **dislike**

Directions: Choose the word from the box that best completes each sentence. Write the word on the line to the left.

react 13. You _____ negatively about all mechanics.

dishonest 14. Not every car-repair shop is _____.

recall 15. Do you _____ the shop we used in June?

distrust 16. You were ready to _____ everything they said.

incorrect 17. You worried that they were _____ about what was wrong.

rebuild 18. But they were able to _____ the engine using good parts.

reuse 19. They were able to _____ a crank shaft from another car.

replace 20. They were also able to _____ the old battery with a new one.

Notes for Home: Your child spelled words with the prefixes *dis-*, *in-*, *mis-*, and *re-*. ***Home Activity:*** Take turns with your child naming and spelling other words that use the same prefixes.

Practice Book 4.5, p. 209

Name______________________________ Amazing Alice!

Technology: Manual

A **manual** is a written set of directions, usually in the form of a booklet or book, that helps readers understand or use something. To understand a manual, you need to know how to follow directions.

Directions: The *Everyday Spelling* CD-ROM contains lessons, games, and activities that can help you learn to spell. Use this page from the manual to answer the questions on the next page.

The *Everyday Spelling* textbook program consists of weekly spelling lessons, review lessons, and cross-cultural lessons. The lockers ("cubbies" in grades 1 and 2) on this screen represent lessons. Selecting locker 1, for example, lets you use the words from Lesson 1. Move the cursor to a number and click on it to choose the words you will use.

Lockers numbered 1–5, 7–11, 13–17, 19–23, 25–29, and 31–35 will take you to the Classroom area, where you will work with that lesson's spelling words. Every sixth lesson is a review lesson. Lockers numbered 6, 12, 18, 24, 30, and 36 will take you to the Testing Center, where you will work with spelling words in review lessons.

Note: In grade 1 there are no spelling lessons 1–6.

Practice Book 4.5, p. 210

Name______________________________ Amazing Alice!

1. What are three different kinds of lessons in the textbook program?
weekly spelling lessons, review lessons, and cross-curricular lessons

2. What does each locker represent? **Each locker represents a lesson.**

3. How can you get to the spelling words for Lesson 5? **Move the cursor to locker 5 and click on it.**

4. Which locker would you click on if you wanted to review spelling words for Lessons 1–5?
locker 6

5. Clicking on lockers will take you to two different areas to work with spelling words. To what two areas can you go?
Classroom area, Testing Center

6. When you click on locker 22, what will happen? **You will go to the Classroom area to work with the spelling words for Lesson 22.**

7. When you click on locker 12, what will happen?
You will go to the Testing Center for a review lesson for Lessons 7–11.

8. Which lessons are review lessons? **6, 12, 18, 24, 30, and 36**

9. Why do you think the manual shows the program's computer screens?
Possible answer: Using pictures of computer screens shows you what you will see and makes the instructions more clear.

10. Why is it important to know how to follow directions to use a manual?
Since manuals are a set of written directions, you need to know how to follow directions to understand and use a manual correctly.

Notes for Home: Your child read a manual for a CD-ROM program and answered questions about it. ***Home Activity:*** Find a user's manual for an appliance or a computer program. Look through the manual with your child and discuss the kinds of information that can be found in it.

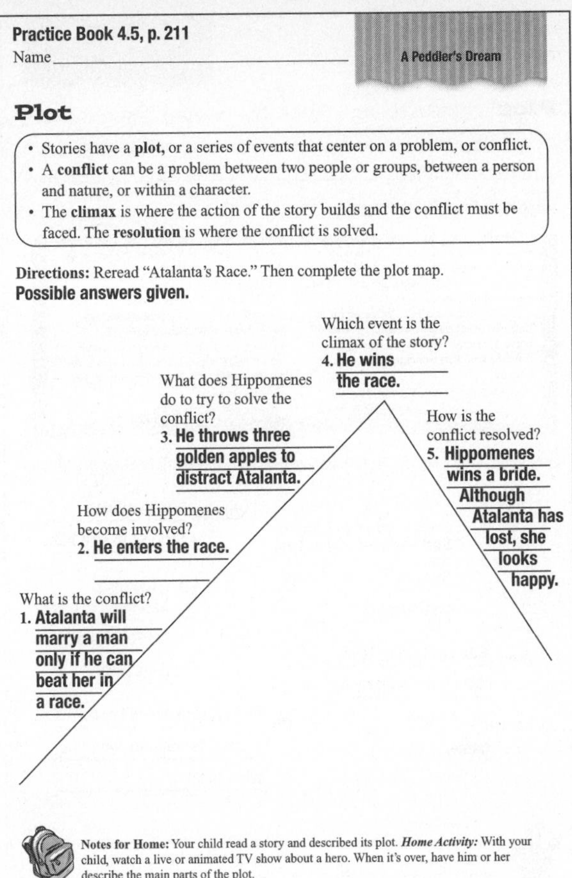

Practice Book 4.5, p. 211
Name______________________________ A Peddler's Dream

Plot

- Stories have a **plot**, or a series of events that center on a problem, or conflict.
- A **conflict** can be a problem between two people or groups, between a person and nature, or within a character.
- The **climax** is where the action of the story builds and the conflict must be faced. The **resolution** is where the conflict is solved.

Directions: Reread "Atalanta's Race." Then complete the plot map.
Possible answers given.

What is the conflict?
1. **Atalanta will marry a man only if he can beat her in a race.**

How does Hippomenes become involved?
2. **He enters the race.**

What does Hippomenes do to try to solve the conflict?
3. **He throws three golden apples to distract Atalanta.**

Which event is the climax of the story?
4. **He wins the race.**

How is the conflict resolved?
5. **Hippomenes wins a bride. Although Atalanta has lost, she looks happy.**

Notes for Home: Your child read a story and described its plot. *Home Activity:* With your child, watch a live or animated TV show about a hero. When it's over, have him or her describe the main parts of the plot.

Plot 477

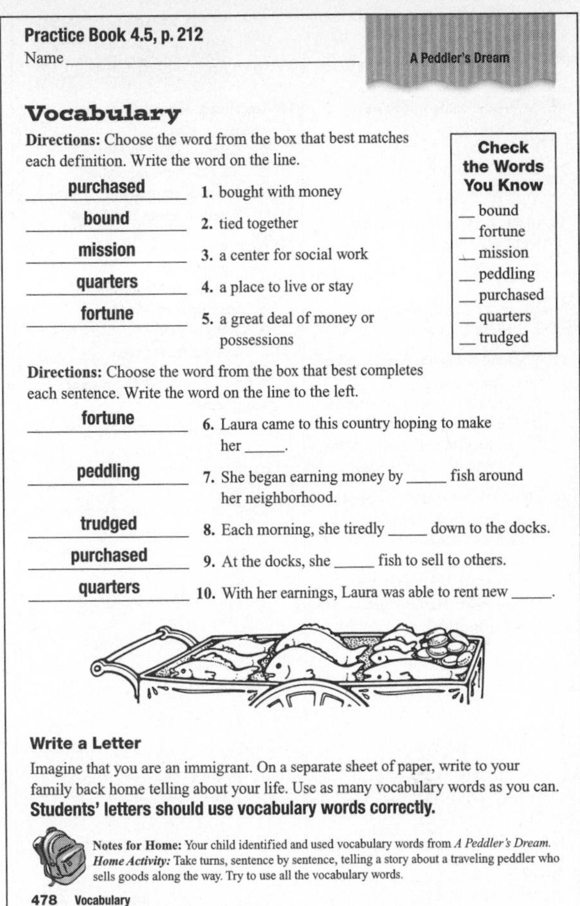

Practice Book 4.5, p. 212
Name______________________________ A Peddler's Dream

Vocabulary

Directions: Choose the word from the box that best matches each definition. Write the word on the line.

Check the Words You Know
__ bound
__ fortune
__ mission
__ peddling
__ purchased
__ quarters
__ trudged

purchased 1. bought with money
bound 2. tied together
mission 3. a center for social work
quarters 4. a place to live or stay
fortune 5. a great deal of money or possessions

Directions: Choose the word from the box that best completes each sentence. Write the word on the line to the left.

fortune 6. Laura came to this country hoping to make her _____.
peddling 7. She began earning money by _____ fish around her neighborhood.
trudged 8. Each morning, she tiredly _____ down to the docks.
purchased 9. At the docks, she _____ fish to sell to others.
quarters 10. With her earnings, Laura was able to rent new _____.

Write a Letter

Imagine that you are an immigrant. On a separate sheet of paper, write to your family back home telling about your life. Use as many vocabulary words as you can.
Students' letters should use vocabulary words correctly.

Notes for Home: Your child identified and used vocabulary words from *A Peddler's Dream*. *Home Activity:* Take turns, sentence by sentence, telling a story about a traveling peddler who sells goods along the way. Try to use all the vocabulary words.

478 Vocabulary

Practice Book 4.5, p. 213
Name______________________________ A Peddler's Dream

Plot

- A story's **plot** is the important parts of a story. These parts include the conflict, or problem, the climax, and the resolution, or outcome.

Directions: Reread this passage from *A Peddler's Dream* in which Solomon wakes up to the noise of fire trucks. Then answer the questions below.

Late one night the clanging of fire trucks awakened him. He jumped from bed and looked out the window. A red glow filled the sky over State House Avenue.

"The store! Marie, it's the store!" he cried.

"Oh, Solomon," she gasped. "It can't be."

Hurriedly he pulled on his trousers and ran out the door.

But it was the store. As Solomon stood watching it burn, Marie joined him, clutching Isaac and Nora by the hand. Rebecca and Ruth were right behind, their eyes big.

"Papa," cried Rebecca, with tears running down her cheeks, "it's ruined. Our nice store is all ruined."

Solomon put one arm around her shoulders, the other around Marie. "Yes, Rebecca, ruined but not finished."

Solomon was true to his word. He rented temporary quarters and purchased new merchandise. In two weeks he reopened for business with a fire sale on the sidewalk.

1. Who are the characters in this passage?
The characters are Solomon and his family.

2. What is the problem these characters have?
There is a fire at Solomon's store.

3. What important thing does Solomon say that shows how he will face the problem?
He says that the store is ruined but not finished.

4. How is the problem solved?
He reopens for business with a fire sale.

5. What if Solomon chose to solve the problem differently? On a separate sheet of paper, write a new ending for this passage. **Check that students' endings follow logically from story events.**

Notes for Home: Your child used story details to identify the plot of a story. *Home Activity:* Read a short folk tale with your child and have him or her identify its most important parts. Discuss the problem that is central to the story and how this problem is resolved.

Plot 479

Practice Book 4.5, p. 215
Name______________________________ A Peddler's Dream

Selection Test

Directions: Choose the best answer to each item. Mark the letter for the answer you have chosen.

Part 1: Vocabulary

Find the answer choice that means about the same as the underlined word in each sentence.

1. She wants to make her fortune.
   A. strong statement
   B. wish for good luck
   (C) large amount of money or property
   D. place built with walls

2. Let's go to the mission.
   F. store that sells many goods
   G. gathering place for travelers
   (H) center for religious or social work
   J. large, stately house

3. His hands were bound.
   (A) tied together
   B. hurt or wounded
   C. icy cold
   D. clasped or folded

4. The children trudged inside.
   F. moved in a group
   G. stumbled and fell
   H. stayed or remained
   (J) walked slowly with effort

5. He earned money by peddling.
   A. riding a bicycle
   (B) carrying and selling goods
   C. fixing things
   D. writing letters

6. We have new quarters.
   F. problems or worries
   G. dream or plan
   (H) place to live or work in
   J. work done by a shopkeeper

7. She purchased some cloth.
   A. made clothes from
   (B) bought
   C. had need of
   D. saved

Part 2: Comprehension

Use what you know about the story to answer each item.

8. Solomon went to America to—
   F. find a wife.
   G. learn to speak English.
   H. explore new lands.
   (J) make his fortune.

480 Selection Test

Practice Book 4.5, p. 216

Name____________________ A Peddler's Dream

9. At first Solomon worked as a—
   A. store clerk.
   (B) peddler.
   C. farmer.
   D. builder.

10. In this story, Solomon faced the problem of how to—
   F. marry a rich woman.
   G. become governor of his state.
   (H) own his own store.
   J. return to Lebanon for good.

11. What did Solomon do after working two years at Hart's?
   A. became the owner of Joseph's
   B. built a house for himself
   (C) returned to Lebanon for Marie
   D. became Mr. Hart's partner

12. More and more people shopped at Hart's Dry Goods when Solomon worked there because he—
   F. lowered the prices.
   (G) made the store run better.
   H. asked Mr. Hart to retire.
   J. told his friends to shop there.

13. The climax of this story comes when—
   A. Solomon lands in America.
   B. Mr. Hart hires Solomon.
   (C) Joseph's burns down.
   D. Solomon opens a new store.

14. What was most important to Solomon's success?
   (F) believing in his dream
   G. learning from Mr. Hart
   H. living in a city
   J. meeting the governor

15. In what way was the fire a good thing for Solomon?
   A. It gave him time to rest from work.
   B. It made people feel sorry for him.
   (C) It gave him a chance to build the store he wanted.
   D. It made him more careful about preventing fires.

Name____________________ A Peddler's Dream

Plot

- A story's **plot** is the important parts of a story. These parts include the conflict, or problem, the climax, and the resolution, or outcome.

Directions: Read the story below.

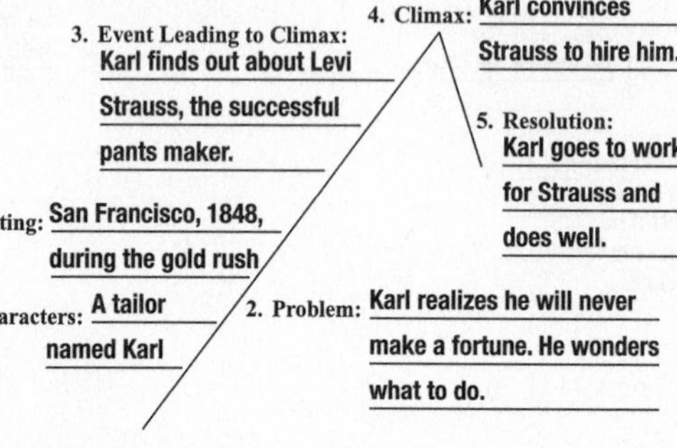

When gold was discovered in California in 1848, Karl was a tailor in San Francisco. Suddenly people left their work and rushed to the gold fields. Karl bought mining tools and went with the others.

After a year and a half of digging for gold, Karl was tired and discouraged. He had not found a fortune. He made just enough to feed himself. Karl wondered if he should keep on.

One day, while Karl was buying work pants, the storekeeper said, "That Levi Strauss is really something. He makes the best work pants!" Karl asked what the man meant. "I can't keep enough in stock!"

Karl was excited. He found Levi Strauss in his small San Francisco pants factory and convinced him that Strauss needed his tailoring skills. Karl sold his miner's tools and went to work making sturdy work pants called *denims* or *jeans*. He was successful, as was Strauss's factory.

Directions: Add story details to complete the plot map. **Possible answers given.**

1. Setting: **San Francisco, 1848, during the gold rush**

Characters: **A tailor named Karl**

2. Problem: **Karl realizes he will never make a fortune. He wonders what to do.**

3. Event Leading to Climax: **Karl finds out about Levi Strauss, the successful pants maker.**

4. Climax: **Karl convinces Strauss to hire him.**

5. Resolution: **Karl goes to work for Strauss and does well.**

Notes for Home: Your child used a plot map to describe the important parts of a story. ***Home Activity:*** Use a plot map to plan a story with your child. Decide what problems your characters will face and how they will solve them.

Practice Book 4.5, p. 217

Name____________________ A Peddler's Dream

Visualizing

REVIEW

Directions: Read the story. Then read each question about the story. Choose the best answer to each question. Mark the letter for the answer you have chosen.

Across the Border

July 4, 1976. Pedro was in the car, heading up the west coast. He gazed at the ocean waves crashing against the shore. Just last week, he had been living across the border in Mexico with his aunt. Then his mother had come to take Pedro and his sister, Pilar, to California. They were all going to live in America.

Pedro could hardly sit still. He imagined his new home with the whitewashed walls, the picket fence, and the yard with chickens. He could smell his mother's cooking.

The car headed away from the coast. It climbed through some hills. Then it went down into a small valley.

The sky darkened. Pedro heard a booming noise. To the right he saw brilliant flashes of color sparkle in the night sky. What a way to celebrate his coming to America!

1. In the car, Pedro—
   A. gets carsick.
   (**B.**) sees the ocean.
   C. sees Mexico.
   D. spots his new home.

2. When Pedro imagines his new home, he—
   F. wants to return to Mexico.
   (**G.**) feels excited.
   H. laughs at his mother.
   J. tells Pilar.

3. The car ride was probably—
   A. uncomfortable.
   (**B.**) interesting.
   C. frightening.
   D. boring.

4. Pedro's new home is probably in—
   F. an apartment building.
   G. the city.
   H. a suburban house.
   (**J.**) the country.

5. The booming noise Pedro hears and the colorful sparkles of light are—
   A. signs of danger.
   B. signs of a thunderstorm.
   (**C.**) fireworks.
   D. especially created for Pedro.

Notes for Home: Your child used story details to visualize or imagine what is happening in a story. ***Home Activity:*** Have your child look carefully at a room, and then give vivid details that would help someone else mentally picture this place.

Name____________________ A Peddler's Dream

Writing Across Texts

Directions: Compare information from *A Peddler's Dream,* the *Welcome to America* graph, and one other source to give an educated guess about the city where Solomon Azar arrived when he first came to the United States. Organize the information in the following table. **Possible answers given.**

Name of the City
1. **New York City**
Evidence and Rationale from Story
2. **Page 480 states that Solomon landed by boat. He landed in a coastal city.**
Evidence and Rationale from Graph
3. **The graph shows that more people landed in New York City than any other place. Therefore, it is most likely that Solomon landed there.**
Evidence and Rationale from Other Source
4. **During the time Solomon came to the U.S., Lebanon was experiencing a time of unrest and many European nations came in to help. Most Europeans landed in New York at Ellis Island, so Solomon probably got help from Europeans and came into New York too.**
Persuasive Opening Sentence
5. **After comparing information from the story, graph, and one other source, I feel very strongly that Solomon Azar probably landed in New York City at Ellis Island.**

Write a Persuasive Paragraph

On a separate sheet of paper, write a persuasive paragraph that tells which city you think Solomon Azar landed in and why. Include the information from your table. **Paragraphs will vary. Check that students use logic and persuasive language to support their position.**

Notes for Home: Your child compared information from several sources to take a persuasive stance and support it in writing. ***Home Activity:*** With your child, review the source material and encourage a discussion about which places were best for newcomers to the United States.

Grammar Practice Book 4.5, p. 106

Name________________________ A Peddler's Dream

Grammar: Pronouns

REVIEW

Directions: Underline each pronoun in the sentences below.

1. For years Ben and I hoped we could sail to America.
2. In 1919 the dream came true for us.
3. We grew up in a little Polish town, but now we were leaving it forever.
4. "I cannot say good-bye to you," sobbed Ben's mother.
5. Watching Ben leave for America was the hardest thing she had ever done.

Directions: Choose a pronoun in ( ) to replace the underlined noun or noun phrase in each sentence. Circle the pronoun you chose.

6. Ben and I were beginning a new life in New York City. (**We**/Us)
7. After our little Polish town, the city seemed so big. (they/**it**)
8. The size and the noise frightened Ben and me. (him/**us**)
9. Some people seemed nice, though, and we became friends with people. (you/**them**)
10. These people helped us find our way around. (**They**/It)
11. We did not know English, so we studied the language. (him/**it**)
12. Our friend Anna spoke English well, and Anna helped us study. (we/**she**)
13. Her husband was a tailor, and the husband found a job for Ben. (**he**/you)
14. We were so grateful to Anna and her husband. (**them**/us)
15. Life was still very hard, but life got better every day. (she/**it**)

Notes for Home: Your child identified and used pronouns—words that take the place of nouns. ***Home Activity:*** Ask your child to tell you some jokes or funny stories. Help your child list the pronouns he or she uses.

Grammar: Pronouns 485

Grammar Practice Book 4.5, p. 107

Name________________________ A Peddler's Dream

Grammar: Subject and Object Pronouns

Subject pronouns are pronouns that are used as the subjects of sentences.

Moesha and I like to travel.

Singular subject pronouns: I, you, he, she, it
Plural subject pronouns: we, you, they

Object pronouns follow action verbs.

Dan Nehmi's parents brought him to this country.

Singular object pronouns: me, you, him, her, it
Plural object pronouns: us, you, them

Directions: Circle the correct pronoun in ( ) to complete each sentence. Write **S** on the line if it is a subject pronoun. Write **O** if it is an object pronoun.

S 1. My brother and (**I**/me) longed to go to America.
S 2. (Us/**We**) heard people say newcomers quickly became rich.
O 3. Our mother said not to believe (**them**/they).
S 4. "But (us/**you**) must go and find out for yourselves."
O 5. Our sister kissed both of (we/**us**).
S 6. "Come with us," (**I**/me) said.
S 7. "(**I**/You) want to stay here with our parents," my sister answered.
O 8. Our father was sorry that we were leaving (**him**/he).
S 9. "(Them/**They**) have a dream," our mother told him.
S 10. "Someday you and (me/**I**) may live in America too."

Notes for Home: Your child chose subject and object pronouns to complete sentences. ***Home Activity:*** Say a sentence with nouns as subject and object: *Mrs. Nehmi told Dan about new customs.* Have your child replace the nouns with pronouns: *She told him about new customs.*

486 Grammar: Subject and Object Pronouns

Grammar Practice Book 4.5, p. 108

Name________________________ A Peddler's Dream

Grammar: Subject and Object Pronouns

Directions: Choose the correct pronoun in ( ) to complete each sentence. Write the pronoun on the line.

you 1. Have (you/she) ever wondered what *success* really means?
it 2. The best way to define (it/her) is by giving examples.
she 3. At first, Amy was afraid of the water, but then (her/she) learned how to swim.
he 4. Luis decided to get 100% on his test, and (he/they) did.
them 5. The twins earned enough money, so their parents let (them/they) go to summer camp.
her 6. Ms. Chang convinced her boss to give (she/her) a better job.
him 7. Aaron's little brother couldn't catch a ball, so Aaron showed (he/him) how.
them 8. Laura and Sandy were confused about math, so they asked Mr. Franklin to help (him/them).
they 9. Some people think success means being rich and famous, but (they/it) may be wrong.
you 10. Now that you've read these examples, what do (they/you) think?

Write an Ad

On a separate sheet of paper, write a Back-to-School ad listing the "Top 5" ways to have success in school. Use both subject pronouns and object pronouns. Underline the pronouns in your ad. **Check that students have underlined each pronoun and that they have correctly used subject and object pronouns.**

Notes for Home: Your child replaced nouns with subject pronouns such as: *I, we, you, he, she, it,* and *they* or object pronouns such as: *me, us, you, him, her, it,* and *them.* ***Home Activity:*** Together, read about a famous person. Ask your child to identify the subject and object pronouns.

Grammar: Subject and Object Pronouns 487

Grammar Practice Book 4.5, p. 109

Name________________________ A Peddler's Dream

Grammar: Subject and Object Pronouns

RETEACHING

Read each pair of sentences. Write a pronoun on each line.

1. A clown and a dog came to school. **They** performed tricks.
2. The dog was good at jumping. The class liked watching **it**.

A **subject pronoun** is used in the subject of a sentence. Subject pronouns are **I, you, she, he, it, we,** and **they.** An object pronoun is used in the predicate of a sentence or in a prepositional phrase. Object pronouns are **me, you, him, her, it, us,** and **them.**

Directions: Circle the subject pronoun in each sentence. Then write it on the line.

1. (**I**) have learned many facts about space from Mr. Turner. **I**
2. (**He**) taught the class how to spot a shooting star. **He**
3. (**It**) is difficult for my sister to do. **It**
4. (**She**) will be in Mr. Turner's class in three years. **She**
5. One day (**we**) will watch shooting stars together. **we**
6. (**They**) are beautiful to see! **They**

Directions: Circle the object pronoun in each sentence. Then write it on the line.

7. Mark gave (**her**) a drawing of the Big Dipper. **her**
8. Did Mark give (**you**) a picture too? **you**
9. Mr. Gomez gave (**us**) star maps. **us**
10. Mr. Gomez keeps (**them**) in the classroom. **them**
11. The star map fascinates (**me**). **me**
12. Nina and Leon looked at (**it**) carefully. **it**

Notes for Home: Your child identified subject and object pronouns in sentences. ***Home Activity:*** Together, read an article in a newspaper. Have your child circle three subject or object pronouns. Then have him or her write new sentences, using pronouns from the article.

488 Grammar: Subject and Object Pronouns

Grammar Practice Book 4.5, p. 110

Name________________ **A Peddler's Dream**

Grammar: Subject and Object Pronouns

Directions: Read the paragraph. Then circle the correct pronoun in ( ) that completes each sentence. Remember:

- **Subject pronouns** are used as subjects in a sentence:
  I, you, he, she, it, we, and they.
- **Object pronouns** are used after action verbs:
  me, you, him, her, it, us, and them.

1.–8.

Grandma invited Tim and (I, me) to spend the holidays with her. Mom and Dad drove (we, us) to the airport. (They, Them) waved as the plane took off into the sky. (We, Us) slept on the plane. A flight attendant had to wake (I, me) up when we landed. (He, Him) carried our bags off the plane. Grandma seemed really excited to see (we, us). (She, Her) had balloons for each of us!

Write a Travel Journal

Write about a trip you would like to take with a friend or a book character. It might be a trip to a place in your town or a trip to a faraway place. Check to make sure you used subject and object pronouns correctly in your description.

Check that students use subject and object pronouns correctly.

Notes for Home: Your child identified subject and object pronouns in a paragraph. ***Home Activity:*** Have your child reread his or her travel journal. Then ask your child to circle the subject pronouns and underline the object pronouns that he or she wrote.

Practice Book 4.5, p. 218

Name________________ **A Peddler's Dream**

Phonics: Words with Silent Consonants *kn, gn, wr, mb*

Directions: Read the words below. One consonant in each word is silent. Write the silent consonant on the line.

1. knee	**k**	**6.** numb	**b**
2. resigned	**g**	**7.** gnarled	**g**
3. wrote	**w**	**8.** knitted	**k**
4. comb	**b**	**9.** wreck	**w**
5. wrap	**w**	**10.** dumb	**b**

Directions: Read the words in the box. Cross out the words that do **not** have silent consonants. Use the remaining words to complete the sentences below. Write the words on the lines to the left.

knocking	~~bit~~	wrong	~~calling~~	~~incorrect~~
designs	gnawed	~~created~~	knots	~~butterflies~~

knocking **11.** Like many Europeans of his time, Jan heard opportunity _____ in America.

designed **12.** Young Jan followed his dream and came to America, where he _____ clothing for a new store.

knots **13.** Now Jan's stomach twisted into _____ as he wondered whether the shop would be a success.

gnawed **14.** He _____ his lips nervously as he unlocked the door for the first day of business.

wrong **15.** The crowd of eager customers showed Jan that his creative ideas had not been _____.

Notes for Home: Your child identified words with *kn, gn, wr,* and *mb* where one consonant in each pair is silent, like *know, sign, write,* and *comb.* ***Home Activity:*** Read a newspaper article with your child. Help your child find words that have silent consonants.

Spelling Workbook 4.5, p. 85

Name________________ **A Peddler's Dream**

Spelling: Words with *kn, gn, wr, mb*

Pretest Directions: Fold back the page along the dotted line. On the blanks, write the spelling words as they are dictated. When you have finished the test, unfold the page and check your words.

1. **knot**	1. This rope has a **knot** in it.
2. **unknown**	2. Where it came from is **unknown**.
3. **know**	3. I do not **know** how much it costs.
4. **knit**	4. We can **knit** these yarns together.
5. **knob**	5. The door **knob** is brass.
6. **kneel**	6. Please **kneel** down.
7. **sign**	7. What does the **sign** say?
8. **design**	8. What a beautiful **design**!
9. **assign**	9. She will **assign** your work later.
10. **writing**	10. He's **writing** the information.
11. **wrist**	11. Wear it on your **wrist**.
12. **wreck**	12. He saw the **wreck** from shore.
13. **wreath**	13. Here is a **wreath** of flowers.
14. **wrench**	14. I need a **wrench** to fix this.
15. **wren**	15. The **wren** is in that tree.
16. **climb**	16. Can you **climb** this hill?
17. **thumb**	17. It is bigger than your **thumb**.
18. **limb**	18. That tree **limb** should be cut off.
19. **comb**	19. **Comb** your hair first.
20. **lamb**	20. The **lamb** bleated for its mother.

Notes for Home: Your child took a pretest on words that have the letters *kn, gn, wr,* and *mb.* ***Home Activity:*** Help your child learn misspelled words before the final test. Your child can underline the word parts that caused the problems and concentrate on those parts.

Spelling Workbook 4.5, p. 86

Name________________ **A Peddler's Dream**

Spelling: Words with *kn, gn, wr, mb*

Word List

knot	knob	assign	wreath	thumb
unknown	kneel	writing	wrench	limb
know	sign	wrist	wren	comb
knit	design	wreck	climb	lamb

Directions: Choose the words from the box where the consonants **k** and **w** are silent. Write the words in the correct column. **Order may vary.**

Silent k	**Silent w**
1. **knot**	7. **writing**
2. **unknown**	8. **wrist**
3. **know**	9. **wreck**
4. **knit**	10. **wreath**
5. **knob**	11. **wrench**
6. **kneel**	12. **wren**

Directions: Choose the word from the box that best matches each clue. Write the word on the line.

lamb **13.** It's the favorite animal of a mother sheep.

thumb **14.** You don't want a hammer to meet this.

comb **15.** You use this to get tangles out of your hair.

design **16.** An architect draws one before starting a new building.

climb **17.** It's how you get to the top.

limb **18.** Going out on one of these can be dangerous.

assign **19.** Your teacher does this with homework.

sign **20.** This is how deaf people communicate.

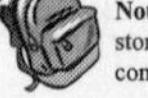

Notes for Home: Your child spelled words with *kn, gn, wr,* and *mb.* ***Home Activity:*** Read a story or newspaper article together. Have your child look for other words that use these letter combinations where one letter is silent.

Spelling Workbook 4.5, p. 87

Name______________________ A Peddler's Dream

Spelling: Words with kn, gn, wr, mb

Directions: Proofread this postcard. Find five spelling mistakes. Use the proofreading marks to correct each mistake.

- Make a capital.
- Make a small letter.
- Add something.
- Take out something.
- Add a period.
- Begin a new paragraph.

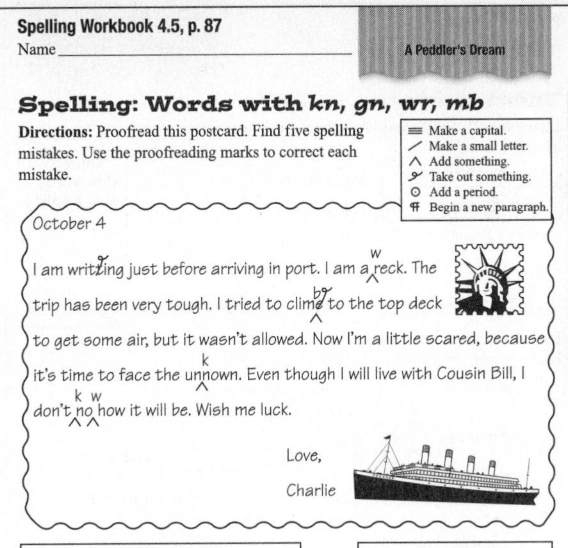

October 4
I am writting just before arriving in port. I am a reck. The trip has been very tough. I tried to climb to the top deck to get some air, but it wasn't allowed. Now I'm a little scared, because it's time to face the unown. Even though I will live with Cousin Bill, I don't no how it will be. Wish me luck.
Love,
Charlie

Spelling Tip

The underlined consonants stand for only one sound: **knot, sign, wrist, comb.**

Write a Postcard Home

Imagine you have traveled far to live in a new country. On a separate sheet of paper, write a postcard home to your family or a friend. Try to use at least three spelling words. **Answers will vary, but each postcard should include at least three spelling words.**

Word List

knot	wrist
unknown	wreck
know	wreath
knit	wrench
knob	wren
kneel	climb
sign	thumb
design	limb
assign	comb
writing	lamb

Notes for Home: Your child spelled words with *kn-, gn-, wr-,* and *mb-*. ***Home Activity:*** Write each spelling word, but leave out the silent consonant *(thum)*. Have your child write each word correctly *(thumb)*.

Spelling Workbook 4.5, p. 88

Name______________________ A Peddler's Dream

Spelling: Words with kn, gn, wr, mb

REVIEW

Word List

knot	knob	assign	wreath	thumb
unknown	kneel	writing	wrench	limb
know	sign	wrist	wren	comb
knit	design	wreck	climb	lamb

Directions: Write the word from the box that belongs in each group.

1. sparrow, canary, **wren**
2. brush, barrette, **comb**
3. sew, weave, **knit**
4. billboard, flyer, **sign**
5. bend, squat, **kneel**
6. chick, calf, **lamb**
7. hammer, screwdriver, **wrench**
8. pinkie, pointer, **thumb**
9. knee, elbow, **wrist**
10. bouquet, bunch, **wreath**
11. branch, arm, **limb**
12. crash, shatter, **wreck**

Directions: Choose the word from the box that best completes each sentence. Write the word on the matching numbered line on the right.

When immigrants came to this country, they faced the **13.** _____. Some immigrants tried to **14.** _____ a plan for their lives. They tried to **15.** _____ the ladder of success. Others had jobs where someone else had to **16.** _____ them work to do. Since factories needed people to do low-paying work, a job might be shaping a **17.** _____ for a door or tying a **18.** _____ in the leather cord that holds a baseball glove together. Reading and **19.** _____ were learned in night school. It was important to **20.** _____ how to use the language in order to succeed in a new country.

13. **unknown**
14. **design**
15. **climb**
16. **assign**
17. **knob**
18. **knot**
19. **writing**
20. **know**

Notes for Home: Your child spelled words with *kn, gn, wr,* and *mb*. ***Home Activity:*** Have your child sort the spelling words by the letter pairs. Together, add other words that use each letter pair *(knight, gnat, wrong, dumb)*.

Practice Book 4.5, p. 219

Name______________________ A Peddler's Dream

Graphs

Graphs show information visually and make it easier for readers to compare types of information. The graph below is called a **circle graph.** It shows how a group of people can be divided into smaller groups. The large group this graph describes is the people who moved to Texas in 1995 from another country. The graph divides the people into five groups: Those who came to Texas from Mexico, Vietnam, India, the Philippines, and elsewhere.

Directions: Use the circle graph to answer the questions that follow.

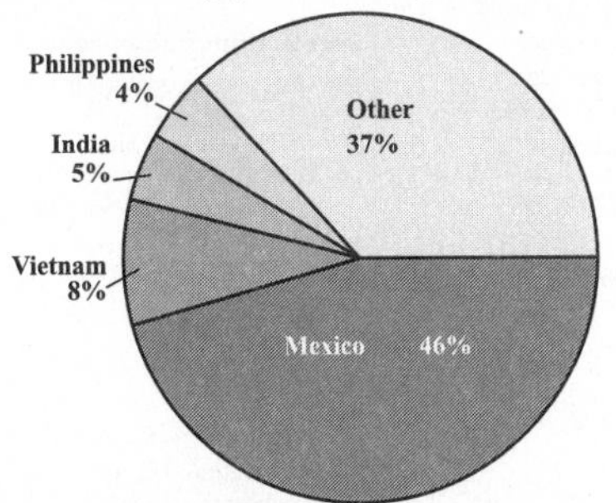

Immigration to Texas, 1995

Source: Department of Justice, Immigration and Naturalization Services

1. From which country did the most number of people come? **Mexico**
2. From which country did the least number of people come? **Philippines**
3. From which two countries did about the same number of people come?
Philippines and India
4. Did more people come from Mexico or from Vietnam, India, and the Philippines combined? How do you know?
Mexico; Possible answer: The wedge for Mexico is larger than the combined wedges for the other three countries.

Practice Book 4.5, p. 220

Name______________________ A Peddler's Dream

Another type of graph is a **bar graph.** The length or height of each bar stands for a number. The bars in this graph show the number of people who moved to Texas in 1995 from another country. The bar graph shows the same data as the circle graph, but in a different way.

Directions: Use the bar graph to answer the questions that follow.

Immigration to Texas, 1995

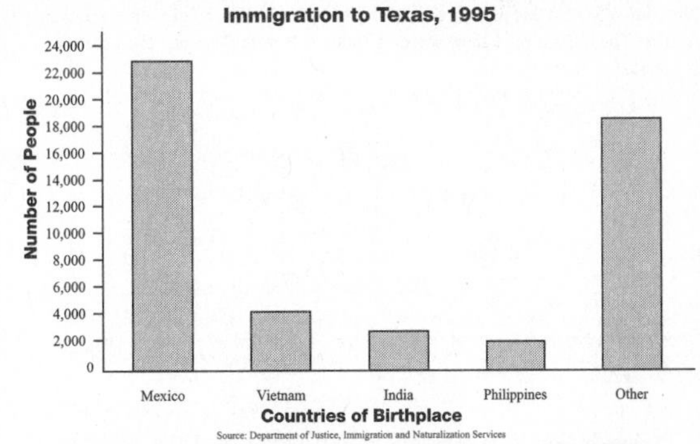

5. About how many people came to Texas from India? **about 2,000**
6. From which country did the greatest number of people come? **Mexico**
7. From which country did about 4,000 people come? **Vietnam**
8. From which two countries did about 2,000 people come? **India and Philippines**
9. About how many more people came from Vietnam than India? **about 2,000**
10. Tell how the two graphs are alike and different. **Possible answer: Alike: Both show the same data. Different: The circle graph shows the data as percents, but the bar graph shows the data as numbers of people.**

Notes for Home: Your child read data from two different graphs. ***Home Activity:*** Look at graphs in a newspaper with your child. Ask your child questions about the data in these graphs. Let your child ask you questions too.

Practice Book 4.5, p. 221
Name________________________ **The Race for the North Pole**

Graphic Sources

- Illustrations, charts, graphs, maps, diagrams, tables, lists, time lines, and scale drawings are kinds of **graphic sources.**
- Maps show places. A **physical map** shows landforms and bodies of water. A **map key** explains symbols used and the scale of distances.

Directions: Reread the introduction to *Polar Lands*. Then use the map to help you answer the questions below. **Possible answers given.**

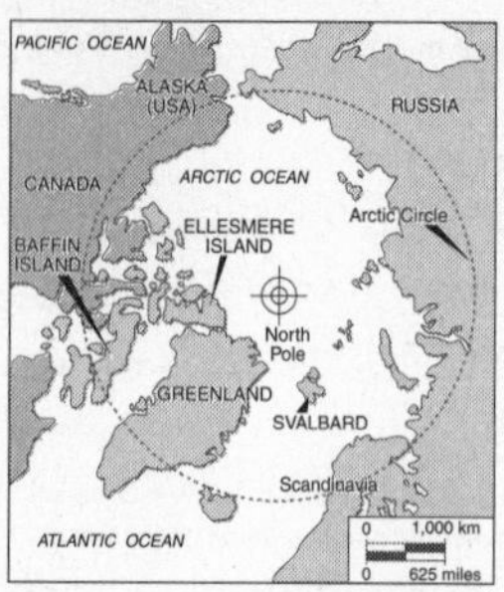

1. Where is the map key? What does it show? **The map key is in the lower right corner. It shows the scale in miles and kilometers.**
2. What is the only U.S. state on the map? **Alaska**
3. What three oceans are shown? **Atlantic, Arctic, Pacific**
4. In which ocean is the North Pole? **the Arctic Ocean**
5. How does the map help you to better understand the article? **Possible answer: The map makes it easier to understand the facts in the article, such as the size of the Arctic Ocean and the closeness of several world powers.**

Notes for Home: Your child studied a map and answered questions about it. ***Home Activity:*** Look at different maps with your child. Take turns asking and answering questions about the maps, such as what areas are shown and how to get from one place to another.

Practice Book 4.5, p. 222
Name________________________ **The Race for the North Pole**

Vocabulary

Directions: Choose the word from the box that best matches each definition. Write the word on the line.

Check the Words You Know
__ adventure
__ glaciers
__ navigate
__ region
__ walruses

adventure 1. an exciting experience
region 2. a place or area
navigate 3. sail or steer a ship
glaciers 4. large masses of ice
walruses 5. large sea animals of arctic areas

Directions: Choose the word from the box that best completes each sentence. Write the word on the line to the left.

glaciers 6. Ice floated in the water. In the distance, Malcolm and Brenna could see enormous _____.
adventure 7. "What an _____!" exclaimed Malcolm. "I never thought I would see anything like that!"
navigate 8. "Can you _____ the ship through that narrow passage?" Brenna asked.
region 9. "Yes," said Malcolm. "I've sailed through a _____ like this before."
walruses 10. "Quick! Follow those _____. They seem to know a way out."

Write About a Scientific Expedition

On a separate sheet of paper, tell what happens to Malcolm and Brenna. Describe what Malcolm has to do to steer the ship in the dangerous Arctic Ocean. Tell what Brenna finds out about icebergs. Use as many vocabulary words as you can.
Students' stories should use vocabulary words correctly.

Notes for Home: Your child identified and used new vocabulary words from "The Race for the North Pole." ***Home Activity:*** Pretend that you and your child are at the North Pole. Use the vocabulary words to act out an adventure.

Practice Book 4.5, p. 223
Name________________________ **The Race for the North Pole**

Graphic Sources

- A **graphic source** is an illustration, a graph, a chart, a map, a diagram, or other visual aid that helps you by showing you what the words say, or by organizing information in a useful way.

Directions: Reread this passage from "The Race for the North Pole" and look at the map. The black arrows show some of Matthew Henson's travels. Then answer the questions below.

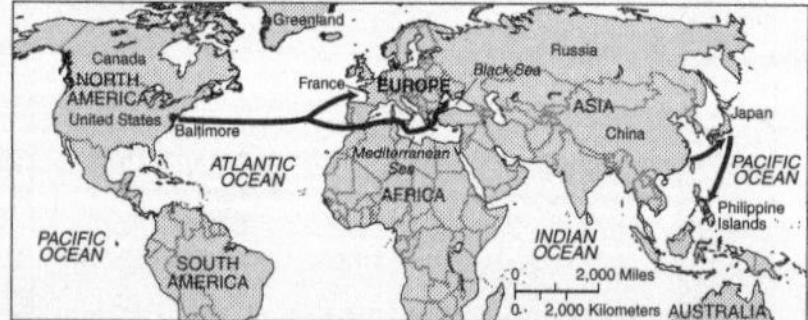

Matthew sailed from China to Japan to the Philippines. He sailed across the Atlantic Ocean to France, Africa, and southern Russia. He even sailed through the Arctic. And all the time, he continued to learn. When Matthew was 19, Captain Childs died and was buried at sea. Heartbroken, Matthew returned to Baltimore.

1. To sail from Japan to the Philippines, Matthew Henson sailed upon which ocean? **Pacific Ocean**
2. To which continents did Matthew Henson sail? **EurAsia (Europe, Asia), Africa, North America**
3. To go from Africa to southern Russia, which seas may Henson have sailed? **Mediterranean Sea, Black Sea**
4. Where is Baltimore? **in eastern United States (or North America)**
5. What information does a map give that helps you to better understand a passage like the one above? Write your answer on a separate sheet of paper. **Possible answer: It shows directions, routes, and the distances.**

Notes for Home: Your child read a story and used a map to understand story details better. ***Home Activity:*** Look at a map with your child (such as a newspaper weather map, a map in an atlas, or a website map). Take turns asking each other questions like the ones above.

Practice Book 4.5, p. 225
Name________________________ **The Race for the North Pole**

Selection Test

Directions: Choose the best answer to each item. Mark the letter for the answer you have chosen.

Part 1: Vocabulary

Find the answer choice that means about the same as the underlined word in each sentence.

1. There are glaciers up ahead.
   A. people who explore
   (B) large masses of ice
   C. shelters made of snow
   D. steep mountains
2. She can navigate the ship.
   F. repair
   G. think of a name for
   H. find
   (J) steer or sail
3. I like that region.
   (A) place or area
   B. type of shirt
   C. old photograph
   D. dessert
4. I described our adventure.
   F. skill or training
   G. way of living
   H. idea or opinion
   (J) exciting experience
5. Jim saw two walruses.
   A. Arctic birds
   B. large fish
   (C) large Arctic sea animals
   D. islands of ice

Part 2: Comprehension

Use what you know about the selection to answer each item.

6. Matthew Henson met Robert Peary when Robert Peary was about to sail to—
   F. France.
   (G) Nicaragua.
   H. Japan.
   J. Russia.
7. Matthew Henson's family moved to Washington, D.C., to—
   A. start a restaurant.
   B. be with their friends.
   (C) escape from racial violence.
   D. live in a big city.
8. Matthew Henson took a job on Captain Childs's ship because he—
   (F) was looking for adventure.
   G. hoped to make a lot of money.
   H. knew how to sail a ship.
   J. wanted to learn to read.

GO ON

Practice Book 4.5, p. 226

Name ____________ The Race for the North Pole

9. Captain Childs helped Matthew Henson mainly by—
   A. paying him lots of money.
   B. bringing him to Robert Peary.
   C. telling him to work harder.
   (D) teaching and encouraging him.

10. Robert Peary first asked Matthew Henson to go with him to the North Pole because—
   F. he enjoyed Matthew Henson's company.
   (G) his other men refused to go.
   H. he thought Matthew Henson was the best man for the trip.
   J. Matthew Henson wanted to be a hero.

11. To survive the Arctic, Matthew Henson used what he learned from—
   A. his father.
   B. Robert Peary.
   (C) the Inuit people.
   D. Captain Childs's crew.

12. Robert Peary and Matthew Henson first tried for the North Pole in—
   F. 1885.
   (G) 1893.
   H. 1902.
   J. 1909.

13. What did Robert Peary probably enjoy most about finally reaching the North Pole?
   A. seeing what it looked like
   B. sharing his victory with Matthew Henson
   (C) becoming famous all over the world
   D. placing a flag there

14. Robert Peary probably treated Matthew Henson differently from his other men because Matthew Henson—
   F. was younger than he.
   G. seemed nervous and afraid.
   H. had so much to learn.
   (J) was an African American.

15. Which sentence states an opinion?
   (A) "Only the bravest person would venture near the North Pole."
   B. "On April 1, 1895, the three men set out for the North Pole."
   C. "They made it as far as Independence Bay."
   D. "On August 3, 1895, the three men returned to Washington."

Name ____________ The Race for the North Pole

Graphic Sources

- A **graphic source** is an illustration, a graph, a chart, a map, a diagram, or other visual aid that helps you by showing you what the words say, or by organizing information in a useful way.

Directions: Read the passage below.

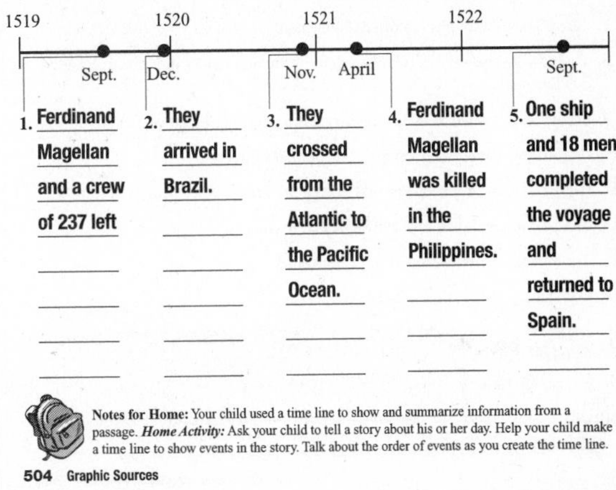
On September 20, 1519, Ferdinand Magellan and his crew of 237 were ready to sail around the world, something that no one had ever done. Three months after they left Spain, they arrived in Brazil. Then they headed south along the coast of South America.

In November, 1520, Ferdinand Magellan's ships crossed from the Atlantic to the Pacific Ocean at the tip of South America. After suffering hunger and illness, the remaining crew reached the Pacific island of Guam on March 6, 1521. By April, they were in the Philippines. But Ferdinand Magellan was killed by warriors there.

Only one ship and 18 men finished the voyage. They returned to Spain on September 8, 1522.

Directions: Write an event from the passage for each date on the time line.
Possible answers given.

Time line: 1519 — 1520 — 1521 — 1522

1. Sept.: Ferdinand Magellan and a crew of 237 left
2. Dec.: They arrived in Brazil.
3. Nov.: They crossed from the Atlantic to the Pacific Ocean.
4. April: Ferdinand Magellan was killed in the Philippines.
5. Sept.: One ship and 18 men completed the voyage and returned to Spain.

Notes for Home: Your child used a time line to show and summarize information from a passage. *Home Activity:* Ask your child to tell a story about his or her day. Help your child make a time line to show events in the story. Talk about the order of events as you create the time line.

Practice Book 4.5, p. 227

Name ____________ The Race for the North Pole

Generalizing

REVIEW

Directions: Read the passage. Then read each question about the passage. Choose the best answer to each question. Mark the letter for the answer you have chosen.

Born to Fly

When Beryl Markham was just three, her parents left England to start a farm in Kenya, East Africa. Most European farmers were quite successful in Kenya, but Beryl's father found his talent in breeding and training horses.

Beryl's life was always full of interesting adventures. While some daughters of European farmers may have been sent to school in England, Beryl was raised in Africa. She learned to speak several African languages and hunted wild game with a spear. She became a horse trainer like her father. Later, she learned to fly an airplane and became a bush pilot.

Few women in the 1930s had the adventures that Beryl did. She became the first person to fly a plane solo nonstop from London to North America. She wrote a best-selling book about her experiences called *West with the Night.*

1. Which word in the first paragraph signals a generalization?
   A. when **C.** Kenya
   (B.) most **D.** just

2. Which of the following statements is a valid generalization from the first paragraph?
   F. Beryl's parents moved when she was three.
   G. Her father became a horse breeder and trainer.
   H. Her father always disliked farming.
   (J.) Most European farmers did quite well in Kenya.

3. Which word in the second paragraph signals a generalization?
   A. while **C.** later
   (B.) always **D.** full

4. Which of these statements is a faulty generalization?
   F. Beryl had many adventures.
   G. Beryl was raised in Africa.
   (H.) All horse trainers learn to fly.
   J. Flying was one of Beryl's many adventures.

5. Which word in the last paragraph signals a generalization?
   (A.) few **C.** wrote
   B. fly **D.** nonstop

Notes for Home: Your child read a passage and identified valid and faulty generalizations. *Home Activity:* Challenge your child to use words like *always, sometimes, never,* or *all* to make a generalization. Discuss whether this generalization is accurate (valid) or not (faulty).

Name ____________ The Race for the North Pole

Writing Across Texts

Directions: Think about how Alice Ramsey from "Amazing Alice!" and Robert Peary from "The Race for the North Pole" are alike. List five ways they are alike in the following table. **Possible answers given.**

How Alice Ramsey and Robert Peary Were Alike
Both Alice Ramsey and Robert Peary did something that had not been done before.
1. **Both were the leaders of their expeditions.**
2. **Both had to "fight" nature to succeed.**
3. **Both were brave.**
4. **Both asked others to help them achieve their goals.**
5. **Both kept trying even when they faced obstacles.**

Write a Paragraph

On a separate sheet of paper, write a paragraph that tells how Alice Ramsey and Robert Peary were alike. Use details from your table in the paragraph.
Paragraphs will vary. Check that students present similarities, not differences.

Notes for Home: Your child compared real-life people from two different stories. *Home Activity:* Read two different stories with your child. Help your child write a paragraph that tells how two characters, one from each story, are similar in personality or behavior.

Grammar Practice Book 4.5, p. 111

Name______________________ The Race for the North Pole

Grammar: Subject and Object Pronouns

REVIEW

Directions: Underline the pronoun in each sentence. Write **S** above the pronoun if it is a subject pronoun. Write **O** if it is an object pronoun.

1. Dolores told me (O) about the thirteenth-century explorer Marco Polo.
2. She (S) had just read a book about this young traveler.
3. At the age of seventeen, he (S) and two family members set out on a long journey.
4. The trip took them (O) from Italy to China, through deserts, mountains, and wondrous cities.
5. It (S) was a difficult journey in 1271, lasting four years.

Directions: Choose the pronoun in ( ) that completes each sentence. Circle the pronoun you chose.

6. Julia and (I/me) are writing a report about the Vikings. — I
7. (They/Them) were also known as Norsemen. — They
8. Their swift ships carried (they/them) far from their homes in Norway, Sweden, and Denmark. — them
9. (They/Them) sailed to North America more than a thousand years ago. — They
10. (We/Us) read about Leif Ericson, one of their leaders. — We
11. (He/Him) may have been the first European to reach North America. — He
12. The land pleased (he/him), and he named it Vinland. — him
13. The Vikings really interested Julia and (I/me). — me
14. One thing puzzled (she/her), though. — her
15. (Her/She) wondered why Christopher Columbus was so much more famous than Leif Ericson. — She

Notes for Home: Your child used the pronouns *I, we, you, he, she, it,* and *they* as subjects and *me, us, you, him, her,* and *them* as objects of verbs. ***Home Activity:*** Together, look for pronouns in a magazine. Decide whether each is a subject or an object pronoun.

Grammar Practice Book 4.5, p. 112

Name______________________ The Race for the North Pole

Grammar: Pronouns and Referents

Pronouns get most of their meaning from the nouns they replace. The noun that a pronoun replaces is its **referent.** It names the person, place, or thing to which the pronoun refers. In the following sentences, the referents are underlined once, and the pronouns are underlined twice.

Jo wants to be an explorer when she grows up.

Soon, Jo and Pavel will visit the Gobi Desert. They can hardly wait!

A pronoun and its referent must agree. In the first example sentence above, the singular subject pronoun *she* agrees with its referent, the singular subject *Jo.* In the next example sentences, the plural subject pronoun *They* agrees with its referent, the compound subject *Jo and Pavel.*

Directions: Match the pronoun with the noun phrase that could be its referent. Write the letter of the referent on the line.

e	1. we	a. Mr. Chin
d	2. they	b. airplane
c	3. she	c. Maggie
b	4. it	d. Tony and Sari
a	5. he	e. Dad and I

Directions: Underline the referent once and the pronoun twice in each sentence.

6. Pavel and Jo can't wait until they go to Nepal.
7. The journey will be long, but it will be fun.
8. Pavel has a new guidebook that will help him.
9. The tickets are expensive, but they are worth it!
10. Pavel went to Nepal last year. It was beautiful.

Notes for Home: Your child connected pronouns to the words to which they refer. ***Home Activity:*** Read a story together and look for nouns and pronouns. For each pronoun, name the noun it replaces.

Grammar Practice Book 4.5, p. 113

Name______________________ The Race for the North Pole

Grammar: Pronouns and Referents

Directions: Circle the correct pronoun in ( ) to complete each sentence. The referents for the pronouns are underlined to help you.

1. Long ago, navigators steering ships had only the stars to guide (he/them). — them
2. The stars look different when you view (it/them) from different parts of the world. — them
3. Navigation takes a long time to learn, but you may find (it/you) worthwhile. — it
4. Sailors who want to be coastal pilots know (it/they) must learn navigation. — they
5. Luisa and I have decided that (she/we) will sail around the world someday. — we

Directions: Revise each sentence. Use pronouns to avoid repeating a noun. Cross out nouns and write new pronouns above the nouns. Circle the referent for each pronoun you used.

6. (Explorers) have interesting lives because ~~explorers~~ they often visit new places.
7. (Ferdinand Magellan) became famous when ~~Ferdinand Magellan~~ he sailed around the globe.
8. (Luisa) plans to sail around the world when ~~Luisa~~ she grows up.
9. (Luisa) will be our navigator because ~~Luisa~~ she has been studying navigation.
10. (Sacajawea) was the guide for (Lewis and Clark.) Without ~~Sacajawea~~ her, ~~Lewis and Clark~~ they would have been lost.

Write an Adventure Story

On a separate sheet of paper, write the story of an explorer. The explorer may be a real person that you know about or an imaginary one. Use at least five pronouns that have referents. When you are finished, identify the referent for each pronoun.

Responses should tell the story of an exploration or an adventure, using at least five pronouns and noting their referents.

Notes for Home: Your child used pronouns to improve sentences and identified the nouns that the pronouns replaced. ***Home Activity:*** Write a few sentences that include pronouns. Ask your child to identify the noun each pronoun replaces.

Grammar Practice Book 4.5, p. 114

Name______________________ The Race for the North Pole

Grammar: Pronouns and Referents

RETEACHING

A referent is a noun or noun phrase that gets replaced by a pronoun.

The referent is underlined. Circle the pronoun that replaces the referent.

Linnea and Jack are hungry before (they) eat dinner.

A **pronoun** gets most of its meaning from the noun or noun phrase it replaces. Its **referent** names the person, place, or thing to which the pronoun refers.

Directions: Circle the pronoun in each sentence. Write each referent on the line.

Walter	1. Walter told Mrs. Chan (he) would water the plants.
Mrs. Chan	2. Mrs. Chan explained how (she) would like the plants to be watered.
plants	3. Many plants from stores come with information about what (they) need to survive.
friend	4. A friend sent a picture (he) had taken of redwood trees.
picture	5. The picture was beautiful, and (it) showed how large the trees were.

Directions: Match the pronoun with the noun or noun phrase that could be its referent. Write the letter of the referent on the line.

d	6. he	a. Linda
e	7. we	b. Jonathan and Chris
b	8. they	c. the truck
c	9. it	d. Pierre
a	10. she	e. Flora and I

Notes for Home: Your child identified pronouns and their referents—the nouns or noun phrases to which pronouns refer. ***Home Activity:*** Together, write a poem about your family. Use at least three pronouns and their referents.

Grammar Practice Book 4.5, p. 115
Name________________ The Race for the North Pole

Grammar: Pronouns and Referents

Directions: Underline the four pronouns in the paragraph. Then list the referents on the lines below.

Carlos studied the five senses with Mrs. Katz. She knows many things about the sense organs. They are the ears, nose, eyes, tongue, and skin. Carlos added a fact about the brain. It works with the eyes. Together they help people to see.

1. **Mrs. Katz** 2. **sense organs** 3. **brain** 4. **eyes and brain**

Directions: Rewrite each sentence. Use a pronoun to replace the underlined referent.

5. Ned and Liz needed a volunteer for an experiment.
They needed a volunteer for an experiment.

6. Liz used a handkerchief for a blindfold.
She used a handkerchief for a blindfold.

7. Ned moved an alarm clock around the room.
He moved an alarm clock around the room.

8. The clock ticked softly at a distance.
It ticked softly at a distance.

9. Now and then Liz asked about the clock.
Now and then she asked about the clock.

10. Volunteers pointed to the sound.
They pointed to the sound.

Write Sentences About Senses

Close your eyes and listen to the sounds around you. Then, on a separate sheet of paper, write sentences about what you heard. Use pronouns and referents in some of your sentences. **Check that students have used pronouns and referents.**

Notes for Home: Your child identified pronouns and referents in sentences. ***Home Activity:*** Have your child write sentences about his or her friends. Challenge your child to use at least three pronouns and their referents.

Grammar: Pronouns and Referents 511

Practice Book 4.5, p. 228
Name________________ The Race for the North Pole

Word Study: Plural Possessives

Directions: To make most words possessive, add an **apostrophe (') and s: the dog's bone.** For plural nouns that end in **-s**, just add the **apostrophe ('): the two dogs' bones.** Complete the table by writing the plural form and the plural possessive form of each noun.

Singular Noun	Plural Noun	Plural Possessive Noun
grandmother	1. **grandmothers**	5. **grandmothers'**
house	2. **houses**	6. **houses'**
teacher	3. **teachers**	7. **teachers'**
Mr. Reed/Mrs. Reed	4. The **Reeds**	8. The **Reeds'**

Directions: Read the paragraph below. You will see many words with apostrophes, including contractions and singular possessives. Find the words that are plural possessives. Circle each plural possessive and write it on the line.

Imagine traveling to the Arctic. You'll have to pack warm clothing to keep out the Arctic's cold. You'll travel on an icebreaker. The ship's prow is built like a snow plow, using heavy blades to break through the ice. Each day's adventures will fill you with wonder. You might hear polar bears' roars or seals' barks. The icebergs' incredible sizes are breathtaking. Watch out for ice floes! The floes' instability often causes crashes. Don't miss gazing at the night sky. The stars' brilliance is amazing, and the Northern Lights' colors dance. Imagine the early explorers' experiences as they first set foot upon this snowy wilderness.

9. **polar bears'**
10. **seals'**
11. **icebergs'**
12. **floes'**
13. **stars'**
14. **Northern Lights'**
15. **explorers'**

Notes for Home: Your child wrote and identified plural possessive nouns, such as: *the dogs' bone.* ***Home Activity:*** Read a story with your child. Point out words with apostrophes, and decide if they are possessives. Next, ask your child if they are plural possessives.

512 Word Study: Plural Possessives

Spelling Workbook 4.5, p. 89
Name________________ The Race for the North Pole

Spelling: Possessives

Pretest Directions: Fold back the page along the dotted line. On the blanks, write the spelling words as they are dictated. When you have finished the test, unfold the page and check your words.

1. **Dad's** — 1. That's **Dad's** seat.
2. **friend's** — 2. I'm going to a **friend's** house.
3. **girl's** — 3. Where is this **girl's** brother?
4. **girls'** — 4. Here are these **girls'** parents.
5. **teacher's** — 5. The **teacher's** bag is on the desk.
6. **teachers'** — 6. Two **teachers'** cars are new.
7. **baby's** — 7. I lost the **baby's** rattle.
8. **babies'** — 8. Both **babies'** smiles were big.
9. **family's** — 9. This is my **family's** car.
10. **families'** — 10. Tom washed both **families'** dogs.
11. **grandma's** — 11. I like my **grandma's** songs.
12. **grandpa's** — 12. I like his **grandpa's** jokes.
13. **brother's** — 13. That's my **brother's** backpack.
14. **brothers'** — 14. Those **brothers'** bikes are cool.
15. **boy's** — 15. I found the **boy's** glove.
16. **boys'** — 16. Three **boys'** bicycles are green.
17. **aunt's** — 17. My **aunt's** hat is straw.
18. **aunts'** — 18. Two **aunts'** houses are near ours.
19. **lady's** — 19. Where is the **lady's** coat?
20. **ladies'** — 20. Both **ladies'** coats are black.

Notes for Home: Your child took a pretest on possessive words—words that tell who owns something. ***Home Activity:*** Help your child learn misspelled words before the final test. Singular nouns add *'s* to show possession. Plural nouns may need other changes besides adding an apostrophe.

Spelling: Possessives 513

Spelling Workbook 4.5, p. 90
Name________________ The Race for the North Pole

Spelling: Possessives

Word List				
Dad's	teacher's	family's	brother's	aunt's
friend's	teachers'	families'	brothers'	aunts'
girl's	baby's	grandma's	boy's	lady's
girls'	babies'	grandpa's	boys'	ladies'

Directions: Choose the word from the box that is the possessive form of each noun below. Write the word on the line.

1. grandma **grandma's**
2. family **family's**
3. brother **brother's**
4. brothers **brothers'**
5. aunt **aunt's**
6. aunts **aunts'**
7. lady **lady's**
8. ladies **ladies'**
9. baby **baby's**
10. babies **babies'**
11. girl **girl's**
12. girls **girls'**
13. teacher **teacher's**
14. families **families'**

Directions: Use the possessive form of the word in ( ) to form a word from the box and complete each sentence. Write the word on the line.

Dad's 15. (Dad) best friend is an Arctic explorer.
friend's 16. His (friend) book on the Arctic was great!
grandpa's 17. It's my (grandpa) favorite book.
boy's 18. The book is about one (boy) travels.
teachers' 19. The parents visited the (teachers) classrooms.
boys' 20. He went to the Arctic, the land of (boys) dreams.

Notes for Home: Your child spelled possessives—words that show possession. ***Home Activity:*** Choose some words from the list. Work with your child to draw a picture and write a caption for each possessive, such as *My Aunts' Spotted Hats.*

514 Spelling: Possessives

Spelling Workbook 4.5, p. 91

Name

The Race for the North Pole

Spelling: Possessives

Directions: Proofread this journal entry. Find five spelling mistakes. Use the proofreading marks to correct each mistake.

Proofreading marks	
≡	Make a capital.
/	Make a small letter.
∧	Add something.
⌫	Take out something.
⊙	Add a period.
¶	Begin a new paragraph.

April 11

On our remote island, the entire family lives in my grandpa's hut. Dad's job is to hunt. Everyone takes care of our family's children. The girls' skirts and boys' pants are very colorful. My grandma's sewing skills are greatly admired. The lady's (ies) hairstyles are very pretty. It is the teachers' responsibility to help pass on the island's traditions.

Spelling Tip

To form possessives of singular nouns, add an **apostrophe (')** and an **-s.** To form possessives of plural nouns that end in **-s,** just add an **apostrophe (').**

Word List

Dad's	grandma's
friend's	grandpa's
girl's	brother's
girls'	brothers'
teacher's	boy's
teachers'	boys'
baby's	aunt's
babies'	aunts'
family's	lady's
families'	ladies'

Write a Journal Entry

Imagine what it would be like to explore a place that no one else has ever seen. On a separate sheet of paper, write a journal entry describing your experience, what you see, and how you feel. Use at least three spelling words. **Answers will vary, but each journal entry should include at least three spelling words.**

Notes for Home: Your child spelled possessives—words that show possession. ***Home Activity:*** Have your child explain to you when to use an apostrophe and *-s* or just an apostrophe to form possessives. Ask him or her to identify the plural possessive spelling words.

Spelling Workbook 4.5, p. 92

Name

The Race for the North Pole

Spelling: Possessives

REVIEW

Word List

Dad's	teacher's	family's	brother's	aunt's
friend's	teachers'	families'	brothers'	aunts'
girl's	baby's	grandma's	boy's	lady's
girls'	babies'	grandpa's	boys'	ladies'

Directions: Write the possessive form of each underlined word below.

friend's 1. the father of my friend

babies' 2. the cries of the babies

baby's 3. the mother of the baby

grandma's 4. the hopes of the grandma

grandpa's 5. the chair of the grandpa

Dad's 6. the shoes of Dad

teachers' 7. the rules of the teachers

lady's 8. the visit of the lady

ladies' 9. the group of the ladies

boy's 10. the friend of the boy

boys' 11. the poems of the boys

families' 12. the dreams of the families

teacher's 13. the books of the teacher

brother's 14. the hat of the brother

Directions: Choose the word in ( ) that best completes each sentence. Write the word on the line.

girl's 15. The (girl's/girls') dream was to be an explorer.

brothers' 16. She had all of her six (brother's/brothers') encouragement.

aunts' 17. Her three (aunt's/aunts') homes were full of travel books.

aunt's 18. Her one (aunt's/aunts') advice was to follow her dream.

family's 19. "You are our (family's/families') bravest person."

girls' 20. "In our family, we care about all (girl's/girls') dreams."

Notes for Home: Your child spelled possessives—words that show possession. ***Home Activity:*** Walk around your home or neighborhood and use possessives to describe things people own. Later, make a list of the possessives you used.

Practice Book 4.5, p. 229

Name

The Race for the North Pole

Atlases/Maps

An **atlas** is a book of maps. A **map** is a drawing of a place. Maps have keys that show what the symbols on the maps mean. A compass shows directions north, south, east, and west. There are many kinds of maps. A picture map shows a place. A road map shows different types of roads. A political map shows city, state, and national boundaries. Physical maps show landforms, such as mountains and valleys. Special purpose maps may show specific information about a subject.

Directions: Admiral Peary made many attempts to reach the North Pole. This map shows the routes he took for each expedition, or trip, and the years he made each attempt. It lists the people who assisted him. Use the map to answer the questions on the next page.

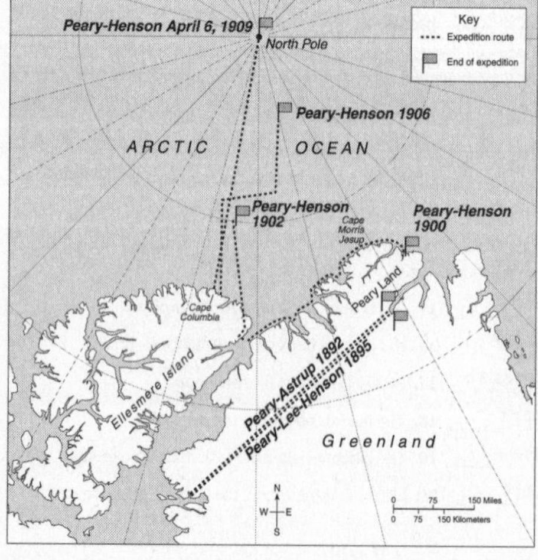

Practice Book 4.5, p. 230

Name

The Race for the North Pole

1. What special purpose does this map have? **It shows the routes Admiral Peary and fellow explorers used in their attempts to reach the North Pole.**

2. What do the dashed lines on the map represent? **the individual routes that Peary and other explorers took**

3. What do the flag symbols on the map represent? **The flag symbols show the end of each expedition.**

4. Why is it important to study the map key? **A map key explains what symbols on the map mean. It helps you read and interpret the map.**

5. How can you tell who made each expedition shown on the map? **The routes are labeled with the names of the explorers.**

6. In which directions did Admiral Peary and Matthew Henson travel during their 1906 expedition to the North Pole? **north and east**

7. Which ocean did Matthew Henson and Admiral Peary travel over to reach the North Pole? **Arctic Ocean**

8. How many expeditions did Admiral Peary make with Matthew Henson? **5**

9. Who traveled with Admiral Peary in 1892 to northern Greenland? **Astrup**

10. How does this map help you understand Admiral Peary and Matthew Henson's work as explorers? **Possible answer: It shows how many attempts and how many years it took before Admiral Peary and Matthew Henson reached the North Pole.**

Notes for Home: Your child read a map and answered questions about it. ***Home Activity:*** Ask your child to draw a map showing the route he or she takes to school. Have your child include a key that explains any symbols, such as a symbol for a post office, bridge, or school.

Practice Book 4.5, p. 231

Name______________________ **Into the Sea**

Author's Purpose

- An **author's purpose** is the reason for writing something.
- Some purposes for writing are to entertain, to inform, to express, and to persuade.

Directions: Reread "Saving Our Wetlands." Then use the questions to help you determine the author's purpose or purposes for the article. **Possible answers given.**

Questions	Answers
Title: What do the title and the subhead reveal about the author's purpose?	1. **The title and subhead tell that the author wants to inform readers about the plight of the wetlands and the importance of wetlands.**
Organization: How does the article's organization help you figure out the author's purpose?	2. **The article is a list of points that tell why wetlands are important.**
Key Words and Phrases: What key words or phrases does the author use that show how he feels about the wetlands?	Wetlands are home to many of the United States' birds.
	3. **Wetlands are being rapidly destroyed.**
	4. **They are among the most important areas on Earth.**

Author's Purpose or Purposes

5. **The author's purpose is to inform the reader about why it is important to save wetlands.**

Notes for Home: Your child read a story and used story details to determine the author's purpose. ***Home Activity:*** With your child, read the editorial page of a newspaper. Ask him or her to find places where the writers inform, entertain, express, and persuade.

Author's Purpose 521

Practice Book 4.5, p. 232

Name______________________ **Into the Sea**

Vocabulary

Directions: Choose the word from the box that best matches each definition. Write the word on the line.

Check the Words You Know
- __ awkward
- __ coral
- __ current
- __ flippers
- __ muscles
- __ protection
- __ ridges
- __ underside

underside 1. bottom side

flippers 2. broad, flat animal body part used for swimming

current 3. a flow of water

awkward 4. uncomfortable; uncoordinated

ridges 5. raised narrow strips

muscles 6. body tissues that move body parts

Directions: Choose the word from the box that best completes each sentence. Write the word on the matching numbered line to the right.

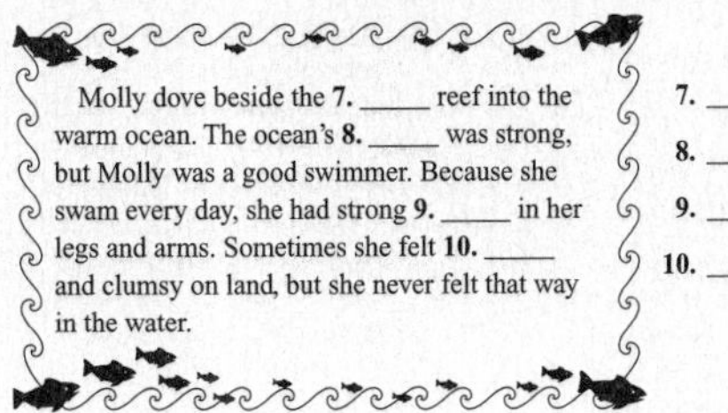

Molly dove beside the **7.** _____ reef into the warm ocean. The ocean's **8.** _____ was strong, but Molly was a good swimmer. Because she swam every day, she had strong **9.** _____ in her legs and arms. Sometimes she felt **10.** _____ and clumsy on land, but she never felt that way in the water.

7. **coral**
8. **current**
9. **muscles**
10. **awkward**

Write a Description

On a separate sheet of paper, write a description of life under the ocean. You might want to find a picture in a book, encyclopedia, or magazine to help you visualize what ocean life is like. Use as many of the vocabulary words as you can in your description. **Students' descriptions should use vocabulary words correctly.**

Notes for Home: Your child identified and used vocabulary words from *Into the Sea.* ***Home Activity:*** Talk with your child about the ocean, looking at pictures of it together if possible. Encourage your child to tell you how the vocabulary words are related to the ocean.

522 Vocabulary

Practice Book 4.5, p. 233

Name______________________ **Into the Sea**

Author's Purpose

- An **author's purpose** is the reason or reasons an author has for writing.
- Four common purposes are to entertain, to inform, to express, and to persuade.

Directions: Reread *Into the Sea.* Then answer the question below. **Possible answers given.**

1. What do you think was the author's purpose or purposes for writing this story? Give examples from the story to support your answer.
inform, persuade; The author gives facts about a sea turtle's life. She encourages people to protect them.

Directions: Read each paragraph. Write the author's purpose on the line after each paragraph and explain your answers.

2. Tony had a "Come as a Turtle" party. Tony's dad came as a sea turtle with a HUGE foam shell, woolly arms and legs, and a ski-mask head. He had to take off the shell to sit down!
entertain; The author presents a funny situation.

3. One of the really cool things about going canoeing is seeing painted turtles sunning themselves on logs. They look like kings. Their bodies seem to be covered in jewels that sparkle in the sun.
express; The author uses sensory details to help readers visualize.

4. Basking turtles live in ponds, streams, lakes, and marshes. They spend most of their time in the water, but they also bask in the sun. Their bodies are encased in bony shells.
inform; The author gives facts about basking turtles.

5. Choose your favorite story. On a separate sheet of paper, describe the author's purpose. Support your answer with examples from the story. **Check that students support their answers with story examples.**

Notes for Home: Your child read several passages and identified the author's purpose. ***Home Activity:*** With your child, look through books, magazines, and newspapers. Find an example of writing for each of the four common purposes listed above.

Author's Purpose 523

Practice Book 4.5, p. 235

Name______________________ **Into the Sea**

Selection Test

Directions: Choose the best answer to each item. Mark the letter for the answer you have chosen.

Part 1: Vocabulary

Find the answer choice that means about the same as the underlined work in each sentence.

1. The fish's mouth has <u>ridges</u>.
   A. sharp teeth
   B. spots of color
   C. moving parts
   (D) raised, narrow strips

2. The fish swam with the <u>current</u>.
   F. type of shark
   G. group of seahorses
   (H) flow of water
   J. large fishing nets

3. The young horse was <u>awkward</u>.
   (A) clumsy
   B. watchful
   C. tired
   D. hungry

4. Baby birds need <u>protection</u>.
   F. warm water
   (G) safety or defense
   H. good food
   J. friends or mates

5. We looked at the <u>coral</u> reef.
   A. having valuable metals
   B. from a sunken ship
   C. filled with silver fish
   (D) made from skeletons of sea animals

6. Seals and whales have <u>flippers</u>.
   F. keen senses
   G. skin with thick layers of fat
   H. eyes without lids
   (J) broad flat body parts used for swimming

7. We'll paint the boat's <u>underside</u>.
   A. back section
   (B) bottom
   C. wall
   D. inside

8. The turtle's <u>muscles</u> are strong.
   F. hard outer shells
   G. gills used for breathing
   H. habits or ways of behaving
   (J) tissues that move parts of the body

GO ON

524 Selection Test

Practice Book 4.5, p. 236

Name________________________ Into the Sea

Part 2: Comprehension

Use what you know about the selection to answer each item.

9. At the beginning of this selection, the turtle has just—
(A) hatched from an egg.
B. eaten a crab.
C. crawled out of the ocean.
D. hidden from a fish.

10. For the first few months of its life, the turtle—
F. builds a nest on a beach.
(G) drifts in a patch of seaweed.
H. rests on the ocean floor.
J. floats on the surface of water.

11. Which animal is still an enemy when the turtle is fully grown?
A. sea gull
B. butterfly fish
(C) shark
D. remora

12. Getting caught in the net was dangerous for the turtle because—
F. a whale had spotted her.
(G) she was almost out of breath.
H. a man was pulling in the net.
J. the net was cutting her shell.

13. The turtle returned to the island where it was born to—
(A) lay its eggs.
B. escape from danger.
C. find its favorite foods.
D. prepare to die.

14. The author's main purpose in this selection is to—
F. show how sea turtles and land turtles are different.
G. tell a funny story about turtles.
H. explain how people can help sea turtles.
(J) describe the life of a sea turtle.

15. The author probably thinks that sea turtles—
(A) must overcome many difficulties to survive.
B. are the most intelligent animals in the world.
C. take excellent care of their young.
D. are gentle, friendly creatures.

Selection Test 525

Name________________________ Into the Sea

Author's Purpose

- An **author's purpose** is the reason or reasons an author has for writing.
- Four common purposes are to entertain, to inform, to express, and to persuade.

Directions: Read the following book titles and descriptions. Then fill in the table below by providing missing purposes or explanations. You may use a purpose more than once. **Possible answers given.**

My Life Among the Sea Turtles—A noted scientist tells of her love for the great beasts, along with fascinating details of their daily life.
Turtles in Space!—Another adventure of the infamous Turtle Terrors. Inside a space shuttle, they make trouble for the astronauts by chomping holes in the shuttle wall and even in a spacesuit!
Natural Beauties—This collection of poems shows the beauty and wonder of turtles—the patterns of their shells, their awkward movements on land, and their graceful swimming.
Save the Sea Turtles!—An animal activist argues for action to protect baby sea turtles and restore sea turtle nesting grounds.
The Family of Turtles—This book is filled with color photographs of turtles in the wild. The notes include facts about each turtle's habitat, food, and egg-laying behavior.

Book Title	Purpose for Writing	Explanation
My Life Among the Sea Turtles	inform, express	1. **tells about turtles; tells of her love for them**
Turtles in Space!	2. **entertain**	It tells a science fiction adventure.
Natural Beauties	3. **express**	Poems show beauty and wonder.
Save the Sea Turtles!	persuade	4. **It tries to get readers to act.**
The Family of Turtles	inform	5. **It gives facts about turtles.**

Notes for Home: Your child used book titles and descriptions to identify an author's purpose. ***Home Activity:*** Read a variety of short newspaper articles, including sports stories and comic strips, with your child. Discuss the author's purpose for each text.

526 Author's Purpose

Practice Book 4.5, p. 237

Name________________________ Into the Sea

Summarizing and Steps in a Process

REVIEW

Directions: Read the passage. Then read each question about the passage. Choose the best answer to each question. Mark the letter for the answer you have chosen.

Turtle Watching

Turtle watching may not be as exciting as whale watching, but you don't have to live near the ocean to do it.

Here's how to find a turtle. If you live where the winter is cold, you must first wait for spring. Then pick a sunny day. Choose a nearby stream with a soft bottom, a lake, a pond, a marsh, or a swamp. There should be a lot of plants. Turtles like them.

After you've chosen a good spot, take an adult with you. Travel on foot or in a small boat. Either way, be quiet. Don't make any sudden moves.

Finally, look for a rock or a log sticking out of the water. You just may see a turtle on it.

Now what? If you want to find out what kind of turtle you are looking at, well, that's another story.

1. The first thing you must do if you want to go turtle watching is—
A. buy a telescope.
B. get a boat.
C. find a stream.
(D) be sure it is not too cold.

2. The next thing you should do is—
F. learn all you can about turtles.
(G) pick a sunny day.
H. travel in a boat.
J. look for a rock.

3. To pick a spot, the first two things you should look for are—
A. water and food.
B. water and rocks.
C. boats and people.
(D) water and plants.

4. Which of the following statements best summarizes the third paragraph?
(F) After finding a location, travel quietly and carefully with an adult by boat or on foot.
G. Take an adult with you.
H. Be quiet and don't move.
J. Travel with an adult either on foot or by small boat.

5. Which clue word signals the last step in finding turtles?
A. then
B. after
(C) finally
D. now

Notes for Home: Your child used story details to recognize steps in a process and to summarize the main idea of a passage. ***Home Activity:*** Together, tell a story about an activity you and your child do. Include steps to follow to do the activity.

Summarizing and Steps in a Process 527

Name________________________ Into the Sea

Writing Across Texts

Directions: Think about the job of Norbert Wu in "I Work in the Ocean." What kinds of careers can you think of that could be connected to the sea turtles described in *Into the Sea?* Brainstorm a list of possible careers and write them in the following table. Then choose a favorite career idea and make a list of reasons why it might be a good career to have. **Possible answers given.**

Possible Sea Turtle Careers	Favorite Career Idea and Why It Might Be a Good Career
1. **turtle keeper at the zoo or nature preserve**	Favorite Career Idea: 6. **documentary filmmaker**
2. **coast guard in charge of stopping egg and shell poachers**	Reasons It Might Be a Good Career: 7. **You get to travel all over the world.**
3. **scientist who studies turtle migration**	8. **You get to swim every day.**
4. **documentary filmmaker**	9. **You get to help people understand the plight of the turtles.**
5. **ecologist who educates the public about the plight of the turtles**	10. **You get to use interesting equipment.**

Write a Paragraph

On a separate sheet of paper, write a paragraph that explains why the career you chose might be a good career to have. Use ideas from your table in the paragraph. **Paragraphs will vary. Check that students have named the career in a topic sentence and included supporting sentences.**

Notes for Home: Your child wrote about an interesting career. ***Home Activity:*** Ask your child to tell about a career he or she might like to have. Visit the library to find books about it. Help your child make a list of things he or she needs to do to accomplish this career goal.

528 Writing Across Texts

Grammar Practice Book 4.5, p. 116

Name ____________ Into the Sea

Grammar: Pronouns and Referents

REVIEW

Directions: Underline the pronoun in each sentence. Then draw a circle around its referent. Hint: One pronoun is a possessive pronoun.

1. Turtles may seem slow and dull, but they are really interesting creatures.
2. Jeff and Josh like turtles so much that they have a pet turtle.
3. Jeff claims that he has trained the turtle to do tricks.
4. The turtle's only "trick," though, is to pull its head inside the shell.
5. Jeff says that seems like an amazing trick to him!

Directions: Write a sentence or a pair of sentences using the nouns and pronouns given. Use each noun as the referent of each pronoun. **Possible answers given.**

6. turtle, it
The turtle moved slowly, but it finally got to the pond.
7. students, they
The students visited the Natural History Museum. There they saw the new turtle exhibit.
8. teacher, him
After our teacher showed a video about turtles, the class asked him many questions.
9. scientist, she
The scientist studies turtles, so she had many interesting things to tell us.
10. turtles, them
I have always liked turtles. Now I am learning more about them.

Notes for Home: Your child matched pronouns with their referents—the nouns they replace in sentences. ***Home Activity:*** With your child, write a story about an animal. Then ask your child to identify the referent of each pronoun in the story.

Grammar Practice Book 4.5, p. 117

Name ____________ Into the Sea

Grammar: Prepositions and Prepositional Phrases

A **preposition** is a word that shows how a word is related to other words in the sentence. A preposition begins a group of words called a **prepositional phrase.** The phrase ends with a noun or pronoun called the **object of the preposition.**

The turtle walked into the sea. The plane flew above the sea.

A prepositional phrase can be used to tell where, when, how, or which one.

Where did the turtle go? It went into the sea.

When did it go? It moved after sunset.

How did it walk? It walked with slow steps.

Which turtle was it? It was the one with a spotted shell.

Common Prepositions				
about	around	between	into	to
above	at	by	of	under
across	behind	for	on	upon
after	below	from	over	with
against	beneath	in	through	without

Directions: Underline the prepositional phrase in each sentence once. Draw a second line under the preposition.

1. The dolphins leaped over the waves.
2. They liked playing in the water.
3. At certain times, they joined the tuna.
4. Many tiny fish swam into view.
5. A baby dolphin swam after them.
6. The crabs walked on the shore.
7. Some hid under the mud.
8. Some dug into the sand.
9. One crab with a heavy shell moved slowly.
10. Another climbed over the log.

Notes for Home: Your child used prepositions, such as *in, on,* and *with,* and prepositional phrases, such as *in the sea.* ***Home Activity:*** Ask your child to tell you the exact location of an object that you name. Then ask the child to identify the prepositions he or she used.

Grammar Practice Book 4.5, p. 118

Name ____________ Into the Sea

Grammar: Prepositions and Prepositional Phrases

Directions: Circle the prepositional phrase that best answers the question in ( ) to complete each sentence.

1. Huge mammals called whales live ____. *(Where?)*
(in the ocean/on land and sea)
2. This has been their home ____. *(When?)*
(for the future/for a long time)
3. Blue whales, killer whales, and others exist ____. *(Where?)*
(on our planet/on small ponds)
4. Some countries protect whales ____. *(How?)*
(through laws/from wild animals)
5. Whales ____ perform well in water shows. *(Which?)*
(with kind trainers/without experience)

Directions: Add a prepositional phrase to each sentence. Begin the phrase with a preposition from the box. **Possible answers given.**

for	to	at	into	toward

6. Rosa dived happily **into the lake**.
7. She swam until her dad waved **to her**.
8. Her dad was pointing **at his watch**.
9. Rosa suddenly felt hungry **for some lunch**.
10. She waved back and swam **toward the beach**.

Write Directions

On a separate sheet of paper, write directions telling how to get to a place that you like to visit. Use at least five prepositions, and underline each one. **Students' directions should be clear and specific, and they should contain at least five prepositions.**

Notes for Home: Your child wrote prepositions, such as *in, for,* and *through,* and prepositional phrases, such as *in the ocean.* ***Home Activity:*** Describe an object's location, using prepositions. Have your child guess the object and identify the prepositions you used.

Grammar Practice Book 4.5, p. 119

Name ____________ Into the Sea

Grammar: Prepositions and Prepositional Phrases

RETEACHING

Choose the preposition in ( ) that makes the most sense in each sentence.

1. We ran (under/down) the path.
2. T.J. called (after/against) you left.

A **preposition** shows how a word is related to one or more other words in the sentence. A preposition is the first word in a **prepositional phrase.** Prepositional phrases can answer the questions **Where? When? How?** and **Which one?** What questions do the two sentences above answer? **Where and when**

Directions: Draw a line from the phrase on the left to the prepositional phrase on the right that best matches it.

1. Luz told Julie to go — to the store.
2. Their mother called — from the basement
3. "There is money — in the jar."
4. "I will go — after this show."
5. "Be back — by four o'clock!"

Directions: Underline the prepositional phrase or phrases in each sentence.

6. My dog is the best dog in the world.
7. He comes when I call, and he walks behind me.
8. If I go to the park, he comes with me.
9. One time I couldn't find him anywhere around the house.
10. I looked under the stairs.
11. I also searched through my bedroom.

Notes for Home: Your child identified prepositions and prepositional phrases in sentences. ***Home Activity:*** Look for prepositional phrases in books or magazines. Have your child identify which questions—*How? When? Where? Which one?*—they answer.

Grammar Practice Book 4.5, p. 120

Name ____________________ Into the Sea

Grammar: Prepositions and Prepositional Phrases

about	above	across	against	behind	by	in	through	to	under	with

Directions: Choose a preposition from the box to complete each sentence. Write it on the line to the left. **Possible answers given.**

to 1. Last weekend my family went _____ a movie.

about 2. The movie was _____ a lot of animals.

in 3. The animals lived _____ a forest.

under 4. Some of them liked to hide _____ the dirt.

above 5. Others swung in trees _____ the ground.

across 6. My favorites were squirrels that ran _____ tree branches.

through 7. Sometimes they flew right _____ the leaves!

against 8. They never crashed _____ anything!

behind 9. My younger stepsister hid _____ her mom.

with 10. She was afraid of the fox _____ sharp teeth.

Directions: Add a prepositional phrase to each sentence. Use a preposition from the box above to begin each prepositional phrase. **Possible answers given.**

11. Kenji hid **by the bed.**
12. He didn't want to be seen **with his pajamas on.**
13. His friends looked **behind the closet door.**
14. One of them saw movement **through the curtains.**
15. Kenji was hiding **against the window.**

Notes for Home: Your child wrote prepositions and prepositional phrases. ***Home Activity:*** Have your child hide four objects in a room. Then have him or her write prepositional phrases as clues for you to find the objects.

Grammar: Prepositions and Prepositional Phrases 533

Practice Book 4.5, p. 238

Name ____________________ Into the Sea

Phonics: Schwa Sound

Directions: The **schwa sound** is an indistinct vowel sound heard in an unstressed syllable. The **a** in **against** and the **o** in **favorite** are examples of the schwa sound. Read each word below. Underline the schwa sound in each word.

1. alone	6. delicate	11. tropical
2. difficult	7. bottom	12. oppose
3. moment	8. across	13. coward
4. around	9. sargassum	14. accuse
5. seasonal	10. surround	15. compete

Directions: Read each sentence below. Say the underlined word carefully to yourself. Listen for the schwa sound. Write the word on the line. Circle the letter or letters that represent the schwa sound.

amazed 16. The more I learn about sea animals, the more amazed I am at how clever they are.

currents 17. For example, some sea animals float with the ocean's currents as they migrate.

attach 18. Some small sea animals attach themselves to larger ones to catch a ride.

plankton 19. Some sea creatures survive by eating small bits of plankton that float in the water.

camouflage 20. Many sea animals camouflage themselves, using their colors to blend in with their environment.

Notes for Home: Your child identified letters that represent the schwa sound, such as the *a* in *against* and the *o* in *favorite*. ***Home Activity:*** Read a story with your child. List words with two or more syllables that have the schwa sound. You can check these words in a dictionary.

534 Phonics: Schwa Sound

Spelling Workbook 4.5, p. 93

Name ____________________ Into the Sea

Spelling: Vowels with No Sound Clues

Pretest Directions: Fold back the page along the dotted line. On the blanks, write the spelling words as they are dictated. When you have finished the test, unfold the page and check your words.

1. **machine**	1. That's a powerful **machine**.
2. **especially**	2. He's **especially** nice.
3. **usually**	3. She's **usually** very quiet.
4. **probably**	4. We're **probably** not going.
5. **giant**	5. It was a **giant** mountain.
6. **buffalo**	6. The **buffalo** grazed peacefully.
7. **Canada**	7. **Canada** is in North America.
8. **canoe**	8. How many can fit in the **canoe**?
9. **relatives**	9. Our **relatives** are coming to visit.
10. **stomach**	10. My **stomach** is full.
11. **moment**	11. Take a **moment** to relax.
12. **cement**	12. The **cement** isn't dry yet.
13. **yesterday**	13. I went to see her **yesterday**.
14. **animals**	14. The **animals** are howling.
15. **iron**	15. The anchor is made of **iron**.
16. **favorite**	16. That's my **favorite** fish.
17. **welcome**	17. We feel **welcome** here.
18. **support**	18. Do you **support** this idea?
19. **suppose**	19. I don't **suppose** you agree.
20. **August**	20. We will see you again in **August**.

Notes for Home: Your child took a pretest on words whose vowel sounds have no sound clues. ***Home Activity:*** Help your child learn misspelled words before the final test. Have your child divide misspelled words into parts (such as syllables) and concentrate on each part.

Spelling: Vowels with No Sound Clues 535

Spelling Workbook 4.5, p. 94

Name ____________________ Into the Sea

Spelling: Vowels with No Sound Clues

Word List

machine	giant	relatives	yesterday	welcome
especially	buffalo	stomach	animals	support
usually	Canada	moment	iron	suppose
probably	canoe	cement	favorite	August

Directions: Choose the word from the box that contains each word below. Write the word on the line.

1. special **especially**	6. usual **usually**
2. ant **giant**	7. buff **buffalo**
3. day **yesterday**	8. come **welcome**
4. port **support**	9. pose **suppose**
5. gust **August**	10. favor **favorite**

Directions: Choose the word from the box that best matches each clue. Write the word on the line.

Canada 11. It's the country north of the United States.

animals 12. These can be wild, or they can be tame.

machine 13. A toaster is one of these, and so is a car.

probably 14. It means the same as "likely."

canoe 15. You paddle in one.

relatives 16. They come to a family reunion.

cement 17. A sidewalk is made of this.

iron 18. Steel is made from this.

moment 19. It's a tiny amount of time.

stomach 20. It's where your food goes after it's swallowed.

Notes for Home: Your child spelled words in which the vowel sound gives no clue to its spelling, such as in *animals*. ***Home Activity:*** Make up memory tricks with your child to help remember correct spellings (*I see the animals.*).

536 Spelling: Vowels with No Sound Clues

Spelling Workbook 4.5, p. 95

Name______________________ Into the Sea

Spelling: Vowels with No Sound Clues

Directions: Proofread this description of a meeting with a turtle. Find five spelling mistakes. Use the proofreading marks to correct each mistake.

≡ Make a capital.
/ Make a small letter.
∧ Add something.
Take out something.
○ Add a period.
¶ Begin a new paragraph.

Welcome to My Home

Have you ever met a turtle eye to eye? It isn't always easy because turtles don't usually let you get that close. But one time, I was on a canoe trip in Canada. We were heading toward a giant rock — or so I thought. It turned out to be probably the largest turtle I've ever seen! Just as we passed it, the turtle stuck its head out of its shell. I think it was as surprised as I was.

(Corrections marked: Wel~~l~~come, can~~ew~~ ∧o, Can~~n~~ada, gi~~e~~∧ant, prob∧baly)

Spelling Tip

In many words, the vowel sound gives no clue to its spelling: **machine, moment, animals, iron, support.** Make up memory tricks to help you remember correct spellings, such as: The **stomach** is an eating **machine.**

Word List

machine	moment
especially	cement
usually	yesterday
probably	animals
giant	iron
buffalo	favorite
Canada	welcome
canoe	support
relatives	suppose
stomach	August

Write a Paragraph

On a separate sheet of paper, write a paragraph describing an interesting experience with an animal. Try to use at least four spelling words. **Answers will vary, but each paragraph should include at least four spelling words.**

Notes for Home: Your child spelled words in which the vowel sound gives no clues to its spelling, such as in *animals*. ***Home Activity:*** Say each spelling word aloud, and have your child write it. Together, check for misspellings and correct them.

Spelling: Vowels with No Sound Clues 537

Spelling Workbook 4.5, p. 96

Name______________________ Into the Sea

Spelling: Vowels with No Sound Clues

REVIEW

Word List

machine	giant	relatives	yesterday	welcome
especially	buffalo	stomach	animals	support
usually	Canada	moment	iron	suppose
probably	canoe	cement	favorite	August

Directions: Write the word from the box that belongs in each group.

1. Mexico, United States, **Canada**
2. kayak, rowboat, **canoe**
3. creatures, beasts, **animals**
4. best, preferred, **favorite**
5. huge, immense, **giant**
6. extremely, unusually, **especially**
7. normally, commonly, **usually**
8. instant, second, **moment**
9. likely, chances are, **probably**
10. guess, assume, **suppose**

Directions: Choose the word from the box that best answers each riddle. Write the word on the line.

stomach 11. Call me tummy or belly, I like bread and jelly.
cement 12. The harder I get, the easier I am to walk on.
machine 13. You can turn me on or turn me off.
welcome 14. This is how the doormat says, "Come in!"
iron 15. If you press on me, I'll press your clothes.
support 16. If I leave, you might fall.
buffalo 17. My body is hairy; I live on the prairie.
relatives 18. You can choose your friends but not these.
yesterday 19. I'm always behind you, never ahead.
August 20. Enjoy this month, summer's almost over.

Notes for Home: Your child spelled words in which the vowel sound gives no clue to its spelling, such as in *animal*. ***Home Activity:*** Play a word scramble game. Each player scrambles the letters of individual spelling words for others to unscramble, such as *onace* for *canoe*.

538 Spelling: Vowels with No Sound Clues

Practice Book 4.5, p. 239

Name______________________ Into the Sea

Diagram/Scale Drawing/ Pictures and Captions

A **diagram** is a special drawing with labels. Diagrams often show how something is made or how it works. A **scale drawing** is a diagram that uses a mathematical scale to help you determine the actual size of the subject. For example, a scale of 1 inch = 1 foot means that one inch on the drawing represents one foot in real life.

Directions: Use this diagram of the skeleton of a sea turtle to answer the questions that follow.

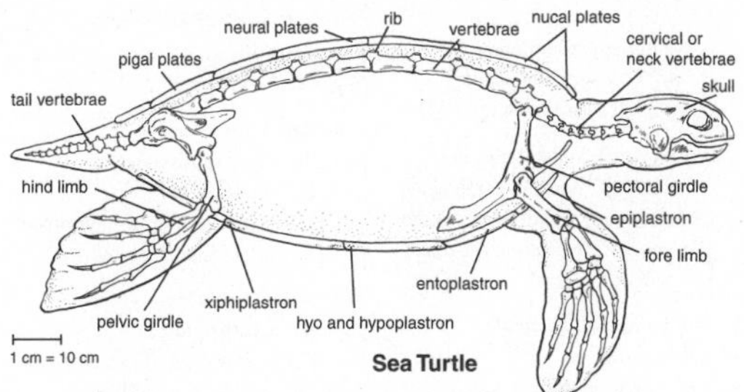

1. One centimeter on the drawing equals how many centimeters on a turtle? **10**
2. About how long is the tail vertebrae of a real sea turtle? **about 20 centimeters**
3. Where are a sea turtle's nucal plates: near the neck, on the back, or near the tail? **near the neck**
4. The vertebrae begin at the neck. Where do they end? **at the tail**
5. What is the name of the bone that forms the sea turtle's head? **skull**
6. A sea turtle has two girdles that help support its shell. What are the full names of the two girdles? **pectoral girdle and pelvic girdle**

Research and Study Skills: Diagram/Scale Drawing/Pictures and Captions 539

Practice Book 4.5, p. 240

Name______________________ Into the Sea

Pictures are photographs or artwork that tell information about characters and events in a story or an article. They can also help set a mood. Sometimes pictures have captions that explain what is happening in a drawing or photograph.

Directions: Use the picture and the caption to answer the questions that follow.

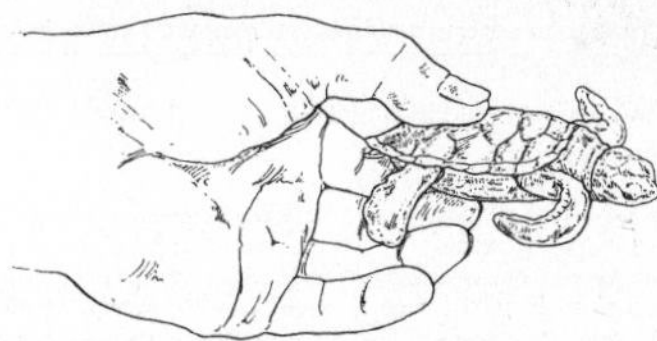

Newly hatched sea turtles are quite small in comparison to their parents. Immediately after hatching on the sandy shores, newborn sea turtles head for the water. This journey is full of danger and many newborn sea turtles become food for hungry birds and other predators.

7. Why do you think the artist included a human hand in this drawing? **The human hand helps show how small a newborn sea turtle is.**
8. Is a newborn sea turtle able to swim right away? How do you know? **Yes, the caption says that newborn sea turtles immediately head for water.**
9. Why is the trip from the hatching site to the sea a dangerous one for newborn sea turtles? **Hungry birds and other predators might eat the newborn sea turtles.**
10. Why is it important to read the labels, scales, and captions for pictures carefully? **Labels, scales, and captions help explain the pictures, so you need to read them carefully to understand the pictures.**

Notes for Home: Your child answered questions about a scale drawing and a picture with a caption. ***Home Activity:*** Ask your child to read captions from newspaper photos and tell you what information the captions provide.

540 Research and Study Skills: Diagram/Scale Drawing/Pictures and Captions

Practice Book 4.5, p. 241
Name______________________

Space Probes to the Planets

Text Structure

- **Text structure** is the way a piece of writing is organized. There are two main kinds of writing, fiction and nonfiction.
- Fiction tells stories of people and events that an author creates. It is usually organized by the order in which things happen. Nonfiction tells of real people and events or tells information about the real world. Some ways to organize nonfiction are cause and effect, problem and solution, and compare and contrast.

Directions: Reread "Out-of-This-World Rocks." Then complete the diagram below. List things that are true about space rocks on the left, things that are true about Earth rocks on the right, and things that are true about both kinds of rocks in the middle. Then describe the type of organization used for this text.

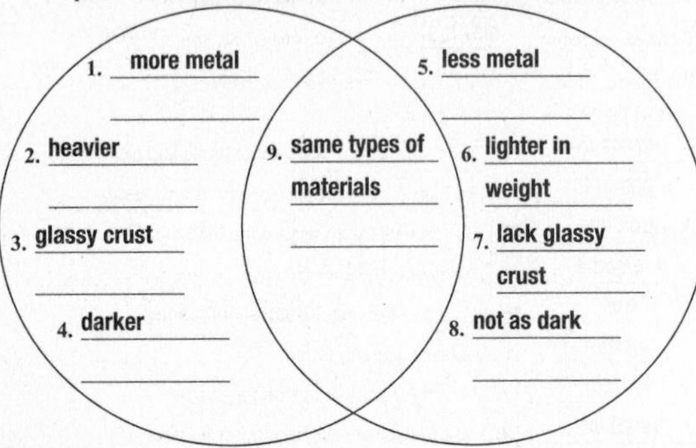

Type of Organization

10. **compare and contrast**

Notes for Home: Your child read an article and identified how information in the article is organized. ***Home Activity:*** Have your child read a newspaper, magazine, or reference book article. Together, look at how the article organizes its information.

Practice Book 4.5, p. 242
Name______________________

Space Probes to the Planets

Vocabulary

Directions: Choose the word from the box that best matches each definition. Write the word on the line.

Check the Words You Know
__ atmosphere
__ craters
__ incredible
__ probes
__ spacecraft

incredible 1. amazing

atmosphere 2. gases that surround a planet

spacecraft 3. vehicle used to fly into outer space

craters 4. holes in ground

probes 5. spacecraft carrying scientific instruments to record information

Directions: Choose the word from the box that best completes each sentence. Write the word on the line to the left.

atmosphere 6. When astronauts land on other planets they cannot breathe because there is no oxygen in the _____.

spacecraft 7. Of course, there is plenty of oxygen inside the _____ in which they travel.

probes 8. Sometimes, it is easier to send space _____ without any astronauts aboard.

incredible 9. The information that scientists can now collect is simply _____!

craters 10. They can even explore the hills and _____ of the moon.

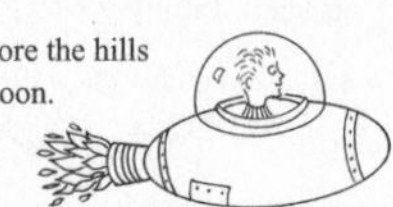

Write a Log Entry

Imagine you are an astronaut. On a separate sheet of paper, write an entry in your log telling about the day you landed on a new planet. Use as many vocabulary words as you can. **Students' logs should use vocabulary words correctly.**

Notes for Home: Your child identified and used vocabulary words from *Space Probes to the Planets.* ***Home Activity:*** Say the definition of each vocabulary word, and have your child tell you what the word is. Alternately, you say the word and have your child supply the definition.

Practice Book 4.5, p. 243
Name______________________

Space Probes to the Planets

Text Structure

- **Text structure** is the way a piece of writing is organized. The two main kinds of writing are fiction and nonfiction.
- Nonfiction tells about the real world. Some ways to organize nonfiction are cause and effect, problem and solution, and compare and contrast.

Directions: Reread the opening passage from *Space Probes to the Planets.* Then answer the questions below.

Have you ever wanted to visit another planet? Ever since the planets were discovered, people have dreamed of visiting them. But the planets are all very hot or very cold, and very far away. Until scientists learn more, a trip to explore them would be unsafe.

In the meantime we've learned a lot about the planets, partly because of space probes. Space probes are spacecraft with no people on them. With the help of computers and radio signals, they can travel to the planets by themselves.

1. Why would a trip to the planets be unsafe?
The planets are too hot or too cold and too far away.

2. How have scientists learned about the planets if they couldn't send people to explore them?
Scientists have sent space probes to find out more about the planets.

3. Why is it safe to use space probes?
The space probes do not have people in them.

4. Which kind of organization does this passage use: cause and effect, problem and solution, or compare and contrast? Explain. **Possible answer: Problem and solution; It describes a problem of using people to explore the planets and tells how space probes have helped solve this problem.**

5. Look at the rest of the story. Choose a passage and tell how it is organized. Write your answer on a separate sheet of paper. **Check that students' identification of text structure is appropriate for the passage selected.**

Notes for Home: Your child used story details to identify the ways the text was organized. ***Home Activity:*** Go to the library with your child and find examples of fiction and nonfiction books about space exploration. Discuss how the writing is organized in each book.

Practice Book 4.5, p. 245
Name______________________

Space Probes to the Planets

Selection Test

Directions: Choose the best answer to each item. Mark the letter for the answer you have chosen.

Part 1: Vocabulary

Find the answer choice that means about the same as the underlined word in each sentence.

1. I know a lot about spacecraft.
   A. science of outer space
   B. outer-space explorers
   C. rocks from outer space
   (D) vehicles for traveling in space

2. It is part of Earth's atmosphere.
   F. materials a planet is made of
   G. planet's distance from the Sun
   (H) mass of gases around a planet
   J. size of a planet

3. This picture is incredible.
   (A) amazing
   B. unclear or hard to see
   C. colorful
   D. old or out of date

4. Probes have been very useful.
   (F) space vehicles that collect and send information
   G. suits worn by astronauts
   H. rocky objects that circle the Sun
   J. maps of the solar system

5. Some planets have craters.
   (A) bowl-shaped holes
   B. rings of gas
   C. thick layers of clouds
   D. mountain ranges

Part 2: Comprehension

Use what you know about the selection to answer each item.

6. Space probes are built to—
   F. carry astronauts.
   G. follow meteoroids.
   (H) travel to or near other planets.
   J. circle Earth's moon.

7. Some probes have—
   A. returned to Earth.
   B. found signs of life on Jupiter.
   C. flown close to Pluto.
   (D) landed on Mars and Venus.

8. One probe showed that Mercury—
   (F) has many craters.
   G. is very cold.
   H. has some small moons.
   J. is getting larger.

GO ON

Practice Book 4.5, p. 246

Name______________________ **Space Probes to the Planets**

9. To find out about Venus, scientists needed to—
A. gather information from Earth.
B. wait for good weather.
C. build a larger probe.
(D) make special cameras.

10. Why do scientists believe there might have been life on Mars?
F. It has a red-orange color.
G. It is the fourth planet from the Sun.
(H) They think it once had rivers of water.
J. It has a rocky surface.

11. What makes scientists think Uranus was knocked over?
A. its hazy glow
(B) the direction of its rings
C. its blue color
D the patterns on its surface

12. The author's main purpose in this selection is to—
(F) describe what the probes have revealed about the planets.
G. explain how scientists solved problems with the probes.
H. tell how probes are different from other space vehicles.
J. tell a fictional story of a probe.

13. This selection presents the planets in order from—
A. largest to smallest.
(B) closest to the Sun to farthest from the Sun.
C. most colorful to least colorful.
D. most like Earth to least like Earth.

14. The author probably thinks that exploring space with probes is—
F. dangerous.
G. wasteful.
H. boring.
(J) useful.

15. Which sentence states an opinion?
A. "The Sun and all the planets and objects that circle it are called the solar system."
(B) "The most exciting information came from pictures the space probes took."
C. "Two of the space probes carry a record that plays sounds from Earth."
D. "They are sending other space probes to the planets to learn more."

Name______________________ **Space Probes to the Planets**

Text Structure

- **Text structure** is the way a piece of writing is organized. The two main kinds of writing are fiction and nonfiction.
- Nonfiction tells about the real world. Some ways to organize nonfiction are cause and effect, problem and solution, and compare and contrast.

Directions: Read the passage below.

Asteroids are tiny planets made of rock or metal. Most of them orbit, or travel in a path, around the Sun between Mars and Jupiter. That part of our solar system is called the *asteroid belt.* Asteroids are usually named by number in order of discovery. Some have been named for make-believe figures or people. The largest asteroid is Ceres. If you could measure it through its middle from side to side, Ceres measures more than 600 miles. The tiniest asteroids are the size of a grain of sand.

Comets are also travelers in the solar system. A comet is a huge lump of ice and rock. It zooms through space in a path around the Sun. As a comet comes close to the Sun, the ice melts. Clouds of dust and gas are released. They follow the comet, shining with reflected sunlight, like a brilliant tail in the sky. Comets are named for the people who discovered them. A comet may be only two miles across, but its tail may be 79,000 miles long!

Directions: For each feature listed in the table, fill in details to compare and contrast asteroids and comets.

Feature	Asteroids	Comets
Orbit	1. **They orbit around the Sun between Mars and Jupiter.**	They zoom in a path around the Sun.
Size	They can be 600 miles thick or the size of a grain of sand.	2. **They can be 2 miles wide with a 79,000-mile tail.**
Made of	3. **They are made of rock or metal.**	4. **They are made of rocks and ice.**
How named	They are usually named by number in order of discovery.	5. **They are named for people who discovered them.**

Notes for Home: Your child read a nonfiction passage that compared and contrasted asteroids and comets. ***Home Activity:*** Help your child write a short nonfiction piece about a topic he or she knows well, such as sports or music. Use comparisons and contrasts to organize the information.

Practice Book 4.5, p. 247

Name______________________ **Space Probes to the Planets**

Graphic Sources

REVIEW

Directions: Read the passage and the table. Then read each question about the passage and the table. Choose the best answer to each question. Mark the letter for the answer you have chosen.

On August 27, 1962, the United States sent a spacecraft to Venus. *Mariner 2* came within 22,000 miles of Venus. Then it lost contact with Earth. Since then, there have been a number of space probes sent to the planets.

Space Probes to the Planets

Spacecraft	Launch Date	Mission
Mariner 6	February 25, 1969	Mars
Pioneer 10	March 3, 1972	Jupiter
Voyager 2	August 20, 1977	Jupiter, Saturn, Uranus, Neptune
Galileo	October 18, 1989	Jupiter

1. The space probe launched in October 1989 was—
A. *Voyager 2.*
B. *Mariner 2.*
C. *Mariner 6.*
(D) *Galileo.*

2. Which planet was explored more than once for the missions listed?
(F) Jupiter
G. Mars
H. Venus
J. Mercury

3. According to the passage and table, the two missions launched in the 1960s were—
A. *Pioneer 10* and *Mariner 2*
B. *Pioneer 10* and *Mariner 6*
(C) *Mariner 2* and *Mariner 6*
D. *Pioneer 10* and *Voyager 2*

4. How many years passed between the first and most recent launch to Jupiter?
F. 5 years
G. 20 years
(H) 17 years
J. 6 years

5. Which probe went to four planets?
A. *Mariner 6*
B. *Galileo*
(C) *Voyager 2*
D. *Pioneer 10*

Notes for Home: Your child answered questions based on information given in a nonfiction passage and table. ***Home Activity:*** Find other examples of tables on cereal boxes, magazines, and newspapers. Ask your child questions that can be answered using data in the tables.

Name______________________ **Space Probes to the Planets**

Writing Across Texts

Directions: Consider what you learned from the selections *Space Probes to the Planets* and "Meet the Universe's Main Attraction . . . Gravity." Imagine you are an astronaut who is walking on another planet for the first time. Use the following table to record ideas about your experience. Compare that planet's gravitational pull with Earth's. **Possible answers given.**

Walking on **Mars**
What I See 1. **I see brownish, red rock as I step out of the spacecraft.**
What I Hear 2. **I hear the sound of my oxygen tank allowing me to breathe.**
What I Smell 3. **I smell plastic, rubber, and nylon as I start to sweat in my suit.**
What I Touch 4. **I collect rock and dust samples in small plastic dishes.**
How I Feel 5. **Since Mars is smaller than Earth, the gravitational pull is less and I feel lighter.**

Write a Journal Entry

On a separate sheet of paper, write a journal entry that describes your visit to another planet. Include ideas you compiled in the table above. **Journal entries will vary. Check that students use sensory details to support their ideas.**

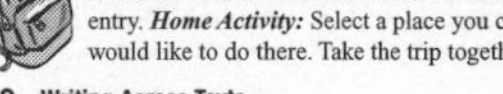

Notes for Home: Your child used the ideas from different stories to write their own journal entry. ***Home Activity:*** Select a place you could visit in a day, and make a list of what you would like to do there. Take the trip together and discuss your journey when you get home.

Grammar Practice Book 4.5, p. 121
Name____________________

Space Probes to the Planets

Grammar: Compound and Complex Sentences

REVIEW

Directions: Write **compound** or **complex** to identify each kind of sentence.

compound 1. Our solar system has nine planets, but it has other parts as well.

compound 2. Asteroids are numerous, and some come near Earth.

complex 3. When an asteroid enters Earth's atmosphere, it is called a *meteor.*

complex 4. If it reaches Earth's surface, it is called a *meteorite.*

compound 5. Comets seem to have tails, but these are just trails of gas and dust.

complex 6. Because the Sun produces both heat and light, it is called a star.

compound 7. Mercury is the closest planet to the Sun, and Venus is the second closest planet.

compound 8. Pluto is thought to be the farthest planet, but there may be more planets beyond it.

Directions: Combine each pair of sentences. Add a connecting word, such as *and, but, or, because, if,* or *when,* to make the kind of sentence shown in ( ). Write your new sentence on the line. **Possible answers given.**

9. Jupiter is the largest planet. It rotates very fast for its size. (compound)
Jupiter is the largest planet, and it rotates very fast for its size.

10. Mercury is close to the Sun. It moves around the Sun in only 88 days. (complex)
Because Mercury is close to the Sun, it moves around the Sun in only 88 days.

Notes for Home: Your child wrote compound and complex sentences. ***Home Activity:*** With your child, write simple sentences about space travel. Work together to try to combine them into compound or complex sentences.

Grammar Practice Book 4.5, p. 122
Name____________________

Space Probes to the Planets

Grammar: Conjunctions

Connecting words such as *and, but,* or *or* are called **conjunctions.** Conjunctions can be used to join words, phrases, or entire sentences. They are used to make compound subjects, predicates, and sentences.

Compound subject: Mercury and Venus are closest to the Sun.
Compound predicate: The probe circled the planet and sent signals.
Compound sentence: We can explore Venus, or we can explore Mars.

- Use *and* to join related ideas: Saturn and Uranus have rings.
- Use *but* to join different ideas: Saturn's rings go around the planet, but Uranus's rings go over it.
- Use *or* to suggest a choice: Would you rather study Saturn or Uranus?

Directions: Underline the conjunction in each sentence.

1. Telescopes and microscopes provide useful information.
2. They have been used to study large and small objects.
3. Would you rather use a telescope or a microscope to look at the moon?
4. A telescope is good for looking at planets, but a microscope is better for looking at germs!
5. An astronomer uses a telescope, but a doctor uses a microscope.

Directions: Choose the conjunction in ( ) to complete each sentence. Write the conjunction on the line.

and 6. The probe sent back pictures (but/and) information.

or 7. Was the information new (or/but) old?

but 8. Some of the information was old, (but/or) most of it was new.

and 9. Both Mercury (and/but) the moon have craters.

but 10. We knew about the moon's craters, (but/or) we did not know about the craters on Mercury.

Notes for Home: Your child used the conjunctions *and, or,* and *but.* ***Home Activity:*** Say some sentences that include *and, or,* or *but.* Ask your child to identify the conjunctions and to describe the words, phrases, or sentences that each conjunction joins.

Grammar Practice Book 4.5, p. 123
Name____________________

Space Probes to the Planets

Grammar: Conjunctions

Directions: Circle the correct conjunction in ( ) to complete each sentence.

1. The scientist looked through the telescope, (and/or) then she scratched her head.
2. Was something wrong with her telescope, (but/or) had she made a great discovery?
3. She blinked (and/or) then peered again at an object on the side of the planet.
4. It did not exactly twinkle, (or/but) it did look like a star!
5. The scientist was excited, (but/or) she decided to stay calm.
6. She called in a friend, (and/or) he thought he saw the same thing.
7. Was it a new star, (and/or) was it just something unimportant?
8. Would they become famous, (and/but) would other scientists respect them?
9. Together, she (and/or) he made an embarrassing but important discovery.
10. A space probe, on its way to explore the riverbeds (but/and) rocks of Mars, was what they had seen.

Write a Note

Imagine planning a long journey to explore a vast place like the ocean floor. On a separate sheet of paper, list the things that you would bring on your journey. Then write a note to yourself so you will remember to take those items. Use conjunctions to join words, phrases, and sentences. **Check to make sure that students have correctly joined words, phrases, or sentences by using *and, but,* or *or.***

Notes for Home: Your child used *and, or,* and *but* to join words, phrases, and sentences. ***Home Activity:*** Say each conjunction and ask your child to say a sentence that includes it. Then invite the child to name a conjunction, and you offer a sentence that includes it.

Grammar Practice Book 4.5, p. 124
Name____________________

Space Probes to the Planets

Grammar: Conjunctions

RETEACHING

Conjunctions can be used to join words, phrases, or sentences. Choose the conjunction **and, but,** or **or** to complete each sentence.

Example A: Marta **and** Sean enjoy soccer.

Example B: Sean likes to be the goalie, **but** Marta likes to play offense.

Example C: After a game, both friends drink a glass of lemonade **and** relax in the shade.

Conjunctions can be used to form compound subjects (Example A), compound predicates (Example C), and compound sentences (Example B).

Use **and** to join related ideas. Use **but** to join contrasting ideas. Use **or** to suggest a choice.

Directions: Choose the conjunction in ( ) that best completes each sentence. Write the conjunction on the line.

and 1. Tara (and/but) Jack raked the garden.

and 2. They were going to plant seeds (but/and) weed the garden.

but 3. Jack wanted to plant vegetables, (but/or) Tara wanted to plant flowers.

or 4. They realized that they didn't have to choose one (and/or) the other.

and 5. Both friends made space in the garden for flowers (and/but) vegetables.

but 6. The garden would be small, (or/but) it didn't matter.

Notes for Home: Your child identified and wrote the conjunctions *and, but,* and *or* in sentences. ***Home Activity:*** Write the words *and, but,* and *or* on cards. Have your child pick a card and make up a sentence with that conjunction.

Grammar Practice Book 4.5, p. 125
Name______________ Space Probes to the Planets

Grammar: Conjunctions

Directions: Underline the conjunction in each sentence.

1. Oceans and lakes have many things in common.
2. They are bodies of water, and they contain fish.
3. You can swim in an ocean or in a lake.
4. You can also go fishing in oceans and lakes.
5. The biggest difference is that lakes have fresh water, but oceans have salt water.

Directions: Finish each sentence by adding the conjunction **and, but,** or **or,** and more information. Write the conjunction on the line. **Possible answers given.**

6. Last week my friends **and I went camping.**
7. They were very excited **, but it rained all day!**
8. My father said I could either **stay home or sleep in a cabin.**
9. I wanted to do both **, but I decided to see my friends.**
10. Today I am going to the park **and looking at pictures of our trip.**

Write a Journal Entry

On a separate sheet of paper, write about a time you had to choose between doing two different things. Use at least three conjunctions.

Students should write detailed journal entries, including at least three conjunctions in their sentences.

Notes for Home: Your child identified conjunctions and wrote them in sentences. ***Home Activity:*** Have your child explain to you the job of each conjunction in a sentence (*and*—joins related ideas; *but*—joins contrasting ideas; *or*—shows a choice).

Practice Book 4.5, p. 248
Name______________ Space Probes to the Planets

Word Study: Syllabication

Directions: A **syllable** is an individual part of a word that you say or hear. For example, **syllable** has three syllables: **syl • la • ble.** When you add a prefix or a suffix to a word, you often add another syllable: **fast • er.** Read the words below. Separate each word into its syllables, using a dot (fast • er).

1. unsafe **un • safe**
2. partly **part • ly**
3. powerful **pow • er • ful**
4. farthest **far • thest**
5. unless **un • less**
6. quickly **quick • ly**
7. disappoint **dis • ap • point**
8. surface **sur • face**

Directions: Read the paragraph below. Say each underlined word to yourself. Count the number of syllables you hear. Write each word in the correct column.

If you could travel to another galaxy, what would you see? What information would you bring back? You would have to travel across the vast distances of space many times more swiftly than you do on Earth. What you'd see would probably be a combination of the beautiful and the incredible. The planets would look colorful against the darkness of space.

2 syllables
9. **swiftly**
10. **darkness**

3 syllables
11. **beautiful**
12. **colorful**

4 syllables
13. **information**
14. **combination**
15. **incredible**

Notes for Home: Your child identified syllables in words with prefixes such as *un • done* and suffixes such as *safe • ly.* ***Home Activity:*** When you read with your child, look for words with prefixes and suffixes. Ask your child to say the words and to clap to show each syllable.

Spelling Workbook 4.5, p. 97
Name______________ Space Probes to the Planets

Spelling: Using Just Enough Letters

Pretest Directions: Fold back the page along the dotted line. On the blanks, write the spelling words as they are dictated. When you have finished the test, unfold the page and check your words.

1. **coming** — 1. I'm **coming** to watch the launch.
2. **always** — 2. It **always** leaves on time.
3. **almost** — 3. We **almost** didn't make it.
4. **didn't** — 4. The launch **didn't** take long.
5. **upon** — 5. Pebbles fell **upon** the surface.
6. **wasn't** — 6. He **wasn't** thinking clearly.
7. **until** — 7. She waited **until** we came.
8. **during** — 8. They cheered **during** liftoff.
9. **want** — 9. We **want** to visit other planets.
10. **father** — 10. My **father** was an astronaut.
11. **hamster** — 11. This is a cute **hamster**.
12. **a lot** — 12. We run around **a lot**.
13. **ugly** — 13. Some people think eels are **ugly**.
14. **washed** — 14. I just **washed** up for dinner.
15. **hotel** — 15. The **hotel** was full.
16. **missed** — 16. We **missed** the show.
17. **eleven** — 17. Climb **eleven** steps to the top.
18. **crazy** — 18. Are you **crazy**?
19. **lazy** — 19. I'm feeling **lazy** today.
20. **feelings** — 20. Don't ignore your **feelings**.

Notes for Home: Your child took a pretest on words with difficult vowel spellings. ***Home Activity:*** Help your child learn misspelled words before the final test. Your child should look at the word, say it, spell it aloud, and then spell it with eyes shut.

Spelling Workbook 4.5, p. 98
Name______________ Space Probes to the Planets

Spelling: Using Just Enough Letters

Word List				
coming	upon	want	ugly	eleven
always	wasn't	father	washed	crazy
almost	until	hamster	hotel	lazy
didn't	during	a lot	missed	feelings

Directions: Write the words from the box that have two syllables. Hint: Don't include the one two-word spelling word. **Order may vary.**

1. **coming**
2. **always**
3. **almost**
4. **didn't**
5. **upon**
6. **wasn't**
7. **until**
8. **during**
9. **father**
10. **hamster**
11. **ugly**
12. **hotel**
13. **crazy**
14. **lazy**
15. **feelings**

Directions: Choose the word from the box that best matches each clue. Write the word in the puzzle.

Down
16. the opposite of *a little* — **a lot**
18. you're clean once you have done this — **washed**

Across
17. the number just after ten — **eleven**
19. it means the same as *desire* — **want**
20. The batter swung and _____. — **missed**

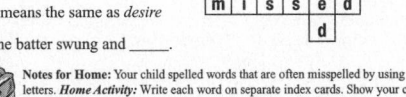

Notes for Home: Your child spelled words that are often misspelled by using too many letters. ***Home Activity:*** Write each word on separate index cards. Show your child the word for a few seconds. Have him or her say it aloud carefully and spell it.

Spelling Workbook 4.5, p. 99

Name ____________________

Space Probes to the Planets

Spelling: Using Just Enough Letters

Directions: Proofread this story about wishing to be an astronaut. Find five spelling mistakes. Use the proofreading marks to correct each mistake.

- ≡ Make a capital.
- / Make a small letter.
- ∧ Add something.
- Take out something.
- ○ Add a period.
- ¶ Begin a new paragraph.

Out of This World

I have allways wanted to be an astronaut. But until last year, I didn't realize that I could be one. My father told me about space camp. My sister thought it was a crazzy idea, but I still went. During space camp I mised my hampster a lot—but not my sister! Yet when I knew my father was comming to pick me up, I wanted to stay longer.

Word List

coming	wasn't	hamster	missed
always	until	a lot	eleven
almost	during	ugly	crazy
didn't	want	washed	lazy
upon	father	hotel	feelings

Write a Short Story

On a separate sheet of paper, write a short story about traveling into space. Try to use at least five spelling words.

Answers will vary, but each story should include at least five spelling words.

Spelling Tip

Pronouncing a word correctly and picturing how it looks can help you avoid writing too many letters.

Notes for Home: Your child spelled words that are often misspelled by using too many letters. ***Home Activity:*** Hold a spelling bee. Include the words on the list plus words from other lessons. Have your child invite classmates or other siblings to participate.

Spelling Workbook 4.5, p. 100

Name ____________________

Space Probes to the Planets

Spelling: Using Just Enough Letters

REVIEW

Word List

coming	upon	want	ugly	eleven
always	wasn't	father	washed	crazy
almost	until	hamster	hotel	lazy
didn't	during	a lot	missed	feelings

Directions: Write the word from the box that belongs with each group.

1. emotions, thoughts, **feelings**
2. arriving, entering, **coming**
3. desire, need, **want**
4. forever, all the time, **always**
5. parent, mother, **father**
6. thirteen, twelve, **eleven**
7. gerbil, mouse, **hamster**
8. unattractive, hideous, **ugly**
9. nuts, loony, **crazy**
10. atop, on, **upon**
11. about, approximately, **almost**
12. much, many, **a lot**
13. inn, lodge, **hotel**
14. cleaned, bathed, **washed**

Directions: Choose the word from the box that best completes each sentence. Write the word on the line to the left.

didn't 15. When the spacecraft took off, it almost _____ go in the right direction.

wasn't 16. But the mission chief _____ too worried.

during 17. That sort of thing often happens _____ the first minute.

until 18. Still, he didn't relax _____ the problem was fixed.

missed 19. Space is lonely, and the astronauts _____ their families.

lazy 20. But astronauts in space have to work hard, so there's no time to be _____.

Notes for Home: Your child spelled words that are often misspelled by using too many letters. ***Home Activity:*** For each spelling word, write a misspelling that includes extra letters. Have your child spell each word correctly.

Practice Book 4.5, p. 249

Name ____________________

Space Probes to the Planets

Take Notes/Record Findings

Taking notes and **recording findings** of what you have read can help you when you are collecting information for a report. It can also help you keep track of information in a story and remember what you have read for a test.

There is no right or wrong way to take notes, but keep these points in mind:

- When you take notes, put what you read into your own words.
- If you're taking notes about a story, include the main characters' names and what you learn about them.
- Include only important details. Use key words, phrases, or short sentences.
- If you're taking notes for a report, be sure to include the source of your information.
- Read over your notes immediately after writing them to make sure you understand them.

Directions: Read the following article about women in space. Record notes on the following page as you read. Then use your notes to summarize the article.

Women have made great contributions to our exploration of space. Did you know that the first woman in space was Valentina Tereshkova? Her flight was on June 16, 1963. She flew in the Soviet spacecraft *Vostok 6.* She spent three days orbiting Earth. Svetlana Savitskaya became the second woman in space in 1982. She was also part of the Soviet space program.

On June 18, 1983, Sally Kristen Ride became the first American woman into space. Sally Ride worked on the *STS-7* and *STS-41-G* space missions. These missions conducted experiments and worked on communication satellite systems.

Since Sally Ride's voyages into space, there have been many women to follow. Shannon Lucid is the woman who has spent the most time in space—more than 222 days. Her first flight was June 1, 1985. Her last flight was March 22, 1996. On this mission, Shannon Lucid spent 188 days in space. This is the longest flight for any U.S. astronaut. She spent this time on the Russian space station *Mir* conducting science experiments.

Practice Book 4.5, p. 250

Name ____________________

Space Probes to the Planets

Notes **Possible answers given.**

1. **Women have done space exploration since 1963.**
2. **Valentina Tereshkova was the first woman in space.**
3. **The Soviets put the first woman in space.**
4. **Svetlana Savitskaya was the second woman in space in 1982.**
5. **The first American woman in space was Sally Kristen Ride in 1983.**
6. **Ms. Ride conducted experiments and worked on communication satellite systems.**
7. **Shannon Lucid spent more time in space than any other female U.S. astronaut.**
8. **Ms. Lucid spent 188 days in space for one mission, the longest U.S. flight.**
9. **Ms. Lucid has conducted science experiments on the space station *Mir.***

Summary

10. **Summaries will vary but should include key information recorded in the notes.**

Notes for Home: Your child recorded notes about an article and used these notes to summarize it. ***Home Activity:*** Have your child take notes while reading a newspaper article or watching a TV program. Have your child use the notes to summarize the article or show.

Name

K-W-L Chart

K-W-L charts should be filled out completely, before and during the research process.

Directions: Write your topic on the first line. In the chart, write what you know about it and what you want to know. As you research, write information to use in your report.

Topic ____________

K What I Know	W What I Want to Know	L What I Learned (Information to Use in My Report)

Notes for Home: Your child has learned about finding information for a research report. ***Home Activity:*** Think of a topic, such as a planet or a space mission. Ask your child what kinds of books or other sources (such as the Internet) may offer information about the topic.

Name

Elaboration

Prepositional Phrases

- You can add information to sentences or make sentences clearer by **using prepositional phrases.** Prepositional phrases begin with **prepositions**—words such as *about, before, from, in, of, on, through,* and *with.*

Directions: Complete each sentence by picking a prepositional phrase that tells more about the topic. Rewrite the sentence with the prepositional phrase at the end. More than one phrase may fit a sentence. Choose one that makes sense.

Prepositional Phrases		
about comets	from a launch pad	of the nine planets
around Saturn	in the night sky	with no moons

Responses will vary. Reasonable answers are given.

1. Circles made of rocks and ice are the rings _____.
Circles made of rocks and ice are the rings around Saturn.

2. My sister knows the names of seven _____.
My sister knows the names of seven of the nine planets.

3. A planet may look like a bright star _____.
A planet may look like a bright star in the night sky.

4. Mercury and Venus are the two planets _____.
Mercury and Venus are the two planets with no moons.

5. It takes power for a rocket to blast off _____.
It takes power for a rocket to blast off from a launch pad.

6. In our classroom, there is a poster _____.
In our classroom, there is a poster about comets.

Notes for Home: Your child has added information to sentences by using prepositional phrases, such as *in the night sky.* ***Home Activity:*** Ask your child to describe various things in space, using prepositional phrases such as *around the Sun* or *on the moon.*

Name

Self-Evaluation

Research Report

Students' responses should show that they have given thought to the research reports they have prepared and written.

Directions: Think about the final draft of your research report. Then answer each question in the chart.

	Yes	No	Not sure
1. Did I find information about interesting questions or central ideas?			
2. Did I present the information from my research clearly?			
3. Did I keep my purpose and audience in mind?			
4. Did I identify sources of special information?			
5. Did I proofread and edit carefully to correct errors?			

6. What is the best part of my research report?

7. Write one thing that you would change about this research report if you had the chance to research or write it again.

Notes for Home: Your child answered questions about writing a research report. ***Home Activity:*** Ask your child what kinds of books or other sources gave the most useful information. Ask if it was hard to find information about the ideas and questions that he or she wanted to research.

Name

Visualizing

- **Visualizing** means forming a mental image as you read.
- To help visualize, look for details that tell how things look, smell, sound, taste, and feel.

Directions: Reread "Seeds." Then complete the word web. List sensory details from the story that help you imagine how things look, taste, and feel. **Possible answers given.**

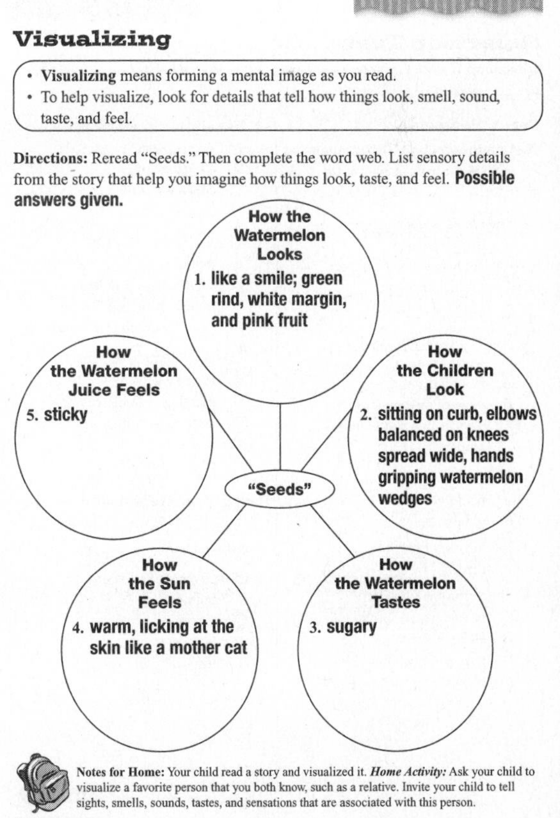

Notes for Home: Your child read a story and visualized it. ***Home Activity:*** Ask your child to visualize a favorite person that you both know, such as a relative. Invite your child to tell sights, smells, sounds, tastes, and sensations that are associated with this person.

Practice Book 4.6, p. 252

Name

Koya's Cousin Del

Vocabulary

Directions: Choose the word from the box that best matches each definition. Write the word on the line.

Check the Words You Know
__ applause
__ auditorium
__ autographs
__ imitation
__ impatient
__ microphones
__ performers

imitation 1. a copying or impersonation of another person or thing

autographs 2. people's signatures

performers 3. people who perform or entertain

impatient 4. not willing to bear delay

microphones 5. instruments for magnifying small sounds

auditorium 6. large room for an audience in a theater or school

Directions: Choose the word from the box that best completes each sentence. Write the word on the line to the left.

performers 7. The _____ arrived ready to sing.

impatient 8. The audience was _____ because they had been waiting a long time.

applause 9. The audience greeted the band's arrival with loud _____.

autographs 10. Afterwards, people asked the band members for their _____.

Write a Music Review

On a separate sheet of paper, write about a concert, music video, or CD that you have enjoyed. Tell what you did and did not like about it. Use as many of the vocabulary words as you can. **Students' music reviews should use vocabulary words correctly.**

Notes for Home: Your child identified and used vocabulary words from the story "Koya's Cousin Del." ***Home Activity:*** Pretend that you and your child are radio announcers at a live concert. Use the vocabulary words to tell what you see and hear.

Practice Book 4.6, p. 253

Name

Koya's Cousin Del

Visualizing

- **Visualizing** means forming a mental image as you read. To help visualize, look for details that tell how things look, smell, sound, taste, and feel.

Directions: Reread what happens in "Koya's Cousin Del." Then answer the questions below. **Possible answers given.**

After dinner, the family gathered in the living room to listen to a tape of Delbert's next album. He had brought it to them as a gift.

"It won't be released until summer," he said. He got up and began dancing. "This is the latest thing from us folks up in the big city."

Koya glanced at her mother and was suprised to see that she was smiling. She never let them dance on the carpet. Whenever she caught them doing it, she would point toward the basement, and they knew they had better get down to the rec room, or they'd be sorry.

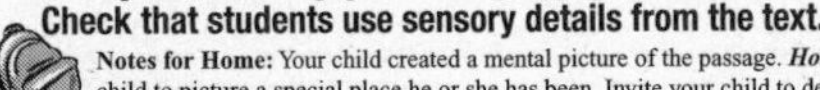

1. Picture the way the family looks as they gather in the living room. How do you think they look?
Their eyes are focused on Del. They smile eagerly waiting to hear the music.

2. Picture Delbert's face as he begins to dance. Describe how you think his face appears.
Del is probably smiling. It is likely that he looks proud and confident as he dances.

3. What sounds can you imagine as Delbert dances?
You can hear the sounds of Del's tape and maybe the sounds of his feet as he dances.

4. How do you imagine the carpet looks in the living room?
It's in good condition since Koya's mother doesn't let people dance on it.

5. Find another place in the story where you get a strong mental image of a scene. On a separate sheet of paper, write a paragraph describing what you visualize.
Check that students use sensory details from the text.

Notes for Home: Your child created a mental picture of the passage. ***Home Activity:*** Ask your child to picture a special place he or she has been. Invite your child to describe what he or she sees when imagining this place.

Practice Book 4.6, p. 255

Name

Koya's Cousin Del

Selection Test

Directions: Choose the best answer to each item. Mark the letter for the answer you have chosen.

Part 1: Vocabulary

Find the answer choice that means about the same as the underlined word in each sentence.

1. The crowd is impatient.
   A. lively and loud
   (B) not happy about waiting
   C. paying attention
   D. satisfied or content

2. We need microphones.
   F. written messages
   G. recordings of music
   H. musical instruments
   (J) devices that make sounds louder

3. I collect autographs.
   A. books about cars
   B. old photographs
   (C) people's signatures
   D. old records and tapes

4. The performers are here.
   (F) people who entertain
   G. close relatives
   H. guests or visitors
   J. people who work at a school

5. The applause made me smile.
   A. joke or story
   (B) clapping
   C. amusing event
   D. letter or note

6. That is a good imitation.
   F. hint or sign
   G. solution to a problem
   H. project or piece of work
   (J) copy of someone or something

7. The auditorium is this way.
   A. test or tryout
   B. building with offices
   (C) large room with a stage and seats
   D. public sale

Part 2: Comprehension

Use what you know about the story to answer each item.

8. Koya's cousin Del is a—
   F. builder.
   (G) singer.
   H. governor.
   J. teacher.

Practice Book 4.6, p. 256

Name

Koya's Cousin Del

9. What did Del do at the airport?
   (A) signed autographs
   B. sang a song
   C. gave tapes away
   D. danced with Koya

10. Who told the secret that Del was at Koya's house?
    (F) Rodney
    G. Loritha
    H. Dr. Hanley
    J. Koya

11. How did most of the crowd outside Koya's house look and act when they saw Del?
    (A) eager and happy
    B. hushed and shy
    C. rough and angry
    D. rude and loud

12. After Del's parents died, Koya's family helped him to—
    F. find a place to live.
    G. write a song about them.
    (H) go back to his music.
    J. start a group with Sherita.

13. When Del sang the first song, he tried to—
    A. sing louder than the drums.
    B. make the students laugh.
    (C) sing in his mother's voice.
    D. get the students to clap.

14. Which sentence helps you see in your mind what Del looked like as he arrived at the airport?
    F. "A man and a woman waiting at the gate had turned to look."
    G. "The young man looked at Delbert and back at the woman as if she were crazy."
    H. "'Del!' he said loudly. 'Your album is bad, man!'"
    (J) "... a young man of medium height and build,... dressed in faded blue jeans and matching jacket."

15. What does Koya think about Del?
    A. She is jealous of him.
    B. She thinks he is vain.
    C. She worries about him.
    (D) She is proud of him.

Name ________________ Koya's Cousin Del

Visualizing

- **Visualizing** means forming a mental image as you read. To help visualize, look for details that tell how things look, smell, sound, taste, and feel.

Directions: Read the story below.

Corey, Pam, Mei-Ling, and Tanya started a band together. Each girl played a different instrument. Corey, the leader, played guitar. She really had to stretch her arms to play the big instrument.

Pam played the clarinet. When she played, her eyes closed and her whole body swayed with the music.

Mei-Ling was the drummer. When Mei-Ling played, she seemed to be moving in all directions. Her hands flew, her elbows jiggled, her knees bounced, and her feet tapped.

Tanya played the bass. Tanya usually had a big, broad smile—except when she played. Then she looked very serious.

Possible answers given.

Directions: Complete the table. Fill in words from the story that help you picture each character. Then tell what you visualized as you read.

Characters	Descriptive Words from the Story
Corey	1. **Corey really had to stretch her arms around the big guitar.**
Pam	2. **Pam's eyes were closed and her whole body swayed to the music.**
Mei-Ling	3. **Mei-Ling's hands flew. She jiggled and bounced and tapped.**
Tanya	4. **Tanya looked very serious.**

5. What I Picture:

I see how the four girls look when playing their instruments. They each have a different playing style.

Notes for Home: Your child created mental images in his or her mind based on story details. ***Home Activity:*** Ask your child to think of a place he or she has been today. Suggest that your child picture the place in his or her mind. Then ask your child to describe it.

Visualizing 573

Practice Book 4.6, p. 257

Name ________________ Koya's Cousin Del

Setting

REVIEW

Directions: Read the story. Then read each question about the story. Choose the best answer to each question. Mark the letter for the answer you have chosen.

A Difficult Concert

Randall and his band got to the auditorium two hours later than planned. It was a cold day, and the roads were icy. Randall had to drive extra carefully to avoid an accident.

While they were driving, Randall had switched on the radio in the van. "Hello, out there!" said the disk jockey cheerfully. "We're going to start our countdown of the year's greatest hits!"

When the band finally got to the auditorium, the crowd was restless. They stamped so hard, the wooden bleachers shook. Even the basketball hoops were shaking. The band ran out onto the stage. "Greetings, everybody!" Randall shouted. "How are things here in Central Valley?"

The crowd cheered. "Are you ready for the year 2000?" he cried. "Here's a song to celebrate the last night of the old year!"

1. Based on the information in the story, what season is it?
   A. summer
   (B.) winter
   C. fall
   D. spring
2. How is Randall affected by the setting during the band's drive?
   F. He is shivering and uncomfortable.
   G. He puts on an extra sweater.
   (H.) He drives more slowly.
   J. He doesn't want to perform.
3. What else is the auditorium used for?
   (A.) a gym
   B. a cafeteria
   C. a town meeting hall
   D. school meetings
4. In what year does the story take place?
   F. 2001
   G. 1899
   H. 2000
   (J.) 1999
5. What holiday is coming up?
   A. Homecoming
   B. Presidents' Day
   C. Thanksgiving
   (D.) New Year's Day

Notes for Home: Your child identified a story's setting—the time and place where it occurs. ***Home Activity:*** Ask your child to identify a favorite book, movie, or television show. Then ask him or her to tell you when and where the story takes place and tell you how he or she knows.

574 Setting

Name ________________ Koya's Cousin Del

Writing Across Texts

Directions: Consider what you learned about how Delbert expressed his creativity in "Koya's Cousin Del." Think of people or characters from other stories in class and consider the ways they expressed themselves creatively. Complete the table below by listing the ways they expressed themselves. **Possible answers given.**

Creativity
Delbert used music to tell others how he felt.
1. **They paint or draw pictures.**
2. **They create gardens.**
3. **They are creative problem-solvers.**
4. **They become actors.**
5. **They are adventurers.**

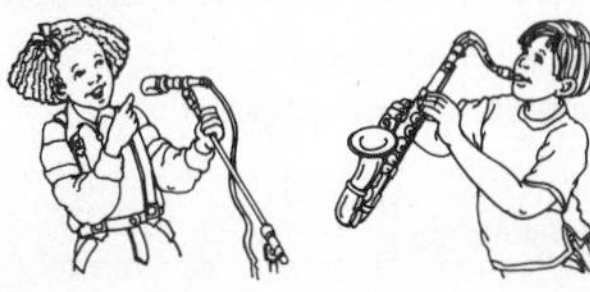

Write a Paragraph

On a separate sheet of paper, write a paragraph that tells about the ways in which people can express themselves creatively. **Students' paragraphs will vary. Check to be sure they include information about people they have read about in this book or have learned about from other sources.**

Notes for Home: Your child used information from many stories to write a paragraph about the ways people express themselves creatively. ***Home Activity:*** Use the creativity of family members as examples. Discuss with your child ways he or she has to express creativity.

Writing Across Texts 575

Grammar Practice Book 4.6, p. 126

Name ________________ Koya's Cousin Del

Grammar: Conjunctions

REVIEW

Directions: Choose the correct conjunction in ( ) to complete each sentence. Write the conjunction on the line.

but 1. It is getting late, (but/or) I want to hear the next band.

and 2. The guitar player (and/but) the keyboard player walked onto the stage together.

or 3. Would the singer (and/or) the drummer be the next one onstage?

and 4. The group played two old hits (and/but) two brand-new songs.

or 5. Should we leave now (but/or) listen to another band?

Directions: Use the conjunction *and, but,* or *or* to combine each pair of sentences. Write your new sentence on the line.

6. The concert was almost sold out. We did get two tickets.
   The concert was almost sold out, but we did get two tickets.
7. Can your brother drive us? Should we take the bus?
   Can your brother drive us, or should we take the bus?
8. The opening band was terrible. We know the second band will be great.
   The opening band was terrible, but we know the second band will be great.
9. The band ran onstage. The crowd went wild.
   The band ran onstage, and the crowd went wild.
10. They opened with their biggest hit. The audience sang along.
    They opened with their biggest hit, and the audience sang along.

Notes for Home: Your child used the conjunctions *and, but,* and *or* to complete or combine sentences. ***Home Activity:*** Give your child two words and a conjunction. Challenge your child to form a sentence. Repeat as many times as you like.

576 Grammar: Conjunctions

Grammar Practice Book 4.6, p. 127
Name______________________________

Koya's Cousin Del

Grammar: Sentences and Punctuation

A **sentence** is a group of words that makes a statement, a question, a command, a request, or an exclamation. It begins with a capital letter and ends with a punctuation mark. One way to tell whether a group of words is a complete sentence is to check whether it expresses a complete thought.

A **declarative sentence** is a sentence that makes a statement. It ends with a period.

I love music.

An **interrogative sentence** asks a question. It ends with a question mark.

Do you love music too?

An **imperative sentence** gives a command or a request. It ends with a period. The first word is usually a verb or *please* followed by a verb. The subject *(you)* is not shown, but it is understood.

Listen to me play the guitar.

An **exclamatory sentence** shows strong feeling. It ends with an exclamation point.

That was so wonderful!

Directions: Match each group of words on the left with a group of words on the right to form complete sentences. Write the letter on the line.

c	1. Did you go	a. study for a long time.
e	2. At the concert,	b. was so talented!
b	3. The lead guitarist	c. to the concert last week?
d	4. I'm going	d. to start taking lessons next week.
a	5. Good musicians must	e. the singer sang a solo.

Directions: Write the correct end punctuation on the line after each sentence.

6. Martin was practicing piano all afternoon **.**
7. Did you know he is playing in the concert **?**
8. Wow, he is a great musician **!**
9. Why didn't he send me an invitation **?**
10. I hope I can go to the concert **. or !**

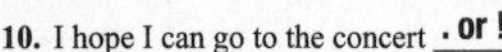

Notes for Home: Your child reviewed sentences and their end punctuation. ***Home Activity:*** Say a sentence and have your child punctuate it with a gesture: pointing a finger for a period, shaking his or her head for a question mark, and clapping hands for an exclamation mark.

Grammar Practice Book 4.6, p. 128
Name______________________________

Koya's Cousin Del

Grammar: Sentences and Punctuation

Directions: Write S on the line if each group of words is a sentence. Write **NS** if the group of words is not a sentence.

S 1. I have been studying music since I was seven years old.
NS 2. For three years!
NS 3. The very first instrument I ever studied was.
S 4. Then I decided to learn piano, so that I could play by myself.
NS 5. The reason I like to play solos?

Directions: Rewrite each sentence with correct capitalization and end punctuation.

6. do you think that it's better to play music by yourself
Do you think that it's better to play music by yourself?

7. if you could play any instrument in the world, what would it be
If you could play any instrument in the world, what would it be?

8. my piano teacher wants me to study harder
My piano teacher wants me to study harder.

9. come to my concert and watch me play
Come to my concert and watch me play.

10. wow, I really love music
Wow, I really love music!

Write a Description of Music

On a separate sheet of paper, write a description of some music that you like. Explain why you like it and tell how the music makes you feel. **Check that students have written complete sentences with correct punctuation.**

Notes for Home: Your child reviewed sentences and their end punctuation. ***Home Activity:*** Have your child read aloud from a favorite story. Encourage your child to use his or her voice to express statements, commands, questions, and exclamations.

Grammar Practice Book 4.6, p. 129
Name______________________________

Koya's Cousin Del

Grammar: Sentences and Punctuation

RETEACHING

A **sentence** is a group of words that makes a statement, a question, a command, a request, or an exclamation. It begins with a capital letter and ends with a punctuation mark.

Read each sentence. Write a punctuation mark that best completes each sentence.

1. Please bring me the book **.**
2. I've never seen anything so amazing **!**
3. Do you know what time it is **?**
4. I am writing a report **.**

An **imperative sentence** gives a command or makes a request and ends with a period. An **exclamatory sentence** shows strong feeling and ends with an exclamation point. An **interrogative sentence** asks a question and ends with a question mark. A **declarative sentence** makes a statement and ends with a period.

Directions: Read each sentence and identify which type it is. Write **declarative**, **exclamatory**, **imperative**, or **interrogative** on the line.

exclamatory 1. What an exciting movie that was!
interrogative 2. Do you know the names of the actors?
declarative 3. Yes, I do.
imperative 4. Please tell me what they are.
interrogative 5. Can you wait until we get home?
imperative 6. Tell me now.
exclamatory 7. You are the most curious person I've ever met!

Notes for Home: Your child correctly punctuated four types of sentences. ***Home Activity:*** Write some sentences without end punctuation. Discuss with your child which punctuation mark (. or ! or ?) best ends each sentence.

Grammar Practice Book 4.6, p. 130
Name______________________________

Koya's Cousin Del

Grammar: Sentences and Punctuation

Directions: Write the correct end punctuation on the line after each sentence.

1. Everyone loved the play **.**
2. Did Sabrina remember all her lines **?**
3. Did you help clean up after the show **?**
4. What a mess it was **!**
5. Hang your costume in the closet **.**
6. Phil fixed a light **.**
7. Wow, what bright lights they are **!**
8. Please fold all those chairs **.**
9. Did you check down that row **?**
10. Brenda swept the stage **.**
11. Does Mr. Carter think we did well **?**
12. He took everyone out for a snack **.**

Directions: Rewrite each sentence with correct capitalization and end punctuation.

13. did you get tickets to the baseball game
Did you get tickets to the baseball game?

14. please get one for me too
Please get one for me too.

15. it will be a fun game
It will be a fun game.

16. what a great time we're going to have
What a great time we're going to have!

Notes for Home: Your child correctly punctuated four types of sentences. **Home Activity:** Listen to a favorite song. Have your child write some of the words to the song and decide which type of punctuation mark (. or ! or ?) to use.

Practice Book 4.6, p. 258
Name______________________ **Koya's Cousin Del**

Word Study: Complex Spelling Patterns

Word List				
steady	reindeer	niece	caught	said
again	veil	brought	piece	bread

Directions: Some letter combinations, such as **ei, ie, ai, ea,** and **gh,** are hard to remember and spell correctly. Read the words in the box. Listen and look for similar letter combinations. Write each word in the correct column.

Words with ei	Words with ie	Words with ai
1. **reindeer**	3. **niece**	5. **said**
2. **veil**	4. **piece**	6. **again**

Words with ea	Words with gh
7. **steady**	9. **brought**
8. **bread**	10. **caught**

Directions: Choose the word from the box that best completes each sentence. Write the word on the line to the left. Not all the words will be used.

said 11. "The winter concert has started," _____ one parent.

steady 12. "I can hear the _____ beat of the school's drummer," the other parent agreed.

brought 13. Opening the door of the auditorium _____ the holiday music into the school corridor.

reindeer 14. The children came out singing, dressed as silly _____.

niece 15. "I think I can recognize my _____ under the horns and bright red nose," said the girl's uncle.

Notes for Home: Your child practiced words with complex spelling patterns. ***Home Activity:*** Encourage your child to keep a list of words he or she has trouble spelling correctly. Set aside time each week to practice spelling these words with your child.

Spelling Workbook 4.6, p. 101
Name______________________ **Koya's Cousin Del**

Spelling: Getting Letters in Correct Order

Pretest Directions: Fold back the page along the dotted line. On the blanks, write the spelling words as they are dictated. When you have finished the test, unfold the page and check your words.

1. **piece** — 1. Would you like a **piece**?
2. **friend** — 2. She's my best **friend**.
3. **field** — 3. There's wheat in that **field**.
4. **believe** — 4. Do you **believe** me?
5. **weird** — 5. They think my cousin is **weird**.
6. **said** — 6. That's what I **said**.
7. **again** — 7. I want to see the movie **again**.
8. **asked** — 8. They **asked** many questions.
9. **only** — 9. We're not the **only** ones.
10. **brought** — 10. Look what we **brought** for you.
11. **height** — 11. He grew in **height**.
12. **weight** — 12. He has gained **weight**.
13. **neighbor** — 13. I'm trying to be a good **neighbor**.
14. **heard** — 14. Everyone has **heard** the secret.
15. **heart** — 15. It nearly broke her **heart**.
16. **tongue** — 16. The soup burned his **tongue**.
17. **rattle** — 17. The baby is shaking the **rattle**.
18. **pickle** — 18. I will have a **pickle** with that.
19. **toes** — 19. His **toes** were frostbitten.
20. **hospital** — 20. I was born in a **hospital**.

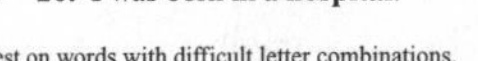

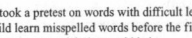

Notes for Home: Your child took a pretest on words with difficult letter combinations. ***Home Activity:*** Help your child learn misspelled words before the final test. See if there are any similar errors and discuss a memory trick that could help.

Spelling Workbook 4.6, p. 102
Name______________________ **Koya's Cousin Del**

Spelling: Getting Letters in Correct Order

Directions: Choose the words from the box that contain the letters **ie** and **ei.** Write the words in the correct column.

Word List	
piece	height
friend	weight
field	neighbor
believe	heard
weird	heart
said	tongue
again	rattle
asked	pickle
only	toes
brought	hospital

Words with ie	Words with ei
1. **piece**	5. **weird**
2. **friend**	6. **height**
3. **field**	7. **weight**
4. **believe**	8. **neighbor**

Directions: Choose the word from the box that best matches each clue. Write the word on the line to the left.

said 9. The past tense of the verb *say*.

again 10. Over and over, or more than once.

heard 11. If you had listened, you would have _____.

heart 12. It beats in your chest.

rattle 13. If you hear a snake doing this, you're in trouble.

pickle 14. This is tasty, but sometimes sour.

hospital 15. Where you go when you're sick.

asked 16. If someone had _____, I would have answered.

only 17. You are my one and _____.

brought 18. It rhymes with *sought.*

toes 19. They're the fingers of your feet.

tongue 20. It should stay in your mouth.

Notes for Home: Your child spelled words with letter combinations that are often mixed up, such as *friend* and *height.* ***Home Activity:*** Say each word twice, and have your child write it. Together, check and correct for any misspellings.

Spelling Workbook 4.6, p. 103
Name______________________ **Koya's Cousin Del**

Spelling: Getting Letters in Correct Order

Directions: Proofread this review of a concert. Find five spelling mistakes. Use the proofreading marks to correct each mistake.

- ≡ Make a capital.
- / Make a small letter.
- ∧ Add something.
- ℘ Take out something.
- ⊙ Add a period.
- ¶ Begin a new paragraph.

"COWBOY BLUES" ARE A GREAT GROUP

Last night, my friend and I haerd some of the best music I have heard in a long time. The "Cowboy Blues" concert was full of songs to touch the haert and set your tose tapping. At the end, the audience cheered wildly, so the group played their most famous song egain. I believe that hearing "Howdy, Nieghbor" was the best part of the evening!

Spelling Tip

Some letter combinations are especially hard to keep in order: **bel<u>ie</u>ve, h<u>ear</u>t, s<u>ai</u>d.** Pay special attention to words with these combinations.

Word List			
piece	said	height	tongue
friend	again	weight	rattle
field	asked	neighbor	pickle
believe	only	heard	toes
weird	brought	heart	hospital

Write a Music Review

On a separate sheet of paper, write your own review of a concert you have heard or of a favorite tape or CD. Tell what you did and didn't like about the music. Use at least five spelling words. **Answers will vary, but each review should include at least five spelling words.**

Notes for Home: Your child spelled words with letter combinations that are often mixed up, such as *friend* and *height.* ***Home Activity:*** Ask your child to name and spell as many words as he or she can think of with the letter combinations *ie* and *ei.*

Spelling Workbook 4.6, p. 104

Name______________________

Koya's Cousin Del

Spelling: Getting Letters in Correct Order

REVIEW

Word List				
piece	weird	only	neighbor	rattle
friend	said	brought	heard	pickle
field	again	height	heart	toes
believe	asked	weight	tongue	hospital

Directions: Choose the word from the box that begins and ends with the same letters as each word below. Write the word on the line.

1. beat	**brought**	**7.** around	**asked**
2. bone	**believe**	**8.** never	**neighbor**
3. filed	**field**	**9.** price	**piece (or pickle)**
4. hall	**hospital**	**10.** true	**tongue**
5. officially	**only**	**11.** peace	**pickle (or piece)**
6. apron	**again**	**12.** wrist	**weight**

Directions: Choose the word from the box that best completes each sentence. Write the word on the line to the left.

heard **13.** We _____ a great concert last night!

weird **14.** At first, the music sounded a bit _____.

friend **15.** My best _____ was starting to get bored.

said **16.** "This is no good!" she _____.

rattle **17.** Then the lead singer shook a huge _____.

height **18.** The guitarist stood up to his full _____.

heart **19.** My _____ began to beat faster.

toes **20.** My friend and I stood on our _____ and cheered.

Notes for Home: Your child spelled words with letters that are often mixed up. ***Home Activity:*** With your child, take turns choosing spelling words. Read a word and ask the other person to spell it. Without looking at the list, tell whether the word was spelled correctly.

Practice Book 4.6, p. 259

Name______________________

Koya's Cousin Del

Poster/Advertisement

A **poster** is a kind of announcement that gives specific facts about an event. It usually answers the questions "Who?" "What?" "When?" "Where?" "Why?"

Directions: This poster gives information about a rock concert. Use the poster to answer the questions that follow.

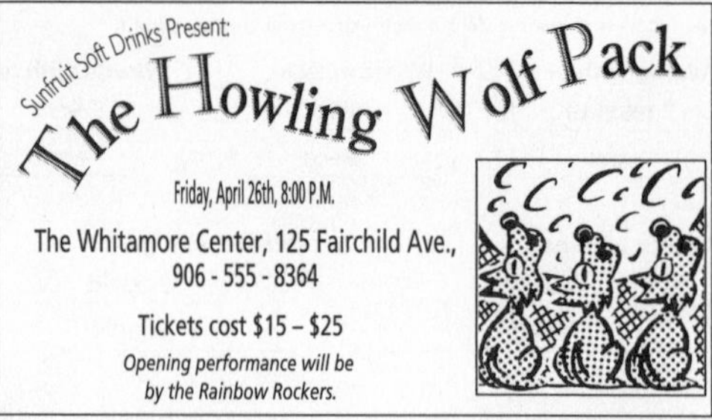

1. What is the name of the main group performing? **The Howling Wolf Pack**

2. What is the name of the group that will be performing first? **The Rainbow Rockers**

3. Where is the concert? **The Whitamore Center, 125 Fairchild Ave.**

4. What date is the concert? **April 26th**

5. Which ticket do you think costs $25—a ticket for a seat close to the stage or far away from the stage? Explain.

Possible answer: The seats close to the stage will probably cost the most because they give you a better view of the concert.

Practice Book 4.6, p. 260

Name______________________

Koya's Cousin Del

An **advertisement** is a kind of announcement that can be found in print or electronic media. The goal of an advertisement is to persuade readers, listeners, or viewers to do something, buy something, or feel a particular way about something.

Directions: Use the video game advertisement to answer the questions that follow.

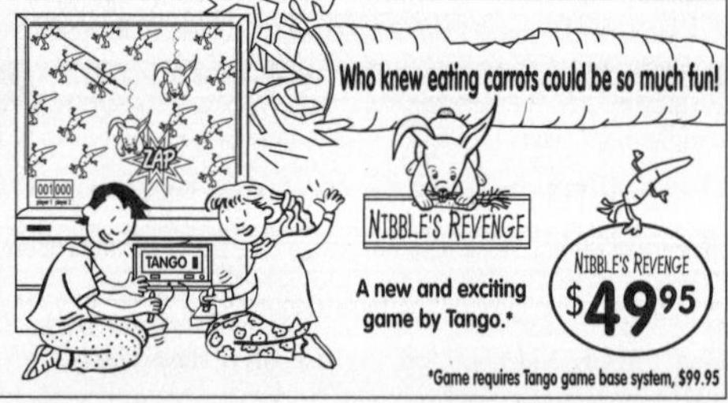

6. What is the purpose of this advertisement? **Its purpose is to get readers to buy the video game.**

7. How do the pictures support this purpose? **Possible answer: The pictures make the game seem fun, and you'll make friends if you own it.**

8. How do the words support this purpose? **Possible answer: Words such as *new* and *exciting* make the game seem interesting and fun in order to persuade readers to buy it.**

9. What do you need to have to play this game? **You need to have the game, a television, and a Tango game base system.**

10. Name one fact and one opinion from the advertisement. **Possible answer: Fact: The game costs $49.95. Opinion: The game is exciting.**

Notes for Home: Your child answered questions about a poster and an advertisement. ***Home Activity:*** Choose an advertisement from the newspaper or a commercial on television. Ask your child to point out some facts and some opinions that the advertisement presents.

Practice Book 4.6, p. 261

Name______________________

Children of Clay

Steps in a Process

- Telling the **steps in a process** is telling the order of steps to complete an action.
- Clue words like *first, next,* and *last* or numbers written by the steps can show when each step is done.

First → Next → Last

Directions: Reread "From Drawing to Carousel Critter." Then complete the flowchart. Put the steps listed in the box in the order they must be done to turn a drawing into a carousel critter.

Possible answers given.

Steps

Enlarge drawing.
Paint animal.
Carve foam animal.
Trace drawing onto foam.
Sand it smooth.
Cover with varnish.
Glue together to make "sandwich."
Add eyes, a mouth, and other details.
Fit pole between cutouts.
Add three coats of fiberglass.
Cut out shapes.

Enlarge drawing.

1. **Trace drawing onto foam.**
2. **Cut out shapes.**
3. **Fit pole between cutouts.**
4. **Glue together to make "sandwich."**
5. **Carve foam animal.**
6. **Add eyes, a mouth, and other details.**
7. **Sand it smooth.**
8. **Add three coats of fiberglass.**
9. **Paint animal.**
10. **Cover with varnish.**

Notes for Home: Your child read a story and identified steps in a process—the steps needed to complete an action. ***Home Activity:*** Together, perform a simple household task, such as putting away groceries or washing dishes. Ask your child to identify each step as it is performed.

Practice Book 4.6, p. 262
Name ____________

Children of Clay

Vocabulary

Directions: Choose the word from the box that best matches each clue. Write the word on the line.

Check the Words You Know
__ figures
__ polish
__ pottery
__ screens
__ symbol

pottery 1. You make this out of clay.

polish 2. This is something you do to make things shiny.

screens 3. People often put these on doors and windows.

symbol 4. This is used to represent something else.

figures 5. These are small pieces of finished pottery.

Directions: Choose the word from the box that best completes each sentence. Write the word on the line to the left.

pottery 6. Tyrone is a skilled potter who makes and sells all different kinds of _____.

figures 7. Tyrone picked up one of the many little clay _____ that he had made.

polish 8. He began to _____ the object to give it a bright shine.

symbol 9. He placed the object next to a plate painted with a _____ representing the sun.

screens 10. Outside, several children peered through the wire _____ to watch Tyrone at work.

Write an Art Review

On a separate sheet of paper, write about a piece of pottery or sculpture, either one you have seen or one you saw in a picture. Tell what the figure looks like and what you like about it. Use as many vocabulary words as you can. **Students' reviews should both describe the art piece and tell what they like about it. They should correctly use included vocabulary words.**

Notes for Home: Your child identified and used vocabulary words from "Children of Clay." ***Home Activity:*** Invite your child to tell you what each vocabulary word means. Together, write a definition for each word. Take turns using these words in sentences.

Practice Book 4.6, p. 263
Name ____________

Children of Clay

Steps in a Process

- Telling the **steps in a process** is telling the order of steps to complete an action.
- Clue words like *first, next,* and *last* or numbers written by the steps can show when each step is done.

Directions: Reread what happens in "Children of Clay" when everyone finishes coiling and forming the clay. Then answer the questions below.

When they finish coiling and forming the clay, everyone carefully puts the pieces out of the way to dry. Big pieces like Nora's figures are wrapped in cloth so that they don't dry too fast and crack. The children know not to touch the clay pieces while they are drying because they are very fragile and will break easily.

A week later, it is time to smooth the pieces with sandpaper. Eliza is very careful as she helps to sand the hands that Devonna made. She sits working with her grandmother Rose, her aunt Rina, and her aunt Tessie, while the younger children play close by.

1. What is the first step after coiling and forming the clay?
Everyone puts the pieces out to dry.

2. What additional step is necessary if the clay pieces are big?
Big pieces need to be wrapped in cloth.

3. How long do the pieces need to dry?
It takes a week for the pieces to dry.

4. What is the final step in the process described here?
The final step is sanding the pieces smooth.

5. Reread the part of the story that describes steps in finishing the clay pieces. On a separate sheet of paper, list these steps.
Finishing steps include coating the pieces with slip, polishing the pieces with stones, painting the pieces, and firing them.

Notes for Home: Your child read a nonfiction passage and identified steps in a process. ***Home Activity:*** Invite your child to watch you perform a simple chore, such as washing the dishes. Ask him or her to list at least three steps in that process.

Practice Book 4.6, p. 265
Name ____________

Children of Clay

Selection Test

Directions: Choose the best answer to each item. Mark the letter for the answer you have chosen.

Part 1: Vocabulary

Find the answer choice that means about the same as the underlined word in each sentence.

1. We used the screens.
   A. rolls of paper
   B. large bottles or jugs
   C. carving tools
   (D) wires woven with small openings

2. He showed us the figures.
   (F) forms or shapes
   G. materials or supplies
   H. large painted pictures
   J. chips of broken clay

3. Now I will polish the dish.
   A. harden by baking
   (B) make smooth and shiny
   C. decorate with designs
   D. show or display

4. These pictures are symbols.
   F. hopes or dreams
   G. ideas shared by many people
   H. strong feelings
   (J) things that stand for something else

5. Show us the pottery.
   A. glass dishes and plates
   B. metal pieces of art
   (C) pots and dishes made of clay
   D. objects carved from wood

Part 2: Comprehension

Use what you know about the selection to answer each item.

6. The family in this selection lives in a—
   (F) Pueblo village.
   G. log cabin.
   H. large city.
   J. ranch house.

7. Which step happens first?
   (A) taking sticks out of the clay
   B. soaking the clay in water
   C. letting the clay dry
   D. wrapping the clay in cloths

8. Sand is added to the clay to—
   F. make the clay thicker.
   (G) keep the clay from cracking when it dries.
   H. get rid of stones and twigs.
   J. make the clay shiny.

Practice Book 4.6, p. 266
Name ____________

Children of Clay

9. Who is Clay-Old-Woman?
   A. the children's grandmother
   B. a woman in the village
   C. a pottery teacher
   (D) a spirit the people believe in

10. What step comes next after the clay is formed into pots and figures?
    (F) They are left to dry.
    G. They are polished.
    H. They are washed.
    J. They are painted.

11. A good polishing stone must be—
    A. light.
    (B) smooth.
    C. pointed.
    D. large.

12. When pottery is "fired," it is—
    F. covered with hot wax.
    G. dipped in boiling water.
    (H) baked to make it hard.
    J. left out in the hot sun.

13. The author's main purpose in this selection is to—
    A. persuade people to make pottery.
    B. tell how to choose well-made pottery.
    (C) explain how one family makes pottery.
    D. describe the village of Santa Clara.

14. What makes this pottery special to the people who buy it?
    F. It has been sanded.
    G. Some of it is plain.
    (H) It is made completely by hand.
    J. Food can be cooked in it.

15. Which sentence best describes the family in this selection?
    A. They spoil the children.
    B. They like to play tricks on one another.
    C. They love to have fun.
    (D) They work well together.

Name______________________ Children of Clay

Steps in a Process

- Telling the **steps in a process** is telling the order of steps to complete an action.
- Clue words like *first, next,* and *last* or numbers written by the steps can show when each step is done.

Directions: Read the passage below. Then complete the flowchart.

Suppose you want to find out about Native American arts, especially pottery. The first thing to do when you are searching for a book is ask the librarian. He or she may have useful ideas.

Next, check the card catalog under the words *Native American* and *pottery.* In the catalog, there is a card for each book. Each card has a book title, a description of the book, and a call number that will help you find the book in the library. Read the descriptions to see which books will be helpful.

Write down the title, author, and number of each book that looks good. Then go find the book on the library shelves. If you can't find it, ask the librarian for help. The librarian can find out if your book has been checked out or is on a special shelf.

Finally, when you do find your book, and it seems to be helpful, check it out!

Step 1: Ask the librarian.

Step 2: In the card catalog, look under the words ***Native American* and *pottery.***

Step 3: Write down **the title, author, and call number.**

Step 4: **Look for your book.**

Step 5: If you can't find the book you need, **ask the librarian.**

Step 6: If you find a book you like, **check it out.**

Notes for Home: Your child used a flowchart to help identify steps in a process. ***Home Activity:*** Ask your child to think of a task he or she usually does, such as making the bed. Invite him or her to tell you each step in that process.

Practice Book 4.6, p. 267

Name______________________ Children of Clay

Main Idea and Supporting Details

REVIEW

Directions: Read the passage. Then read each question about the passage. Choose the best answer to each question. Mark the letter for the answer you have chosen.

The Pueblo People

The Pueblo are one of the oldest peoples in North America. The Pueblo are descended from an even older Southwestern culture called the Anasazi, which is Navajo for "ancient ones." Their villages developed in what is now the Southwestern area of the United States, including parts of Arizona, New Mexico, Colorado, and Utah.

Pueblo means "village" in Spanish. Pueblo homes are apartment-like buildings made of stone or adobe. An underground room, called a *kiva,* is used for special ceremonies.

Today, pueblo villages may still be made of adobe or stone. Like the old villages, rooms are often added onto a building to make more room as a village grows. An entire village might live in one building. Unlike the earlier buildings, these modern-day Pueblo buildings often have windows and doors.

1. The main idea of the whole passage is that the Pueblo—
   - A. live in apartments.
   - (B.) have a long history.
   - C. live in the Southwest.
   - D. have special ceremonies.

2. A key word to the main idea in the first paragraph is—
   - (F.) oldest.
   - G. developed.
   - H. Arizona.
   - J. Utah.

3. The second paragraph tells about the Pueblo's—
   - (A.) homes.
   - B. economy.
   - C. religious beliefs.
   - D. ancestors.

4. The last paragraph—
   - F. describes the Anasazi.
   - (G.) compares old and modern Pueblo villages.
   - H. explains how to make adobe bricks.
   - J. describes the Pueblo people.

5. Which of the following does **not** support the main idea of the passage?
   - A. The Pueblo are one of the oldest peoples in North America.
   - B. The Pueblo are descendents of the Anasazi.
   - C. Modern Pueblo villages are similar to old villages.
   - (D.) A kiva is a room used for special ceremonies.

Notes for Home: Your child identified the main idea and details of a passage. ***Home Activity:*** Read a brief newspaper article about a local person, place, or event. Ask your child to tell you the main idea. Take turns telling details from the story.

Name______________________ Children of Clay

Writing Across Texts

Directions: Using information from "Children of Clay" and "Clay Old Woman and Clay Old Man," fill in the five most important steps in the making of Pueblo pottery on the flowchart below. **Students' answers will vary. Check to make sure that their steps are the most important ones and are in time order.**

How to Make Pueblo Pottery

1. **Cleaned clay is mixed with fine, white sand.**
2. **Several days later, the clay is molded into animal shapes or pots.**
3. **The pieces are sanded a week later.**
4. **The pieces are coated and polished.**
5. **Several weeks later, the clay shapes are fired over burning wood.**

Write a How-to List

Using information from "Children of Clay" and "Clay Old Woman and Clay Old Man," write a numbered how-to list on the making of Pueblo Indian pottery. Be sure to include the most important steps in the process. Write your list on a separate sheet of paper. **Lists will vary. Be sure that lists are in chronological order and that no irrelevant details are included.**

Notes for Home: Your child combined information from two selections to create a how-to list for making pottery. ***Home Activity:*** Ask your child to select an activity such as making a bed or riding a bicycle. Together, list the steps included in the process of doing the activity.

Grammar Practice Book 4.6, p. 131

Name______________________ Children of Clay

Grammar: Proper Nouns and Adjectives

REVIEW

Directions: Rewrite each sentence correctly. Capitalize the proper nouns and adjectives.

1. ms. sams talked about the art of native peoples of north america.
   Ms. Sams talked about the art of native peoples of North America.
2. Groups in the great plains, such as the sioux, decorated with beads.
   Groups in the Great Plains, such as the Sioux, decorated with beads.
3. In the united states, ancient stone dwellings are found in the southwest.
   In the United States, ancient stone dwellings are found in the Southwest.
4. Hundreds of families lived in these dwellings in arizona and new mexico.
   Hundreds of families lived in these dwellings in Arizona and New Mexico.
5. The american museum of natural history has a fine collection of native art.
   The American Museum of Natural History has a fine collection of native art.
6. Have you seen any mexican art?
   Have you seen any Mexican art?
7. Mexican art is another kind of american art.
   Mexican art is another kind of American art.
8. Many items show a spanish influence.
   Many items show a Spanish influence.
9. Art is important to canadian groups too.
   Art is important to Canadian groups too.
10. For example, inuit sculptures are world famous.
    For example, Inuit sculptures are world famous.

Notes for Home: Your child capitalized proper nouns and proper adjectives. ***Home Activity:*** Ask your child to write a paragraph about a place he or she would like to visit. Encourage your child to use proper nouns and adjectives in the paragraph.

Grammar Practice Book 4.6, p. 132

Name____________________ Children of Clay

Grammar: Capitalization

Use these rules for **capitalization:**

- Capitalize the first word of a sentence.

  My friend is an artist.

- Capitalize the first word and every important word of a proper noun. Remember, proper nouns name particular people, places, or things.

  His name is Joseph Stephens. He wrote a book called *How to Paint.*

- Capitalize the first letter of an abbreviation. An abbreviation is a shortened form of a word. It usually ends with a period. State name abbreviations use two capital letters and no periods.

  He lives in Flagstaff, AZ. His address is 182 Cottonwood St.

- Capitalize titles before people's names.

  Capt. Alice Stephens is his wife.

Directions: Rewrite each sentence, using correct capitalization.

1. mrs. johnson is a very good artist.

Mrs. Johnson is a very good artist.

2. she lives in phoenix, az, in a big house.

She lives in Phoenix, AZ, in a big house.

3. her address is 17 bluebird road.

Her address is 17 Bluebird Road.

4. she teaches a class called "drawing can be fun!"

She teaches a class called "Drawing Can Be Fun!"

5. she has visited all 50 states, including alaska and hawaii.

She has visited all 50 states, including Alaska and Hawaii.

Notes for Home: Your child practiced capitalizing proper nouns, abbreviations, and titles. ***Home Activity:*** Write down the names and addresses of some of your child's friends and relatives, without capitalizing them. Help him or her to capitalize each word correctly.

Grammar: Capitalization 599

Grammar Practice Book 4.6, p. 133

Name____________________ Children of Clay

Grammar: Capitalization

Directions: Write C on the line for each group of words that is correctly capitalized. If a group of words is not correctly capitalized, rewrite it on the line, using correct capitalization.

Answer	Item
She created a new painting.	**1.** she created a new painting.
C	**2.** Capt. Martin Anderson
Yuma, AZ	**3.** yuma, az
The Life of the Buffalo	**4.** *The Life of the buffalo*
Mr. Peter Alvarez	**5.** mr. peter alvarez
C	**6.** 1313 Blue View Terrace
Los Angeles, CA	**7.** los angeles, ca

Directions: Rewrite each sentence on the line, using proper capitalization.

8. frank has been an artist all his life.

Frank has been an artist all his life.

9. his best friend is dr. russell mears.

His best friend is Dr. Russell Mears.

10. together they wrote a book called *we are native americans.*

Together they wrote a book called *We Are Native Americans.*

Write a Review

On a separate sheet of paper, write a review of a movie, book, or video you liked. Compare it to at least two other works. Remember to capitalize each proper noun you use in your review. **Students should include the names of at least three titles in their reviews, using correct capitalization.**

Notes for Home: Your child practiced capitalizing proper nouns, abbreviations, and titles. ***Home Activity:*** Write down some silly titles for books, movies, or videos without capitalizing them. Have your child correct the capitalizations.

600 Grammar: Capitalization

Grammar Practice Book 4.6, p. 134

Name____________________ Children of Clay

Grammar: Capitalization

RETEACHING

Underline the sentence that is capitalized correctly.

1. I live at 2121 Dobson Ave.

2. my favorite book is called *cats and dogs.*

Use a **capital letter** to begin a **sentence.** Capitalize the first word and every important word of a **proper noun.** Proper nouns can be people, places, or things. Capitalize the first letter of an **abbreviation.** Also capitalize **titles** before people's names.

Directions: Capitalize each sentence correctly and write it on the line.

1. i live at 1501 kenmore st.

I live at 1501 Kenmore St.

2. my sister turned six years old on may 6, 2000.

My sister turned six years old on May 6, 2000.

3. dr. peter montgomery is my dentist.

Dr. Peter Montgomery is my dentist.

Directions: Write **correct** on the line next to each group of words that is capitalized correctly. Rewrite the others on the line, using correct capitalization.

Answer	Item
Mrs. Joanna Thornton	**4.** mrs. joanna thornton
correct	**5.** December 31, 1902
the book *How I Learned Italian*	**6.** the book *How I learned italian*
correct	**7.** Boston, Massachusetts
He likes to write songs.	**8.** he likes to write songs.

Notes for Home: Your child practiced capitalizing proper nouns, abbreviations, and titles. ***Home Activity:*** Have your child explain rules for using capital letters when writing.

Grammar: Capitalization 601

Grammar Practice Book 4.6, p. 135

Name____________________ Children of Clay

Grammar: Capitalization

Directions: Look at each underlined word or group of words. Some of them have mistakes. Find twelve capitalization mistakes in the paragraph. Rewrite the incorrect words, using capital letters correctly.

my friend mr. Applebee has lived on town square st. for a long time. He has been teaching me how to play the piano since last march. He teaches kids from other families in harpersville too. On september 12, we will have a recital. Everyone in the town will be there, including capt. Maria Lopez from the police department. I am a little nervous, but mrs. applebee told me not to be scared. she gave me a book called *Your first recital* by r. j. Martin. now I'm ready!

1. **My**	7. **Capt. Maria Lopez**
2. **Mr. Applebee**	8. **Mrs. Applebee**
3. **Town Square St.**	9. **She**
4. **March**	10. ***Your First Recital***
5. **Harpersville**	11. **R. J. Martin**
6. **September 12**	12. **Now**

Directions: Rewrite each sentence, using correct capitalization.

13. rita and tony are going to visit their aunt and uncle.

Rita and Tony are going to visit their aunt and uncle.

14. aunt gina and uncle andrew live in atlanta, georgia.

Aunt Gina and Uncle Andrew live in Atlanta, Georgia.

15. they are planning to visit the fernbank museum of natural history.

They are planning to visit the Fernbank Museum of Natural History.

16. they haven't seen their aunt and uncle since january two years ago!

They haven't seen their aunt and uncle since January two years ago!

Notes for Home: Your child corrected mistakes in capitalization. ***Home Activity:*** Write (without capital letters) a list of titles and authors of books your child has read. Have him or her capitalize the titles and authors correctly.

602 Grammar: Capitalization

Practice Book 4.6, p. 268
Name________________ Children of Clay

Word Study: Irregular Plurals

Directions: Most plurals are formed by adding **-s** or **-es.** Some words change their spelling to become plural. Some words have the same singular and plural form. Both of these types of words are called **irregular plurals.** Read each word below. Write the plural form of the word on the line.

1. child	children	**6.** person	people
2. deer	deer	**7.** foot	feet
3. sheep	sheep	**8.** fish	fish
4. man	men	**9.** woman	women
5. moose	moose	**10.** goose	geese

Directions: Each sentence below has two plural nouns. Circle the plural nouns in each sentence. Then write just the irregular plurals on the lines.

One day last summer we went to a shop where two (women) make musical (instruments.) On (Saturdays,) (visitors) could make something to play too. We built shoe-box (guitars,) then tapped our (feet) to the music we made. We sang (songs) about (fish) swimming upstream and one funny song about a humpback whale. (People) listened and sang along, and the (children) had a lot of fun.

11. women
12. feet
13. fish
14. people
15. children

Notes for Home: Your child wrote irregular plural words, such as *children, deer,* and *feet.* ***Home Activity:*** Write plural words on index cards. Include examples of irregular plurals. Ask your child to sort the words into two piles—regular and irregular.

Spelling Workbook 4.6, p. 105
Name________________ Children of Clay

Spelling: Capitalization and Abbreviation

Pretest Directions: Fold back the page along the dotted line. On the blanks, write the spelling words as they are dictated. When you have finished the test, unfold the page and check your words.

1. Memorial Day	**1.** It's a **Memorial Day** picnic.
2. Christmas	**2.** Will you be home for **Christmas**?
3. May	**3.** My birthday is in **May**.
4. June	**4.** They were married in **June**.
5. September	**5.** School starts in **September**.
6. Hanukkah	**6. Hanukkah** candles are burning.
7. Kwanzaa	**7.** There's a **Kwanzaa** fest tonight.
8. Chinese New Year	**8. Chinese New Year** is coming up!
9. Valentine's Day	**9.** I got a card for **Valentine's Day**.
10. November	**10.** We will visit you in **November**.
11. Sun.	**11.** Today is **Sun.**, March 8.
12. Dec.	**12.** We fly out on **Dec.** 19.
13. Dr.	**13.** This is my mom, **Dr.** Nunez.
14. Mrs.	**14.** She's also called **Mrs.** Nunez.
15. Rd.	**15.** They live on Sheraton **Rd.**
16. Feb.	**16.** It's on **Feb.** 14, I think.
17. Wed.	**17.** The tickets say "**Wed.,** May 1."
18. Ms.	**18.** My name is **Ms.** Wood.
19. Mr.	**19.** His name is **Mr.** Delmar.
20. Ave.	**20.** They live on Atlantic **Ave.**

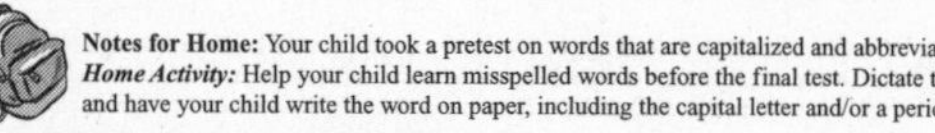

Notes for Home: Your child took a pretest on words that are capitalized and abbreviated. ***Home Activity:*** Help your child learn misspelled words before the final test. Dictate the word and have your child write the word on paper, including the capital letter and/or a period.

Spelling Workbook 4.6, p. 106
Name________________ Children of Clay

Spelling: Capitalization and Abbreviation

Directions: Choose the words from the box that name holidays or months. Write the words in the correct columns. **Order may vary**

Holidays	Months
1. Memorial Day	7. May
2. Christmas	8. June
3. Hanukkah	9. September
4. Kwanzaa	10. November
5. Chinese New Year	11. Dec.
6. Valentine's Day	12. Feb.

Word List	
Memorial Day	Sun.
Christmas	Dec.
May	Dr.
June	Mrs.
September	Rd.
Hanukkah	Feb.
Kwanzaa	Wed.
Chinese New Year	Ms.
Valentine's Day	Mr.
November	Ave.

Directions: Choose an abbreviation from the box that best completes each sentence. Write the abbreviation on the line to the left. Use an abbreviation only once.

Dr. **13.** If you're ill, we can go see _____ Levenson.
Mrs. (Dr.) **14.** We're going to meet Mr. Jones and his wife, _____ Jones.
Ms. **15.** My neighbor, _____ Winston, says she doesn't want to get married.
Rd. (Ave.) **16.** I live at 38 Kingston _____.
Ave. (Rd.) **17.** My best friend lives at 857 Rushmore _____.
Sun. **18.** _____ is a weekend day.
Wed. **19.** _____ is in the middle of the week.
Mr. **20.** Our plumber is _____ George Smith.

Notes for Home: Your child spelled abbreviations and words that are always capitalized. ***Home Activity:*** Make a list with your child of other abbreviations and proper nouns that require capital letters.

Spelling Workbook 4.6, p. 107
Name________________ Children of Clay

Spelling: Capitalization and Abbreviation

Directions: Proofread this letter. Find five spelling mistakes. Use the proofreading marks to correct each mistake.

≡ Make a capital.
/ Make a small letter.
∧ Add something.
Take out something.
⊙ Add a period.
¶ Begin a new paragraph.

Dear ms. Duke,

This coming may, on Memmorial Day, my family and I will be visiting your town. I would love to visit your pottery workshop. If you agree, please send directions to my mother, Mrs. Kim Lee, at 100 Coldfield rd., Denver, CO 35009. Thank you!

Sincerely,

Mr Vernon Lee

Spelling Tip

Holidays, days and months of the year, titles, and words that are part of an address are always capitalized: **Kwanzaa, November.** Abbreviations should be capitalized and followed by a period: **Dr., Mrs.**

Word List	
Memorial Day	Sun.
Christmas	Dec.
May	Dr.
June	Mrs.
September	Rd.
Hanukkah	Feb.
Kwanzaa	Wed.
Chinese New Year	Ms.
Valentine's Day	Mr.
November	Ave.

Write a Letter

On a separate sheet of paper, write a reply from Ms. Duke, inviting Vernon Lee to visit her pottery workshop. Use at least four spelling words, including at least one abbreviation. **Answers will vary, but each letter should include at least four spelling words, including at least one abbreviation.**

Notes for Home: Your child spelled abbreviations and words that are always capitalized. ***Home Activity:*** Say the full word for one of the abbreviations on the list and have your child write the abbreviation. Make sure he or she includes capital letters and periods.

Spelling Workbook 4.6, p. 108
Name______________

Children of Clay

Spelling: Capitalization and Abbreviation

REVIEW

Directions: Choose the word from the box that is an abbreviation for each word below. Write the word on the line.

Word List	
Memorial Day	Sun.
Christmas	Dec.
May	Dr.
June	Mrs.
September	Rd.
Hanukkah	Feb.
Kwanzaa	Wed.
Chinese New Year	Ms.
Valentine's Day	Mr.
November	Ave.

1. doctor **Dr.**
2. mister **Mr.**
3. avenue **Ave.**
4. road **Rd.**
5. Wednesday **Wed.**
6. Sunday **Sun.**
7. December **Dec.**
8. February **Feb.**

Directions: Choose the word from the box that best matches each clue. Write the word on the line.

9. fifth month **May**
10. sixth month **June**
11. ninth month **September**
12. eleventh month **November**
13. title for a married woman **Mrs.**
14. title for a married or unmarried woman **Ms.**
15. February 14 **Valentine's Day**
16. holiday to remember soldiers who have died **Memorial Day**
17. Jewish eight-day "festival of lights" **Hanukkah**
18. December 25 **Christmas**
19. African American celebration that starts on December 26 **Kwanzaa**
20. four-day festival that features dragons and firecrackers **Chinese New Year**

Notes for Home: Your child spelled abbreviations and words that are always capitalized. ***Home Activity:*** Play a holiday game with your child. Give a clue about a holiday and invite your child to identify the holiday and spell it correctly.

Practice Book 4.6, p. 269
Name______________

Children of Clay

Dictionary

A **dictionary** is a book of words and their meanings. A **glossary** is a short dictionary at the back of some books that contain the definitions for words used in a specific book. You can use a **dictionary** or **glossary** to find a word's meaning.

Here are some things to know about using a dictionary:

- The words at the top of a dictionary page are called **guide words.** They show the first and last words on the page.
- If your word fits alphabetically between the two guide words, it is included on that page.
- When you find your word, you will see letters and symbols in parentheses. This **pronunciation key** tells how to say the word.
- The **definition** tells the meaning of the word. Choose the definition that makes the most sense in the sentence containing the word. Example sentences and illustrations may help define the word. Sometimes there is more than one meaning for a word.
- The **part of speech** tells how the word is used, such as a verb or noun.

Directions: Use these dictionary entries to answer the questions that follow.

polish/power

pol•ish (pol ´ ish), **1** to make or become smooth and shiny: *to polish shoes. The silverware polished beautifully.* **2** a substance used to give smoothness or shine: *silver polish.* **3** Smoothness or shininess: *The polish of the furniture reflected our faces like a mirror.* 1,2 *verb,* 2,3 *noun, plural* **po • lish • es.**

pot•ter•y (pot ´ ər ē), pots, dishes, or vases made from clay and hardened by heat. *noun.*

scrawl/script

scrawl (skrȯl), **1** to write or draw poorly or carelessly. **2** poor, careless handwriting. 1 *verb,* 2 *noun.*

scream (skrēm), **1** to make a loud, sharp, piercing cry. People scream in fright, in anger, and in excitement. **2** a loud, sharp, piercing cry. 1 *verb,* 2 *noun.*

1. What are the guide words for the page on which the entry word *scream* appears? **scrawl and script**
2. What part of speech is listed for the third definition of *polish?* **noun**
3. How many syllables are in *pottery?* **three**

Practice Book 4.6, p. 270
Name______________

Children of Clay

4. What part of the entry for *polish* tells what the word sounds like? Write that part here. **(pol´ ish)**
5. Does the *e* in *pottery* sound like the *e* in *scream?* **no**
6. List one other word that might appear on a page that has *polish* and *power* as its guide words. **Possible answer: pour**
7. What is the plural form of *polish?* **polishes**
8. How many definitions does *scream* have? **two**
9. What part of speech is listed for the first definition of *scream?* **verb**
10. How many definitions does *polish* have? **three**
11. Which of the four words listed is used as a noun only? **pottery**
12. List one word that might appear on the page just before the page with *scrawl.* **Possible answer: scrap**
13. How is the word *scrawl* used in the following sentence? *He scrawled his signature on the check.* **It is used as a verb.**
14. Write the meaning of *scream* that is used in this sentence: *I scream every time I see a spider.* **to make a loud, sharp, piercing cry**
15. Write a sentence using the third definition of *polish.* **Possible answer: The polish on the hood of the car gleamed in the sunlight.**

Notes for Home: Your child practiced using a dictionary. ***Home Activity:*** Read a news article with your child and have him or her circle any unfamiliar words. Together, look up these words in a dictionary and discuss their meanings.

Practice Book 4.6, p. 271
Name______________

Coming Home

Fact and Opinion

- A **statement of fact** tells something that can be proved true or false.
- A **statement of opinion** tells your ideas or feelings. It cannot be proved true or false, but it can be supported by facts and reasons. Sometimes statements of opinion begin with clues such as *I believe.*

Directions: Reread the book review of *Naomi's Geese.* Then complete the tables. Identify statements of fact and statements of opinion from the review. Some have been done for you. **Possible answers given.**

Fact
The book is about Naomi and two geese.
The reviewer's family moved to a lake in Maine.
1. **Geese migrate.**
2. **Loons were at the lake in Maine.**
3. **Loons are curious and will come close.**

Opinion
I was worried about the loons.
I like how the geese called pieces of bread "fluffy white things."
4. **Most people who like nature will like this book.**
5. **Anyone between the ages of nine and thirteen would like the book.**

Notes for Home: Your child read a book review and identified statements of fact and opinion. ***Home Activity:*** Choose a recent family event, such as a visit to a relative's house. Take turns telling statements of fact and opinion about the event.

Practice Book 4.6, p. 272

Name______________________ Coming Home

Vocabulary

Directions: Choose the word from the box that best matches each clue. Write the word on the line.

Check the Words You Know
__ dreamer
__ drifted
__ heroes
__ librarians
__ rusty
__ tremble

rusty 1. It's what your bike will become if you leave it out in the rain.

dreamer 2. It's what you are if you spend more time asleep than awake.

heroes 3. These are people who do things that other people admire.

librarians 4. These are people who can't keep their hands off a good book.

Directions: Choose the word from the box that best replaces each underlined word or words. Write the word on the line.

heroes 5. Traci had many people she admired.

librarians 6. She loved books, and so she also admired people who ran libraries.

dreamer 7. Traci was a person who had a lot of dreams.

rusty 8. One day in the attic, she found an old metal box that was covered in rust.

tremble 9. She thought she had found a hidden treasure, and she began to shake with excitement.

drifted 10. The box held old postcards of an uncle who had wandered from one interesting town to another.

Write a Poem

On a separate sheet of paper, write a poem about a wish or a dream. Use vocabulary words in your poem. **Students' poems should use vocabulary words correctly.**

Notes for Home: Your child identified and used vocabulary words from *Coming Home: From the Life of Langston Hughes. Home Activity:* Ask your child to write six sentences, each one including a different vocabulary word.

Practice Book 4.6, p. 273

Name______________________ Coming Home

Fact and Opinion

- A **statement of fact** tells something that can be proved true or false.
- A **statement of opinion** tells your ideas or feelings. It cannot be proved true or false.

Directions: Reread what happens in *Coming Home: From the Life of Langston Hughes* when Langston's mother comes to visit him. Then follow the instructions below.

Other times Langston's ma would come to Lawrence. Once it wasn't the best of times for her. Money was scarce. She snapped at Langston and it hurt.

Later that evening they went to St. Luke's Church where Langston's ma was giving a performance. She told him that she had a wonderful surprise for him. That he was going to be on the stage with her. That he was going to be a star, just like she was going to be.

Langston didn't like the surprise. That evening he was the one with the surprise. As his ma introduced him, behind her back Langston made faces: He crossed his eyes, stretched his mouth, and imitated her. Everyone burst out laughing.

1. Tell whether this statement is fact or opinion: "Once it wasn't the best of times for her." Explain your answer.
opinion; You couldn't prove that it wasn't the best of times.

2. Tell whether this statement is fact or opinion: "Money was scarce." Explain your answer.
fact; You could determine the amount of money they had.

3. Give a statement of fact from the second paragraph.
Possible answer: They went to St. Luke's Church.

4. Tell an opinion that Langston's mother expresses in the second paragraph.
Possible answer: She had a wonderful surprise for him.

5. Reread the story. On a separate sheet of paper, write three statements of fact about Langston Hughes and two statements of opinion about him. **Check that students correctly distinguish between statements of fact and opinion.**

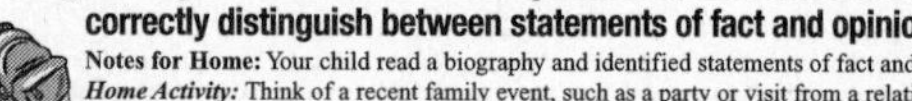

Notes for Home: Your child read a biography and identified statements of fact and opinion. *Home Activity:* Think of a recent family event, such as a party or visit from a relative. Ask your child to tell two facts and two opinions about the event.

Practice Book 4.6, p. 275

Name______________________ Coming Home

Selection Test

Directions: Choose the best answer to each item. Mark the letter for the answer you have chosen.

Part 1: Vocabulary

Find the answer choice that means about the same as the underlined word in each sentence.

1. The leaves began to tremble.
   - **(A)** move or shake
   - B. grow quickly
   - C. change color
   - D. wither and die

2. The pot is rusty.
   - F. large and heavy
   - G. having many dents or bumps
   - H. dripping or leaking
   - **(J)** covered with a reddish coating

3. Every child needs heroes.
   - A. true friends
   - **(B)** people who are admired
   - C. wise teachers
   - D. thoughtful adults

4. He has always been a dreamer.
   - F. one who is usually sad
   - G. person who acts young
   - **(H)** one who imagines how things might be
   - J. person who causes harm

5. The librarians can help us.
   - A. ideas that are written down
   - B. people who write books
   - C. collections of things to read
   - **(D)** persons who work in libraries

6. People drifted through the park.
   - **(F)** moved easily or without care
   - G. searched or looked about
   - H. whispered or spoke softly
   - J. rushed by

Part 2: Comprehension

Use what you know about the selection to answer each item.

7. Langston Hughes grew up in—
   - A. Mexico.
   - **(B)** Kansas.
   - C. Oklahoma.
   - D. New York.

8. In his early years, Langston dreamed mostly of—
   - F. becoming an actor.
   - G. meeting famous people.
   - H. learning to play jazz music.
   - **(J)** living with his pa and ma.

GO ON

Practice Book 4.6, p. 276

Name______________________ Coming Home

9. You can tell from this selection that Langston's mother—
   - **(A)** cared a lot about her acting career.
   - B. wanted Langston to be a dancer.
   - C. liked living in different places.
   - D. wanted Langston to be a writer.

10. How did Langston feel when he went to live with the Reeds?
    - F. frightened and sad
    - G. selfish and spoiled
    - H. lonesome and bored
    - **(J)** happy and loved

11. Langston loved to tell his friends stories about—
    - A. his mother and father.
    - B. performing on stage.
    - **(C)** black people he admired.
    - D. visiting the library.

12. Langston Hughes became a—
    - **(F)** writer.
    - G. teacher.
    - H. congressman.
    - J. preacher.

13. Which sentence states a fact?
    - A. "Living with Granma wasn't easy."
    - B. "Auntie Reed's church was all right."
    - **(C)** "One day she took Langston all the way to Topeka to hear Booker T. Washington speak."
    - D. "The singing and preaching felt so familiar."

14. Which sentence best describes Langston Hughes?
    - **(F)** He found home in his heart.
    - G. He liked to be alone.
    - H. He counted on other people to help him.
    - J. He felt sorry for himself.

15. Which sentence states an opinion?
    - A. Langston was chosen class poet.
    - B. After school, he'd run and play with friends.
    - C. Granma used to work on the Underground Railroad.
    - **(D)** Buffalo soldiers were the bravest of all.

Name______________________ Coming Home

Fact and Opinion

- A **statement of fact** tells something that can be proved true or false.
- A **statement of opinion** tells ideas or feelings. It cannot be proved true or false.

Directions: Read the passage below.

Gwendolyn Brooks is one of the greatest poets of our time. She has won many awards. She was the first African American to receive the Pulitzer Prize, a famous prize for the best book of the year. She was also chosen *poet laureate* of Illinois. (A poet laureate is an honored and official poet.)

Brooks was born on June 7, 1917, in Topeka, Kansas. Her first books, *A Street in Bronzeville* and *Annie Allen*, are full of beautiful but sad poems.

Brooks taught poetry for many years. She believes children are important poets. She is a generous person. She has given her own money for poetry prizes to elementary and high school poets.

Brooks has also written books to help young people write poetry: *Young Poets' Primer* and *Very Young Poets*. She is an excellent teacher and a great writer.

Directions: Use statements from the passage to complete the table.
Possible answers given.

Statements of Fact (can be proved true or false)	Statements of Opinion (tells ideas and feelings)
She received a Pulitzer Prize.	She is one of the greatest poets of our time.
1. **She has taught poetry.**	She has written many beautiful poems.
2. **She has given her own money for prizes.**	3. **She is a generous person.**
4. **She has written books for young people.**	5. **She is an excellent teacher.**

Notes for Home: Your child has read a biography and identified statements of fact and opinion. ***Home Activity:*** Ask your child to think of the last time your family ate dinner together. Invite him or her to tell you two facts and two opinions about that dinner.

Practice Book 4.6, p. 277

Name______________________ Coming Home

Paraphrasing

REVIEW

Directions: Read the passage. Then read each question about the passage. Choose the best answer to each question. Mark the letter for the answer you have chosen.

Carl Sandburg: American Poet

Carl Sandburg wrote poems that found the beauty in ordinary people. His poetry shows his belief in "the common folk" and in their power to make the world a better place.

Sandburg worked many different jobs. For a while, he was a soldier. He did hard physical labor. He wrote for a newspaper. All of these experiences helped shape his poetry.

In addition to his poetry, Sandburg wrote a famous biography of President Abraham Lincoln. He also wrote children's books. The most famous is called *Rootabaga Stories.*

1. Sandburg wrote—
   - A. long poems.
   - B. poems about nature.
   - (C.) poems about ordinary people.
   - D. poems about famous people.
2. Sandburg's work—
   - (F.) helped him write his poetry.
   - G. prevented him writing poetry.
   - H. was separate from his poetry.
   - J. paid a lot of money.
3. Complete this paraphrase of the last paragraph: Sandburg also wrote —
   - A. children's stories.
   - (B.) a biography of Lincoln and children's stories.
   - C. a biography of Lincoln.
   - D. *Rootabaga Stories.*
4. Which detail would probably not be part of a paraphrase of the passage?
   - F. Sandburg wrote poems about ordinary people.
   - G. He worked many different jobs.
   - H. He wrote children's books and a biography.
   - (J.) He wrote *Rootabaga Stories.*
5. Complete this paraphrase of the whole passage: Carl Sandburg was an American poet who—
   - A. worked at different jobs and wrote books as well as poetry.
   - (B.) showed his belief in ordinary people through his writing.
   - C. wrote a famous biography.
   - D. worked many hard jobs.

Notes for Home: Your child read a passage and identified statements that paraphrased the passage's main ideas. ***Home Activity:*** Tell your child about something you did together today. Ask your child to paraphrase your story by retelling it in his or her own words.

Name______________________ Coming Home

Writing Across Texts

Directions: Consider what you already know and what you read in the selections *Coming Home* and "Koya's Cousin Del." What did coming home mean to Del and Langston Hughes? Complete the table below to explain how each character felt about home. **Possible answers given.**

Del's Feelings About Home	Langston Hughes's Feelings About Home
He loved spending time with his family.	He did not like how quiet it was.
1. **He wanted to share his new music with his family members first.**	6. **He dreamt of having his family together in one home.**
2. **It was a place he could share his dreams.**	7. **It was a place where his grandma told wonderful stories.**
3. **After his parents died, it was the only place he was comfortable.**	8. **Home was a place where there was lots of food and hugs.**
4. **He paid for damage and picked up litter to keep the neighborhood looking nice.**	9. **Home could be a theater, or a song, or a church.**
5. **Singing songs about his mother reminded Del of home.**	10. **He realized that home was inside him.**

Write a Paragraph

On a separate sheet of paper, write a paragraph that compares and contrasts what Koya's cousin Del and Langston Hughes felt about coming home. Use the information in your table to help you write your paragraph.

Paragraphs will vary. Check that students have used details from both selections in their paragraphs.

Notes for Home: Your child compared the feelings of characters in two different selections. ***Home Activity:*** Read other selections with your child and have your child find similarities and differences among the characters.

Grammar Practice Book 4.6, p. 136

Name______________________ Coming Home

Grammar: Compound Subjects and Objects

REVIEW

Directions: Combine each set of sentences by using a compound subject. Write your new sentence on the lines. (Remember, verbs must agree with the subject.)

1. Harlem is located in New York City. Greenwich Village is located in New York City also.
   Harlem and Greenwich Village are located in New York City.
2. Many workers settled in Harlem in the 1920s. Many artists settled there too.
   Many workers and artists settled in Harlem in the 1920s.
3. Writers made Harlem the center of African American culture. Musicians and artists did too.
   Writers, musicians, and artists made Harlem the center of African American culture.

Directions: Combine each set of sentences by using a compound object. Write your new sentence on the lines.

4. Musicians from the South brought jazz to Harlem. They brought other exciting music as well.
   Musicians from the South brought jazz and other exciting music to Harlem.
5. People everywhere were reading novels about African American life. They also were reading poems and plays about African American life.
   People everywhere were reading novels, poems, and plays about African American life.

Notes for Home: Your child combined sentences by using compound subjects and objects. ***Home Activity:*** Challenge your child to make up sets of sentences for you to combine using compound subjects and compound objects.

Grammar Practice Book 4.6, p. 137

Name_______________

Coming Home

Grammar: Commas

A **series** is a group of items. Items in sentences can be nouns, verbs, or other words. In a sentence, commas are used to separate items in a series.

Langston Hughes, Nella Larsen, and Zora Neale Hurston were all Harlem writers.

When you speak to, or address, a person by name, you are using a name in **direct address.** Commas are used when the name is at the beginning, in the middle, or at the end of a sentence.

Louis, have you read the biography of Langston Hughes?
No, Tanya, I haven't.
Why not, Louis?

Commas are also used in dates and addresses:

- between the day and the month: *Friday, June 4*
- between the date and the year: *Tanya was born on June 5, 1991.*
- between the city and the state: *Burlington, Vermont*
- after the street address, the city, and the Zip Code, if the address appears in the middle of a sentence: *She moved to 23 W. 5th St., Columbus, Ohio 43216, when she was five.*

Directions: Add commas as needed to each sentence.

1. Tanya is reading about writers,painters,and musicians who lived in Harlem.
2. Her favorite writers are Langston Hughes,Richard Wright,and Jessie Faucet.
3. Tanya,what are you doing?
4. I am reading,Mother.
5. I have to finish this book,call Grandma,and write my report.
6. Tanya's grandma lives in Marquette,Michigan 49855,near a lake.
7. She was born on March 9,1942,and lived in Harlem for many years.
8. Tanya plans to do her research,organize her notes,and write her report.
9. Grandma,have you ever read any books by Langston Hughes?
10. Yes,Tanya,he is one of my favorite writers.

Notes for Home: Your child used commas to separate items in a series, with names used in direct address, in dates, and in addresses. ***Home Activity:*** Look through a book with your child and ask him or her to explain why commas are used as they are.

Grammar: Commas 621

Grammar Practice Book 4.6, p. 138

Name_______________

Coming Home

Grammar: Commas

Directions: Add commas as needed to each sentence.

1. Keisha,Jennifer,and Otto had to choose a subject for a school report.
2. Keisha,help us pick a famous writer.
3. Otto and Jennifer weren't sure if they wanted to write about an author,a songwriter,or a poet.
4. They knew that Langston Hughes wrote books,stories,poems,and plays.
5. They began their research on Friday,January 16.
6. Their report was due in two weeks on Friday,January 30.
7. They went to the library,bookstores,and the school's computer lab.
8. Jennifer took lots of books home,read them,and returned them to the library.
9. Keisha even wrote to a library at 1185 6th Ave.,New York,New York 10036,to get more information.
10. The information arrived on Monday,January 26.
11. Otto's mother,sister,and brother helped him do research on the Internet.
12. At last, the three friends finished their report on Thursday,January 29.
13. They read the report to their teacher,classmates,and the school principal.
14. Everyone agreed it was the best report their school in Newark,New Jersey,had ever seen!
15. Class,let's applaud these three students!

Write a Letter

Write a letter to a favorite author. List at least three of your favorite books by that author and describe some of the things you like about them. Remember to use commas in your letter. **Letters should include at least one series of three, with commas used correctly.**

Notes for Home: Your child used commas in a series, in direct address, and in dates and addresses. ***Home Activity:*** Ask your child to name three of something, such as three favorite colors. Then have him or her write the three in a list, using commas correctly.

622 Grammar: Commas

Grammar Practice Book 4.6, p. 139

Name_______________

Coming Home

Grammar: Commas

RETEACHING

Underline the sentence in which commas are used correctly.

1. He read many books, written in Chicago Illinois.
2. Laura, Danielle, and Sophie are going to the show. (underlined)
3. Alicia are you, coming too?

Use **commas** to separate items in a **series.** Also use a comma to separate a name in **direct address** from the rest of the sentence. In a **date,** use commas between the day and the month, and between the date and the year. In an **address,** use a comma between the city and the state, and after the street address, the city, and the Zip Code if the address is in the middle of a sentence.

Directions: Add commas to each sentence as needed.

1. Andreas left Alaska on July 17,1996.
2. A book,a game,a rope,and a box sat on the windowsill.
3. Bill,do you know where your brother is?
4. Pants,more socks,and a shirt covered a chair.
5. Karen,bring me the new blanket.
6. A bank,another game,and a horseshoe were on the rug.
7. His desk was dirty,wobbly,and messy.
8. Jeanne lives at 1002 Sue Parkway,Ann Arbor,MI 48103.
9. Some marbles,a pencil,and a sweater were under his bed.
10. José was born on October 1,1990.

Notes for Home: Your child corrected sentences by adding commas. ***Home Activity:*** Write a brief letter to your child, leaving out commas in dates, series, and addresses. Have your child correct the letter by adding commas where they belong.

Grammar: Commas 623

Grammar Practice Book 4.6, p. 140

Name_______________

Coming Home

Grammar: Commas

Directions: Add commas where they are needed in these sentences.

1. Puerto Rico,Jamaica,and Hispaniola are all Caribbean islands.
2. The weather in Puerto Rico is usually warm,breezy,and pleasant.
3. The beaches,tropical forests,and water attract many tourists.
4. Children play,swim,and build sand castles along the beaches.
5. Some of Puerto Rico's major products are milk,eggs,and coffee.

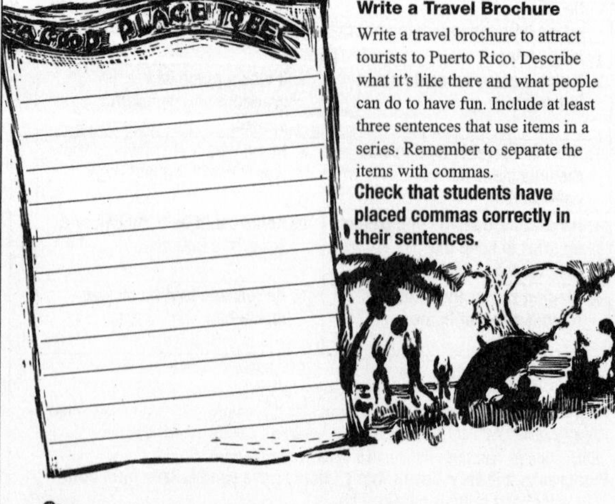

Write a Travel Brochure

Write a travel brochure to attract tourists to Puerto Rico. Describe what it's like there and what people can do to have fun. Include at least three sentences that use items in a series. Remember to separate the items with commas.

Check that students have placed commas correctly in their sentences.

Notes for Home: Your child identified and wrote commas in a series of items in sentences. ***Home Activity:*** Have your child write sentences that list what he or she will do over the weekend. Remind your child to include commas between items in the list.

624 Grammar: Commas

Practice Book 4.6, p. 278

Name________________________ Coming Home

Phonics: Consonant Sounds /k/ and /f/

Word List				
books	enough	America	trophy	kitchen
family	beautiful	Kansas	tracks	Buffalo

Directions: Read the words in the box. Listen for words that have the sound /k/ and words that have the sound /f/. Write each word in the correct column. **Order may vary.**

Words with the sound /k/	Words with the sound /f/
1. books	6. enough
2. America	7. trophy
3. kitchen	8. family
4. Kansas	9. beautiful
5. tracks	10. Buffalo

Directions: Read each sentence below. Listen for the word that has the sound /k/ or /f/. Circle the word and write it on the line. Underline the letters that stand for the sound /k/ or /f/.

backyard 11. As he played in his backyard the young boy heard the whistle of the passing train.

fence 12. He ran to the fence to watch the train go by.

himself 13. "Someday, I hope to ride on the train," he said to himself.

clickety-clack 14. He listened to the clickety-clack of the wheels.

laughed 15. He laughed and waved at people in the train.

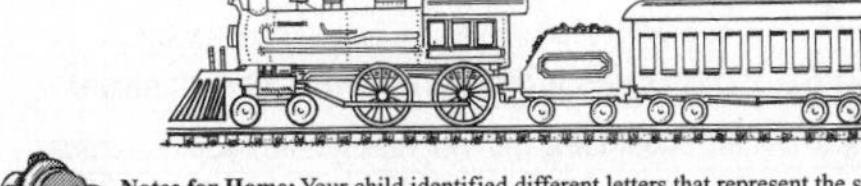

Notes for Home: Your child identified different letters that represent the sound /k/, *(c, k, ck)* and the sound /f/, *(f, ff, gh, ph)*. ***Home Activity:*** While reading with your child, take turns trying to find words with these two sounds.

Spelling Workbook 4.6, p. 109

Name________________________ Coming Home

Spelling: Words with /k/ and /f/

Pretest Directions: Fold back the page along the dotted line. On the blanks, write the spelling words as they are dictated. When you have finished the test, unfold the page and check your words.

1. care — 1. Take **care** when you travel.
2. because — 2. I'm going **because** I have to.
3. cover — 3. This blanket will **cover** me well.
4. record — 4. His time broke the world **record**.
5. brake — 5. Hit the **brake**; we need to stop.
6. Kansas — 6. **Kansas** is a prairie state.
7. track — 7. I can't keep **track** of all this.
8. pocket — 8. Put this in your **pocket**.
9. snack — 9. She ate an apple for a **snack**.
10. attack — 10. The bear cubs will not **attack**.
11. stiff — 11. Our hands are **stiff** and cold.
12. muffin — 12. This **muffin** tastes good.
13. giraffe — 13. The **giraffe** ate its fill of leaves.
14. enough — 14. They have eaten **enough**.
15. laughed — 15. We **laughed** at his joke.
16. rough — 16. The trail was **rough** to climb.
17. photo — 17. Who is that in the **photo**?
18. alphabet — 18. The **alphabet** soup is ready.
19. dolphin — 19. The **dolphin** swims quickly.
20. elephant — 20. Look at the gray **elephant**.

Notes for Home: Your child took a pretest on words that have the /k/ and /f/ sound. ***Home Activity:*** Help your child learn misspelled words before the final test. Your child can underline the word parts that caused the problems and concentrate on those parts.

Spelling Workbook 4.6, p. 110

Name________________________ Coming Home

Spelling: Words with /k/ and /f/

Word List				
care	brake	snack	giraffe	photo
because	Kansas	attack	enough	alphabet
cover	track	stiff	laughed	dolphin
record	pocket	muffin	rough	elephant

Directions: Choose the words from the box that have the consonant sound /f/. Write the words in the correct columns. **Order may vary.**

Spelled ph	Spelled ff	Spelled gh
1. photo	5. stiff	8. enough
2. alphabet	6. muffin	9. laughed
3. dolphin	7. giraffe	10. rough
4. elephant		

Directions: Choose the word from the box that best matches each clue. Write the word on the line.

pocket 11. Unlike golf, a hole in one of these isn't good.

snack 12. It's something you eat between two meals.

track 13. You can run on one, or race a car on one.

care 14. Never say, "I don't ____ about you."

because 15. Ask why, and the answer may start with this word.

Kansas 16. It's where Dorothy and Toto came from.

brake 17. If you're going too fast, do this.

attack 18. An animal might do this if cornered.

cover 19. It wraps around the pages of a book.

record 20. If you set one of these, you should be proud.

Notes for Home: Your child spelled words with the consonant sounds /k/ and /f/. ***Home Activity:*** Read the words on the list aloud, one at a time. Ask your child to tell you the letters that represent either the sound /k/ or /f/ in each word.

Spelling Workbook 4.6, p. 111

Name________________________ Coming Home

Spelling: Words with /k/ and /f/

Directions: Proofread this invitation to a poetry reading. Find five spelling mistakes. Use the proofreading marks to correct each mistake.

≡ Make a capital.
/ Make a small letter.
∧ Add something.
Take out something.
⊙ Add a period.
¶ Begin a new paragraph.

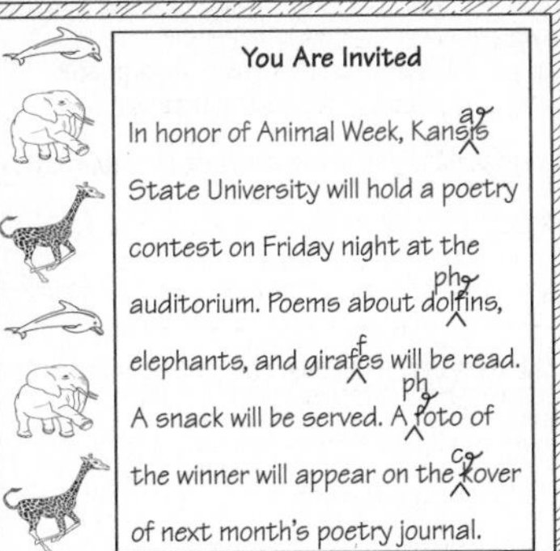

You Are Invited
In honor of Animal Week, Kansis State University will hold a poetry contest on Friday night at the auditorium. Poems about dolfins, elephants, and girafes will be read. A snack will be served. A foto of the winner will appear on the kover of next month's poetry journal.
as
ph
f
ph
co

Spelling Tip

The sound /k/ can be spelled **c, k,** or **ck.** The sound /f/ can be spelled **ff, gh,** or **ph.** It's hard to tell when you have to use **ck** or when a simple **c** or **k** will do. Check the invitation to make sure words with these consonant sounds are spelled correctly.

Word List				
care	brake	snack	giraffe	photo
because	Kansas	attack	enough	alphabet
cover	track	stiff	laughed	dolphin
record	pocket	muffin	rough	elephant

Write an Invitation

On a separate sheet of paper, write an invitation to a poetry reading. Try to use at least three spelling words. **Answers will vary, but each invitation should include at least three spelling words.**

Notes for Home: Your child spelled words with the consonant sounds /k/ and /f/. ***Home Activity:*** Have your child think of words that are similar to the spelling words (for example: *careful, snacking, pocketful*), and have him or her try to spell these longer words.

Spelling Workbook 4.6, p. 112

Name____________________ Coming Home

Spelling Words with /k/ and /f/ REVIEW

Word List				
care	brake	snack	giraffe	photo
because	Kansas	attack	enough	alphabet
cover	track	stiff	laughed	dolphin
record	pocket	muffin	rough	elephant

Directions: Choose the word from the box that rhymes with each word below. Write the word on the line. Use a word only once.

1. sack **snack (or attack or track)**
2. fake **brake**
3. socket **pocket**
4. sniff **stiff**
5. puffin **muffin**
6. raft **laughed**
7. hover **cover**
8. stack **attack (or snack or track)**
9. rack **track (or snack or attack)**
10. pause **because**
11. sword **record**
12. staff **giraffe**

Directions: Choose the word from the box that best replaces each underlined word. Write the word on the line to the left.

rough 13. Being a poet can be a little difficult.

care 14. Many people don't think about poetry.

enough 15. But if you want it a lot, you can be a poet.

photo 16. You might not have your picture in the paper.

Kansas 17. People might not know your name in a Midwestern state.

alphabet 18. But you'll make good use of the letters.

elephant 19. You can write about a big gray animal.

dolphin 20. Or you can write about a porpoise, if you prefer.

Notes for Home: Your child spelled words with consonant sounds /k/ and /f/. ***Home Activity:*** Write the spelling words in a list, but spell some words incorrectly. Challenge your child to check the list and correct any misspellings.

Practice Book 4.6, p. 279

Name____________________ Coming Home

Organize and Present Information/Draw Conclusions

Before you prepare a report, you need to organize your information. For example, you might make a story map to record ideas about plot, setting, and characters in a story. You might use a cluster web to show facts and details about a person, place, or thing.

Directions: Reread *Coming Home.* Then complete the cluster web to give facts and details that you learned about Langston Hughes. Then answer the question that follows. **Answers will vary. Check that students have listed facts and details from the selection.**

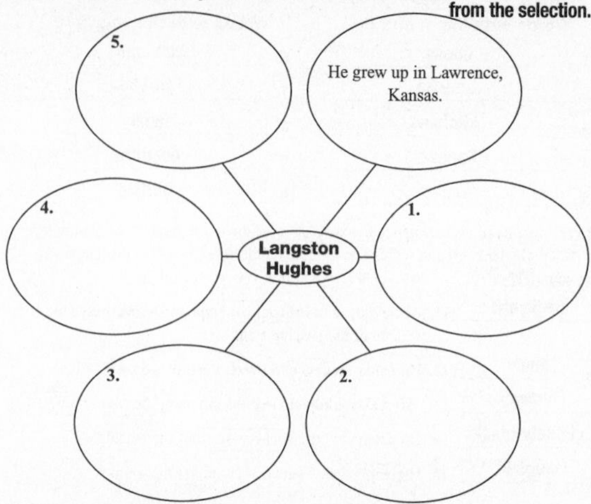

6. Did you find it helpful to organize information in a cluster web? Explain.

Possible answer: Yes, a cluster web is helpful because it lets you record important facts and details about Langston Hughes. It helps you remember what you read about him.

Practice Book 4.6, p. 280

Name____________________ Coming Home

After you have collected information for a report, you have to present it to others. You could present your report orally, write a report or a story, draw a time line or make a drawing with captions. In your presentation, you should draw conclusions about the information you've organized to explain what it means.

Directions: Read each topic. Decide whether a written report, a time line, or a picture with captions would be the best method of presentation. Give an explanation to support each answer. **Possible answers given. Accept any reasonably supported answers.**

7. NASA space launches

A time line would be the best because you could show when important launches happened.

8. poets of the 1950s

A written report would be the best because you could include information about several different poets.

9. life cycle of a tree

A picture with captions would be best because you could show each stage of a tree's life cycle.

10. Choose a strategy for organizing information, such as a story map, a time line, or a table. Explain why this strategy is useful for organizing information.

Answers will vary. Students' explanations should tell how the strategy helps organize information.

Notes for Home: Your child learned how to organize and present information. ***Home Activity:*** Work with your child to organize a story about his or her life. Use a time line to show important events. Have your child tell his or her story to family members or friends.

Practice Book 4.6, p. 281

Name____________________ Out of the Blue

Main Idea and Supporting Details

- The **topic** is what a paragraph or article is all about.
- The **main idea** is the most important idea about the topic. Sometimes it is stated, and sometimes you have to figure it out and put it into your own words.
- **Supporting details** are small pieces of information that tell more about the main idea.

Directions: Reread "Working on the Railroad." Then complete the diagram by finishing the sentences that tell about the article's main idea and some of its supporting details.

Main Idea
1. Because railroad work was difficult and dangerous, **many railroad workers created inventions to make their jobs easier and safer.**

Supporting Details
2. The brakeman was in danger because **he might be crushed between two cars.**
3. Andrew Beard created **the Jenny Coupler.**
4. Railroad firemen had to **keep the engine fueled and oiled.**
5. Elijah McCoy invented **a self-lubricating cup.**

Notes for Home: Your child read an article and identified its main idea and some of its supporting details. ***Home Activity:*** Read a news article with your child. Together, identify the main idea of the article and take turns naming the supporting details.

Practice Book 4.6, p. 282

Name ______________________ Out of the Blue

Vocabulary

Directions: Choose the word from the box that best matches each definition. Write the word on the line.

Check the Words You Know

__ almanac
__ calendar
__ circulating
__ electricity
__ experiment
__ inventions
__ mysterious
__ theory

calendar 1. chart showing months, weeks, days, and dates of a year

electricity 2. form of energy that can produce light, heat, or motion

mysterious 3. hard to explain or understand

theory 4. explanation based on observation and reasoning

experiment 5. a trial or a test to find out something

Directions: Choose the word from the box that best matches each clue. Write the word on the line.

almanac 6. It has useful information.

circulating 7. This is what library books are doing.

inventions 8. These often become everyday tools, like toasters, automobiles, and computers.

electricity 9. This runs your refrigerator and lights your house.

theory 10. Scientists use observation to help create this idea.

Write a Description

Imagine a new invention that would do some chore that you hate. On a separate sheet of paper, write a description of this invention and how it works. Use as many vocabulary words as you can. **Students should use vocabulary words correctly.**

Notes for Home: Your child identified and used vocabulary words from "Out of the Blue." ***Home Activity:*** Read each vocabulary word to your child and ask him or her to tell you what it means.

Practice Book 4.6, p. 283

Name ______________________ Out of the Blue

Main Idea and Supporting Details

- The **main idea** is the most important idea about the topic.
- **Supporting details** are small pieces of information that tell more about the main idea.

Directions: Reread the following passage in "Out of the Blue." Then answer the questions below.

Philadelphia suited young Benjamin perfectly. He lived on High Street, the busiest and noisiest street in town. On one end of the street was the Delaware River to jump into when he felt like a goat leap. On the other end of the street was Debbie Read, whom he courted and married.

Benjamin and Debbie were married in 1730. Benjamin was twenty-four years old now and getting ahead in the world. He had his own printshop, owned his own newspaper, and because he was such a good printer, he did the printing for the government of Pennsylvania. (He always used the blackest ink and the whitest paper he could find.) In addition, Debbie and Benjamin ran a store in the front of their house.

1. What is the main idea in the first paragraph? **Possible answers given.**
Philadelphia suited young Benjamin perfectly.

2. Is the main idea in the first paragraph stated? Explain.
stated; It is the first sentence of the paragraph.

3. What is the main idea in the second paragraph?
Benjamin was getting ahead in the world.

4. What are two examples of supporting details in the second paragraph?
He had his own printshop. He owned his own newspaper.

5. On a separate sheet of paper, tell the main idea of "Out of the Blue," and give two supporting details. **Main idea: Benjamin Franklin was an important inventor who had lots of good ideas. Supporting details: He started the first circulating library in America. He invented a new kind of stove.**

Notes for Home: Your child read a biography and identified its main ideas and supporting details. ***Home Activity:*** Read a newspaper article with your child. Ask your child to tell you the most important idea of the story. Take turns identifying supporting details.

Practice Book 4.6, p. 285

Name ______________________ Out of the Blue

Selection Test

Directions: Choose the best answer to each item. Mark the letter for the answer you have chosen.

Part 1: Vocabulary

Find the answer choice that means about the same as the underlined word in each sentence.

1. Where is the new <u>calendar</u>?
   A. large, heavy book
   (B) chart of months and days
   C. list of places to see
   D. book of telephone numbers

2. There was no <u>electricity</u>.
   (F) form of energy
   G. equipment used by scientists
   H. disagreement
   J. chance for people to vote

3. The <u>inventions</u> worked.
   A. wise sayings
   (B) things created or thought up
   C. money set aside and saved
   D. builders or carpenters

4. We will do an <u>experiment</u>.
   (F) trial or test
   G. report
   H. performance
   J. job or chore

5. The <u>almanac</u> is amusing.
   A. daily journal kept to record a person's ideas and activities
   B. postcard or letter
   (C) yearly publication of brief information on many subjects
   D. storybook with pictures

6. She is a <u>mysterious</u> woman.
   F. very pretty
   G. old and wise
   H. highly skilled
   (J) hard to understand

7. His <u>theory</u> interests me.
   A. training or education
   B. something made to be displayed
   C. way of behaving
   (D) explanation based on observing

8. This is a <u>circulating</u> library book.
   F. popular or well liked
   (G) passing from person to person
   H. easily torn or ripped
   J. uncommon or difficult to find

GO ON

Practice Book 4.6, p. 286

Name ______________________ Out of the Blue

Part 2: Comprehension

Use what you know about the selection to answer each item.

9. In Philadelphia, Ben Franklin got a job with a—
   A. clothing maker.
   (B) printer.
   C. watchmaker.
   D. sailor.

10. Members of the Leather Apron Club met every week to—
    (F) talk about ideas.
    G. print newspapers.
    H. do experiments.
    J. make clothes.

11. You know that young Ben Franklin had many interests because he—
    A. went to work when he was 17.
    B. lived in Philadelphia.
    (C) owned a printshop, a newspaper, and a store.
    D. made friends easily.

12. Publishing his almanac gave Ben Franklin a chance to—
    (F) use his sense of humor.
    G. write about electricity.
    H. sell his inventions.
    J. tell how hurricanes move.

13. What is the main idea of this selection?
    A. Ben Franklin should have been a scientist.
    B. Ben Franklin improved the lives of people in Philadelphia.
    C. Most people liked Ben Franklin's ideas.
    (D) Ben Franklin had many ideas, but his big one was that lightning is electricity.

14. Which sentence states an opinion?
    F. Electricity and lightning are the same.
    (G) Lightning is as mysterious as heaven.
    H. Electricity is attracted to pointed iron rods.
    J. Ben Franklin felt an electric shock through a key tied to a kite.

15. In his lifetime, Ben Franklin was best known for his—
    A. magic squares.
    (B) ideas about electricity.
    C. household inventions.
    D. writings about comets.

Name___________________ Out of the Blue

Main Idea and Supporting Details

- The **main idea** is the most important idea about the topic.
- **Supporting details** are small pieces of information that tell more about the main idea.

Directions: Read the passage below.

Elijah McCoy was a famous inventor. He invented many things, including a folding ironing board, treads for tires, and a lawn sprinkler. He is best known for making different parts of a steam engine.

Elijah McCoy's inventions were popular. Because people wanted to be sure they were getting one of his inventions, not an imitation, they asked for "the real McCoy." This familiar phrase now means "the real thing" and not an imitation.

Elijah McCoy had a hard life before he became famous. His parents were slaves who had escaped from Kentucky to Canada. The McCoys had to work hard to take care of their twelve children.

Elijah McCoy first went to school in Canada. Later he learned to be an engineer in Edinburgh, Scotland. After Edinburgh, he went to Detroit. But he faced prejudice there. No one would hire him as an engineer, so he found work taking care of engines. That is when he invented better parts for steam engines.

Directions: Complete the diagram by telling the main idea of the passage. Then list supporting details that tell more about the main idea. **Supporting details will vary. Check that each detail tells more about the main idea. Possible answers given.**

Main Idea
1. Elijah McCoy was **a famous inventor.**

Supporting Details
He made parts of a steam engine.
2. **His inventions were popular.**
3. **He was an engineer.**
4. **He invented an ironing board.**
5. **He invented a lawn sprinkler.**

Notes for Home: Your child identified the main idea and supporting details in a passage. ***Home Activity:*** Tell your child about a place that you plan to visit. Give a few examples of things you will do. Ask your child to tell where you are going (main idea) and what you will do there (details).

Name___________________ Out of the Blue

Generalizing

REVIEW

Directions: Read the story. Then read each question about the story. Choose the best answer to each question. Mark the letter for the answer you have chosen.

Lydia LaRue: Great Inventor

Lydia LaRue wanted to be a great inventor. Her first invention was a new kind of alarm clock. A rooster crowed, which was supposed to wake up a mouse, who started running on a little wheel. The little wheel made a ball fall into a glass of water. Being splashed by the water woke the person up.

The first day Lydia tried out her invention, the rooster overslept. The second day, the mouse didn't wake up. By the third day, the water had dried up.

Lydia's second invention was a special kind of washing machine. In the bottom of the machine were three big fish. They were supposed to swim and splash, moving the water. However, the fish got sick from the laundry soap, so Lydia set them free.

"I'll never give up," Lydia vowed. "A person who works hard can always succeed."

1. Which generalization about Lydia's inventions is valid?
   - (A.) They are complicated.
   - B. They are simple.
   - C. They work well.
   - D. They are expensive.
2. Which generalization about Lydia's inventions is faulty?
   - (F.) They involve electricity.
   - G. They involve animals.
   - H. They involve water.
   - J. They imitate existing machines.
3. Which generalization about Lydia's first invention is valid?
   - A. Each part involved animals.
   - B. Each part involved water.
   - C. Each part involved electricity.
   - (D.) Each part failed to work.
4. Which of the following statements is a generalization?
   - F. Lydia has animals.
   - G. Lydia invents machines.
   - H. Lydia and Ben Franklin are both inventors.
   - (J.) Complicated ideas often do not work.
5. What clue word tells you that Lydia's last statement is a generalization?
   - A. I'll
   - B. works
   - C. hard
   - (D.) always

Notes for Home: Your child identified valid, or accurate, generalizations and faulty, or inaccurate, generalizations. ***Home Activity:*** Use the words *always, never, sometimes,* and *most* to make a broad statement about several things that is a valid generalization.

Name___________________ Out of the Blue

Writing Across Texts

Directions: Use information from "Out of the Blue" and "A Really Bright Idea" to compare the two inventors Benjamin Franklin and Thomas Edison. Fill in five facts about each inventor.

Possible answers given.

Benjamin Franklin	Thomas Edison
Born in 1706 in Boston.	His first invention was an electrical vote recorder in 1869.
1. **ran a printshop**	6. **received 1,093 patents**
2. **married Debbie in 1730**	7. **set up an invention factory in Menlo Park, New Jersey**
3. **invented the Franklin stove**	8. **designed the first power station**
4. **published an almanac**	9. **developed the first light bulb**
5. **discovered that lightning and electricity are the same**	10. **died in 1931**

Write a Comparison/Contrast Paragraph

On a separate sheet of paper, write a paragraph in which you compare and contrast the inventors Benjamin Franklin and Thomas Edison. Support your statements with information from "Out of the Blue" and "A Really Bright Idea." **Paragraphs will vary. Check to make sure students have used details from both selections.**

Notes for Home: Your child combined and used information from two texts. ***Home Activity:*** As you read other stories and articles together, encourage your child to compare and contrast related information found in these reading materials.

Name___________________ Out of the Blue

Grammar: Commas

REVIEW

Directions: Add a comma where needed to each sentence.

1. The typewriter was invented in 1867,and this invention changed the world.
2. The typewriter seems old-fashioned now,but it was an important invention.
3. The typewriter speeded up writing,and it also brought more women into offices.
4. Was the telephone invented at the same time,or did it come along later?
5. Alexander Graham Bell was the inventor and the first user of the telephone,and he introduced it in 1876.
6. Tape recorders may seem modern,but they first appeared in 1899.
7. Did Gabriel D. Fahrenheit invent the thermometer,or was it invented by Anders Celsius?
8. Actually, Galileo invented the thermometer in 1593,and Gabriel D. Fahrenheit created the mercury thermometer.
9. An alcohol thermometer was invented in 1641,but Gabriel D. Fahrenheit's use of mercury in 1714 made it more accurate.
10. Anders Celsius developed a metric scale for the thermometer in 1742,and most thermometers today show both Fahrenheit and Celsius scales.
11. If you were around before 1849,you had trouble holding things together.
12. When the safety pin appeared in 1849,life became easier.
13. "After Velcro was invented in 1948," I said, "life became easier still."
14. If you wore a turtleneck sweater,you didn't need either invention.
15. "Because humans are creative," my friend said, "new inventions appear every day."

Notes for Home: Your child used commas with compound sentences and complex sentences. ***Home Activity:*** Dictate sentences to your child from a book or a magazine. Challenge your child to add commas where needed.

Grammar Practice Book 4.6, p. 142

Name______________________ Out of the Blue

Grammar: Quotations and Quotation Marks

A speaker's exact words are called a **quotation.** When you write a quotation, use **quotation marks (" ")** at the beginning and end of the speaker's exact words.

Ben Franklin said, "Early to bed and early to rise makes a man healthy, wealthy, and wise."

Rules:

- Begin the quotation with a capital letter.
- If the quotation comes last in a sentence, use a comma to separate it from the rest of the sentence.
- If the quotation comes first, use a comma, a question mark, or an exclamation mark to separate the quotation from the rest of the sentence.
- Periods and commas at the end of quotations appear before the quotation mark.
- If the quotation is a question or an exclamation, place the question mark or exclamation mark before the quotation marks at the end of the speaker's words.

"I like to experiment with my new science kit," said John.
"Don't blow up the house!" his sister joked.

Directions: Rewrite each sentence, adding quotation marks.

1. Have you seen the new invention Ben made? asked Letitia.
"Have you seen the new invention Ben made?" asked Letitia.

2. I haven't seen it yet, answered Thomas.
"I haven't seen it yet," answered Thomas.

3. I can't wait to see it! said Letitia.
"I can't wait to see it!" said Letitia.

4. Thomas said, I heard it can light up a whole room!
Thomas said, "I heard it can light up a whole room!"

5. Should I wear my sunglasses? asked Letitia.
"Should I wear my sunglasses?" asked Letitia.

Notes for Home: Your child used quotation marks to set off a speaker's exact words. ***Home Activity:*** Look at a favorite book with your child. Help him or her find examples of quotation marks. Talk about how they are used.

Grammar Practice Book 4.6, p. 143

Name______________________ Out of the Blue

Grammar: Quotations and Quotation Marks

Directions: Add quotation marks and the correct punctuation to each sentence.

1. Madeleine said, "I'm going to try my own experiment!"
2. "No, you're not," said her teacher.
3. "Why not?" asked Madeleine.
4. Her teacher explained, "You have to do a lot of research before you try an experiment."
5. "I guess I'd better think about it carefully," said Madeleine.

Directions: Write sentences on the lines below to continue the conversation between Madeleine and her teacher. Use quotation marks in each sentence. **Possible answers given.**

6. **"What would you like to try?" asked the teacher.**
7. **Madeleine replied, "I'm interested in changing forms of matter."**
8. **The teacher said, "Let's work with water."**
9. **"We can make it freeze and melt," said Madeleine.**
10. **"Are you ready to get started?" asked her teacher.**

Write a Conversation

On a separate sheet of paper, write a conversation between two friends talking about a science experiment or an invention. Use quotation marks to show each speaker's exact words. Remember to put all punctuation that goes with the quotation *inside* the quotation marks.
Check that quotations are correctly punctuated.

Notes for Home: Your child practiced using quotation marks to enclose a speaker's exact words. ***Home Activity:*** Say three sentences and invite your child to record each one, using quotation marks, the proper punctuation, and the phrase: _____ *said.*

Grammar Practice Book 4.6, p. 144

Name______________________ Out of the Blue

Grammar: Quotations and Quotation Marks

RETEACHING

Read the sentences. Circle all the quotation marks. Underline all the periods, commas, question marks, and exclamation marks.

1. "I like to see the stars," Kirsten said.
2. "When should we look?" her brother asked.
3. Their mother called, "Come right now!"

Notice that a comma or an end mark always separates the quotation from the speaker.

Use **quotation marks** to show the exact words of a speaker. Place a comma, period, question mark, or exclamation mark just before the second quotation mark.

Directions: The exact words of the speaker are underlined. Write quotation marks where needed.

1. "I found my telescope," called Kirsten.
2. "Will you look at the stars tonight?" asked her mother.
3. "I will if the sky is clear," replied Kirsten.
4. "Mars also will be in view," added her brother.
5. Her father asked, "Are you excited?"
6. "I can't wait!" cried Kirsten.

Directions: Write the correct punctuation marks in the spaces.

7. _"_ I'd love to travel in space _!_ _"_ exclaimed Kirsten _._
8. _"_ Do you want to go to a certain planet _?_ _"_ asked her mother _._

Notes for Home: Your child identified and punctuated quotations. ***Home Activity:*** Have your child interview you and summarize your responses to his or her questions. Remind your child to use quotation marks to show the exact words you used.

Grammar Practice Book 4.6, p. 145

Name______________________ Out of the Blue

Grammar: Quotations and Quotation Marks

Directions: Write each sentence, adding quotation marks and other correct punctuation marks where needed.

1. I found a bird's nest in this tree said Scott.
"I found a bird's nest in this tree," said Scott.

2. What kind of nest is it asked Mark.
"What kind of nest is it?" asked Mark.

3. The nest has blue eggs in it replied Scott.
"The nest has blue eggs in it," replied Scott.

4. Don't touch the eggs Lea pleaded.
"Don't touch the eggs!" Lea pleaded.

5. I would never do that Scott said.
"I would never do that," Scott said.

Directions: Write the necessary four punctuation marks in each sentence.

6. _"_ I've read many books about bird nests _,_ _"_ said Scott _._
7. _"_ Can you tell us an interesting fact _?_ _"_ asked Lea _._
8. Scott said happily _,_ _"_ One kind of bird doesn't build a nest _._ _"_
9. _"_ What does the bird do with its eggs _?_ _"_ asked Mary _._
10. _"_ It lays one egg on a branch and sits on it _,_ _"_ stated Scott _._
11. Lea exclaimed _,_ _"_ That's really amazing _!_ _"_

Write a Conversation

Check that students correctly punctuate their conversations, including quotation marks.

On a separate sheet of paper, write a conversation between you and a friend about a bird you have read about or seen. Include quotations in your conversation.

Notes for Home: Your child wrote and punctuated quotations—the exact words of a speaker. ***Home Activity:*** Have your child write an imaginary conversation between himself or herself and a famous person. Remind your child to use quotation marks.

Practice Book 4.6, p. 288

Name______________________ **Out of the Blue**

Word Study: Suffixes

Directions: Letters added to the end of base words are called **suffixes.** Suffixes can change the meaning of the base words. Add a suffix to each word below to make a new word. Write each new word on the line. Hint: You might need to change some letters in the base word.

1. bright + -en = **brighten**
2. creative + -ity = **creativity**
3. educate + -ion = **education**
4. bother + -some = **bothersome**
5. pass + -ive = **passive**
6. transport + -ation = **transportation**
7. divide + -sion = **division**

Directions: Read each sentence below. Look for words that use one of the suffixes listed above. Write the word on the line. Then circle the suffix.

electricity 8. Electricity was an amazing discovery.

motivation 9. The need for a better source of energy was a strong motivation.

deepen 10. People tested their ideas to deepen their understanding of this new energy source.

invention 11. An experiment was one way to test an invention.

effective 12. To be effective, an experiment must be carefully controlled.

information 13. Much information can be gained by testing.

creation 14. The creation of the first light bulb is a day to remember.

troublesome 15. An inventor's hard work should never be viewed as troublesome.

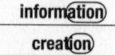

Notes for Home: Your child built new words by adding suffixes such as *-en (lengthen). Home Activity:* Challenge your child to find words in print with suffixes. Start a three-column chart to write the base word, the suffix, and the word with the suffix added.

Spelling Workbook 4.6, p. 113

Name______________________ **Out of the Blue**

Spelling: Suffixes -less, -ment, -ness

Pretest Directions: Fold back the page along the dotted line. On the blanks, write the spelling words as they are dictated. When you have finished the test, unfold the page and check your words.

1. **helpless**	1. Don't look so **helpless**.
2. **careless**	2. Don't be **careless** with the paint.
3. **hopeless**	3. Things are not **hopeless**.
4. **spotless**	4. The room was **spotless**.
5. **breathless**	5. I was **breathless** from running.
6. **worthless**	6. That old rag is **worthless**.
7. **useless**	7. The broken mop is **useless**.
8. **payment**	8. I will use a check for **payment**.
9. **statement**	9. I gave a **statement** to the press.
10. **movement**	10. I saw **movement** in the grass.
11. **pavement**	11. The **pavement** was wet with rain.
12. **treatment**	12. The **treatment** was expensive.
13. **punishment**	13. What should be my **punishment**?
14. **goodness**	14. He was full of **goodness**.
15. **softness**	15. I felt the **softness** of the pillow.
16. **brightness**	16. The **brightness** hurt his eyes.
17. **business**	17. What's your **business** here?
18. **greatness**	18. I see the **greatness** of the woods.
19. **fairness**	19. In all **fairness**, you're right.
20. **darkness**	20. The **darkness** frightened him.

Notes for Home: Your child took a pretest on words that include the suffixes *-less, -ment,* and *-ness. Home Activity:* Help your child learn misspelled words before the final test. Have your child divide misspelled words into parts (such as syllables) and concentrate on each part.

Spelling Workbook 4.6, p. 114

Name______________________ **Out of the Blue**

Spelling: Suffixes -less, -ment, -ness

Word List				
helpless	breathless	statement	punishment	business
careless	worthless	movement	goodness	greatness
hopeless	useless	pavement	softness	fairness
spotless	payment	treatment	brightness	darkness

Directions: Choose the word from the box that is formed by adding the suffix **-less** or **-ness** to each base word. Write the word on the line.

1. spot **spotless**
2. dark **darkness**
3. breath **breathless**
4. fair **fairness**
5. worth **worthless**
6. great **greatness**
7. use **useless**
8. busy **business**
9. help **helpless**
10. bright **brightness**
11. care **careless**
12. soft **softness**
13. hope **hopeless**
14. good **goodness**

Directions: Add the suffix **-ment** to each word in ( ) to form a word from the box and complete each sentence. Write the word on the line.

statement 15. The great inventor made a (state) to the press.

treatment 16. She said, "I have invented a (treat) for colds and flu."

payment 17. "I did not do it for (pay)."

movement 18. Just then, there was a (move) in the crowd.

pavement 19. Another woman ran in from the (pave) outside.

punishment 20. "This impostor deserves (punish)," she cried, "because I am the true inventor!"

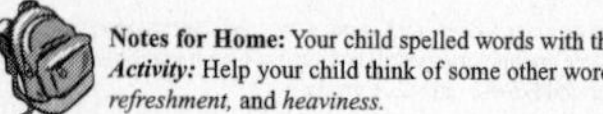

Notes for Home: Your child spelled words with the suffixes *-less, -ment,* and *-ness. Home Activity:* Help your child think of some other words with these suffixes, such as *fearless, refreshment,* and *heaviness.*

Spelling Workbook 4.6, p. 115

Name______________________ **Out of the Blue**

Spelling: Suffixes -less, -ment, -ness

Directions: Proofread this news story about an inventor. Find five spelling mistakes. Use the proofreading marks to correct each mistake.

≡ Make a capital.
/ Make a small letter.
∧ Add something.
Take out something.
⊙ Add a period.
¶ Begin a new paragraph.

INVENTOR MAKES STATEMENT

Today Pete Vargas, inventor of a famous treatmen[t] used to increase the softness and brit[gh]ness of carpets, spoke at the Porta Linda City Business Center. "In all fairnes[s]," said the inventor, "I owe much of my greatness~~e~~ to my colleagues. Without them, my own discoveries would have been worthless. Therefore, any pa~~i~~[y]ment I receive, I always share with them."

Spelling Tip

When **-less, -ment,** or **-ness** is added to most base words, the base stays the same. If the base word ends in a **consonant** and **y,** change the **y** to **i** before adding the suffix: **business.**

Word List		
helpless	payment	softness
careless	statement	brightness
hopeless	movement	business
spotless	pavement	greatness
breathless	treatment	fairness
worthless	punishment	darkness
useless	goodness	

Write a News Story

On a separate sheet of paper, write your own news story about an imaginary inventor's visit to your town. Use at least four spelling words.

Answers will vary, but each news story should include at least four spelling words.

Notes for Home: Your child spelled words with the suffixes *-less, -ment,* and *-ness. Home Activity:* Say some base words from the list, such as *good, punish,* and *use.* Ask your child to add one of the suffixes to make the whole word. Then have your child spell the word.

Spelling Workbook 4.6, p. 116

Name

Out of the Blue

Spelling: Suffixes *-less*, *-ment*, *-ness* REVIEW

Word List				
helpless	breathless	statement	punishment	business
careless	worthless	movement	goodness	greatness
hopeless	useless	pavement	softness	fairness
spotless	payment	treatment	brightness	darkness

Directions: Unscramble the letters to form a word from the box. Write the word on the line.

1. neatresgs **greatness**
2. soognesd **goodness**
3. inesfars **fairness**
4. sinbuess **business**
5. nessfost **softness**
6. sardknes **darkness**
7. muiphsnent **punishment**
8. tovemmen **movement**
9. mavepent **pavement**
10. meattrent **treatment**
11. meanttest **statement**
12. sbraleehts **breathless**

Directions: Choose the word from the box that has the same meaning as the underlined word or words. Write the word on the line to the left.

hopeless 13. "It's without hope!" Yoshi said.
worthless 14. "This invention is without worth!"
helpless 15. "I feel so unable to do anything."
careless 16. "It's not as though I have been inattentive."
spotless 17. "I kept all my equipment completely clean."
useless 18. "Yet this worthless rocket won't fly!"
brightness 19. Suddenly, a strong light filled the room.
payment 20. "This is the reward for all my hard work," he said . . .

Notes for Home: Your child spelled words with the suffixes *-less, -ment,* and *-ness. **Home Activity:*** Look at the words on the list that end with *-less.* Challenge your child to add the suffix *-ly* to each and use it in a sentence.

Spelling: Suffixes *-less, -ment, -ness* 651

Practice Book 4.6, p. 289

Name

Out of the Blue

Study Strategies

Study Strategies help you focus on the most important parts of what you read. **Skimming and scanning** are two ways of looking at written materials quickly, focusing only on important parts.

Skimming is looking at a story or article quickly to find out what it is about. When skimming, you do not read the entire story. You look for highlights, such as titles and captions. Skimming helps you decide whether you want to read the text and whether it is useful for your research and study purposes.

Scanning is looking for key words or ideas. You can scan when you need to answer a specific question. Read the sentences around the key words to find the answer to your question.

Directions: Skim the article on the next page to answer the questions below.

1. Who is the article about? **Thomas Jefferson**
2. What can you learn by reading this article? **You can learn about things Thomas Jefferson invented.**
3. How many different inventions are mentioned? What are they? **three; revolving closet, revolving bookstand, the Great Clock**
4. Would you read this article if you needed information about things Thomas Jefferson did when he was the President of the United States? Explain. **No, the article focuses on Thomas Jefferson as an inventor.**
5. Would you read this article if you needed information about important accomplishments Thomas Jefferson made in his lifetime? Explain. **Yes, the article tells about some of his important inventions.**

652 Research and Study Skills: Study Strategies

Practice Book 4.6, p. 290

Name

Out of the Blue

Thomas Jefferson: Inventor

While Thomas Jefferson is mostly known for being a brilliant politician, he was also quite an inventor. Many of his inventions were items he used in his house. They were things that made life easier for him.

Revolving Closet

One of his inventions helped him get dressed in the morning. At the end of his bed he had a revolving closet. It was a long pole that reached from floor to ceiling. This pole had forty-eight arms. Each arm held one item of clothing. Jefferson could turn the arms with a long stick making it easier to find the clothes he wanted to wear.

Revolving Bookstand

Another item Jefferson is believed to have invented is a revolving bookstand. Jefferson joined five bookstands and placed them on a revolving platform. Using this device, he was able to review different books with ease.

The Great Clock

One of Jefferson's most impressive creations was his Great Clock. This clock had two faces. The outside face had only an hour hand. This, he felt, was all the information workers needed. Its gong chimed the hour loud enough to be heard from 3 miles away. The inside face had hour, minute, and second hands. The weights that moved the clock's hands also indicated the day of the week.

Directions: Read each question. Determine the key word or phrase you will scan for to find the information. Write the key word or phrase. Then scan the text above to find the answer to each question. **Possible key words given.**

6. Which invention did Thomas Jefferson use to find clothes more easily? **key word: clothes; answer: revolving closet**
7. From how many miles away could the Great Clock chime be heard? **key word: miles; answer: 3 miles**
8. Which invention did Thomas Jefferson use for reviewing several books at a time? **key word: books; answer: revolving bookstand**
9. What portion of the Great Clock did Jefferson feel was most useful for workers? **key word: workers; answer: the outside clock face with only an hour hand**
10. What did the Great Clock's inside face show? **key phrase: inside face; answer: hour, minute, and second hands**

Notes for Home: Your child skimmed and scanned an article to find necessary information quickly. ***Home Activity:*** Give your child a newspaper article you have read. Ask questions that can be answered by scanning (looking for key words) the article.

Research and Study Skills: Study Strategies 653

Practice Book 4.6, p. 291

Name

Chocolate Is Missing

Author's Purpose

- An **author's purpose** is the reason for writing something.
- Some purposes for writing are to entertain, to inform, to express, and to persuade.

Directions: Reread "Breakfast with Brede." Then complete the web. Identify the author's purpose and give four clues that helped you decide.

Author's Purpose or Purposes
1. **to entertain.**

2. Grandpa says scones are like **horses' hooves.**

3. Brede says scones are like camels' **heels.**

4. Brede says scones are like elephants' **toenails.**

5. Why isn't Andrew allowed to finish speaking? **The narrator interrupts him before he says something really horrible.**

Notes for Home: Your child identified the author's purpose in a story. ***Home Activity:*** Ask your child to pick a favorite story. Ask him or her to identify the author's purpose. Then have your child support his or her answer with examples from the story.

656 Author's Purpose

Practice Book 4.6, p. 292
Name____________________ Chocolate Is Missing

Vocabulary

Directions: Choose the word from the box that best matches each definition. Write the word on the line.

Check the Words You Know
__ angle
__ approach
__ brag
__ chocolate
__ poster
__ presence

brag 1. boast
poster 2. large printed sheet or notice on a wall
angle 3. point of view
presence 4. ability to project a sense of ease
approach 5. come near

Directions: Choose the word from the box that best completes each sentence. Write the word on the line to the left.

angle 6. Dottie is a detective who always has an interesting _____ on any problem.
chocolate 7. One day, Myron had lost a candy bar made from his favorite kind of_____.
brag 8. Right away, Dottie began to _____ to others that she could easily solve the mystery.
presence 9. Dottie's certainty and strong _____ made Myron believe that his candy bar would be found fast.
approach 10. "If you have seen the candy bar, come forward and _____ me," said Dottie. "There is a reward—another candy bar!"

Write a Detective Story

On a separate sheet of paper, tell the story of a classroom detective. Tell what the mystery is, who the detective is, and what he or she does to solve the mystery. Use as many vocabulary words as you can.
Students should correctly use included vocabulary words.

Notes for Home: Your child identified and used vocabulary words from "Chocolate Is Missing." ***Home Activity:*** With your child, act out the roles of a detective questioning a suspect. Try to use as many vocabulary words as you can.

Practice Book 4.6, p. 293
Name____________________ Chocolate Is Missing

Author's Purpose

- An **author's purpose** is the reason or reasons the author has for writing.
- Four common author's purposes are to entertain, to inform, to express, and to persuade.

1. Reread "Chocolate Is Missing." Tell what you think the author's purpose or purposes were for writing this story. Explain your answer.
to entertain; The author tells a suspenseful and humorous story.

Directions: Tell what the author's purpose or purposes were for writing each passage below. Explain your answer.

2. I love my cat, Tomiddy. He snuggles up next to me when I read and keeps me company. When I'm feeling blue, I pick Tomiddy up and give him a big hug. I push my face into his soft, comforting fur. He purrs and purrs. A Tomiddy hug is good for cheering me up.
to express; The author tells her feelings about her cat.

3. Guinea pigs belong to a family of rodents that are native to South America. Other members of this family are rock cavies and mountain cavies. Rodents have unusually long, sharp front teeth that keep growing. Rodents' unusual ability to gnaw keeps their teeth sharp!
to inform; The author gives facts about guinea pigs.

4. *All Creatures Great and Small* is a wonderful book about an English veterinarian and his animal cases. The stories are interesting, and the book is well written and easy to read. If you like reading about animals, you really should look at this fascinating book.
to persuade; The author tries to get readers to read a specific book.

5. Think about other stories you have read in class. On a separate sheet of paper, name a story or article that was written for each of the four common purposes listed above. Explain your choices.
Check that explanations support the author's purpose.

Notes for Home: Your child read several passages and identified the reason or reasons an author has for writing. ***Home Activity:*** Ask your child to think of a favorite book. Encourage him or her to tell you why the author wrote the book.

Practice Book 4.6, p. 295
Name____________________ Chocolate Is Missing

Selection Test

Directions: Choose the best answer to each item. Mark the letter for the answer you have chosen.

Part 1: Vocabulary

Find the answer choice that means about the same as the underlined work in each sentence.

1. Jay has a different angle.
   Ⓐ point of view
   B. troubled or worried feeling
   C. person who offers help
   D. notebook divider

2. The girls looked at the poster.
   F. open drawer
   G. small card sent by mail
   H. secret message
   Ⓙ printed notice hung on a wall

3. Mr. Jones changed his approach.
   Ⓐ way of working on a task
   B. tone of voice
   C. time and place for a meeting
   D. way a person looks

4. I tried not to brag.
   F. complain
   G. become confused
   Ⓗ boast
   J. worry

5. Here is some chocolate.
   A. dark-gray color
   B. strong, sweet odor
   C. small box or container
   Ⓓ substance used in candies and other foods

6. Rena has great presence.
   F. duties or jobs
   G. ability to imagine
   H. gift given to another person
   Ⓙ sense of being sure of oneself

Part 2: Comprehension

Use what you know about the story to answer each item.

7. How is Gayle different from Lila?
   Ⓐ Gayle is taller and wider.
   B. Gayle cares more about Chocolate.
   C. Gayle is a better writer.
   D. Gayle is not as logical.

8. In this story, Chocolate is a—
   F. cat.
   Ⓖ guinea pig.
   H. snake.
   J. rabbit.

GO ON

Practice Book 4.6, p. 296
Name____________________ Chocolate Is Missing

9. What happened next after the class found that Chocolate was gone?
   A. Lila and Eddie looked for Chocolate.
   Ⓑ Lila and Gayle made posters.
   C. Lila realized Chocolate had escaped.
   D. Lila and Gayle talked to Michael.

10. The author probably included Lila's list of suspects to show—
    F. how smart Lila is.
    G. that Chocolate was stolen.
    Ⓗ that Lila was a bit silly.
    J. which students could not be trusted.

11. Lila was not ready to do her oral report because she—
    A. knew Mr. Sherman would understand how busy she was.
    B. did not want to talk in front of the class.
    Ⓒ forgot about it while searching for Chocolate.
    D. did not want to learn about Brazil.

12. Chocolate probably hid in Mr. Sherman's desk because she—
    F. found lots of food there.
    G. was afraid of the children.
    Ⓗ needed a safe place for her babies.
    J. was sick.

13. The author's main purpose in this selection is to—
    Ⓐ tell an amusing story.
    B. explain how to solve mysteries.
    C. describe a class of students.
    D. give tips for keeping class pets.

14. Near the end of the story, it is suggested that Lila was jealous of—
    F. Mr. Todd.
    Ⓖ Rita Morgan.
    H. Michael Watson.
    J. Eddie English.

15. Mr. Sherman was probably most impressed that Lila—
    A. pretended to be a detective.
    Ⓑ worked so hard to find Chocolate.
    C. knew so much about Brazil.
    D. was Gayle's best friend.

STOP

Name______________________________ **Chocolate Is Missing**

Author's Purpose

- An **author's purpose** is the reason or reasons the author has for writing.
- Four common author's purposes are to entertain, to inform, to express, and to persuade.

Directions: Read the story below.

You might think that a chicken is a funny kind of class pet to have. But I'm telling you, Cedric the Chicken is the best! He is a lot of fun to watch, and he is smart and loyal. I think every class should have a chicken as a class pet.

You might think chickens are boring, but you need to change your thinking on that! For example, did you know that new chicks can live for a week without eating? And while you may think chickens are as American as a certain fried chicken restaurant, they're originally from Asia.

Cedric can always tell when it's time for lunch. He lets us know by cackling until we notice. When there's chicken for lunch, he puts up a big fuss. He'd rather we ate peanut butter and jelly. We love our class pet—even if he's different from most!

Directions: Complete the table. Fill in a statement from the story for each purpose listed. **Possible answers given.**

Author's Purpose	Statement from Story
To persuade	I think every class should have a chicken as a class pet.
To persuade	1. **You might think chickens are boring, but you need to change your thinking on that!**
To inform	2. **New chicks can live for a week without eating.**
To inform	3. **Chickens are originally from Asia.**
To entertain	4. **He'd rather we ate peanut butter and jelly.**
To express	5. **We love our class pet…**

Notes for Home: Your child identified statements that showed an author's reasons for writing a story. ***Home Activity:*** Look at a newspaper with your child. Discuss, for example, how the purpose for writing the comics may be different from writing an article.

Practice Book 4.6, p. 297

Name______________________________ **Chocolate Is Missing**

Plot

REVIEW

Directions: Read the story. Then read each question about the story. Choose the best answer to each question. Mark the letter for the answer you have chosen.

Penny's Parrot

All her life, Penny had lived in sunny southern California. When she heard that her family was moving to Alaska, Penny felt sad.

However, Penny soon discovered that she liked sledding and skating. She also liked her new friends at school.

But Penny's parrot seemed very sad. It was home alone all day in Penny's house. Penny discovered that parrots like warm weather! Penny's house was too cold during the day when no one was home.

Penny decided to bring her parrot to school. The parrot was happy with the warm classroom—and Penny's class had a new pet!

1. What happens to Penny at the beginning of the story?
   - (A.) She moves to Alaska.
   - B. She moves to California.
   - C. She learns to skate.
   - D. She gets a parrot.

2. What problem does Penny have?
   - F. She hates the cold.
   - G. She has no friends.
   - (H.) Her parrot is sad.
   - J. Her parrot is noisy.

3. What causes Penny's problem?
   - A. Alaska is not a good place to live.
   - (B.) The parrot doesn't like the cold house.
   - C. Alaska is a big state.
   - D. Penny is very shy.

4. How does Penny solve her problem?
   - F. She feeds her parrot.
   - G. She gives her parrot away.
   - H. She makes new friends.
   - (J.) She brings her parrot to school.

5. Why does this action solve Penny's problem?
   - A. The class likes her better now.
   - B. She doesn't have to take care of her parrot anymore.
   - (C.) The parrot has a warmer place to live.
   - D. Her parrot makes less noise.

Notes for Home: Your child answered questions about a story's plot. ***Home Activity:*** Plan a story with your child. Describe when and where the story will take place, who the characters are, what problem they'll face, and how they'll solve it.

Name______________________________ **Chocolate Is Missing**

Writing Across Texts

Directions: Use information from "Chocolate Is Missing" and *Komodo Dragons* in Unit 2 to fill in the table, using words and phrases from the box below. **Possible answers given. Animal traits within each box can be given in any order.**

are not social	are social
come from Indonesia	need a small cage
can eat a water buffalo	eat carrots, lettuce, apples, spinach
come from Brazil	makes an excellent classroom pet
would not be suitable as a classroom pet	have razor-sharp teeth

Guinea Pigs	Komodo Dragons
Traits have curly brown fur	**Traits** have leathery, scaly skin
1. **eat carrots, lettuce, apples, spinach**	6. **can eat a water buffalo**
2. **need a small cage**	7. **come from Indonesia**
3. **come from Brazil**	8. **have razor-sharp teeth**
4. **are social**	9. **are not social**
What Kind of Class Pet Would a Guinea Pig Make?	**What Kind of Class Pet Would a Komodo Dragon Make?**
5. **makes an excellent classroom pet**	10. **would not be suitable as a classroom pet**

Write a Comparison/Contrast Paragraph

On a separate sheet of paper, write a comparison/contrast paragraph about guinea pigs and komodo dragons; conclude whether and why each animal would (or would not) be a good classroom pet. Refer to your table when writing. Remember to use descriptive details about each animal. **Paragraphs will vary. Check to make sure that students have used details from both selections in making their comparisons and contrasts.**

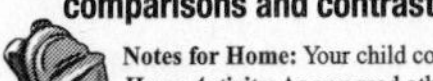

Notes for Home: Your child combined information from more than one reading selection. ***Home Activity:*** As you read other stories or articles about animals, encourage your child to identify the similarities and differences between animals.

Grammar Practice Book 4.6, p. 146

Name______________________________ **Chocolate Is Missing**

Grammar: Quotations

REVIEW

Directions: Draw a circle around any letter that should be capitalized. If no letters need to be capitalized, write N on the line.

________ 1. "(w)here's the white mouse?" Jenny asked.

________ 2. "The white mouse?" said Jamal. "(i)t's in its cage."

N 3. "If you look," replied Jenny, "you'll see it's not there."

________ 4. "That's not good. (w)here could it be?" Jamal asked.

________ 5. Jenny answered, "(w)e'd better start looking for it."

Directions: Each sentence is missing a punctuation mark—a comma, a period, or a question mark. Write the mark where it is needed. Use an insert symbol (^) if necessary.

6. "I don't see the mouse anywhere**,**" complained Jamal.
7. Jenny replied, "Well, let's keep looking**.**"
8. "Could one of the kids have taken it home**^?**" asked Jamal.
9. "It's possible," said Jenny**,** "but the teacher didn't mention it."
10. Jamal said, "I just hope it's all right**.**"
11. Suddenly Jamal said**,** "What's that?"
12. "What's what**^?**" asked Jenny.

Directions: Write a sentence that uses each group of words as a quotation. **Possible answers given.**

13. what's that spot of white over there
"What's that spot of white over there?" replied Jamal.

14. it looks like a mouse to me
Jenny smiled and said, "It looks like a mouse to me."

15. it looks okay!
"It looks okay!" exclaimed Jamal happily.

Notes for Home: Your child reviewed the use of capital letters and punctuation with quotations in sentences. ***Home Activity:*** Work with your child to write a short story about a pet and its owners. Include dialogue. Have your child write out the story.

Grammar Practice Book 4.6, p. 147

Name________________ Chocolate Is Missing

Grammar: Review of Compound and Complex Sentences

A **compound sentence** contains two simple sentences. They are joined by a comma and a conjunction such as *and, but,* or *or.* The two sentences must have ideas that go together.

Two Sentences: Steve was a pet detective. He found my dog, Misty.

Compound Sentence: Steve was a pet detective, and he found my dog, Misty.

A **complex sentence** is made by combining a simple sentence with a group of words that cannot stand on its own as a sentence. The group of words is joined to the sentence with a word such as *because* or *when.*

He likes dogs because they are usually friendly.

When he feels sad, he takes his dog for a walk.

Directions: Write whether each sentence is **compound** or **complex.**

compound 1. Our cat was lost, and we didn't know where to look.

compound 2. The detective came, and she began looking for our cat.

complex 3. When she found our cat, we cheered loudly.

compound 4. The detective was smart, and she was good at her job.

complex 5. Because she knew just where to look, we found our cat!

Directions: Match each group of words on the left with a group on the right to make a compound or a complex sentence. Write the letter on the line.

c 6. Joe hired us to find his pet frog

a 7. We knew that the frog would be tired,

b 8. We looked outside for the frog,

e 9. We wanted to take a rest,

d 10. When we finally found the frog,

a. and it would be hungry too.

b. and we also looked inside.

c. because it was lost.

d. Joe was happy and relieved.

e. but we knew we had to keep looking.

Notes for Home: Your child reviewed compound and complex sentences. ***Home Activity:*** Look at a favorite book with your child. Invite him or her to find examples of compound and complex sentences.

Grammar Practice Book 4.6, p. 148

Name________________ Chocolate Is Missing

Grammar: Review of Compound and Complex Sentences

Directions: Join the two sentences to form a compound sentence. Use *and* and a comma to combine them. Write the compound sentence on the line.

1. Being a detective is hard. It requires a lot of work.

Being a detective is hard, and it requires a lot of work.

2. I have a good memory. I never forget a face.

I have a good memory, and I never forget a face.

3. My teacher thinks I would be a good detective. Someday I might try to be one.

My teacher thinks I would be a good detective, and someday I might try to be one.

Directions: Add a simple sentence to each sentence part to form a complex sentence. **Possible answers given.**

4. When I have a great idea, **I like to work on it right away.**

5. When I'm not sure that I'll remember my idea, **I write it down.**

Write a What-If Story

What would happen if you had a really great idea? Write a story about it on a separate sheet of paper. Use at least two compound and two complex sentences.

Check that students use a conjunction and a comma to join two related sentences to form a compound sentence. Their complex sentences should include a sentence part and a complete sentence.

Notes for Home: Your child reviewed compound and complex sentences. ***Home Activity:*** You can form complex sentences with your child by saying: "*If I were a ____, I would . . .*" Take turns filling in the blank and completing the sentence. *(If I were a dog, I would run around all day.)*

Grammar Practice Book 4.6, p. 149

Name________________ Chocolate Is Missing

RETEACHING

Grammar: Review of Compound and Complex Sentences

Combine the sentences to form a compound sentence.

1. Reading was his favorite subject. He read widely.

Reading was his favorite subject, and he read widely.

Combine the groups of words to form a complex sentence.

2. We wanted to leave. Because we were tired.

We wanted to leave because we were tired.

A **compound sentence** contains two simple sentences joined by a comma and a conjunction such as **and, but,** or **or.** The simple sentences must have ideas that go together. A **complex sentence** is made by combining a simple sentence with a group of words that cannot stand alone as a sentence.

Directions: Combine each pair of sentences to form a compound sentence. Use **and** and a comma to combine them. Write each new sentence on the line.

1. Ben lived a full life. His achievements were many.

Ben lived a full life, and his achievements were many.

2. His brother printed a newspaper. Ben wrote for it.

His brother printed a newspaper, and Ben wrote for it.

Directions: Write whether each sentence is **compound** or **complex.**

complex 3. Daniel missed the directions because he was late.

compound 4. Dori enjoyed singing, and she sang every day.

complex 5. When we walked outside, we noticed it was raining.

compound 6. We are going to Grandpa's house, and he will make us pancakes.

Notes for Home: Your child identified compound and complex sentences. ***Home Activity:*** Ask your child to give you an example of a compound sentence and a complex sentence. Challenge him or her to explain the differences between the two.

Grammar Practice Book 4.6, p. 150

Name________________ Chocolate Is Missing

Grammar: Review of Compound and Complex Sentences

Directions: Combine each pair of word groups to make a compound or a complex sentence. Write each sentence on the lines.

1. Many cartoonists begin with a pencil outline. They use a pen in a later step.

Many cartoonists begin with a pencil outline, and they use a pen in a later step.

2. Movement is shown by using lines. Speech is shown by putting words in a balloon.

Movement is shown by using lines, and speech is shown by putting words in a balloon.

3. After drawings are scanned into a computer Computer operators can shade areas of the images.

After drawings are scanned into a computer, computer operators can shade areas of the images.

4. The pictures can be seen on a computer screen. They can be sent to other computers.

The pictures can be seen on a computer screen, and they can be sent to other computers.

5. When the pictures are placed in a form for a newspaper page The page is prepared for printing.

When the pictures are placed in a form for a newspaper page, the page is prepared for printing.

Notes for Home: Your child identified compound and complex sentences. ***Home Activity:*** Together, write a silly story about two animals. Use at least one compound sentence and one complex sentence in the story.

Practice Book 4.6, p. 298

Name____________________ **Chocolate Is Missing**

Word Study: Word Building

Directions: Add a suffix to each word below to make a new word. Write each new word on the line. Hint: The spelling of some words may change slightly when the suffix is added. Use a dictionary if necessary.

1. explain + -ation = **explanation**
2. imagine + -ation = **imagination**
3. describe + -tion = **description**
4. inform + -ation = **information**
5. drama + -tic + -al + -ly = **dramatically**

Directions: Read each word below. Write each base word and suffix in the correct column. Remember to adjust the spelling of the base word if needed.

	Word		Base Word		Suffix
6.	interrogation	=	**interrogate**	+	**ion**
7.	nomination	=	**nominate**	+	**ion**
8.	investigation	=	**investigate**	+	**ion**
9.	maintenance	=	**maintain**	+	**ance**
10.	rectangular	=	**rectangle**	+	**ular**

Directions: Sometimes when a suffix is added to a base word, some sounds in the word change. Read the pairs of words below. Listen for the syllable that is stressed. Underline the stressed syllable in each word, for example: **music** and **musician.**

11. nominate nomination
12. maintain maintenance
13. interrogate interrogation
14. rectangle rectangular
15. investigate investigation

Notes for Home: Your child listened for the ways in which words can change when a suffix is added. ***Home Activity:*** With your child, think of words that have suffixes. Clap each syllable as you say the word, clapping more loudly for the one that is stressed.

Spelling Workbook 4.6, p. 117

Name____________________ **Chocolate Is Missing**

Spelling: Related Words

Pretest Directions: Fold back the page along the dotted line. On the blanks, write the spelling words as they are dictated. When you have finished the test, unfold the page and check your words.

1.	**able**	1.	Are you **able** to understand?
2.	**ability**	2.	I'm sure of your **ability**.
3.	**sign**	3.	Please **sign** here.
4.	**signal**	4.	What will be our **signal**?
5.	**mean**	5.	I don't know what you **mean**.
6.	**meant**	6.	That's what I **meant**.
7.	**deal**	7.	All right, it's a **deal**.
8.	**dealt**	8.	He **dealt** me these cards.
9.	**soft**	9.	The ice cream is **soft**.
10.	**soften**	10.	Let the butter **soften** a little.
11.	**relate**	11.	I can **relate** to that.
12.	**relative**	12.	He is my oldest **relative**.
13.	**heal**	13.	This will help it **heal** faster.
14.	**health**	14.	She's in very good **health**.
15.	**meter**	15.	The desk is a **meter** long.
16.	**metric**	16.	We will use the **metric** system.
17.	**compose**	17.	Let her **compose** the note.
18.	**composition**	18.	That was a fine **composition**.
19.	**crumb**	19.	There's hardly a **crumb** left.
20.	**crumble**	20.	First, we will **crumble** this bread.

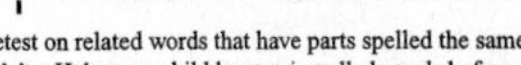

Notes for Home: Your child took a pretest on related words that have parts spelled the same but pronounced differently. ***Home Activity:*** Help your child learn misspelled words before the final test by underlining the parts that are different in each pair and concentrating on those.

Spelling Workbook 4.6, p. 118

Name____________________ **Chocolate Is Missing**

Spelling: Related Words

		Word List		
able	mean	soft	heal	compose
ability	meant	soften	health	composition
sign	deal	relate	meter	crumb
signal	dealt	relative	metric	crumble

Directions: Choose the word from the box that has a related word part that is spelled the same but pronounced differently. Write the word on the line.

1. able	**ability**	6. meter	**metric**
2. crumb	**crumble**	7. deal	**dealt**
3. sign	**signal**	8. heal	**health**
4. compose	**composition**	9. soft	**soften**
5. mean	**meant**	10. relate	**relative**

Directions: Choose the word from the box that best matches each clue. Write the word on the line.

11. the basic measurement of the metric system **meter**
12. capable or competent **able**
13. not hard **soft**
14. an arrangement between two people **deal**
15. connect in thought or meaning **relate**
16. make better, like a wound **heal**
17. a billboard is an example **sign**
18. create a piece of music **compose**
19. not nice **mean**
20. a morsel, or a tiny piece **crumb**

Notes for Home: Your child spelled related words that have parts that are spelled the same but are pronounced differently. ***Home Activity:*** Say one of the words on the list. Invite your child to say and spell the related word. Point out the differences in how the related words are said.

Spelling Workbook 4.6, p. 119

Name____________________ **Chocolate Is Missing**

Spelling: Related Words

Directions: Proofread this list of instructions for taking care of a class pet. Find five spelling mistakes. Use the proofreading marks to correct each mistake.

- ≡ Make a capital.
- / Make a small letter.
- ∧ Add something.
- Take out something.
- ⊙ Add a period.
- ¶ Begin a new paragraph.

Taking Care of "Hamlet," the Class Hamster

1. Look at the sine over his cage. It says, "Don't tease the hamster." That's what we say, and that's what we meen!
2. When Hamlet gets hungry, do not crumbel cookies or cupcakes into his cage. Cookie crumbs are not good for his helth!
3. When Hamlet is sleeping, you don't have to speak in a sofft voice. But please don't yell at him! He might get scared.

Spelling Tip

Pay close attention to related words. They often have parts that are spelled the same but pronounced differently: **sign, signal.**

		Word List		
able	mean	soft	heal	compose
ability	meant	soften	health	composition
sign	deal	relate	meter	crumb
signal	dealt	relative	metric	crumble

Write a List of Instructions

On a separate sheet of paper, write your own instructions for taking care of a class pet. Use at least two pairs of related spelling words. **Answers will vary, but each set of instructions should include at least two pairs of related spelling words.**

Notes for Home: Your child spelled related words that have parts that are spelled the same but are pronounced differently. ***Home Activity:*** Write the shorter of a pair of related words. Then write an "equation" to show how to form the longer word (*relate – e + ive = relative*).

Spelling Workbook 4.6, p. 120

Name_______________ Chocolate Is Missing

Spelling: Related Words

REVIEW

Word List

able	mean	soft	heal	compose
ability	meant	soften	health	composition
sign	deal	relate	meter	crumb
signal	dealt	relative	metric	crumble

Directions: Choose the word from the box that rhymes with each word below. Write it on the line to the right. Then, beside it, write the related word.

thumb 1. **crumb** 7. **crumble**

often 2. **soften** 8. **soft**

bean 3. **mean** 9. **meant**

fine 4. **sign** 10. **signal**

inflate 5. **relate** 11. **relative**

heater 6. **meter** 12. **metric**

Directions: Choose the word from the box that best completes each sentence. Write the word on the line to the left.

health 13. One day our class rabbit was in poor ____.

heal 14. "The vet can ____ him," said our teacher.

able 15. We knew the vet would be ____ to cure the rabbit.

ability 16. The vet has the ____ to cure most pet problems.

dealt 17. The vet came and ____ with the problem.

compose 18. We decided to ____ a song in honor of the vet.

composition 19. The vet loved our ____.

deal 20. We made a ____ with the vet to call her for all our pet problems.

Notes for Home: Your child spelled related words that have parts that are spelled the same but are pronounced differently. ***Home Activity:*** Write each spelling word on separate index cards. Mix the cards. When a pair is drawn, the player must use one word in a sentence.

Practice Book 4.6, p. 299

Name_______________ Chocolate Is Missing

Technology: Electronic Media

There are many resources you can use to find information, such as books, newspapers, magazines, and people. You can also use **electronic media,** which include things such as audiotapes, videotapes, films, and computers. CD-ROM encyclopedias and the Internet are two ways to gather information using a computer.

Directions: Review the list of resources that give information about guinea pigs. Use the list to tell which resource you would choose for each situation described on the next page.

Books *(Nonfiction)*
Guinea Pigs: How to Care for Them, Feed Them, and Understand Them by Katrin Behrend
I Love Guinea Pigs by Dick King-Smith
The Guinea Pig, An Owner's Guide by Audrey Pavia

Books *(Fiction)*
Bedtime by Kate Duke
Olga De Polga by Michael Bond

Organizations
Guinea Pig Adoption Network
Home for Unwanted and Abandoned Guinea Pigs

Internet Web Pages
Todd's Guinea Pig Hutch
Carlo's Guinea Pig Site

Internet Mailing Lists*
Gpigs

Internet Newsgroups*
Pets: Guinea Pigs

Internet Sound Files*
"Need food" sound
Guinea pig's chuckle

Videos
Pocket Pet Series Featuring: Guinea Pigs

CD-ROMs
The ABC's of Caring for a Guinea Pig

*Mailing lists and newsgroups are discussions conducted on the Internet. People post questions and answers about a specific topic. You automatically receive mailing list posts in e-mail. You have to go to a newsgroup site to read news posted by other members of the newsgroup. An Internet sound file is a short audio recording of a specific sound. You can save the file and play the sound over and over again.

Practice Book 4.6, p. 300

Name_______________ Chocolate Is Missing

1. You are giving a presentation on guinea pigs to your class. You want to let students know how to adopt a guinea pig.
Organizations: Guinea Pig Adoption Network

2. Also as part of your presentation, you want the class to hear the sound guinea pigs make when they are hungry.
Internet Sound Files: "Need food" sound

3. You are interested in receiving information through e-mail about the care of guinea pigs.
Internet Mailing List: Gpigs

4. Your class is creating a Web page about your class pet—a guinea pig named Honey. You are responsible for finding out what kinds of information you should include in a web page.
Internet Web Pages: Todd's Guinea Pig Hutch or Carlo's Guinea Pig Site

5. Choose one of the electronic media resources from the list. Give an example of a research project where a student might use this resource. Tell why this resource best suits the purposes of the project.
Answers will vary. Be sure that the choice of electronic media does suit the purpose of the project described.

Notes for Home: Your child chose resources for completing projects. ***Home Activity:*** Visit a library with your child. Many libraries have media centers that provide public access to electronic media. Discuss the resources available and how your child might use them for study or research.

Name_______________

Supporting an Opinion

Supporting an Opinion graphic organizer should be filled out completely.

Directions: Write your opinion in the top box. Then record facts, reasons and examples that support your opinion. Choose the most persuasive fact, reason, or example and write it on the lines at the bottom of the page.

I think that _______________

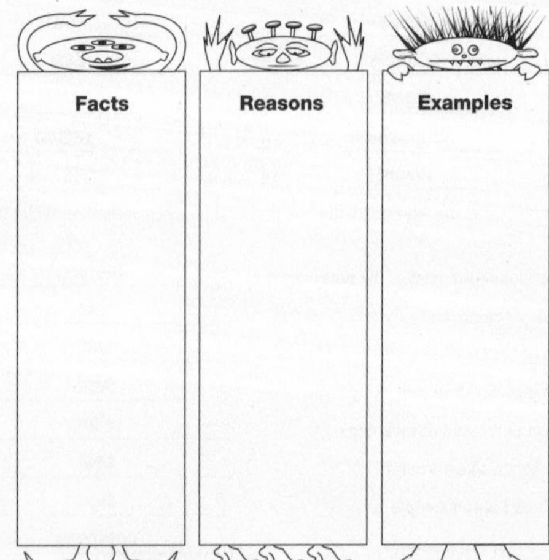

Most persuasive fact, reason, or example: _______________

Notes for Home: Your child has been learning how to support an opinion in order to be persuasive. ***Home Activity:*** Ask your child to persuade you to try a certain kind of food.

Name________________________________

Elaboration

Combine Sentences

- When you write, you can elaborate by **combining short, choppy sentences** into one longer, more interesting sentence.
- You can make a compound sentence by joining sentences with *and, but,* or *or.*
- You can make a complex sentence by joining short sentences with words such as *when, if,* or *because*.

Directions: Use the word in parentheses to combine the sentences. Remember to capitalize the first word of your new sentence. **Responses will vary. Reasonable answers are given.**

1. (because) Chocolate the guinea pig was missing. Lila began an investigation.
Because Chocolate the guinea pig was missing, Lila began an investigation.

2. (or) Was Chocolate stolen? Did she escape from her cage?
Was Chocolate stolen, or did she escape from her cage?

3. (and) Lila made a list of suspects. She read the list to Gayle.
Lila made a list of suspects, and she read it to Gayle.

4. (if) Chocolate escaped from her cage. Where is she now?
If Chocolate escaped from her cage, where is she now?

5. (and) Lila searched the classroom. Eddie English helped her.
Lila searched the classroom, and Eddie English helped her.

6. (when) Lila fell down. She saw Chocolate and her babies in the drawer.
When Lila fell down, she saw Chocolate and her babies in the drawer.

Notes for Home: Your child combined short sentences into compound or complex sentences. ***Home Activity:*** To practice forming complex sentences, ask your child to think of sentences beginning with the words *when, if,* and *because* and say them to you.

Name________________________________

Self-Evaluation Guide

Persuasive Argument

Students' responses should show that they have given thought to the persuasive arguments that they have written.

Directions: Think about the final draft of your persuasive argument. Then answer each question below.

	Yes	No	Not sure
1. Did I state my opinion at the beginning of the argument?			
2. Did I use good reasons, facts, and examples to persuade my reader?			
3. Are my reasons organized in order of importance?			
4. Did I use persuasive words in my argument?			
5. Did I proofread and edit carefully to avoid errors?			

6. What is the best reason you used in your persuasive argument?

7. How would you change this persuasive argument if you were writing it for a different audience than your classmates? Explain.

Notes For Home: Your child has been learning to write a persuasive argument. ***Home Activity:*** Ask your child to think of a favorite leisure activity and give three reasons to persuade someone to try it.

Teacher's Notes